Common Organic Functions

Class	Formula	Functional Group	IUPAC Prefix or Suffix
acyl halide	$\overset{O}{\overset{\|}{R C}}X$	$\overset{O}{\overset{\|}{-C}}X$	-oyl halide
alcohol	ROH	—OH	-ol
aldehyde	$\overset{O}{\overset{\|}{R C}}H$	$\overset{O}{\overset{\|}{-C}}H$	-al
alkane	RH	none	-ane
alkene	$R_2C=CR_2$	$\overset{\diagdown}{\diagup}C=C\overset{\diagup}{\diagdown}$	-ene
alkyne	$RC\equiv CR$	$-C\equiv C-$	-yne
amide	$\overset{O}{\overset{\|}{R C}}NR_2$	$\overset{O}{\overset{\|}{-C}}N-$	-amide
amine	R_3N	$-\overset{\|}{N}-$	amino-
arene	ArH	(benzene ring)	
azide	RN_3	$-N=\overset{+}{N}=\overset{-}{N}$	azido-
carboxylic acid	$\overset{O}{\overset{\|}{R C}}OH$	$\overset{O}{\overset{\|}{-C}}OH$	-oic acid
ester	$\overset{O}{\overset{\|}{R C}}OR$	$\overset{O}{\overset{\|}{-C}}O-$	
ether	R_2O	—O—	alkoxy-
halide	RF	—F	fluoro-
	RCl	—Cl	chloro-
	RBr	—Br	bromo-
	RI (RX)	—I (—X)	iodo- (halo-)
ketone	$\overset{O}{\overset{\|}{R C}}R$	$\overset{O}{\overset{\|}{-C}}-$	-one
nitrile	$RC\equiv N$	$-C\equiv N$	-nitrile
nitro compound	RNO_2	$-NO_2$	nitro-
phenol	ArOH	—OH	
sulfide	R_2S	—S—	alkylthio-
sulfone	$\overset{O}{\overset{\|}{R \underset{\underset{O}{\|}}{S}}}R$	$\overset{O}{\overset{\|}{-\underset{\underset{O}{\|}}{S}}}-$	
sulfonic acid	RSO_3H	$\overset{O}{\overset{\|}{-\underset{\underset{O}{\|}}{S}}}OH$	-sulfonic acid
sulfoxide	$\overset{O}{\overset{\|}{R S}}R$	$\overset{O}{\overset{\|}{-S}}-$	
thiol	RSH	—SH	-thiol

Approximate Nmr Chemical Shifts

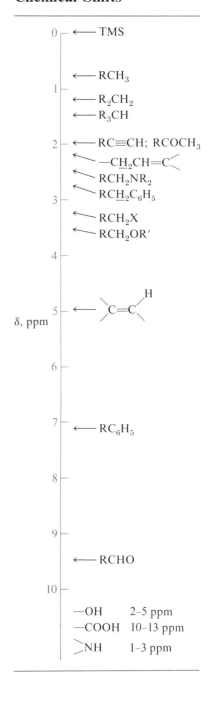

δ, ppm

—OH	2–5 ppm
—COOH	10–13 ppm
⟩NH	1–3 ppm

Symbols for Amino Acids

Ala	alanine
Arg	arginine
Asn	asparagine
Asp	aspartic acid
Cys	cysteine
Gln	glutamine
Glu	glutamic acid
Gly	glycine
His	histidine
Ile	isoleucine
Leu	leucine
Lys	lysine
Met	methionine
Phe	phenylalanine
Pro	proline
Ser	serine
Thr	threonine
Trp	tryptophan
Tyr	tyrosine
Val	valine

Greek Alphabet

Lower Case	Capital	Name
α	A	alpha
β	B	beta
γ	Γ	gamma
δ	Δ	delta
ϵ	E	epsilon
ζ	Z	zeta
η	H	eta
θ	Θ	theta
ι	I	iota
κ	K	kappa
λ	Λ	lambda
μ	M	mu
ν	N	nu
ξ	Ξ	xi
o	O	omicron
π	Π	pi
ρ	P	rho
σ	Σ	sigma
τ	T	tau
υ	Υ	upsilon
ϕ	Φ	phi
χ	X	chi
ψ	Ψ	psi
ω	Ω	omega

Chemical Abbreviations

Ac	acetyl,	$CH_3\overset{O}{\overset{\|}{C}}-$
Boc	t-butoxycarbonyl,	$(CH_3)_3CO\overset{O}{\overset{\|}{C}}-$
n-Bu	n-butyl,	$CH_3CH_2CH_2CH_2-$
t-Bu	t-butyl,	$(CH_3)_3C-$
Cbz	benzyloxycarbonyl,	$C_6H_5CH_2O\overset{O}{\overset{\|}{C}}-$
DCC	dicyclohexylcarbodiimide,	$C_6H_{11}N{=}C{=}NC_6H_{11}$
DIBAL	diisobutylaluminum hydride,	$[(CH_3)_2CHCH_2]_2AlH$
diglyme	bis(2-methoxyethyl) ether,	$(CH_3OCH_2CH_2)_2O$
DMF	dimethylformamide,	$(CH_3)_2NCHO$
DMSO	dimethyl sulfoxide,	$(CH_3)_2SO$
DNP	2,4-dinitrophenyl,	$2,4\text{-}(O_2N)_2C_6H_3-$
Et	ethyl,	CH_3CH_2-
glyme	1,2-dimethoxyethane,	$CH_3OCH_2CH_2OCH_3$
HMPT	hexamethylphosphoric triamide,	$[(CH_3)_2N]_3PO$
LAH	lithium aluminum hydride,	$LiAlH_4$
LDA	lithium diisopropylamide,	$LiN[CH(CH_3)_2]_2$
Me	methyl,	CH_3-
PPA	polyphosphoric acid	
THF	tetrahydrofuran,	$\overline{CH_2CH_2CH_2CH_2O}$
TMS	tetramethylsilane,	$(CH_3)_4Si$
Ts	p-toluenesulfonyl,	$p\text{-}CH_3C_6H_4SO_2-$

Equilibria and Free Energy

$$A \rightleftharpoons B \qquad K = \frac{[B]}{[A]}$$

$$\Delta G° = -RT \ln K$$

K	Percent B	Percent A	$\Delta G°$, kcal mole^{-1} (25°)
0.0001	0.01	99.99	+5.46
0.001	0.1	99.9	+4.09
0.01	0.99	99.0	+2.73
0.1	9.1	90.9	+1.36
0.33	25	75	+0.65
1	50	50	0
3	75	25	−0.65
10	90.9	9.1	−1.36
100	99.0	0.99	−2.73
1000	99.9	0.1	−4.09
10000	99.99	0.01	−5.46

Introduction to Organic Chemistry

THIRD EDITION

Introduction to Organic Chemistry

Andrew Streitwieser, Jr.
Clayton H. Heathcock
UNIVERSITY OF CALIFORNIA, BERKELEY

Macmillan Publishing Company   *New York*

Collier Macmillan Publishers   *London*

Earlier editions, copyright © 1976 and 1981 by Macmillan Publishing Co., Inc. Selected illustrations have been reprinted from *Orbital and Electron Density Diagrams: An Application of Computer Graphics,* by Andrew Streitwieser, Jr., and Peter H. Owens, copyright © 1973 by Macmillan Publishing Co., Inc.

Macmillan Publishing Company
866 Third Avenue, New York, New York 10022

Collier Macmillan Canada, Inc.

Library of Congress Cataloging in Publication Data

Streitwieser, Andrew,
  Introduction to organic chemistry.

  Includes index.
  1. Chemistry, Organic. I. Heathcock, Clayton H.
II. Title.
QD251.2.S76 1985   547   84-15399
ISBN 0-02-418140-4 (Hardcover Edition)
ISBN 0-02-946720-9 (International Edition)

Printing: 1 2 3 4 5 6 7 8   Year: 5 6 7 8 9 0 1 2 3

ISBN 0-02-418140-4

Preface

Organic chemistry is a live, changing science. New concepts, tools, and reactions are being continually developed and affect the teaching of the science even at the introductory level. The science is so large and encompasses so much that those of us concerned with teaching the subject to new generations of students keep searching for the best way. So it is that textbooks spawn new editions. We are gratified by the response to previous editions of our textbook and are indebted to numerous teachers and students of organic chemistry for suggested improvements to make our text still better.

The biggest change to be noticed in this new edition is the introduction of color. A common comment with previous black-and-white printed editions was that in many reactions students could not easily locate the site of reaction. Experienced organic chemists view structures as a unified *gestalt* and see quickly where structural change has occurred in a reaction. The inexperienced student needs to search for such changes. The use of color helps by ''spotlighting'' where the action is. We have also used color to indicate the essential stoichiometry of many reactions, showing where specific atoms go in a manner resembling the use of isotopic labels. That is, we have tried to use color as a pedagogic tool and not just for aesthetics.

The changes include some reorganization. Organometallic chemistry has been brought in early, at the same time as alkyl halides in Chapter 8, in order to include displacement reactions of metallated acetylenes in Chapter 12 and Grignard reactions in the chemistry of aldehydes and ketones (Chapter 14). The treatment of transition metal organometallic chemistry is now one of the special topics in the final chapter. Nuclear magnetic resonance has been deferred to Chapter 13 in order to first get a rapid start on organic reactions with a few important functional groups. The chemistry of nitriles has traditionally been included with that of carboxylic acid derivatives, but this placement produces an awkward situation since all of the other functional derivatives of carboxylic acids contain carbonyl groups. We solved this problem in this edition by treating the carbon-nitrogen triple bond with the carbon-carbon triple bond in Chapter 12. The result is a happy combination, which we think instructors will like, and a more manageable size for Chapter 18 on derivatives of carboxylic acids.

Another major change in this edition is the introduction of frontier orbital concepts. This application of molecular orbital theory has become so important in organic chemistry that we thought it should now be introduced in the first course. Because of the long involvement of one of us in molecular orbital interpretations of organic chemistry, many readers of our past editions had expressed surprise that our text made so little use of the theory. We are convinced that resonance theory, with its symbolism rooted in conventional structures, is a sound way to teach much organic chemistry, and will continue to be so, but some areas of the subject are well suited for·a molecular orbital approach. Nevertheless, the molecular orbital theory has been written as a separate chapter, Chapter 21, and it can be skipped by those who prefer a conventional treatment.

Other changes include the expansion of the sulfur and phosphorus chapter (Chapter 25) to include silicon, reflecting the growing importance of this element in organic chemistry. To make room for this new material we have deleted some traditional reactions that are no longer important, and we have reduced the number of variations of other reactions.

The number of exercises has been greatly increased; virtually every section now has one or more exercises to test the student's understanding and these exercises are now numbered. We are pleased that Professor Paul A. Bartlett has again prepared a Student Study Guide that includes answers to most of the exercises and problems, as well as numerous supplemental problems. In addition, the Student Study Guide contains useful outlines of the essential points of each chapter, tips for effective study strategies, and an extensive appendix of reactions, keyed by page to the text itself.

We have retained many of the attributes of the past editions that we regard as their strengths: explanations of physical properties and phenomena, use of specific examples for reactions with experimental details, descriptive chemistry of important inorganic reagents, and up-to-date values of important properties such as acidities, bond dissociation energies, etc. We have retained the stereoscopic projections to emphasize the three-dimensional nature of organic structures. We only hope that with the growing capabilities of computer graphics, stereo viewers will become increasingly available to the reader.

As in previous editions, we have many people to thank for their comments, corrections and suggestions. Some to whom we are particularly indebted include Professors T. Tidwell, Toronto; K. Mislow, Princeton; H. Koch, Ithaca College; W. Jorgensen, Purdue; G. Daub, New Mexico; V. Jager, Wurzburg; and Dr. D. Golden, Stanford Research Institute. A special debt of thanks is due to Professor Costas Issidorides, American University of Beirut, who critically evaluated the entire 1200 pages of the Second Edition and made hundreds of useful suggestions, many of which have been incorporated in this Edition. We are also indebted to Dr. Arnold Falick, of the University of California at San Francisco, who assisted greatly in the modernization of our treatment of mass spectrometry (Chapter 32).

We are especially grateful to two of our Berkeley graduate students, Peter Connolly and Terry Rosen, who devoted many hours of their time to the task of redoing all of the NMR and CMR spectra in a more modern format, using a 180-MHz, Fourier-Transform spectrometer.

Berkeley, California

A. Streitwieser, Jr.
C. H. Heathcock

Contents

A Note to the Student

Before you begin your adventure in organic chemistry it is perhaps appropriate for you to take a few minutes to plan your journey. The first chapter of this book provides a succinct history of the development of chemical science up to the beginnings of organic chemistry in the middle of the last century. Immediately following is a brief review of the important concepts of orbitals and chemical bonds. Although Chapter 2 is a review of topics you learned in your general chemistry course, it is essential that you be familiar with this material before proceeding with your study. Therefore, take an hour or so to go over this chapter and work the problems, even if your instructor does not specifically repeat the review material in lecture. The Lewis structures and simple hybrid orbitals and bond concepts reviewed in this chapter are fundamental to the chemistry that follows.

Chapters 3 and 4 are intended to introduce you to the two important aspects of organic chemistry—structures and reactions. Although some general chemistry courses will have covered the subject matter of these two chapters, many will not. Again, you should be thoroughly acquainted with the material in Chapters 3 and 4 before going further.

In Chapter 5 you will encounter the simplest organic compounds, those made up solely of carbon and hydrogen. This chapter also introduces two basic principles—thermodynamics and conformations. In Chapter 6 you will find the first detailed study of an organic reaction, free radical halogenation, and you will be able to put into practice the general ideas of reaction mechanisms and thermodynamics presented in Chapters 4 and 5. Chapter 7 will introduce you to a fascinating topic—stereochemistry. This special aspect of molecular structure is of fundamental importance to organic chemistry and to biochemistry. Although you may find thinking in three dimensions difficult at first, practice pays off. Once you can freely visualize organic compounds as three-dimensional objects just like the familiar objects of everyday life, you will discover that organic chemistry is suddenly ''much easier'' than you thought.

Chapter 8 introduces two new groups of organic compounds, those containing halogen atoms and those with carbon-metal bonds. New structures are involved, and your repertoire of reactions will start to grow. The displacement reaction, which is treated in Chapter 9, is one of the most important reactions in organic chemistry. It is important that you grasp the mechanism of this reaction because you will find that the same relationships of structure and reactivity occur over and over again. By acquiring an early understanding of the principles of the displacement reaction, you can avoid mindlessly memorizing dozens of reactions; you will be able to recognize that many ''new'' reactions are only different versions of reactions you already understand.

As you progress in your study of organic chemistry, you will discover that the science is conveniently organized in terms of functional groups—the parts of organic compounds other than the carbon-carbon and carbon-hydrogen single bonds that are common to all organic structures. The next group of three chapters systematically treats the chemistry of alcohols and ethers (Chapter 10), alkenes (Chapter 11), alkynes and nitriles (Chapter 12). In each of these chapters the topical sequence is similar.

1. The functional group itself—its characteristic geometry and its effect on the geometry of the hydrocarbon part of the molecule containing it.

2. How compounds of the class are named.
3. The common physical properties of the class of compounds under consideration.
4. The chemical reactions that are characteristic of the functional group, to which the bulk of the chapter is devoted.

In most organic reactions one functional group is typically transformed into another. Thus, you will find that an organic reaction can usually be thought of both as an attribute of a given class of compounds and as a method of preparation of another class of compounds. In this book you will find that reactions are generally introduced as a property of a class of compounds. However, each functional group chapter also contains a section on preparative methods. In general, the emphasis in these preparation sections is on the practical aspects of the reactions rather than on the mechanistic aspects.

With the chemistry of several key functional groups and a number of structures and reactions under our belts we now shift gears and turn in Chapter 13 from chemical reactivity back to chemical structure. In this chapter you will have your first encounter with spectroscopy, which is the principal way modern organic chemists find out how the atoms of a molecule are joined together. In all, four sections of the book are devoted to various forms of spectroscopy—Chapter 13 (nuclear magnetic resonance spectroscopy), Chapter 15 (infrared spectroscopy), Section 21.6 (ultraviolet spectroscopy), and Chapter 32 (mass spectroscopy). Each kind of spectroscopy gives us different pieces of the molecular jigsaw puzzle, but nuclear magnetic resonance spectroscopy is the most important. In subsequent chapters on functional groups the discussion of physical properties includes spectroscopy.

After Chapter 13 on nuclear magnetic resonance spectroscopy, Chapter 14 on the important carbonyl functional group in aldehydes and ketones, and Chapter 15 on infrared spectroscopy, we come to a convenient break in the sequence. Chapter 16 is rather different from the other chapters in the book in that it is essentially a review of the organic chemistry learned up to that point. In some ways, learning organic chemistry is like learning a language. The simple reactions and mechanistic principles are like the vocabulary of the language. As in learning a language, you must first learn the vocabulary. However, if you only know the words of a language you will not be able to compose a poem, or even rent a hotel room with hot and cold running water. It is necessary also to learn how the words are put together to make sentences—the grammar and syntax of the language. In organic chemistry we learn to put several simple reactions together to achieve an overall transformation that cannot be accomplished by any single reaction. Chapter 16 will give you an opportunity to practice multistep synthesis using the reactions you have learned. This chapter is followed by two more chapters or carbonyl-containing functional groups, the carboxylic acids and their derivatives.

In the first half of the book, you will have considered the typical chemical properties of molecules having a single functional group. In Chapter 19 you will discover that compounds having two functional groups can have properties that are very different from those of compounds having only one of the groups. This study of "conjugated systems" is fundamental to the understanding of aromatic chemistry (Chapters 20 and 22) and provides a convenient way of introducing some new concepts in molecular orbital theory (Chapter 21). This theory is especially important in applications to conjugated and "aromatic" compounds and related reactions and has had a major impact on modern organic chemistry.

The remainder of the book contains a good deal of chemistry of such "polyfunctional" compounds. For example, Chapter 26 discusses aromatic halogen- and oxygen-containing compounds, and Chapter 27 treats the special chemistry of compounds with two oxygen-containing functional groups. Chapters 28 and 29 cover the chemistry of two important families of polyfunctional "natural products"—carbohydrates and amino acids.

Up to Chapter 22 your study of organic chemistry will have dealt with compounds made up mainly of carbon, hydrogen, oxygen and the halogens. In Chapters 23–25 you will encounter organic compounds of nitrogen, phosphorus, sulfur, and silicon. Of these compounds, the amines (Chapter 23) are the most important, but the other nitrogen functions (Chapter 24) play a significant role, especially in aromatic chemistry. Although your instructor may choose to omit Chapter 25 (sulfur, phosphorus, and silicon compounds), if you are bound for a career in medicine or in the health sciences, you will want at least to read through this chapter.

Chapters 30 and 31 deal with further aspects of aromatic chemistry. The astute student will recognize that there are virtually no new concepts in these two chapters; rather, they serve to add flesh to the bones of the subject. However, it is interesting flesh, and the future chemical engineer or physician will find in these chapters many hints of things to come.

The final chapters of the book are optional reading. Chapter 32 introduces mass spectroscopy and Chapter 33 is an introduction to the literature of chemistry. Although you may not need to use the chemical literature at this point in your career, many of you will need this knowledge later. Chapter 33 will give you a start at the appropriate time. Finally, Chapter 34 is a collection of brief essays on topics somewhat beyond the scope of a general introduction. These essays are provided to give the interested student a glimpse of some of the exciting areas of modern research.

It is also appropriate at this point to mention several tools we have provided to assist you in learning organic chemistry. The first is the "indented sections," which are in smaller type and, as a further aid to their recognition, are set apart by brackets at the top and bottom. These sections, which are found at various points within each chapter, contain several types of information. Some give more detailed information on the topic immediately preceding. Others contain specific reaction conditions for a reaction that has been used for an example. Still others convey information of interest about specific compounds, often inorganic compounds that are employed as reagents in organic chemistry. These indented sections are set apart so that they may be skipped over by the student who is just reviewing the important principles of the chapter. Our rule of thumb at Berkeley is that the material in these sections is for enrichment, and that students are not held responsible for it on examinations. You should ask your instructor about the policy in your course.

A second invaluable tool is the exercises and problems in each chapter. The exercises, which occur in most sections, are often cast in the form of "drill" to provide you with immediate practice in using new principles or reactions that have just been introduced. For many of you, these exercises will seem ridiculously easy, as you will be asked to write out equation you have just learned. However, they are an important part of the learning process. Everyone has had the experience of "daydreaming" while reading merrily along. It is possible to read several pages and be totally unconscious of what you have read. The exercises force you to pause periodically and check to see that you have really been assimilating what you have been reading. The problems at the end of each chapter also contain some drill questions, but the parts of a single question may draw from many different sections of the chapter. Thus, these questions provide for a second check on your retention of the various reactions and principles you have studied. There are also "thought questions" that ask you to take several reactions or principles and put them together to solve a problem or in some cases to extend your knowledge and discover something yourself.

To enable you to derive the greatest benefit from the exercises and problems, we have prepared a Student Study Guide. This paperback book contains worked-out answers to all of the exercises and problems as well as a key-word index and study hints for each chapter. In addition, the study guide contains supplemental problems, with answers. It is important that you give any problem a good try before looking up the answer. It is human nature to quit worrying about a problem as soon as the answer is known, and it is also true that we learn more from a problem we have labored over than from one we haven't given much thought to.

One teaching device we have used requires special mention—the three-dimensional stereoscopic projections that are distributed throughout the book. These computer-generated images are designed so that you may see the figure in three dimensions. By using a suitable viewer one may cause each eye to focus independently on one of the two images of such a projection, and there is an illusion of depth to the resulting picture one sees. An inexpensive cardboard viewer is available from the Taylor-Merchant corporation, 212 West 35 Street, New York, NY 10001. Most bookstores will not stock these viewers unless the Professor in a course requests it. If your bookstore does not have a supply of viewers, ask that they be ordered. It is actually possible, albeit a bit more difficult, to see a stereo image without the special viewer. To do this, hold the page about 20 inches from your eyes and focus on a point behind the book in such a way that the two images merge. Generally, the merged image will suddenly seem three dimensional. One caution: with this method the right eye will sometimes focus on the left image and vice versa. The result is the perception of the mirror image, a concern when precise stereochemistry is important, as in Chapter 7.

The stereo pictures should be considered as an adjunct to and not a substitute for molecular models. We urge you to acquire and regularly use a set of molecular models; most bookstores stock one or more relatively inexpensive student sets as learning aids for organic chemistry courses. Organic structures are three-dimensional structures, and practice with models is essential to give proper meaning to the structural symbols commonly recorded on two-dimensional pages.

With these general suggestions in mind, it remains only for us to wish you luck as you set out upon your journey through organic chemistry. Both of us look back with fond remembrance upon our own discovery of this fascinating subject; we hope that you will find it as rewarding.

Andrew Streitwieser, Jr.
Clayton H. Heathcock

Chapter 1

Introduction

Although chemistry did not emerge as a coherent science until the seventeenth century, its roots extend back into antiquity. Chemical changes were probably first brought about by paleolithic man when he discovered that he could make fire and use it to warm his body and roast his food. Being a curious and a resourceful creature, man observed and exploited other natural phenomena as well. By neolithic times he had discovered such arts as smelting, glass making, the dyeing of textiles, and the manufacture of beer, wine, butter, and cheese. However, matter and changes of matter were not systematically discussed in a theoretical sense until the period of the Greek philosophers, beginning in about 600 B.C. One popular theory that emerged during this period saw all matter as being made up of the four "elemental" substances: fire, earth, air, and water. For a time, the atomist school, of which Democritus (ca. 460-370 B.C.) was the chief spokesman, gained popularity. The atomists considered all matter to be made up of hypothetical particles called atoms, of which there were assumed to be but a finite number of different kinds. Although the atomists held sway for several centuries, the notion was highly speculative, being based on nothing directly observable. The demise of this theory was foreshadowed when it was rejected by the highly respected Aristotle; its burial was assured with the advent of stoicism and the subsequent rise of the popular religious movements in the Western world. The idea of fundamental particles was not resurrected for almost two millenia.

Around the time of Christ, the Greek philosophers of Alexandria hit upon the idea of changing (or "transmuting") base metals such as lead and iron into gold and silver. Although alchemy was first practiced in a serious sense by the Greeks, it quickly spread to other cultures and continued as a lively discipline throughout the world for over a thousand years. This alchemical period has often been put down as a "dark age" of science. However, there is nothing inherently wrong with the notion that one metal may be transformable into another. Chemistry is, in fact, based upon changes in the state of matter. The alchemists had no way of recognizing the elemental nature of the metals with which they dealt.

Although they were uniformly unsuccessful in their quest for the philosopher's stone, the alchemists contributed a great deal to chemical technology. Not only did they develop numerous processes for the production of relatively pure compounds but they also invented tools and apparatus—beakers, flasks, funnels, mortars, crucibles—many of which persist in similar form to the present day. Perhaps the most important invention of alchemy was the still. The important technique of distillation was probably discovered by the early Greek alchemists when they noticed condensate on the lid of a vessel in which some liquid was being heated. It was only a short step from this observation to the realization that this technique could be used to separate volatile substances from nonvolatile animal and vegetable matter. Although the still was quite inefficient in its infancy, its design improved steadily. By 1300 actual fractionation was being practiced, and alcoholic distillates of fairly high alcohol concentration were available. The production of whiskey and brandy became an established industry in short order.

The invention and development of the still had an interesting consequence in another area—medicine. Through the Middle Ages, medicine was practiced as a mystical blend of magic and folklore. It had long been noticed that certain animal and plant substances seemed to possess curative powers. With the advent of the still, it became possible to concentrate the "essence" of various natural materials. The use of various distillates as medical remedies quickly became a widespread practice. For several hundred years, physicians and their associates distilled all manner of natural substances. In the process, a number of relatively pure organic compounds were isolated, such as acetic acid from vinegar and formic acid from ants.

During this pre-1600 period, as the tools for handling matter were being developed and as a number of relatively pure chemical substances were being discovered, there was not much serious experimentation and no advance at all in the theory of matter. However, during the seventeenth and eighteenth centuries, chemistry was born as a science in Europe. The first area of serious investigation was gases. Although Boyle, Hales, Cavendish, Priestley, and Scheele made important breakthroughs, it was Antoine Laurent Lavoisier (1743-1794) who laid the real foundation for modern chemistry. During the "pneumatic chemistry" period (1650-1750), there had evolved a theory that explained combustion with the aid of a substance called *terra pinquis*, or "phlogiston." It was believed that almost every kind of matter contained a certain amount of phlogiston, and that fire caused transfer of the phlogiston to another body. The phlogiston theory was a step away from the purely qualitative notions of chemistry that had existed since the time of the Greek philosophers toward quantitation of chemical change. However, it was Lavoisier who first realized that the gain in weight that occurs during combustion and calcination is due to the combination of the substance being heated with a component of the air. It was during the 1770s that Lavoisier carried out the quantitative experiments with Priestley's "dephlogisticated air" that subsequently led him to recognize its elemental nature; the name oxygen was first used in a memoir dated September 5, 1775. The characterization of oxygen as an elemental substance allowed quantitative studies of combustion and led rapidly to the notion of combining weights. By 1789, Lavoisier had assembled a Table of the Elements, containing 33 substances, most of which appear in the modern periodic table.

In this formative stage in the science of chemistry, the substances derived from the animal and vegetable worlds were largely ignored. These materials were recognized as being different—more complex—than the compounds of the atmosphere or those compounds derived from the mineral kingdom. Lavoisier himself noted that "organic compounds," as they came to be known, differed from the inorganic compounds in that they all seemed to be composed of carbon and hydrogen and occasionally nitrogen or phosphorus. For a time it was thought that organic compounds did not obey the new law of definite proportions, and people came to believe that a "vital force," present only in living organisms, was responsible for the production of organic compounds.

The vitalism theory persisted until the middle of the nineteenth century. In 1828 Friedrich Wöhler, while a medical student at the University of Heidelberg, reported that, upon treating lead cyanate with ammonium hydroxide, he obtained urea. Since urea was a well-known organic compound, having been isolated from human urine by Roulle in about 1780, Wöhler had succeeded in preparing an organic compound in the laboratory for the first time. In a letter to Jöns Jakob Berzelius, a leading Swedish chemist, Wöhler proclaimed, "I must tell you that I can make urea without the use of kidneys, either man or dog. Ammonium cyanate is urea." Although the synthesis of urea was recognized as an important accomplishment by the leading chemists of the day, the concept of vitalism did not die quickly. It was not until the synthetic work of

Kolbe in the 1840s and Berthelot in the 1850s that the demise of vitalism was complete.

At this time, chemists recognized that it was not the vital force that imparted uniqueness to organic chemistry but rather the simple fact that organic compounds are all compounds of carbon. This definition—**organic chemistry is the chemistry of carbon compounds**—has persisted. During the eighteenth and nineteenth centuries, analytical methods were also being perfected. With the advent of these methods, particularly the technique of combustion analysis, organic chemistry began to take on new dimensions. For the first time accurate formulas were available for fairly complicated organic compounds. There ensued a confusing period, which lasted from about 1800 until about 1850, during which various theories were advanced in an attempt to explain such complexities as isomerism (the existence of two compounds with the same formula) and substitution (the replacement of one element by another in a complex organic formula). Organic chemistry began to emerge from this chaotic period in 1852 when Edward Frankland advanced the concept of valence. In 1858, Friedrich August Kekulé and Archibald Scott Couper, working independently, introduced a simple, but exceedingly important, concept. Making use of the new structural formulas shown, which had come into vogue since 1850, Kekulé and Couper proposed that the carbon atom is always tetravalent and that carbon atoms have the ability to link to each other.

$$\left.\begin{array}{c} H \\ H \\ H \end{array}\right\}N \qquad \left.\begin{array}{c} H \\ H \end{array}\right\}O \qquad \left.\begin{array}{c} C_2H_5 \\ H \end{array}\right\}O \qquad \left.\begin{array}{c} C_2H_5 \\ C_2H_5 \end{array}\right\}O$$

$$\text{ammonia} \qquad\qquad \text{water} \qquad\qquad \text{alcohol} \qquad\qquad \text{ether}$$

A third event that ushered organic chemistry into its modern period was the demonstration by Stanislao Cannizzaro in 1858 that Avogadro's hypothesis, available since 1811, allowed the determination of accurate molecular weights for organic compounds. With this last piece of the structural puzzle available, it was possible to think in terms of molecular structure and the chemical bond. Kekulé introduced the idea of a bond between atoms and depicted it with his "sausage formulas" in the first edition of his textbook in 1861.

methane   methyl chloride   carbon dioxide

ethyl chloride   ethyl alcohol

In the century since Kekulé, organic chemistry has matured as a scientific discipline in its own right. Well over 95% of all known chemical compounds are compounds of carbon. Over one half of present-day chemists classify themselves as organic chemists. The organic chemical industry plays a major role in world economy. For example, one commercial herbicide (Roundup™, marketed by the Monsanto Chemical Company) had 1983 sales of more than $1 billion, and is currently a significant factor in increasing agricultural yields and therefore the availability of food, both in industrialized and third-world countries. Finally, because organic chemicals are literally the "stuff of life,'' the significant advances in unravelling the nature of life are discoveries in organic chemistry.

Why study organic chemistry? There are different answers to this question depending upon who you are. It may be that you will devote your life to a career in organic chemistry per se, although if this is the case, you probably do not know it yet. Or you may plan to specialize in some other area of chemistry and want a knowledge of organic chemistry as an adjunct to your specialty area. You may be a future chemical engineer; if so, organic chemistry will be an important part of your life, since most of the industrial processes you will encounter will be organic reactions. If you are headed for medicine or nursing, you should be aware of the fact that sales of pharmaceutical products amounted to over $10 billion in 1983 and that chemotherapy is one of the major techniques in modern medicine. You may be going into biochemistry, molecular biology, or some other life science to which organic chemistry is essential; biochemistry is simply a study of organic chemistry as it goes on in living organisms, and the molecules of molecular biology are organic molecules.

Even if you do not have any of the foregoing reasons to study organic chemistry, there is a purely intellectual justification. The previous arguments are vocational motivations. But organic chemistry also provides a fascinating area of natural philosophy for the student who wants to obtain a broad liberal arts education. If you approach the subject in the proper frame of mind, you will find it to be an extremely stimulating intellectual pursuit. The subject has a highly logical structure. As you will see, organic chemists make much use of symbolic logic, the logical principle of analogy, and deductive reasoning. In fact, it has been intimated that medical school admission boards value organic chemistry courses as much for the exercise in logical thinking that they provide as for their factual content.

Finally, organic chemistry has a unique content as an art form. The building up of complex molecular architecture by appropriate choice of a sequential combination of reactions provides syntheses that are described as ''elegant'' and ''beautiful.'' The design of an experiment in reaction mechanism can be similarly imaginative. Such elegantly conceived experiments can evoke that delightful feeling of pleasure that one obtains from the appreciation of human creativity—but only in the mind of the knowledgeable spectator. These unique works of art can only be appreciated by those who know some organic reactions and have tried to design some simple syntheses and experiments themselves, such as those suggested in problem sets throughout this textbook. Only one who has played chess can feel that special pleasure of following a game between Grand Masters.

Chapter 2
Electronic Structure and Bonding

2.1 Periodic Table

The periodic table of the elements was developed just over 100 years ago. At that time it was an empirical organization based on the chemical and physical properties of the known elements. The table now embraces over 100 elements. Compounds of carbon, organic compounds, are known that contain virtually all of the elements except the noble gases. However, only a small part of this organization is important in the introductory study of organic chemistry. In the condensed form of the periodic table shown in Table 2.1, the most important elements are emphasized with color; these are C, H, N, O, S, Mg, Cl, Br, and I. Secondary but still important elements are in italics: Li, B, F, and P.

TABLE 2.1 Abbreviated Periodic Table

first period:	H							He
second period:	*Li*	· Be	*B*	C	N	O	*F*	Ne
third period:	Na	Mg	Al	Si	*P*	S	Cl	Ar
							Br	
							I	

2.2 Lewis Structures

The "noble" gases, He, Ne, Ar, Kr, Xe, and Ra, are almost inert chemically. Paradoxically, it is this very inert character that dominates much of the chemistry of all the rest of the elements. The noble gases have characteristic numbers of electrons, 2 for helium, 10 for neon (2 + 8), 18 for argon (2 + 8 + 8), and so on. They are described as having "filled shells" or, for neon and argon, as having filled outer **octets**. Other elements can achieve such stable electronic configurations by gaining or losing electrons.

The energy required to lose an electron is known as the **ionization potential**, IP.

$$M \longrightarrow M^+ + e^- \qquad \Delta H° = IP$$

For elements at the far left of the periodic table, loss of an electron produces the electronic configuration of the next lower noble gas.

$$Li \xrightarrow{-e^-} Li^+$$

3 electrons   2 electrons
(same as helium)

$$Na \xrightarrow{-e^-} Na^+$$

11 electrons   10 electrons
(same as neon)

Such elements have relatively low ionization potentials and are described as being **electropositive**.

The energy liberated when an electron is acquired is called the **electron affinity**, EA.

$$X + e^- \longrightarrow X^- \qquad -\Delta H^\circ = EA$$

The electron affinity of an atom is also the ionization potential of the corresponding anion. Elements at the far right of the periodic table readily acquire electrons to produce the stable electronic configuration of the next higher noble gas.

$$F \quad + e^- \longrightarrow \quad F^-$$

9 electrons   10 electrons
(same as neon)

$$Cl \quad + e^- \longrightarrow \quad Cl^-$$

17 electrons   18 electrons
(same as argon)

Such elements have relatively high electron affinities and are described as being **electronegative**.

The electrons outside the shell of the next lower noble gas are the **valence electrons** and are the only ones normally included in symbols. The above ionization processes are then symbolized as follows.

$$Li\cdot \longrightarrow Li^+ + e^- \qquad IP = 123.6 \text{ kcal mole}^{-1},^* \; 517.1 \text{ kJ mole}^{-1}$$

$$Na\cdot \longrightarrow Na^+ + e^- \qquad IP = 118.0 \text{ kcal mole}^{-1}, \; 493.7 \text{ kJ mole}^{-1}$$

$$:\ddot{F}\cdot + e^- \longrightarrow :\ddot{F}:^- \qquad EA = 78.3 \text{ kcal mole}^{-1}, \; 327.6 \text{ kJ mole}^{-1}$$

$$:\ddot{C}l\cdot + e^- \longrightarrow :\ddot{C}l:^- \qquad EA = 83.3 \text{ kcal mole}^{-1}, \; 348.5 \text{ kJ mole}^{-1}$$

Electropositive elements such as the alkali metals tend to lose electrons to electronegative elements such as the halogens to form pairs of ions. Such compounds are described as having ionic bonding. Typical examples are lithium chloride (Li^+ :Cl:$^-$) and sodium fluoride (Na^+ :F:$^-$).

For elements in the middle of the periodic table, too much energy is required to gain or lose sufficient electrons to form similar octet ions. Compare the energy required to generate a triply positive boron or quadruply positive carbon with the energies required to form Li^+ or Na^+.

$$\cdot\dot{B}\cdot \longrightarrow 3\,e^- + B^{3+} \qquad IP = 870.4 \text{ kcal mole}^{-1}, \; 3642 \text{ kJ mole}^{-1}$$

$$\cdot\dot{\underset{\cdot}{C}}\cdot \longrightarrow 4\,e^- + C^{4+} \qquad IP = 1480.7 \text{ kcal mole}^{-1}, \; 6195 \text{ kJ mole}^{-1}$$

Consequently, such elements tend to acquire their electron octets by sharing electrons, as in the following examples.

---

* Another system of units that is being adopted in many parts of the world is known as SI (*Système International d'Unités*). In this international system of units, the unit of energy is the joule, J; 1 cal = 4.184 J. The six fundamental units in SI are length = meters (m), mass = kilograms (kg), time = seconds (s), electrical current = amperes (A), temperature = degrees Kelvin (K), and luminosity = candelas (cd). These units are modified by 10^3 (kilo), 10^6 (mega), 10^{-3} (milli), 10^{-6} (micro), 10^{-9} (nano), 10^{-12} (pico). Many traditional units are still in common use among chemists. Examples are calories (cal), kilocalories (kcal), and centimeters (cm). In this text we will generally use such traditional units but will often include the SI units as well for comparison.

$$H:\overset{\overset{\displaystyle H}{..}}{\underset{\displaystyle H}{C}}:H \qquad H:\overset{\overset{\displaystyle H}{..}}{\underset{\displaystyle H}{N}}: \qquad H:\overset{..}{\underset{..}{O}}:H \qquad H:\overset{\overset{\displaystyle H}{..}}{\underset{\displaystyle H}{C}}:\overset{..}{\underset{..}{F}}:$$

methane   ammonia   water   methyl fluoride

Such bonds are described as **covalent bonds**.

The symbols used to describe the foregoing examples are called **Lewis structures**. Such structures not only provide simple and convenient representations of ions and compounds but are also valuable in providing an accurate accounting for electrons. They form an important basis for predicting relative stabilities. Lewis structures are important in the study of organic chemistry and the student should be able to write them with facility. The following general rules are useful for deriving suitable structures.

1. *All valence electrons are shown.* The total number of such electrons is equal to the sum of the numbers contributed by each atom, with addition or subtraction of another number to account for any ionic charge. Some examples are worked out in Table 2.2.

TABLE 2.2 Valence Electrons

Species	Atomic Contributions	−	Cation Charges	+	Anion Charges	=	Total Valence Electrons
CH_4	$4(C) + 4 \times 1\,(H) = 8$	−	0	+	0	=	8
NH_3	$5(N) + 3 \times 1\,(H) = 8$	−	0	+	0	=	8
H_2O	$6(O) + 2 \times 1\,(H) = 8$	−	0	+	0	=	8
H_3O^+	$6(O) + 3 \times 1\,(H) = 9$	−	1	+	0	=	8
HO^-	$6(O) + \quad 1\,(H) = 7$	−	0	+	1	=	8
BF_3	$3(B) + 3 \times 7\,(F) = 24$	−	0	+	0	=	24
NO_2^-	$5(N) + 2 \times 6\,(O) = 17$	−	0	+	1	=	18
CO_3^{2-}	$4(C) + 3 \times 6\,(O) = 22$	−	0	+	2	=	24

2. *Each element should, to the greatest extent possible, have a complete octet.* Exceptions are hydrogen, which has a duet shell, and elements beyond the first row, such as sulfur and phosphorus, which may accommodate more than eight valence electrons ("expand their octets") in certain circumstances.

Correct Structure   *Incorrect Structures*

$:\overset{..}{O}::C::\overset{..}{O}: \qquad\qquad :\overset{..}{O}:C::\overset{..}{O}: \qquad :\overset{..}{O}:C:\overset{..}{O}: \qquad :\overset{..}{O}::C:\overset{..}{O}:$

$H:\overset{..}{\underset{..}{Cl}}: \qquad\qquad\qquad :H:\overset{..}{\underset{..}{Cl}}:$

$:N:::N: \qquad\qquad\qquad :N::N: \qquad :\overset{..}{N}:\overset{..}{N}:$

3. *Formal charges are assigned by dividing each bonding pair of electrons equally between the bonded atoms.* The number of electrons "belonging" in this way to each atom is compared with the neutral atom and appropriate positive or negative charges are assigned. Lone pairs "belong" to a single atom.

$H:\overset{\overset{\displaystyle H}{..}}{\underset{\displaystyle H}{N^+}}:H \qquad H:\overset{\overset{\displaystyle H}{..}}{\underset{\displaystyle H}{C}}:\overset{..}{\underset{..}{O}}:^- \qquad {}^-:\overset{\overset{\displaystyle :\overset{..}{O}:^-}{}}{\underset{\displaystyle :\overset{..}{O}:_-}{O}}:S^{2+}:\overset{..}{O}:^-$

ammonium ion   methoxide ion   sulfate ion

In $NH_4{}^+$, each electron pair is divided between N and H. This gives one electron for each H, the same as a hydrogen atom. The N has a total of 4, one less than atomic nitrogen; hence, the formal charge of $+1$ is associated with N. This procedure assigns the entire positive charge of $(NH_4)^+$ to the nitrogen; in practice, the electrons are spread over the entire molecule. However, this method of assigning formal charges does keep strict account of the total numbers of electrons and charges present and, when used with care, it helps to interpret chemistry. For example, the formal charge of -1 assigned to the oxygen of methoxide ion helps to explain why this ion is a strong base that readily adds a proton to the oxygen.

The example of sulfate ion is more complex. Some students tend to write this ion as $^-:\!\ddot{O}\!:\!\ddot{O}\!:\!S\!:\!\ddot{O}\!:\!\ddot{O}\!:^-$, an arrangement that has the proper number of valence electrons and a less complex formal structure assignment. However, sulfate ion is known experimentally to have each oxygen bound to sulfur in an equivalent manner.

When a species has an incomplete octet, it is usually unstable or highly reactive. Examples are methyl cation and methyl radical.

$$
\begin{array}{cc}
\text{H} & \text{H} \\
\text{H}:\overset{..}{\underset{+}{\text{C}}}:\text{H} & \text{H}:\overset{..}{\underset{.}{\text{C}}}:\text{H} \\
\text{methyl cation} & \text{methyl radical}
\end{array}
$$

Multiple bonds are handled in a straightforward manner, by the use of either two or three pairs of electrons.

$$
\begin{array}{ccc}
\text{H}\!\!\overset{.}{}\quad\overset{.}{}\!\!\text{H} & & \\
\quad\text{C}::\text{C} & \text{H}:\text{C}:::\text{C}:\text{H} & ^-:\text{C}:::\text{N}: \\
\text{H}\,\overset{.}{}\quad\overset{.}{}\,\text{H} & & \\
\text{ethylene} & \text{acetylene} & \text{cyanide ion}
\end{array}
$$

A further simplifying convention is to replace each electron-pair bond by a line. For convenience, electron pairs are frequently omitted, unless needed to call attention to a particular property of the molecule.

$$
\begin{array}{cccc}
\text{H} & \text{H} & \text{O}^- & \text{H} \\
| & | & | & | \\
\text{H}\!-\!\overset{+}{\text{N}}\!-\!\text{H} & \text{H}\!-\!\text{C}\!-\!\text{O}^- & ^-\text{O}\!-\!\overset{2+}{\text{S}}\!-\!\text{O}^- & \text{H}\!-\!\overset{+}{\text{C}}\!-\!\text{H} \\
| & | & | & \\
\text{H} & \text{H} & \text{O}_- & \\
\end{array}
$$

$$
\begin{array}{cccc}
\text{H} & \text{H}\text{H} & & \\
| & \quad\diagdown\quad\diagup & & \\
\text{H}\!-\!\text{C}\!-\!\text{H} & \quad\text{C}\!=\!\text{C} & \text{H}\!-\!\text{C}\!\equiv\!\text{C}\!-\!\text{H} & ^-\text{C}\!\equiv\!\text{N} \\
| & \quad\diagup\quad\diagdown & & \\
\text{H} & \text{H}\text{H} & & \\
\end{array}
$$

In these symbolic representations, the lone-pair electrons are understood to be present and their presence is signified by appropriate formal charges. This is another reason for assigning formal charges properly. *The use of such symbols is widespread in organic chemistry, and practice in reading and writing these electronic representations cannot be overemphasized.* The simplified symbols correspond to the notational system proposed by Kekulé and Couper in 1858 (Chapter 1). Such symbols, in which each electron-pair bond is represented by a line and the lone-pair electrons are omitted, are frequently called **Kekulé structures**.

The use of a "dative" or "coordinate covalence" bond is sometimes convenient. In this convention, an arrow represents a two-electron bond in which both electrons are considered to "belong" to the donor atom for the bookkeeping purpose of assigning formal charges.

$$\text{H—O—N}^{+}\diagdown\!\!\!\begin{smallmatrix}O\\\\O^{-}\end{smallmatrix} \quad \text{or} \quad \text{H—O—N}\diagdown\!\!\!\begin{smallmatrix}O\\\\O\end{smallmatrix}$$

This type of symbolism finds most use in representing ligands in inorganic complexes and will rarely be used in this text.

EXERCISE 2.1 Rewrite the following Kekulé structures as Lewis structures, including all of the valence electrons.

(a) chloride ion, Cl^-

(b) water, H—O—H

(c) hydroxide ion, H—O$^-$

(d) hypochlorite ion, Cl—O$^-$

(e) ammonia, H—N—H
            |
            H

(f) cyanogen fluoride, F—C≡N

(g) nitric oxide, NO

(h) hydronium ion, H_3O^+

(i) sodium cation, Na^+

(j) helium, He

(k) hydrogen peroxide, H—O—O—H

(l) carbon dioxide, O=C=O

2.3 Geometric Structure

One of the really important achievements of the physics of a half century ago was the determination of crystal structures by x-ray diffraction. Other methods that may be used for the precise determination of molecular structures include electron diffraction and microwave spectroscopy. These experimental approaches have yielded a wealth of detailed structures at the molecular level. For example, H_2O is known to have a structure with a bent H—O—H angle of 104.5° and an oxygen-hydrogen bond distance of 0.96 Å [1 Å $\equiv 1 \times 10^{-8}$ cm $\equiv$ 100 pm (picometers, SI units)].

$$\text{H} \diagup\!\!\!\underset{104.5°}{\overset{O}{}}\!\!\!\diagdown \text{H} \quad (0.96\,\text{Å})$$

It should be emphasized that water is not a rigid molecule with the atoms fixed in this geometry. The atoms are constantly in motion, even at a temperature of absolute zero. This motion is conveniently described in terms of the bending and stretching of bonds. At any instant of time, the actual O—H distance may vary from 0.96 Å by several hundredths of an Ångstrom, but the average distance will be that given. Similarly, bond angles are constantly changing, and the value given is an average value.

An important result has emerged from these many structural studies. Specific bonds retain a remarkably constant geometry from one compound to another. For example, the oxygen-hydrogen bond distance is almost always 0.96–0.97 Å.

Compound	O—H Bond Distance, Å
HO—H, water	0.96
HOO—H, hydrogen peroxide	0.97
H_2NO—H, hydroxylamine	0.97
CH_3O—H, methyl alcohol	0.96

In fact, it is this consistency that allows us to treat the oxygen-hydrogen bond as an individual unit in different compounds.

Lewis structures can be useful in the interpretation of bond distances. For example, the nitrogen-oxygen bond distance is longer in hydroxylammonium ion than in nitronium ion.

$$H_3\overset{+}{N}—OH \qquad O=\overset{+}{N}=O \;\equiv\; :\overset{..}{O}::\overset{+}{N}::\overset{..}{O}:$$

1.45 Å   1.15 Å

hydroxylammonium ion   nitronium ion

The hydroxylammonium ion should not be confused with ammonium hydroxide, $NH_4^+\ OH^-$. The hydroxylammonium ion is an ammonium ion with one hydrogen replaced by an OH group. In the ammonium ion there are four nitrogen-hydrogen bonds; in the hydroxylammonium ion, there are three nitrogen-hydrogen bonds and one nitrogen-oxygen bond.

In $HONH_3^+$, one electron pair binds the nitrogen to the oxygen, and the compound is said to have a nitrogen-oxygen **single bond**. In NO_2^+, the Lewis structure shows that each nitrogen-oxygen bond involves two pairs of electrons and is therefore said to be a **double bond**. At the equilibrium bond distance the electrostatic forces between the negative electrons and positive nuclei are balanced. For the nitrogen-oxygen single bond, two bonding electrons are involved, and the balance of attraction and repulsion occurs at an internuclear distance of 1.45 Å. For the nitrogen-oxygen double bond, more electrons are involved with consequent greater net electrostatic attraction to the nuclei. The increased internuclear repulsion required to balance this additional attraction occurs at the shorter distance of 1.15 Å.

EXERCISE 2.2 On the basis of the Lewis structure you wrote for nitric oxide in Exercise 2.1, what nitrogen-oxygen bond distance would you expect?

EXERCISE 2.3 In the following comparisons of bonds, determine which bond is the shorter:
(a) CO in H—C—O—H   (b) NO in O=N—O—H
               ‖
               O
(c) CO in H_3C—O—H or H_2C=O

2.4 Resonance Structures

In some cases, it is not possible to describe the electronic structure of a species adequately with a single Lewis structure. An example is nitryl chloride, NO_2Cl.

nitryl chloride

The Lewis structure shown has one nitrogen-oxygen single bond and one nitrogen-oxygen double bond. However, it has been determined experimentally that both nitrogen-oxygen bonds are equivalent. Furthermore, the nitrogen-oxygen bond distance of 1.21 Å is intermediate between the nitrogen-oxygen single- and double-bond distances described in the previous section. Actually, two alternative structures, which differ only in the positions of electrons, may be written for nitryl chloride.

The actual electronic structure of NO_2Cl is a *composite* or *weighted average* of the two Lewis structures. The alternative structures are called **resonance structures**, and the molecule is said to be a **resonance hybrid**. Resonance structures may be defined as alternative representations of the electronic configuration of a fixed set of nuclei.

It is important to recognize that nitryl chloride *has only one geometric structure:* that in which the two nitrogen-oxygen bonds are equivalent. It is *not* $Cl-N\overset{O}{\underset{O^-}{\diagup}}$ half of the time and $Cl-N\overset{O^-}{\underset{O}{\diagup}}$ the other half. It is a hybrid in the same sense that a mule is a hybrid of a horse and a donkey. Resonance structures are necessary only because of inadequacies in our simplified system for describing bonding and electron distribution in molecules. When one conventional Lewis structure does not adequately describe what we know to be the actual structure of a species, we use two or more structures (resonance structures) for the species and bear in mind that the species has some characteristics of each structure.

Resonance structures are written with a double-headed arrow, and the resonance hybrid is frequently written with dotted lines to represent partial bonds. Even in such cases, the individual Lewis structures provide an accurate accounting of the electrons and are frequently preferred to dotted-line formulas. In the case of nitryl chloride, the Lewis structures indicate that the nitrogen-oxygen bond is halfway between single and double, and we expect an intermediate bond distance. Because each nitrogen-oxygen bond is single in one resonance structure and double in the other, the nitrogen-oxygen bond in the resonance hybrid is said to have a **bond order** of $1\frac{1}{2}$.

Another species that is not adequately described by a single structure is formate ion, HCO_2^-. As in the case of nitryl chloride, formate ion is a hybrid of two resonance structures.

$$\left[\begin{array}{c} H{:}C{\overset{:\ddot{O}:^{-}}{\underset{:\ddot{O}:}{\diagup}}} \\ \\ \updownarrow \\ \\ H{:}C{\overset{:\ddot{O}}{\underset{:\ddot{O}:_{-}}{\diagup}}} \end{array}\right] \equiv \left[\begin{array}{c} H{-}C{\overset{O^{-}}{\underset{O}{\diagup}}} \\ \\ \updownarrow \\ \\ H{-}C{\overset{O}{\underset{O_{-}}{\diagup}}} \end{array}\right] \equiv H{-}C{\overset{O^{\frac{1}{2}-}}{\underset{O^{\frac{1}{2}-}}{\diagup}}}$$

Both of the carbon-oxygen bonds have a bond order of $1\frac{1}{2}$. Accordingly, the carbon-oxygen bond distance of 1.26 Å is intermediate between the carbon-oxygen double-bond distance of 1.20 Å in $H_2C{=}O$ and the carbon-oxygen single-bond distance of 1.43 Å in $HO{-}CH_3$.

Carbonate ion, CO_3^{2-}, is somewhat more complicated in that three resonance structures are required. The resonance hybrid has three equivalent carbon-oxygen bonds, each having a bond order of $1\frac{1}{3}$. Because the carbon-oxygen bonds in carbonate ion (order $1\frac{1}{3}$) have more single-bond character than those in formate ion (order $1\frac{1}{2}$), they are slightly longer (1.28 Å).

$$\left[^{-}O{-}C{\overset{O}{\underset{O_{-}}{\diagup}}} \longleftrightarrow O{=}C{\overset{O^{-}}{\underset{O_{-}}{\diagup}}} \longleftrightarrow {}^{-}O{-}C{\overset{O^{-}}{\underset{O}{\diagup}}}\right]$$

EXERCISE 2.4 One resonance structure for ozone, O_3, is $^{-}O{-}O^{+}{=}O$. Write two Lewis resonance structures showing all valence electrons and compare the expected oxygen-oxygen bond length with that of hydrogen peroxide (Exercise 2.1).

In each of the foregoing examples, the important resonance structures are equivalent. In some cases, a species is best described by two or more resonance structures that are not energetically equivalent. One such species is protonated formaldehyde, $(H_2COH)^+$. Formaldehyde itself may be represented by a Lewis structure in which there are two carbon-hydrogen single bonds and a carbon-oxygen double bond (Exercise 2.3).

$$\begin{array}{c} H \\ {:}C{::}\ddot{O}{:} \\ H \end{array} \equiv \begin{array}{c} H \\ \diagdown C{=}O \\ \diagup \\ H \end{array}$$

formaldehyde

In protonated formaldehyde, an additional oxygen-hydrogen single bond is present. Two Lewis structures may be written for $(H_2COH)^+$.

$$\left[\begin{array}{c} H \\ {:}C{::}\overset{+}{O}{:}H \\ H \\ \updownarrow \\ H \\ {:}\overset{+}{C}{:}\ddot{O}{:}H \\ H \end{array}\right] \equiv \left[\begin{array}{c} H \\ \diagdown C{=}\overset{+}{O}H \\ \diagup \\ H \\ \updownarrow \\ H \\ \diagdown \overset{+}{C}{-}\ddot{O}H \\ \diagup \\ H \end{array}\right] \equiv \begin{array}{c} H \\ \diagdown {}^{\delta+}C{\cdots}{}^{\delta+}OH \\ \diagup \\ H \end{array}$$

In one structure there is a carbon-oxygen double bond, and the positive charge is assigned to oxygen. This **oxonium ion structure** is analogous to the hydronium ion, H_3O^+.

$$
\begin{array}{cc}
\text{H} & \text{H} \\
\ddot{}+ & \ddot{} \\
:\text{C}::\ddot{\text{O}}:\text{H} & \text{H}:\ddot{\text{O}}:^+ \\
\text{H} & \text{H}
\end{array}
$$

$$
\begin{array}{cc}
\text{oxonium ion structure} & \text{hydronium ion}
\end{array}
$$

In the alternative structure there is a carbon-oxygen single bond, and the positive charge is assigned to carbon. This **carbocation structure** is analogous to the methyl cation, CH_3^+.

$$
\begin{array}{cc}
\text{H} & \text{H} \\
+\ddot{} & \ddot{} \\
\dot{\text{C}}:\ddot{\text{O}}:\text{H} & \text{H}:\text{C}^+ \\
\text{H} & \text{H}
\end{array}
$$

$$
\begin{array}{cc}
\text{carbocation structure} & \text{methyl cation}
\end{array}
$$

Which structure more adequately represents protonated formaldehyde? The carbon-oxygen bond length in $(H_2COH)^+$ is 1.27 Å, which is much closer to the normal carbon-oxygen double-bond length of 1.20 Å than to the normal carbon-oxygen single-bond length of 1.43 Å. On this basis, we conclude that $(H_2COH)^+$ is more nearly described by the oxonium ion structure than by the carbocation structure. However, the carbon-oxygen bond length is significantly longer than a normal double bond, and calculations show that there is a substantial partial positive charge on carbon. We shall see in Chapter 14 that much of the chemistry of $(H_2COH)^+$ is best explained by the contribution of the less important carbocation structure.

Again, let us reiterate that *neither oxonium nor carbocation structure provides a totally accurate description of* $(H_2COH)^+$. The actual ion is a resonance hybrid of the two structures. It "looks" more like the oxonium ion structure than the carbocation structure, and it has some of the characteristics of each. The carbon-oxygen bond order is something between 1 and 2, but closer to 2. The positive charge is spread over both atoms, but is mostly borne by oxygen. Because oxygen is more electronegative than carbon, the positive charge would normally be on carbon. However, in this structure, carbon does not have an electron octet. In order for carbon to fill its octet, the positive charge must be borne by the more electronegative oxygen. *In cases such as this, the more important resonance structure is generally that one with all octets filled, even if a positive charge is assigned to the more electronegative atom.*

An extreme example of this principle is trifluoromethyl cation, CF_3^+. It has been calculated that the carbon-fluorine bond length in this ion is 1.27 Å, much less than the normal carbon-fluorine single bond length of 1.38 Å. Thus, the fluoronium ion structure is a major contributor to the resonance hybrid, even though the positive charge must be assigned to fluorine, the most electronegative of all of the elements.

$$
\left[
\begin{array}{c}
:\ddot{\text{F}}: \\
:\ddot{\text{F}}:\text{C}^+ \\
:\ddot{\text{F}}: \\
\updownarrow \\
:\ddot{\text{F}}: \\
:\overset{+}{\ddot{\text{F}}}::\text{C} \\
:\ddot{\text{F}}:
\end{array}
\right]
\equiv
\left[
\begin{array}{c}
\text{F} \\
\text{F}\!-\!\text{C}^+ \\
\text{F} \\
\updownarrow \\
\text{F} \\
\overset{+}{\text{F}}\!=\!\text{C} \\
\text{F}
\end{array}
\right]
$$

Another interesting example is provided by protonated methyleneimine, $(H_2CNH_2)^+$. The carbon-nitrogen bond length of 1.29 Å is almost exactly the same as the carbon-nitrogen double-bond length in methyleneimine itself (1.27 Å) and is much less than the normal carbon-nitrogen single-bond length of 1.47 Å.

methyleneimine
C=N length = 1.27 Å

protonated methyleneimine
C—N length = 1.29 Å

methylamine
C—N length = 1.47 Å

In this case, the ammonium ion structure dominates the hybrid even more than the oxonium ion structure does in the case of $(H_2COH)^+$ because the difference in electronegativity between carbon and nitrogen is less than that between carbon and oxygen.

In summary, let us set out some empirical rules for assessing the relative importance of the resonance structures of molecules and ions:

1. Resonance structures involve *no* change in the positions of nuclei; only the electron organization is involved.
2. Structures in which all first-row (second-period) atoms have filled octets are more important than structures with unfilled octets. The contribution of the non-octet structure increases as the difference in electronegativity between the atoms increases.

More Important   *Less Important*

3. The more important structures are those involving a minimum of charge separation.

More Important   *Less Important*

In cases such as these, however, the less important charge-separated structure still contributes significantly, and we shall find this contribution useful in interpreting some chemical reactions.

In some cases, Lewis structures with complete octets cannot be written without charge separation. In such alternative structures, the more important structure is again that in which the negative charge is borne by the more electronegative element and the positive charge by the more electropositive element.

More Important *Less Important*

$$\left[\; H-\underset{\underset{H}{|}}{\overset{+}{C}}=\overset{-}{\underset{..}{N}}=\overset{-}{\underset{..}{N}}: \quad \longleftrightarrow \quad H-\underset{\underset{H}{|}}{\overset{..}{C}}-\overset{+}{N}\equiv N: \; \right]$$

diazomethane

$$\left[\; H-\underset{\underset{H}{|}}{\overset{H}{\underset{|}{C}}}-C\equiv\overset{+}{N}-\overset{-}{\underset{..}{O}}: \quad \longleftrightarrow \quad H-\underset{\underset{H}{|}}{\overset{H}{\underset{|}{C}}}-\overset{..}{C}=\overset{+}{N}=\overset{-}{\underset{..}{O}}: \; \right]$$

acetonitrile oxide

Elements beyond the second period form structures with an apparent expansion of their octets. Examples are provided by sulfur hexafluoride, SF_6, and phosphorus pentachloride, PCl_5. Such compounds are probably best considered in terms of "no-bond" contributions. See how the P-Cl bond-length variations can be explained by simple octet resonance structures.

In the same manner, some compounds of these elements are often written as resonance hybrids with expanded octet resonance structures. An example is sulfuric acid.

The normal Lewis octet structure at the far left has a formal charge of $+2$ on sulfur. Sulfuric acid is known to be a strong acid, and the high formal charge on sulfur helps to explain the ease of loss of a proton.

EXERCISE 2.5 In this section we have made use of the concept of bond order and the generalization that the higher the bond order (degree of bonding), the shorter (and stronger) the bond. An example is the application to nitric acid and nitrate ion. Write two equivalent resonance structures for nitric acid and three for nitrate ion. Rank these three different types of nitrogen-oxygen bonds in order of length.

2.5 Atomic Orbitals

Careful use of Lewis structures and the related straight-line structural shorthand is clearly important in understanding the physical and chemical properties of molecules.

But these structures are themselves only symbolic representations of electronic structures. In the real world, electrons do not stand still in octets. A more complete understanding of the chemical bond and the structure of molecules requires a discussion of the modern theory of electronic structure in terms of wave functions or orbitals. Unfortunately, this theory involves new and unfamiliar concepts that do not relate to human experience. Atomic and molecular orbitals are usually covered in depth in courses on physical chemistry, but the qualitative aspects are so important to understanding modern organic chemistry that a brief survey of some results of quantum mechanics is highly desirable at this point. In the next few sections, we shall review those aspects of atomic and molecular orbital theory that are particularly important in the study of organic chemistry.

As mentioned in Section 2.1, the periodic table of the elements was first conceived in a purely empirical fashion. The various known elements were arranged into groups and rows on the basis of similarities in their chemical and physical properties. The "periodicity" of the table first became understandable with the early development of electronic theory. This early theory was based on the Bohr model, which is often taught by comparing an atom to a miniature solar system in which electrons are pictured as revolving in fixed orbits around a nucleus much as planets revolve about the sun.

With the advent of quantum mechanics about a half century ago, this analogy was shown to be seriously deficient in an extremely important respect. A basic tenet of quantum mechanics is the **Heisenberg uncertainty principle**, which states that it is not possible to determine simultaneously both the precise position and momentum of an electron. In other words, the laws of nature are such that we cannot determine an exact trajectory for an electron. The best we can do is to describe a probability distribution that gives the probability of finding an electron in any region around a nucleus. The mathematical description that leads to this probability distribution has the same form as that which describes a wave. Thus, we may use the mathematics and concepts of wave motion to describe electron distributions. Consequently, it is common to refer to the motion of an electron around a nucleus as a "wave motion" or in terms of a "wave function." This does not mean that the electron actually bobs up and down like a cork in a stormy sea. It is only a convenient phrase that helps to characterize the mathematical equations that describe the electron probability distribution.

In quantum mechanics, an **atomic orbital** is defined as a one-electron wave function, ψ. For each point in space there is associated a number whose square is proportional to the probability of finding an electron at that point. Such a probability function corresponds to the more useful concept of an **electron density** distribution. The mathematical function that describes an atomic orbital has all of the properties associated with waves; hence, it is called a **wave function**. It has a numerical magnitude (its amplitude), which can be either positive or negative (corresponding to a wave crest or a wave trough, respectively), and nodes. A **node** is the region where a crest and a trough meet. For the three-dimensional waves characteristic of electronic motion, the nodes are two-dimensional surfaces at which $\psi = 0$. Consequently, atomic orbitals may be characterized by their corresponding nodes as given by quantum numbers (Table 2.3).

If one recognizes the relationship between quantum numbers and the number and character of the nodes in a wave, it is clear why quantum numbers are integers; that is, it is meaningless to talk of a fraction of a node. In labeling a particular atomic orbital, the principal, azimuthal, and magnetic quantum numbers are specified. The three quantum numbers are expressed in the order nlm, but in a particular manner. The principal quantum number n is given as the appropriate integer. The azimuthal number l is expressed in code, where $0 = s$, $1 = p$, $2 = d$, and $3 = f$. In spatial descriptions m

TABLE 2.3 Atomic Quantum Numbers

Quantum Number	Symbol	Possible Values	Relationship to Nodes
principal	n	1, 2, 3, . . .	one more than the total number of nodes[a]
azimuthal or angular momentum	l	0, 1, . . . , $n-1$	number of nonspherical nodes
magnetic	m	$-l, . . . , 0, . . . +l$	character (planes or cones) and orientation of nonspherical nodes
spin	—	$-\frac{1}{2}, +\frac{1}{2}$	none

[a] Because atomic orbitals are exponential functions, they have very small values at distances far from the nucleus but never reach zero. The extra node could therefore be taken at infinity, but such a node could never be represented in conventional symbols. If the node "at infinity" is included, the principal quantum number is the same as the total number of nodes.

is not given explicitly, but is implied in a subscript code that defines the orientation of the orbital.

Examples

$1s$ no nodes. This wave function is a spherically symmetric function whose numerical value decreases exponentially from the nucleus.

$2s$ one spherical node

$2p_x$ one node, the yz-plane

$2p_y$ one node, the xz-plane

$2p_z$ one node, the xy-plane

These orbitals are the most important for the organic compounds we will study. They are usually represented symbolically as in Figure 2.1. The plus and minus signs

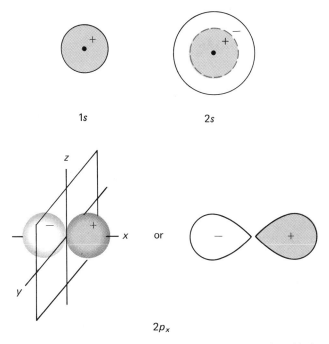

FIGURE 2.1 Symbolic representation of some atomic orbitals.

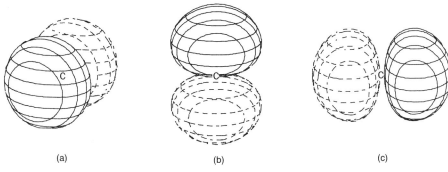

FIGURE 2.2   Perspective diagrams of $2p_x$-, $2p_y$-, and $2p_z$-orbitals.

in Figure 2.1 have no relationship to electric charge. They are simply the arithmetic signs associated with the wave function, much as a positive sign for an ocean wave is a wave crest and a negative sign denotes a wave trough. We shall see in the next section that the positive and negative signs determine how two or more wave functions combine when they interact.

In the symbolic representations given in Figure 2.1, the solid line represents the angular part of the wave function and defines a three-dimensional closed surface. A useful approximation is to regard the surface as a locus of points of constant value of ψ such that some given, but arbitrary, proportion of the total electron density is contained within the surface. For example, the value of ψ may be selected so that the resulting surface will enclose 80%, 90%, 95%, and so on of the electron density. The dotted lines in Figure 2.1 represent nodal surfaces. Remember that at the nodal surface the value of the wave function is zero. These nodes are a sphere for the 2s-orbital and a plane for the 2p-orbital. The strange shape of the p-orbital is determined by the central attractive force of the nucleus and the constraint of a planar node. The representation of 2p-orbitals in Figure 2.2 gives a better perspective for the three-dimensional shape and shows the three orthogonal directions of p_x-, p_y-, and p_z-orbitals.

2.6 Electronic Structure of Atoms

The Pauli principle applied to atoms states that no two electrons can have identical quantum numbers. Three quantum numbers characterize an atomic orbital. Electrons have a fourth quantum number associated with the characteristics of spin. This quantum number may have a value of either $+\frac{1}{2}$ or $-\frac{1}{2}$. Consequently, each atomic orbital may have associated with it no more than two electrons, and these two electrons must have "opposite spin."

In general, the more nodes a wave function has, the higher is its energy. In atoms that have more than one electron, the energies of atomic orbitals increase in the order $1s < 2s < 2p < 3s < 3p$, and so on (see Figure 2.3).

The first electron is put into the lowest energy atomic orbital, 1s, to produce the hydrogen atom. The helium atom has two electrons, and the second electron can also be put into a 1s-orbital if the second electron has a spin opposite that of the first electron. These two electrons "fill" the 1s-shell, and helium has the filled-shell configuration characteristic of noble gases. Thus, hydrogen and helium constitute the "first period" of the periodic table. The third electron of lithium must be put into a higher energy atomic orbital, 2s. The fourth electron of beryllium can also be put into the 2s-orbital if its spin is opposite that of the third electron. The 2s-orbital is now also filled, and the additional electrons of the first row (second period) elements must go

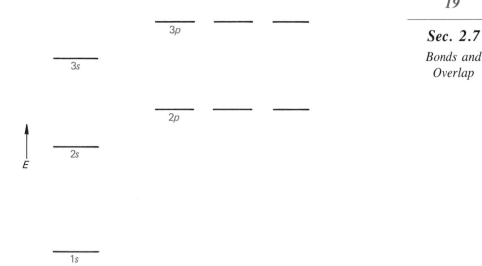

FIGURE 2.3 Order of energy levels in an atom with more than one electron.

into $2p$ atomic orbitals. The $2p_x$-, $2p_y$-, and $2p_z$-orbitals may each accept two electrons, giving a total of six for the p-set. Consequently, eight electrons fill the $n = 2$ shell and again give the stable filled-shell electronic configuration characteristic of the noble gases.

The process of filling successive atomic orbital levels with electron pairs is used to build up the entire periodic table. The atomic configurations of the first ten elements are summarized in Table 2.4. Each filled principal quantum shell corresponds to a stable noble gas. Other elements react in such a way as to achieve the stability associated with filled orbital shells. One way of achieving this higher stability is by combining atomic orbitals into molecular orbitals, as discussed in the next section.

TABLE 2.4 Electronic Configurations of Some Elements

First Period		Second Period	
H	$1s$	Li	$1s^22s$
He	$1s^2$	Be	$1s^22s^2$
		B	$1s^22s^22p$
		C	$1s^22s^22p^2$
		N	$1s^22s^22p^3$
		O	$1s^22s^22p^4$
		F	$1s^22s^22p^5$
		Ne	$1s^22s^22p^6$

2.7 Bonds and Overlap

One of the useful concepts derived from treating atomic orbitals as wave functions is that two such orbitals may overlap to form a bond. The combination of two waves having the same sign is *reinforcing* (Figure 2.4). This is true for light waves, sound waves, or the waves of an ocean. It is also true for the combination of two electron waves or wave functions having the same sign.

FIGURE 2.4 Two interacting waves or wave functions of the same sign add or **reinforce**.

The increased magnitude of the wave function between the atoms corresponds to higher electron density in this region. Electrons are attracted electrostatically to both nuclei, and the net effect of increased electron density between the nuclei counterbalances the internuclear repulsion. The result is a **covalent bond**. An example is the combination of two $1s$ atomic orbitals to give a new wave function. This wave function now encompasses both nuclei and is therefore called a **molecular orbital**. Figure 2.5 shows a symbolic representation of a molecular orbital (b) formed by the overlap of two atomic orbitals as in (a). Part (c) of Figure 2.5 is a contour diagram that depicts the value of the wave function in such a covalent bond as a function of distance from the nuclei, which are symbolized by the two heavy dots. The diagram represents a plane passing through the nuclei; each contour line connects points having the same value of the wave function in the same way that a contour line on a map connects points having the same altitude relative to sea level. In the example shown, all of the contours are positive. Figure 2.5d is a perspective view of a contour surface of such an orbital for a given contour value. Each bond that we have heretofore symbolized by a shared electron pair or by a straight line may now be interpreted as a ''two-center'' molecular orbital (an orbital encompassing two nuclei). Each such two-center molecular orbital contains two electrons of opposite spin.

When two waves of opposite sign interact, they interfere or cancel each other. It is this characteristic of waves that can produce regions of darkness in the interaction of two light beams or regions of silence from the combination of two sound waves. At the point of interference the wave function has the value of zero; that is, interference of waves creates a node. The same pattern holds for electron waves. The interaction of two orbitals of opposite sign produces a node between the nuclei, as illustrated in

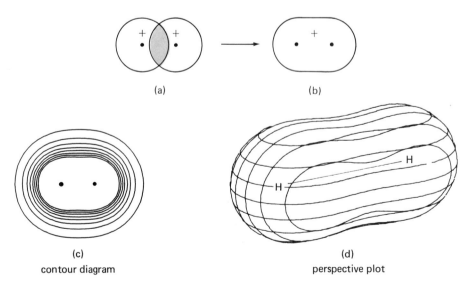

(a)   (b)

(c)   (d)
contour diagram   perspective plot

FIGURE 2.5 The combination of two H $1s$ orbitals to form an H_2 molecular orbital.

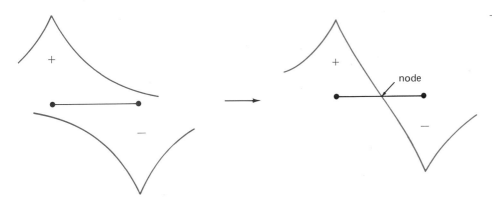

FIGURE 2.6 Interaction of two waves of opposite sign gives subtraction or **interference**.

Figure 2.6. Because there is no electron density at a node, the net effect is a reduced electron density between the nuclei which does not compensate for the nuclear repulsion, and the result is a higher energy or lower stability than that which corresponds to the two orbitals before interacting. Such a molecular orbital is called **antibonding**. A diagram of such an antibonding molecular orbital is shown in Figure 2.7.

The interaction of two orbitals can be positive or reinforcing to give a bonding molecular orbital, or the combination can be negative or interfering to give an antibonding molecular orbital. The bonding combination corresponds to a decrease in energy (greater stability); the antibonding combination corresponds to an increase in energy (lower stability). Two atomic orbitals give rise to two molecular orbitals. The two paired electrons of opposite spin available for the bond can be put into the bonding molecular orbital. We will not refer to antibonding molecular orbitals for most of the normal compounds important in organic chemistry, but we will make extensive use of them in Chapter 21.

The energy relationships of two combining orbitals are summarized in Figure 2.8. Note how the energies of the two starting orbitals separate or spread apart when they interact to form the two molecular orbitals. The amount of the separation depends on the degree to which the orbitals occupy the same space or **overlap**. A slight overlap gives two molecular orbitals that differ little in energy; a large overlap results in strong energy separation such as that shown in Figure 2.8. For axially symmetric orbitals, such as *p*-orbitals, the greatest overlap occurs when the orbitals are allowed to interact along the nuclear axis, that is, to form straight bonds. We shall see later that if orbitals are so constrained that overlap is not along the internuclear axis, the resulting "bent bonds" (Figure 2.9b and c) are weaker than equivalent straight bonds (Figure 2.9a).

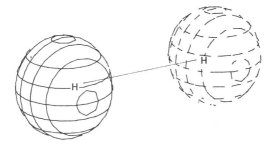

FIGURE 2.7 A two-center antibonding molecular orbital. The dashed lines indicate a wave function of negative sign.

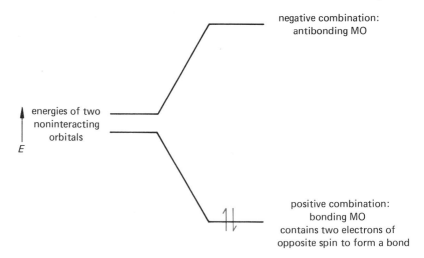

FIGURE 2.8 Energy relationships of combining orbitals.

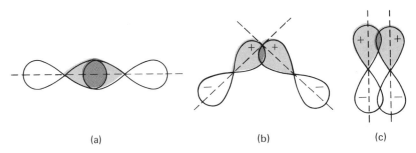

FIGURE 2.9 Illustrating the overlap of two *p*-orbitals (*a*) along the internuclear axis and (*b* and *c*) off the internuclear axis. The bonding molecular orbital resulting from the overlap in (*a*) has lower energy than the other two.

2.8 Hybrid Orbitals and Bonds

When more than two valence electrons on the same atom are involved in bonding, the individual bonds are not generally describable in terms of overlap of simple atomic orbitals as in the foregoing example. Consider the molecule BeH_2 as an example. Spectroscopic measurements show that the two beryllium-hydrogen bonds are of equal length. These two bonds clearly cannot be described adequately by using the beryllium 2*s*-orbital for one bond and a 2*p*-orbital for the other. These two orbitals have different spatial extensions and different energies and would be expected to give different bonds. The bonding can be explained if we construct *two equivalent* **hybrid** *orbitals* by combining the 2*s*- and a 2*p*-orbital. This is done mathematically by taking the sum and the difference of the two orbitals, as in Figure 2.10. This example shows how the mathematical signs of wave functions enter into arithmetic operations.

The two orbitals that result from this operation are designated *sp*-hybrid orbitals because they are each constructed from equal amounts of an *s*- and a *p*-orbital. The *sp*-hybrid orbital is shown in contour form in Figure 2.11a and as the three-dimensional perspective plot in Figure 2.11b. The two hybrid orbitals are each well suited to form a bond by overlapping with a hydrogen 1*s*-orbital. They are equivalent and are directed opposite each other. Furthermore, the two lobes of a hybrid orbital are unequal in

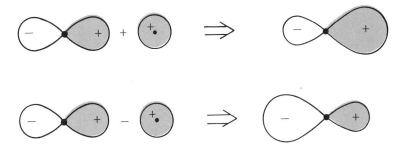

FIGURE 2.10 Mathematical combination of *s*- and *p*-orbitals to form two *sp*-hybrid orbitals.

''size''—the larger lobe can overlap well with another orbital. That is, overlap at the large lobe can occur readily in a straight line to produce stronger bonding.

Why does beryllium form bonds in this manner rather than by overlap of the simple atomic orbitals? The answer is simply that stronger bonds and a more stable structure result when the system H—Be—H is linear and the two bonds are of equal length. In this manner *the two electron pairs involved in the bonds are directed as far apart from each other as possible*. This principle is a useful guide for predicting the geometry of a molecule in which several groups are bonded to a central atom. In general, the bonding may be described by constructing as many hybrid orbitals from the simple *s*- and *p*-atomic orbitals as are needed to accommodate all of the valence electrons associated with the central atom. In the BeH_2 example, we used one *s*- and one *p*-orbital and constructed two equivalent hybrids. Each such hybrid is described as 50% *s* and 50% *p*. In constructing such combinations, we must again obey the *rule of conservation of orbitals*. We must end up with as many orbitals as we started with. The beryllium atom has, of course, two remaining *p*-orbitals that are not occupied by electrons in the molecule BeH_2.

As a further example, consider a species in which three groups are to be bonded to a central atom. From an *s*-orbital and two *p*-orbitals—for example, a p_x- and a p_y-orbital—we may construct three equivalent sp^2-hybrids. Each such hybrid is $\frac{1}{3}$ *s* and $\frac{2}{3}$ *p*. The three equivalent hybrids lie in the *xy*-plane (the same plane defined by the two *p*-orbitals) and are directed 120° from each other (Figure 2.12).

Methyl cation, CH_3^+, is an example of such a species. It is planar and the three carbon-hydrogen bonds are equal in length. It may be regarded as being derived from overlap of three equivalent carbon sp^2-orbitals with hydrogen 1*s*-orbitals. Each bond

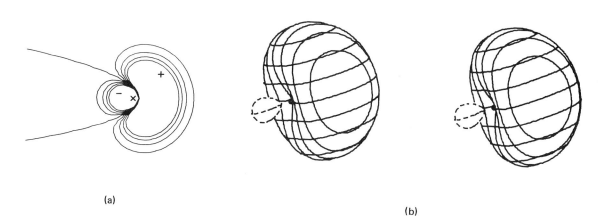

(a)

(b)

FIGURE 2.11 Contour and perspective plots of an *sp*-hybrid orbital.

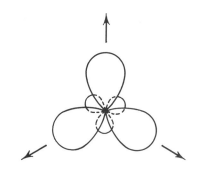

FIGURE 2.12 Three sp^2-hybridized orbitals.

may be represented as C_{sp^2}—H_{1s}. The remaining carbon p-orbital is perpendicular to the molecular plane and contains no electrons. In this process of conceptual development, we have used the sequence of combining three atomic orbitals to form three hybrid orbitals (Figure 2.12) that are allowed to overlap (Figure 2.13a) to form three two-center molecular orbitals (Figure 2.13b). Each of these molecular orbitals contains two electrons, and the carbon also has two electrons in its $1s$ orbital that are not normally represented in our simple valence symbols.

Finally, from an s-orbital and three p-orbitals we may derive four sp^3-hybrids directed to the corners of a tetrahedron with an interorbital angle of 109.5°, the tetrahedral angle. Each such hybrid orbital is 25% s and 75% p. A three-dimensional perspective plot of one sp^3-hybrid orbital is shown in Figure 2.14. Note that the ''small lobe'' is much larger than in the sp-hybrid depicted in Figure 2.11b.

The tetrahedral structure of methane, CH_4, is illustrated in stereo plot in Figure 2.15a or by the perspective model in Figure 2.15b. Each bond between C and H may be described as a C_{sp^3}—H_{1s} bond. Each such bond is derived by the interaction of a C_{sp^3}-hybrid orbital with a hydrogen $1s$, as in Figure 2.15c, to produce the resulting two-center molecular orbital shown in Figure 2.15d. The actual wave function—the mathematical form of the molecular orbitals—for which Figure 2.15d is only a symbolic representation is shown in contour form in Figure 2.15e.

The hybrid orbitals considered thus far are equivalent, but it is not necessary that all orbitals on an atom be equivalent when the molecule lacks symmetry. It is possible to have a hybrid orbital that is, for example, 23% s and 77% p. In NH_3, for example, the H—N—H angle of 107.1° does not correspond to any simple hybrid. Recall that sp^3-hybridization corresponds to a bond angle of 109.5°, sp^2-hybridization corresponds to 120°, and pure p-orbitals form a 90° angle. In addition to its three nitrogen-hydrogen bonds, ammonia also has a nonbonding pair of electrons on the nitrogen. These elec-

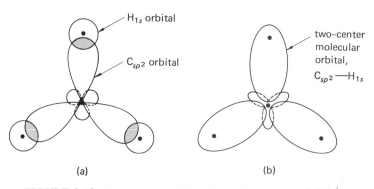

      (a)   (b)

FIGURE 2.13 Development of the electronic structure of CH_3^+.

FIGURE 2.14 Three-dimensional perspective view of an sp^3-hybrid orbital.

trons are in an orbital that has more *s*-character than a simple sp^3-orbital. Consequently, the three hybrid orbitals that overlap with the three hydrogen atoms contain less *s*-character than a sp^3-orbital (actually, these orbitals are each approximately 23% *s* and 77% *p*).

Electrons in *s*-orbitals have lower energy than electrons in *p*-orbitals. Therefore, bonds with more *s*-character tend to be stronger. However, an electron pair in a bond is affected by two nuclei, whereas nonbonding electrons are attracted only by a single

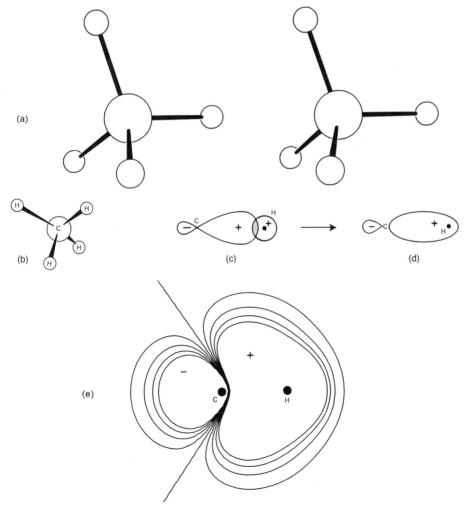

FIGURE 2.15 Methane, CH_4, and its C_{sp^3}—H_{1s} bond.

nucleus. Hence, *s*-character is more important for lone-pair electrons than for bonding electron pairs. In dividing the available *s*-orbital among bonds and lone pairs, the lone pairs generally receive a higher proportion.

This type of result is general. In water, for example, the H—O—H angle is 104.5° and each oxygen-hydrogen bond clearly involves an oxygen hybrid with more *p*-character than the nitrogen hybrid in ammonia. The two oxygen lone pairs require a large fraction of the available oxygen 2*s*-orbital. In HF, the hydrogen-fluorine bond is an almost pure F_{2p}—H_{1s} bond, and the fluorine 2*s*-orbital is used almost entirely for the three hybrid orbitals that contain the lone pairs. Nevertheless, despite these complexities, it is frequently convenient and sufficient to regard the two-center molecular orbitals that comprise electron-pair covalent bonds as being composed *approximately* of simple hybrids: sp, sp^2, sp^3, and so on.

EXERCISE 2.6 The bond angle in H_2S is 93.3°. How would you describe the sulfur-hydrogen bond in terms of simple hybrids?

The total electron density distribution in a molecule is real in the sense that it can, in principle, be seen and measured. However, in order to understand such electron distributions, we generally dissect the total system into component parts that we can work with conceptually through the manipulation of symbols. Our concepts of orbitals, hybrids, and bonds should be regarded in this light. In principle, there are many possible ways of dissecting a total molecular electron density distribution into smaller and smaller parts. Our traditional way is merely one such method, but it is a method having historical roots and having evolved a grammar and language of its own. It is also a system that can be represented by simple symbols and serves as a powerful and widespread method for correlating and predicting a wide range of chemistry. As such, this symbolism and language have permeated many neighboring sciences such as biochemistry and molecular biology.

PROBLEMS

1. Write a valid Lewis structure for each of the following inorganic compounds.
    (a) bisulfate ion, HSO_4^-
    (b) amide ion, NH_2^-
    (c) nitrite ion, NO_2^- (arranged ONO)
    (d) dinitrogen trioxide, N_2O_3 (arranged ONONO)
    (e) nitrous oxide, N_2O (arranged NNO)
    (f) hydroxylamine anion, $(ONH_2)^-$
    (g) nitronium ion, NO_2^+ (arranged ONO)
    (h) cyanamide, H_2NCN
    (i) nitrosonium ion, NO^+
    (j) hydrazoic acid, HN_3 (arranged HNNN)
    (k) azide ion, N_3^- (arranged NNN)
    (l) carbonate ion, CO_3^{2-}
    (m) cyanic acid, OCNH

2. Write out the Lewis structures and corresponding Kekulé structures for each of the following organic compounds.
    (a) ethyl cation, $CH_3CH_2^+$
    (b) ethyl radical, CH_3CH_2
    (c) ethyl anion, $CH_3CH_2^-$
    (d) methylacetylene, $CH_3C{\equiv}CH$
    (e) methyl ethyl ketone, $CH_3COCH_2CH_3$
    (f) dimethyl ether, CH_3OCH_3

(g) methylamine, CH_3NH_2
(h) methylammonium cation, $CH_3NH_3^+$
(i) methoxide ion, CH_3O^-
(j) methyloxonium ion, $CH_3OH_2^+$
(k) vinyl chloride, $CH_2=CHCl$
(l) formyl cation, HCO^+ (arranged HCO)

3. For each of the following compounds, describe each bond in terms of its component atomic orbitals.
   (a) ethane, CH_3CH_3
   (b) ethyl anion, $CH_3CH_2^-$
   (c) ethyl cation, $CH_3CH_2^+$
   (d) methylborane, CH_3BH_2
   (e) methylberyllium hydride, CH_3BeH
   (f) methanol, CH_3OH

4. Which of the following pairs of Kekulé structures do *not* constitute resonance structures?

(a) $CH_3\overset{O}{\overset{\|}{C}}-O^-$ and $CH_3\overset{O^-}{\overset{|}{C}}=O$

(b) $CH_3\overset{O}{\overset{\|}{C}}-OH$ and $CH_3\overset{OH}{\overset{|}{C}}=O$

(c) $CH_3\overset{O}{\overset{\|}{C}}CH_3$ and $CH_3\overset{OH}{\overset{|}{C}}=CH_2$

(d) $^+CH_2-CH=CH_2$ and $CH_2=CH-\overset{+}{C}H_2$

(e) $CH_2=CH-\overset{O}{\overset{\|}{C}}H$ and $^+CH_2-CH=\overset{O^-}{\overset{|}{C}}H$

(f) $CH_3CH=CHCH_3$ and $CH_3CH_2CH=CH_2$

(g) $CH_2=C=CH_2$ and $CH_3C\equiv CH$

(h) $H-C\equiv\overset{+}{N}H$ and $H-\overset{+}{C}=NH$

(i) $CH_3-\underset{+}{\overset{O}{\overset{\|}{N}}}-O^-$ and $CH_3-\underset{+}{\overset{O^-}{\overset{|}{N}}}=O$

(j) $CH_3\overset{OH}{\overset{|}{C}}HCH_3$ and $CH_3CH_2\overset{OH}{\overset{|}{C}}H_2$

(k) $CH_3N=C=O$ and $CH_3O-C\equiv N$

(l) $CH_3N=C=O$ and $CH_3\overset{+}{N}\equiv C-O^-$

(m) $^-O-\overset{+}{O}=O$ and $O=\overset{+}{O}-O^-$

(n) $\overset{.}{N}=O$ and $^-N=O\cdot{}^+$

(o)   HOCN   and   HNCO

5. For each of the following resonance hybrids, rank the contributing structures in order of their relative importance.

(a) $H-\overset{:O:}{\overset{\|}{C}}-\overset{..}{N}H_2 \longleftrightarrow H-\overset{:O:^-}{\overset{|}{C}}=\overset{+}{N}H_2$

(b) $H-\overset{:O:}{\overset{\|}{C}}-\overset{..}{C}H_2 \longleftrightarrow H-\overset{:O:^-}{\overset{|}{C}}=CH_2$

(c) $H-\overset{:O:}{\overset{\|}{C}}-\overset{-}{\overset{..}{N}}H \longleftrightarrow H-\overset{:O:^-}{\overset{|}{C}}=\overset{..}{N}H$

(d) $CH_2=CH-\overset{\overset{\displaystyle :O:}{\|}}{C}H \longleftrightarrow {}^+CH_2-CH=\overset{\overset{\displaystyle :\overset{\cdot\cdot}{O}:^-}{|}}{C}H \longleftrightarrow {}^-\overset{\cdot\cdot}{C}H_2-CH=\overset{\overset{\displaystyle :O:^+}{|}}{C}H$

(e)

(f) $H-\overset{\overset{\displaystyle :\overset{+}{O}H}{\|}}{C}-\overset{\cdot\cdot}{O}H \longleftrightarrow H-\overset{\overset{\displaystyle :\overset{\cdot\cdot}{O}H}{|}}{C}=\overset{\cdot\cdot}{O}H^+$

(g) $CH_3-\overset{+}{N}\equiv C-O^- \longleftrightarrow CH_3-{}^-N-C\equiv O^+$

(h) $^-O-\overset{\cdot}{O}=O \longleftrightarrow O=O=O$

(i) $\overset{\cdot}{N}=O \longleftrightarrow {}^-N=O\cdot^+$

(j) $HONC \longleftrightarrow HO\overset{+}{N}\equiv C^-$

(k) $CH_2=C=O \longleftrightarrow \overset{-}{C}H_2-C\equiv O^+$

6. Use the information given on page 6 to show that the reaction $Na\cdot + Cl\cdot \longrightarrow Na^+ + Cl^-$ is endothermic in the gas phase. Sodium chloride has m.p. 801°C and boils at 1465°C. The vapor consists of ion pairs, $Na^+ Cl^-$, held together by electrostatic attraction at a bond distance of 2.36 Å. A proton and electron at a distance of 1 Å have an electrostatic attraction of 330 kcal mole^{-1}. What is the electrostatic energy of a proton and electron at the bond distance of sodium chloride? As a model for $Na^+ Cl^-$, is this value enough to make the reaction $Na\cdot + Cl\cdot \longrightarrow Na^+ Cl^-$ exothermic?

Chapter 3

Organic Structures

3.1 Introduction

By the middle of the nineteenth century, organic chemistry was being actively explored in Europe. Many new compounds had been isolated from natural sources, and it was found increasingly that one organic compound could be transformed into another. However, the fundamental concept of **structure** had not yet evolved. The atomic theory of matter was well established, and it was clear that, by and large, inorganic compounds could be characterized by simple formulas, such as NH_3, P_2O_5, HNO_3, or H_2SO_4.* The satisfying theory of valency was well on its way to providing organization to the multitude of known chemical substances. However, some vexing problems remained, largely with the ''organic'' compounds. For example, ''marsh gas'' (methane) was shown to have the formula CH_4, which agreed with the quadrivalence of carbon in inorganic compounds such as CS_2. However, ''olefiant gas'' (ethylene) was found to have the formula C_2H_4, in which the apparent valence of carbon was two. To make matters worse, a gaseous hydrocarbon (acetylene) discovered by Edmund Davy in 1836 was found to have the formula C_2H_2 in which carbon had the ridiculous valence of one!

A second difficult problem was presented by the phenomenon of **isomerism** (the existence of two or more compounds having the same molecular formula). Isomerism had first been discovered in the 1820s by Liebig and Wöhler when they found that silver cyanate (AgNCO) and silver fulminate (AgONC) have the same atomic composition. Joseph Louis Gay-Lussac made the then-revolutionary suggestion that the two compounds differed ''in the way the elements were combined together.'' From this point on, it was clear that a formula alone was not adequate to characterize a compound uniquely.

The third important event which paved the way for the invention of chemical structures was the discovery of **substitution reactions** (replacement of an atom or group of atoms in a compound by another atom or group of atoms). Although substitution had been noted in the late eighteenth century, it was first actively investigated by Dumas and his protégé Auguste Laurent in the 1830s and 1840s. One of the first substitution reactions studied was halogenation (Chapter 6). For example, it was found that chlorine combines with many organic compounds by replacing hydrogen atoms one-for-one, as in the conversion of methane to chloroform.

$$CH_4 + 3\,Cl_2 \longrightarrow CHCl_3 + 3\,HCl$$

---

* Actually, the formulas in use in the early nineteenth century were not standardized, since different chemists were prone to use different atomic weights for various elements. For example, the German chemist Justus von Liebig used C = 6, O = 8, while the French chemist Jean Baptiste André Dumas used C = 6, O = 16. In Sweden, Berzelius used atomic weights that agree with the present-day values, but he also used double volume formulas. In this section, we use only the modern formulas.

However, it was also found that in some compounds all of the hydrogens did not seem to be equivalent. For example, acetic acid was found to undergo substitution of only three of its four hydrogens, no matter how vigorous the reaction conditions. The product, trichloroacetic acid, had properties which differed only quantitatively from those of acetic acid itself.

$$HC_2H_3O_2 + 3\,Cl_2 \longrightarrow HC_2Cl_3O_2 + 3\,HCl$$

Thus, it became increasingly clear that it must matter how a given hydrogen is joined to the remainder of the molecule.

At the time, a considerable controversy raged over the work of Laurent and Dumas. In fact, strange as it may now seem, the very existence of substitution was not even accepted by Berzelius, since it appeared to be leading toward nullification of the "dualistic theory," of which he was the architect and principal advocate. The controversy was not solely the result of inflexibility on the part of Berzelius, since Dumas was prone to make rather rash extensions of his experiments, such as his claim that even carbon atoms were susceptible to substitution by halogens. The argument eventually led Wöhler, who was something of a practical joker, to perpetrate an amusing hoax. In an article published in the German journal *Liebigs Annalen* under the pen name S. C. H. Windler, Wöhler described work on the reaction of chlorine with manganese acetate, $Mn(C_2H_3O_2)_2$. He reported that the hydrogen was first replaced by chlorine as expected. However, he reported that on longer reaction the oxygen and manganese were also replaced and that finally even the carbon was replaced by chlorine. There was obtained a substance which analyzed for 100% chlorine, but which had all the physical and chemical properties of manganese acetate!

Gradually, it came to be realized that the atoms in a molecule are "hooked together" in a certain way and that this assembly or structure is a more accurate way of describing a substance than a simple molecular formula. As shown on page 3, the first attempts to depict structures were fairly clumsy. However, these initial attempts to depict the manner in which a compound's atoms are joined together soon gave way to a standard formalism in which a line was used to symbolize a point of connection, or "bond," between two atoms. With this simple concept came the realization that "valency," which worked so well for inorganic compounds, could be easily extended to organic compounds by the expedient of using "double" and "triple" bonds, as in ethylene and acetylene.

$$\begin{array}{cc} H \\ \diagdown \\ C{=}C \\ \diagup \diagdown \\ H H \end{array} \qquad H{-}C{\equiv}C{-}H$$

It was much later that the idea of the electron-pair (covalent) bond was introduced, and the lines of the nineteenth century acquired a physical significance as shown in the Lewis "electron dot" structures we reviewed in Chapter 2. In modern orbital terms each of these lines represents a two-center molecular orbital "localized" on a pair of atoms and derived from the overlap of two atomic or hybrid orbitals. These **structural formulas** are often further abbreviated for convenience by omitting the lines. The resulting expressions are called **condensed formulas**.

$$\begin{array}{ccc} H & & H \\ | & & | \\ H{-}C{-}H \equiv CH_4 & & H{-}C{-}\ddot{C}\ddot{l}{:} \equiv CH_3Cl \\ | & & | \\ H & & H \end{array}$$

methane   methyl chloride

$$\underset{\displaystyle H}{\overset{\displaystyle H}{H-\underset{|}{\overset{|}{C}}-\ddot{\underset{\displaystyle ..}{O}}-H}} \equiv \underset{\displaystyle H}{\overset{\displaystyle H}{H-\underset{|}{\overset{|}{C}}-O-H}} \equiv CH_3OH$$

methyl alcohol

An important characteristic of organic compounds is the ubiquity of carbon-carbon bonds. Although some other atoms can bond to themselves to form short or long chains, carbon is unique in the extent and versatility of its catenation (chain formation; L., *catena*, a chain). Such carbon-carbon bonds are treated in the same way as others, as shown by the following examples.

$$\underset{\displaystyle H\ H}{\overset{\displaystyle H\ H}{H-\underset{|}{\overset{|}{C}}-\underset{|}{\overset{|}{C}}-H}} \equiv CH_3CH_3 \qquad \underset{\displaystyle H\ H}{\overset{\displaystyle H\ H}{H-\underset{|}{\overset{|}{C}}-\underset{|}{\overset{|}{C}}-Cl}} \equiv CH_3CH_2Cl$$

ethane   ethyl chloride

$$\underset{\displaystyle H\ H}{\overset{\displaystyle H\ H}{H-\underset{|}{\overset{|}{C}}-\underset{|}{\overset{|}{C}}-O-H}} \equiv CH_3CH_2OH \qquad \underset{\displaystyle H\ H\ H}{\overset{\displaystyle H\ H\ H}{H-\underset{|}{\overset{|}{C}}-\underset{|}{\overset{|}{C}}-\underset{|}{\overset{|}{C}}-H}} \equiv CH_3CH_2CH_3$$

ethyl alcohol   propane

These compounds involve carbon-hydrogen bonds that are all approximately $C_{sp^3}-H_{1s}$. Correspondingly, all of these carbon-hydrogen bonds are about the same length, 1.10 Å. Similarly, all of the carbon-carbon bonds in these compounds are approximately $C_{sp^3}-C_{sp^3}$, and these bond lengths are all about the same, 1.54 Å.

Compounds with multiple bonds can also be represented by condensed formulas.

$$\underset{\displaystyle H \qquad H}{\overset{\displaystyle H \qquad H}{C=C}} \equiv CH_2=CH_2 \qquad H-C\equiv C-H \equiv HC\equiv CH$$

ethylene   acetylene

The carbon-hydrogen bonds in ethylene are approximately $C_{sp^2}-H_{1s}$ and are slightly shorter than the $C_{sp^3}-H_{1s}$ bonds in ethane. Similarly, the carbon-hydrogen bonds in acetylene are approximately $C_{sp}-H_{1s}$ and are shorter still. The double and triple carbon-carbon bonds in ethylene and acetylene are also shorter and stronger than the single carbon-carbon bond and are discussed in detail in subsequent chapters (Sections 11.1 and 12.1).

Further examples in which several different types of bonds are involved are

$$\underset{\displaystyle H \quad\ \ H}{\overset{\displaystyle H\ \ O\ \ H}{H-\underset{|}{\overset{|}{C}}-\overset{\parallel}{C}-\underset{|}{\overset{|}{C}}-H}} \equiv CH_3COCH_3 \qquad \underset{\displaystyle Cl}{\overset{\displaystyle Cl}{H-\underset{|}{\overset{|}{C}}-Cl}} \equiv CHCl_3$$

acetone   chloroform

$$O=C=O \equiv CO_2 \qquad \underset{\displaystyle H}{\overset{\displaystyle H\ \ O}{H-\underset{|}{\overset{|}{C}}-\overset{\parallel}{C}-O-H}} \equiv CH_3COOH$$

carbon dioxide   acetic acid

In our subsequent discussion of organic structures, we shall make frequent use of these simple bonding concepts and symbols. We shall find them to be common and powerful devices for understanding physical properties and reactions. Organic structures are generally so large and complex that it is essential to have such systematic methods for dissecting the whole molecule into component parts and individual bonds.

EXERCISE 3.1 Write structural and condensed formulas for two compounds having the formula C_4H_{10} and three compounds having the formula C_5H_{12}.

3.2 Functional Groups

One consequence of the Laurent-Dumas investigations of substitution during the 1830s and 1840s was the evolution of the "type theory." It was gradually recognized that organic compounds can be organized in a certain rather small number of "types," each of which show similar chemical properties. The type theory was greatly extended in the 1840s and 1850s, principally by August Wilhelm von Hofmann at the Royal College of Chemistry and Alexander William Williamson at University College, both in London. Hofmann studied the relationship between ammonia and the group of organic compounds known as amines, and showed that the amines can be prepared from ammonia by the successive replacement of one, two, or three hydrogens of ammonia by organic groups. Furthermore, the amines all show the characteristic basic properties of ammonia. Accordingly, Hofmann suggested that amines are organic molecules of the "ammonia type."

$$\left.\begin{array}{l} H \\ H \\ H \end{array}\right\} N \qquad \left.\begin{array}{l} C_2H_5 \\ H \\ H \end{array}\right\} N \qquad \left.\begin{array}{l} C_2H_5 \\ C_2H_5 \\ H \end{array}\right\} N \qquad \left.\begin{array}{l} C_2H_5 \\ C_2H_5 \\ C_2H_5 \end{array}\right\} N$$

$$\text{ammonia} \qquad \text{ethylamine} \qquad \text{diethylamine} \qquad \text{triethylamine}$$

At about the same time as Hofmann was investigating amines, Williamson carried out research on the relationship of water, alcohols, and ethers and eventually realized that, just as there is an ammonia type of organic compound, alcohols and ethers belong to a "water type."

$$\left.\begin{array}{l} H \\ H \end{array}\right\} O \qquad \left.\begin{array}{l} C_2H_5 \\ H \end{array}\right\} O \qquad \left.\begin{array}{l} C_2H_5 \\ C_2H_5 \end{array}\right\} O$$

$$\text{water} \qquad \text{ethyl alcohol} \qquad \text{ethyl ether}$$

Chemists were quick to realize the power of this new idea of grouping the rapidly expanding plethora of organic molecules into a relatively small number of types, characterized by similar chemical properties. For example, the OH group in water reacts avidly with potassium to form potassium hydroxide and molecular hydrogen.

$$H_2O + K \longrightarrow K^+ OH^- + \tfrac{1}{2} H_2$$

Under the type theory, it is no surprise to find that the same reaction occurs with methyl alcohol.

$$CH_3OH + K \longrightarrow CH_3O^- K^+ + \tfrac{1}{2} H_2$$

Furthermore, a large number of different alcohols are known. Each consists of an OH group attached to a carbon framework, and all show this same reaction. Because of this constancy in the chemical properties of the OH group, it is unnecessary to study in detail the reactions of each of these many alcohols. Instead, it suffices to study alcohols as a class of organic compounds characterized by the chemical properties of the hydroxy group. This is a fortunate situation, for it gives organic chemistry a logical and systematic structure. There are a number of atoms or groups of atoms that show a relative constancy of properties when attached to different carbon chains. In modern terminology, such groups of atoms are called **functional groups**. The OH group is an example of a functional group. In this book, we will organize our systematic study of organic chemistry according to the chemistry of the important functional groups.

The simplest organic compounds are those that have no functional groups. These compounds consist only of carbon and hydrogen and are molecules in which carbons are joined to each other only by single bonds. These **saturated hydrocarbons** (''saturated'' means having no double or triple bonds) may be noncyclic (the **alkanes**) or cyclic (the **cycloalkanes**). They form the framework to which functional groups may be attached. The symbol R is often used to denote an alkyl group, the simplest being the methyl group, CH_3. Since the simplest alkane is methane, CH_4, we see that with this symbolism the alkane class may be represented by RH. We shall see in Chapter 6 that alkanes undergo only a limited number of reactions—precisely because they have no functional groups.

Some Alkanes

$$CH_4 \qquad CH_3CH_3 \qquad CH_3CH_2CH_3 \qquad CH_3CH_2CH_2CH_3$$

Some Cycloalkanes

In a similar manner, all hydrocarbons containing one or more carbon-carbon double bonds form a logical class, the **alkenes**. The hydrocarbons having a carbon-carbon triple bond form a third structurally similar set, the **alkynes**.

Some Alkenes

Some Alkynes

$$CH_3-C\equiv C-H \qquad CH_3CH_2CH_2-C\equiv C-CH_3 \qquad H-C\equiv C-H$$

We will find a number of reactions characteristic of carbon-carbon multiple bonds that are not shared by single bonds.

Organic compounds that contain carbon-oxygen single bonds are classed as **alcohols** or **ethers**, depending on whether or not the oxygen is also bonded to a hydrogen.

Some Alcohols

Some Ethers

$$CH_3—O—CH_3 \quad CH_3—O—CH\genfrac{}{}{0pt}{}{\diagup CH_3}{\diagdown CH_3} \quad \begin{array}{c} H_2C—CH_2 \\ | \qquad \backslash \\ H_2C \qquad CH_2 \\ \diagdown \quad O \quad \diagup \end{array}$$

The carbon-oxygen double bond, the carbonyl group, is found in **aldehydes** and **ketones**. When the carbonyl group is bonded to an OH group, it becomes a carboxy group. Compounds containing this functional group are called **carboxylic acids**.

Some Aldehydes

$$H_2C{=}O \qquad CH_3\overset{\overset{\textstyle O}{\|}}{C}H \qquad CH_3CH_2\overset{\overset{\textstyle O}{\|}}{C}H$$

Some Ketones

$$CH_3\overset{\overset{\textstyle O}{\|}}{C}CH_3 \qquad CH_3\overset{\overset{\textstyle CH_3}{|}}{C}H{-}\overset{\overset{\textstyle O}{\|}}{C}CH_3 \qquad \begin{array}{c} H_2C—C{=}O \\ | \qquad | \\ H_2C—CH_2 \end{array}$$

Some Carboxylic Acids

$$H\overset{\overset{\textstyle O}{\|}}{C}OH \qquad CH_3\overset{\overset{\textstyle O}{\|}}{C}OH \qquad \begin{array}{c} CH_2 \\ \diagup \quad \diagdown \\ H_2C{-}CHCOOH \end{array}$$

Table 3.1 lists a number of the important functional groups. The structures and names of these groups should be committed to memory. They form an essential part of the language of organic chemistry. In our subsequent studies we will develop the chemistry of the individual functional groups in terms of structural and electronic theory, nomenclature (names), physical properties, the preparation from other functional groups, and the characteristic reactions that produce other groups.

Interconversions of functional groups constitute a large proportion of organic chemistry. After the individual groups have been studied, the effect of one group on another can be considered, for the organic chemistry of compounds with more than one functional group is not simply the sum of the parts. Groups affect each other, sometimes in complex ways. One of the reasons for studying the theory of organic chemistry is that the mutual interactions of functional groups can be understood.

The aromatic ring in Table 3.1 is written with three carbon-carbon double bonds. Nevertheless, we shall see later (Chapters 20 and 22) that compounds containing this ring system differ substantially in their chemistry from the alkenes. Compounds containing this ring system are known collectively as **aromatic compounds**. Compounds with no aromatic ring are known as **aliphatic compounds**.

EXERCISE 3.2 Using R = ethyl, write structural and condensed formulas for one example each of an alkene, an alkyne, an alcohol, an ether, an aldehyde, a ketone, a carboxylic acid, an amine, and a nitrile.

TABLE 3.1

Class	General Structure	Characteristic Functional Group	Example
alkanes	R—H	none	CH_4
alkenes	$\begin{array}{c}RR_2\\ \diagdown\diagup\\ C{=}C\\ \diagup\diagdown\\ R_1R_3\end{array}$	$\diagdown C{=}C\diagup$	$CH_3CH{=}CH_2$
aromatic ring	$\begin{array}{c}R_2R_3\\ C{-}C\\ R_1{-}CC{-}R_4\\ C{=}C\\ R_6R_5\end{array}$	$\begin{array}{c}C{-}C\\ {-}CC{-}\\ C{=}C\end{array}$	$\begin{array}{c}CH{-}CH\\ CH_3{-}CCH\\ CH{=}CH\end{array}$
alkynes	R—C≡C—R′	—C≡C—	CH_3—C≡C—CH_3
alkyl halides	RF, RCl, RBr, RI	—F, —Cl, —Br, —I	CH_3Cl
alcohols	R—OH	—OH	CH_3OH
ethers	R—O—R′	—O—	CH_3OCH_3
amines			
primary amines	$R{-}NH_2$	$-NH_2$	CH_3NH_2
secondary amines	R—NH—R′	$\diagdown N{-}H$	CH_3NHCH_3
tertiary amines	$\begin{array}{c}R{-}N{-}R'\\ \vert\\ R''\end{array}$	$\diagdown N{-}$	$\begin{array}{c}CH_3NCH_3\\ \vert\\ CH_3\end{array}$
thiols	R—SH	—SH	CH_3SH
sulfides	R—S—R′	—S—	CH_3SCH_3
disulfides	R—S—S—R′	—S—S—	CH_3SSCH_3
boranes	R_3B	$\begin{array}{c}-B-\\ \vert\end{array}$	$(CH_3)_3B$
organometallic	RM, R_2M, R_3M	—M	$CH_3Li, (CH_3)_2Mg, (CH_3)_3Al$
aldehydes	$\begin{array}{c}O\\ \parallel\\ R{-}C{-}H\end{array}$	$\begin{array}{c}O\\ \parallel\\ {-}C{-}H\end{array}$	$\begin{array}{c}O\\ \parallel\\ CH_3{-}C{-}H\end{array}$
ketones	$\begin{array}{c}O\\ \parallel\\ R{-}C{-}R'\end{array}$	$\begin{array}{c}O\\ \parallel\\ {-}C{-}\end{array}$	$\begin{array}{c}O\\ \parallel\\ CH_3{-}C{-}CH_3\end{array}$
imines	$\begin{array}{c}N{-}R'\\ \parallel\\ R{-}C{-}R''\end{array}$	$\begin{array}{c}N{-}\\ \parallel\\ {-}C{-}\end{array}$	$\begin{array}{c}N{-}CH_3\\ \parallel\\ CH_3{-}C{-}H\end{array}$
carboxylic acids	$\begin{array}{c}O\\ \parallel\\ R{-}C{-}OH\end{array}$	$\begin{array}{c}O\\ \parallel\\ {-}C{-}OH\end{array}$	$\begin{array}{c}O\\ \parallel\\ H{-}C{-}OH\end{array}$

35

TABLE 3.1 (continued)

Class	General Structure	Characteristic Functional Group	Example
esters	$R-\overset{\displaystyle O}{\overset{\|}{C}}-OR'$	$-\overset{\displaystyle O}{\overset{\|}{C}}-O-$	$CH_3-\overset{\displaystyle O}{\overset{\|}{C}}-OCH_3$
amides	$R-\overset{\displaystyle O}{\overset{\|}{C}}-NR'_2$	$-\overset{\displaystyle O}{\overset{\|}{C}}-N\big\langle$	$CH_3-\overset{\displaystyle O}{\overset{\|}{C}}-NH_2$
acyl halides	$R-\overset{\displaystyle O}{\overset{\|}{C}}-X$	$-\overset{\displaystyle O}{\overset{\|}{C}}-X$	$CH_3-\overset{\displaystyle O}{\overset{\|}{C}}-Cl$
nitriles	$R-C\equiv N$	$-C\equiv N$	$CH_3C\equiv N$
nitro compounds	$R-NO_2$	$-NO_2$	CH_3-NO_2
sulfones	$R-SO_2-R'$	$-SO_2-$	$CH_3-SO_2-CH_3$
sulfonic acids	$R-SO_2-OH$	$-SO_2-OH$	CH_3-SO_2-OH

3.3 The Shapes of Molecules

The Kekulé-Couper concept of bonds and the powerful organizational theory of types, or functional groups, catalyzed an explosive period in the development of the new science of organic chemistry. There remained to be recognized one important aspect of molecular structure. It was the German chemist Johannes Wislicenus who first conceived of the idea of molecular shape. Wislicenus studied pairs of isomeric organic compounds and concluded in 1873 that "If molecules can be structurally identical and yet possess dissimilar properties, this can be explained only on the ground that the difference is due to a different arrangement of the atoms in space." In 1874, the Dutch chemist Jacobus Hendricus van't Hoff and the French chemist Joseph Achille Le Bel independently suggested that the four valences of a carbon atom are oriented in space in a tetrahedral manner. That is, the four hydrogens of methane may be viewed as occupying the four corners of a regular tetrahedron (Figure 2.15).

Molecular shape is a fundamental concept in organic chemistry. Molecules are three-dimensional, and the spatial interactions between different parts of a molecule can be very important in determining the chemical and physical properties of a compound. Consequently, the student must cultivate the ability to think of organic molecules as "objects" having a definite shape. Since this is a difficult task for most people, especially with complex molecules, various aids to visualization are employed. One such technique, which we shall use in this book, is stereoscopic projection (see the list of stereo drawings on page xvii).

Other tools which are indispensable for visualizing spatial interactions in molecules are **molecular models**. Since bonds in organic compounds are formed from hybrid orbitals which approximate simple sp-, sp^2-, and sp^3-hybrids, and bond angles and distances are relatively constant from one molecule to another, it is possible to use simple objects as models for various atoms. These objects may be joined together in the same manner as "Tinkertoys" to produce models of molecules. Various types of model sets are available for this purpose. Some are expensive precision constructions used primarily for research purposes, but several are relatively inexpensive and are designed for student use in the study of organic chemistry. Some of the sets available are summarized below and illustrated in Figure 3.1.

Dreiding stereomodels are skeletal models constructed from welded stainless steel tubing. The bond lengths and angles are precisely proportional to the average molecular dimensions. They are relatively expensive and are widely used by professional chemists for research purposes.

The Theta Molecular Model Set marketed by John Wiley & Sons uses small plastic nuclei like "jacks" and plastic tubing. The Prentice-Hall Framework molecular models are similar, but use metal nuclei. The Allyn and Bacon Molecular Model Set uses round plastic nuclei and a more flexible type of bond. The HGS-Maruzen models use polyhedral plastic atoms with holes drilled to accommodate bonds. Models such as these are relatively inexpensive and are indispensable as an aid in visualizing three-dimensional aspects of organic structures and reactions.

Corey-Pauling-Koltun (CPK™) molecular models are an example of space-filling models. The models are constructed from an acrylic polyester plastic and are proportional to the covalent and atomic radii of the atoms. They are held together by connectors made of a hard rubber-like elastomer. They are fairly expensive and are mainly used by professional chemists for constructing models where a knowledge of molecular shape and intramolecular interactions is important.

EXERCISE 3.3 Using your molecular model set, construct models of some of the organic molecules previously illustrated in this chapter.

FIGURE 3.1 Some molecular model representations of ethyl alcohol, CH_3CH_2OH. Models used are (*a*) Allyn and Bacon, (*b*) HGS Maruzen, (*c*) Theta, (*d*) Framework, (*e*) Dreiding, and (*f*) CPK™.

3.4 The Determination of Organic Structures

In previous sections, we have reviewed some basic concepts of electronic structure and bonding and have introduced the subject of organic structures and functional groups. In subsequent chapters, we shall take up the structures and chemical reactions of various classes of organic compounds and examine them in detail. At this point, an additional question must be addressed before we embark upon our systematic study of organic chemistry. How does the chemist know the structure of a compound? The question is an important one, and it is encountered over and over again by researchers in the field. In fact, the rate of development of organic chemistry as a science has been intimately related to our ability to *determine structure*.

Mentally transport yourself back a hundred years—imagine that you are a nine-teenth-century scientist and have laboriously purified an organic substance from some source. How do you determine its structure? It is possible to measure various physical properties such as boiling point, melting point, density, and refractive index. A catalog of these properties constitutes the **characterization** of a compound. Just as no two people have identical fingerprints, no two compounds have all physical properties in common. It is relatively easy to assemble a list of physical properties for the compound and to decide that it is different from other previously isolated substances. Your new compound also undergoes various chemical reactions, and from its behavior with vari-ous reagents you may be able to decide what kinds of functional groups are present. For example, suppose that your material reacts with sodium to produce hydrogen gas. Since simple alcohols such as methyl alcohol are known to undergo this reaction, you can make the deduction that your new compound contains the functional group OH. But still, from all these data, how do you write a molecular structure for the com-pound? This problem challenged chemists for over a hundred years.

The first major breakthrough came with the development of methods of elemental analysis. The first attempts to determine the elemental compositions of organic com-pounds were made by Lavoisier in the late eighteenth century in connection with his pioneering work on the reactions of oxygen. Lavoisier examined the combustion prod-ucts from various compounds and could deduce which elements were present in the substance burned. For example, combustion of methane gives carbon dioxide and water. Hence, methane must be built up from carbon and hydrogen in some way.

$$\text{methane} + O_2 \longrightarrow CO_2 + H_2O$$

Although Lavoisier attempted to quantitate combustion as a method to determine accu-rate formulas for organic compounds, the apparatus at his disposal was not sufficiently accurate for him to obtain precise formulas. The next significant advance came in 1831 when Liebig developed the Lavoisier method into a precise quantitative technique. For the first time, it was possible to determine accurate empirical formulas for organic compounds. In connection with methods for the determination of molecular weights, it was then possible to determine molecular formulas.

The method of combustion analysis, as developed by Liebig, is conceptually very simple. A weighed quantity of the sample to be analyzed is burned in the presence of red-hot copper oxide, which is reduced to metallic copper. The sample is swept through the combustion tube with pure oxygen gas, which reoxidizes the copper to copper oxide.

$$C_{10}H_{14} + 27\,CuO \longrightarrow 10\,CO_2 + 7\,H_2O + 27\,Cu$$
naphthalene

$$2\,Cu + O_2 \longrightarrow 2\,CuO$$

The combustion products are swept through a calcium chloride tube, which absorbs the water formed, and then through a tube containing aqueous potassium hydroxide, which absorbs the carbon dioxide produced. The two tubes are weighed before and after combustion to determine the weights of water and carbon dioxide produced. From the weights of the two products, the weight of sample burned, and the atomic weights of carbon and hydrogen, it is possible to compute an empirical formula for the substance burned.

$$\text{weight of H in sample} = \text{weight of } H_2O \times \frac{2.016}{18.016}$$

$$\text{weight of C in sample} = \text{weight of } CO_2 \times \frac{12.01}{44.01}$$

$$\% \text{ H in sample} = \frac{\text{weight of H}}{\text{weight of sample}} \times 100$$

$$\% \text{ C in sample} = \frac{\text{weight of C}}{\text{weight of sample}} \times 100$$

If the percentages of carbon and hydrogen do not add up to 100 and no other element has been detected by qualitative tests, the deficiency is taken as the percentage of oxygen.

As an example, consider the analysis of propyl alcohol, C_3H_8O. An ideal analysis on a 0.500-g sample would give 0.600 g of H_2O and 1.099 g of CO_2. The calculations proceed as follows.

$$\text{weight of H in sample} = 0.600 \text{ g} \times \frac{2.016}{18.016} = 0.067 \text{ g}$$

$$\text{weight of C in sample} = 1.099 \text{ g} \times \frac{12.01}{44.01} = 0.300 \text{ g}$$

$$\% \text{ H in sample} = \frac{0.067}{0.500 \text{ g}} \times 100 = 13.4$$

$$\% \text{ C in sample} = \frac{0.300}{0.500} \times 100 = 60.0$$

The percentages of hydrogen and carbon add up to 73.4%, and the remaining 26.6% is taken as the percentage of oxygen in the sample. In actual practice, the analytical values are usually accurate to $\pm 0.3\%$.

EXERCISE 3.4 How much CO_2 and H_2O are produced by the combustion of 3.74 mg of $C_6H_{12}O$?

From the elemental analysis of a compound, one may easily calculate its **empirical formula**, which expresses the ratio of the elements present. In the present case, for example, the analysis tells us that 100 g of propyl alcohol contains 60.0 g of carbon, 13.4 g of hydrogen, and 26.6 g of oxygen. Dividing each of these weights by the appropriate atomic weights gives us the number of moles of each element in 100 g of sample.

$$\frac{60.0}{12.01} = 5.00 \text{ moles of carbon}$$

$$\frac{13.4}{1.008} = 13.29 \text{ moles of hydrogen}$$

$$\frac{26.6}{16} = 1.66 \text{ moles of oxygen}$$

This calculation gives us an empirical formula of $C_{5.00}H_{13.29}O_{1.66}$. However, because the atoms in a molecule must be present in whole numbers, the initially derived formula must be normalized. If we divide each of the factors derived above by the smallest, we have

$$C_{5.00/1.66}H_{13.29/1.66}O_{1.66/1.66} = C_{3.01}H_{8.01}O_{1.00}$$

Thus, the empirical formula of propyl alcohol is calculated from its elemental analysis to be C_3H_8O. The molecular formula expresses the total number of each atom present and is the same as the empirical formula or some multiple of it. For example, if the molecular formula of propyl alcohol were $C_6H_{16}O_2$, the percentages of carbon, hydrogen, and oxygen would be the same. (Actually, because of the rules of valence, $C_6H_{16}O_2$ is an impossible formula, as a little trial and error will readily reveal.)

EXERCISE 3.5 Combustion of 0.250 g of di-*n*-butyl ether gives 0.677 g of CO_2 and 0.311 g of H_2O. Calculate the empirical formula of di-*n*-butyl ether.

The Lavoisier-Liebig method of analysis provided a tremendous boost to the development of organic chemistry but required relatively large amounts of sample, on the order of 0.25-0.50 g. In 1911 Fritz Pregl introduced a technique of microanalysis that allows combustion analysis to be carried out with only 3-4 mg of sample. Elements such as N, S, Cl, Br, I, and P are determined on a micro scale by other analytical methods that we shall not detail. Highly accurate molecular formulas may now be determined on a few micrograms of substance by the technique of high-resolution mass spectrometry (Chapter 32).

From the molecular formula, the next step is to derive a molecular structure. How are the atoms bonded to one another? For our present example of C_3H_8O, which of the following structures corresponds to propyl alcohol?

As indicated previously, some insight may be gained by a consideration of the gross chemical properties of the material. For example, if we know that the compound reacts with sodium to liberate hydrogen, this would indicate the presence of the OH functional group and would eliminate the third possible structure above. In a similar manner, an examination of other chemical properties could lead to the elimination of other candidate structures. For example, we shall see in later chapters that the OH functional group has slightly different chemical properties when it is bonded to a carbon having two hydrogens than when it is bonded to a carbon having only one hydrogen. Thus, a careful consideration of the properties of a substance could eventually lead to a structure consistent with all the data. The modern chemist relies heavily on spectroscopic methods for the determination of structure. As we shall see in subsequent chapters, spectroscopy is the experimental evaluation of the manner in which a substance interacts with electromagnetic radiation. Thus, by examining the various spectra of a material, the chemist is evaluating a physical property of the substance. In fact, this particular physical property is a very powerful one. In our study of organic chemistry we shall consider various kinds of spectroscopy: nuclear magnetic resonance (Chapter 13), infrared spectroscopy (Chapter 15), mass spectrometry (Chapter 32), and ultraviolet spectroscopy (Chapter 21).

EXERCISE 3.6 Elemental analysis of an organic compound reveals it to have the empirical formula C_3H_6O. Determination of its molecular weight gives a value of 57 ± 2. These data, together with the rules of valence, are compatible with eight structures. Write these eight structures. What two structures are possible if the infrared spectrum of the unknown compound reveals the presence of a carbon-oxygen double bond?

3.5 n-**Alkanes, the Simplest Organic Compounds**

The straight-chain alkanes constitute a family of hydrocarbons in which a chain of CH_2 groups is terminated at both ends by a hydrogen. They have the general formula $H(CH_2)_nH$ or C_nH_{2n+2}. Such a family of compounds, which differ from each other by the number of CH_2 groups in the chain, is called an **homologous series**. The individual members of the family are known as **homologs** of one another. Straight-chain alkanes are called **normal alkanes**, or simply **n-alkanes**, to distinguish them from the branched alkanes, which we shall study later.

Alkanes are sometimes called **saturated** hydrocarbons. This term means that the carbon skeleton is ''saturated'' with hydrogen. That is, in addition to its bonds to other carbons, each carbon bonds to enough hydrogens to give a maximum covalence of 4. The general formula for a n-alkane is C_nH_{2n+2} because there are two hydrogens bonded to each carbon atom of the chain plus one additional hydrogen bonded to each end of the chain. In saturated hydrocarbons, there are only single bonds. Later, we shall study **unsaturated** hydrocarbons, compounds that contain double and triple carbon-carbon bonds. The normal alkanes are named according to the number of carbon atoms in the chain (Table 3.2).

TABLE 3.2

n	Name	Formula
1	methane	CH_4
2	ethane	CH_3CH_3
3	propane	$CH_3CH_2CH_3$
4	butane	$CH_3CH_2CH_2CH_3$
5	pentane	$CH_3(CH_2)_3CH_3$
6	hexane	$CH_3(CH_2)_4CH_3$
7	heptane	$CH_3(CH_2)_5CH_3$
8	octane	$CH_3(CH_2)_6CH_3$
9	nonane	$CH_3(CH_2)_7CH_3$
10	decane	$CH_3(CH_2)_8CH_3$
11	undecane	$CH_3(CH_2)_9CH_3$
12	dodecane	$CH_3(CH_2)_{10}CH_3$
13	tridecane	$CH_3(CH_2)_{11}CH_3$
14	tetradecane	$CH_3(CH_2)_{12}CH_3$
15	pentadecane	$CH_3(CH_2)_{13}CH_3$
20	eicosane	$CH_3(CH_2)_{18}CH_3$
21	heneicosane	$CH_3(CH_2)_{19}CH_3$
22	docosane	$CH_3(CH_2)_{20}CH_3$
30	triacontane	$CH_3(CH_2)_{28}CH_3$
40	tetracontane	$CH_3(CH_2)_{38}CH_3$

These names derive from the generic name alkane with the **alk-** stem replaced by a stem characteristic of the number of carbons in the chain. The names of the first four members of this series—methane, ethane, propane, and butane—came into widespread use before any attempts were made to systematize the names of organic compounds. The remaining names derive quite obviously from Greek numbers; compare **pent**agon, **oct**al, **dec**imal, and so on. The student should memorize the names of the *n*-alkanes up through dodecane and know the logical procedure for developing names for larger compounds.

A "group" is a portion of a molecule in which a collection of atoms is considered together as a unit. For purposes of naming more complicated compounds, it is necessary to have names for such groups. A group name is derived by replacing the -**ane** of the corresponding alkane name by the suffix -**yl**.

Alkane	*Group*	*Sample Molecule*
CH_4	$CH_3—$	$CH_3—OH$
meth**ane**	meth**yl** group	methyl alcohol
CH_3CH_3	$CH_3CH_2—$	$CH_3CH_2—Cl$
eth**ane**	eth**yl** group	ethyl chloride
$CH_3CH_2CH_3$	$CH_3CH_2CH_2—$	$CH_3CH_2CH_2—Br$
prop**ane**	prop**yl** group	propyl bromide

> **EXERCISE 3.7** Write the structures of the pentyl group and of pentyl iodide.

3.6 Systematic Nomenclature

There is only one compound having each of the formulas CH_4, C_2H_6, and C_3H_8. There are two **isomeric** compounds having the formula C_4H_{10}. **Isomers** are defined as compounds that have identical formulas but differ in the nature or sequence of bonding of their atoms or in the arrangement of their atoms in space. One of the C_4H_{10} isomers is *n*-butane, discussed previously. The other is isobutane.

$$CH_3CH_2CH_2CH_3 \qquad CH_3—\overset{\displaystyle CH_3}{\underset{\displaystyle H}{\overset{|}{\underset{|}{C}}}}—CH_3$$

n-butane   isobutane

In general, isomers have different physical and chemical properties. For example, with the two C_4H_{10} compounds, isobutane has the lower melting point and boiling point. The lower boiling point reflects the branched-chain structure of isobutane, which provides less effective contact area for van der Waals attraction.

Interconversion of the two butane isomers requires breaking bonds. Since carbon-carbon bonds have bond strengths of about 80 kcal mole^{-1}, these isomers are completely stable under normal conditions. Interconversion requires very high temperatures or special catalysts.

There are three C_5H_{12} isomers.

$$CH_3CH_2CH_2CH_2CH_3 \qquad CH_3CH_2\overset{\displaystyle CH_3}{\overset{|}{C}}HCH_3 \qquad CH_3—\overset{\displaystyle CH_3}{\underset{\displaystyle CH_3}{\overset{|}{\underset{|}{C}}}}—CH_3$$

pentane   isopentane   neopentane

TABLE 3.3 Number of Isomers of C_nH_{2n+2}

n	Number of Isomers
4	2
5	3
6	5
7	9
8	18
9	35
10	75
12	355
15	4,347
20	366,319

The prefix **iso-** serves to name one of these isomers, the one with the greatest structural similarity to isobutane. The third isomer was named neopentane, the prefix **neo-** being derived from the Greek word for "new." With more carbons the number of possible isomers increases rapidly. As shown in Table 3.3, there are 5 possible hexanes, 9 heptanes, and 75 decanes, and with larger alkanes the number of possible isomers becomes astronomic. Is is obviously not possible to coin a set of unique prefixes like iso- and neo- to name all of the dodecane isomers, or, for that matter, even the heptane isomers. Clearly, it is essential that a method of systematic nomenclature be devised, so that each different compound may be assigned an unambiguous name.

This problem was first addressed by an International Congress of Chemists, held in Geneva in 1892. The forty chemists in attendance at this meeting adopted a set of systematic rules for naming organic compounds. For the most part, the Geneva rules were based on a suggestion originally made by Laurent, whereby hydrocarbons are the base compounds, with other classes of compounds being treated as substitution products. The International Congresses evolved into an organization now known as the International Union of Pure and Applied Chemistry (IUPAC), which maintains several committees whose job it is to see that the rules for systematic nomenclature are continually updated.

The IUPAC system of alkane nomenclature is based on the simple fundamental principle of considering all compounds to be **derivatives of the longest single carbon chain** present in the compound. Appendages to this chain are designated by appropriate prefixes. The chain is then numbered from one end to the other. The end chosen as number 1 is that which gives the *smaller number at the first point of difference*.

$$\underset{1 \quad 2 \quad 3 \quad 4 \quad 5}{CH_3\overset{\overset{\displaystyle CH_3}{|}}{C}HCH_2CH_2CH_3} \qquad \underset{1 \quad 2 \quad 3 \quad 4 \quad 5 \quad 6}{CH_3CH_2\overset{\overset{\displaystyle CH_3}{|}}{C}HCH_2CH_2CH_3}$$

2-methylpentane (not 4-methylpentane)   3-methylhexane (not 4-methylhexane)

EXERCISE 3.8 Write the structure of 3-ethylhexane. Why is 2-ethylhexane not a possible name under the IUPAC system?

When there are two or more identical appendages, the modifying prefixes di-, tri-, tetra-, penta-, hexa-, and so on are used, but every appendage group still gets its own number.

$$CH_3CCH_2CH_2CH_3$$

with CH_3 groups above and below the second carbon

2,2-dimethylpentane
(not 2-dimethylpentane)

$$CH_3C-CH_2-CCH_3$$

with CH_3 groups above and below

2,2,4-tetramethylpentane

EXERCISE 3.9 (a) Write the structure of 2,3,4-trimethyloctane. (b) Why is 1,4-dimethyl-butane an incorrect name?

When two or more appendage locants are employed, the longest chain is numbered from the end which produces the lowest series of locants. When comparing one series of locants with another, that series is lower which contains the *lower number at the first point of difference*.

$$CH_3CH_2CHCHCH_3$$

with CH_3 groups

2,3-dimethylpentane
(not 3,4-dimethylpentane)

$$CH_3CHCH_2CH_2CHCHCH_2CH_3$$

with CH_3 groups

2,5,6-trimethyloctane
(not 3,4,7-trimethyloctane)

$$CH_3CHCH_2CHCH_2CH_2CHCH_3$$

with CH_3 groups

2,4,7-trimethyloctane
(not 2,5,7-trimethyloctane)

$$CH_3CCH_2CHCH_3$$

with CH_3 groups

2,2,4-trimethylpentane
(not 2,4,4-trimethylpentane)

EXERCISE 3.10 Two possible names for an alkane are 2,3,5-trimethylhexane and 2,4,5-trimethylhexane. Which is correct?

Groups derived from the terminal position of a *n*-alkane are named as discussed in Section 3.5. Several other common groups have special names that must be memorized by the student.

$$CH_3CH-$$

isopropyl

$$CH_3CHCH_2-$$

isobutyl

$$CH_3CH_2CH-$$

sec-butyl

$$CH_3C-$$

tert-butyl
or *t*-butyl

$$CH_3CCH_2-$$

neopentyl

A more complex appendage group is named as a derivative of the **longest carbon chain in the group** starting from the carbon that is attached to the principal chain. The description of the appendage is distinguished from that of the principal chain by enclosing it in parentheses.

$$CH_3$$
$$|$$
$$H-C-CH_3$$
$$|$$
$$H-C-CH_3$$
$$|$$
$$CH_3CH_2CH_2CH_2CHCH_2CH_2CH_2CH_3$$

5-(1,2-dimethylpropyl)nonane

When two or more appendages of different nature are present, they are cited as prefixes in alphabetical order. Prefixes specifying the number of identical appendages (di-, tri-, tetra-, and so on) and hyphenated prefixes (*tert-* or *t-*, *sec-*) are ignored in alphabetizing except when part of a complex substituent. The prefixes cyclo-, iso-, and neo- count as a part of the group name for purposes of alphabetizing.

$$CH_3 \qquad\qquad CH_3CHCH_3$$
$$| \qquad\qquad\qquad |$$
$$CH_3CH_2CCH_2CH_3 \quad CH_3CH_2CH_2CHCHCH_2CH_2CH_3$$
$$| \qquad\qquad\qquad\qquad |$$
$$CH_2CH_3 \qquad\qquad CH_2CH_2CH_3$$

3-ethyl-3-methylpentane   4-isopropyl-5-propyloctane

EXERCISE 3.11 Which three of the following names are incorrect according to the IUPAC rules?
(a) 2-methyl-4-ethylheptane   (b) 3-ethyl-2,2-dimethylhexane
(c) 2-isopropyl-3-methylhexane   (d) 4-isopropyl-3-ethylheptane?
What is the correct name in each case?

When chains of equal length compete for selection as the main chain for purposes of numbering, that chain is selected which has the greatest number of appendages attached to it.

$$CH_2CH_3$$
$$|$$
$$CH_3-C-CH_3$$
$$|$$
$$CH_2$$
$$|$$
$$CH_3CH_2CH_2CH_2CH_2CHCH_2CHCH_2CH_3$$
$$|$$
$$CH_2CH_3$$

5-(2-ethylbutyl)-3,3-dimethyldecane
[not 5-(2,2-dimethylbutyl)-3-ethyldecane]

When two or more appendages are in equivalent positions, the lower number is assigned to the one that is cited first in the name (that is, the one that comes first in the alphabetic listing).

$$CH_3CH_2 \quad CH_3 \qquad\qquad CH_3CHCH_3$$
$$| \qquad | \qquad\qquad\qquad\qquad |$$
$$CH_3CH_2CHCH_2CHCH_2CH_3 \quad CH_3CH_2CH_2CHCHCH_2CH_2CH_3$$
$$| $$
$$CH_2CH_3$$

3-ethyl-5-methylheptane   4-ethyl-5-isopropyloctane
(not 5-ethyl-3-methylheptane)   (not 4-isopropyl-5-ethyloctane)

Note that the direction of numbering of the main chain may already have been decided by application of a higher priority rule.

$$\begin{array}{cc} CH_3 & CH_2CH_3 \\ | & | \\ CH_3CH_2CCH_2CH_2CHCH_2CH_3 \\ | \\ CH_3 \end{array}$$

6-ethyl-3,3-dimethyloctane
[3,3,6 is lower than 3,6,6 at
the first point of difference]

$$\begin{array}{cc} CH_3 & CH_2CH_3 \\ | & | \\ CH_3CHCH_2CH_2CH_2CHCH_2CH_3 \end{array}$$

6-ethyl-2-methyloctane
(2,6 is lower than 3,7)

> The complete IUPAC rules actually allow a choice regarding the order in which the appendage groups may be cited. One may cite the appendages alphabetically, as above, or in order of increasing complexity. In this book, we shall adhere to the alphabetic order in citing appendage prefixes. The alphabetic order is also used by *Chemical Abstracts* for indexing purposes.

The prefix halo- is used as a generic expression for the halogens, which are treated in the same manner as alkyl appendages for purposes of nomenclature. The individual halogen prefixes are fluoro-, chloro-, bromo-, and iodo-.

$$\begin{array}{cc} Cl & CH_3 \\ | & | \\ CH_3CHCH_2CHCH_3 \end{array}$$

2-chloro-4-methylpentane

$$\begin{array}{c} CH_2Cl \\ | \\ CH_3CH_2CHCH_2CH_3 \end{array}$$

3-(chloromethyl)pentane

$ClCH_2CH_2CH_2CH_2Br$

1-bromo-4-chlorobutane

$$\begin{array}{c} CH_3 \\ | \\ BrCH_2CHFCHCH_2I \end{array}$$

1-bromo-2-fluoro-4-
iodo-3-methylbutane

$BrCH_2CH_2CHBrCH_2Br$

1,2,4-tribromobutane

> **EXERCISE 3.12** Why is the name 4-chloro-2-methylpentane incorrect? Write the structure of 2,6-dichloro-4-ethylheptane. If the two chlorine substituents of this compound are replaced by iodines, what is the correct IUPAC name of the resulting compound?

As with many other classes of organic compounds, haloalkanes can be named with systematic names, such as the foregoing, or with "common names" (names which evolved before attempts were made to systematize nomenclature). Simple haloalkanes are often named as though they were salts of alkyl groups—as alkyl halides.

CH_3F

methyl fluoride

$(CH_3)_2CHBr$

isopropyl bromide

$$\begin{array}{c} CH_3 \\ | \\ CH_3CCH_2I \\ | \\ CH_3 \end{array}$$

neopentyl iodide

$$\begin{array}{c} CH_3 \\ | \\ CH_3CHCH_2Cl \end{array}$$

isobutyl chloride

Nomenclature is an essential element of organic chemistry for several reasons. First, it is our basic tool for communicating about the subject. It is not always convenient to draw a structure on every bottle we want to label or for every compound we want to talk about. Therefore, it is important that we be able to assign a name to every compound, and it is essential that the name we use correspond to only one compound. This is the most fundamental rule of nomenclature. If more than one structure can be written which corresponds to a name, or if the name is so ambiguous that no unique structure can be written, then the name is incorrect.

However, another important use of nomenclature is in searching the chemical literature for the physical and chemical properties of various compounds. We shall consider the chemical literature in Chapter 33; however, a brief mention at this point is appropriate to the subject of nomenclature. New chemical information is made public for the first time as scientific **papers** which appear in various chemical magazines called **journals**. Examples are the *Journal of the American Chemical Society*, the *Journal of Organic Chemistry*, and *Chemische Berichte*. Hundreds of such journals are published, mostly on a monthly or twice-monthly basis. The back issues of these basic journals contain all of the accumulated knowledge of the science and are known collectively as the **chemical literature**. To facilitate the retrieval of information from this mass of data, the American Chemical Society publishes a reference journal known as *Chemical Abstracts*. This journal is published twice monthly and contains short abstracts of all of the chemical papers published in the basic journals. At the end of each year, an extensively cross-referenced index is published. At the end of each 5-year period (10-year period before 1957), a cumulative index covering that period is published.

In order to search the chemical literature for a compound *by name* it is necessary to know the correct name of any given structure. For such a name search to be successful, it follows that every structure must correspond to *only one name*. The IUPAC system is one example of an attempt to construct such an unambiguous system of nomenclature. The actual rules are quite extensive and allow for all sorts of special situations. More complete versions of the rules may be found in standard reference works such as the *Chemical Rubber Handbook of Physics and Chemistry*. Unfortunately, the rules as they have been formulated are not totally unambiguous, and all of the special situations which may arise have not been anticipated. Moreover, in some situations the rule makers have been permissive rather than compulsory, as in allowing the retention of certain common names and in allowing a choice in deciding which appendage is cited first in a name. Therefore, one finds that the same compound may be named several different ways in different important reference works. In fact, in the most important reference source, *Chemical Abstracts*, one will find that the name used for a compound has often been changed over the years. Indeed, many of the names currently in use by *Chemical Abstracts* bear little resemblence to those derivable under the IUPAC rules. Fortunately, the necessity of using compound names only for searching the literature is partially alleviated by the existence of formula indices. A welcome development of the ''computer age'' is the ability to conduct literature searches by computer, using a graphical symbol for the structure of a compound, rather than a name.

Nevertheless, if the student is to learn organic chemistry effectively, it is essential that he or she thoroughly learn the simplified IUPAC system that we have presented in this Section, and which may be summarized as follows.

1. Find the longest carbon chain in the compound.
2. Name each appendage group that is attached to this principal chain.
3. Alphabetize the appendage groups.
4. Number the principal chain from one end in such a way that the smaller number is used at the first point of difference in the two possible series of locants.
5. Name the parent alkane using the set of names summarized in Table 3.2 and assign to each appendage group a number signifying its point of attachment to the principal chain.

We shall see that this basic system is used in naming all other classes of organic compounds. For naming substances which have functional groups, the foregoing system is simply modified by the use of appropriate prefixes or suffixes. For example, the characteristic suffix denoting the functional group OH is **-ol** and that for the group NH_2 is **-amine**. Thus, alcohols and amines are named as follows:

$$CH_3$$
$$CH_3CH_2CHCH_2CH_2OH \qquad CH_3CH_2CH_2CH_2CH_2NH_2$$
3-methyl-1-pentanol   1-pentanamine

Complete details on the modifications which are necessary to adapt the basic system to a given class of compound will be given when we discuss each class.

PROBLEMS

1. Calculate the elemental composition of each of the following compounds.
   (a) 2,2-dimethylhexane
   (b) ethyl acetate (fingernail polish remover), $C_4H_8O_2$
   (c) nitromethane (racing engine fuel), CH_3NO_2
   (d) trinitrotoluene (TNT), $C_7H_5N_3O_6$

2. A series of compounds was analyzed by the Liebig method. In each case, the specified amount of sample was burned and the indicated quantity of CO_2 and H_2O was obtained. Calculate the empirical formula for each unknown compound.
   (a) 5.20 mg of sample gave 14.3 mg of CO_2 and 5.80 mg of H_2O.
   (b) 3.81 mg of sample gave 12.3 mg of CO_2 and 3.90 mg of H_2O.
   (c) 2.58 mg of sample gave 5.87 mg of CO_2 and 2.40 mg of H_2O.
   (d) 3.10 mg of sample gave 4.54 mg of CO_2 and 1.86 mg of H_2O.

3. From the analytical values for each compound, derive its empirical formula.
   (a) hexanol: 70.4% C, 13.9% H
   (b) benzene: 92.1% C, 7.9% H
   (c) pyrrole: 71.6% C, 7.5% H, 20.9% N
   (d) morphine: 71.6% C, 6.7% H, 4.9% N
   (e) quinine: 74.1% C, 7.5% H, 8.6% N
   (f) DDT: 47.4% C, 2.6% H, 50.0% Cl
   (g) vinyl chloride: 38.3% C, 4.8% H, 56.8% Cl
   (h) thyroxine: 23.4% C, 1.4% H, 65.3% I, 1.8% N

4. In each of the following examples, qualitative analysis shows the presence of no elements other than C, H, and O. Calculate the empirical formula for each case.
   (a) Combustion of 0.0132 g of camphor gave 0.0382 g of CO_2 and 0.0126 g of H_2O.
   (b) Combustion of 1.56 mg of the sex-attractant of the common honey bee (*Apis mellifera*) gave 3.73 mg of CO_2 and 1.22 mg of H_2O.
   (c) Benzo[*a*]pyrene is a potent carcinogenic compound that has been detected in tobacco smoke. Combustion of 2.16 mg gave 7.50 mg of CO_2 and 0.92 mg of H_2O.

5. Halogen may be determined by burning the sample under conditions such that the halogen is converted into halide ion, which is then determined by titration with standard silver nitrate solution. Carbon and hydrogen are determined by conversion into CO_2 and H_2O as usual. Calculate the empirical formula for the following case: 2.03 mg of sample gave 4.44 mg of CO_2 and 0.91 mg of H_2O; a separate 5.31 mg sample gave a chloride solution which required 4.80 mL of 0.0110 N AgNO$_3$.

6. Write condensed formulas and IUPAC names for the eight isomers having the molecular formula $C_5H_{11}Br$.

7. Write condensed formulas for seven isomers having the molecular formula $C_4H_{10}O$.

8. Write condensed formulas for the eight isomers having the molecular formula C_7H_{16}. Give the IUPAC name for each isomer.

9. How many monochloro derivatives may be formed from the eight alkanes in problem 8?

10. The empirical formula C_4H_8 may correspond to many molecular formulas: C_8H_{16}, $C_{12}H_{24}$, etc. Explain why the empirical formula C_5H_{12} can only correspond to one molecular formula.

11. Convince yourself by trial and error that the molecular weight of an organic compound containing only carbon, hydrogen, and oxygen will always be an even number and that the molecular weight for compounds having an odd number of nitrogens will be an odd number.

12. Each of the following molecules contains one principal functional group. Locate and name the group, and classify the molecule for each case.

(a)

(b)

(c)
$$CH_2\text{—}CH_2$$
$$CH_2\text{—}CHOH$$

(d)
$$CH_3\text{—}\overset{\overset{\displaystyle CH_3}{|}}{\underset{\underset{\displaystyle CH_3}{|}}{C}}\text{—}\overset{\overset{\displaystyle CH_3}{|}}{\underset{\underset{\displaystyle CH_3}{|}}{C}}\text{—}Cl$$

(e)
$$CH_3\text{—}\overset{\overset{\displaystyle CH_3}{|}}{\underset{\underset{\displaystyle CH_3}{|}}{C}}\text{—}CH_2\text{—}\overset{\overset{\displaystyle O}{||}}{C}\text{—}OH$$

(f)

(g)

(h)

(i)
$$\overset{\overset{\displaystyle SH}{|}}{CH_3CHCH_3}$$

(j)

(k)

(l)
$$CH_3\text{—}\overset{\overset{\displaystyle CH_3}{|}}{\underset{\underset{\displaystyle CH_3}{|}}{C}}\text{—}NH_2$$

(m)
$$CH_3\text{—}\overset{\overset{\displaystyle CH_3}{|}}{CH}\text{—}C\equiv CH$$

(n) $CH_3CH_2CH_2CH_2Li$

13. Write the structural formula corresponding to each of the following common names.
   (a) neopentane   (b) isobutane   (c) *t*-butyl bromide
   (d) isobutyl iodide   (e) isopropyl chloride   (f) *sec*-butyl bromide

14. Write the structural formula corresponding to each of the following IUPAC names.
    (a) 3,4,5-trimethyl-4-propyloctane
    (b) 3-ethyl-3-fluorohexane
    (c) 6-(3-methylbutyl)undecane
    (d) 4-*t*-butylheptane
    (e) 2-methylheptadecane
    (f) 4-(1-chloroethyl)-3,3-dimethylheptane
    (g) 6,6-dimethyl-5-(1,2,2-trimethylpropyl)dodecane
    (h) 5,5-diethyl-2-methylheptane

15. Give the IUPAC name for each of the following compounds.

(a) $(CH_3)_2CHCH_2CH_2CH(CH_3)_2$

(b)
$$CH_3CH_2CHCH_2CCH_2CHCH_2CH_3$$
with substituents CH_3, CH_3, CH_2CH_3 on the chain and CH_3 below.

(c)
$$CH_3CH_2CH_2CHCH_2CH_3$$
with $CH_3CHCH_2CH_3$ substituent above.

(d)
$$CH_3CHCH_2CHCH_2Br$$
with Cl and CH_3 substituents above.

(e)
$$(CH_3)_3CCH_2CHCHCH_2CH_2CH_3$$
with I and CH_2CH_3 substituents above.

(f)
$$CH_3CH_2CHCH_2CH_2CCH_2CH_3$$
with CH_3CHCH_3 and CH_2CH_3 above and CH_3 below.

(g)
$$(CH_3CH_2CCH_2CH_2CH_2)_3CH$$
with CH_3 above and CH_3 below.

(h) $(CH_3CH_2)_4C$

(i)
$$(CH_3CH_2)_2CHCHCH_2CH_3$$
with CH_3 above.

(j)
$$(CH_3CH_2)_2CHCCH_2CH_3$$
with CH_3 above and CH_3 below.

16. Explain why each of the following names is incorrect.
    (a) methylheptane   (b) 4-methylhexane
    (c) 3-propylhexane   (d) 3-isopropyl-5,5-dimethyloctane
    (e) 3-methyl-4-chlorohexane   (f) 2,2-dimethyl-3-ethylpentane
    (g) 3,5,6,7-tetramethylnonane   (h) 2-dimethylpropane

Chapter 4
Organic Reactions

4.1 Introduction

The two principal components of organic chemistry are **structure** and **reactions**. Each of these components has experimental and theoretical aspects, and they are interrelated. Structures in terms of bond angles and bond distances are available from the interpretation of experimentally obtained rotational spectra and x-ray or electron diffraction patterns. In Chapter 2 we reviewed the symbolism used to represent such structures—structural formulas and Lewis structures—and their modern significance in terms of atomic, hybrid, and molecular orbitals.

In this chapter we introduce some concepts concerning reactions. Many reactions are known in organic chemistry that allow us to convert one structure to another. In this connection we must distinguish between **equilibrium** and **rate**. Equilibrium refers to the relative amounts of reactants and products expected by thermodynamics, *if a suitable pathway exists between them*. A simple example is glucose in the presence of oxygen. These two reagents can exist together for indefinite periods without change, but if the sugar is ignited it will burn to produce the equilibrium products CO_2 and H_2O. Alternatively, the same result is accomplished in living organisms by a series of catalysts (enzymes) that allow this oxidation to occur in a sequence of controlled steps.

Reactants can reach equilibrium at a variety of rates ranging from immeasurably slow to exceedingly fast. The rate at which equilibrium is reached depends on the reaction and on the structures of the reactants. Consequently, we will be much concerned with the effect of structural change on reactivity. We will also find that many reactions are characteristic of individual functional groups and form much of the chemistry of functional groups. Finally, we will also be concerned with the pathway, or *mechanism*, by which reactants find their way to products.

4.2 An Example of an Organic Reaction: Equilibria

Although methyl chloride is a gas at room temperature, it is sufficiently soluble in water to give a solution of about $0.1\ M$ concentration. If the solution also contains hydroxide ion, reaction occurs to form methyl alcohol and chloride ion.

$$\text{HO}^- + \underset{\substack{\text{methyl}\\\text{chloride}}}{\text{CH}_3\text{Cl}} \rightleftharpoons \underset{\substack{\text{methyl}\\\text{alcohol}}}{\text{CH}_3\text{OH}} + \text{Cl}^- \qquad (4\text{-}1)$$

At equilibrium all four compounds are present, but the equilibrium constant K is such an exceedingly large number that the amount of methyl chloride present in the equilibrium mixture is vanishingly small.

$$K = \frac{[\text{CH}_3\text{OH}][\text{Cl}^-]}{[\text{CH}_3\text{Cl}][\text{OH}^-]} = 10^{16}$$

If the reaction started with 0.1 M CH_3Cl and 0.2 M NaOH, at the end of the reaction we would have a solution of 0.1 M CH_3OH, 0.1 M NaCl, 0.1 M NaOH, and 10^{-17} M CH_3Cl. That is, 1 mL of such a solution would contain only a few thousand molecules of CH_3Cl.

Such a reaction is said to **go to completion**. In practice a reaction may be considered to go to completion if the final equilibrium mixture contains less than about 0.1% of reactant.

The reaction of methyl chloride and hydroxide ion may also be characterized by the **Gibbs standard free energy change at equilibrium**, $\Delta G°$.

$$\Delta G° = -RT \ln K$$

For reaction (4-1), $\Delta G°$ is -22 kcal mole^{-1}, a rather large value. We may speak of this reaction as having a large **driving force**. That is, the driving force for a reaction is a qualitative description of an equilibrium property and is related to the overall free energy change. For comparison, $\Delta G°$ for a reaction that proceeds to 99.9% at equilibrium is 4.1 kcal mole^{-1} at 25°C.

There is an important difference between ΔG and $\Delta G°$. The free energy of a given system is ΔG. The free energy of that system with the components in their standard states is $\Delta G°$. For gases, the standard state is generally the corresponding ideal gas at 1 atm pressure. For solutions, the standard state is normally chosen to be the ideal 1 M solution. The standard free energy of a system $\Delta G°$ is defined as the free energy ΔG of an ideal solution in which each reactant and product is present in a concentration of 1 M. For such a system, $\Delta G = \Delta G°$. When reaction reaches equilibrium, the free energy of the system $\Delta G = 0$. The concentrations of the components at this point are given as

$$\Delta G = \Delta G° + RT \ln K$$

where

$$K = \frac{[\text{products}]_{eq}}{[\text{reactants}]_{eq}}$$

Hence, the standard free energy is given by

$$\Delta G° = -RT \ln K$$

Note also that the units of K are determined by the standard states.

The Gibbs standard free energy may be dissected into **enthalpy** and **entropy** components, $\Delta H°$ and $\Delta S°$, respectively.

$$\Delta G° = \Delta H° - T \Delta S°$$

Enthalpy is the heat of reaction and is generally associated with bonding. If stronger bonds are formed in a reaction, $\Delta H°$ is negative and the reaction is **exothermic**. A reaction with positive $\Delta H°$ is **endothermic**. Entropy may be thought of simply as freedom of motion. The more a molecule or portion of a molecule is restricted in motion, the more negative is the entropy. Both the formation of stronger bonds and greater freedom of motion can contribute to a favorable driving force for reaction (negative $\Delta G°$).

For reaction (4-1), $\Delta H° = -18$ kcal mole^{-1} and $\Delta S° = +13$ eu (ΔS is usually expressed as entropy units, eu, which mean cal deg^{-1} mole^{-1}). The driving force in this case comes mostly from bond energy changes; a carbon-oxygen bond is stronger than a carbon-chlorine bond. The formation of stronger bonds is usually an important component of the driving force of a reaction.

In the vapor phase, where intermolecular interactions are negligible, the strength of the internal bonds in a molecule is especially important in determining its stability. In solutions, however, one must also consider the intermolecular interactions with solvent molecules (**solvation**). Solvent interactions that involve varying degrees of ionic and covalent bonding are particularly important for ions. They provide the main driving force for breaking up the stable crystal lattices when ionic substances dissolve. Although solvation of an ion provides bonding stabilization which is reflected in $\Delta H°$, it is partially offset by a decrease in entropy $\Delta S°$. The crowding of several solvent molecules around an ion restricts the freedom of motion of these molecules. In the present case the entropy of reaction $\Delta S°$ is positive because chloride ion is less strongly solvated than hydroxide ion. That is, the solvent molecules are less restricted after reaction than before. Since $\Delta S°$ is positive, the quantity $(-T\Delta S°)$ contributes a negative value to $\Delta G°$ and provides an additional driving force for reaction to occur.

EXERCISE 4.1 Using the basic thermodynamic relationships given in this section, calculate $\Delta G°$ and the equilibrium constant K for a reaction that has $\Delta H° = -10$ kcal mole^{-1} and $\Delta S° = -22$ eu (a) if the reaction is carried out at 27°C (300 K or Kelvin) and (b) if the reaction temperature is 227°C.

4.3 Reaction Kinetics

Because it has such a large driving force, it seems remarkable that the reaction of methyl chloride with hydroxide ion is relatively slow. For example, a 0.05 M solution of methyl chloride in 0.1 M aqueous sodium hydroxide will have reacted only to the extent of about 10% after 2 days at room temperature. It is an important principle in all reactions that favorable thermodynamics is not enough; a suitable reaction pathway is essential.

Reactions generally involve an **energy barrier** that must be surmounted in going from reactants to products. This barrier exists because molecules generally repel each other as they are brought together and reactants must be forced close to each other to cause the bond changes involved in reaction. The resulting energy barrier is called the **activation energy** or the **enthalpy of activation** and is symbolized by $\Delta H^{\ddagger}$. In the reaction of methyl chloride with hydroxide ion, $\Delta H^{\ddagger}$ is about 25 kcal mole^{-1}. This appears to be a rather formidable hurdle when one realizes that the average kinetic energy of molecules at room temperature is only about 0.6 kcal mole^{-1}. However, this latter number is only an average. Molecules are continually colliding with each other at rapid rates and exchanging kinetic energy. At any given instant some molecules have less than this average energy, some have more, and a few even have very large energies—like 25 kcal mole^{-1}.

The relative number of molecules with any given energy is given by the Boltzmann distribution function, shown schematically in Figure 4.1. Most of the molecules have an energy close to the average energy represented by the large hump. Only the minute fraction of molecules in the far end of the asymptotic tail have sufficient energy to overcome the barrier to reaction. Thus, only a very small number of the collisions between methyl chloride and hydroxide ion involve sufficient energy to result in reaction.

At a higher temperature, the average kinetic energy of the molecules is greater, and the entire distribution function is shifted to higher energies, as shown by the dashed curve in Figure 4.1. The fraction of molecules with kinetic energy sufficient for reac-

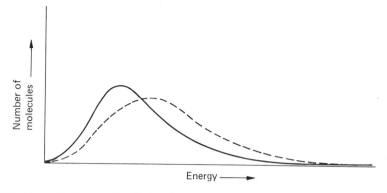

FIGURE 4.1 A Boltzmann distribution function. Dashed line shows a higher temperature.

tion is larger, and the rate of reaction is correspondingly larger. For example, the reaction of methyl chloride with hydroxide ion is 25 times faster at 50°C than it is at 25°C. A useful rule of thumb for many organic reactions is that a 10° change in temperature causes a two- to threefold change in rate of reaction.

The rate of a chemical reaction depends not only on the fraction of molecules that have sufficient energy for reaction but also on their concentration because this determines the probability of an encounter that could lead to reaction. Reaction rates are directly proportional to the concentrations of the reactants, and the proportionality constant is called a **rate constant, k**. The reaction of methyl chloride with hydroxide ion is an example of a **second-order reaction**, since the rate depends on two concentrations.

$$\text{rate} = k[CH_3Cl][OH^-] \tag{4-2}$$

"Rate" involves a change in concentration of something per unit time, usually expressed as moles per liter per second, $M\ \sec^{-1}$. In equation (4-2), therefore, k must have units of $M^{-1}\ \sec^{-1}$.

$$(M^{-1}\ \sec^{-1})(M)(M) = M\ \sec^{-1}$$

The "something" whose concentration is changing is either a reactant or a product.

$$\text{rate} = -\frac{\Delta[CH_3Cl]}{\Delta t} = -\frac{\Delta[OH^-]}{\Delta t} = \frac{\Delta[CH_3OH]}{\Delta t} = \frac{\Delta[Cl^-]}{\Delta t} \tag{4-3}$$

The minus signs for the reactants indicate that their concentrations decrease with increasing time. All of the changes shown are equal by stoichiometry.

In the language of calculus, this rate equation becomes

$$-\frac{d[CH_3Cl]}{dt} = -\frac{d[OH^-]}{dt} = \frac{d[CH_3OH]}{dt} = \frac{d[Cl^-]}{dt} = k[CH_3Cl][OH^-]$$

The actual value of k at 25°C is $6 \times 10^{-6}\ M^{-1}\ \sec^{-1}$.

The reaction of methyl chloride with hydroxide ion may be compared with its reaction with water. The reaction with water is an example of a **first-order reaction**. The reaction involves water molecules, but, because water is the solvent, it is present in large excess. Therefore the concentration of water remains effectively the same, even after all of the methyl chloride has reacted. Since the concentration of water appears not to change during the reaction, it does not appear in the kinetic expression; thus the rate of reaction depends only on the concentration of methyl chloride.

$$\text{rate} = k[CH_3Cl] \qquad\qquad (4\text{-}4)$$

Because only one concentration is involved, equation (4-4) is the equation of a first-order reaction. The rate is a change in concentration per unit time, for example, moles per liter per second, $M\ \text{sec}^{-1}$. Therefore, k has the units of sec^{-1}. For methyl chloride at 25°C, $k = 3 \times 10^{-10}\ \text{sec}^{-1}$.

The reaction of methyl chloride with water is experimentally a first-order reaction because the concentration of one reactant (water) does not change significantly during the reaction. A second-order reaction becomes effectively a first-order reaction if the concentration of one component is much greater than the other. For example, in the reaction of a solution of $0.01\ M\ CH_3Cl$ with $1\ M\ NaOH$ the concentration of hydroxide ion changes from $1\ M$ to $0.99\ M$ during the reaction. That is, its concentration remains essentially constant and the reaction of methyl chloride under these conditions appears to be a first-order reaction with a rate constant of $6 \times 10^{-6}\ \text{sec}^{-1}$. Such a reaction is also called a **pseudo first-order reaction**.

The student should be careful not to confuse "rate" and "rate constant." The rate constant k for a reaction is simply a numerical measure of how fast a reaction can occur if the reactants are brought together. It relates the actual concentrations of the reactants to the rate of reaction, which is the "through-put" or "flux" of the reaction.

EXERCISE 4.2 Using the rate constant $k = 6 \times 10^{-6}\ M^{-1}\ \text{sec}^{-1}$ for the reaction of methyl chloride with hydroxide ion, calculate the initial rate of reaction for each of the following initial reactant concentrations.
(a) $0.1\ M\ CH_3Cl$ and $1.0\ M\ OH^-$ (b) $0.1\ M\ CH_3Cl$ and $0.1\ M\ OH^-$
(c) $0.01\ M\ CH_3Cl$ and $0.01\ M\ OH^-$
Compare each of these initial rates with the rate of reaction when 90% of the methyl chloride has reacted.

4.4 Reaction Profiles and Mechanism

In the reaction of methyl chloride and hydroxide ion atoms must move around and bonds must change in order that the products methyl alcohol and chloride ion may be produced. One of the important concepts in organic chemistry involves the consideration of the structure of the system as reaction proceeds. Each configuration of the atoms during the process of changing from reactants to products has an associated energy. Since reaction generally involves bringing the reactants close together and breaking bonds, these structures generally have higher energy than the isolated reactants. That is, as the reactants approach each other and start to undergo the molecular changes that will eventually result in products, the potential energy of the reacting system increases. As the reaction encounter continues, the potential energy continues to increase until the system reaches a structure of **maximum energy**. Thereafter the changes that result in the final products continue, but the structures represent lower and lower energy until the products are fully formed.

The difference in the energy of the isolated reactants and the maximum energy structure which the system passes through on the path to products is the **activation energy** of the reaction. This maximum energy corresponds to a definite structure called the **transition state**. The measure of the progress of reaction from reactants to products is the **reaction coordinate**. This coordinate is usually not specified in detail because the qualitative concept is usually sufficient, but in our reaction, for example, it could be represented by the carbon-oxygen bond length or the carbon-chlorine bond length as the reaction progresses, or by the net electronic charge on chlorine. Whatever measure is used, the general reaction profile is given by Figure 4.2. In this figure, the energy shown is the potential energy. This quantity is related to but is not identical with $\Delta H°$. Similarly, the difference in potential energy between reactants and products contributes to $\Delta G°$ for the reaction. The magnitude of this difference determines the *position* of equilibrium. The magnitude of the activation energy determines the *rate* at which equilibrium is established.

The energy quantities involved in reactions are given more precise definitions in the **theory of absolute rates.** In this theory the transition state is characterized by the dynamic properties: free energy, enthalpy, and entropy. The rate constant for reaction is related to the Gibbs free energy difference between the transition state, sometimes called an **activated complex,** and the reactant state by the equation

$$k = \nu^{\ddagger} e^{-\Delta G^{\ddagger}/RT} = \nu^{\ddagger} e^{-\Delta H^{\ddagger}/RT} e^{\Delta S^{\ddagger}/R}$$

The proportionality constant, $\nu^{\ddagger}$ is a kind of frequency. Its magnitude is 6.2×10^{12} sec^{-1} at 25°C, a magnitude comparable to ordinary vibration frequencies. In fact, the reaction process can be described as one of the modes of vibration of the activated complex. For this reason, the activated complex or transition state is not a normal molecule and is only a transient phase in the course of reaction.

The structure of the transition state is an important feature of a reaction. If we can estimate its energy, we can predict the reaction rate, at least roughly. For example, a transition state in which several bonds are broken is likely to correspond to high energy and a slow reaction. Furthermore, and most important, from the structure of the transition state we can often evaluate how a given change in structure will change the rate. Unfortunately, we cannot directly observe a transition state-we cannot take its spec-

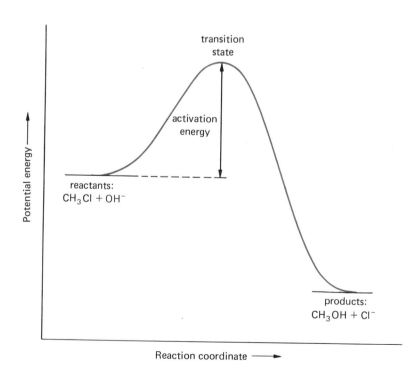

FIGURE 4.2 A reaction profile for the reaction $CH_3Cl + OH^- \longrightarrow CH_3OH + Cl^-$.

trum or determine its structure by x-ray diffraction. Instead, we must infer its structure indirectly.

The reaction of hydroxide ion with methyl chloride is an example of a general reaction known as an S_N2 reaction, which we will study in Chapter 8. The structure of the transition state will be developed at that time. We will find, for example, that the S_N2 reaction probably involves a single step with one transition state, as suggested in Figure 4.2. Many other reactions, however, involve more than one step. A reaction profile such as that in Figure 4.3 is not uncommon. Such a reaction involves one or more intermediates, and each intermediate is flanked by transition states. Reaction intermediates correspond to energy minima on the reaction coordinate diagram. They may be sufficiently stable that they can be isolated and stored in bottles, or they may have such fleeting existence that their presence must be inferred from subtle observations of cleverly designed experiments.

The **reaction mechanism** is a sequential account of each transition state and intermediate in a total reaction. The overall rate of reaction is determined approximately by the transition state of highest energy in the sequence, so that this structure has particular importance. The step involving this transition state is often called the **rate-determining** step.

The reaction profile shown in Figure 4.3 corresponds to the equations

$$\text{reactants} \underset{k_{-1}}{\overset{k_1}{\rightleftharpoons}} \text{intermediate} \underset{k_{-2}}{\overset{k_2}{\rightleftharpoons}} \text{products}$$

The relative energies in this figure correspond to rate constants having the relationships

$$k_{-1} > k_1 > k_2 > k_{-2}$$

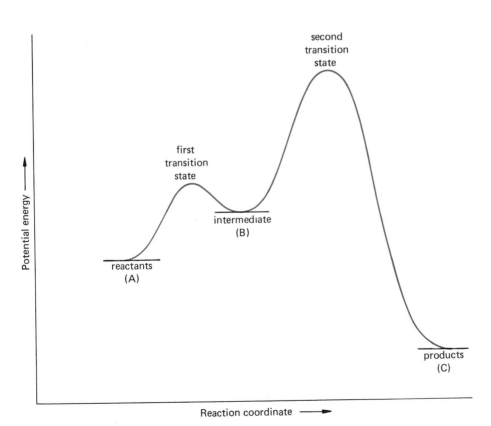

FIGURE 4.3 Profile of a more complex reaction that involves an intermediate.

Remember that the lower the energy barrier, the larger the rate constant. Because it is the highest point between reactants and products, the second transition state in Figure 4.3 corresponds to the rate-determining step.

Again, it must be emphasized that rate constant and rate are not the same. For example, in Figure 4.3 the first step has a greater rate constant than the second step (i.e., $k_1 > k_2$). It is also clear from the graph that since B is less stable than A, the equilibrium between A and B is such that the concentration of B at any given time is much less than the concentration of A, or $[A] > [B]$. Thus, the first step in the reaction has a faster *rate* than the second ($k_1[A] > k_2[B]$).

As a further example of this point, consider the reaction coordinate diagram for a two-step reaction shown in Figure 4.4. Again, the highest energy transition state occurs in the second step, which is therefore the rate-determining step. In this example $k_2 > k_1$. However, since $[A] >> [B]$, the rate of the first step is still faster than the rate of the second.

An example of a reaction with intermediates is the hydrolysis of ethyl acetate with aqueous sodium hydroxide.

$$\underset{\text{ethyl acetate}}{CH_3\overset{\overset{O}{\|}}{C}OCH_2CH_3} + OH^- \xrightarrow[H_2O]{25°} \underset{\text{acetate ion}}{CH_3CO_2^-} + \underset{\text{ethyl alcohol}}{CH_3CH_2OH}$$

This example illustrates the way in which organic reactions are typically written. The arrow shows the direction of the reaction and implies that the equilibrium lies far to the right. Reaction conditions such as solvent, temperature, and any catalysts used are written with the arrow as shown. Abbreviations are often used in this convention. An example is the use of the symbol Δ for heat. If the reaction mixture shown was heated or refluxed in order to speed reaction, we could represent the reaction as

$$CH_3\overset{\overset{O}{\|}}{C}OCH_2CH_3 + OH^- \xrightarrow[H_2O]{\Delta} CH_3CO_2^- + CH_3CH_2OH$$

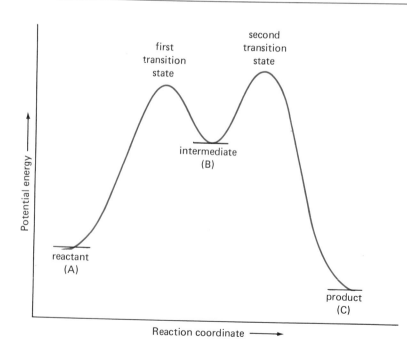

FIGURE 4.4 Profile of another two-step reaction.

FIGURE 4.5 Reaction profile for hydrolysis of an ester.

The rate expression for this reaction is

$$\text{rate} = 0.1 \, [OH^-][CH_3COOCH_2CH_3]$$

The second-order rate constant $0.1 \, M^{-1} \, \text{sec}^{-1}$ is relatively large and corresponds to a rather fast reaction. As we shall learn in Chapter 18, the mechanism of this reaction appears to be

$$CH_3\overset{O}{\overset{\|}{C}}OCH_2CH_3 + OH^- \rightleftharpoons CH_3\overset{O^-}{\underset{OH}{\overset{|}{C}}}OCH_2CH_3$$

$$CH_3\overset{O^-}{\underset{OH}{\overset{|}{C}}}OCH_2CH_3 \longrightarrow CH_3COOH + CH_3CH_2O^-$$

The reaction is effectively irreversible because the strong base $CH_3CH_2O^-$ reacts immediately with acetic acid to produce ethyl alcohol and acetate ion.

$$\underset{\text{acetic acid}}{CH_3COOH} + CH_3CH_2O^- \xrightarrow{\text{fast}} CH_3CO_2^- + CH_3CH_2OH$$

The reaction profile for this reaction is shown in Figure 4.5.

Reaction profiles such as those in Figures 4.2-4.5 can be useful because they illustrate a rather complex pattern in a diagrammatic way that is easy to visualize. But such diagrams have only a qualitative significance. The reason is that the rate constant for a given reaction step depends on the Gibbs free energy difference between the reactants and transition state, $\Delta G^{\ddagger}$, a thermodynamic quantity that has significance only for a statistical collection of species. It is not defined for the distorted structures that result as the reactant molecule is changing to the product molecule. The potential energy is defined for individual molecules and distorted structures, but is only one component of the free energy. Nevertheless, it is generally (but not always) true that a larger potential energy increase between reactants and transition state is associated with a larger $\Delta G^{\ddagger}$ and a smaller rate constant. Moreover, for these same reasons the term "rate-determining step" has only approximate significance. In multistep reactions the actual rate of reaction may be a complex function of time and reactant concentrations that does not lend itself to a simple pictorial representation.

The elucidation of reaction mechanisms is a fascinating branch of organic chemistry. In our study of organic chemistry, we will deal frequently with reaction mechanisms because they help enormously in our classification and understanding of the vast array of organic reactions known. In some important cases, such as the hydrolysis of ethyl acetate, we will also study some of the experimental evidence from which the reaction mechanisms and transition state structures have been deduced.

> **EXERCISE 4.3** Construct a reaction coordinate diagram for a reaction $A \rightleftharpoons B \rightleftharpoons C$ in which the relative stabilities of the three species are $C > A > B$ and for which the relative order of the four rate constants is $k_2 > k_{-1} > k_1 \gg k_{-2}$. Which is the rate-determining step in your diagram? What is the relative order of the four free energies of activation, $\Delta G^{\ddagger}$? Of the two forward steps, which has the faster rate? Is there any way you can adjust the relative levels within the foregoing specified conditions so that the rate of the other step becomes faster?

4.5 Acidity and Basicity

One of the most important reactions in chemistry is that associated with acidity and basicity. **Acidity** refers to the loss of a proton.

$$HY \rightleftharpoons H^+ + Y^-$$

Such reactions can be measured for the gas phase and are invariably highly endothermic. For example,

$$HCl(g) \rightleftharpoons H^+(g) + Cl^-(g) \qquad \Delta H^\circ = 328.8 \text{ kcal mole}^{-1}$$

This reaction is extremely endothermic because a bond is broken and charges are separated; both of these processes require energy. In aqueous solution acidity is defined in terms of a dissociation equilibrium involving solvated species.

$$HCl(aq) \rightleftharpoons H^+(aq) + Cl^-(aq)$$

The species $H^+(aq)$ is often written as H_3O^+ for convenience. However, in actuality even more extensive solvation occurs involving hydrogen bonds to the oxygens of other water molecules.

$$H_2O\text{----}H \diagdown \overset{+}{\underset{\underset{\overset{|}{OH_2}}{H}}{O}} \diagup H\text{----}OH_2$$

Similarly, the Cl^- ion is solvated by hydrogen bonds to water molecules.

$$H-O-H$$
$$H-O-H----Cl^- ----H-O-H$$
$$H-O-H$$

Hydrogen bonds will be discussed in greater detail in Section 10.3. They result from the electrostatic attraction between lone-pair electrons, such as those on oxygen and chlorine, and hydrogens that are bound to an electronegative element. Such hydrogens are good "receptors" for these electrostatic bonds because of the partial positive charge they bear. These solvation bonds are sufficiently strong in the aggregate to compensate for the energy that must be supplied to break the hydrogen-chlorine bond and the electrostatic energy required to separate negative from positive charges.

Acidity measurements have been made in many different solvents. Nevertheless, water is by far the most common solvent and is assumed to be the reference solvent if none is specified. *The acidity of an acid HA in water is defined as the equilibrium constant for the reaction*

$$HA(aq) \xrightleftharpoons{K} H^+(aq) + A^-(aq)$$

$$K = \frac{[H^+][A^-]}{[HA]}$$

The equilibrium constants for acid dissociations are normally symbolized as K_a. Note that the concentration of water does not appear in the expression and that K_a normally has units of M or moles liter^{-1}.

Acidity equilibrium constants vary over a wide range. Acids with $K_a > 1$ are referred to as strong acids; acids with $K_a < 10^{-4}$ are weak acids, and many compounds are very weak acids for which K_a is exceedingly small. For example, methane is a very weak acid with $K_a \cong 10^{-50}$. This number is so small (it corresponds to approximately one pair of dissociated ions per universe of solution) that it is known only approximately and must be measured indirectly.

Acidity equilibrium constants are usually expressed as an exponent of 10 in order to accommodate this large range of possible values. The pK_a is defined as the negative exponent of ten, or as

$$pK_a = -\log K_a$$

The pK_a values for some common acids are summarized in Table 4.1. A more extensive list is given in Appendix IV. The term "acidity" is also used in a qualitative sense to refer to acidic character relative to water. Solutions of acids that are substantially more acidic than water have significant hydrogen ion concentrations. That is, their aqueous solutions have pH values less than 7. Recall that the pH is defined as the negative logarithm of the hydrogen-ion concentration.

$$pH = -\log [H^+]$$

Neutral water has $[H^+] = 1.0 \times 10^{-7}$ M or pH = 7.0. Solutions with pH < 7 are "acidic" and have a distinctive sharp taste at the tip of the tongue. The strong acids HI, HBr, HCl, HNO$_3$, and H$_2$SO$_4$ are commonly referred to as "mineral acids." Their solutions have the low pH values characteristic of solutions that are "acidic." Acetic acid is a weaker acid, but its aqueous solutions also have pH values that are definitely "acidic." Alcohols have about the same acidity as water itself and are therefore not "acidic" in this sense.

TABLE 4.1 Acidities of Common Acids at 25°C

Name	Formula	pK_a
acetic acid	CH_3COOH	4.76
ammonium ion	NH_4^+	9.24
hydriodic acid	HI	−5.2
hydrobromic acid	HBr	−4.7
hydrochloric acid	HCl	−2.2
hydrocyanic acid	HCN	9.22
hydrofluoric acid	HF	3.18
hydrogen selenide	H_2Se	3.71
hydrogen sulfide	H_2S	6.97
methyl alcohol	CH_3OH	15.5
nitric acid	HNO_3	−1.3
nitrous acid	HNO_2	3.23
phosphoric acid	H_3PO_4	2.15 (7.20, 12.38)[a]
phenol	C_6H_5OH	10.00
sulfuric acid	H_2SO_4	−5.2 (1.99)[a]
water	H_2O	15.74

[a] Values in parentheses are the constants for dissociation of the second and third protons from phosphoric acid and the second proton from sulfuric acid.

EXERCISE 4.4 Calculate the pH of a solution of 1 mole of each of the following acids in 1 L of water.
(a) HI   (b) HCl   (c) HF   (d) acetic acid   (e) H_2S

Table 4.1 gives second and third dissociation constants where appropriate. Thus, HSO_4^- with $pK_a = 1.99$ is about as acidic as the first dissociation of H_3PO_4, $pK_a = 2.15$. The acidity of $H_2PO_4^-$, $pK_a = 7.20$, is comparable to that of H_2S, $pK_a = 6.95$, and both pK_as are comparable to the pH of neutral water, 7. The significance of this point is apparent from the following analysis. When an acid is exactly 50% dissociated, the remaining acid concentration [HA] is equal to the concentration of the conjugate anion [A^-]. For such a case, the hydrogen-ion concentration of the solution is numerically equal to the acidity constant, or pH = pK_a.

$$K = \frac{[A^-][H^+]}{[HA]}$$

$$pK = -\log K = -\log [H^+] = pH$$

For aqueous solutions pK_a values in the range of about 2–12 are known fairly accurately. The acidity constants of stronger acids ($pK_a < 2$) are known with less precision because such acids are extensively dissociated in aqueous solution.

EXERCISE 4.5 Determine the concentrations of H^+, A^-, and undissociated acid, HA, for a 1 *M* solution of an acid having a $pK_a = -2$.

We have discussed acidity in terms of the process of acid HA giving up a proton to the solvent water. But the process is an equilibrium, the reverse of which involves the reaction of the conjugate anion A^- to accept a proton from the solvent. We could speak equally of the acidity of HA or of the **basicity** of A^-.

$$HA \rightleftharpoons H^+ + A^-$$

conjugate   conjugate
acid   base

The stronger HA is as an acid, the weaker A⁻ is as a base. Conversely, a strong base has a weak conjugate acid. Because of these relationships basicity is generally characterized in terms of the acidity of the conjugate acid.

> **EXERCISE 4.6** For each of the acids listed in Table 4.1 write the conjugate base and give an evaluation of the basicity considering hydroxide ion to be a relatively strong base.

The relationship between structure and acidity is extremely important in chemistry, and we shall refer frequently throughout our study of organic chemistry to the acidities of different functional groups and the manner in which these acidities change as the structure is perturbed. We shall find that the mechanisms of many organic reactions involve intermediates functioning in one way or another as acids or bases. For comparisons of the acidities of two or more compounds, some generalizations are useful. Removing a proton from a molecule involves breaking a bond to hydrogen and putting a negative charge on the remaining system. Thus, weaker bonds generally lead to greater acidity. As we move from element to element down the periodic table, bond strengths diminish because valence atomic orbitals become larger and more diffuse and their overlap to a hydrogen $1s$-orbital is less effective. This factor can have a dominating effect on acidity. Compare the acidity series $H_2O < H_2S < H_2Se$ and $HF < HCl < HBr < HI$.

Stabilization of the negative charge on an anion also generally results in greater acidity of the acid from which it is derived. Along any given row of the periodic table electronegativity increases as we move to the right. This is the dominating factor in such acidity comparisons as $HF > H_2O$ and $HCl > H_2S$. Stabilization of the anion can also result from more extensive distribution of charge. We will learn many examples of this principle as we develop the chemistry of various functional groups in subsequent chapters. The presence of a formal positive charge results in a dramatic increase in acidity because of the electrostatic attraction between positive and negative charges. Some examples are

$$
\begin{array}{cc}
\overset{\displaystyle O^-}{\underset{\displaystyle O_-}{HO-\overset{|}{\underset{|}{S^{2+}}}-OH}} & > & \overset{\displaystyle O^-}{HO-\overset{|}{\underset{\cdot\cdot}{S^+}}-OH}
\end{array}
$$

sulfuric acid   sulfurous acid

$$
\overset{\displaystyle O^-}{O=\overset{|}{N^+}-OH} > O=\overset{\cdot\cdot}{N}-OH
$$

nitric acid   nitrous acid

A simple corollary is that a nearby negative charge will reduce acidity because of charge repulsion in the resulting anion. Thus the second dissociation constants are generally smaller than the first. Examples of such acidity orders are

$$
\overset{\displaystyle O^-}{\underset{\displaystyle O_-}{HO-\overset{|}{\underset{|}{S^{2+}}}-OH}} > \overset{\displaystyle O^-}{\underset{\displaystyle O_-}{HO-\overset{|}{\underset{|}{S^{2+}}}-O^-}}
$$

$$\overset{\displaystyle OH}{\underset{\displaystyle OH}{^-O-\overset{|}{\underset{|}{P^+}}-OH}} \;>\; \overset{\displaystyle O^-}{\underset{\displaystyle OH}{^-O-\overset{|}{\underset{|}{P^+}}-OH}} \;>\; \overset{\displaystyle O^-}{\underset{\displaystyle O_-}{^-O-\overset{|}{\underset{|}{P^+}}-OH}}$$

Another important effect in many kinds of anions is resonance stabilization. Recall from page 12 that the electronic structure of formate ion cannot be represented accurately by a single Lewis structure but requires two equivalent structures:

$$H-C\overset{\displaystyle O}{\underset{\displaystyle O^-}{\big<}} \;\longleftrightarrow\; H-C\overset{\displaystyle O^-}{\underset{\displaystyle O}{\big<}}$$

The negative charge is divided between two oxygens; that is, each oxygen bears only one half of a negative charge. Accordingly, each oxygen is less basic than an oxygen with a full charge such as hydroxide ion or methoxide ion, or equivalently, the conjugate acid is more acidic. Thus, the carboxylic acids are more acidic than alcohols. This an important point and we shall discuss it again in greater detail in Chapter 17. The fundamental principle involved will also enter into some reactions of acetate ion to be studied in Chapter 9.

To summarize, acidity and basicity are important chemical properties. Many organic reactions involve proton-transfer equilibria, and we need to appreciate the effect of structural change on such equilibria. Moreover, some organic compounds are related chemically to corresponding inorganic acids. For example, methanesulfonic acid, CH_3SO_3H, is related to sulfuric acid, $HOSO_3H$, and is also a strong acid. Ethylamine, $CH_3CH_2NH_2$, is related to ammonia, NH_3, and has comparable base strength. Some important generalizations are

1. Acidity of Y—H increases as Y is further down a given column of the periodic table.
2. Acidity of Y—H increases as Y is toward the right along a given row of the periodic table.
3. Nearby positive charges increase acidity; negative charges decrease acidity.
4. Resonance stabilization of anion increases acidity. This effect will be discussed more in later chapters.

PROBLEMS

1. In this chapter we discuss the hydrolysis of methyl chloride in aqueous solution. Consider the same reaction in the gas phase at 25°C:

$$CH_3Cl + H_2O \; \Longrightarrow \; CH_3OH + HCl$$

(a) $\Delta H° = 7.3$ kcal mole^{-1}; $\Delta S° = 0.3$ eu. Calculate $\Delta G°$.
(b) Calculate the equilibrium constant.
(c) Can this reaction be said to ''go to completion'' in the direction shown?

2. Consider the equilibrium between butane and ethane plus ethylene.

$$C_4H_{10} \; \Longrightarrow \; C_2H_6 + C_2H_4$$

(a) At 25°C $\Delta H° = 22.2$ kcal mole^{-1} and $\Delta S° = 33.5$ eu. What is $\Delta G°$? On which side does the equilibrium lie?

(b) Calculate $\Delta G°$ at 800 K (527°C) and determine the position of equilibrium.

(c) How does the relative effect of $\Delta H°$ and $\Delta S°$ change with temperature? (Actually, $\Delta H°$ and $\Delta S°$ change somewhat with temperature, but the effect is not large enough to change the qualitative result.)

3. (a) At room temperature what change in free energy in units of kcal mole^{-1} will change an equilibrium constant by a factor of 10? By a factor of 100? This energy quantity is a handy number to remember.

(b) These numbers can be converted to equivalent ΔH and ΔS values. Consider ΔG for the factor of 10 change in equilibrium constant. What is the equivalent value for ΔH in kcal mole^{-1} if $\Delta S = 0$; what is the equivalent value for ΔS in eu (cal deg^{-1} mole^{-1}) if $\Delta H = 0$?

4. During the course of reaction, the concentration of reactants decreases; hence, the rate of reaction is reduced.

(a) In the example of 0.05 M methyl chloride and 0.10 M OH$^-$ discussed on page 51, what is the rate of reaction at the start of the reaction, using the rate constant given on page 54?

(b) Using this rate, determine the time required for 10% reaction. What are the concentrations of reactants after 10% reaction? What is the rate of reaction at this point? Using this rate, determine how long it takes for the second 10% of reaction to occur.

(c) Repeat the calculation to estimate the time for 50% completion of the reaction.

5. The equilibrium reaction in the gas phase of ethylene and HCl to give ethyl chloride, $C_2H_4 + HCl = C_2H_5Cl$, has a favorable enthalpy, $\Delta H° = -15.5$ kcal mole^{-1}, but an unfavorable entropy, $\Delta S° = -31.3$ eu.

(a) Why is the entropy negative?

(b) What is $\Delta G°$ at room temperature (25°C)?

(c) If the reaction mixture started with 1 atm pressure each of HCl and C_2H_4, what pressure of each is left at equilibrium?

(d) For the system to be at equilibrium with all three components present in equal amounts, what total pressure is required? Incidentally, in this system a mixture of pure, dry HCl and C_2H_4 will not react at room temperature. Establishment of the equilibrium requires a suitable catalyst.

6. Consider the following reaction sequence in which B is an intermediate. Sketch energy profiles for each of the possible relationships among rate constants shown.

$$A \underset{k_2}{\overset{k_1}{\rightleftharpoons}} B$$

$$B \overset{k_3}{\longrightarrow} C$$

The back-reaction from C is negligible.

(a) k_1 and k_2 large; k_3 small.

(b) k_1 large; k_2 and k_3 large, but $k_2 > k_3$.

(c) k_1 and k_3 large; k_2 small.

(d) k_1 small; k_2 and k_3 large, but $k_3 > k_2$.

Identify the rate-determining transition state for each of the four cases.

7. Consider the hypothetical two-step reaction

$$A \underset{k_2}{\overset{k_1}{\rightleftharpoons}} B \underset{k_1}{\overset{k_2}{\rightleftharpoons}} C$$

that is described by the following energy profile.

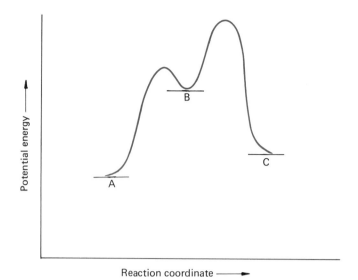

(a) Is the overall reaction (A ⟶ C) exothermic or endothermic?

(b) Label the transition states. Which transition state is rate-determining?

(c) What is the correct order of magnitude of rate constants?

    (i) $k_1 > k_2 > k_3 > k_4$

    (ii) $k_2 > k_3 > k_1 > k_4$

    (iii) $k_4 > k_1 > k_3 > k_2$

    (iv) $k_3 > k_2 > k_4 > k_1$

(d) Which is the thermodynamically most stable compound?

(e) Which is the thermodynamically least stable compound?

8. *t*-Butyl chloride reacts with hydroxide ion according to the following equation.

$$CH_3-\overset{\overset{\displaystyle CH_3}{|}}{\underset{\underset{\displaystyle CH_3}{|}}{C}}-Cl + OH^- \overset{k}{\rightleftharpoons} CH_3-\overset{\overset{\displaystyle CH_3}{|}}{\underset{\underset{\displaystyle CH_3}{|}}{C}}-OH + Cl^-$$

        t-butyl chloride   *t*-butyl alcohol

We will learn in Chapter 9 that the reaction is believed to proceed by the following mechanism.

$$(1)\ CH_3-\overset{\overset{\displaystyle CH_3}{|}}{\underset{\underset{\displaystyle CH_3}{|}}{C}}-Cl \underset{k_2}{\overset{k_1}{\rightleftharpoons}} CH_3-\overset{\overset{\displaystyle CH_3}{|}}{\underset{\underset{\displaystyle CH_3}{|}}{C}}+ + Cl^-$$

$$(2)\ CH_3-\overset{\overset{\displaystyle CH_3}{|}}{\underset{\underset{\displaystyle CH_3}{|}}{C}}+ + OH^- \underset{k_4}{\overset{k_3}{\rightleftharpoons}} CH_3-\overset{\overset{\displaystyle CH_3}{|}}{\underset{\underset{\displaystyle CH_3}{|}}{C}}-OH$$

The order of rate constants is $k_3 > k_2 > k_1 \gg k_4$.

(a) Construct a reaction coordinate diagram for the reaction.

(b) Is the first step exothermic or endothermic?

(c) Is the overall reaction exothermic or endothermic?

(d) Does the first or second step govern the rate of disappearance of *t*-butyl chloride?

9. Ammonia is a weak acid with a pK_a estimated as 34. The conjugate anion NH_2^-, amide ion, is available as alkali metal salts such as sodium amide, $NaNH_2$. Calculate the pH of a solution prepared by adding 0.1 mole of sodium amide to 1 L of water. Does this pH differ appreciably from that of a solution prepared from 0.1 mole of NaOH in 1 L of water? How does the pK_a of phosphine, PH_3, compare with that of ammonia?

10. Hydride ion, H^-, is known in the form of salts such as sodium hydride, NaH. When sodium hydride is added to water, it is converted completely into hydrogen. What does this say about H_2 as an acid relative to water?

11. Explain the following acidity orders using the principles summarized on page 64.
    (a) $H_2SO_4 > HSO_4^-$
    (b) Nitric acid ($HONO_2$) > nitrous acid (HONO)
    (c) $H_2Te > H_2Se$
    (d) Nitrous acid > hydroxylamine (H_2NOH)
    (e) $H_2S > PH_3$
    (f) Perchloric acid ($HOClO_3$) > hypochlorous acid (HOCl)

    (g) Oxalic acid $(HO-\overset{\overset{O}{\|}}{C}-\overset{\overset{O}{\|}}{C}-OH)$ > hydrogen oxalate ion $(HO-\overset{\overset{O}{\|}}{C}-CO_2^-)$
    (h) A sulfinic acid (RSO_2H) > a sulfenic acid (RSOH)

12. Consider the reaction of A + B as a second-order reaction for which rate $= k[A][B]$. If A and B start off with equal concentrations, how has the rate changed at 50% reaction?

13. (a) The reaction of methyl chloride with water was described as a first-order reaction because the concentration of water does not change during the reaction. If the reaction with water is exactly analogous to the reaction with hydroxide ion, we should write the kinetic equation as

$$\text{rate} = k_2[CH_3Cl][H_2O]$$

What is the value of $[H_2O]$ in this expression?
    (b) Because $[H_2O]$ remains constant, this case is an example of pseudo first-order kinetics. For the expression

$$\text{rate} = k_1[CH_3Cl]$$

we found that $k_1 = 3 \times 10^{-10}$ sec^{-1}. Using the value of $[H_2O]$ found above, derive k_2. How does the value of k_2 for the reaction of methyl chloride with water compare with that for reaction with hydroxide ion?
    (c) For a first-order reaction, the time for half of the remaining reactant to react—the half-life—is given by $t_{1/2} = 0.693/k$. From the value of k_1, calculate the half-life in years of an aqueous solution of methyl chloride.

14. Problem 4 was solved in an approximate manner. Using the methods of differential and integral calculus, derive the exact answers.

Chapter 5

Alkanes

5.1 *n*-Alkanes: Physical Properties

Table 5.1 lists the boiling points, melting points, and densities of some *n*-alkanes. These properties vary in a regular manner. Note that the alkanes from methane through butane are gases at room temperature, pentane boils just above room temperature, and the remaining alkanes show regular increases in boiling point with each additional methylene unit. This regularity of physical properties stems from a regularity of structure. In all of the alkanes the bonds to carbon are nearly tetrahedral and the carbon-hydrogen bond lengths are all essentially constant at 1.095 ± 0.01 Å. Similarly, the carbon-carbon bonds are uniformly 1.54 ± 0.01 Å in length.

The boiling point of a substance is defined as the temperature at which its vapor pressure is equal to the external pressure, usually 760 mm. The vapor pressure of a compound is inversely related to the energy that causes the molecules to attract one another. If the intermolecular attractive force is weak, little energy must be supplied in order for vaporization to occur and the compound has a high vapor pressure. If the intermolecular attractive force is large, more energy must be supplied to cause vaporization and the compound has a low vapor pressure. Interactions between neutral molecules generally result from **van der Waals forces**, dipole-dipole electrostatic attraction, and hydrogen bonding. For hydrocarbons, only the van der Waals interaction is

TABLE 5.1 Physical properties of *n*-Alkanes

Hydrocarbon	Boiling Point, °C	Melting Point, °C	Density[a] d^{20}
methane	−161.7	−182.5	
ethane	−88.6	−183.3	
propane	−42.1	−187.7	0.5005
butane	−0.5	−138.3	0.5787
pentane	36.1	−129.8	0.5572
hexane	68.7	−95.3	0.6603
heptane	98.4	−90.6	0.6837
octane	125.7	−56.8	0.7026
nonane	150.8	−53.5	0.7177
decane	174.0	−29.7	0.7299
undecane	195.8	−25.6	0.7402
dodecane	216.3	−9.6	0.7487
tridecane	235.4	−5.5	0.7564
tetradecane	253.7	5.9	0.7628
pentadecane	270.6	10	0.7685
eicosane	343	36.8	0.7886
triacontane	449.7	65.8	0.8097
polyethylene			0.965

[a] Note that densities vary with temperature; d^{20} refers to the density in grams per milliliter at 20°C.

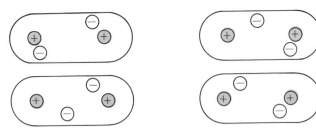

FIGURE 5.1 Van der Waals attraction. Electronic motion is such as to produce net electrostatic attraction at every instant.

important. This force of attraction results from an electron correlation effect also called the **London force** or **dispersion force**.

Although we normally think of atoms and molecules in terms of smeared-out electron-density distributions, it should be emphasized that this is a time-average picture. At any given instant the electrons are positioned as far from each other as possible, although these positions are different from one instant to the next. Consider the simplified models shown in Figure 5.1. The system of charges on the left has a small net attraction that binds the two molecules together. In the system on the right, the electrons have all moved but there is still net attraction. The motion of the electrons is mutually correlated to produce net attraction at all times. This attractive force is sensitive to distance and varies as $1/r^6$. It is significant only for molecules close to each other—but not too close. As molecules get too close, the electron charge clouds overlap appreciably and electron repulsion dominates.

Van der Waals attraction depends on the approximate "area" of contact of two molecules—the greater this area, the greater is the attractive force. Each additional methylene unit provides an additional area of contact that increases the total attractive force and gives rise to a greater boiling point. The energy of attraction per methylene group is approximately $1-1.5$ kcal mole^{-1}. Van der Waals forces are even greater in solids, and there is also a progressive change in melting point with increasing chain length, as shown in Table 5.1.

Because of the tetrahedral nature of carbon, alkane chains tend to have a zigzag geometry. For example, one of the geometric arrangements adopted by butane is shown in stereo-plot form in Figure 5.2. This type of zigzag arrangement of butane and pentane is symbolized in Figure 5.3.

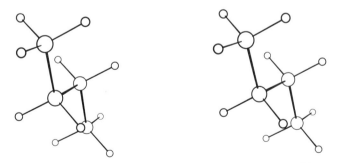

FIGURE 5.2 Stereo representation of one conformation of butane.

FIGURE 5.3 Zigzag geometry of alkanes.

5.2 *n*-Alkanes: Barriers to Rotation

Experiments of various sorts have shown that the methyl groups of ethane are free to **rotate** with respect to each other about the carbon-carbon single bond. Two extreme structures are possible, the **eclipsed** and **staggered** forms (Figure 5.4). In the eclipsed form, the carbon-hydrogen bonds of one methyl group are "lined up" with those of the other. In the staggered form, each carbon-hydrogen bond of one methyl group bisects a H—C—H angle of the other methyl group, when the molecule is viewed along the carbon-carbon bond axis. The eclipsed form of ethane is 3 kcal mole^{-1} higher in energy than the more stable staggered form.

Structures that differ only by rotation about one or more bonds are defined as **conformations** of a compound. In order to represent the three-dimensional character of such conformations, two useful systems are commonly employed. In Figure 5.5 the eclipsed and staggered conformations of ethane are depicted as "sawhorse" structures. In this kind of representation a dashed bond projects away from the viewer, a heavy wedge bond projects toward the viewer, and a normal bond lies in the plane of the page.

Another useful representation is the **Newman projection**. Newman projections for eclipsed and staggered ethane are shown in Figure 5.6. In a Newman projection the carbon-carbon bond is being viewed end on. The nearer carbon is represented by a point. The three other groups attached to that carbon radiate as three lines from the point. The farther carbon is represented by a circle with its bonds radiating from the edge of the circle. These projections show that a rotation of 60° about the C—C axis

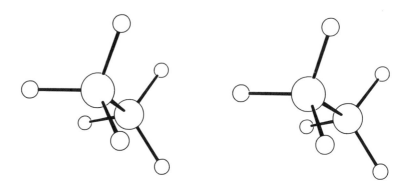

(a) eclipsed structure of ethane

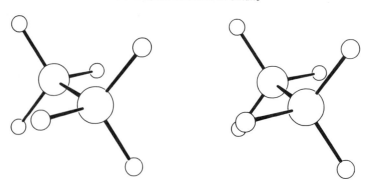

(b) staggered structure of ethane

FIGURE 5.4 Stereo plots illustrating the eclipsed and staggered structures of ethane.

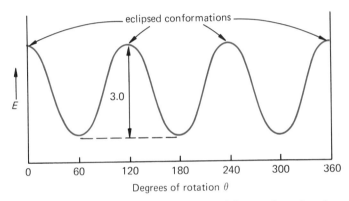

FIGURE 5.5 Sawhorse structures illustrating the eclipsed and staggered conformations of ethane.

(a) eclipsed   (b) staggered

FIGURE 5.6 Newman projections illustrating the eclipsed and staggered conformations of ethane.

FIGURE 5.7 Potential energy of ethane as a function of degree of rotation about the carbon-carbon bond.

converts the staggered form to the eclipsed structure. As the rotation is continued another 60°, a new staggered conformation is produced, which is identical with the first staggered conformation. A plot of potential energy versus degree of rotation for one complete 360° rotation about the carbon-carbon bond in ethane is shown in Figure 5.7.

Thus, in rotating about the carbon-carbon bond, there is a 3.0 kcal mole^{-1} energy barrier in passing from one staggered conformation to another. The instability of the eclipsed form of ethane appears to result from repulsion of some of the hydrogen orbitals. The hydrogen orbitals on one methyl group are rather far from those on the other, but they are closer in the eclipsed conformation than in the staggered one. The internuclear H-H distance in staggered ethane is 2.55 Å, whereas it is only 2.29 Å in the eclipsed form. Orbital overlap between hydrogens on adjacent atoms is antibonding or repulsive. At these distances the magnitude of this repulsion is small, only about 1 kcal mole^{-1} per pair of hydrogens, but this small energy effect has staggering structural consequences. As we shall see, staggered conformations are the general rule for alkane chains and cycloalkane rings.

In propane the barrier to rotation now involves the interaction of one C—CH$_3$ bond with a carbon-hydrogen bond, as well as two C—H:C—H interactions. Consequently,

FIGURE 5.8 Most stable conformation of propane.

the rotational barrier is slightly higher in energy at 3.4 kcal mole^{-1}. The most stable conformation is again the staggered one, as illustrated in Figure 5.8.

A potential energy plot for rotation about the C-2—C-3 bond in butane is shown in Figure 5.9. The conformations at the various unique maxima and minima are depicted in Figure 5.10, both as Newman projections and as stereo plots. Note that there are two different kinds of staggered conformation: **anti**, in which the two methyl groups attached to carbons 2 and 3 are farthest apart, and **gauche**, in which these two methyl groups are adjacent. These two kinds of staggered conformation have different energies. The anti conformation is more stable than the gauche by 0.9 kcal mole^{-1}. At room temperature butane is a mixture of 72% anti and 28% gauche conformations.

If these two structures could be isolated, they would have different physical properties such as density, spectra, and melting points. However, the energy barrier separating them is rather small, only 3.8 kcal mole^{-1}. A barrier of such magnitude is far too small to permit isolation of the separate anti and gauche conformations at normal temperatures. In order to separate these two species, one would have to slow the conversion by working at very low temperatures, below approximately −230°C.

Also note that there are two distinct eclipsed conformations. One of these maxima is passed in rotation from the anti to a gauche conformation. In this conformation, there are two CH₃:H and one H:H eclipsed interactions. This conformation is 3.8 kcal mole^{-1} less stable than the anti conformation. The other eclipsed conformation, which is passed in rotation from one gauche conformation to the other, has one CH₃:CH₃ and two H:H eclipsed interactions. Its energy is about 4.5 kcal mole^{-1} above that of the anti conformation.

Finally, note that the gauche conformations labeled B and E, although energetically equivalent, are not really the same. They are actually mirror images of one another. They are the same only in the sense that your right and left hands are the same. We shall return to this phenomenon in Chapter 7.

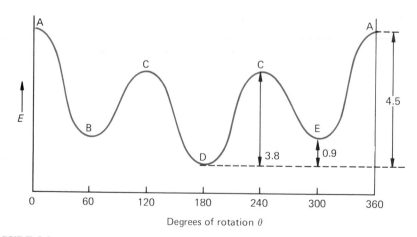

FIGURE 5.9 Potential energy of butane as function of degree of rotation about the C-2—C-3 bond.

(a) eclipsed (A)

H₃C CH₃

H   H
H   H

(b) *gauche* (B)

CH₃

H   CH₃

H   H

H

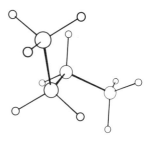

(c) eclipsed (C)

H CH₃

H   CH₃
H   H

(d) *anti* (D)

CH₃

H   H

H   H

CH₃

(e) *gauche* (E)

CH₃

CH₃   H

H   H

H

FIGURE 5.10 Conformations of butane.

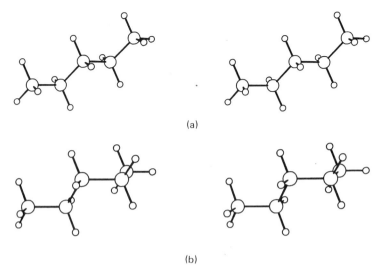

(a)

(b)

FIGURE 5.11 Stereo representations of two pentane conformations: *(a)* anti-anti; *(b)* anti-gauche.

The same principles apply to larger alkanes. In general, the most stable structure of a given compound is the completely staggered one with all alkyl groups having an anti relationship to one another. However, keep in mind that gauche conformations are only slightly less stable, and there will always be a sizable fraction of the molecules with these conformations. The two conformations of pentane given here are shown in stereo-plot form in Figure 5.11.

When writing the structures of such compounds, it is usually not convenient to depict the full geometry as is done in the preceeding structures. It is important to recognize that a given structure may be written in many ways. For example, the various structures that follow all represent pentane.

$$CH_3-CH_2-CH_2-CH_2-CH_3 \qquad \begin{array}{l} CH_3-CH_2-CH_2 \\ \qquad\qquad\quad | \\ \qquad\qquad CH_2-CH_3 \end{array} \qquad \begin{array}{l} CH_3-CH_2 \\ \qquad\quad | \\ \qquad CH_2 \\ \qquad\quad | \\ \qquad CH_2-CH_3 \end{array}$$

$$\begin{array}{ccc} & CH_2 & CH_2 \\ & \diagup\quad\diagdown & \diagup\quad\diagdown \\ CH_3 & CH_2 & CH_3 \end{array} \qquad \begin{array}{cc} & CH_2 \\ & \diagup\quad\diagdown \\ CH_3 & CH_2 \\ & CH_2 \\ & \diagdown \\ & CH_3 \end{array}$$

EXERCISE 5.1 Using molecular models, compare the gauche and anti conformations of butane. Estimate the distance between different pairs of hydrogens. Which pair of hydrogens is closest together? Compare this separation with that of the eclipsed hydrogens in ethane. Does this comparison suggest a principal reason for the higher energy of the gauche conformation?

5.3 Branched-Chain Alkanes

The branched-chain alkanes also exist as mixtures of rapidly interconverting staggered conformations. For example, the two staggered conformations of 2-methylbutane for rotation about the C-2—C-3 bond, $(CH_3)_2CH-CH_2CH_3$, are shown in Figure 5.12.

FIGURE 5.12   Staggered conformations of 2-methylbutane.

The rotational barrier separating these two conformations is about 5 kcal mole^{-1}. At room temperature 2-methylbutane exists as a mixture of the two conformations, 90% of the one with only one gauche interaction and 10% of the one with two gauche interactions.

According to the definition of isomers given in Section 5.2, different conformations of a compound are isomers since they have the same formula but differ in the arrangement of the atoms in space. However, it is convenient to distinguish such isomers, which rapidly interconvert at ordinary temperatures, from other kinds of isomers that interconvert only at high temperatures or not at all. Consequently, we refer to these easily interconvertible spatial isomers as **conformational isomers**, or as **conformations**, to distinguish them from **structural isomers**, such as butane and 2-methylpropane.

Physical properties for some branched hydrocarbons are summarized in Table 5.2. Branched-chain hydrocarbons are more compact than their straight-chain isomers. Thus, there is less surface area per unit mass, and van der Waals interactions between molecules are weaker. For this reason, branched hydrocarbons tend to have lower boiling points and melting points than their straight-chain isomers. However, when a molecule has sufficient symmetry, it forms a crystal lattice *more* easily and therefore has a higher melting point but a relatively low boiling point. For an example of such a case, compare the melting points of pentane, 2-methylbutane and 2,2-dimethylpropane. An extreme example is given by 2,2,3,3-tetramethylbutane, which boils only a few degrees above its melting point. Hydrocarbons having a high degree of symmetry or "ball-like" character tend to sublime rather than boil. On heating they pass directly from the solid to vapor state without passing through the intermediate liquid state.

This result can be cast into entropy concepts in a straight-forward way. In the crystal, molecules are locked in and have greatly restricted movement. In the liquid phase, molecules have enhanced freedom of movement. Consequently, the entropy of melting is a positive quantity whose magnitude is a measure of this increased freedom of movement. The entropy of melting of pentane is +14 eu, whereas that of 2,2-dimethylpropane is only +3 eu. Both molecules have increased freedom of translational motion in the liquid hydrocarbon. In addition, pentane has a floppy chain with many rotational degrees of freedom so that the liquid hydrocarbon is a mixture of many staggered conformational isomers having relatively high entropy. Rotation about the carbon-carbon bonds in 2,2-dimethylpropane, however, always gives back the same structure, and it has a lower entropy. Note that 2-methylbutane has an intermediate value of the entropy of melting of +11 eu.

EXERCISE 5.2   Write Newman projections for two different staggered conformations of 2,3-dimethylbutane for rotation about the C-2—C-3 bond.

EXERCISE 5.3   Draw a potential energy diagram (see Figure 5.9) for rotation about the C-2—C-3 bond of 2,3-dimethylbutane.

TABLE 5.2 Physical Properties of Some Branched Alkanes

	Boiling Point, °C	Melting Point, °C	Density d^{20}
2-methylpropane	−11.7	−159.4	0.5572
2-methylbutane	29.9	−159.9	0.6196
2,2-dimethylpropane	9.4	−16.8	0.5904
2-methylpentane	60.3	−153.6	0.6532
3-methylpentane	63.3		0.6644
2,2-dimethylbutane	49.7	−100.0	0.6492
2,3-dimethylbutane	58.0	−128.4	0.6616
2,2,3,3-tetramethylbutane	106.3	100.6	0.6568

For relatively simple organic structures, such as the examples discussed so far in this chapter, it is possible to use condensed structural formulas, in which each carbon and hydrogen is explicitly shown. However, for more complex molecules, these formulas are rather awkward, and an even more highly abbreviated representation is used. In these **line structures** an alkane chain is represented by a zigzag line. The ends and each "bend" in the line represent a carbon atom. Hydrogens are not shown; each carbon is understood to have enough hydrogens to satisfy its tetravalency. Thus, pentane and octane are depicted as

$$\equiv \quad CH_3CH_2CH_2CH_2CH_3$$

pentane

$$\equiv \quad CH_3CH_2CH_2CH_2CH_2CH_2CH_2CH_3$$

octane

Branched alkanes are represented in an analogous fashion, using a branched line. Remember that there is either one or no hydrogens at a branch point, depending on the number of carbons attached to that position.

2,3-dimethylhexane   2,2-dimethylheptane   3-ethylhexane

Substituent groups such as halogens are shown as

2-chloro-3-methylbutane   2,2-dichloropentane

EXERCISE 5.4 Write the simple line structures corresponding to the following alkanes and compare with complete structures.
(a) 2-methylnonane   (b) 2,3,3-trimethylpentane
(c) 3-ethyl-4-methylnonane   (d) 3-(chloromethyl)-3-methylhexane

5.4 Cycloalkanes

Carbon chains can also form rings. Because there are no ends to the carbon chain in a cyclic alkane, the general formula is $(CH_2)_n$ or C_nH_{2n}. Like straight-chain alkanes, they are saturated hydrocarbons. They are named according to the number of carbons in the ring with the prefix **cyclo-**.

$$\begin{array}{ccc}
\text{CH}_2 & \text{H}_2\text{C—CH}_2 & \text{CH}_2 \\
\diagup \quad \backslash & | \quad\quad | & \diagup \quad\quad \backslash \\
\text{H}_2\text{C—CH}_2 & \text{H}_2\text{C—CH}_2 & \text{H}_2\text{C} \quad\quad \text{CH}_2 \\
& & \text{H}_2\text{C—CH}_2
\end{array}$$

cyclopropane   cyclobutane   cyclopentane

The physical properties of some cycloalkanes are summarized in Table 5.3. Note that their symmetry and more restricted rotations result in higher melting points and boiling points than comparable *n*-alkanes.

Because of symmetry, there is only one monosubstituted cycloalkane, and a number to designate the position of the appendage is not necessary.

methylcyclohexane   ethylcyclopentane

When there is more than one substituent, numbers are required. One substituent is always given the number 1, and the other is given the next lowest possible number.

1,1-dimethyl-3-propylcyclohexane

In more complex compounds, the cycloalkyl radical may be named as a prefix.

3-cyclopropylpentane   2-cyclobutyl-3-methylbutane

TABLE 5.3 Physical Properties of Some Cycloalkanes

	Boiling Point, °C	Melting Point, °C	Density d^{20}
cyclopropane	−32.7	−127.6	
cyclobutane	12.5	−50.0	
cyclopentane	49.3	−93.9	0.7457
cyclohexane	80.7	6.6	0.7786
cycloheptane	118.5	−12.0	0.8098
cyclooctane	150.0	14.3	0.8349

Cycloalkanes are usually symbolized by simple geometric figures in which a carbon atom with its appropriate number of attached hydrogens is understood to be present at each apex. Thus, the four smallest cycloalkanes are depicted as

cyclopropane   cyclobutane   cyclopentane   cyclohexane

Simple substituted cycloalkanes are depicted by the appropriate geometric figure, with attached substituent groups.

methylcyclohexane   1,1-dibromocyclobutane

1-chloro-3-methylcyclopentane   2-cyclohexyl-4-methylpentane

The alkanes and cycloalkanes are the parent structures in the general class of aliphatic compounds. Most of the chemistry of cycloalkanes is similar to that of the alkanes. There are some differences in stability and in their conformations, which will be discussed in Sections 5.6 and 7.7, respectively.

EXERCISE 5.5 Using simple geometric figures and line structures, depict the following compounds. Compare your structures with complete structural representations.
(a) 1,1,3-trimethylcyclohexane   (b) 3-cyclopentylpentane
(c) 1-chloro-4-chloromethylcyclohexane   (d) 1,1,2,2-tetramethylcyclopropane

---

5.5 Heats of Formation

The **heat of formation** of a compound from its elements in their standard states is a thermodynamic property with considerable use in organic chemistry. This quantity, symbolized ΔH_f°, is defined as the enthalpy of the reaction of elements in their standard states to form the compound. The standard state of each element is generally the most stable state of that element at 25°C and 1 atm pressure. The standard state of carbon is taken as the graphite form, whereas those of hydrogen and oxygen are H_2 and O_2 gases, respectively. By definition, ΔH_f° for an element in its standard state is zero. The standard heat of formation of butane is -30.36 ± 0.16 kcal mole^{-1} and that of 2-methylpropane is -32.41 ± 0.13 kcal mole^{-1}.

$$4 \text{ C (graphite)} + 5 \text{ H}_2(g) = n\text{-C}_4\text{H}_{10}(g) \qquad \Delta H^\circ \equiv \Delta H_f^\circ(n\text{-C}_4\text{H}_{10})$$
$$= -30.36 \text{ kcal mole}^{-1}$$

$$4 \text{ C (graphite)} + 5 \text{ H}_2(g) = (\text{CH}_3)_3\text{CH}(g) \qquad \Delta H^\circ \equiv \Delta H_f^\circ(i\text{-C}_4\text{H}_{10})$$
$$= -32.41 \text{ kcal mole}^{-1}$$

We shall see in Chapter 6 how these hypothetical enthalpies of reaction are determined. For now, suffice it to say that they *can* be determined, although indirect methods are required. The ΔH_f° of a compound may either be negative, as in the two foregoing examples, or positive. A negative ΔH_f° means that heat would be liberated if the compound could be prepared directly by combination of its elements. That is, butane and 2-methylpropane are both more stable (have lower enthalpy) than four carbon atoms and five hydrogen molecules in their standard states. The heats of formation of the butane isomers reveal that 2-methylpropane is more stable than butane by 2.05 kcal mole^{-1}. Thus, in the following hypothetical equilibrium, 2-methylpropane would predominate.

$$CH_3CH_2CH_2CH_3 \underset{}{\overset{K}{\rightleftharpoons}} CH_3\overset{\overset{\displaystyle CH_3}{|}}{C}HCH_3 \qquad \Delta H^\circ = -2.05 \text{ kcal mole}^{-1}$$

The heats of formation of these two hydrocarbons are depicted graphically in Figure 5.13. In using energy diagrams such as these, remember that down represents less energy and greater stability ("downhill in energy"), whereas up represents higher energy and lower stability.

Some values for heats of formation are listed in Table 5.4. A more complete list is given in Appendix I. These ΔH_f° values are useful for estimating possible reactions, providing that a pathway or reaction mechanism is possible. For example, the hydrogenation of butane to ethane is exothermic by 10 kcal mole^{-1}.

$$\begin{array}{cccc} & C_4H_{10} & + H_2 = & 2\,C_2H_6 \\ \Delta H_f^\circ: & -30.4 & + 0 & 2 \times -20.2 \end{array} \qquad \Delta H^\circ = -10.0 \text{ kcal mole}^{-1}$$

If a suitable catalyst or reaction pathway could be found, this reaction would proceed toward the right. However, no such catalyst or pathway is known at ordinary temperatures. The reaction remains hypothetical even though, if realized, it would be exothermic. This example illustrates the difference between thermodynamics and kinetics. A given reaction may have favorable thermodynamics but will occur only if a pathway with a sufficiently low activation barrier can be found. Because of the importance of pathways our studies of organic reactions will also often include discussions of reaction mechanism. The importance of enzymes in biochemical reactions is that they provide such pathways for reaction.

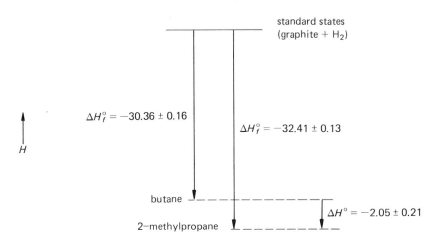

FIGURE 5.13 The heats of formation of butane and 2-methylpropane, illustrating the use of ΔH_f° values to compute ΔH° for a simple reaction.

TABLE 5.4 Some Heats of Formation

Compound	Heat of Formation at 25°C ΔH_f°, kcal mole^{-1}
CH_4	-17.9
CH_3CH_3	-20.2
$CH_3CH_2CH_3$	-24.8
$CH_3CH_2CH_2CH_3$	-30.4
$(CH_3)_3CH$	-32.4
$CH_3CH_2CH_2CH_2CH_3$	-35.1
$(CH_3)_2CHCH_2CH_3$	-36.9
$(CH_3)_4C$	-40.3
CO	-26.4
CO_2	-94.1
$H_2O(g)$	-57.8
$H_2O(l)$	-68.3
H_2	0
O_2	0
C (graphite)	0

EXERCISE 5.6 Using the heats of formation given in Table 5.4, construct a diagram analogous to Figure 5.13 showing the relative energies of pentane, 2-methylbutane, and 2,2-dimethylpropane. Note that each new branch provides 2–3 kcal mole^{-1} in stabilization.

The hydrogenation of ethylene to ethane is also highly exothermic.

$$C_2H_4 + H_2 = C_2H_6$$
$$12.5 + 0 \quad -20.2 \qquad \Delta H^\circ = -32.7 \text{ kcal mole}^{-1}$$

In this case a number of catalysts are known that provide reaction pathways, and this reaction is an important general reaction of alkenes (Section 11.6).

One important limitation on the use of heats of formation is that equilibria are determined by free energy rather than by enthalpy alone.

$$\Delta G^\circ = -RT \ln K = \Delta H^\circ - T\Delta S^\circ$$

That is, an entropy change plays a large role in determining an equilibrium constant. For example, in the equilibrium between *n*-butane and 2-methylpropane discussed previously, ΔH° is -2.05 kcal mole^{-1}, but ΔG° is only -0.89 kcal mole^{-1}, corresponding to an equilibrium constant at 25°C of 4.5. Since entropy is a measure of freedom of motion, the largest entropy changes result from a difference in numbers of molecules on the two sides of an equilibrium. The magnitude of this effect depends on physical state (gas, liquid, and so on), molecular weight, and temperature. For a gas at ordinary temperature and pressure, a difference of one molecule on the two sides of an equilibrium (for example, A = B + C) corresponds to about 30-40 eu, which is equivalent to 9–12 kcal mole^{-1} in enthalpy at room temperature. At higher temperatures any entropy change has a still greater effect. For example, at 25°C the conversion of butane to one molecule of ethane and one of ethylene is highly endothermic.

$$C_4H_{10} = C_2H_6 + C_2H_4$$
$$\Delta H_f^\circ: \quad -30.4 \quad -20.2 \quad 12.5$$

$$\Delta H^\circ = \Delta H_f^\circ(\text{products} = -20.2 + 12.5) - \Delta H_f^\circ(\text{reactants} = -30.4)$$
$$= +22.6 \text{ kcal mole}^{-1}$$

Even though this reaction involves one molecule going to two, the resulting ΔS° of 33 eu still leaves a positive free energy change at room temperature: $\Delta G^\circ = +12.7$ kcal mole^{-1}. At 500°C, although the equilibrium is still highly endothermic in enthalpy, the positive entropy change gives a ΔG° of -3.8 kcal mole^{-1}. The equilibrium now favors the products. As we shall see in Section 6.2, this reaction is involved in the refining of petroleum ("cracking"). However, the thermodynamics of the molecules demands that the reaction be carried out at high temperature, as the foregoing simple calculations show.

EXERCISE 5.7 Calculate ΔH° for the reaction of hydrogen with 2-methylbutane to give ethane and propane.

5.6 Cycloalkanes: Ring Strain

Ring strain is an energy effect that can be seen clearly in the heats of formation of the cycloalkanes. In alkanes each CH_2 group contributes about -5 kcal mole^{-1} to ΔH_f° of a molecule. That is, the heats of formation of compounds differing by only one CH_2 differ by a regular increment of about 5 kcal mole^{-1}.

$$\Delta H_f^\circ, \text{ kcal mole}^{-1}$$

$$4\,C + 5\,H_2 \longrightarrow n\text{-}C_4H_{10} \qquad -30.4$$
$$5\,C + 6\,H_2 \longrightarrow n\text{-}C_5H_{12} \qquad -35.1$$
$$6\,C + 7\,H_2 \longrightarrow n\text{-}C_6H_{14} \qquad -39.9$$

Since cycloalkanes have the empirical formula $(CH_2)_n$, one can obtain the ΔH_f° for each each CH_2 group by simply dividing ΔH_f° for the molecule by n. The heats of formation for a number of cycloalkanes are tabulated in Table 5.5. Examination of the table shows that most of these cycloalkanes have less negative values of $\Delta H_f^\circ/n$ than the alkane value of about -5 kcal mole^{-1}. That is, many cycloalkanes have a higher energy content per CH_2 group than a typical acyclic alkane. This excess energy is called **ring strain**. The total excess energy of a cycloalkane is simply the excess energy per CH_2 multiplied by the number of CH_2 groups in the particular cycloalkane.

Cyclohexane shows essentially no ring strain; its CH_2 groups have essentially the same ΔH_f° as those of normal alkanes. For the purpose of computing the ring strain of a particular cycloalkane, cyclohexane is considered to be strain-free; it is the standard for comparison. For cyclohexane $\Delta H_f^\circ = -29.5$ kcal mole^{-1} and $\Delta H_f^\circ/n = -29.5/6 = -4.92$ kcal mole^{-1}. This value is taken as ΔH_f° for a "strainless" CH_2 group. For example, ΔH_f° for a hypothetical "strainless" cyclopentane would be 5×-4.92 kcal mole$^{-1} = -24.6$ kcal mole^{-1}. Hence, the strain energy of cyclopentane $= (-18.4) - (-24.6) = +6.2$ kcal mole^{-1}. In other words, cyclopentane is 6 kcal mole^{-1} less stable than it would be if each CH_2 group were in some hypothetical strain-free state.

EXERCISE 5.8 Using the data in Table 5.5, verify that the total strain energy of cyclooctane is 10 kcal mole^{-1}.

TABLE 5.5 ΔH_f° of Cycloalkanes, $(CH_2)_n$

n	Cycloalkane	ΔH_f°, kcal mole^{-1}	$\Delta H_f^\circ/n$, kcal mole^{-1} per CH_2 group	Total Strain Energy, kcal mole^{-1}
2	ethylene	+12.5	+6.2	22
3	cyclopropane	+12.7	+4.2	27
4	cyclobutane	+6.8	+1.7	26
5	cyclopentane	−18.4	−3.7	6
6	cyclohexane	−29.5	−4.9	(0)
7	cycloheptane	−28.2	−4.0	6
8	cyclooctane	−29.7	−3.7	10
9	cyclononane	−31.7	−3.5	13
10	cyclodecane	−36.9	−3.7	12
11	cycloundecane	−42.9	−3.9	11
12	cyclododecane	−55.0	−4.6	4
13	cyclotridecane	−58.9	−4.5	5
14	cyclotetradecane	−57.1	−4.1	12
15	cyclopentadecane	−72.0	−4.8	2
16	cyclohexadecane	−76.9	−4.8	2

The inherent ring strain of a given molecule results from three distinct conditions: bond strain ("bent bonds"), eclipsing of adjacent pairs of carbon-hydrogen bonds, or transannular nonbonded interaction (the "bumping together" of two hydrogens that are bonded to atoms "across the ring" from one another).

A bond is strongest when it is formed by the overlap of two atomic orbitals along the internuclear bond axis. The strength of the bond is reduced if overlap of the constituent orbitals is not along the bond axis.

stronger,
more efficient overlap

weaker,
less efficient overlap

The structure of cyclopropane is shown in Figure 5.14. For purely geometric reasons the internuclear C—C—C angle in cyclopropane is 60°. The natural bond angle for C_{sp^3}-orbitals overlapping linearly would be 109.5°. Even with pure p-orbitals the natural bond angle cannot be less than 90°. In practice, the carbon-carbon bonds in cyclopropane do have more p-character than normal sp^3. As a result, the orbitals form bent bonds (Figure 5.15). Consequently, the carbon-carbon bonds in cyclopropane are weaker than those in normal alkanes. This reduced bond strength shows up as a ring strain in the ΔH_f°.

To compensate for the fact that extra p-character is used in the carbon-carbon bonds of cyclopropane, extra s-character is used for the carbon-hydrogen bonds. Consequently, these bonds are somewhat shorter and stronger than alkyl carbon-hydrogen bonds, and the H—C—H bond angle is greater than tetrahedral. Another factor that contributes to the ring strain in cyclopropane is the eclipsing of the carbon-hydrogen bonds. Recall that the eclipsed conformation of ethane is 3.0 kcal mole^{-1} less stable than the staggered conformation; each pair of eclipsed hydrogens raises the energy by 1.0 kcal mole^{-1} (Section 5.2). In cyclopropane there are six pairs of eclipsed hydro-

(a)

(b)

FIGURE 5.14 Cyclopropane: *(a)* stereo representation; *(b)* geometric structure.

gens, which could contribute a maximum of 6 kcal mole^{-1} to the energy of the molecule. However, the eclipsed hydrogens are farther apart in cyclopropane than they are in ethane because of the small C—C—C angle in the former. Therefore, the actual magnitude of the eclipsing interaction is somewhat less than the maximum of 6 kcal mole^{-1}.

In cyclobutane the internuclear angles of 90° are not as small as in cyclopropane. The carbon-carbon bonds are not as bent, and there is less strain per bond. However, there are four strained bonds rather then three, and there are eight pairs of eclipsed hydrogens rather than six. Also the eclipsing in a planar cyclobutane would be more important than in cyclopropane because the hydrogens are closer. The result is that the total ring strain in the two compounds is about the same.

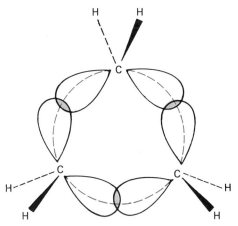

FIGURE 5.15 Orbital structure of cyclopropane ring showing bent-bond strain.

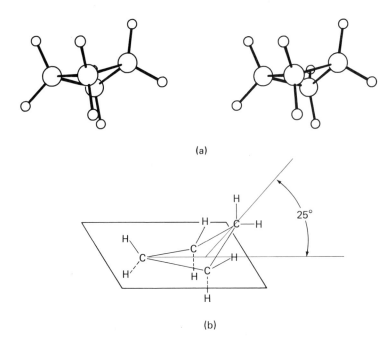

(a)

(b)

FIGURE 5.16   Bent cyclobutane: *(a)* stereo representation; *(b)* illustrating the angle of bend.

Since three points define a plane, the carbon framework of cyclopropane must have a planar structure. However, cyclobutane can exist in a nonplanar conformation. Spectroscopic studies show that cyclobutane and many of its derivatives do have nonplanar structures in which one methylene group is bent at an angle of about 25° from the plane of the other three ring carbons. In this structure, shown in Figure 5.16, some increase in bond-angle strain is compensated by the reduction in the eclipsed-hydrogen interactions.

A planar pentagonal ring structure for cyclopentane would have C—C—C angles of 108°, a value so close to the normal tetrahedral angle of 109.5° that no important strain effect would be expected. However, all of the hydrogens are completely eclipsed in such a structure and it would have about 10 kcal mole^{-1} of strain energy.

The molecule finds it energetically worthwhile to twist somewhat from a planar conformation. The actual structure has the "envelope" shape shown in Figure 5.17. The additional bond-angle strain involved in this structure is more than compensated by the reduction in eclipsed hydrogens. The out-of-plane methylene group is approximately staggered with respect to its neighbors.

Cyclohexane is the most important of the carbocycles; its structural unit is widespread in compounds of natural origin. Its importance no doubt stems from the fact that

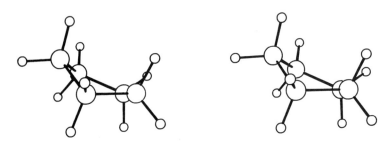

FIGURE 5.17   Stereostructure of cyclopentane.

(a)

(b)

FIGURE 5.18 Chair conformation of cyclohexane: *(a)* stereo representation; *(b)* conventional perspective drawing.

it can adopt a conformation that is essentially strain-free. This structure, shown in Figure 5.18, is known as a **chair conformation**. In this structure the bond angles are all close to tetrahedral, and all pairs of hydrogens are completely staggered with respect to each other. The latter point can easily be seen by looking down each carbon-carbon bond in turn to produce the Newman projections shown in Figure 5.19. Cyclohexane has neither bond-angle strain nor eclipsed-hydrogen strain.

The chair conformation has two distinct types of hydrogens. These different hydrogens correspond to two sets of exocyclic bonds, the **axial** and **equatorial** bonds shown in Figure 5.20.

The chair conformation of cyclohexane is so important that the student should learn to draw it legibly. Notice should be taken of the sets of parallel lines in the structure shown in Figure 5.21. The molecular axis shown in Figure 5.21 is a threefold axis; rotation by 120° about this axis leaves the molecule unchanged.

Cyclohexane is a dynamic structure. A concerted rotation about the carbon-carbon bonds changes one chair conformation to another in which the axial and equatorial bonds have changed places. This change is shown in Figure 5.22, in which two sets of bonds are marked by open and filled circles. The conversion of cyclohexane from one chair form to another is a conformational change that involves only rotation about carbon-carbon bonds. The process has an energy barrier of 10.8 kcal mole^{-1}.

FIGURE 5.19 Newman projections of carbon-carbon bonds in cyclohexane.

axial   equatorial

FIGURE 5.20 Cyclohexane bonds.

The larger cycloalkanes are less important, and we will not dwell on them. In general, the medium-ring cycloalkanes C_7–C_{12} have conformations in which some form of hydrogen repulsion is inescapable. When the carbocyclic ring is sufficiently large, the constraint of ring formation is no longer significant. This point is reached by about C_{15}. Segments of such rings behave much as long, linear alkanes; in such large rings there are generally a number of possible conformations in which the hydrogens are sufficiently separated and staggered from each other.

EXERCISE 5.9 Using a molecular model set, construct a model of cyclohexane. Place the model in a chair conformation (reference to the stereoscopic projection of cyclohexane in Figure 5.22 may be useful in this regard), and identify the axial and equatorial hydrogens. Mark the end of one of the carbon-hydrogen bonds. Experiment with "flipping" the model from one chair conformation to the other, noting that the marked hydrogen is in an axial position in one conformation and in an equatorial position in the other.

EXERCISE 5.10 Practice drawing a chair conformation of cyclohexane, paying careful attention to the sets of parallel lines as shown in Figure 5.22. Compare the drawing you have made to the molecular model you constructed in Exercise 5.9. Draw a chair conformation of chlorocyclohexane in which the substituent is axial and one in which the substituent is equatorial. Do not include the hydrogens. Show your drawings to your professor or teaching assistant and see if he or she can tell which is which.

---

threefold axis
of symmetry

FIGURE 5.21 Construction of chair conformations.

colored balls equatorial

(a)

colored balls axial

(b)

FIGURE 5.22 Two chair conformations of cyclohexane: *(a)* colored balls equatorial; *(b)* colored balls axial. Left: normal projection; right: stereo.

5.7 Occurrence of Alkanes

Alkanes are widespread natural products on earth. They are primarily the product of living processes. Methane is produced by the anaerobic bacterial decomposition of vegetable matter under water. Because it was first isolated in marshes, it was long called "marsh gas." It is also an important constituent of the gas produced in some sewage-disposal processes. Methane also occurs in the atmosphere of coal mines, where it is called "fire damp" because of the explosive nature of methane-air mixtures.

Natural gas is a mixture of gaseous hydrocarbons and consists primarily of methane and ethane, along with small amounts of propane. Natural gas production in the United States in 1981 was 20.2 trillion (20.2×10^{12}) cubic feet (ft^3), corresponding to about 10^{11} lb or 360 million tons of methane! (It is interesting to note that this production was 10% lower than it was for the year 1978.) The smaller alkanes are also by-products of petroleum refining operations. For example, propane is the major constituent of liquefied petroleum gas (LPG), a domestic fuel used in mobile homes, among other places.

Petroleum itself is a complex mixture of hydrocarbons, mostly alkanes and cycloalkanes. It is the end result of the decomposition of animal and vegetable matter which has been buried in the earth's crust for long periods of time. The hydrocarbon mixture collects as a viscous black liquid in underground pockets, whence it is obtained by drilling wells. The resulting crude oil is refined by distillation into useful fuels and lubricants. Crude oil has a very broad boiling range. The more volatile constituents are propane, which is used as LPG, and butane, which is used as a chemical raw material Light petroleum ether consists of pentanes and hexanes and boils at 30-60°C. Ligroin is a mixture of heptanes and boils at 60-90°C. These relatively volatile mixtures are often used as solvents, both in industry and in chemical laboratories. The most important petroleum distillates are gasoline and heating oils.

Fractional distillation of a typical crude oil yields the following fractions.

	Boiling Range, °C
natural gas (C_1 to C_4)	below 20
petroleum ether (C_5 to C_6)	30–60
ligroin or light naphtha (C_7)	60–90
straight-run gasoline (C_6 to C_{12})	85–200
kerosene (C_{12} to C_{15})	200–300
heating fuel oils (C_{15} to C_{18})	300–400
lubricating oil, greases, paraffin wax, asphalt (C_{16} to C_{24})	over 400

In 1981 total world production of crude oil was 20.4 billion barrels (bbl). About 45% of this total was converted into gasoline, 31% into heating oils, and the remainder into a variety of products, including kerosene, jet fuel, and petrochemical feedstocks.

One of the major problems facing mankind is energy. As consumption increases, the supply of nonrenewable fossil fuels obviously decreases. A large fraction of the world's crude oil reserve is under the control of a group of Middle Eastern and South American countries that have banded together and formed an organization known as the Organization of Petroleum Exporting Countries (OPEC). In 1974, as an aftermath of the armed conflict between Israel and several Arab countries, OPEC severely limited production and curtailed crude oil exports, in an action known as the "Arab oil embargo." Subsequently, prices of crude oil have increased dramatically. In the industrialized Western world, there has been a strong emphasis on conservation, with the result that demand for petroleum products leveled off in about 1978. Between 1978 and 1981 worldwide crude oil production amounted to 65 billion bbl (compared with 62 billion bbl in the preceding 3-year period). At the same time, the dramatic increases in the price of crude oil resulted in intensified exploration. Since 1978, new discoveries have added 94 billion bbl to the "proven reserves" (unmined oil that is economically recoverable using only existing technology), so that reserves have actually increased by 29 billion bbl since 1978. Furthermore, proven reserves of natural gas increased in the same period from 1,743 to 2,017 trillion ft^3, the increase of 274 trillion ft^3 being equivalent to about 40 billion bbl of crude oil. Hence, the total proven reserves of crude oil and natural gas have actually increased dramatically since 1978. However, even though discoveries of new deposits have kept pace with usage so far, it is clear that one day the known reserves will begin to decline and we must eventually turn to alternative sources of fuel.

Although other sources of energy will undoubtedly replace the fossil fuels as energy sources, there will still be a need for the fossil fuels as a source of **carbon**. At present, petroleum and coal hydrocarbons are the basic raw materials of much of the chemical industry. As the reserves become depleted, it is essential that we develop new sources of carbon raw materials to augment and eventually replace petroleum and natural gas. One possible source is shale oil, petroleum that is not collected in pockets from which it is easily retrieved but is interspersed throughout a porous rock formation. There are enormous reserves of shale oil, particularly in the Western Rockies of the United States, and active research is directed toward improving the economics and solving the ecological problems associated with its recovery.

An obvious source of additional petroleum is the vegetable matter from which it derives in the first place. However, the natural production of petroleum by the decomposition of vegetation requires eons of time. Some current research is directed toward developing ways to speed up this process, since vegetation may be grown relatively quickly and is therefore replaceable.

Hydrocarbons also result from some inorganic reactions. Examples are the production of methane by the hydrolysis of beryllium carbide or aluminum carbide.

$$Be_2C + 4 H_2O \longrightarrow CH_4 + 2 Be(OH)_2$$

$$Al_4C_3 + 12 H_2O \longrightarrow 3 CH_4 + 4 Al(OH)_3$$

Methane and ethane are odorless, but many of the higher hydrocarbons have distinctive odors. In spite of the absence of typical functional groups, hydrocarbons can effect the changes at olfactory centers that we sense as odor. In addition, it has recently been found that a number of alkanes function as **pheromones**, chemicals that are used for communication in nature. For example, 2-methylheptadecane and 17,21-dimethylheptatriacontane are the sex-attractants for the tiger moth and the tsetse fly, respectively.

EXERCISE 5.11 Write a line structure for the tsetse fly sex-attractant. (Refer to Table 3.2.).

PROBLEMS

1. Give the IUPAC name for each of the following compounds.

(a) (b) (c) (d) (e) (f) (g) (h)

2. Using line structures and geometric figures, depict the following compounds.
   (a) 3-ethyl-3-cyclopentylhexane   (b) 1,1-dichloro-3-ethylcyclohexane
   (c) isopropylcyclohexane   (d) 3,3-dichloropentane
   (e) cyclohexylcyclohexane   (f) 2-methyl-3-isopropylheptane

3. Write the structures of the nine possible heptane isomers and assign IUPAC names. The b.p. of heptane is 101°C. By referring to the b.p.s of the isomeric hexanes in Table 5.2, estimate

the b.p.s of the heptane isomers. Check your answers by looking up these compounds in the *Handbook of Chemistry and Physics* or *Lange's Handbook of Chemistry*. Not all of these hydrocarbons are listed in these handbooks. Browse through your library and see if you can find their properties in other reference works.

4. Write Newman projections showing the possible staggered conformations about the C-2—C-3 bond of pentane. Which ones correspond to the two stereo projections shown in Figure 5.11?

5. Write Newman projections and "sawhorse" structures for the three possible staggered conformations of 2,3-dimethylbutane. Note that two of these conformations are equivalent. The two different types of conformation differ in enthalpy by 0.9 kcal mole^{-1}. Which has the lower energy? Assume that $\Delta G° = \Delta H°$ and calculate the equilibrium composition at room temperature and compare your answer with that given for butane on page 72.

6. Examine a molecular model of adamantane. Give a rough estimate of its b.p. Would you expect the m.p. to be far below the b.p.? Look up its m.p. and b.p. in a handbook.

7. With a set of molecular models find each of the four staggered conformations of pentane. Sketch each of these structures using dashed bonds and wedges as appropriate. Try to rank these conformations in order of increased energy (remember that a gauche conformation is less stable than an anti conformation).

8. For each of the following compounds, construct a potential energy diagram for rotation about the C-2—C-3 bond. For each unique energy maximum or minimum, illustrate the structure with a Newman projection.
   (a) 2-methylbutane   (b) 2,2-dimethylbutane   (c) 2,2,3,3-tetramethylbutane

9. Using the heats of formation in Appendix I, calculate $\Delta H°$ for each of the following reactions.

   (a) $CH_2=CH_2$ (ethylene) $+ H_2 \longrightarrow CH_3CH_3$
   (b) $CH_2=CH_2 + HCl \longrightarrow CH_3CH_2Cl$
   (c) $CH_2=CH_2 + H_2O \longrightarrow CH_3CH_2OH$ (ethanol)

   What do your calculations tell you about the equilibrium constant for each reaction? What do they tell you about the rates of the three reactions?

10. Ethylcyclohexane and cyclooctane are isomers. Using the heats of formation of the two cycloalkanes (Appendix I) and assuming $\Delta H° = \Delta G°$, calculate the equilibrium constant for the equilibrium

cyclooctane   ethylcyclohexane

The actual equilibrium constant at 25°C is 6.7×10^8. Explain.

11. Draw a Newman projection for the C-1—C-2 bond of methylcyclohexane with the methyl group in the equatorial position (see Figure 5.19). Note that the methyl group is anti with respect to C-3 of the ring. Now draw a Newman projection for the conformation having an axial methyl group. What is the relationship of the methyl group and the C-3 ring carbon? By analogy to the conformational analysis of butane, which conformation of methylcyclohexane do you think is more stable?

12. We found in Section 5.5 that at 25°C the equilibrium butane $\rightleftharpoons$ 2-methylpropane has $\Delta H° = -2.05$ kcal mole^{-1}; however, $\Delta G°$ is only -0.89 kcal mole^{-1}. Calculate the entropy change for the reaction and explain the direction of the effect. Calculate the equilibrium constant at 25°C.

13. The definition of free energy of formation, $\Delta G_f°$, is analogous to that of the enthalpy of formation, $\Delta H_f°$. Some values of $\Delta G_f°$ (25°C, gas) are pentane, -2.00; 2-methylbutane, -3.54; 2,2-dimethylpropane, -3.64 kcal mole^{-1}. Calculate the composition of the equilibrium mixture of these three isomers at 25°C.

14. Careful inspection of the heats of formation in Table 5.4 will show regular increments per CH_2 group in a homologous series. In fact, $\Delta H_f°$ increments can be associated with the groups

$$CH_3, \quad \diagdown CH_2 \diagup, \quad -\overset{|}{\underset{|}{C}}H \quad \text{and} \quad -\overset{|}{\underset{|}{C}}-$$

Determine average values for these groups from Table 5.4, or, if you have access to a small computer, calculate the values that give the best least squares fit to the experimental data. Use your results to estimate $\Delta H_f°$ for hexane, 2-methylpentane, 3-methylpentane, 2,2-dimethylbutane, and 2,3-dimethylbutane. Compare with the experimental values in Appendix I.

You can see how far your "group equivalents" will go by comparing your calculated value with the experimental $\Delta H_f°$ for nonane of -54.7 kcal mole^{-1}. You should agree to several tenths of a kilocalorie per mole. However, compare your calculated value for 2,2,4,4-tetramethylpentane with the experimental $\Delta H_f°$ of -57.8 kcal mole^{-1}. Why is there a discrepancy? (*Hint*: Look at a molecular model. Will steric interferences or strain increase or decrease $\Delta H_f°$?)

15. 2-Methylpropane is thermodynamically more stable than butane. Which has the lower boiling point? Is there any relationship between thermodynamic stability and boiling point? Would you expect such a relationship between thermodynamic stability and melting point?

Chapter 6

Reactions of Alkanes

6.1 Bond-Dissociation Energies

Heat is kinetic energy. When a substance is heated, this kinetic energy increases the motion of atoms and molecules. When a molecule is heated, much of the added energy goes into translational motion, and the molecules move about faster relative to one another. However, some of the energy absorbed appears as increased vibrational and rotational motion. Figure 6.1 is a schematic diagram of the potential energy of a diatomic molecule as a function of the bond distance. It shows the vibrational quantum states for bond stretching. At room temperature, only the lowest quantum state is significantly populated.

Remember that even at absolute zero the atoms are still vibrating. If the atoms were at rest, we would know both their position and momentum exactly—in violation of the Heisenberg uncertainty principle. This lowest vibrational quantum state has an energy ϵ_0 above the potential minimum. The quantity ϵ_0 is called the zero-point energy of the vibration.

As heat is applied, higher vibrational states are increasingly populated. In the higher vibrational quantum states, the average bond distance during a vibration is greater. When sufficient energy D is absorbed, the bond breaks. The distance between the nuclei increases to infinity and two separated atoms result.

$$A—B \longrightarrow A\cdot + \cdot B$$

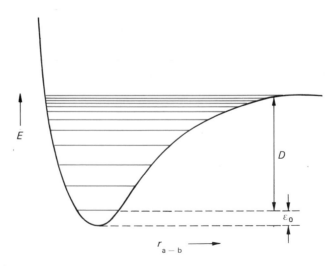

FIGURE 6.1 Schematic diagram of the potential function for a diatomic molecule. Horizontal lines represent the various vibrational energy levels.

For polyatomic molecules diagrams such as Figure 6.1 are more complicated because they are multidimensional. Instead of the energy quantity D we refer instead to the enthalpy of a bond-dissociation reaction, ΔH°. The enthalpy value for a bond-dissociation reaction is generally called the **bond-dissociation energy** and is given the special symbol DH°.

When methane is heated to a high temperature dissociation occurs to give a hydrogen atom and methyl radical.

$$H—CH_3 \longrightarrow H\cdot + \cdot CH_3$$

For this reaction DH° is 105 kcal mole^{-1}.

Bond-dissociation energies are often measured at rather high temperatures. Because enthalpies generally vary somewhat with temperature, they are usually extrapolated back to room temperature for convenience. That is, DH° values refer to 25°C. Bond-dissociation reactions are difficult to measure accurately and DH° values are rarely known more accurately than about ± 1 kcal mole^{-1}.

A DH° of 105 kcal mole^{-1} represents a rather strong bond. Temperatures of the order of 1000°C are required for dissociation of methane to occur at an appreciable rate. A carbon-hydrogen bond in ethane has a slightly lower DH° (98 kcal mole^{-1}), but DH° for the carbon-carbon bond is only 90 kcal mole^{-1}. Consequently, when ethane is heated, C—C fission occurs more rapidly than does C—H fission.

$$H_3C—CH_3 \longrightarrow 2\ CH_3\cdot$$

This reaction occurs at about 700°C.

In general, pyrolysis of a compound results in fission of the weakest bond. The products are **free radicals**.

Free radicals contain an odd number of electrons. The Lewis structure for methyl radical is

$$\begin{array}{c} H \\ \cdot\cdot \\ H:C\cdot \\ \cdot\cdot \\ H \end{array}$$

Alkyl radicals can exist only at low concentrations at ordinary temperatures. Nevertheless, many such radicals have been "seen" by various spectroscopic methods. For example, methyl radical has been shown by spectroscopic measurements to be essentially flat—all four atoms lie in the same plane. Free radicals are important intermediates in many organic reactions, and we shall encounter them in this context later in this chapter.

The bond-dissociation energies, DH°, of several hydrocarbons are listed in Table 6.1. A more extensive table for a variety of compounds is given in Appendix II.

Note that DH° depends on the character of the radical products. The DH° for dissociation of a terminal C—H of an alkane is always about 98 kcal mole^{-1}. The product of this bond cleavage is called a **primary** alkyl radical. It has the structure $RCH_2\cdot$, where R is any alkyl group.

$$CH_3CH_3 \longrightarrow CH_3CH_2\cdot + H\cdot \qquad \Delta H^\circ = 98 \text{ kcal mole}^{-1}$$

When an interior carbon-hydrogen bond of a linear alkane is broken, the product $R_2CH\cdot$ is a **secondary** alkyl radical. Such bonds have a lower DH° of 95 kcal mole^{-1}.

$$CH_3CH_2CH_3 \longrightarrow CH_3\overset{\cdot}{C}HCH_3 + H\cdot \qquad \Delta H^\circ = 95 \text{ kcal mole}^{-1}$$

TABLE 6.1 Bond-Dissociation Energies for Some Alkanes[a]

Compound	$DH°$, kcal mole^{-1}	Compound	$DH°$, kcal mole^{-1}
CH_3-H	105	CH_3-CH_3	90
C_2H_5-H	98	$C_2H_5-CH_3$	86
$CH_3CH_2CH_2-H$	98	$C_3H_7-CH_3$	87
$(CH_3)_2CHCH_2-H$	98	$C_2H_5-C_2H_5$	82
$(CH_3)_2CH-H$	95	$(CH_3)_2CH-CH_3$	86
$(CH_3)_3C-H$	93	$(CH_3)_3C-CH_3$	84

[a] The bond dissociated is shown as a bond.

A carbon-hydrogen bond at a branch point is the weakest type of carbon-hydrogen bond. Such bonds have $DH°$ of about 93 kcal mole^{-1}. The product is a **tertiary** alkyl radical, $R_3C\cdot$.

$$\underset{\overset{|}{CH_3}}{CH_3CHCH_3} \longrightarrow \underset{\overset{|}{CH_3}}{CH_3\underset{\cdot}{C}CH_3} + H\cdot \qquad \Delta H° = 93 \text{ kcal mole}^{-1}$$

The relative stability of alkyl radicals depends on the number of alkyl groups attached to the radical carbon; alkyl radicals have the order of stability

$$\text{tertiary} > \text{secondary} > \text{primary} > \text{methyl}$$

The same principle applies to carbon-carbon bonds. The strength of this bond also depends on the relative stabilities of the radical products.

$$CH_3CH_3 \longrightarrow 2\ CH_3\cdot \qquad \Delta H° = 90 \text{ kcal mole}^{-1}$$

$$\underset{\overset{|}{CH_3}}{\overset{\overset{\displaystyle CH_3}{|}}{CH_3CCH_3}} \longrightarrow \underset{\overset{|}{CH_3}}{\overset{\overset{\displaystyle CH_3}{|}}{CH_3C\cdot}} + CH_3\cdot \qquad \Delta H° = 84 \text{ kcal mole}^{-1}$$

Additional carbon-carbon bond-dissociation energies are also tabulated in Table 6.1.

Consider fission of the two types of carbon-hydrogen bonds in 2-methylpropane (Table 6.1). In order to break one of the terminal carbon-hydrogen bonds, 98 kcal mole^{-1} of energy must be absorbed. In order to break the carbon-hydrogen bond at the branch point, only 93 kcal mole^{-1} is required.

$$\underset{\overset{|}{CH_3}}{CH_3CHCH_3} \nearrow \underset{\overset{\overset{\displaystyle CH_3}{|}}{}}{CH_3CHCH_2\cdot} + H\cdot \qquad \Delta H° = 98 \text{ kcal mole}^{-1}$$

$$\searrow \underset{\overset{|}{CH_3}}{\overset{\overset{\displaystyle CH_3}{|}}{CH_3C\cdot}} + H\cdot \qquad \Delta H° = 93 \text{ kcal mole}^{-1}$$

We start at the same point for the two reactions and, because one of the products is the same in each case ($H\cdot$), the difference in $\Delta H°$s for these reactions is a direct measure of

FIGURE 6.2 The $DH°$s for the two carbon-hydrogen bonds in 2-methylpropane.

the difference in stability of the two alkyl radicals. *The t-butyl radical is more stable than the isobutyl radical by 5 kcal mole^{-1}* (Figure 6.2).

These results can also be expressed in terms of heats of formation. The heat of formation of a radical is derived from the $\Delta H_f°$ of the reactants and the $DH°$ of the bond-breaking reaction; for example,

$$H_2 \longrightarrow 2H\cdot \quad \Delta H° = DH° = 104 \text{ kcal mole}^{-1}$$

$$\Delta H_f°(H\cdot) = [DH° + H_f(H_2)] \div 2 = 52 \text{ kcal mole}^{-1}$$

$$\Delta H_f°[(CH_3)_2CHCH_2\cdot] = \Delta H_f°[(CH_3)_3CH] + DH°[(CH_3)_2CHCH_2{-}H] - \Delta H_f°(H\cdot)$$

$$= -32.4 + 98 - 52 = 14 \text{ kcal mole}^{-1}$$

Heats of formation of some radicals are summarized in Table 6.2. A more complete list is given in Appendix I.

TABLE 6.2 Heats of Formation of Some Radicals

Compound	$\Delta H_f°$, kcal mole^{-1} at 25°C	Compound	$\Delta H_f°$, kcal mole^{-1} at 25°C
H·	52	$(CH_3)_3C\cdot$	9
$CH_3\cdot$	35	$CH_3CH_2CH_2CH_2\cdot$	16
$C_2H_5\cdot$	26	$(CH_3)_2CHCH_2\cdot$	14
$CH_3CH_2CH_2\cdot$	21	$CH_3CH_2\overset{\cdot}{C}HCH_3$	13
$(CH_3)_2CH\cdot$	18		

EXERCISE 6.1 For each of the reactions discussed in this section, calculate the bond-dissociation energies using the $\Delta H_f°$ values in Table 6.2 and Appendix I.

6.2 Pyrolysis of Alkanes: Cracking

When a molecule is broken up by heat, the process is called **pyrolysis** (Gk., *pyros*, fire; *lysis*, a loosening). When alkanes are pyrolyzed, the carbon-carbon bonds cleave to produce smaller alkyl radicals. With higher alkanes, the cleavage occurs randomly along the chain.

$$CH_3CH_2CH_2CH_2CH_3 \Bigg\langle \begin{array}{l} \longrightarrow CH_3\cdot + CH_3CH_2CH_2CH_2\cdot \\ \\ \longrightarrow CH_3CH_2\cdot + CH_3CH_2CH_2\cdot \end{array}$$

One possible reaction that these radicals may undergo is recombination to form an alkane. A mixture of different alkanes is produced.

$$CH_3\cdot + CH_3\cdot \longrightarrow CH_3CH_3$$
$$CH_3\cdot + CH_3CH_2\cdot \longrightarrow CH_3CH_2CH_3$$
$$CH_3CH_2\cdot + CH_3CH_2CH_2CH_2\cdot \longrightarrow CH_3CH_2CH_2CH_2CH_2CH_3$$

Another reaction that occurs is disproportionation. In this process one radical transfers a hydrogen atom to another radical to produce an alkane plus an alkene.

$$CH_3CH_2\cdot + CH_3CH_2CH_2\cdot \longrightarrow CH_3CH_3 + CH_3CH=CH_2$$

The net result of pyrolysis is the conversion of a large alkane to a mixture of smaller alkanes and alkenes. This reaction is not a useful one in the organic laboratory, where the aim is generally to produce a single pure compound in high yield. However, thermal cracking of hydrocarbons has been an important industrial process. As it comes from the ground, crude oil varies widely in composition depending on its source. For example, fractional distillation of a typical light oil affords 35% gasoline, 15% kerosene, and only a trace of asphalt, the balance being mainly high-boiling heating and lubricating oils. On the other hand, a typical "heavy oil" affords only 10% gasoline, 10% kerosene, and 50% asphalt. In order to reduce the average molecular weight of heavy oils and increase the production of the desirable more volatile fractions, various cracking techniques have long been employed. The oldest such method was the thermal-cracking method. However, thermal cracking has all but disappeared in recent years, although the process (which is actually more complex than indicated in the simple equation on this page) is still used to some extent for the production of low molecular weight alkenes. Modern cracking methods employ various catalysts, mainly composed of alumina and silica, which accomplish degradation of the large hydrocarbons into smaller ones at lower temperatures. Catalytic cracking probably involves cationic rather than free-radical intermediates.

EXERCISE 6.2 2-Methylbutane has three different carbon-carbon bonds that can break in the initial thermal cracking process. Give the disproportionation products expected from the radicals produced in each case. From consideration of bond-dissociation energies determine which products predominate.

6.3 Halogenation of Alkanes

When a mixture of methane and chlorine is heated to about 120°C or irradiated with light of a suitable wavelength, a highly exothermic reaction occurs.

$$CH_4 + Cl_2 \xrightarrow[\text{or light}]{\text{heat}} \underset{\text{methyl chloride}}{CH_3Cl} + HCl \qquad \Delta H° = -24.7 \text{ kcal mole}^{-1}$$

This reaction is a significant industrial process for preparing methyl chloride. It has limited usefulness as a laboratory preparation because the reaction does not stop with the introduction of a single chlorine. As the concentration of methyl chloride builds up, it undergoes chlorination in competition with methane.

$$CH_3Cl + Cl_2 \longrightarrow CH_2Cl_2 + HCl$$
methylene chloride

$$CH_2Cl_2 + Cl_2 \longrightarrow CHCl_3 + HCl$$
chloroform

$$CHCl_3 + Cl_2 \longrightarrow CCl_4 + HCl$$
carbon tetrachloride

The actual product of the reaction of methane and chlorine is a mixture of methyl chloride (b.p. $-24.2°C$), methylene chloride (CH_2Cl_2, b.p. $40.2°C$), chloroform ($CHCl_3$, b.p. $61.2°C$), and carbon tetrachloride (CCl_4, b.p. $76.8°C$). The composition of the mixture depends on the relative amounts of starting materials used and the reaction conditions. In this case it is easy to separate the products by fractional distillation because of the difference in boiling points.

A good deal of experimental evidence is in accord with the following mechanism for the chlorination of methane. The reaction begins with the **homolysis** of a chlorine molecule to two chlorine atoms (equation 6-1).

$$Cl_2 \xrightarrow[\text{or } h\nu]{\Delta} 2\ Cl\cdot \qquad (6\text{-}1)$$

When a covalent bond breaks in such a way that each fragment retains one electron of the bond, the process is called **homolytic cleavage** or **homolysis**.

$$A:B \longrightarrow A\cdot + B\cdot$$

When one fragment retains both electrons, the process is termed **heterolytic cleavage** or **heterolysis**.

$$A:B \longrightarrow A + B:$$

Since molecular chlorine has a rather low bond-dissociation energy ($DH° = 58$ kcal mole^{-1}), chlorine atoms may be produced by light of relatively long wavelength or by heating to moderate temperatures (equation 6-1). Once chlorine atoms are present in small amount, a **chain reaction** commences. A chlorine atom reacts with a methane molecule to give a methyl radical and HCl (equation 6-2). The methyl radical then reacts with a chlorine molecule to give methyl chloride and a chlorine atom (equation 6-3).

$$Cl\cdot + CH_4 \rightleftharpoons CH_3\cdot + HCl \qquad \Delta H° = +2 \text{ kcal mole}^{-1} \qquad (6\text{-}2)$$

$$CH_3\cdot + Cl_2 \longrightarrow CH_3Cl + Cl\cdot \qquad \Delta H° = -26.7 \text{ kcal mole}^{-1} \qquad (6\text{-}3)$$

The chlorine atom produced in equation (6-3) can react with another methane molecule to continue the chain. Reaction (6-1) is called the **initiation** step, and reactions (6-2) and (6-3) are called the **propagation** steps.

In principle, only one chlorine molecule need homolyze in order to convert many moles of methane and chlorine to methyl chloride and HCl. In practice, the chain process only goes through, on the average, about 10,000 cycles before it is terminated. Termination occurs whenever two radicals happen to collide, for example, equations (6-4) and (6-5).

$$CH_3 \cdot + Cl \cdot \longrightarrow CH_3Cl \qquad (6\text{-}4)$$

$$CH_3 \cdot + CH_3 \cdot \longrightarrow CH_3CH_3 \qquad (6\text{-}5)$$

Another possible termination step involves the collision of two chlorine atoms—reverse of the initiation step (equation 6-1). However, when two chlorine atoms collide to form Cl_2, the resulting molecule has as vibrational energy all of the kinetic energy of translation of the two atoms. This energy is always in excess of the bond energy, and the two atoms simply separate again. Only if collision occurs in the presence of a third body or on the wall of the reaction vessel to remove some of this energy does the chlorine molecule formed stay intact.

$$Cl \cdot + Cl \cdot + M \longrightarrow Cl_2 + M$$

This fundamental principle holds for all radical recombinations; a third body is required to remove the excess energy.

Other reactions that may (and probably do) occur are unproductive and do not terminate the chain reaction.

$$CH_4 + CH_3 \cdot \longrightarrow CH_3 \cdot + CH_4$$

$$Cl_2 + Cl \cdot \longrightarrow Cl \cdot + Cl_2$$

Let us look at each of the foregoing propagation steps in some detail. Reaction (6-2) is slightly endothermic and reversible, but it has a low activation energy of only about 4 kcal mole^{-1}. The reaction may be considered in further detail in terms of attack by Cl· on hydrogen.

$$Cl \cdot + H-CH_3 \longrightarrow [Cl \cdots H \cdots CH_3]^{\ddagger} \longrightarrow Cl-H + \cdot CH_3$$

The H—Cl and H—CH_3 bonds have similar strength [the $DH°$'s are 103 and 105 kcal mole^{-1}, respectively (Appendix II)]. As the chlorine-hydrogen bond forms and becomes stronger, the hydrogen-carbon bond becomes weaker and breaks. The product methyl radical appears to be planar (Figure 6.3). Methyl radical can be described to a good approximation in terms of three C_{sp^2}—H_{1s} bonds with the odd electron contained in the remaining C_{2p}-orbital. At the transition state the methyl group has started to flatten out from its original tetrahedral structure.

For the reverse process, $HCl + CH_3 \cdot \longrightarrow CH_4 + Cl \cdot$, the same mechanism applies in reverse. The carbon radical attacks the hydrogen of HCl at the rear of the hydrogen-chlorine bond and a carbon-hydrogen bond begins to form. As the forming carbon-hydrogen bond distance decreases and the bond strength increases, the remaining carbon-hydrogen bonds begin to bend back toward their tetrahedral geometry in CH_4. At the same time, the hydrogen-chlorine bond distance increases.

FIGURE 6.3 Methyl radical.

FIGURE 6.4 Stereo representation of the transition state for the reaction $CH_4 + Cl\cdot \rightleftharpoons$ $CH_3\cdot + HCl$.

A stereo representation of the transition state is shown in Figure 6.4.

The structure of the transition state is the same for both directions by the **principle of microscopic reversibility**. That is, the reverse reaction from products to reactants must have the same reaction mechanism as the forward reaction. If it did not, we could, in principle, set up a perpetual motion machine in violation of the second law of thermodynamics.

An equivalent description may be given in orbital terms. As the chlorine orbital containing one electron overlaps with the hydrogen $1s$-orbital, electron repulsion causes a decrease in the overlap of the H_{1s}-orbital with the C_{sp^3}-orbital, and the carbon-hydrogen bond begins to lengthen and become weaker. As this carbon-hydrogen bond gets weaker, it has less demand for s-orbital character, and the carbon s-orbital is used more for bonding to the other carbon-hydrogen bonds. Rehybridization occurs progressively from sp^3 toward sp^2. The carbon begins to flatten out, and the remaining carbon-hydrogen bonds become somewhat shorter and stronger. The structure of the transition state is depicted in terms of component atomic orbitals in Figure 6.5. A reaction coordinate diagram for reaction (6-2) is shown in Figure 6.6.

FIGURE 6.5 Orbital description of the transition state for the reaction $CH_4 + Cl\cdot \rightleftharpoons$ $CH_3\cdot + HCl$.

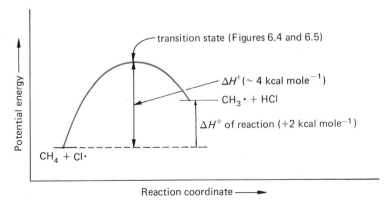

FIGURE 6.6 Reaction profile for the reaction $CH_4 + Cl\cdot \rightleftharpoons CH_3\cdot + HCl$.

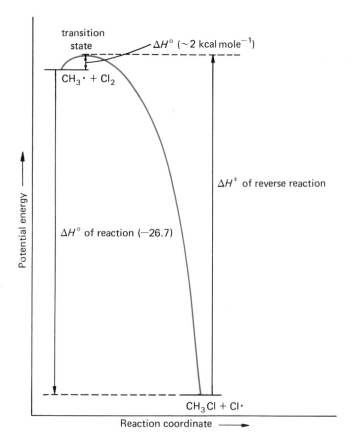

FIGURE 6.7 Reaction profile for the reaction $CH_3\cdot + Cl_2 \rightleftharpoons CH_3Cl + Cl\cdot$.

FIGURE 6.8 Stereo representation of the transition state for the reaction $CH_3\cdot + Cl_2 \rightleftharpoons CH_3Cl + Cl\cdot$.

Reaction (6-3) has a small activation energy of about 2 kcal mole^{-1}. This reaction is rapid and highly exothermic. The reverse reaction is highly endothermic and has a correspondingly high activation energy of $26.7 + 2 \cong 29$ kcal mole^{-1}. Consequently, the overall forward reaction is effectively irreversible. A reaction coordinate diagram for this step is shown in Figure 6.7. The transition state for this reaction is one in which the carbon-chlorine bond is partly formed and the chlorine-chlorine bond is partly broken.

$$[CH_3\cdots\cdots Cl\cdots Cl]^\ddagger$$

A stereo representation of this transition state is given in Figure 6.8.

The overall $\Delta H°$ of the net chlorination reaction may be obtained by summing equations (6-2) and (6-3).

$$\Delta H°, \; kcal \; mole^{-1}$$

(6-2): $CH_4 + \cancel{Cl}\cdot \longrightarrow \cancel{CH_3}\cdot + HCl \qquad\qquad +2$

(6-3): $\cancel{CH_3}\cdot + Cl_2 \longrightarrow CH_3Cl + \cancel{Cl}\cdot \qquad\qquad -26.7$

$\overline{\qquad\qquad CH_4 + Cl_2 \longrightarrow CH_3Cl + HCl \qquad\qquad -24.7 \qquad}$

Note that $\Delta H°$ for the initiation step is *not* added to the $\Delta H°$ values for the propagation steps in deriving $\Delta H°$ for the overall reaction. If one does this, one is actually calculating $\Delta H°$ for another reaction.

$$\Delta H°, \; kcal \; mole^{-1}$$

$Cl_2 \longrightarrow 2\,Cl\cdot \qquad\qquad +58$

$CH_4 + \cancel{Cl}\cdot \longrightarrow \cancel{CH_3}\cdot + HCl \qquad\qquad +\;2$

$\cancel{CH_3}\cdot + Cl_2 \longrightarrow CH_3Cl + \cancel{Cl}\cdot \qquad\qquad -26.7$

$\overline{Cl_2 + CH_4 + Cl_2 \longrightarrow CH_3Cl + HCl + 2\,Cl\cdot \qquad +33.3}$

This equation is just the sum of the overall chlorination reaction and the chlorine homolysis.

This is often a point of confusion because the student reasons that heat had to be put in to initiate the reaction. However, the question is not how much heat is applied, but what is $\Delta H°$, the *heat of the reaction*?

Chlorination of higher alkanes is similar to chlorination of methane except that the product mixtures are more complex. Ethane gives not only ethyl chloride, but also 1,1-dichloroethane and 1,2-dichloroethane.

$$CH_3CH_3 + Cl_2 \longrightarrow CH_3CH_2Cl + HCl$$

$$CH_3CH_2Cl + Cl_2 \longrightarrow \underset{\text{1,1-dichloroethane}}{CH_3CHCl_2} + \underset{\text{1,2-dichloroethane}}{ClCH_2CH_2Cl} + HCl$$

EXERCISE 6.3 Write equations showing the initiation, propagation, and termination steps for the monochlorination of ethane. Compute the $\Delta H°$ for each step and the overall $\Delta H°$ of the reaction. Write equations for the chain propagation steps involved in the formation of the two dichloroethanes.

With propane, two monochloro products may be formed. Both *n*-propyl chloride and isopropyl chloride are formed, but not in equal amounts.

$$CH_3CH_2CH_3 + Cl_2 \longrightarrow \underset{\substack{(43\%) \\ \textit{n}\text{-propyl chloride}}}{CH_3CH_2CH_2Cl} + \underset{\substack{(57\%) \\ \text{isopropyl chloride}}}{CH_3CHClCH_3}$$

In carbon tetrachloride solution at 25°C, the two isomers are produced in the relative amounts 43:57. Further reaction gives a mixture of the four possible dichloropropanes.

Let us examine the monochlorination of propane in greater detail. Recall that $DH°$ for the secondary hydrogen in propane is about 3 kcal mole^{-1} lower than $DH°$ for the primary hydrogen (Table 6.1). We might anticipate, then, that the secondary hydrogen would be removed by a chlorine atom more easily than a primary hydrogen. However, there are six primary hydrogens that may be replaced, whereas there are only two secondary hydrogens. The **relative reactivity** per hydrogen is then

$$\frac{\text{secondary}}{\text{primary}} = \frac{57/2}{43/6} = \frac{4}{1}$$

A similar trend is noticed in the monochlorination of 2-methylpropane, which gives 36% *t*-butyl chloride and 64% isobutyl chloride.

$$(CH_3)_3CH + Cl_2 \longrightarrow (CH_3)_3CCl + (CH_3)_2CHCH_2Cl$$

(36%)   (64%)

t-butyl chloride   isobutyl chloride

The relative reactivity of tertiary and primary hydrogens on a per-hydrogen basis is

$$\frac{\text{tertiary}}{\text{primary}} = \frac{36/1}{64/9} = \frac{5.1}{1}$$

Thus, the relative rates of reaction of different hydrogens with Cl· are just as we expect on the basis of $DH°$ for the various hydrogens

tertiary > secondary > primary

However, the degree of preference is relatively low. That is, there is less difference between the activation energies for the various reactions than there is between the heats of reaction (Figure 6.9).

For example, in chlorination of propane, the Cl· can abstract a hydrogen from the methyl group or from the methylene group. In the former case $\Delta H°$ is -5 kcal mole^{-1}, and in the latter it is -8 kcal mole^{-1}. Thus, the difference in heats of reaction $\Delta H° = 3$ kcal mole^{-1}. However, $\Delta H^{\ddagger}$ for abstraction of a CH$_2$ hydrogen is 3 kcal mole^{-1}, whereas $\Delta H^{\ddagger}$ for abstraction of a hydrogen from a CH$_3$ group is 2 kcal mole^{-1}; the difference in activation energies $\Delta H^{\ddagger} = 1$ kcal mole^{-1}. This result becomes reasonable when one realizes that in the transition state the free radical is not yet fully formed. Whatever it is that causes a secondary free radical to be more stable than a primary free radical will also affect the two transition states. However, that effect will be muted in the transition state to the extent that carbon has not achieved complete free radical character.

With more complicated alkanes, chlorination mixtures are hopelessly complex. Hence, chlorination of alkanes is not a good general reaction for preparing alkyl chlorides. There is only one type of compound for which chlorination has practical utility in laboratory preparations. When all hydrogens are equivalent, there is only one possible monochloro product. In such cases the desired product can generally be separated from hydrocarbon and di- and higher chlorinated species by fractional distillation. Two examples are the chlorination of cyclohexane and 2,2-dimethylpropane.

cyclohexyl chloride

$$CH_3-\underset{\underset{CH_3}{|}}{\overset{\overset{CH_3}{|}}{C}}-CH_3 + Cl_2 \longrightarrow CH_3-\underset{\underset{CH_3}{|}}{\overset{\overset{CH_3}{|}}{C}}-CH_2Cl + HCl$$

neopentyl chloride

The handling of gaseous chlorine in the laboratory is frequently inconvenient and such chlorinations are often done with sulfuryl chloride, SO_2Cl_2, instead.

FIGURE 6.9 Reaction profiles for the reaction of Cl· with C_3H_8.

Sulfuryl chloride is a colorless liquid, b.p. 69°C, produced by reaction of Cl_2 and SO_2. It fumes in moist air because it reacts rapidly with water according to the equation

$$SO_2Cl_2 + 2\,H_2O \longrightarrow 2\,HCl + H_2SO_4$$

When sulfuryl chloride is used as a chlorinating agent, a special initiator must be used to provide the free radicals that start the chain reaction. Peroxides are often used for this purpose because the oxygen-oxygen bond is weak and readily broken at relatively low temperatures (see Appendix II).

$$ROOR \longrightarrow 2\,RO·$$

The chlorination of cyclohexane by sulfuryl chloride provides a typical example.

$$\bigcirc + SO_2Cl_2 \longrightarrow \overset{Cl}{\bigcirc} + HCl + SO_2$$

A mixture of 1.8 mole of cyclohexane, 0.6 mole of sulfuryl chloride, and 0.001 mole of benzoyl peroxide, $(C_6H_5COO)_2$, is refluxed for 1.5 hr. Fractional distillation gives 89% of chlorocyclohexane, b.p. 143°C, and 11% of a mixture of dichlorocyclohexanes.

EXERCISE 6.4 Write the structures expected from the monochlorination of 2-methylbutane. Using relative reactivities of 1:4:5 for replacement of primary, secondary, and tertiary hydrogens, determine the percent of each of the monochloro compounds expected in the product mixture.

EXERCISE 6.5 Each of the following hydrocarbons contains no double or triple bonds and reacts with chlorine to give a single monochloride. Deduce the structure of each hydrocarbon and its chloride.
(a) C_8H_{18} (b) C_8H_{16} (c) C_8H_8

TABLE 6.3
$CH_4 + X_2 = CH_3X + HX$

X	ΔH°, kcal mole^{-1}
F	-102.8
Cl	-24.7
Br	-7.3
I	$+12.7$

The mechanism for chlorination may also be applied to the other halogens, but the actual reactions show important differences. The overall enthalpies of halogenation of methane by various halogens are summarized in Table 6.3.

The reaction with fluorine is so highly exothermic that controlled fluorination is difficult to accomplish. The energy liberated is sufficient to break most bonds. The hydrogen-fluorine bond is so strong ($DH^\circ = 136$ kcal mole^{-1}) that the following reaction is endothermic by only 7 kcal mole^{-1}.

$$CH_4 + F_2 \longrightarrow CH_3\cdot + F\cdot + HF \qquad \Delta H^\circ = +7 \text{ kcal mole}^{-1}$$

Consequently, when methane and fluorine are mixed, a few radicals form spontaneously and initiate chain reactions. The heat liberated by this reaction causes a rapid rise in temperature, and more bonds break to form radicals, which initiate more chain reactions. A radical chain reaction that is highly exothermic and produces radicals faster than they are destroyed results in an explosion. Organofluorine compounds are important because they frequently have unique and desirable properties. However, they are generally *not* made by direct fluorination, and this reaction is not a general laboratory preparation.

Iodination is at the opposite extreme. As shown in Table 6.3, the reaction of methane with iodine is endothermic. In fact, methyl iodide reacts with HI to generate CH_4 and I_2. Iodine atoms are relatively unreactive. For example, reaction with methane is so endothermic that no significant reaction occurs at ordinary temperatures.

$$CH_4 + I\cdot \longrightarrow HI + CH_3\cdot \qquad \Delta H^\circ = +34 \text{ kcal mole}^{-1}$$

Any iodine atoms produced ultimately dimerize to reform I_2.

The bromination of methane is less exothermic than is chlorination. Of the two chain propagation steps only one is relatively exothermic.

$$CH_4 + Br\cdot \longrightarrow CH_3\cdot + HBr \qquad \Delta H^\circ = +18 \text{ kcal mole}^{-1}$$
$$CH_3\cdot + Br_2 \longrightarrow CH_3Br + Br\cdot \qquad \Delta H^\circ = -25 \text{ kcal mole}^{-1}$$

Consequently, bromination is much slower than chlorination. It is instructive to examine the bromination of methane from a mechanistic standpoint. The two propagation steps are plotted in reaction coordinate form in Figures 6.10 and 6.11.

In its reactions with other alkanes, bromine is a much more *selective* reagent than chlorine. For example, bromination of propane at 330°C in the vapor phase gives 92% isopropyl bromide and only 8% *n*-propyl bromide.

$$CH_3CH_2CH_3 + Br_2 \longrightarrow CH_3CH_2CH_2Br + (CH_3)_2CHBr$$
$$ (8\%) \qquad\qquad (92\%)$$
$$ \textit{n}\text{-propyl bromide} \quad \text{isopropyl bromide}$$

The hydrogen abstraction steps for formation of the two isomers are

FIGURE 6.10 Reaction profile for the reaction $CH_4 + Br\cdot \rightleftharpoons CH_3\cdot + HBr$.

$$CH_3CH_2CH_3 + Br\cdot \longrightarrow CH_3CH_2CH_2\cdot + HBr \qquad \Delta H° = +10 \text{ kcal mole}^{-1}$$
$$CH_3CH_2CH_3 + Br\cdot \longrightarrow (CH_3)_2CH\cdot + HBr \qquad \Delta H° = +7 \text{ kcal mole}^{-1}$$

The two reactions are plotted in reaction coordinate form in Figure 6.12.

The rates of reaction of a bromine atom with the two types of hydrogen in propane are given by

$$\text{rate } (1°) = k_{1°}[CH_3CH_2CH_3][Br\cdot]$$
$$\text{rate } (2°) = k_{2°}[CH_3CH_2CH_3][Br\cdot]$$

FIGURE 6.11 Reaction profile for the reaction $CH_3\cdot + Br_3 \rightleftharpoons CH_3Br + Br\cdot$.

$\Delta\Delta H^{\ddagger} = 3.0 \text{ kcal mole}^{-1}$

$CH_3CH_3CH_2\cdot + HBr$

$\Delta\Delta H^{\circ} = 3.5 \text{ kcal mole}^{-1}$

$(CH_3)_2CH\cdot + HBr$

$CH_3CH_2CH_3 + Br\cdot$

Reaction coordinate ⟶

FIGURE 6.12 Reaction profiles for the reaction of Br· with C_3H_8.

The ratio of the products formed is simply the ratio of the two rate constants.

$$\frac{\text{rate } (2^{\circ})}{\text{rate } (1^{\circ})} = \frac{k_{2^{\circ}}}{k_{1^{\circ}}}$$

For two similar reactions such as these, the ratio of the rate constants is related in an exponential manner to the two activation energies. The reaction with the larger activation energy has the smaller rate constant. In the chlorination of propane $\Delta\Delta H^{\ddagger}$ is only 1 kcal mole^{-1}, and consequently chlorination is relatively nonselective. For bromination $\Delta\Delta H^{\ddagger}$ is 3 kcal mole^{-1}, and hence bromination gives a greater *ratio* of secondary to primary products.

EXERCISE 6.6 From the difference in activation energies of 3 kcal mole^{-1} calculate the relative reactivity of secondary and primary hydrogens for vapor phase bromination at 330°C.

The selectivity of bromine relative to chlorine is even more apparent when there are tertiary hydrogens in the alkane. For example, 2,2,3-trimethylbutane undergoes bromination to give more than 96% of the tertiary bromide, even though the alkane has only one tertiary hydrogen and fifteen primary hydrogens.

$$(CH_3)_3CCH(CH_3)_2 + Br_2 \xrightarrow[CCl_4]{h\nu} (CH_3)_3CCBr(CH_3)_2$$
$$(>96\%)$$

Thus, bromination is a somewhat more useful process for preparative purposes than chlorination. However, when there is only one tertiary hydrogen and many secondary hydrogens in a molecule, complex mixtures will still be produced.

EXERCISE 6.7 Using the data in Appendices I and II calculate the heats of reaction for

$$(CH_3)_3CH + X_2 \longrightarrow (CH_3)_3CX + HX$$

for $X_2 = F_2$, Cl_2, Br_2, and I_2.

6.4 Combustion of Alkanes

In terms of the mass of material involved, combustion of alkanes is one of the most important organic reactions. All burning of natural gas, gasoline, and fuel oil involves mostly the combustion of alkanes. However, this combustion is an atypical organic reaction in two respects. First, mixtures of alkanes are normally the "reactants" in this reaction. Second, the desired product of the reaction is not the chemical products but the heat of reaction. Indeed, the chemical products are frequently undesirable, and their sheer mass creates significant problems of disposal. The equation for complete combustion of an alkane is simple.

$$C_nH_{2n+2} + \left(\frac{3n + 1}{2}\right)O_2 \longrightarrow n\,CO_2 + (n + 1)\,H_2O$$

However, many combustion processes, such as the burning of gasoline in an internal combustion engine, do not result in complete combustion. In an automobile, 1 gal of gasoline produces more than 1 lb of carbon monoxide. There are many other products resulting from incomplete combustion. Among these other products are aldehydes (RCHO), compounds that contribute significantly to the smog problem.

The mechanism by which alkanes react with oxygen is a complex one that has not been worked out in detail. There are many partially oxidized intermediates. Radical chain steps are certainly involved. An especially important reaction is the combination of alkyl radicals with oxygen to give alkylperoxy radicals, which abstract hydrogen from an alkane to give intermediate alkyl hydroperoxides.

$$R\cdot + O_2 \longrightarrow ROO\cdot$$
$$ROO\cdot + RH \longrightarrow ROOH + R\cdot$$

Alkyl hydroperoxides contain a weak oxygen-oxygen bond ($DH° \cong 44$ kcal mole^{-1}), which breaks readily at elevated temperatures to produce more radicals.

$$ROOH \longrightarrow RO\cdot + HO\cdot$$

Thus combustion is another example of a radical-multiplying reaction, which leads to explosions under proper conditions.

When such an explosion occurs in the reaction chamber of an internal combustion engine, the piston is driven forward with a violent, rather than a gentle, stroke. Such premature explosions cause the phenomenon known as "knocking." The tendency of a fuel to cause engine knock depends markedly on the nature of the hydrocarbons used. In general, branching of an alkane chain tends to inhibit knocking. The knocking characteristic of a fuel is expressed quantitatively by an "octane number." On this arbitrary scale, heptane is given a value of 0 and 2,2,4-trimethylpentane ("isooctane") is assigned the value of 100. An octane number of 86, typical of a medium-grade "standard" or "regular" gasoline, has a knocking characteristic equivalent to that of a mixture of 86% 2,2,4-trimethylpentane and 14% heptane. The octane rating may be upgraded by the addition of small amounts of tetraethyllead ($C_2H_5)_4$Pb, which is called an "antiknock" agent. Its function is to control the concentration of free radicals and prevent the premature explosions that are characteristic of knocking. In recent years, the proliferation of "catalytic converters" for smog control has reduced the use of leaded fuel, since the lead compounds produced in the combustion process inactivate the catalysts. Thus, for environmental protection reasons, there has been a shift away from the use of lead compounds for increasing the octane rating of gasoline. This may be accomplished by various "reforming" processes, which cause straight-chain alkanes to be rearranged to their branched-chain isomers and to cycloalkanes, which have intrinsically higher octane ratings. However, the additional processing requires the expenditure of additional energy and entails additional losses of a limited raw material. For this reason, there is currently an active program under way to find other compounds that will improve the knocking characteristics of gasoline without damaging smog-control devices. Two leading candidates are *t*-butyl alcohol and methyl *t*-butyl ether (Chapter 10).

The **heat of combustion** is defined as the enthalpy of the complete oxidation. The heat of combustion of a pure alkane can be measured experimentally with high precision ($\pm 0.02\%$) and constitutes an important thermochemical quantity. For example, the heat of combustion of butane is $\Delta H^\circ = -634.82 \pm 0.15$ kcal mole^{-1}, whereas that of 2-methylpropane is $\Delta H^\circ = -632.77 \pm 0.11$ kcal mole^{-1}. The general equation for combustion of these two isomers is the same.

$$C_4H_{10} + 6\tfrac{1}{2}\,O_2 \longrightarrow 4\,CO_2 + 5\,H_2O$$

Heats of combustion are often expressed in terms of $H_2O(l)$ as one product. To avoid confusion with other energy terms in this text we have given values for the heats of combustion with $H_2O(g)$ as one product. This difference is the heat of vaporization of water, 10.52 kcal mole^{-1}.

A direct comparison of these two heats of combustion shows that the branched hydrocarbon is 2.0 kcal mole^{-1} more stable than the straight-chain hydrocarbon at room temperature (Figure 6.13). The products, carbon dioxide and water, are more stable than the reactants. Because the products have a lower energy content, energy is released as heat—the heat of combustion. The less stable the reactants, the more heat is evolved. Since butane has a heat of combustion of greater magnitude than 2-methylpropane, butane must have a higher energy content and is less stable thermodynamically than 2-methylpropane.

It is from accurate heats of combustions that heats of formation (Section 5.5) have been determined. Figure 6.14 illustrates the relationship between heats of combustion and heats of formation for *n*-butane and 2-methylpropane. Note that the conversion of the heats of combustion to heats of formation requires only the heats of combustion of graphite and of hydrogen.

EXERCISE 6.8 The heats of combustion of graphite (per carbon) and hydrogen (H_2) are -94.05 and -57.80 kcal mole^{-1}, respectively. From the heats of combustion of butane and 2-methylpropane shown in Figure 6.14, calculate ΔH_f° for both hydrocarbons and compare with the values in Figure 6.14.

FIGURE 6.13 Illustrating the heats of combustion of butane and 2-methylpropane.

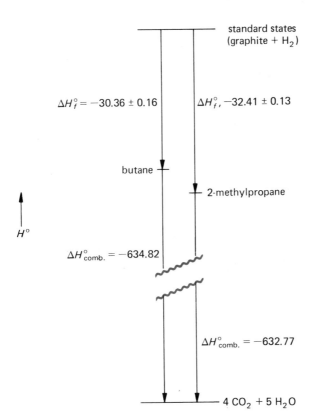

FIGURE 6.14 The relationship between the heats of formation and combustion of butane and 2-methylpropane.

EXERCISE 6.9 From heats of formation given in Appendix I, calculate the heats of combustion of pentane, 2-methylbutane and 2,2-dimethylpropane.

6.5 Average Bond Energies

Appendix I includes heats of formation for a number of free atoms. With these values we can calculate **heats of atomization**, the enthalpy required to dissociate a compound into all of its constituent atoms. For example, the heat of atomization of methane is 397 kcal mole^{-1}.

$$CH_4 = C + 4 H$$
$$\Delta H_f^\circ: \quad -17.9 \quad 170.9 + (4 \times 52.1) \qquad \Delta H^\circ = 397.2 \text{ kcal mole}^{-1}$$

Note that ΔH_f° of atomic carbon is much higher than ΔH_f° of C(graphite), carbon bound as graphite, which is defined as the standard state. Graphite has strong carbon-carbon bonds that must be broken to obtain carbon atoms. The heat of formation of carbon atoms is actually the heat of atomization of graphite per carbon.

This reaction requires breaking four carbon-hydrogen bonds. Hence, we can consider each bond to have an **average bond energy** of 397/4 = 99 kcal mole^{-1}. Note that this number differs from the bond-dissociation energy of methane (DH° = 105 kcal mole^{-1}), which is the energy required to break only one carbon-hydrogen bond in methane.

A similar calculation for ethane gives 674.6 kcal mole^{-1} as the heat of atomization required to break six carbon-hydrogen bonds and one carbon-carbon bond. If we assume that the average carbon-hydrogen bond energy in ethane is the same as it is in methane, we obtain $675 - (6 \times 99) = 81$ kcal mole^{-1}, a number that we could call the average bond energy of the carbon-carbon bond in ethane. If the same technique is applied to propane, we find a carbon-carbon bond energy similar to that in ethane.

In practice, data for a large number of compounds have been used to derive best overall values for such average bond energies. A table of such values is given in Appendix III. With this table one can calculate heats of atomization that are accurate to a few kilocalories per mole. The use of such a table is important for determining the approximate energy content of molecules whose heats of formation have not been determined experimentally or are too unstable to be isolated. Note that the results are only approximations. Butane and 2-methylpropane, for example, have the same numbers of carbon-carbon and carbon-hydrogen bonds. Such an approximate calculation using average bond energies results in identical heats of atomization; however, accurate heats of combustion show that butane and 2-methylpropane differ in energy content by 2.0 kcal mole^{-1}. Nevertheless, such approximate values will be found to have important uses in our study of organic chemistry.

EXERCISE 6.10   Use the average bond energies given in Appendix III to estimate the heat of reaction for chlorination of methane. Compare your answer with that obtained by using heats of formation of reactants and products.

EXERCISE 6.11   From Appendix I calculate the heats of atomization of butane and 2-methylpropane. Compare these values with the approximate one obtained from the use of average bond energies (Appendix III).

PROBLEMS

1. (a) What products are expected from thermal-cracking of pentane?
   (b) Write reaction mechanisms leading to each product.
   (c) From heats of formation calculate the enthalpy of each of the net reactions involved.

2. (a) Using the appropriate $DH°$ values from Appendix II, calculate $\Delta H°$ for each of the following reactions.
   $Br_2 \longrightarrow 2\ Br\cdot$
   $CH_3CH_3 + Br\cdot \longrightarrow CH_3CH_2\cdot + HBr$
   $CH_3CH_2\cdot + Br_2 \longrightarrow CH_3CH_2Br + Br\cdot$
   (b) What is the overall $\Delta H°$ for bromination of ethane?
   $CH_3CH_3 + Br_2 \longrightarrow CH_3CH_2Br + HBr$
   (c) How does this value compare with that obtained using heats of formation?

3. In the course of the bromination of ethane (problem 2), both bromine atoms and ethyl radicals will be present but not in equal amounts. Which is present in larger quantity? Explain.

4. The reaction of the unusual hydrocarbon spiropentane with chlorine and light is one of the best ways of preparing chlorospiropentane.

$$\underset{\text{spiropentane}}{\begin{array}{c}\text{H}_2\text{C} \qquad \text{CH}_2 \\ \text{C} \\ \text{H}_2\text{C} \qquad \text{CH}_2\end{array}} \quad \xrightarrow[h\nu]{\text{Cl}_2} \quad \underset{\text{chlorospiropentane}}{\begin{array}{c}\text{H}_2\text{C} \qquad \text{CHCl} \\ \text{C} \\ \text{H}_2\text{C} \qquad \text{CH}_2\end{array}}$$

(a) Explain why chlorination is such a useful preparative method in this case.

(b) Write the reaction mechanism.

5. For each of the following compounds, write the structures of all of the possible monochlorination products and predict the relative amounts in which they will be produced.

(a) butane   (b) 2,3-dimethylbutane   (c) 2,2,4-trimethylpentane

(d) 2,2,3-trimethylbutane   (e) pentane

6. Answer problem 5 for bromination, using the relative reactivities of carbon-hydrogen bonds toward bromine atoms at 40°C: primary, 1; secondary, 220; tertiary, 19,000.

7. In the chlorination of ethane, the observed reaction is

$$\text{CH}_3\text{CH}_3 + \text{Cl}_2 \longrightarrow \text{CH}_3\text{CH}_2\text{Cl} + \text{HCl}$$

An alternative reaction that might have occurred is

$$\text{CH}_3\text{CH}_3 + \text{Cl}_2 \longrightarrow 2\,\text{CH}_3\text{Cl}$$

(a) Calculate $\Delta H°$ for each reaction.

(b) Propose a radical chain mechanism by which the alternative reaction might occur. Calculate $\Delta H°$ for each of the propagation steps.

(c) Suggest a reason why the alternative reaction does not occur.

8. From the average bond energies in Appendix III calculate the heat of atomization of cyclopropane. Compare the the value derived from heats of formation in Appendix I. Do average bond energies take ring strain into account? Does this result suggest how average bond energies can be used to estimate ring strain? The unusual molecule cubane, C_8H_8 (see Exercise 6.5) has $\Delta H_f° = 148.7$ kcal mole^{-1}. Estimate its strain energy by comparing its heat of atomization with that calculated from average bond energies.

9. From the heats of formation given in Appendix I calculate the heat of combustion of cyclopropane and cyclohexane. For combustion of an equal weight under the same conditions, which is the better fuel?

10. Chlorine fluoride, ClF, is a colorless gas (b.p. $-101°C$) which behaves chemically as a reactive halogen. In principle, it can react with methane in two alternative ways

$$\text{CH}_4 + \text{ClF} \begin{array}{c} \nearrow \text{CH}_3\text{F} + \text{HCl} \\ \searrow \text{CH}_3\text{Cl} + \text{HF}\end{array}$$

(a) From $\Delta H_f°$ (ClF) $= -12.2$ kcal mole^{-1} and other data in Appendix I, calculate $\Delta H°$ for both reactions.

(b) $\Delta S°$ for both reactions is expected to be approximately the same; therefore, which set of products is expected to predominate at equilibrium?

(c) The reaction mechanism involves radical chain reactions similar to the reactions with chlorine except that the reaction of methyl radical with ClF can take two possible courses.

$$\text{CH}_3{}^\cdot + \text{ClF} \begin{array}{c}\nearrow \text{CH}_3\text{Cl} + \text{F}^\cdot \\ \searrow \text{CH}_3\text{F} + \text{Cl}^\cdot\end{array}$$

What is the difference in $\Delta H°$ for these two reactions? To the extent that the difference in activation energies reflects the difference in $\Delta H°$, which reaction is expected to be the faster?

11. Nitromethane, CH_3NO_2, is prepared by reaction of methane with nitric acid in the gas phase at temperatures over 400°C. Appendix I includes values for some nitrogen compounds. Calculate $\Delta H°$ (298 K) for the equilibrium

$$CH_4 + HNO_3 \rightleftharpoons CH_3NO_2 + H_2O$$

It may seem strange that such an exothermic reaction requires such a high temperature. The actual reaction steps are believed to be

$$CH_4 + \cdot NO_2 \rightleftharpoons CH_3\cdot + HNO_2$$

$$HNO_2 + HNO_3 \rightleftharpoons 2\,NO_2\cdot + H_2O$$

$$CH_3\cdot + NO_2\cdot \rightleftharpoons CH_3NO_2$$

Calculate $\Delta H°$ for each step. Which step is expected to be the slow step that requires the high temperature? The reaction is initiated by traces of oxygen or radicals to produce some $NO_2\cdot$ radicals which start the reaction. Note that this reaction sequence involves a radical chain propagation. Nitrogen dioxide is a rather stable radical, and its concentration in the reaction mixture is relatively high. It reacts rapidly with the methyl radicals and keeps these radicals at a very low concentration so that alternative free radical chain reactions are kept to minor importance; that is, nitrogen dioxide scavenges the methyl radicals. List several possible reactions of methyl radicals with nitric acid to produce methyl alcohol or nitromethane directly and show that these reactions are exothermic.

Nitrogen dioxide is a resonance-stabilized radical in which the odd electron can be placed on both oxygens and nitrogen. Write Lewis structures to demonstrate this point. In view of these structures it may seem surprising that methyl radical reacts with the nitrogen of NO_2. Actually, reaction at oxygen also occurs to give methyl nitrite, CH_3ONO. Compare $\Delta H°$ for this reaction with that for production of nitromethane:

$$CH_3NO_2 \longleftarrow CH_3\cdot + NO_2\cdot \longrightarrow CH_3ONO$$

Methyl nitrite is unstable under the reaction conditions and gives other products. The entire reaction is complex, and the discussion has treated only the most important of the many reactions that actually occur in this system.

12. In the chlorination of methane, the propagation steps (equations 6-2 and 6-3) do not have the same activation energies, as shown by Figures 6.6 and 6.7. However, by varying the relative concentrations of the methane and chlorine, either step can be made to be the slow step. Explain. Which step is rate-determining when $[CH_4] = [Cl_2]$? Under these conditions of relative concentrations, which free radical will be present in higher concentration, $CH_3\cdot$ or $Cl\cdot$? Show that the nature of the principal termination step depends on which propagation step is faster.

13. The description of rotational barriers in the alkanes (Section 5.2) was actually oversimplified, since, like all motion, the torsional motion around a carbon-carbon bond is quantized and a molecule will exist in one or more torsional-rotational states. Construct a more accurate version of Figure 5.9 to show this quantization. Assume that the zero-point energy level is about 0.5 kcal mole^{-1} above the potential minimum and that the torsional quantum levels are separated by about 1.0 kcal mole^{-1} increments. Which quantum level corresponds to continuous, uninhibited rotation about the bond?

Chapter 7

Stereoisomerism

7.1 Chirality and Enantiomers

The two objects depicted in Figure 7.1 appear to be identical in all respects. For every edge, face, or angle on one there is a corresponding edge, face, or angle on the other. And yet the two objects are not superimposable upon each other and are therefore *different objects*. They are related to one another as an object is related to its mirror image.

Another pair of familiar objects that are related to each other in this way are your right and left hands. They are (to a first approximation) identical in all respects. Yet your right hand will fit into a right glove and not into a left glove. The general property of "handedness" is called **chirality**. An object that is not superimposable upon its mirror image is **chiral**. If an object and its mirror image can be made to coincide in space, then they are said to be **achiral**.

EXERCISE 7.1 Which of the following familiar objects are chiral?
(a) a football   (b) an egg   (c) a corkscrew
(d) a golf club   (e) a crescent wrench   (f) a person
(g) a catcher's mitt (h) a spiral staircase (i) a pencil
(j) a calculator   (k) a pair of scissors (l) a screw-cap bottle
(m) a Greek vase   (n) a portrait

Careful inspection of 2-iodobutane reveals that it is a chiral compound. There are actually two isomeric 2-iodobutanes, which are nonsuperimposable mirror images (Figure 7.2). Two compounds that differ in handedness in this way are called **enantiomers** and are said to have an **enantiomeric** relationship to each other. In order to

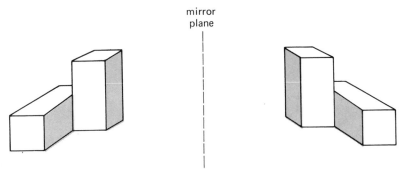

mirror
plane

FIGURE 7.1   Two nonsuperimposable mirror-image objects.

convert one of the enantiomeric 2-iodobutanes into the other, it is necessary either to break and reform bonds or to distort the molecule through a planar geometry. Either process requires substantial energy; consequently, there is a rather large energy barrier to interconversion of enantiomers of this type. The two enantiomeric forms of 2-iodobutane may be kept in separate flasks or bottles for an indefinite period of time; under normal conditions they show no tendency to interconvert. This type of isomerism is called stereoisomerism. **Stereoisomers** are compounds that have the same sequence of covalent bonds and differ in the relative disposition of their atoms in space.

2-Iodobutane owes its chirality to C-2, which has four different groups attached to it (C_2H_5, CH_3, I, H). If the positions of any pair of these four different substituents are exchanged, the enantiomeric structure is produced. Such a carbon is referred to as a **stereocenter**.

> From the time of Le Bel and van't Hoff, an atom with four different substituents was called an "asymmetric atom." It is true that compounds with one such atom are truly asymmetric in the sense that they lack symmetry. However, as we shall see, it is possible for molecules that have atoms with four different substituents to also have various symmetry elements, including planes of symmetry. Use of the term "asymmetric atom" in such a case is confusing. The term *stereocenter* avoids such confusion.

Notice that 1,1-dichloroethane, which has three different groups attached to C-1 (CH_3, Cl, H), is achiral; it is superimposable upon its mirror image (Figure 7.3). When a compound has one stereocenter, its molecules are always chiral. However, a stereocenter is not a necessary condition for chirality, as we shall soon see. Also, as we shall see in Section 7.5, a molecule may still be achiral if it contains more than one stereocenter.

FIGURE 7.2   The mirror-image relationship of the two 2-iodobutanes.

FIGURE 7.3 The achirality of 1,1-dichloroethane.

EXERCISE 7.2 Which of the following compounds has a stereocenter?
(a) 3-chloropentane   (b) 3-methylhexane
(c) 1-bromo-1-chloroethane   (d) bromocyclobutane

Two of the conformational isomers of butane (Section 5.2) also have an enantio-meric relationship to each other (Figure 7.4). However, in this case, the two enantio-mers may interconvert simply by rotation about the central carbon-carbon bond.

Since rotational barriers are generally rather small, enantiomers such as these intercon-vert rapidly at room temperature. The individual enantiomers could be obtained in a pure state only by working at exceedingly low temperatures, on the order of $-230°C$ (page 72). Note that the enantiomeric gauche butanes do not have stereocenters. In-stead, these molecules are chiral because of the presence of a **stereoaxis**.

EXERCISE 7.3 Construct molecular models of the two enantiomeric forms of gauche butane. Confirm that the two enantiomers are not superimposable and that rotation about the C-2—C-3 bond interconverts them.

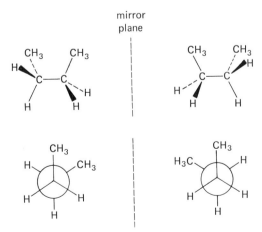

FIGURE 7.4 The enantiomeric relationship between the two gauche conformations of butane.

7.2 Physical Properties of Enantiomers: Optical Activity

Most of the physical properties of the two enantiomeric 2-iodobutanes are identical. They have identical melting points, boiling points, solubilities in common solvents, densities, refractive indices, and spectra. However, they differ in one important respect—the way in which they interact with **polarized light**.

Light may be treated as a wave motion of changing electric and magnetic fields which are at right angles to each other. When an electron interacts with light, it oscillates at the frequency of the light in the direction of the electric field and in phase with it. In normal light, the electric field vectors of the light waves are oriented in all possible planes. **Plane-polarized** light is light in which the electric field vectors of all of the light waves lie in the same plane, the plane of polarization.

normal light   plane–polarized light

Plane-polarized light may be produced by passing normal light through a polarizer, such as a polaroid lens or a device known as a Nicol prism.

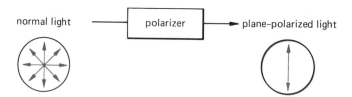

In a molecule, an electron is not free to oscillate equally in all directions. That is, its polarizability is "anisotropic," which means different in different directions. When electrons in molecules oscillate in response to plane-polarized light, they generally tend, because of their anisotropic polarizability, to oscillate out of the plane of polarization. Because of its interaction with the oscillating electrons, the light has its electric and magnetic fields changed. Thus, when plane-polarized light interacts with a molecule, the plane of polarization rotates slightly. However, in a large collection of achiral molecules, for any orientation of a molecule that changes the plane of polarization of the light, there is apt to be another molecule with a mirror-image orientation which has the opposite effect. Consequently, when a beam of plane-polarized light is passed through such a compound, it emerges with the plane of polarization unchanged.

However, for molecules of a chiral compound, such as one of the enantiomeric 2-iodobutanes, no such mirror-image orientations exist, and the plane of polarization of the light is usually measurably altered in its passage through the sample. Such compounds are said to be **optically active**. If a compound causes the plane of polarization to rotate in a clockwise (positive) direction on facing the beam, it is said to be **dextrorotatory**. If it causes the plane to rotate in a counterclockwise (negative) direction, it is called **levorotatory**. The amount by which the plane is rotated is expressed as the angle of rotation α and by the appropriate sign which shows whether rotation is in the dextro (+) or levo (−) sense.

Rotations are measured with a device called a **polarimeter**. Since the degree of rotation depends on the wavelength of the light used, monochromatic light (light having a single wavelength) is necessary. Common polarimeters use the sodium D line (5890 Å). The monochromatic light is first passed through the polarizer (usually a Nicol prism), from which it emerges polarized in one plane. The plane-polarized light is then passed through a tube that contains the sample, either as a liquid or dissolved in some achiral solvent. It emerges from the sample with the plane of polarization rotated in either the plus or minus direction by some amount. The light beam then passes through a second Nicol prism, which is mounted on a circular marked dial (the analyzer). The analyzer is rotated by an amount sufficient to allow the light beam to pass through at maximum intensity. Readings are compared with and without the sample tube to obtain the rotation value. Precision polarimeters using the sodium yellow line (D line) or the mercury green line are generally precise to about ± 0.01°. Modern spectropolarimeters use photocells in place of visual observation and can give even more precise data over a wide spectral region. A schematic representation of a polarimeter is shown in Figure 7.5.

The student may easily experience the phenomenon of optical rotation by performing a simple experiment. Take two pairs of Polaroid sunglasses and line them up, one in front of the other. Look through one lens of each pair of glasses at a bright light. Now rotate one of the lenses. When the glasses are parallel, the maximum amount of light is transmitted. When they are oriented at right angles to each other, no light is transmitted. What you have constructed is a simple polarimeter. The first pair of glasses corresponds to the polarizer and the second to the analyzer. Now dissolve several tablespoons of table sugar (sucrose, an optically active compound) in a small glass of water and place the glass between the two sunglasses. Again rotate one pair of glasses and note that the orientation for maximum and minimum transmission of light is now different. It is easier to observe the change at the point of minimum transmission.

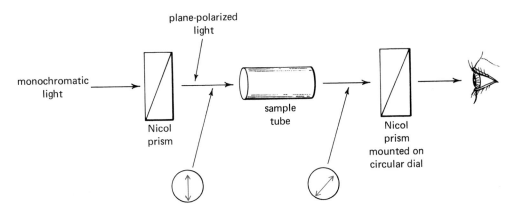

FIGURE 7.5 Polarimeter schematic.

The observed angle of rotation α is proportional to the number of optically active molecules in the path of the light beam. Therefore, α is proportional to the length of the sample tube and to the concentration of the solution being observed. The **specific rotation [α]** is obtained by dividing α by the concentration (expressed in g mL^{-1} solution) and by the length of the cell, l (expressed in decimeters). The wavelength of light used is given as a subscript, and the temperature at which the measurement was made is given as a superscript.

$$[\alpha]_D^t = \frac{\alpha}{l \cdot c} \quad \text{(for solutions)}$$

The decimeter is used as the unit of length simply because a 1-dc (10-cm) tube is a common length for measurements of rotation. For a pure liquid the definition of c (g mL^{-1}) is simply the density of the compound, d.

$$[\alpha]_D^t = \frac{\alpha}{l \cdot d} \quad \text{(for liquids)}$$

When the temperature is not given, the rotation is assumed to be that at room temperature, generally 25°C,

---

Actually, it is not possible to determine whether the rotation is $(+)$ or $(-)$ from a single measurement. Is a reading of 60° to be interpreted as $+60°$ or $-300°$? The sign may be determined by measuring the rotation at different sample concentrations. For example, if a 1 M sample gives a reading of 60° on the polarimeter, this may be either $+60°$ or $-300°$. For a 1.1 M sample, the values would be either $+66°$ or $-330°$, which are easily distinguished.

As was mentioned earlier, enantiomers differ from one another in the manner in which they interact with plane-polarized light. In fact, two enantiomers cause the plane of polarization to rotate by exactly the same amount, but in *opposite* directions. For example, one of the two enantiomeric 2-iodobutanes has $[\alpha]_D^{24°} = +15.9°$, and the other has $[\alpha]_D^{24°} = -15.9°$. This knowledge still does not tell us which enantiomer is which. *There is no simple relationship between the sign of α and the absolute stereostructure of a molecule.*

Absolute stereostructure can be determined by x-ray diffraction using a technique known as anomalous dispersion. Although the technique is too sophisticated to discuss here, suffice it to say that absolute stereostructures for some optically active compounds have been established in this way. Once the absolute stereostructures for a few optically active compounds are known, other molecular configurations may be determined by correlating them chemically with the compounds of known structure. We shall show how this is done in later sections. By these methods, the structures of $(+)$- and $(-)$-2-iodobutane are known to be

(+)-2-iodobutane
$[\alpha]_D^{24°} = +15.9°$

(−)-2-iodobutane
$[\alpha]_D^{24°} = -15.9°$

EXERCISE 7.4 The specific rotation of sucrose is $+66°$. Assuming that 5 tablespoons weighs 60 g and that a small glass 5 cm in diameter holds 300 mL of solution, calculate how much rotation should have been observed in the experiment described on page 117.

119

Sec. 7.3

*Nomenclature of
Enantiomers:
The R,S
Convention*

7.3 Nomenclature of Enantiomers: The *R,S* Convention

Suppose we have one bottle containing only one of the two enantiomeric 2-iodobutanes and another bottle containing only the other enantiomer. What labels do we attach to the two bottles? We cannot simply label each bottle "2-iodobutane" because they contain different compounds. We can label the bottles "(+)-2-iodobutane" and "(−)-2-iodobutane." By this we mean: "this bottle contains the 2-iodobutane that rotates the plane of polarized light in the dextro sense" and "this bottle contains the 2-iodobutane that rotates the plane of polarized light in the levo sense." Since it has also been determined which absolute stereostructure corresponds to (+)-2-iodobutane, these labels are sufficient to define unambiguously which compounds are in the bottles.

However, if a chemist were to encounter a bottle labeled (+)-2-iodobutane, chances are that he or she would not know which of the two possible absolute configurations correspond to dextrorotation. For this reason, it is highly desirable to have a system whereby the absolute configuration may be specified in the name of the compound. A system of nomenclature for this purpose was first introduced by R. S. Cahn and Sir Christopher Ingold of University College, London, in 1951. The proposal was subsequently modified in collaboration with Vlado Prelog, of the Swiss Federal Institute of Technology and has since been adopted for this purpose by the IUPAC. The Cahn-Ingold-Prelog system is also called the *R,S* convention, or the "sequence rule."

The application of the sequence rule to naming enantiomers which owe their chirality to one or more stereocenters is straightforward and involves the following simple steps.

1. Identify the four different substituents attached to the stereocenter. Assign to each of the four substituents a priority 1, 2, 3, or 4 using the sequence rule, such that 1 > 2 > 3 > 4.
2. Orient the molecule in space so that one may look down the bond from the stereocenter to the substituent with lowest priority, 4.

When one looks along that bond, one will see the stereocenter with the three attached substituents 1, 2, and 3 radiating from it like the spokes of a wheel. Trace a path from 1 to 2 to 3. If the path describes a clockwise motion, then the stereocenter is called *R* (L., *rectus*, right). If the path describes a counterclockwise motion, then the stereocenter is called *S* (L., *sinister*, left).

Stereo representations of *R* and *S* structures are shown in Figure 7.6.

The actual sequence rule is the method whereby the four substituents are assigned priorities 1, 2, 3, and 4 so that the symbols *R* and *S* may be assigned. There are a number of parts to the sequence rule, but we need only consider four aspects of it.

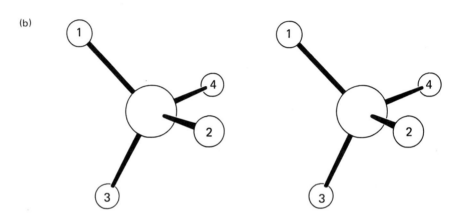

FIGURE 7.6 Stereo diagrams of a stereocenter, illustrating the arrangement of 1, 2, 3, and 4 priority groups for assignment of configurations as (*a*) *S* and (*b*) *R*.

1. If the four atoms directly attached to the stereocenter are different, **higher atomic number takes precedence over lower**. For example, in 1-bromo-1-chloroethane, the four atoms attached to the stereocenter are ranked Br > Cl > C > H.

$$3\,H_3C \qquad H\,4$$
$$C$$
$$1\,Br \qquad Cl\,2$$

(*S*)-1-bromo-1-chloroethane

Note that, in applying this aspect of the sequence rule, only the atoms attached *directly to the stereocenter* are considered. For example, in 1-chloro-1-fluoropropane, the four *groups* attached to C-1 are ranked Cl > F > CH_2CH_3 > H. For stereocenters that have three groups and a lone pair, the lone pair has the lowest priority (i.e., the lone pair is treated as having an atomic number of zero).

EXERCISE 7.5 Write a three-dimensional structure for (*R*)-1-chloro-1-fluoropropane.

2. In cases where two of the attached atoms are isotopes of each other, **higher atomic mass has priority over lower**. In 1-deuterio-1-fluoroethane, the four groups are therefore ranked F > C > D > H.

(R)-1-deuterio-1-fluoroethane

3. For many chiral compounds, two of the atoms directly attached to the stereocenter will be the same. In this case, work outward concurrently along the two chains atom by atom until a point of difference is reached. **The priorities are then assigned at that first point of difference**, using the same considerations of atomic number and atomic mass. In 2-iodobutane, the iodine is assigned priority 1 and the hydrogen is assigned priority 4. The two remaining groups are —CH$_2$—CH$_3$ and —CH$_2$—H. The first point of difference is at the two carbons attached to the stereocenter. The group —CH$_2$—CH$_3$ takes priority over —CH$_2$—H because carbon has a higher atomic number than hydrogen. Thus, we may assign R and S configurations to the two enantiomers as

(S)-2-iodobutane   (R)-2-iodobutane

For 4-chloro-2-methyloctane, the four atoms attached to the stereocenter are Cl (1), H (4), C, and C. In order to rank the isobutyl and *n*-butyl groups, we work along the chains until we reach the second carbon from the stereocenter before we reach a point of difference. The group —CH$_2$CH(CH$_3$)$_2$ takes priority over —CH$_2$CH$_2$CH$_2$CH$_3$ because at the first point of difference the carbon in isobutyl has *two other carbons* attached to it, whereas the analogous carbon in *n*-butyl has only *one other attached carbon*.

EXERCISE 7.6   Write the structure of (S)-3-chloro-2,6-dimethylheptane.

Note that the configuration R or S is assigned by considering only the *first* point of difference as one works out the two chains, even if other differences exist further out the chain. For example, in 1,3-dichloro-4-methylpentane, the priority order of the four groups attached to the stereocenter is Cl > —CH(CH$_3$)$_2$ > —CH$_2$CH$_2$Cl > H. In this case, the isopropyl and 2-chloroethyl groups are ranked on the basis of the fact that the isopropyl group has two carbons and one hydrogen bonded to the indicated carbon, while the 2-chloroethyl group has one carbon and two hydrogens attached to the analogous carbon.

EXERCISE 7.7   Assign R and S configurations to the following compounds.

(a)   (b)

---

4. **Double and triple bonds are treated by assuming that each such bonded atom is duplicated or triplicated.** For example, a carbon that is doubly bonded to oxygen is considered to be bonded to *two oxygens*.

$$\underset{O}{\overset{O}{\parallel}}{-}\overset{}{C}{-}H \equiv -\overset{O-C}{\underset{O}{\overset{|}{C}}}{-}H \qquad \underset{O}{\overset{O}{\parallel}}{-}\overset{}{C}{-}CH_3 \equiv -\overset{O-C}{\underset{O}{\overset{|}{C}}}{-}CH_3$$

EXERCISE 7.8 What is the absolute configuration of the following dihydroxy aldehyde (glyceraldehyde)?

$$\underset{HO}{\overset{H}{\diagdown}}\overset{\overset{\displaystyle O}{\overset{\parallel}{CH}}}{\underset{CH_2OH}{\diagup}}C$$

For a carbon-carbon double bond, *both* doubly-bonded carbons are considered to be duplicated.

$$-CH{=}CH_2 \equiv -\overset{\overset{\displaystyle C}{|}}{\underset{\underset{\displaystyle H}{|}}{C}}{-}\overset{\overset{\displaystyle C}{|}}{\underset{\underset{\displaystyle H}{|}}{C}}{-}H$$

Thus, the group —CH=CH₂ takes priority over the group —CH(CH₃)₂. In this example, the first carbon of each group is considered to be bonded to two carbons and one hydrogen, so that a priority cannot be assigned on the basis of this position. However, C-2 of the —CH=CH₂ group is considered to be bonded to one carbon and two hydrogens, while the analogous carbon in the —CH(CH₃)₂ group is considered to be bonded to three hydrogens.

$$-\overset{\overset{\displaystyle C}{|}}{\underset{\underset{\displaystyle H}{|}}{C}}{-}\overset{\overset{\displaystyle C}{|}}{\underset{\underset{\displaystyle H}{|}}{C}}{-}H \; > \; -\overset{\overset{\displaystyle CH_3}{|}}{\underset{\underset{\displaystyle H}{|}}{C}}{-}\overset{\overset{\displaystyle H}{|}}{\underset{\underset{\displaystyle H}{|}}{C}}{-}H$$

EXERCISE 7.9 What are the absolute configurations of the following compounds?

(a) $$\underset{(CH_3)_2CH}{\overset{CH_3CH=CH}{\diagdown}}C\overset{H}{\underset{OH}{\diagup}}$$
(b) $$\underset{CH_3}{\overset{HC\overset{\displaystyle O}{\parallel}}{\diagdown}}C\overset{H}{\underset{C\equiv N}{\diagup}}$$

It is important to remember that the *R* and *S* prefixes discussed in this section are nomenclature devices. They specify the absolute configuration of individual molecules. The terms (+) and (−) refer to the experimental property of optical activity.

7.4 Racemates

When equal amounts of enantiomeric molecules are present together, the sample is said to be **racemic**. Such a mixture is also called a **racemate**. Since a racemate contains equal numbers of dextrorotating and levorotating molecules, the net optical rotation is

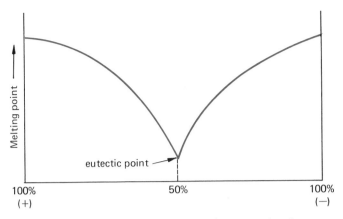

FIGURE 7.7 Melting point diagram for a racemic mixture.

zero. A racemate is often specified by prefixing the name of the compound with the symbol ($\pm$), for example, ($\pm$)-2-iodobutane.

The physical properties of a racemate are not necessarily the same as those of the pure enantiomers. A sample composed solely of right-handed molecules experiences different intermolecular interactions than a sample composed of equal numbers of right- and left-handed molecules. (In order to verify this in a simple way, use your right hand to shake hands with another person. The interaction is clearly different depending on whether the other person extends his right or his left hand.)

A racemate may crystallize in several ways. In some cases, separate crystals of the (+) and ($-$) forms result. In this case, the crystalline racemate is a mechanical mixture of two different crystalline compounds and is called a **racemic mixture**. The melting-point diagram for such a mixture is like that for any other mixture of two compounds (Figure 7.7). The eutectic point in such a case is always at the 50:50 point. Addition of a little of either pure enantiomer will cause the melting point of the mixture to increase. The racemate may also crystallize as a **racemic compound**. In this case only one type of crystal is formed, and it contains equal numbers of (+) and ($-$) molecules. The racemic compound acts as though it were a separate compound; its melting point is a peak on the phase diagram. However, the racemic compound may melt either higher or lower than the pure enantiomers. Addition of a small amount of either pure enantiomer causes a melting-point depression (Figure 7.8).

Because of these differential intermolecular interactions, racemates frequently differ from the pure enantiomers in other physical properties. Differences have been observed in density, refractive index, and in various spectra.

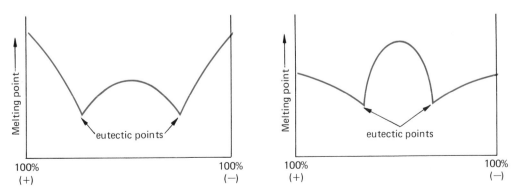

FIGURE 7.8 Representative melting point diagrams for racemic compounds.

The process whereby a pure enantiomer is converted into a racemic mixture is called **racemization**. Racemization may be accomplished in a trivial sense by simply mixing equal amounts of two pure enantiomers. Racemization may also result from chemical interconversion; we shall see many examples of this in future chapters. We have already encountered one racemization process in Section 7.1, the interconversion of the two enantiomeric gauche forms of butane by rotation about the central carbon-carbon bond.

7.5 Compounds Containing More Than One Stereocenter: Diastereomers

If a molecule has more than one stereocenter, the number of possible stereoisomers is correspondingly larger. Consider 2-chloro-3-iodobutane as an example. There are four isomers, which are depicted in Figure 7.9. Of the four stereoisomeric 2-chloro-3-iodobutanes, two pairs bear an enantiomeric relationship to one another. The 2R,3R and 2S,3S compounds are one enantiomeric pair, and the 2R,3S and 2S,3R compounds are another enantiomeric pair. As with the other enantiomeric pairs previously discussed, the 2R,3R and 2S,3S compounds have identical boiling points, melting points, densities, solubilities, and spectra. They cause the plane of polarized light to rotate to the same degree but in opposite directions; one is dextrorotatory, and the other is levorotatory. A similar correspondence in physical properties is observed for the 2R,3S and 2S,3R compounds.

Compounds that are stereoisomers of one another, but are not enantiomers, are called **diastereomers** and are said to have a **diastereomeric** relationship. The stereoisomeric relationships for a compound having two unlike stereocenters are summarized in schematic form in Figure 7.10.

In general, the maximum number of possible stereoisomers for a compound having n stereocenters is given by 2^n. Thus, for a compound with one stereocenter, there are $2^1 = 2$ stereoisomers. For a compound with two stereocenters, there may be $2^2 = 4$ stereoisomers. In some cases, there are fewer than the maximum number of possible stereoisomers. As an example, consider 2,3-dichlorobutane. The 2R,3R and 2S,3S compounds are enantiomers of one another.

FIGURE 7.9 Stereoisomers of 2-chloro-3-iodobutane.

125

Sec. 7.5

*Compounds
Containing More
Than One
Stereocenter:
Diastereomers*

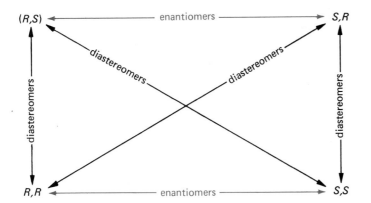

FIGURE 7.10 Stereoisomeric relationships for a compound having two unlike stereocenters.

mirror plane

(2S,3S)-2,3-dichlorobutane   (2R,3R)-2,3-dichlorobutane

However, careful inspection reveals that the 2R,3S and 2S,3R compounds are actually the *same* compound (mentally perform a 180° rotation of the entire molecule about the axis of the C-2—C-3 bond).

mirror plane

(2S,3R)-2,3-dichlorobutane (meso)

Since this isomer of 2,3-dichlorobutane is achiral, it is not optically active. Such a compound, which has stereocenters yet is achiral, is called a **meso** compound. It is important not to confuse meso compounds with racemates, which are actually equimolar mixtures of two enantiomers. Both show no optical activity, but a meso compound is a single achiral substance, whereas a racemate is a 50 mole % mixture of two chiral substances.

Meso compounds may be recognized by looking for a plane or a point of symmetry *within a molecule* which has stereocenters. When such an element of symmetry exists, the maximum number of possible stereoisomers is less than 2^n. In one of the eclipsed conformations of *meso*-2,3-dichlorobutane the plane of symmetry is clearly obvious.

plane of symmetry

A point of symmetry may be seen in one of the staggered conformations.

$$Cl \quad H \qquad\qquad CH_3$$
$$C \!-\!\bullet\!-\! C$$
$$H_3C \qquad\qquad H \quad Cl$$

center of symmetry

An object has a point of symmetry (or is centrosymmetric) when the identical environment is encountered at the same distance in both directions along any line through a given point.

EXERCISE 7.10 The tsetse fly sex-attractant (page 89) has the $17R,21S$ configuration. Is it a meso compound, or does it show optical activity?

In writing more complex structures than we have considered heretofore in this Chapter, it is often convenient to employ the line structures that were introduced in Chapter 5 (page 76). In such structures, an emboldened line represents a part of the molecule that projects *forward* from the general plane of the molecule and a dashed line represents a part of the molecule that projects *away* from the general plane of the molecule. Remember that hydrogens are not shown in these simplified drawings, even if attached to a stereocenter.

Cl	Cl
(S)-3-chloroheptane	$(4R,5S)$-5-chloro-4-ethyl- 2,8-dimethylnonane

---

EXERCISE 7.11 Write line structures for (R)-2-chloro-5-methylhexane and $(2R,4S)$-2,4-dichloropentane. The latter compound is meso. Identify an internal symmetry element in the drawing you have made.

7.6 Stereoisomeric Relationships in Cyclic Compounds

Chlorocyclopropane and 1,1-dichlorocyclopropane are achiral molecules, as can be readily be deduced from the fact that each has an internal plane of symmetry. For both molecules, the symmetry plane includes C-1 and its two substituents and bisects the C-2—C-3 bond.

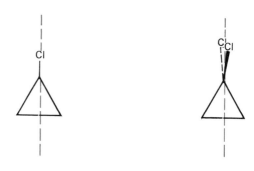

For 1,2-dichlorocyclopropane there are three stereoisomers. In one of the isomers, the two chloro substituents are on the same side of the plane of the ring. This isomer is called *cis*-1,2-dichlorocyclopropane (L., *cis*, on this side). This isomer also contains a symmetry plane, and is therefore achiral (even though it has two stereocenters).

In the other two stereoisomeric 1,2-dichlorocyclopropanes, the two chloro substituents are attached to opposite sides of the cyclopropane ring. These isomers are called trans (L., *trans*, across). Neither of these isomers have an internal symmetry plane. Indeed, as the following structures show, the two *trans*-1,2-dichlorocyclopropanes are enantiomers.

The set of stereoisomeric 1,2-dichlorocyclopropanes is completely analogous to the set of stereoisomeric 2,3-dichlorobutanes we discussed in Section 7.5. The cis isomer has the *R,S* configuration and is a meso compound. It has a diastereomeric relationship to each of the trans isomers, which have *R,R* and *S,S* configurations, respectively.

EXERCISE 7.12 Construct molecular models of the three stereoisomeric 1,2-dichlorocyclopropanes. Verify that the two trans isomers have a mirror-image relationship. Find the internal symmetry plane in the cis isomer. Assign *R* and *S* configurations to the two stereocenters in each of the three isomers you have constructed.

Chlorocyclohexane and 1,1-dichlorocyclohexane are analogous to their cyclopropane counterparts. Both have symmetry planes, which include C-1 and its two substituents. In these molecules, the internal symmetry planes also pass through C-4 and its two substituents. The symmetry planes are clearly evident in "flat" projection structures of the two compounds.

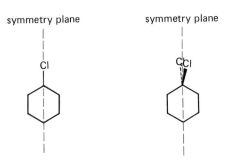

In the chair perspective structure of 1,1-dichlorocyclohexane, the symmetry plane may also be seen, but with somewhat more difficulty.

1,1-dichlorocyclohexane

Chlorocyclohexane can exist in two different chair conformations since the chloro group may be either axial or equatorial. As shown by the following structural drawings, both conformations have an internal symmetry plane, and are therefore achiral.

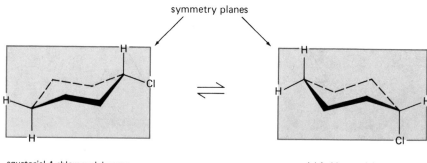

equatorial 1-chlorocyclohexane   axial 1-chlorocyclohexane

The two chair conformations of 1-chlorocyclohexane actually have a diastereomeric relationship, since they are stereoisomers that do not have a mirror-image relationship. However, as we saw in Section 5.6, the energy barrier for the conversion of one cyclohexane chair conformation to another is on the order of 10 kcal mole^{-1}. Thus, at normal temperatures, they are in rapid equilibrium. In fact, the situation is analogous to that seen with butane (Sections 5.2 and 7.1), where the two enantiomeric gauche conformations are in rapid equilibrium.

For 1,4-dichlorocyclohexane, there are a cis and a trans isomer. Both have an internal symmetry plane and are thus achiral.

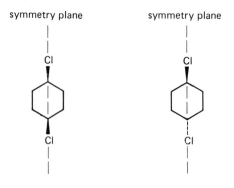

cis-1,4-dichlorocyclohexane   *trans*-1,2-dichlorocyclohexane

EXERCISE 7.13 Construct molecular models of *cis-* and *trans*-1,4-dichlorocyclo-hexane. Note that the trans isomer has two *different* chair conformations. Identify the symmetry plane in each of these isomers. What relationship do the two chair conformations of the cis isomer have?

The 1,3-dichlorocyclohexane stereoisomers comprise an interesting case. A plane of symmetry is apparent in the cis isomer. Since this isomer has stereocenters, *cis*-1,3-dichlorocyclohexane is a meso compound.

symmetry plane

(1*R*,3*S*)-1,3-dichlorocyclohexane

However, no symmetry plane exists in the trans isomer. Thus, as is the case with *trans*-1,2-dichlorocyclopropane, there are two enantiomeric *trans*-1,3-dichloro-cyclohexanes.

mirror plane

(1*R*,3*R*)-1,3-dichlorocyclohexane   (1*S*,3*S*)-1,3-dichlorocyclohexane

Note that with the absolute configuration of each stereocenter specified it is not necessary to specify that either is a trans isomer.

EXERCISE 7.14 Construct molecular models of the two enantiomeric *trans*-1,3-dichloro-cyclohexanes. Convince yourself that there are no conformations in which the two isomers are superimposable.

7.7 Conformations of Substituted Cyclohexanes

As we saw in the preceding section, a monosubstituted cyclohexane can exist in two different conformations, since the substituent can be either axial or equatorial. The two chair conformations of methylcyclohexane are shown in Figure 7.11. It is instructive to

FIGURE 7.11 Chair conformations of methylcyclohexane.

FIGURE 7.12   Newman projections of methylcyclohexane.

look at Newman projections of the ring C-1—C-2 bond of methylcyclohexane (Figure 7.12). In the equatorial conformation, the methyl group is anti to the C-3 CH_2 group of the ring, whereas in the axial conformation these groups have a gauche relationship. The interaction of a methyl hydrogen with the axial hydrogen of the C-3 CH_2 group is much like the interaction of the corresponding hydrogens in a gauche conformation of butane (Section 5.2). Recall that this interaction in butane causes an enthalpy increase of 0.9 kcal mole^{-1}. There are two such interactions in axial methylcyclohexane— between the methyl group and the C-3 CH_2 and the C-5 CH_2, as shown in Figure 7.12. Correspondingly, the axial conformation of methylcyclohexane is expected to be about 1.8 kcal mole^{-1} less stable than the equatorial conformation. This difference in energy for the two conformations may be approximated as $\Delta G°$ and transformed into an equilibrium constant for the equilibrium between the two isomers at 25°C:

$$\Delta G° = -RT \ln K$$
$$(-1.8 \text{ kcal mole}^{-1}) = -(1.987 \times 10^{-3} \text{ kcal mole}^{-1} \text{ deg}^{-1})(298 \text{ deg}) \ln K$$
$$K = 21$$

Thus, at 25°C, methylcyclohexane exists as an equilibrium mixture of the two conformations, with 95% of the molecules having the equatorial-methyl structure and 5% having the axial-methyl structure. Because of interaction of axial groups with the other axial hydrogens on the same side of the ring, axial conformations of substituted cyclohexanes are generally less stable than the corresponding equatorial conformations. Actual energy differences for various substituents, expressed as $\Delta G°$ values, are summarized in Table 7.1.

Bulky groups such as isopropyl and *t*-butyl have such strong interactions in the axial position that the proportion of axial conformation in the equilibrium mixture is small. For example, the $\Delta G°$ of 3.1 kcal mole^{-1} for the group C_6H_5 (phenyl) corresponds to an equilibrium constant at 25°C of 189; for phenylcyclohexane 995 out of every 1000 molecules have the C_6H_5 group equatorial.

EXERCISE 7.15   Calculate the equilibrium constants for the axial $\rightleftharpoons$ equatorial equilibria in isopropylcyclohexane and *t*-butylcyclohexane.

TABLE 7.1 Conformational Energies for Monosubstituted Cyclohexanes

Group	$-\Delta G°$ (axial $\rightleftharpoons$ equatorial), kcal mole^{-1} (25°C)
F	0.25
Cl	0.5
Br	0.5
I	0.45
OH	1.0
CH$_3$	1.7
CH$_2$CH$_3$	1.8
C≡CH	0.41
CH(CH$_3$)$_2$	2.1
C(CH$_3$)$_3$	~5–6
C$_6$H$_5$	3.1
COOH	1.4
CN	0.2

Like other substituted cyclohexanes, 1,1-dimethylcyclohexane can exist in two chair conformations. In each conformation, one methyl group is axial and one is equatorial.

cis-1,4-dimethylcyclohexane

Of course, the $\Delta G°$ for this equilibrium is zero, and the corresponding equilibrium constant is 1.

The lower energy of equatorial substituents compared to axial is also seen in the disubstituted compounds. For example, *trans*-1,4-dimethylcyclohexane ($\Delta H_f° = -44.1$ kcal mole^{-1}) is more stable than the cis isomer ($\Delta H_f° = -42.2$ kcal mole^{-1}) by 1.9 kcal mole^{-1}. In the trans isomer both methyl groups can be accommodated in equatorial positions, whereas in the cis hydrocarbon one methyl must be axial.

Both *cis*- and *trans*-1,4-dimethylcyclohexane can exist in two chair conformations. For the cis isomer, the two conformations are of equal energy, since each has one axial substituent and one equatorial substituent.

cis-1,4-dimethylcyclohexane, $\Delta G° = 0$

For the trans isomer, one conformation has both substituents axial and the other has both substituents equatorial. The diequatorial conformation predominates greatly at equilibrium ($\Delta G° \cong 3.4$ kcal mole^{-1}).

trans-1,4-dimethylcyclohexane, $\Delta G° \cong 3.4$ kcal mole^{-1}

For 1,3-dimethylcyclohexane the cis isomer is more stable than the trans. In *cis*-1,3-dimethylcyclohexane both methyls can be equatorial, whereas one methyl must be axial in the trans isomer.

| *cis*-1,3-dimethylcyclohexane | *trans*-1,3-dimethylcyclohexane |
| both methyls equatorial | one methyl equatorial |

The *t*-butyl group is so bulky that it effectively demands an equatorial position. Indeed, an axial *t*-butyl group represents so strained a structure that the $\Delta G°$ value in Table 7.1 for the difference between axial and equatorial *t*-butyl groups is only a rough estimate. In *cis*-1-*t*-butyl-4-methylcyclohexane, for example, the conformation with axial methyl and equatorial *t*-butyl groups dominates completely.

EXERCISE 7.16 Using the data in Table 7.1, estimate the equilibrium constant for the foregoing equilibrium.

When excessive strain is involved, a distortion of the cyclohexane ring occurs. For example, phenyl and *t*-butyl are both rather bulky groups. A crystal structure analysis of a compound that has a *cis*-1-*t*-butyl-4-phenylcyclohexane structure shows that the ring has been stretched out somewhat but still has essentially a chair conformation with axial phenyl and equatorial *t*-butyl groups.

In *trans*-1,3-di-*t*-butylcyclohexane a chair cyclohexane ring would require one *t*-butyl group to be axial as in Figure 7.13. Actually, in this compound the cyclohexane ring is twisted in order to avoid placing the *t*-butyl group in an axial position. This new conformation of cyclohexane is related to the hypothetical **boat** conformation shown in Figure 7.14. In this confirmation, however, two of the hydrogens are so close together that a slight further twisting occurs to give the so-called "twist-form" or "skew-boat" structure as shown in Figure 7.15. This skew-boat form occurs in several compounds containing bulky groups but is not an important conformation for cyclohexane itself. In the skew-boat conformation several hydrogens are partially eclipsed. The structure has a strain energy of about 5 kcal mole^{-1} relative to chair cyclohexane.

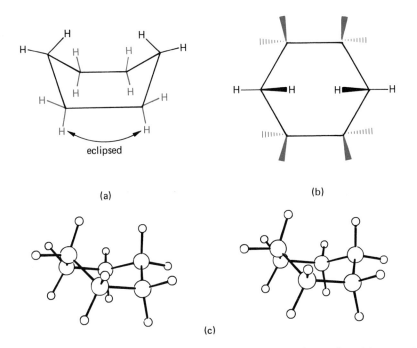

FIGURE 7.13   Conformations of *trans*-1,3-di-*t*-butylcyclohexane.

(a)   (b)

(c)

FIGURE 7.14   Boat conformation of cyclohexane: (*a*) side view; (*b*) top view; (*c*) stereo view.

FIGURE 7.15   Skew-boat conformation of cyclohexane. The hydrogens are omitted for clarity.

EXERCISE 7.17 Construct a molecular model of cyclohexane and place it in the ideal boat conformation depicted in Figure 7.14. Note that four of the ring carbons (C-2, C-3, C-5, and C-6) lie in a common plane, and that C-1 and C-4 are tipped above this plane. Verify that this conformation has four eclipsed H:H interactions. Note that one of the C-1 hydrogens is very close to one of the C-4 hydrogens. With a ruler, measure the distance between these hydrogens and compare with the distance between a pair of eclipsed hydrogens. Now manipulate your model so that its carbon skeleton matches the representation of the twist-boat conformation shown in Figure 7.15. Note that in this conformation, all H:H interactions are minimized.

7.8 Chemical Reactions and Stereoisomerism

When a chemical reaction involves only achiral reactants, solvents, and reagents, the reaction products must be either achiral or, if chiral, they must be racemates. As an example, consider the monochlorination of butane. After the monochlorobutane fraction has been isolated, it is found to be a mixture of 1-chlorobutane and 2-chlorobutane. The 1-chlorobutane is, of course, achiral. The 2-chlorobutane formed in the reaction is a racemate, an equimolar mixture of (R)-2-chlorobutane and (S)-2-chlorobutane.

$$CH_3CH_2CH_2CH_3 + Cl_2 \xrightarrow{h\nu} CH_3CH_2CH_2CH_2Cl +
\begin{cases}
CH_3CH_2{-}\overset{\displaystyle Cl}{\underset{\displaystyle H}{C}}{-}CH_3 \\
\\
CH_3CH_2{-}\overset{\displaystyle H}{\underset{\displaystyle Cl}{C}}{-}CH_3
\end{cases}$$

Moreover, recall that the reactive intermediate in the reaction leading to 2-chlorobutane is the *sec*-butyl free radical, which is approximately planar. Being planar, it is achiral and may react with Cl_2 on either of its faces. Reaction on one face yields (R)-2-chlorobutane, and reaction on the other side yields (S)-2-chlorobutane. Since reaction is equally probable on the two faces, a racemate results. Consequently, any reaction that involves an achiral intermediate will give racemic products.

(S)-2-chlorobutane   (R)-2-chlorobutane

This result may also be discussed in terms of the relative rates of two competing reactions, *sec*-butyl free radical reacting with Cl_2 to give either (R)- or (S)-2-chlorobutane. The transition states for the two reactions are depicted as follows.

Notice that transition state A leading to the *R* enantiomer and transition state B leading to the *S* enantiomer are themselves enantiomeric. Because they are enantiomeric, they have identical physical properties, including bond angles, bond lengths, and free energies of formation. Since the two competing reactions begin at the same place and pass through transition states of equal energy, they have identical activation energies, and a 50:50 mixture of (*R*)- and (*S*)-2-chlorobutane results (Figure 7.16).

In Sections 4.2 and 4.3, we briefly considered the reaction of methyl chloride with hydroxide ion, in which the hydroxy group replaces the chloro group. Analogous reactions occur with other alkyl halides. For example, the enantiomeric 2-iodobutanes undergo a similar reaction. As we shall see in the next chapter, an **inversion of absolute configuration** takes place in this reaction, so that (*R*)-2-iodobutane gives (*S*)-2-butanol and (*S*)-2-iodobutane gives (*R*)-2-butanol.

FIGURE 7.16 An achiral intermediate gives enantiomeric transition states with equal activation energies.

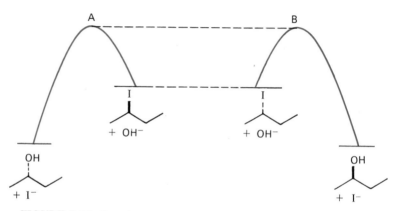

(R)-2-iodobutane   (S)-2-butanol

(S)-2-iodobutane   (R)-2-butanol

In the next chapter, we shall study this kind of reaction in detail. For now, let us only note that the **principle of enantiomeric transition states** that we have just learned demands that the two reactions take place with precisely the same rate. This may be readily appreciated by inspection of Figure 7.17. Since (R)- and (S)-2-iodobutane are enantiomeric, they have equal free energies of formation. Similarly, the transition states leading from each enantiomer to the respective alcohols (A and B) bear an enantiomeric relationship. Consequently, the energies of activation for the two reactions must be identical.

FIGURE 7.17 Enantiomers react with achiral reagents with equal rates.

PROBLEMS

1. Calculate $[\alpha]_D$ for each of the following compounds.
   (a) A 1-M solution of 2-chloropentane in chloroform in a 10-cm cell gives an observed α of $+3.64°$.
   (b) A solution containing 0.96 g of 2-bromooctane in 10 mL of ether gives an observed α of $-1.80°$ in a 5-cm cell.

2. How many stereoisomers may exist for each of the following compounds?

   (a) $CH_3CH-CHCH_3$ with OH OH

   (b) $CH_3CH_2CH-CHCH_3$ with OH OH

   (c) $CH_3CH-CHCH_3$ with Cl OH

   (d) $CH_3CH-CH-CHC_2H_5$ with Cl Cl Cl

   (e) $CH_3CH-CH-CHCH_3$ with OH Cl Cl

   (f) $CH_3CH_2CCH_3$ with Cl (below) Cl

3. For parts (a)-(e) of problem 2, show which pairs of stereoisomers are enantiomeric and which pairs are diasteromeric. Assign *R* or *S* to each stereocenter.

4. For each of the following compounds assign *R* or *S* to each stereocenter.

(a)

(b)

(c)

(d)

(e)

(f)

(g)

(h)

5. For each of the following compounds, assign *R* or *S* to each stereocenter.

(a)   (b)   (c)   (d)

6. Write structures for each of the following compounds.
   (a) (1*R*,3*R*)-1,3-dichlorocyclohexane
   (b) (3*S*,4*R*)-3-chloro-4-methylhexane
   (c) the meso isomer of 1,3-dimethylcyclopentane
   (d) an optically active isomer of 1,2-dimethylcyclobutane

7. Write structures for all of the stereoisomeric 2,4-dichloro-3-methylpentanes. Identify the two meso forms.

8. Given the Newman projection

Is this structure *R* or *S*? Determine whether each of the following structural symbols is equivalent to the above Newman projection or to its enantiomer.

(a)   (b)   (c)   (d)

9. How many stereoisomers exist for 1,3-dichloro-2,4-dimethylcyclobutane? Write all the structures. Which are chiral and which are achiral? Identify all planes and points of symmetry in the various structures.

10. Assign *R* or *S* to each stereocenter in the following compounds.

11. A fifth sub-rule of the sequence rule (Section 7.3) provides that when two substituents are identical except in absolute sense of chirality, *R* configuration takes precedence over *S* configuration. Using this sub-rule, assign configurational labels to the stereocenters in the following compounds.

12. Draw a chair perspective structure for *cis*-1,2-dimethylcyclohexane. Is the molecule in the conformation you have drawn chiral or achiral? Now draw the structure for the other chair conformation. What relationship do the two conformations have?

13. From the data in Table 7.1, calculate the percentage of molecules having the substituent in the equatorial position for each of the following compounds.

14. Using the conformational energies in Table 7.1 as a guide, estimate the difference in energy between the diaxial and diequatorial conformers of *trans*-1,4-dichlorocyclohexane. Experimentally, it is found that the diequatorial conformer predominates in the equilibrium, as expected. However, for *trans*-1,2-dichlorocyclohexane, the diaxial conformer is found to predominate at equilibrium. Explain.

15. Draw Newman projections for the C-1—C-2 bond, the C-1—C-6 bond, and the C-2—C-3 bonds of *cis*- and *trans*-1,2-dimethylcyclohexane (for the trans isomer, use the diequatorial conformation). Identify all gauche interactions involving the methyl groups. Estimate the difference in energy in the two isomers. How does your estimate compare with the difference in energy calculated from the heats of formation given in Appendix I?

16. Make perspective structural drawings of the two chair conformations of *cis*-1,3-dimethylcyclohexane. Assuming that the only important interactions are the *gauche*-butane interactions involving the methyl groups, estimate the difference in energy in the two isomers. The actual difference is not known accurately, but it has been estimated to be greater than 5 kcal mole^{-1}. Can you offer an explanation for the difference between this value and the value you estimated?

17. (*S*)-1-Chloro-2-methylbutane has been shown to have (+) rotation. Among the products of light-initiated chlorination are (−)-1,4-dichloro-2-methylbutane and (±)-1,2-dichloro-2-methylbutane.
    (a) Write out the absolute configuration of the (−)-1,4-dichloro-2-methylbutane produced by the reaction and assign the proper *R* or *S* label. What relationship does this example show between sign of rotation and configuration?

(b) What does the fact that the 1,2-dichloro-2-methylbutane produced is totally racemic indicate about the reaction mechanism and the nature of the intermediates?

18. Consider the chlorination of (S)-2-fluorobutane. The monochlorination fraction of the reaction product contains 1-chloro-2-fluorobutane, 2-chloro-2-fluorobutane, 2-chloro-3-fluorobutane, and 1-chloro-3-fluorobutane.

(a) The 1-chloro-2-fluorobutane constitutes 1% of the monochloro product. What is the absolute configuration of this material (R or S)?

(b) The 1-chloro-3-fluorobutane constitutes 26% of the monochloro product. What is its absolute configuration?

(c) The 2-chloro-2-fluorobutane fraction amounts to 31% of the monochloro product. This material is found to be racemic. How do you explain this result?

(d) Careful examination of the 2-chloro-3-fluorobutane product reveals that it is actually a mixture consisting of 16% of the 2S,3S diastereomer and 24% of the 2R,3S diastereomer. Can you offer an explanation for the fact that these two isomers are not produced in equal amounts? [Hint: Construct a reaction coordinate diagram analogous to Figure 7.16.]

Chapter 8

Alkyl Halides and Organometallic Compounds

8.1 Structure of Alkyl Halides

Alkyl halides are the first group of organic compounds we will study in which there is a functional group. The halogen group can be converted into several other functional groups, and some of these reactions are among the most important in organic chemistry.

The carbon atoms in alkyl halides are essentially tetrahedral. The carbon-halogen bond may be regarded to a good approximation as resulting from overlap of a C_{sp^3} orbital with a hybrid orbital from the halogen. Molecular orbital calculations suggest that the hybrid halogen orbital is mostly p, with only a small amount of s-character. In methyl fluoride, for example, the hybrid orbital from fluorine in the carbon-fluorine bond is calculated to be about 15% s and 85% p. The reason for the relatively small amount of s-character is that the halogen has three lone pairs and most of the X_{2s} atomic orbital is used to bind these lone-pair electrons. Only a small amount of s-orbital is available for the orbital bonded to carbon. Note that the hybridization of the halogen must be computed; it is not amenable to experimental tests with currently available methods.

The carbon-halogen bond lengths of the methyl halides are shown in Table 8.1. The size of the halogen atoms increases as we go down the periodic table. The fluorine atom is somewhat larger than hydrogen, but smaller than carbon: compare the C—F bond distance of 1.39 Å with C—C, 1.54 Å, and C—H, 1.10 Å. The higher halogens are all substantially larger than carbon.

The *van der Waals radius* of a group is the effective size of the group. As two molecules approach each other, the van der Waals attractive force (Section 5.1) increases to a maximum, then decreases and becomes repulsive (Figure 8.1). The van der Waals radius is defined as one-half the distance between two equivalent atoms at the point of the energy minimum. It is an equilibrium distance and is usually evaluated from the structures of molecular crystals. Van der Waals radii for several atoms and groups are summarized in Table 8.2. The van der Waals radius of bromine (1.95 Å) is about the same as that for a methyl group (2.0 Å).

TABLE 8.1 Bond Lengths of Methyl Halides

Compound	r_{C-X}, Å
CH_3F	1.39
CH_3Cl	1.78
CH_3Br	1.93
CH_3I	2.14

FIGURE 8.1 Van der Waals forces.

**TABLE 8.2 Van der Waals
Radii, Å**

H	N	O	F
1.2	1.5	1.4	1.35
CH_2	P	S	Cl
2.0	1.9	1.85	1.8
CH_3			Br
2.0			1.95
			I
			2.15

Although the carbon-halogen bonds in alkyl halides are covalent, they have a polar character because halogens are more electronegative than carbon. That is, the "center of gravity" of the electron density does not coincide with the center of nuclear positive charge. This imbalance results in a **dipole moment** μ, which is expressed as the product of the charge q and the distance of separation d: $\mu = q \times d$. The distance involved has direction; hence, dipole moments are vectors. In the case of methyl halides this vector is directed along the carbon-halogen bond and is usually symbolized as

$$\overset{\longmapsto}{CH_3 - X}$$

The direction of the arrow is from positive to negative charge. The magnitudes of the dipole-moment vectors for methyl halides are summarized in Table 8.3. Since the charge involved is on the order of 10^{-10} esu and the distance is on the order of 10^{-8} cm, dipole moments are on the order of 10^{-10} esu cm. This unit is named the Debye, abbreviated D, after the late Professor Peter Debye who discovered this molecular property. Thus, if a positive charge and a negative charge of 10^{-10} esu are separated by 10^{-8} cm, the system has a dipole moment of 1 Debye or 1 D.

EXERCISE 8.1 The electron charge is 4.8×10^{-10} esu. Using the bond distances in Table 8.1 calculate the fraction of an electronic charge at the ends of the carbon-halogen bond that would give rise to the dipole moments in Table 8.3. Note that fluorine is more electronegative than chlorine but gives rise to a smaller carbon-halogen dipole moment because of its shorter bond distance.

142

Chap. 8

*Alkyl Halides
and
Organometallic
Compounds*

**TABLE 8.3 Dipole
Moments of Methyl
Halides (Vapor Phase)**

Compound	μ, D
CH_3F	1.82
CH_3Cl	1.94
CH_3Br	1.79
CH_3I	1.64

8.2 Physical Properties of Alkyl Halides

The lower molecular weight *n*-alkyl halides are gases at room temperature. Starting with *n*-butyl fluoride, *n*-propyl chloride, ethyl bromide, and methyl iodide, the alkyl halides are liquids at room temperature. This result comes mostly from the increasing effective "size" of the halogens as we proceed down the periodic table. We saw in the previous section how this changing size is reflected in increasing carbon-halogen bond distances along the series from fluorine to iodine. Increasing size carries with it an increase in the effective "area of contact" at the van der Waals radius that produces van der Waals attraction.

However, size does more than increase this area of contact. We learned on page 69 that van der Waals attraction results from the mutual correlation of electronic motions. The movement of one electron describes a changing electric field. The ability of a second electron to respond to such a changing field is measured by its **polarizability**. The smaller and "tighter" the atom, the lower the polarizability of its electrons and the lower the van der Waals attraction for a given area of contact. Consequently, along the series F, Cl, Br, I the polarizability increases. Furthermore, lone-pair electrons are generally held more loosely than bonding electrons and can be more polarizable. Although bromine has a van der Waals radius similar to that of a methyl group, it has much higher polarizability, and an alkyl bromide, RBr, has a much higher boiling point than that of the corresponding RCH_3. We have emphasized the role of van der Waals attractions in boiling points, but it should be mentioned that molecular weight also plays a role because of the effect of mass on kinetic energy. Along a given homologous series, however, the van der Waals force depends on the overall size of the molecule which, in turn, parallels the molecular weight.

> The tightly held electrons and consequent low polarizability of fluorine results in the unique and distinctive properties of fluorocarbons, compounds composed entirely of carbon and fluorine. The boiling points of fluorocarbons are much closer to those of related hydrocarbons than might have been expected from the difference in molecular weights or size; for example, C_2H_6 has b.p. $-89°C$; C_2F_6 has b.p. $-79°C$.

Increasing the alkyl chain also causes a normal progressive increase in boiling point. As with alkanes themselves, branched systems have lower boiling points than isomeric linear systems. Some boiling point data are summarized in Table 8.4 and in Figure 8.2.

Alkyl halides are insoluble in water but soluble in most organic solvents. They vary greatly in stability. Monofluoroalkanes are difficult to keep pure; on distillation they tend to lose HF to form alkenes. Chlorides are relatively stable and generally can be purified by distillation. However, higher molecular weight tertiary alkyl chlorides tend

TABLE 8.4 Boiling Points of Alkyl Halides (RX)

			Boiling Point, °C			
R	X =	H	F	Cl	Br	I
CH_3-		−161.7	−78.4	−24.2	3.6	42.4
CH_3CH_2-		−88.6	−37.7	12.3	38.4	72.3
$CH_3(CH_2)_2-$		−42.1	−2.5	46.6	71.0	102.5
$CH_3(CH_2)_3-$		−0.5	32.5	78.4	101.6	130.5
$CH_3(CH_2)_4-$		36.1	62.8	107.8	129.6	157.
$(CH_3)_2CH-$		−42.1	−9.4	34.8	59.4	89.5
$(CH_3)_2CHCH_2-$		−11.7		68.8		
$CH_3CH_2\overset{\displaystyle CH_3}{\underset{\displaystyle \mid}{CH}}-$		−0.5		68.3	91.2	120.
$(CH_3)_3C-$		−11.8		50.7	73.1	dec.

to lose HCl on heating and must be handled more carefully. Indeed, this property holds for most tertiary alkyl halides. Note in Table 8.4 that *t*-butyl iodide decomposes on attempted distillation at atmospheric pressure.

Chloroform slowly decomposes on exposure to light. This tendency is diminished by the presence of small amounts of alcohol. Commercially available chloroform has about 0.5% alcohol added as a stabilizer. Alkyl bromides and iodides are also light sensitive. Upon exposure to light they slowly liberate the free halogen and turn brown or violet, respectively. Thus, these halides are generally stored in opaque vessels or brown bottles and should generally be redistilled before use.

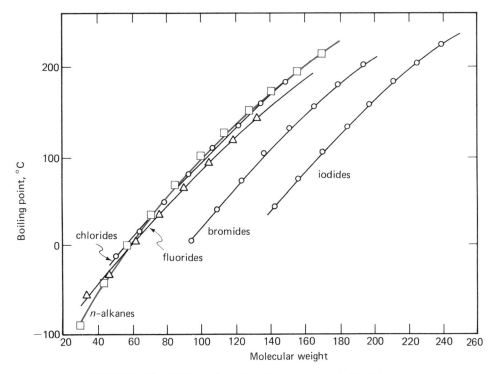

FIGURE 8.2 Boiling points of *n*-alkanes and *n*-alkyl halides.

EXERCISE 8.2 (a) Which has the higher melting point, *n*-butyl bromide or *t*-butyl bromide? Explain. Compare your answer with melting points found in a handbook. (b) From the generalizations and data provided in this section and in Chapter 5, estimate the boiling points of $CH_3CH_2CH(CH_3)CH_2CH_2Cl$ and $CH_3CH_2CH_2CH(C_2H_5)CH_2Cl$. Look up these boiling points in a handbook.

8.3 Conformations of Alkyl Halides

Barriers to rotation about carbon-carbon bonds bearing halogens are comparable to those in hydrocarbons, and these compounds also prefer staggered conformations. Some rotation barriers are summarized in Table 8.5. Note that there is no simple relationship between the barrier and the size of the halogen. One reason is that as the size of a halogen increases, its bond length to carbon also increases. The same principle operates in the halogenated cyclohexanes; recall that the halogens show a relatively small and almost constant preference for the equatorial conformation (Table 7.1). In alkyl halides where rotation involves eclipsing C—H with C—H and C—H with C—X, the barriers are about 3.2-3.7 kcal mole^{-1}. Even for hexafluoroethane, where rotation involves eclipsing three pairs of carbon-fluorine bonds, the barrier is only 3.9 kcal mole^{-1}. However, rotation of one carbon-chlorine bond past another is more difficult; the barrier in hexachloroethane is 10.8 kcal mole^{-1}.

1,2-Dichloroethane, like butane, exists in two conformations, gauche and anti.

gauche   anti

One conformation is converted to another by rotating a carbon-chlorine bond past a carbon-hydrogen bond. It is not necessary to rotate C—Cl past C—Cl. Accordingly, the barrier between these conformations is only about 3.2 kcal mole^{-1}, not much different than for rotation in ethyl chloride.

We saw in Chapter 5 that the gauche and anti conformations of butane differ in energy by about 0.9 kcal mole^{-1}. We might expect, therefore, that the two analogous

TABLE 8.5 Barriers to Rotation in Alkyl Halides

Compound	Rotation Barrier, kcal mole^{-1}
$CH_3—CH_2F$	3.3
$CH_3—CF_3$	3.25
$CF_3—CF_3$	3.9
$CH_3—CH_2Cl$	3.7
$CCl_3—CCl_3$	10.8
$CH_3—CH_2Br$	3.7
$CH_3—CH_2I$	3.2

conformations of 1,2-dichloroethane will also have different energies. In fact, in the vapor phase, the anti conformation is more stable by 1.2 kcal mole^{-1}. Remarkably, however, the energy difference in the pure liquid is about zero!

How do we account for this interesting observation? One explanation involves two opposing factors, dipole repulsion and van der Waals attraction. Each carbon-chlorine bond has an associated dipole moment. The electrostatic repulsion for two dipoles oriented in the anti conformation is lower than that for two dipoles oriented in the gauche conformation.

gauche conformation   anti conformation

The other factor involved is van der Waals attraction. Two chlorines separated by little more than the sum of their van der Waals radii attract each other in exactly the same manner as two neighboring alkanes (Section 5.2). Such van der Waals attraction is especially important for the large halogen atoms because the lone-pair electrons are spread through a relatively large volume and respond easily to changing neighboring charge fields. That is, such electrons have relatively high polarizability.

The net result for the gauche and anti conformations is a balance. Van der Waals attraction favors the gauche conformation, but dipole-dipole repulsion favors the anti conformation. In the vapor phase the dipole effect dominates, and the anti structure is more stable. In the liquid phase there are many other molecules close by that reduce the importance of the intramolecular dipole factor. The two effects now just cancel.

8.4 Some Uses of Halogenated Hydrocarbons

The simple alkyl halides and polyhaloalkanes are readily available and are used extensively as solvents. Chlorides are most important because of the low cost of chlorine relative to bromine and iodine. In fact, chlorine is one of the basic raw materials of the chemical industry. In 1983 the United States produced 9,960,000 tons of chlorine, most of which was used to produce chlorinated hydrocarbons.

The polychloromethanes are produced industrially by the chlorination of methane. Carbon tetrachloride has been used extensively in drycleaning establishments. However, it must be handled with care because it is an accumulative poison that causes liver damage. Consequently, its use in drycleaning has declined. Chloroform was once used as an anesthetic, but its use for this purpose has now been abandoned because it is toxic and a suspected carcinogen. More recently, the mixed halogenated compound $CF_3CHClBr$, ''Halothane,'' has found important use as an inhalative anesthetic because it is effective and relatively nontoxic.

Several theories have been proposed for the action of anesthetics, but the detailed mode of action is not yet known. Anesthetics can be chemically inert; for example, xenon has anesthetic action. Different compounds vary in the concentration required; even nitrogen under pressure functions as an anesthetic. Nitrogen narcosis is a danger to deep divers. It is remarkable that the effective concentration of an anesthetic is species-independent. The same partial pressure of anesthetic functions as well in man as in a goldfish. The application of anesthetics needs to be carefully monitored. Lethal concentrations are typically only about double the useful anesthetic concentration.

146

Chap. 8

*Alkyl Halides
and
Organometallic
Compounds*

A number of partially fluorinated alkanes are widely marketed for use as cooling fluids in refrigeration systems and as aerosol propellants. These compounds are often known by their trade names.

Compound	Trade Name	Systematic Name
$CFCl_3$	Freon 11	trichlorofluoromethane
CF_2Cl_2	Freon 12	dichlorodifluoromethane
CF_3Cl	Freon 13	chlorotrifluoromethane
CF_4	Freon 14	tetrafluoromethane

Ethyl chloride is used as a local anesthetic. It is a gas at ambient temperature (b.p. 12°C) and is kept in pressurized containers. When it is sprayed onto the skin, rapid vaporization occurs. The heat required to cause vaporization is drawn from the local surroundings, in this case the skin, and the resultant cooling deadens the nerve endings.

Another significant use of chlorinated hydrocarbons is as pesticides, a general term that includes fungicides, herbicides, insecticides, fumigants, and rodenticides. There are three main types of pesticides in use: carbamates, organophosphorus compounds, and chlorinated hydrocarbons. The use of such compounds for the control of disease-bearing pests has increased sharply during the past three decades.

The most well-known pesticide is DDT, which has been used extensively since 1939.

1,1,1-trichloro-2,2-bis(*p*-chlorophenyl)ethane
DDT

DDT is effective against many organisms, but its most spectacular success has been in control of the *Anopheles* mosquito, which transmits malaria. Malaria has been a scourge of mankind for centuries. According to the World Health Organization, malaria is still the chief cause of human death in the world, aside from natural causes. The disease acquired its name in ancient Rome (L. *mala*, bad; *aria*, air), where it was believed to be a result of the bad air in the city. It is actually caused by a parasite of the *Plasmodium* family which infects and ruptures erythrocytes in the blood stream. The organism has a complex life cycle requiring both vertebrate and invertebrate hosts. Humans are infected by sporozoites of the organism that are injected into the bloodstream by the bite of an infected mosquito.

Although malaria may be treated, the most effective method of controlling it is to eliminate the insect vector that is essential for its transmission. DDT is especially effective for this purpose, and malaria has been essentially eliminated from large areas of the world through its use. It has been estimated that because of the efficacy of DDT in checking malaria and other mosquito-borne diseases (yellow fever, encephalitis), more than 75 million human deaths have been averted. A striking example is Sri Lanka (the island of Ceylon). In 1934-35, there were 1.5 million cases of malaria resulting in 80,000 deaths. After an intensive mosquito abatement program using DDT, malaria effectively disappeared and there were only 17 cases reported in 1963. When the use of DDT was discontinued in Sri Lanka, malaria rebounded, and there were over 600,000 cases reported in 1968 and the first quarter of 1969.

In spite of its obvious value in combatting diseases such as malaria, DDT has been abused. It is a "hard" insecticide, in that its residues accumulate in the environment. Although it is not especially toxic to mammals (the fatal human dose is 500 mg kg^{-1} of body weight, about 35 g for a 150 lb person), it is concentrated by lower organisms such as plankton and accumulates in the fatty tissues of fish and birds. The toxicity of DDT was first noted in 1949 by the Fish and Wildlife Service, but indiscriminate use as an agricultural pesticide for the control of crop-destroying pests continued to grow. In 1962, following the publication of *Silent Spring* by the late biologist Rachel Carson, an intensive campaign against the use of pesticides such as DDT commenced. In 1972 its use as an agricultural pesticide in the United States was banned by the Environmental Protection Agency. Active research is being directed toward developing new types of pesticides that are species-specific and biodegradable and will not accumulate in the environment.

Alkyl halides are important as reagents. Many reactions are known for transforming the halogens to other functional groups. For industrial reactions, chlorides are used almost exclusively because of the high cost of bromine and iodine. For laboratory uses, where cost is not as great a consideration, bromides are used preferentially because alkyl bromides are generally more reactive than alkyl chlorides. Methyl iodide is a commonly used laboratory reagent because it is the only methyl halide that is liquid at room temperature. The preparation of alkyl halides from alcohols and alkenes will be discussed in Chapters 10 and 11, respectively.

Another important use of alkyl halides is in the preparation of organometallic compounds. We will next turn our attention to this group.

8.5 Nomenclature of Organometallic Compounds

Organometallic compounds are substances in which an organic group is bonded directly to a metal, R—M. They are named by prefixing the name of the metal with the appropriate organic group name. The names are written as one word.

$(CH_3)_3CLi$	$(CH_3CH_2)_2Mg$	$(CH_3)_3Al$
t-butyllithium	diethylmagnesium	trimethylaluminum
$(CH_3CH_2CH_2)_2Cd$	$(CH_3CH_2)_2Zn$	$(CH_3)_2Hg$
dipropylcadmium	diethylzinc	dimethylmercury
CH_3Cu	$(CH_3)_4Si$	$(CH_3CH_2)_4Pb$
methylcopper	tetramethylsilicon	tetraethyllead

Compounds of boron, tin, and silicon are also named as derivatives of the simple hydrides: borane, BH_3; stannane, SnH_4; and silane, SiH_4. These compounds are indexed by *Chemical Abstracts* in this manner.

$(CH_3CH_2)_3B$	$(CH_3CH_2)_4Sn$	$(CH_3)_3SiCH_2CH_3$
triethylborane	tetraethylstannane	ethyltrimethylsilane

In some organometallic compounds, the valences of the metal are not all utilized in bonding to carbon but include bonds to inorganic atoms as well. Such compounds are named as organic derivatives of the corresponding inorganic salt.

CH_3CH_2MgBr	CH_3HgCl	$CH_3CH_2AlCl_2$
ethylmagnesium bromide	methylmercuric chloride	ethylaluminum dichloride

---

EXERCISE 8.3 Provide an acceptable name for each of the following compounds.
(a) $(CH_3)_2CHMgCl$ (b) $(CH_3)_4Si$ (c) $CH_3CH_2CH_2CH_2Li$ (d) $(CH_3)_4Pb$
(e) $(CH_3)_2Sn(CH_2CH_3)_2$

148

Chap. 8

Alkyl Halides
and
Organometallic
Compounds

8.6 Structures of Organometallic Compounds

Since metals are **electropositive** elements, carbon-metal bonds can have a high degree of **ionic character**. That is, dipolar resonance structures are often important contributors to the structures of such compounds.

$$\left[R\!-\!M \longleftrightarrow R^- \; M^+ \right] \equiv \overset{\delta-}{R}\!-\!\overset{\delta+}{M}$$

The degree of covalency of such carbon-metal bonds depends markedly on the metal and is related to the metal's **electronegativity**. Electronegativity is a measure of the ability of an element to attract or to hold onto electrons. Linus Pauling has established a semiquantitative scale in which each element is assigned an electronegativity value. On this scale a larger number signifies a greater affinity for electrons. When two elements of differing electronegativity are bonded, the bond is polar with the "center of gravity" of electron density in the bond closer to the more electronegative element. The greater the difference in electronegativity, the more polar is the bond. Pauling electronegativities for some of the elements are listed in Table 8.6.

Note that, in Table 8.6, carbon is assigned an electronegativity of 2.5, a value midway between the extremes. Fluorine, the most electronegative element, has a value of 4.1, and the alkali metals, the most electropositive elements, have values of 1 or less. Thus, the bond in lithium fluoride is virtually completely ionic. That is, the two bonding electrons are associated almost solely with F^-, and the lithium-fluorine bond is almost totally electrostatic. We have already discussed the polarity of the carbon-fluorine bond, which is understood in terms of the difference in electronegativity between carbon (2.5) and fluorine (4.1). The electron density in the carbon-fluorine bond concentrates towards fluorine.

Because lithium is so much less electronegative than carbon, we expect the electrons in the carbon-lithium bond to be polarized towards carbon. The concept of relative electronegativity is thus useful for understanding the relative polarities of different bonds. But the argument is oversimplified because the electronic structure of bonds depends not just on relative electronegativities but also on the effectiveness of orbital overlap. The valence orbitals of the alkali metals are highly diffuse and their overlap with other orbitals is generally ineffective. For example, the difference between the electronegativities of lithium and carbon, 1.5, is the same as that between carbon and

TABLE 8.6 Electronegativity Values for Some Elements

IA	IIA	IB	IIB	IIIA	IVA	VA	VIA	VIIB
H 2.2								
Li 1.0	Be 1.5			B 2.0	C 2,5	N 3.1	O 3.5	F 4.1
Na 0.9	Mg 1.2			Al 1.5	Si 1.7	P 2.1	S 2.4	Cl 2.8
K 0.8	Ca 1.0	Cu 1.9	Zn 1.6	Ga 1.8	Ge 2.0	As 2.2	Se 2.5	Br 2.7
		Ag 1.9	Cd 1.7	In 1.5	Sn 1.7	Sb 1.8	Te 2.0	I 2.2
Cs 0.7			Hg 1.9	Tl 2.0	Pb 1.6	Bi 1.7		

fluorine. Both bonds are polar but the lithium-carbon bond is almost as ionic as the lithium-fluorine bond, whereas the carbon-fluorine bond is a strong covalent bond. Organometallic compounds of the alkali metals may be regarded simply as essentially ionic salts of the alkali metal cation and an organic anion called a **carbanion.**

The ionic character of alkyllithium, alkylsodium, and alkylpotassium compounds is manifest in their structures. Methylpotassium displays almost classic salt-like behavior. Its crystal structure is similar to that of NaCl; each potassium ion is symmetrically surrounded by six methyl anions and vice versa. Alkyllithium compounds generally form aggregates of tetramers, hexamers, and so on, that are usually soluble in organic solvents, even hydrocarbons. Some such aggregates have appreciable volatility. These aggregates can be thought of as ionic clusters with a hydrocarbon-like exterior.

With the less electropositive metals, such as Be, Mg, B, and Al, the carbon-metal bonds are polar but still partially covalent. The metals in these compounds generally do not have an inert gas configuration. This electron deficiency has several structural consequences. For example, **three-center two-electron** bonds are encountered commonly. An example is trimethylaluminum, which exists as a dimer in which two aluminum atoms are bridged by two methyl groups (Figure 8.3a). The three-center bond may be thought of as arising by the mutual overlap of an orbital from each aluminum with an sp^3-orbital of carbon (Figure 8.3b). In this way both aluminum atoms achieve an octet electronic configuration. Structural symbols such as Figure 8.3a are in common use but can be confusing because they do not correspond to a Lewis structure in which each line represents two electrons. An alternative symbolism has been suggested, shown in Figure 8.3c, in which $\bot$ represents a three-center two-electron bond.

Beryllium compounds are frequently highly toxic and are not important in organic chemistry. Magnesium compounds are particularly important. Dialkylmagnesium compounds exist as polymeric structures in the solid phase or in hydrocarbon solvents (Figure 8.4a). Note how bridging three-center two-electron bonds accomplish electron octets around each magnesium in the polymer. These compounds are usually soluble in ether solvents because the monomeric dialkylmagnesium compounds are coordinated to two ether oxygens (Figure 8.4b). In these structures the availability of oxygen lone pairs obviates the need for three-center two-electron bonds to provide octets for the magnesium. Such coordination is usually represented with a dative bond as shown in Figure 8.4b.

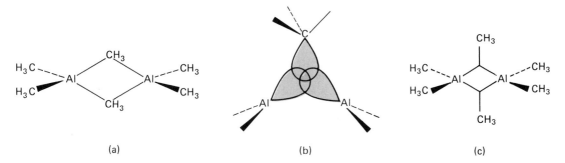

(a)   (b)   (c)

FIGURE 8.3 (*a*) Trimethylaluminum dimer. (*b*) Three orbitals overlap to give a molecular orbital containing two electrons. (*c*) Structure showing the $\bot$ symbol for a three-center two-electron bond.

150

Chap. 8

*Alkyl Halides
and
Organometallic
Compounds*

(a) (b)

FIGURE 8.4 (a) Dialkylmagnesium polymer. (b) Dialkylmagnesium coordinated to two ether molecules. Note the use of arrows to show the dative or coordinative "donor" bonds.

EXERCISE 8.4 Write a Lewis structure for dimethylmagnesium coordinated to two molecules of dimethyl ether, $(CH_3)_2O$. Include all electrons and formal charges and compare with the structure using dative bonds.

Alkylmagnesium halides, also known as **Grignard reagents**, are important organometallic compounds that have many uses in synthesis. In dilute ether solution (about 0.1 M), Grignard reagents exist as monomers in which the magnesium is coordinated to two solvent molecules; their structures are similar to that of dialkylmagnesium (Figure 8.4b). However, in more concentrated solution (0.5–1 M) the principal species is a dimer in which two magnesium atoms are bridged by two bromines (Figure 8.5). In this structure each magnesium acquires its octet by additional coordination with one bromine from the other RMgBr and an ether oxygen. The bridging bonds in this structure make effective use of the additional lone-pair electrons available on the halogen. Note that the bridging bromines are *not* involved in three-center two-electron bonds because each magnesium-bromine bond involves a separate pair of electrons.

Because of the high ionic character of these carbon-metal bonds they generally react avidly with water and other compounds containing relatively acidic hydrogens. The reaction is essentially an acid-base reaction with the proton being transferred to the carbanion, a strong base. Recall that methane ($pK_a \cong 50$), for example, is a much weaker acid than water, and its conjugate base, methide ion, is a much stronger base than hydroxide ion.

$$H_3C\colon^- \ Li^+ \ + \ H_2O \ \rightleftharpoons \ H_3C{-}H \ + \ Li^+ \ OH^-$$
$$pK_a = 16.7 \qquad\qquad pK_a \cong 50$$

In compounds of metals in groups IV and V (Si, Ge, Sn, Pb, Sb, Bi), there are sufficient electrons for the metals to engage in normal covalent bonding. Furthermore, since these metals tend to be much nearer to carbon in electronegativity than metals of groups I-III, the carbon-metal bonds are not very polar. These organometallic compounds tend to resemble conventional organic compounds in their properties. For example, tetramethylsilane and tetramethyllead are similar in structure to neopentane. The metal in each case has tetrahedral geometry (sp^3-hybridization) and makes covalent bonds to the four methyl groups.

tetramethylsilicon
(tetramethylsilane)
b.p. 26.5°C

tetramethyllead
b.p. 110°C

FIGURE 8.5 Methylmagnesium bromide dimer in ether.

Trimethylantimony and trimethylbismuth have pyramidal structures in which the metal has an unshared electron pair, similar to that in ammonia (page 24).

trimethylantimony
b.p. 80.6°C

trimethylbismuth
b.p. 110°C

8.7 Physical Properties of Organometallic Compounds

The melting points and boiling points of some simple organometallic compounds are summarized in Table 8.7. If sufficient caution is exercised, many organometallics may be prepared and handled in the same manner as other organic compounds. However, as we have seen, many types of organometallics react vigorously with water or other protic compounds; they also react with oxygen. Consequently, care must be taken in performing such operations as distillation and recrystallization.

Many of the organometallic compounds in Table 8.7 decompose in water, but they are soluble in various inert aprotic organic solvents. Typical solvents are ethers and

TABLE 8.7 Physical Properties of Organometallic Compounds

Compound	Melting Point, °C	Boiling Point, °C
CH_3CH_2Li	95	subl. 95 (aggregated)
$(CH_3)_2Mg$	240	(probably polymeric)
$(CH_3)_3Al$	0	130
CH_3AlCl_2	73	97–100 (100 torr)
$(CH_3)_2Cd$	−4.5	106
$(CH_3)_2Hg$	—	96
CH_3CH_2HgCl	193	subl. 40
$(CH_3)_3Ga$	−19	56
$(CH_3)_3Te$	38.5	147
$(CH_3)_4Si$	—	26.5
$(CH_3)_4Ge$	−88	43
$(CH_3)_4Sn$	−55	78
$(CH_3)_4Pb$	−27.5	110

152

Chap. 8

*Alkyl Halides
and
Organometallic
Compounds*

alkanes. Because of their solubility in convenient organic solvents and their extreme reactivity, a number of the organometallic compounds used in organic syntheses are normally not purified but are prepared and used in such solutions without isolation.

8.8 Preparation of Organometallic Compounds

A. Reaction of an Alkyl Halide with a Metal

Reaction of the metal with an alkyl halide is most generally used for the laboratory preparation of organolithium and organomagnesium compounds. The reaction is normally carried out by treating the metal with an ether or hydrocarbon solution of the alkyl halide.

$$\underset{\underset{CH_3}{|}}{\overset{\overset{CH_3}{|}}{CH_3CCl}} + Mg \xrightarrow{\text{ether}} \underset{\underset{CH_3}{|}}{\overset{\overset{CH_3}{|}}{CH_3CMgCl}}$$

A solution of 227 g of *t*-butyl chloride in 1300 mL of dry ether is stirred in contact with 61 g of magnesium turnings for 6-8 hr. A cloudy gray solution is obtained that is approximately 2 *M* in *t*-butylmagnesium chloride. This solution is used directly for further reactions.

This type of reaction is an example of a heterogeneous reaction—a reaction that occurs at the interface between two different phases. The alkyl halide in solution must react with magnesium on the surface of solid magnesium. In such reactions the surface area and its character are important. In the preparation of Grignard reagents, the magnesium is usually in the form of metal shavings or turnings. The reaction mechanism consists of the following steps.

$$R\!-\!X + \overset{\wr}{\underset{\wr}{Mg}} \longrightarrow R\cdot + X\!-\!\overset{\wr}{\underset{\wr}{Mg}}$$

$$R\cdot + X\!-\!\overset{\wr}{\underset{\wr}{Mg}} \longrightarrow R\!-\!Mg\!-\!X$$

Reaction of RX at the magnesium surface produces an alkyl radical and a Mg-X species probably still associated with the metal surface. The resulting free radical, R·, then reacts with the ·MgX to produce the Grignard reagent, RMgX. The principal side reactions involve alternative reactions of organic radicals, mostly dimerization and disproportionation (page 96).

$$CH_3CH_2CH_2CH_2\cdot + CH_3CH_2CH_2CH_2\cdot \longrightarrow CH_3CH_2CH_2CH_2CH_2CH_2CH_2CH_3$$
$$CH_3CH_2CH_2CH_2\cdot + CH_3CH_2CH_2CH_2\cdot \longrightarrow CH_3CH_2CH_2CH_3 + CH_3CH_2CH\!=\!CH_2$$

However, for simple alkyl halides the yields of alkylmagnesium halide are high—frequently above 90%. The reaction works well with chlorides, bromides, and iodides. Reaction of alkyl chlorides is frequently somewhat sluggish and iodides are generally expensive. Hence, alkyl bromides are common laboratory reagents in Grignard syntheses.

A suitable solvent is essential for formation of the Grignard reagent because of the necessity for solvating the magnesium, as discussed in Section 8.6. The reaction is commonly carried out by adding an ether solution of the alkyl halide to magnesium turnings stirred in ether. The reaction is exothermic, particularly with bromides and iodides, and a reflux condenser is provided for returning the boiling ether. Anhydrous conditions must be maintained throughout the reaction, since Grignard reagents react rapidly with traces of moisture.

Alkyllithium compounds are prepared in the same manner.

$$CH_3CH_2CH_2CH_2Br + 2Li \xrightarrow{\text{ether}} CH_3CH_2CH_2CH_2Li + LiBr$$

A solution of 68.5 g of *n*-butyl bromide in 300 mL of dry ether is added slowly to 8.6 g of lithium wire. The mixture is stirred at $-10°C$ for about 1 hr, during which time all of the lithium dissolves. The resulting ether solution of *n*-butyllithium is stored under nitrogen in a well-stoppered flask.

The reaction of alkyl halides with lithium is probably similar to that with magnesium; that is, alkyl radicals are probably produced at the surface of the lithium metal and react further with the metal surface.

Although many other organometallic compounds may be prepared by direct reaction of the metal with an alkyl halide (for example, C_2H_5ZnI, CH_3HgCl), a more convenient and general laboratory method is metal exchange with an organolithium or organomagnesium compound (next section).

EXERCISE 8.5   Write the structure and name of each organometallic compound derived from reaction of (a) methyl iodide, (b) cyclohexyl bromide, and (c) 2-chloro-2-methylbutane with magnesium and with lithium.

B. Reaction of Organometallic Compounds with Salts

One of the most useful methods for preparing organometallic compounds in the laboratory is the exchange reaction of one organometallic with a salt to give a new organometallic and a new salt.

$$RM + M'X \rightleftharpoons RM' + MX \qquad (8\text{-}1)$$

This is an equilibrium process, and the equilibrium constant is dominated by the relative electronegativity (or electropositivity) of the two metals. In general, the halide ion is more electronegative than carbon and tends to be associated with the cation of the more electropositive metal. Recall that the more electropositive elements are those that are down and to the left in the periodic table. For example, Grignard reagents react readily with cadmium chloride to give organocadmium compounds and magnesium chloride. Magnesium is to the left of cadmium in the periodic table and is more electropositive [electronegativities are 1.2 and 1.7, respectively (Table 8.6)].

$$2 CH_3CH_2MgCl + CdCl_2 \xrightarrow{\text{ether}} (CH_3CH_2)_2Cd + 2 MgCl_2$$

In a similar way, Grignard reagents may be used to prepare tetraalkylsilanes and dialkylmercury compounds.

$$4 CH_3MgCl + SiCl_4 \longrightarrow (CH_3)_4Si + 4 MgCl_2$$

154

Chap. 8

Alkyl Halides
and
Organometallic
Compounds

$$2\ CH_3CH_2\overset{\overset{\displaystyle CH_3}{|}}{C}HMgCl + HgCl_2 \longrightarrow (CH_3CH_2\overset{\overset{\displaystyle CH_3}{|}}{C}H)_2Hg + 2\ MgCl_2$$

EXERCISE 8.6 From inspection of a periodic table of the elements, and Table 8.6, predict the direction of each of the following equilibria:
(a) $2\ (CH_3)_3Al + 3\ ZnCl_2 \rightleftharpoons 3\ (CH_3)_2Zn + 2\ AlCl_3$
(b) $2\ (CH_3)_2Hg + SiCl_4 \rightleftharpoons (CH_3)_4Si + 2\ HgCl_2$
(c) $(CH_3)_2Mg + CaBr_2 \rightleftharpoons (CH_3)_2Ca + MgBr_2$

8.9 Reactions of Organometallic Compounds

A. Hydrolysis

Organometallic compounds in which the metal has an electronegativity value of about 1.7 or less (Table 8.6) react with water to give the hydrocarbon and a metal hydroxide. The more electropositive the metal is, the faster is the hydrolysis. As mentioned earlier, alkyllithium, alkylmagnesium, and alkylaluminum compounds react violently with water.

$$CH_3Li + H_2O \longrightarrow CH_4 + LiOH$$
$$CH_3CH_2MgBr + H_2O \longrightarrow CH_3CH_3 + HOMgBr$$
$$(CH_3)_3Al + 3\ H_2O \longrightarrow 3\ CH_4 + Al(OH)_3$$

Such compounds react similarly with other hydroxylic compounds, such as alcohols and carboxylic acids.

$$CH_3-\overset{\overset{\displaystyle CH_3}{|}}{\underset{\underset{\displaystyle CH_3}{|}}{C}}-Li + CH_3OH \longrightarrow CH_3\overset{\overset{\displaystyle CH_3}{|}}{C}HCH_3 + CH_3O^- Li^+$$

They also react with other compounds having relatively acidic hydrogens, such as thiols and amines.

Since the product of hydrolysis is an alkane, hydrolysis is not a very useful preparative reaction. However, it is important to recognize the limitation that this ready hydrolysis puts on the use of such organometallic compounds for other purposes. For example, it is not possible to prepare a Grignard reagent from an alkyl halide that also has an acidic hydrogen in the molecule, such as $ClCH_2CH_2CH_2OH$.

One important use for such hydrolysis reactions is **specific deuteriation**. When one carries out the hydrolysis with heavy water, deuterium oxide, the product is an alkane containing a deuterium at the position formerly occupied by the metal.

$$CH_3CH_2\overset{\overset{\displaystyle CH_3}{|}}{\underset{\underset{\displaystyle MgBr}{|}}{C}}CH_3 + D_2O \longrightarrow CH_3CH_2\overset{\overset{\displaystyle CH_3}{|}}{\underset{\underset{\displaystyle D}{|}}{C}}CH_3 + DOMgBr$$

2-methylbutane-*2-d*

The nomenclature used for isotopically labeled compounds is implied in this example. The use of *-d* for deuterium and *-t* for tritium is common although more generally the isotope is specified by the atomic symbol and a prefix superscript giving the atomic mass of the isotope; for example, our labeled compound may also be named as 2-methylbutane-2-^2H. Finally, deuterium may be specified by a prefix as in 2-deuterio-2-methylbutane.

Heavy water is readily available, and this reaction is an excellent way of making hydrocarbons "labeled" with deuterium in a specific position. After reaction, the magnesium salts are removed, and the ether solution of the labeled hydrocarbon is dried and distilled. In subsequent chapters we will see several examples of the use of labeled compounds in studies of reaction mechanisms.

Alkylzinc and alkylcadmium compounds also react with protic materials, but their reactions are not so vigorous. Compounds of silicon, tin, mercury, and lead are unaffected by water, but in acidic solution they also undergo hydrolysis.

$$(C_2H_5)_4Si + 4\,HCl \xrightarrow{\;H_2O\;} 4\,CH_3CH_3 + SiCl_4$$

EXERCISE 8.7 Suggest how each of the following deuterated compounds can be prepared from a hydrocarbon.
(a) cyclohexane-*d*
(b) 2-methylpropane-*2-d*
(c) 1-deuterio-2,2-dimethylpropane

B. Reaction with Halogens

Most organometallic reagents react vigorously with chlorine and bromine.

$$RM + Cl_2 \longrightarrow RCl + M^+\,Cl^-$$

The reaction is not preparatively useful because the product is an alkyl halide and organometallic compounds are frequently derived from alkyl halides.

C. Reaction with Oxygen

Organic compounds of many metals react rapidly with oxygen. Some are so reactive that they spontaneously inflame in air, often with spectacular consequences.

Alkylboranes burn with a brilliant green flame. In his graduate student days, one of the authors was briefly immersed in a sea of such green fire. Only the wearing of safety glasses and rapid reflexes of a lab partner with a fire extinguisher allowed the current textbook to come to fruition.

Because of this reactivity, it is common to carry out organometallic reactions under an inert atmosphere such as nitrogen or argon. Oxidation is a side reaction of Grignard reactions run in the presence of air. In refluxing diethyl ether, a common solvent for Grignard syntheses, the ether vapor forms a suitable "blanket" of inert atmosphere.

These few reactions do little more than hint at the great versatility and usefulness of organometallic compounds in organic synthesis but we will encounter many more examples as we study the chemistry of individual functional groups.

156

Chap. 8

Alkyl Halides
and
Organometallic
Compounds

PROBLEMS

1. Write structures and IUPAC names for all structural isomers corresponding to each of the following formulas.

    (a) C_3H_7Cl (b) C_4H_9Br (c) $C_5H_{11}I$

    (d) $C_5H_{14}Sn$ (e) $C_4H_{10}Mg$ (f) C_4H_9Li

2. Write Newman projections for the conformations of 1,1,2-trichloroethane. Two of these are the same, and the third is different. The two types of conformation differ in energy by 2.6 kcal mole^{-1} in the vapor phase. Which is the more stable? This energy difference reduces to 0.2 kcal mole^{-1} in the liquid. Explain why. Interconversion of the two similar conformations requires about 2 kcal mole^{-1}, but conversion of either to the third structure requires about 5 kcal mole^{-1}. Explain why these two rotation barriers differ.

3. Show how the following conversions may be accomplished.

    (a) $(CH_3)_3CCH(CH_3)_2 \longrightarrow (CH_3)_3CCD(CH_3)_2$

    (b) $CH_3CH_2CHClCH_3 \longrightarrow \left(CH_3CH_2\overset{\overset{\displaystyle CH_3}{|}}{C}H \right)_4 Sn$

    (c) $(CH_3)_3CCH_2Cl \longrightarrow (CH_3)_3CCH_2Br$

    (d) $CH_3CH_2Cl \longrightarrow (CH_3CH_2)_2Cd$

    (e) $(CH_3)_3CCl \longrightarrow [(CH_3)_3C]_2Hg$

4. Predict whether the equilibrium constant will be greater than or less than unity for each of the following reactions.

    (a) $2 (CH_3)_3Al + 3 CdCl_2 \rightleftharpoons 3 (CH_3)_2Cd + 2 AlCl_3$

    (b) $(CH_3)_2Hg + ZnCl_2 \rightleftharpoons (CH_3)_2Zn + HgCl_2$

    (c) $2 (CH_3)_2Mg + SiCl_4 \rightleftharpoons (CH_3)_4Si + 2 MgCl_2$

    (d) $CH_3Li + HCl \rightleftharpoons CH_4 + LiCl$

    (e) $(CH_3)_2Zn + 2 LiCl \rightleftharpoons 2 CH_3Li + ZnCl_2$

5. (a) Dimethylberyllium has a polymeric structure analogous to that described for dimethylmagnesium in Figure 8.4a. By contrast, di-t-butylberyllium is monomeric. Suggest a reason for the difference and predict the geometry of di-t-butylberyllium.

    (b) Dimethylmercury is monomeric. Predict its geometry. The measured dipole moments of $(CH_3)_2Hg$ and $(C_2H_5)_2Hg$ are $\mu = 0.0$ D. Explain.

6. Trimethylborane reacts with methyllithium to give a product having the formula $C_4H_{12}BLi$. Propose a structure for this substance. What is the hybridization of boron? Describe the geometry of the species.

7. Write the structures of the eight compounds having the formula $C_5H_{11}D$. Which two of these isomers can be prepared in good yield from alkanes using reactions you have learned in the last two chapters? Explain why the other six isomers cannot be prepared in this way.

8. In the formation of Grignard reagents from magnesium and alkyl halides, the most frequent side reactions are dimerization and disproportionation.

Propose a mechanism for these side reactions.

Chapter 9

Nucleophilic Substitution

9.1 The Displacement Reaction

The replacement of the halogen in an alkyl halide by another group is one of the most important reactions in organic chemistry. In Section 4.2, we took a brief look at one such reaction, the reaction of methyl chloride with hydroxide ion.

$$HO^- + CH_3Cl \xrightarrow{H_2O} CH_3OH + Cl^-$$

We learned that this reaction is effectively irreversible and is a rather slow reaction at room temperature. By raising the temperature the reaction rate is increased.

Another example is the reaction of ethyl bromide with potassium iodide in acetone solution.

$$CH_3CH_2Br + K^+ I^- \xrightarrow{acetone} CH_3CH_2I + KBr\downarrow$$

In this case the reaction is reversible; that is, the equilibrium constant is not a large number. Nevertheless, the reaction proceeds virtually to completion because potassium iodide is soluble in acetone and potassium bromide is not.

The foregoing reactions are but two of a large number of closely related reactions that have in common the replacement of one Lewis base by another. Recall that a Lewis base has a lone pair of electrons available for bonding. We shall first look at reactions in which the *leaving group* is a halide ion but we shall see later that these reactions are not limited to alkyl halides. Many Lewis bases qualify as suitable *incoming groups* in such reactions. Some additional examples are summarized in Table 9.1.

Many of the examples given in Table 9.1 involve anions as incoming groups. Some of these anions are rather strong bases; that is, they are the conjugate bases of weak acids. Examples are hydroxide ion, HO^-, and ethoxide ion, $C_2H_5O^-$. Others, such as cyanide ion, CN^-, azide ion, N_3^-, and acetate ion, $CH_3CO_2^-$, are the conjugate bases of moderately strong acids and are weaker bases than hydroxide ion. Halide ions are the weak conjugate bases of rather strong mineral acids, the hydrohalic acids, such as HCl and HI. When used in displacement reactions, such bases are referred to as **nucleophilic reagents** or simply as **nucleophiles** (L., *nucleus*, kernel; Gr., *philos*, loving; hence "nucleus loving"). The reaction is then also called a **nucleophilic displacement reaction**.

A number of the nucleophiles listed in Table 9.1 are neutral molecules. The reaction of trimethylphosphine with ethyl bromide may be written

$$(CH_3)_3 P\!:\; + \quad CH_2\!-\!Br \longrightarrow (CH_3)_3 \overset{+}{P}CH_2CH_3\; Br^-$$
$$\hspace{3.5cm} CH_3$$

The phosphorus in the phosphine has a lone pair of electrons that bonds to the methylene group in the product. Thus, trimethylphosphine is a neutral nucleophilic reagent.

157

TABLE 9.1 Some Displacement Reactions with Ethyl Bromide

Attacking Reagent		Product	
Formula	Name	Formula	Name
HO^-	hydroxide ion	C_2H_5OH	ethyl alcohol
$C_2H_5O^-$	ethoxide ion	$CH_3CH_2OCH_2CH_3$	diethyl ether
HS^-	hydrosulfide ion	CH_3CH_2SH	ethanethiol
SCN^-	thiocyanate ion	CH_3CH_2SCN	ethyl thiocyanate
CN^-	cyanide ion	CH_3CH_2CN	ethyl cyanide propionitrile
N_3^-	azide ion	$CH_3CH_2N_3$	ethyl azide
NH_3	ammonia	$CH_3CH_2NH_3^+\ Br^-$	ethylammonium bromide
H_2O	water	$CH_3CH_2OH_2^+\ Br^-$	ethyloxonium bromide
$CH_3CO_2^-$	acetate ion	$CH_3CO_2C_2H_5$	ethyl acetate
NO_3^-	nitrate ion	$CH_3CH_2ONO_2$	ethyl nitrate
$P(CH_3)_3$	trimethylphosphine	$C_2H_5P(CH_3)_3^+\ Br^-$	ethyltrimethyl-phosphonium bromide
$N(C_2H_5)_3$	triethylamine	$(C_2H_5)_4N^+\ Br^-$	tetraethylammonium bromide
$S(C_2H_5)_2$	diethyl sulfide	$(C_2H_5)_3S^+\ Br^-$	triethylsulfonium bromide

> **EXERCISE 9.1** Give the structure and name of the product of the displacement reaction of each of the nucleophiles in Table 9.1 with methyl iodide. For each case, identify the lone-pair electrons that bond to carbon in the product.

9.2 Mechanism of the Displacement Reaction

Two important tools in studying the mechanism of a reaction are the **reaction kinetics** and **stereochemistry**. The reaction kinetics can reveal the *composition* of the rate-determining transition state, and stereochemical studies with chiral molecules help to determine its *structure*. We will demonstrate the application of these tools to the displacement reaction of alkyl halides with acetate ion. The reaction of methyl iodide with lithium acetate in methanol solution produces methyl acetate and is effectively irreversible. The reactants and products are all soluble in the alcohol; hence, this is a *homogeneous* reaction.

$$CH_3CO_2^- + CH_3{-}I \longrightarrow CH_3\overset{\overset{\displaystyle O}{\|}}{C}{-}OCH_3 + I^-$$

The condensed formula given for acetate ion, $CH_3CO_2^-$, is a shorthand for the two resonance structures that show that the negative charge in acetate ion is divided between the two oxygens (pages 12 and 64):

$$CH_3CO_2^- \equiv CH_3\overset{\overset{\displaystyle O}{\|}}{C}{-}O^- \longleftrightarrow CH_3\overset{\overset{\displaystyle O^-}{|}}{C}{=}O$$

The rate of the reaction may be determined by following the rate of disappearance of reactants or the rate of formation of products. It is proportional to the product of the concentrations of the two reactants.

$$\text{rate} = -\frac{d[CH_3I]}{dt} = -\frac{d[CH_3CO_2{}^-]}{dt} = \frac{d[CH_3CO_2CH_3]}{dt} = \frac{d[I^-]}{dt}$$

$$= k[CH_3I][CH_3CO_2{}^-]$$

This equation is expressed in the symbolism of calculus. The expression

$$-\frac{d[CH_3I]}{dt}$$

means simply the rate with which the concentration of CH_3I changes with time. The negative sign indicates that the concentration of CH_3I decreases as time increases.

The concentrations of $CH_3CO_2CH_3$ and LiI may be determined at different times during the reaction by chemical or spectroscopic analysis. As the reaction proceeds, the concentrations of the reactants become reduced and the rate of reaction decreases. For example, at 60°C, with the two reactants each present in an initial concentration of 0.1 M, the reaction is 50% complete in 20 hr but only 90% complete after 180 hr. Furthermore, the reaction has an activation energy, $\Delta H^{\ddagger}$, of 24 kcal mole^{-1}; it is about 80 times faster at 60°C than it is at 25°C. This activation energy is considerably higher than those of the free radical reactions we studied in Chapter 6.

When the rate of a chemical reaction depends on the concentration of two species, as in this case, it is said to display **second-order kinetics**. Both components are present in the rate-determining transition state. This suggests a **bimolecular** mechanism, one in which one molecule of each reactant collide and react. The relatively high activation energy shows that only a minute fraction of such collisions actually result in reaction—those involving reactant molecules with sufficient kinetic energy.

The **molecularity** of a reaction is defined as the number of reactant molecules involved in the rate-determining transition state. It is sometimes, but not always, equal to the kinetic order of the reaction. For example, consider a reaction of the type

$$A + B \underset{\substack{k_{-1} \\ \text{fast}}}{\overset{k_1}{\rightleftharpoons}} C \xrightarrow[\text{slow}]{k_2} D$$

The rate of appearance of the product D is given by the rate law

$$\begin{matrix}\text{rate of} \\ \text{formation of D}\end{matrix} = \frac{d[D]}{dt} = \frac{k_1 k_2}{k_{-1}}[A][B] = k'[A][B]$$

which shows second-order kinetics. However, in the slow step (k_2), the rate-determining step, only one molecule, species C, is involved. Hence, the reaction is unimolecular.

The **stereochemistry of reaction** refers to the relative configurations of the leaving group and entering group bonded to a stereocenter in the reactant and product, respectively. This stereochemistry cannot be determined for methyl iodide because it is not chiral. But many such reactions have been carried out with optically active compounds in which the leaving group has been bonded to the stereocenter. These experiments have shown that in such displacement reactions every replacement of the leaving group by the incoming group occurs with *inversion of configuration*. For example, the reaction of (R)-2-bromobutane with acetate ion produces (S)-2-butyl acetate.

This example poses the problem of relating the configurations of the reactant and product. Remember that there is no necessary relation between the sign of rotation and the structural configuration. We will not discuss the specific example shown here, but in subsequent studies of different functional groups we will encounter many similar examples where such configurations have been interrelated. One such example is given at the end of this chapter.

EXERCISE 9.2 For each of the following displacement reactions write the structure of the product with inversion of configuration.

(a) (S)-$CH_3CH_2CH_2CHDCl$ + $CH_3CO_2^-$

(b)

+ $P(CH_3)_3$

(c)

+ CN^-

Consideration of the second order reaction kinetics and the stereochemistry of the reaction leads to a mechanism in which the entering nucleophilic reagent attacks the carbon atom at the rear of the bond to the leaving group. During reaction, the carbon forms a progressively stronger bond to the attacking group, while the bond to the leaving group is being weakened. During this change, the other three bonds to the central carbon progressively flatten out and end up on the other side of the carbon in a manner similar to the spokes of an umbrella inverting in a windstorm.

The foregoing equation illustrates the use of a curved arrow as a symbol for the flow of electrons in the course of the reaction. This symbolism finds much use in organic chemistry. An electron pair is thought of as originating at the end of an arrow and flowing in the direction of the point. In this case, a pair of electrons belonging to acetate ion flows toward the bromine-bearing carbon and eventually forms a new carbon-oxygen bond. Simultaneously, the pair of electrons comprising the carbon-bromine bond flows away from carbon and eventually ends up as a fourth lone pair on the product bromide ion. The transition state is shown in brackets. The dotted lines indicate a partially formed or partially broken bond. The symbols δ^- indicate that the negative charge is spread over both entering and leaving groups in the transition state. Using curved arrows, the entire reaction can be symbolized as follows with the transition state being implied.

EXERCISE 9.3 For each of the reactions in Exercise 9.2, write Lewis structures showing the electrons around the reacting carbon and use curved arrows to show the electron flow corresponding to the displacement reaction.

During the course of the reaction, the reacting system has greater potential energy than either the reactants or the products. The two weak bonds to the entering and leaving groups are weaker than the single bond in either the reactant or the product. Hence, energy is required in order for reaction to occur. The necessary potential energy is supplied by the conversion of kinetic energy. Only the minute fraction of reactants that have sufficient kinetic energy can react. Furthermore, even if the colliding reactants have sufficient kinetic energy, they must have the proper orientation or they will simply bounce apart. It is important to remember that the transition state is a point of maximum energy. It is not a discrete molecule that can be isolated and studied. In fact, the whole act of displacement occurs in the space of about 10^{-12} sec, the period of a single vibration, so the system has the transition-state geometry for only a fleeting moment.

This reaction mechanism may be generalized. The general reaction is called an S_N2 reaction for **substitution, nucleophilic, bimolecular**. The geometry of the transition state appears to be that in which the incoming and leaving groups are both weakly bonded to carbon in a linear fashion and in which the three remaining bonds to carbon lie in a plane perpendicular to the two weak bonds. The mechanism for reaction of an entering group Y^- and a leaving group X^- is shown in Figure 9.1, where the structure of the reacting system is illustrated at several points along the reaction coordinate. At

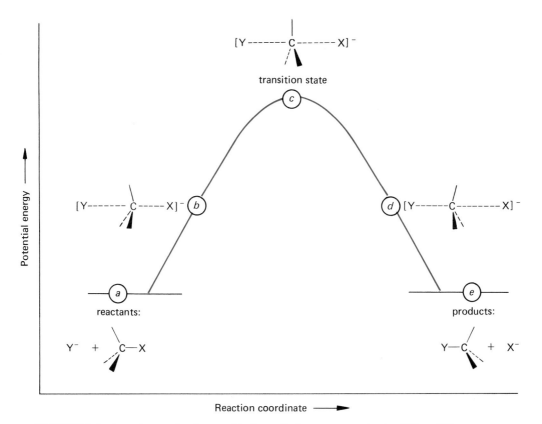

FIGURE 9.1 Reaction mechanism profile for a displacement reaction by Y^- on RX.

point (b) the C-X bond has started to lengthen and the central carbon has started to flatten out. At the transition state, point (c), the central carbon is approximately flat and both bonds to the leaving and entering groups are long. Point (d) occurs on the final road to products (e); the central carbon has bent, the C-Y bond is approaching normal length, and the leaving group X is receding. The structures at points (a) through (e) are represented in stereo form in Figure 9.2.

The reaction can also be followed by changes in orbitals. Both reactant and product are tetrahedral and the central carbon has sp^3-hybrid orbitals. As reaction occurs, the orbital to the leaving halide has greater p-character and the three remaining bonds to the central carbon develop greater s-character. In the transition state structure, the weak bonds to X and Y may be considered to derive from overlap of their orbitals with the two lobes of a p-orbital on the central carbon. The other three bonds to this carbon are formed from sp^2-hybrid orbitals, as shown in Figure 9.3.

Table 9.1 shows that the mechanism label S_N2 covers a wide variety of specific reactions. All of these reactions are bimolecular and occur with inversion of configura-

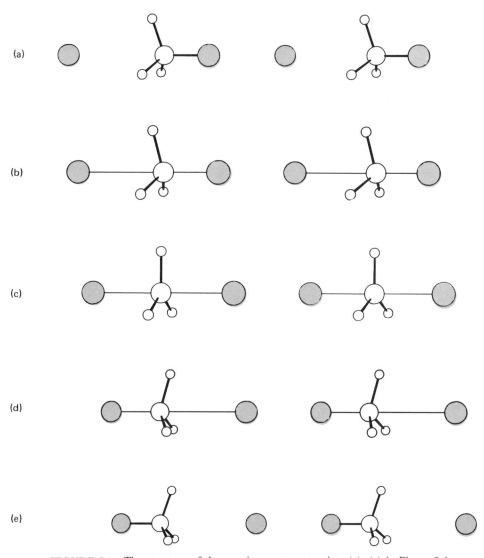

FIGURE 9.2 The structure of the reaction system at points (a)–(e) in Figure 9.1.

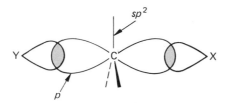

FIGURE 9.3 Orbital formulation of the transition state of a displacement reaction.

tion at the reacting carbon. In such reactions we need to be concerned not only with the position of equilibrium but with rate. The reactions can range from incredibly fast at low temperatures to painfully slow even at higher temperatures, depending on the nature of the alkyl group, the nucleophile, the solvent, and the leaving group. We shall discuss each of these variables in turn. The important principles that enter into evaluating the effects of these variables recur frequently in organic chemistry and therefore warrant careful study at this time. Moreover, we shall see how a knowledge of transition state structure helps to rationalize a large body of diverse facts.

> **EXERCISE 9.4** Displacement reactions can be carried out in which the entering and leaving groups are the same. Consider the reaction of *cis*-1-iodo-4-methylcyclohexane with iodide ion in acetone. What is the product of this displacement reaction? What is the composition of the mixture when equilibrium is reached (note Table 7.1, page 131)?

9.3 Effect of Alkyl Structure on Displacement Reactions

A large variety of alkyl halides undergo substitution by the S_N2 mechanism. The ease of reaction depends markedly upon the structure of the alkyl group to which the halogen is attached. Reactivities vary widely and in a consistent manner. Branching of the chain at the carbon where substitution occurs (the α-carbon) has a significant effect on the rate of reaction. Relative rates of S_N2 reactions for methyl, ethyl, isopropyl, and *t*-butyl halides are approximately as shown in Table 9.2.

> This use of the Greek alphabet is widespread in organic chemistry, and it is important to learn the first few letters, at least through delta (the entire Greek alphabet is given inside the front cover of this book). Many of the letters, small and capital, have evolved standard meanings in the mathematical and physical sciences (for example, the number π). In organic chemistry, the lowercase letters are used more frequently than the capital letters.

TABLE 9.2 Effect of Branching at the α-Carbon on the Rate of S_N2 Reactions

Alkyl Halide	Relative Rate
CH_3—	30
CH_3CH_2—	1
$(CH_3)_2CH$—	0.02
$(CH_3)_3C$—	~0

FIGURE 9.4 Effect of α-branching on S_N2 reactions.

These effects on reaction rate are interpreted with the concept of **steric hindrance** to attack of the attacking nucleophile. The rear of a methyl group is relatively open to such attack, and methyl compounds are generally quite reactive in displacement reactions. As the hydrogens of the methyl group are replaced successively by methyl groups, the area in the rear of the leaving group becomes more encumbered. It becomes more difficult for the attacking group to approach closely enough to the rear of the C—X bond for reaction to occur, and the rate of reaction diminishes (Figure 9.4).

A similar effect may be seen in branching at the β-carbon. Some typical relative rates are shown in Table 9.3. This reduction in rate is also attributable to steric hindrance. In one conformation, the rear of a *n*-propyl carbon is seriously blocked (Figure 9.5a), but in two other conformations the situation is no worse than for ethyl (Figure 9.5b). Consequently, *n*-propyl halides undergo S_N2 displacement only slightly less readily than do ethyl halides.

For the isobutyl group, it is possible to rotate both of the β-methyl groups out of the way of the attacking group, but the resulting conformation is highly congested and has relatively high energy (Figure 9.6). Accordingly, isobutyl halides are much less reactive than either ethyl or *n*-propyl compounds.

TABLE 9.3 **Effect of Branching at the β-Carbon on the Rate of S_N2 Reactions**

Alkyl Halide	Relative Rate
CH_3CH_2-	1
$CH_3CH_2CH_2-$	0.4
$(CH_3)_2CHCH_2-$	0.03
$(CH_3)_3CCH_2-$	0.00001

165

Sec. 9.3

*Effect of Alkyl
Structure on
Displacement
Reactions*

FIGURE 9.5 S_N2 attack at two conformations of *n*-propyl compounds.

Neopentyl halides are particularly interesting because there is no conformation in which a blocking methyl group can be avoided (Figure 9.7). Neopentyl halides are unreactive in S_N2 reactions except under very drastic conditions.

Substitution of sites more remote than the β-carbon has little or no effect on the ease of S_N2 reactions. For example, *n*-butyl and *n*-pentyl halides react at essentially the same rate as *n*-propyl halides.

The type of steric interaction we have discussed here forces groups to bend away from each other. Such deformation often forces orbitals to overlap in a noncolinear fashion. Recall that the resulting bent bonds are weaker than the corresponding straight bonds (Section 5.6).

In summary, the effect of the structure of the alkyl group on the rate of S_N2 reaction is apparent in two ways.

1. **Branching at the α-carbon hinders reaction: rate order is methyl > primary > secondary > tertiary.**
2. **Branching at the β-carbon hinders reaction: neopentyl compounds are particularly unreactive.**

Displacements that proceed by the S_N2 mechanism are most successful with primary compounds having no branches at the β-carbon. Yields are poor to fair with secondary halides and with primary halides having branches at C-2. Neopentyl systems undergo the reaction only under very drastic conditions, and tertiary halides rarely react by this mechanism. When the rate of the S_N2 reaction is slowed down by these structural

FIGURE 9.6 S_N2 reaction at isobutyl systems.

FIGURE 9.7 S_N2 reaction at neopentyl compounds.

effects, alternative side reactions begin to compete. With tertiary halides, and to an important degree with secondary and highly branched primary halides, the side reactions tend to dominate. The most important of these side reactions is *elimination* to form alkenes. This reaction will be discussed in Sections 9.6 and 11.5.

EXERCISE 9.5 For each of the following pairs of alkyl groups indicate which member is the more reactive in S_N2 reactions.

(a)

(b)

(c)

(d)

9.4 Nucleophilicity and Solvent Effects

A. Solvent Properties

The solvent plays an important role in determining the rate of a displacement reaction. For example, the reaction of acetate ion with methyl iodide that we examined earlier is over ten million times faster in dimethylformamide than in methanol.

$$(CH_3)_2NCHO$$

dimethylformamide (DMF)

In this section we will study some of the factors that give rise to such large rate variations.

Nucleophilic displacement reactions involve ions either as nucleophiles or as products. For this reason relatively polar solvents are required. A polar solvent is one having a relatively high dipole moment and dielectric constant.

The dielectric constant of a substance is the factor by which an electrostatic interaction in a vacuum is reduced by a medium of the substance. Coulomb's law for the electrostatic interaction of two charges, q_1 and q_2, separated by a distance r in a medium of dielectric constant D is given as

$$E = \frac{q_1 q_2}{Dr}$$

As the dielectric constant is reduced, the electrostatic interactions between ions increases and they combine together to form ion pairs and insoluble crystals.

$$M^+ + X^- \rightleftharpoons M^+ \ X^- \rightleftharpoons (M^+X^-)$$
$$\text{ion pair} \qquad \text{crystal}$$

Ion pairs are relatively unreactive in S_N2 reactions.

Polar solvents orient around ions such that their dipole moments provide electrostatic attraction to both anions and cations.

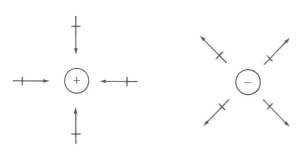

This attraction of ions and dipoles is one of the microscopic mechanisms that leads to the macroscopic property of a high dielectric constant.

Examples of compounds that are important as solvents in displacement reactions are summarized in Table 9.4. It is convenient to consider them in two categories: *hydroxylic* (water, alcohols) and *polar aprotic* (acetonitrile, dimethylformamide, dimethyl sulfoxide, acetone). Hydroxylic solvents have hydroxy groups that can hydrogen bond with anions. Polar aprotic solvents are polar solvents that have no hydroxy groups.

The pronounced effects of solvent with different nucleophiles are exemplified by the data in Table 9.5. This table gives the free energies of activation for reaction of many of the nucleophiles in Table 9.5 with methyl iodide at 25°C in dimethylformamide, a representative polar aprotic solvent, and in methanol, a representative hydroxylic solvent. The two solvents have about the same dielectric constant but much different rate effects. The relative reactivity of a nucleophile is referred to as its *nucleophilicity*. The representative data in Table 9.5 show that nucleophilicity (the tendency to react with carbon) is not the same as basicity (the tendency to react with a proton) and that nucleophilicity is sensitive to solvent.

TABLE 9.4 Properties of Solvents

	Boiling Point °C	Dipole Moment μ, D (g)	Dielectric Constant ϵ (25°C)
water, H_2O	100	1.85	78.5
methanol, CH_3OH	65	1.70	32.6
ethanol, CH_3CH_2OH	78.5	1.69	24.3
acetonitrile, CH_3CN	81.6	3.92	36.2
dimethylformamide, DMF, $HCON(CH_3)_2$	153	3.82	36.7
dimethyl sulfoxide, DMSO, CH_3SOCH_3	189	3.96	49
acetone, CH_3COCH_3	56.5	2.88	20.7
hexamethylphosphoric triamide, HMPT, $[(CH_3)_2N]_3PO$	232	4.30[a]	30

[a] In solution.

TABLE 9.5 Free Energies of
Activation for Reaction of
Nucleophiles with Methyl Iodide
at 25°C in Methanol and in
Dimethylformamide (DMF)

Nucleophile	DMF	CH_3OH
CN^-	14.0	21.8
$CH_3CO_2^-$	15.7	25.1
NO_2^-	16.8	22.5
N_3^-	16.8	23.0
Cl^-	16.9	25.0
Br^-	17.3	23.0
SCN^-	19.0	22.0
I^-	20.9	18.0
$(CH_3)_2S$	21.8	23.6

To put the numbers in this table in practical perspective, note that a value of $\Delta G^{\ddagger}$ of 22.5 kcal mole^{-1} corresponds to a reaction having a half-life of approximately 1 hr with a reagent concentration of 1 M. Recall also that a change of 1.4 kcal mole^{-1} corresponds approximately to a factor of ten in rate.

B. Polar Aprotic Solvents

As summarized in Table 9.5, many anions are satisfactory nucleophiles in polar aprotic solvents. The list includes nucleophiles that are somewhat basic (cyanide ion, acetate ion) as well as the conjugate bases of strong acids (halide ions). The reactivity depends primarily on the standard free energy—the thermodynamic driving force—of reaction. That is, in these solvents the more exothermic the reaction, the more readily it occurs. Figure 9.8 is a general reaction profile for these reactions.

As in the case of the free-radical reactions we have already studied, one important component of the driving force is the bond strength of the new bond formed compared to that of the carbon-halogen bond being broken. Thus, groups in which the nucleophilic center is a first row atom (O, N) tend to be more reactive. Among halide ions, the reactivity order is $Cl^- > Br^- > I^-$. Since we are now dealing with charge changes, another important component is the relative electron affinity of the nucleophile compared to the leaving group. The more readily a group can give up an electron, the greater is its nucleophilicity and the more facile is its reaction. A factor that stabilizes an anion would be expected generally to reduce the rate of reaction.

C. Hydroxylic Solvents

A glance at Table 9.5 shows that nucleophiles are generally much less reactive in methanol than in dimethylformamide, usually by several powers of ten. The reason for this difference is that hydroxylic solvents solvate an ion by hydrogen bonding. Hydrogen bonding is especially important for small anions with concentrated charges. The transition state behaves as a much larger ion that is less stabilized by hydrogen bonding. Thus, nucleophiles that are solvated by hydrogen bonding must weaken these bonds during the course of reaction and are consequently less reactive.

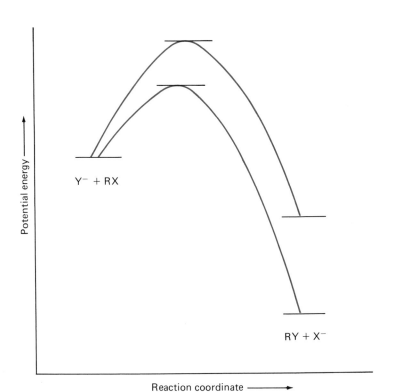

FIGURE 9.8 S_N2 reactions in polar aprotic solvents: the greater the driving force, the faster the reaction.

hydrogen-bond solvation
more important for smaller atoms
(C, N, O, F)

much larger ion
hydrogen-bond solvation less important

The effect is particularly important for first-row ions—ions with negative charge on N, O, and F. This effect leads to large reactivity changes between hydroxylic and polar aprotic solvents. Acetate ion, which is highly nucleophilic in dimethylformamide, is relatively much less reactive in methanol. The reactivity order for halide ions is the reverse of that in dimethylformamide; in methanol the order is now $I^- > Br^- > Cl^-$. The smaller chloride ion is more hydrogen bonded in methanol than are the larger halide ions; this factor is more important in hydroxylic solvents than is the greater carbon-chlorine bond strength compared to carbon-bromine and carbon-iodine. In general, nucleophiles with second row and larger atoms are less hydrogen bonded in hydroxylic solvents and are relatively more nucleophilic compared to polar aprotic solvents. Compare, for example, the relative nucleophilicities of thiocyanate ion (SCN^-) in methanol and in dimethylformamide (Table 9.5).

EXERCISE 9.6 Table 9.5 lists nucleophiles in order of decreasing reactivity in dimethylformamide. Rewrite the table in order of decreasing reactivity in methanol.

Despite the generally lesser reactivity in hydroxylic solvents, methanol and ethanol are still important solvents for carrying out displacement reactions. The reason is simply that they are inexpensive, relatively inert, and dissolve many organic substrates and inorganic salts. Sometimes some water is added to increase the solubility of the inorganic salt used as the displacing agent.

$$CH_3O^- + CH_3CH_2CH_2CH_2Br \xrightarrow{CH_3OH} CH_3CH_2CH_2CH_2OCH_3 + Br^-$$

> *n*-Butyl bromide is refluxed with sodium methoxide in methanol for $\frac{1}{2}$ hr. Water is added, and the organic layer is separated, dried, and distilled to give methyl *n*-butyl ether.

$$Na^+SCN^- + CH_3\overset{\overset{\displaystyle Br}{|}}{C}HCH_3 \xrightarrow[H_2O]{C_2H_5OH} CH_3\overset{\overset{\displaystyle SCN}{|}}{C}HCH_3 + Na^+Br^-$$

> Isopropyl bromide and sodium thiocyanate (NaSCN) are refluxed in 90% aqueous ethanol for 6 hr. The precipitated sodium bromide is filtered. The filtrate is diluted with water and extracted with ether. Distillation gives isopropyl thiocyanate, $(CH_3)_2CHSCN$, in 76-79% yield.

In summarizing the effect of structure on nucleophilicity the following generalizations are useful. Nucleophiles with second row and larger atoms at the nucleophilic center tend to have useful reactivity. Nucleophiles with first row atoms at the nucleophilic center tend to be relatively more nucleophilic in polar aprotic solvents but less so in hydroxylic solvents. When the attacking atom remains the same, stronger bases are also more nucleophilic. For example, methoxide ion is a stronger base than acetate ion and is generally also more reactive in S_N2 reactions.

EXERCISE 9.7 The average $\Delta G^{\ddagger}$ in Table 9.5 is 20 kcal mole^{-1}, which corresponds to $\log k = -2$ or $k = 1 \times 10^{-2}$ M^{-1} sec^{-1}. Consider the reaction of 0.1 *M* methyl iodide with 1 *M* nucleophile having this rate constant. How long would it take to achieve 99.9% reaction (10 half-lives)? Note that under these conditions the nucleophile concentration changes only from 1 *M* to 0.9 *M* and the reaction becomes pseudo-first order.

D. Ambient Nucleophiles

Halide ions, acetate ion, and many other nucleophiles can react at only one atom in the system either as bases or as nucleophiles. Similarly, sulfate ion is straightforward in its reaction with either H^+ or CH_3I in an S_N2 reaction. Both types of reaction occur at an oxygen

sulfate ion

bisulfate ion

methyl sulfate ion

Sulfite ion, however, behaves quite differently. In hydroxylic solvents it reacts with a proton mainly on oxygen to form bisulfite ion and with methyl iodide on sulfur to form the methanesulfonate ion.

$$HO-\overset{\overset{\displaystyle O^-}{|}}{\underset{\displaystyle \cdot\cdot}{S^+}}-O^-$$

bisulfite ion

$$^-O-\overset{\overset{\displaystyle O^-}{|}}{\underset{\displaystyle \cdot\cdot}{S^+}}-O^-$$

sulfite ion

$$^-O-\overset{\overset{\displaystyle O^-}{|}}{\underset{\underset{\displaystyle CH_3}{|}}{S^{2+}}}-O^-$$

methanesulfonate ion

The oxygen in sulfite ion is the more basic atom and prefers to attack H^+, but the oxygens are also solvated by hydrogen bonding. The lone pair on sulfur is the more nucleophilic center and it has preference in the S_N2 transition state. Sulfate ion has no lone pair on sulfur, and both reactions have no alternative but to occur at the oxygen. Thiosulfate ion is a simple sulfur analog of sulfate. This ion reacts with methyl iodide exclusively on sulfur, even though there are three oxygens and only one sulfur.

$$^-S-\overset{\overset{\displaystyle O^-}{|}}{\underset{\underset{\displaystyle O_-}{|}}{S^{2+}}}-O^- + CH_3I \longrightarrow CH_3S-\overset{\overset{\displaystyle O^-}{|}}{\underset{\underset{\displaystyle O_-}{|}}{S^{2+}}}-O^- + I^-$$

thiosulfate ion   methylthiosulfate ion

Finally, there are some nucleophiles that show measurable nucleophilic properties at two different atoms. Nitrite ion is an example. The ion undergoes protonation exclusively on oxygen to give nitrous acid.

$$\left[^-O-\ddot{N}=O \longleftrightarrow O=\ddot{N}-O^- \right] \overset{H^+}{\longrightarrow} HO-\ddot{N}=O$$

nitrite ion   nitrous acid

However, the reaction of nitrite ion with methyl iodide gives both methyl nitrite and nitromethane.

$$CH_3O-\ddot{N}=O$$

methyl nitrite

$$^-O-\ddot{N}=O + CH_3I$$

$$\left[CH_3-\overset{+}{N}\overset{\nearrow O}{\underset{\searrow O^-}{}} \longleftrightarrow CH_3-\overset{+}{N}\overset{\nearrow O^-}{\underset{\searrow O}{}} \right]$$

nitromethane

In this case both nitrogen and oxygen are first-row elements and have comparable nucleophilicities. The ratio of the products actually depends on the reaction conditions. Another example is the reaction of methyl iodide with cyanide ion. In addition to methyl cyanide, the major product, small amounts of methyl isocyanide are also produced.

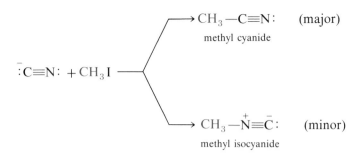

Anions such as these, which can react at two different positions, are called ambident (L., *ambo*, both; *dentis*, tooth), "two-fanged" nucleophiles.

EXERCISE 9.8 The sodium salt of methylsulfinic acid reacts with methyl iodide in methanol to give a mixture of two isomeric products. What are the structures of these two products?

$$CH_3\overset{\overset{\displaystyle O}{\|}}{\underset{..}{S}}-OH \xrightarrow{\text{NaOH}} \xrightarrow{\text{CH}_3\text{I}} \textbf{A} \ (C_2H_6SO_2) + \textbf{B} \ (C_2H_6SO_2)$$

9.5 Leaving Groups

Alkyl chlorides, bromides, and iodides all react satisfactorily by the S_N2 mechanism. The ease of reaction is dependent on the nature of the leaving group, alkyl iodides reacting most rapidly and alkyl chlorides most slowly. Alkyl fluorides are essentially unreactive by the S_N2 mechanism. Since chlorine is much cheaper than bromine, alkyl chlorides are the least expensive alkyl halides. However, for laboratory uses where only small amounts of material are involved, alkyl bromides are commonly used because they are 50-100 times more reactive than the corresponding chlorides. Iodides are somewhat more reactive than bromides but are quite a bit more expensive, and this slightly increased reactivity does not justify their additional cost. In industrial processes, where massive amounts of materials are involved and cost is a prime consideration, alkyl chlorides are used almost exclusively.

The S_N2 reaction is not restricted to alkyl halides. Any group that is the conjugate base of a strong acid can act as a leaving group. An example is bisulfate ion, HSO_4^-, which is the conjugate base of sulfuric acid, pK_a −5. Dimethyl sulfate is an inexpensive commercial compound, and reacts readily by the S_N2 mechanism. The leaving group is the methyl sulfate ion, which is similar in its base strength to bisulfate ion.

$$CH_3CH_2CH_2O^- + CH_3O-\overset{\overset{\displaystyle O^-}{|}}{\underset{\underset{\displaystyle O^-}{|}}{S^{2+}}}-OCH_3 \longrightarrow CH_3CH_2CH_2OCH_3 + {}^-O-\overset{\overset{\displaystyle O^-}{|}}{\underset{\underset{\displaystyle O^-}{|}}{S^{2+}}}-OCH_3$$

methyl sulfate ion

The chief disadvantage of dimethyl sulfate is its toxicity. It is water soluble and reacts readily with the nucleophilic groups in body tissues and fluids. Although dimethyl sulfate is the only sulfate in common use, alkyl sulfonates are often employed. Sulfonic acids, RSO_2OH, are similar to sulfuric acid in acidity, and the sulfonate ion, RSO_3^-, is an excellent leaving group. Alkyl benzenesulfonates, alkyl *p*-toluesulfonates, and alkyl methanesulfonates are extremely useful substrates for S_N2 reactions. These compounds are readily prepared from alcohols as described in Sections 10.6.B and 25.5).

methyl
benzenesulfonate

ethyl
p-toluenesulfonate

methyl
methanesulfonate

One instructive example of the use of such sulfonates in studying reaction mechanisms is shown by the following sequence of reactions involving chiral compounds and compounds enriched with the oxygen isotope ^{18}O. The butyl alcohol enriched with ^{18}O as shown can be converted to the acetate without loss of the oxygen isotope, which shows that the carbon-oxygen bond has not been broken in the process. Under these conditions the optically active (+)-alcohol is converted to acetate also having (+) optical rotation. Since the carbon-oxygen bond remains intact during this reaction, whatever the configuration the (+) alcohol has at the stereocenter must be the same configuration in the (+) acetate. Similarly, the formation of the sulfonate ester as shown also proceeds with retention of the configuration at the stereocenter. When the sulfonate is treated with acetate ion in a displacement reaction, the acetate formed has lost the ^{18}O label; that is, the old carbon-oxygen bond was broken in order to form the new bond to an oxygen of the acetate. This reaction produces acetate having an optical rotation opposite that of acetate produced directly from the alcohol. The displacement reaction must have proceeded with complete inversion of configuration. Many experiments of this type were used to form the generalization discussed above in Section 9.2 that S_N2 reactions occur with inversion of configuration.

The facility with which a group can function as a leaving group in an S_N2 reaction may be gauged approximately by its basicity. If a group is a weak base (that is, the conjugate base of a strong acid), it will generally be a "good" leaving group. This is readily understood on recalling that the leaving group L gains electron density in going from the reactant to the transition state.

The more this electron density or negative charge is stabilized, the lower is the energy of the transition state and the faster is the rate of reaction. The degree to which a group can accommodate a negative charge is also related to its affinity for a proton, its basicity. The acids HCl, HBr, HI, and H_2SO_4 are all strong acids because the anions Cl^-, Br^-, I^-, and HSO_4^- are stable anions. These anions are also good leaving groups in S_N2 reactions.

Hydrocyanic acid (HCN) is a weak acid ($pK_a = 10$) and the displacement of cyanide is never observed.

$$N:^- + RCN \longrightarrow\!\!\!/\!\!\!\longrightarrow R-N + CN^-$$

Hydrazoic acid (HN_3) and acetic acid (CH_3CO_2H) are also weak acids (pK_as of 5.8 and 4.8, respectively). Correspondingly, azide ion and acetate ion are poor leaving groups.

$$N:^- + R-N_3 \longrightarrow\!\!\!/\!\!\!\longrightarrow RN + N_3^-$$

$$N:^- + R-\overset{\overset{\textstyle O}{\|}}{O}CH_3 \longrightarrow\!\!\!/\!\!\!\longrightarrow RN + CH_3CO_2^-$$

The reason that alkyl fluorides are ineffective substrates in S_N2 reactions is related to the relatively low acidity of HF ($pK_a = 3$).

EXERCISE 9.9 Write out the complete displacement reactions of trimethylamine, $(CH_3)_3N$, with (a) $CH_3SO_2OCH_3$ and (b) $(CH_3)_3S^+$. Use curved arrows to show the electronic changes involved.

9.6 Elimination Reactions

One of the side reactions that occurs in varying degrees in displacement reactions is the elimination of the elements of HX to produce an alkene.

$$B:^- \overset{\frown}{} H-\overset{|}{\underset{|}{C}}\overset{\curvearrowright}{}\overset{|}{\underset{|}{C}}-X \longrightarrow BH + \overset{\diagdown}{}C=C\overset{\diagup}{} + X^-$$

Under appropriate conditions, this reaction can be the principal reaction and becomes a method for preparing alkenes. Accordingly, it is discussed in more detail in Section 11.5.A. For the present, it suffices to know that this reaction occurs by attack of a base on a hydrogen with concomitant formation of a carbon-carbon double bond and breaking of the carbon-halogen bond to form halide ion.

Mechanistically, the reaction is classified as **bimolecular elimination**, or **E2**. Since attack on a proton is involved, it is the basicity, rather than the nucleophilicity, of the Lewis base that is important. Strongly basic species such as alkoxide or hydroxide ions favor elimination; highly nucleophilic species such as second- and third-row elements favor substitution. For example, the S_N2 and E2 reactions of 3-bromo-2-methylbutane with chloride ion in acetone occur at about equal rates.

With acetate ion, however, elimination is about 8 times faster than substitution.

The structure of the substrate compound is also important in determining the substitution/elimination ratio. Straight-chain primary compounds show little tendency toward elimination because the alternative S_N2 reaction is relatively rapid. For example, ethyl bromide reacts with N_3^-, Cl^-, or $CH_3CO_2^-$ in acetone to give only substitution products. Even the strong base sodium ethoxide in ethanol gives virtually none of the elimination product. However, with more highly branched compounds, the S_N2 reaction is slower, and attack at hydrogen can compete more favorably. Consequently, larger amounts of the elimination product are obtained. Some data are presented in Table 9.6 for the reactions of various alkyl halides with acetate ion in acetone.

Note the resulting generalizations that elimination by-products are quite minor with simple primary halides, but with branching at either the α- or β-carbon, the alkene elimination products become increasingly important. The behavior of tertiary halides is more complex. Since they undergo S_N2 reactions so very slowly, one would expect that tertiary halides would give complete elimination, even with weak bases. However, tertiary halides can undergo substitution by another mechanism (next section). Consequently, the elmination/substitution ratio for tertiary halides is highly dependent on reaction conditions. In general, they give mainly the elimination products, especially under conditions that favor the bimolecular mechanism (high concentrations of strong base).

The distinction between *nucleophilicity* and *basicity* helps us to understand some of the chemistry of organo-alkali metal compounds. We would normally expect that carbanions generated as the alkali metal salts of hydrocarbons (Section 8.6) would be excellent nucleophiles. But they are also very strong bases. Alkylsodium and -potassium compounds do react with straight chain halides to give higher alkanes—this is probably the reaction that occurs when alkyl halides are allowed to react with sodium or potassium metals.

$$2 \ CH_3CH_2CH_2Br + 2 \ Na \longrightarrow CH_3CH_2CH_2CH_2CH_2CH_3 + 2 \ NaBr$$

The initially formed carbanion salt displaces halide from a molecule of alkyl halide that has not yet reacted.

$$CH_3CH_2CH_2Br + 2 \ Na \longrightarrow CH_3CH_2CH_2:^- Na^+ + NaBr$$
$$CH_3CH_2CH_2:^- + CH_3CH_2CH_2Br \longrightarrow CH_3CH_2CH_2CH_2CH_2CH_3 + Br^-$$

TABLE 9.6 Substitution and Elimination with Acetate Ion

$$R-Br + CH_3CO_2^- \xrightarrow{acetone} R-\overset{\overset{\displaystyle O}{\|}}{O}CCH_3 + Br^-$$

RBr	Percent Substitution	Percent Elimination
CH_3CH_2Br	100	0
$(CH_3)_2CHBr$	100	0
$(CH_3)_2CHCHBrCH_3$	11	89
$(CH_3)_3CBr$	0	100

The reaction is limited in its usefulness. Branched chain systems generally give largely or entirely elimination.

EXERCISE 9.10   In each of the following pairs of reactions which gives more of the elimination product?

(a) I^- + ([structure with Cl] or [structure with Cl])

(b) $(CH_3CO_2^-$ or $CH_3CH_2O^-)$ + [structure with Cl]

(c) [structure] $^- Na^+$ + ([structure with Cl] or [structure with Cl])

(d) ([structure with Cl] or [structure with Cl]) + CN^-

9.7 S$_N$1 Reactions: Carbocations

Ethyl bromide reacts rapidly with ethoxide ion in refluxing ethanol (78°C); reaction is complete after a few minutes. If ethyl bromide is refluxed in ethanol not containing any added sodium ethoxide, S$_N$2 displacement still occurs, but the reaction is exceedingly slow. After refluxing for 4 days, the reaction is only 50% complete. This reactivity difference is due to the fact that the negatively charged ethoxide ion is much more nucleophilic than the neutral ethanol molecule. On an equal concentration basis, ethoxide ion is more than 10,000 times more reactive than ethanol itself. In general, anions are much more basic and nucleophilic than their conjugate acids.

$$CH_3O^- > CH_3OH$$

$$CH_3S^- > CH_3SH$$

$$CH_3CO_2^- > CH_3COOH$$

$$SO_3^{2-} > HSO_3^-$$

We saw earlier that tertiary alkyl halides rarely react by the S$_N$2 mechanism. Yet *t*-butyl bromide reacts quite rapidly in pure ethanol; in refluxing ethanol the half-life for reaction is only a few minutes! Various observations show that this reaction does not proceed by an S$_N$2 displacement even though the principal product is ethyl *t*-butyl ether, $(CH_3)_3COCH_2CH_3$. For example, the addition of ethoxide ion to an ethanol solution of ethyl bromide causes a large increase in the rate of reaction. The rate law for the reaction of ethyl bromide is

$$\text{rate} = k_1[C_2H_5Br] + k_2[C_2H_5Br][C_2H_5O^-]$$

The first term represents the reaction of ethyl bromide with neutral ethanol; because ethanol is the solvent and its concentration remains virtually unchanged, its concentration does not appear in the rate equation. The second term represents the reaction of ethyl bromide with ethoxide ion. For ethyl bromide, as we saw above, the reaction with ethoxide is much faster than the reaction with ethanol, that is, $k_2 \gg k_1$. Since k_1 is so small relative to k_2, the rate expression is approximately

$$\text{rate} = k_2[C_2H_5Br][C_2H_5O^-]$$

The rate of reaction of t-butyl bromide (t-BuBr) is given by a similar equation.

$$\text{rate} = k_1[t\text{-BuBr}] + k_2[t\text{-BuBr}][C_2H_5O^-]$$

Here, however, the second term is unimportant; $k_1 \gg k_2$. Addition of sodium ethoxide has no effect on the rate of reaction. Therefore, in this case the rate is effectively

$$\text{rate} = k_1[t\text{-BuBr}]$$

This is true only for small concentrations of sodium ethoxide. High concentrations of strong base lead to formation of alkene by a competing elimination reaction (Section 9.6).

This change in kinetic behavior is indicative of a change in mechanism. With the tertiary alkyl halide, the rear of the molecule is effectively blocked and the $S_N 2$ mechanism cannot operate. However, a competing mechanism is possible. A great deal of experimental work over the past several decades has established that this mechanism involves two steps. In the first step, ionization of the carbon-bromine bond occurs and an intermediate **carbocation** is produced. The carbocation then reacts rapidly with solvent or whatever nucleophiles are around.

(1) $\underset{\underset{CH_3}{|}}{\overset{\overset{CH_3}{|}}{CH_3C}}Br \underset{}{\overset{slow}{\rightleftharpoons}} \underset{\underset{CH_3}{|}}{\overset{\overset{CH_3}{|}}{CH_3C^+}} + Br^-$

(2) $\underset{\underset{CH_3}{|}}{\overset{\overset{CH_3}{|}}{CH_3C^+}} + C_2H_5OH \overset{fast}{\longrightarrow} \underset{\underset{CH_3}{|}\ H}{\overset{\overset{CH_3}{|}}{CH_3C}}\overset{+}{O}CH_2CH_3 \longrightarrow \underset{\underset{CH_3}{|}}{\overset{\overset{CH_3}{|}}{CH_3C}}OCH_2CH_3 + H^+$

When a compound reacts with the solvent, as is the case here, the process is called a **solvolysis reaction**. This solvolysis reaction is classified mechanistically as **unimolecular nucleophilic substitution** or $S_N 1$ because only one species is involved in the rate-limiting step. A reaction coordinate diagram for the reaction is shown in Figure 9.9. In the intermediate carbocation, the central carbon has only a sextet of electrons (compare with the Lewis structure of methyl cation, Section 2.2). In orbital terms, the ion is best described in terms of a central sp^2-hybridized carbon with an empty p-orbital (Figure 9.10).

We have already encountered *carbanions* (Section 8.6). The terms *carbocation* and *carbanion* are generic names for organic cations R^+ and anions R^-, respectively. For many years the term *carbonium ion* was used as a generic name for organic cations having an electron-deficient carbon with a sextet of electrons. The term carbonium ion has been considered to be nonsystematic because comparable oxonium ions (for example, H_3O^+)

and ammonium ions (NH_4^+) have electron octets; the term *carbenium ion* has been suggested instead, but is not yet in common use. To avoid confusion, we will frequently use the term carbocation as a generic name for organic cations with positive formal charge on carbon, but specific ions will be referred to as alkyl cations (methyl cation, *t*-butyl cation, etc.).

Note that alkyl cations are planar; the central carbon and its three attached atoms all lie in one plane. The structure is favored because it places the three groups as far apart from one another as possible and allows the carbocation to achieve the strongest bonds and lowest energy. This electronic structure can also be understood on the basis that electrons in a 2*s*-orbital are more stable than electrons in a 2*p*-orbital. By using the *s*-orbital to form three sp^2-hybrid orbitals, it is involved most effectively in bonding; the remaining 2*p*-orbital is left vacant.

It is important to point out that cations are highly reactive reaction intermediates. They have only a short, but finite, lifetime in solution. Under normal conditions they cannot be observed directly in the reaction mixture because they react almost as soon as they are produced. However, carbocations vary widely in stability with structure. The enthalpies for ionization of various alkyl halides *in the gas phase* are summarized in Table 9.7. Note that ethyl cation is more stable than methyl cation, but *n*-propyl and *n*-butyl cations are of similar stability. These systems may be described as *primary carbocations*, RCH_2^+. Isopropyl cation is an example of a *secondary carbocation*, R_2CH^+, and *t*-butyl cation is a *tertiary carbocation*.

CH_3^+ methyl cation
$CH_3CH_2^+$ ethyl cation, a *primary carbocation*
$(CH_3)_2CH^+$ isopropyl cation, a *secondary carbocation*
$(CH_3)_3C^+$ *t*-butyl cation, a *tertiary carbocation*

Table 9.7 shows that the relative stabilities of various cations are

$$\text{tertiary} > \text{secondary} > \text{primary} > \text{methyl}$$

FIGURE 9.9   Reaction coordinate diagram for the solvolysis of *t*-butyl bromide.

FIGURE 9.10   The *t*-butyl cation.

Note that the difference in the ionization energy between methyl chloride and *t*-butyl chloride is 76 kcal mole^{-1} in the gas phase. In solution, the ions are solvated and ionization is facilitated. Consequently, the $\Delta H°$ for ionization is much lower than given in Table 9.7. Thus, the energy required to ionize *t*-butyl chloride in hydroxylic solvents is low enough that reaction proceeds at normal rates. Tertiary alkyl cations are rather common intermediates in organic reactions. Secondary alkyl cations are considerably less stable and much more difficult to produce, but they do occur as intermediates in some reactions. Primary alkyl cations are so much less stable that they virtually never occur as reaction intermediates in solution. These generalizations may be summarized as follows.

Alkyl Group	Occurrence of Carbocation Intermediates in Solution	Occurrence of S$_N$2 Displacement Reactions
tertiary	common	rare
secondary	sometimes	sometimes
primary	rare	common
methyl	never	common

The order of stabilities of carbocations is in large part to be attributed to the greater polarizability of alkyl groups compared to hydrogen. Another factor is an interesting aspect of overlapping orbitals. Consider the methyl cation, CH_3^+. The carbon-hydrogen bonds in methyl cation lie in the nodal plane of the vacant $2p_z$-orbital and hence cannot overlap with it. In the ethyl cation, $CH_3CH_2^+$, there can be some overlap between this empty orbital and one of the bonds of the methyl group (Figure 9.11). This type of overlap is readily shown by quantum mechanical calculations. It has the effect of stabilizing the ion because electron density from an adjacent bond can "spill over" into the empty orbital. This results in spreading the positive charge over a larger

**TABLE 9.7 Enthalpy for Ionization
of Alkyl Chlorides in the Gas Phase**

$$RCl \longrightarrow R^+ + Cl^-$$

R	$\Delta H°$, kcal mole^{-1}
CH_3	229
CH_3CH_2	190
$CH_3CH_2CH_2$	193
$CH_3CH_2CH_2CH_2$	193
$(CH_3)_2CH$	168
$(CH_3)_3C$	153

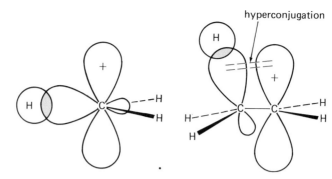

FIGURE 9.11   Overlap of a carbon-hydrogen bond orbital with the empty *p*-orbital of a carbocation.

volume. We shall see frequently that ions with concentrated charge are less stable and more reactive than ions in which the charge is spread over a greater volume. As more alkyl groups are attached to the cationic carbon, it becomes even more stable.

The interaction of a bond orbital with a *p*-orbital as shown in Figure 9.11 is referred to as *hyperconjugation*. Its relationship to *conjugation* will become apparent when we get to Chapter 20.

The relative stabilities of carbocations can be understood on the basis of simple electrostatics. Electrons are attracted to nuclei and are repelled by other electrons. The electrons in a bond repel each other, but they are prevented from getting too far apart because of their attraction to the two nuclei in the bonded atoms. When there is an adjacent atom with a vacant orbital available for overlap and a positive charge, the original bonding pair of electrons can reduce their mutual repulsion by getting farther apart; they can do this and still maintain the stability of being associated with a positive nucleus. Electron repulsion is decreased in such a carbocation and it is convenient to describe the result in terms of a spreading out of positive charge.

The first step of the S_N1 reaction is an ionization process, that involves separation of charge.

$$R-X \longrightarrow R^+ \; X^-$$

Accordingly, the reaction is highly sensitive to solvent effects. The reaction is rapid in aqueous and hydroxylic solvents and slow in nonpolar solvents.

The solvolysis reaction of tertiary alkyl halides is only in part an S_N1 reaction. The intermediate carbocation can react rapidly in several alternative ways. Two of these reaction paths are

1. Reaction with any nucleophiles present (the S_N1 process)
2. Elimination of a proton (the El process).

These reactions are illustrated by the behavior of *t*-butyl bromide in ethanol at 25°C. The solvolysis product, ethyl *t*-butyl ether, is produced along with a significant amount of the elimination product, an alkene.

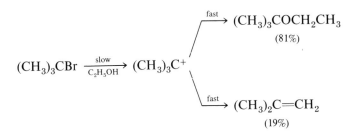

In a mixed solvent, the carbocation can react with both components in addition to eliminating a proton. For example, in a mixture of 80% ethanol and 20% water, *t*-butyl bromide gives three products.

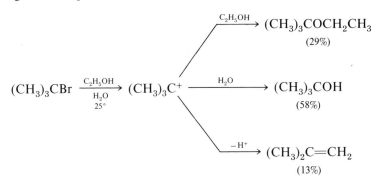

Because product mixtures are so frequently obtained, solvolysis reactions are generally not important synthetic methods. Such reactions have been studied in great detail over the past several decades, but primarily for the purpose of evaluating the properties and relative stabilities of carbocations.

EXERCISE 9.11 When cyclopentyl chloride is refluxed with a solution of sodium thiocyanate in methanol the principal product is cyclopentyl thiocyanate. Under the same conditions, however, 1-chloro-1-methylcyclopentane gives principally 1-methoxy-1-methylcyclopentane. Explain.

9.8 Ring Systems

Cyclic systems provide some special features in substitution reactions of alkyl halides. For example, the reaction of amines with alkyl halides is a typical S_N2 reaction (Section 23.6.A).

$$RCH_2NH_2 + R'CH_2Br \longrightarrow RCH_2\overset{+}{N}H_2CH_2R' + Br^-$$

When both functional groups are present in the same molecule, the reaction is an **intramolecular** S_N2 reaction, which creates a ring. Ring formation necessarily has been initiated at the transition state; hence, the relative energies of transition states depend on the ring size. Relative rates for reactions of ω-bromoalkylamines, $Br(CH_2)_{n-1}NH_2$, are given in Table 9.8.

Omega, ω, is the last letter of the Greek alphabet and its use conveniently designates substituents at the end of the alkyl chain, as in the forgoing example.

**TABLE 9.8 Relative Rates of
Cyclization of Aminoalkyl Halides**

$$Br(CH_2)_{n-1}NH_2 \longrightarrow (CH_2)_{n-1}NH_2{}^+ \, Br^-$$

n (Ring Size)	Relative Rate
3	0.1
4	0.002
5	100
6	1.7
7	0.03
10	10^{-8}
12	10^{-5}
14	3×10^{-4}
15	3×10^{-4}
17	6×10^{-4}

1-Amino-4-bromobutane, which gives a five-membered ring, is the most reactive compound, followed by 1-amino-5-bromopentane, which gives a six-membered ring. We see that the stability of the ring is not the only factor—the probability that the ends can get together is also important. The three-membered ring, for example, has high energy, but the functional groups are so close together that ring formation is relatively probable. The pattern shown in Table 9.8 is common. The general order of ring formation in intramolecular S_N2 reactions is $5 > 6 > 3$ with other rings being formed much more slowly.

Large rings are relatively unstrained, but the groups are so far apart that their probability of getting together for reaction is low. Indeed, it becomes more probable for reaction of one amino group to occur with another bromide. That is, **intermolecular** S_N2 reaction is an important side reaction for such cases unless conditions of high dilution are used. At ordinary concentrations the reaction product is a polymer chain.

Displacement reactions on cyclic compounds show large effects of ring size. Table 9.9 summarizes some relative rates of reaction of alkyl bromides with lithium iodide in acetone.

Halocyclopropanes are relatively unreactive in S_N2 reactions. At the transition state of an S_N2 reaction, the central carbon has sp^2-hybridization in which the normal bond

**TABLE 9.9 Relative Rates
of Reaction of Alkyl
Bromides with Lithium
Iodide in Acetone**

Alkyl Group	Relative Rate
Isopropyl	1.0
Cyclopropyl	<0.0001[a]
Cyclobutyl	0.008
Cyclopentyl	1.6
Cyclohexyl	0.01
Cycloheptyl	1.0
Cyclooctyl	0.2

[a] Approximate upper limit; no reaction was detected.

FIGURE 9.12   Transition state for S$_N$2 reaction on a cyclopropyl halide.

FIGURE 9.13   Transition state for S$_N$2 reaction with cyclohexyl compounds.

angle is 120°. The imposition of such an increased bond angle on a cyclopropyl ring would result in additional bond angle strain (Figure 9.12). The same effect is apparent in the slow reactions of cyclobutyl systems, but since the bond angle strain is less, the effect is not as great.

Cyclopentyl compounds undergo S$_N$2 reactions at rates comparable to open-chain systems. The reactions usually proceed in good yield.

Cyclohexyl compounds react rather slowly in S$_N$2 reactions. Ring strain does not appear to be an important factor for five- and six-membered rings, but a novel kind of strain involving axial hydrogens does appear to be significant for cyclohexyl systems (Figure 9.13). Because the displacement reaction has a reduced rate, elimination reactions to alkenes are frequently important side reactions with cyclohexyl compounds and often dominate. For larger rings, the reactions are roughly comparable to open-chain systems.

EXERCISE 9.12   In each of the following pairs, which is more reactive in S$_N$2 reactions?
(a) cyclobutyl bromide, cyclopentyl bromide
(b) cyclohexyl iodide, 3,3-dimethylcyclohexyl iodide
(c) cyclopropyl chloride, cyclopropylmethyl chloride

PROBLEMS

1. Predict the principal product of each of the following reactions:

(a) [cyclopentyl chloride structure] + K$^+$ I$^-$ $\xrightarrow{\text{acetone}}$

(b) [1-chloro-1-methylcyclopentane structure] + K$^+$ I$^-$ $\xrightarrow{\text{acetone}}$

(c) $CH_3I + Na^+ \ SCN^- \ \xrightarrow[\Delta]{CH_3OH}$

(d) $(CH_3CH_2)_3CCl + Na^+ \ OCH_3^- \ \xrightarrow[\Delta]{CH_3OH}$

(e)

$+ Na^+ \ CN^- \ \xrightarrow{DMF}$

(f) $(H_3C)_2NCH_2CH_2CH_2CH_2Br \ \xrightarrow{DMF}$

(g) $(CH_3)_3CCl + Na \ \xrightarrow{ether}$

(h) $(CH_3)_2CHCH_2CH_2Br + CH_3CO_2^- \ Na^+ \ \xrightarrow[\Delta]{C_2H_5OH}$

(i) $CH_3CH_2CH_2I + Na^+ \ NO_2^- \ \xrightarrow{DMSO}$

(j) $(CH_3)_2CHCH_2Cl + Na^+ \ N_3^- \ \xrightarrow[\Delta]{CH_3OH}$

2. (R)-2-Butanol, labeled with ^{18}O, is subjected to the following sequence of reactions.

$$\underset{\displaystyle CH_3CH_2\overset{\displaystyle \overset{^{18}OH}{|}}{C}HCH_3}{} \xrightarrow{CH_3SO_2Cl} \underset{\displaystyle CH_3CH_2\overset{\displaystyle \overset{^{18}OSO_2CH_3}{|}}{C}HCH_3}{} \xrightarrow[\underset{dioxane}{H_2O}]{OH^-} \underset{\displaystyle CH_3CH_2\overset{\displaystyle \overset{OH}{|}}{C}HCH_3}{} + CH_3SO_2{-}^{18}O^-$$

What is the absolute configuration of the 2-butanol product?

3. 2-Bromo-, 2-chloro- and 2-iodo-2-methylbutanes react at different rates with pure methanol but produce the same mixture of 2-methoxy-2-methylbutane and alkenes as products. Explain these results in terms of the reaction mechanism.

4. Explain each of the following observations.
   (a) (S)-3-Bromo-3-methylhexane reacts in aqueous acetone to give racemic 3-methyl-3-hexanol.

$$\underset{\displaystyle \underset{\displaystyle \underset{CH_3}{|}}{CH_3CH_2CH_2\overset{\displaystyle \overset{Br}{|}}{C}CH_2CH_3}}{} \xrightarrow[acetone]{H_2O} (\pm)\underset{\displaystyle \underset{\displaystyle \underset{CH_3}{|}}{CH_3CH_2CH_2\overset{\displaystyle \overset{OH}{|}}{C}CH_2CH_3}}{}$$

   (b) (R)-2-Bromo-2,4-dimethylhexane reacts in aqueous acetone to give optically active 2,4-dimethyl-2-hexanol.

5. For each of the following pairs of reactions, predict which one is faster and explain why.

   (a) $(CH_3)_2CHCH_2Cl + N_3^- \ \xrightarrow{C_2H_5OH} (CH_3)_2CHCH_2N_3 + Cl^-$

   $(CH_3)_2CHCH_2I + N_3^- \ \xrightarrow{C_2H_5OH} (CH_3)_2CHCH_2N_3 + I^-$

   (b) $(CH_3)_3CBr \ \xrightarrow[\Delta]{H_2O} (CH_3)_3COH + HBr$

   $(CH_3)_2CHBr \ \xrightarrow[\Delta]{H_2O} (CH_3)_2CHOH + HBr$

   (c) $CH_3CH_2\overset{\displaystyle \overset{CH_3}{|}}{C}HCH_2Br + SH^- \longrightarrow CH_3CH_2\overset{\displaystyle \overset{CH_3}{|}}{C}HCH_2SH + Br^-$

   $CH_3CH_2CH_2CH_2Br + SH^- \longrightarrow CH_3CH_2CH_2CH_2SH + Br^-$

(d) $CH_3CH_2Br + CN^- \xrightarrow[\text{(solvent)}]{CH_3OH} CH_3CH_2CN + Br^-$

$CH_3CH_2Br + CN^- \xrightarrow[\text{(solvent)}]{(CH_3)_2NCHO} CH_3CH_2CN + Br^-$

(e) $(CH_3)_2CHBr + NH_3 \xrightarrow{CH_3OH} (CH_3)_2CH\overset{+}{N}H_3\ Br^-$

$CH_3CH_2CH_2Br + NH_3 \xrightarrow{CH_3OH} CH_3CH_2CH_2\overset{+}{N}H_3\ Br^-$

(f) $CH_3I + Na^+\ OH^- \xrightarrow{H_2O} CH_3OH + Na^+\ I^-$

$CH_3I + Na^+\ ^-O_2CCH_3 \xrightarrow{H_2O} CH_3O_2CCH_3 + Na^+\ I^-$

(g) $CH_3Br + (CH_3)_3N \longrightarrow (CH_3)_4N^+\ Br^-$

$CH_3Br + (CH_3)_3P \longrightarrow (CH_3)_4P^+\ Br^-$

(h) $SCN^- + CH_3CH_2Br \xrightarrow{aq.\ C_2H_5OH} CH_3CH_2SCN + Br^-$

$SCN^- + CH_3CH_2Br \xrightarrow{aq.\ C_2H_5OH} CH_3CH_2NCS + Br^-$

(i) $N_3^- + (CH_3)_2CHCH_2Br \xrightarrow{C_2H_5OH} (CH_3)_2CHCH_2N_3 + Br^-$

$C_6H_5S^- + (CH_3)_2CHCH_2Br \xrightarrow{C_2H_5OH} (CH_3)_2CHCH_2SC_6H_5 + Br^-$

[*Note:* $pK_a(HN_3) \cong pK_a(C_6H_5SH)$.]

(j) $CH_3CO_2^- +$ Cl–[square] $\longrightarrow$ CH_3COO–[square] $+ Cl^-$

$CH_3CO_2^- +$ Cl–[cyclopentane] $\longrightarrow$ CH_3COO–[cyclopentane] $+ Cl^-$

(k) $^-OCH_2CH_2Cl \longrightarrow CH_2\!\!\overset{O}{\diagup\!\!\diagdown}\!\!CH_2 + Cl^-$

$^-OCH_2CH_2CH_2Cl \longrightarrow$ [four-membered ring: O—CH₂ / CH₂—CH₂] $+ Cl^-$

6. Of the following nucleophilic substitution reactions, which ones will probably occur and which will probably not occur or be very slow. Explain.

(a) $CH_3CN + I^- \longrightarrow CH_3I + CN^-$
(b) $CH_3F + Cl^- \longrightarrow CH_3Cl + F^-$
(c) $(CH_3)_3COH + NH_2^- \longrightarrow (CH_3)_3CNH_2 + OH^-$
(d) $CH_3OSO_2OCH_3 + Cl^- \longrightarrow CH_3Cl + CH_3OSO_3^-$
(e) $CH_3NH_2 + I^- \longrightarrow CH_3I + NH_2^-$
(f) $CH_3CH_2I + N_3^- \longrightarrow CH_3CH_2N_3 + I^-$
(g) $CH_3CH_2OH + F^- \longrightarrow CH_3CH_2F + OH^-$
(h) cyclopropyl bromide $+ N(CH_3)_3 \longrightarrow C_3H_5N(CH_3)_3^+\ Br^-$

7. Give a specific example of two related reactions having different rates for which each of the following is the principal reason for the relative reactivities.
(a) The less basic leaving group is more reactive.
(b) A nitrogen anion is hydrogen bonded more strongly than a sulfur anion.
(c) Tertiary carbocations are more stable than secondary carbocations
(d) Steric hindrance.
(e) Protic solvents can form hydrogen bonds.

8. Of the following statements, which are true for nucleophilic substitutions occurring by the S_N2 mechanism?
   (a) Tertiary alkyl halides react faster than secondary.
   (b) The absolute configuration of the product is opposite to that of the reactant when an optically active substrate is used.
   (c) The reaction shows first-order kinetics.
   (d) The rate of reaction depends markedly on the nucleophilicity of the attacking nucleophile.
   (e) The probable mechanism involves only one step.
   (f) Carbocations are intermediates.
   (g) The rate of reaction is proportional to the concentration of the attacking nucleophile.
   (h) The rate of reaction depends on the nature of the leaving group.

9. Answer problem 8 for nucleophilic substitutions occurring by the S_N1 mechanism.

10. Consider the reaction of isopropyl iodide with various nucleophiles. For each pair, predict which will give the larger substitution/elimination ratio.
    (a) SCN^- or OCN^- (b) I^- or Cl^-
    (c) $N(CH_3)_3$ or $P(CH_3)_3$ (d) CH_3S^- or CH_3O^-

11. When a solution of *cis*-1-*t*-butyl-4-chlorocyclohexane in ethanol is refluxed for several hours, the major product is found to be *trans*-1-*t*-butyl-4-ethoxycyclohexane. However, if the solution is also made 2.0 *M* in sodium ethoxide, the major product after the same treatment is found to be 4-*t*-butylcyclohexene. Explain.

12. Appendix I gives some heats of formation for anions in the gas phase. Use these data to compute the $\Delta H°$ for those S_N2 reactions listed in Table 9.5 for which sufficient data are available. Do these heats of reaction correlate with the reaction rates in either DMF or methanol? What do the results imply?

13. The reaction of methyl bromide with methylamine to give dimethylammonium bromide is a typical S_N2 reaction that shows second-order kinetics.

$$CH_3Br + CH_3NH_2 \longrightarrow (CH_3)_2NH_2{}^+ \; Br^-$$

However, the analogous cyclization of 4-bromobutylamine shows first-order kinetics. Explain.

The foregoing **intramolecular** displacement reaction is a useful method for making cyclic amines. However, a competing side reaction is the intermolecular displacement

$$Br(CH_2)_4NH_2 + Br(CH_2)_4NH_2 \longrightarrow Br(CH_2)_4\overset{\overset{\displaystyle H}{|}}{\underset{\underset{\displaystyle H}{|}}{N}}{}^+(CH_2)_4NH_2 \; Br^-$$

Suggest the experimental conditions to minimize this side reaction.

14. Chloroacetic acid is more acidic than acetic acid by 1.9 pK units. Chloroacetate ion is 10 times less reactive than acetate ion in an S_N2 reaction with methyl iodide in methanol. What do these data suggest concerning the the amount of negative charge left on the carboxylate group in the transition state?

15. Optically active 3-bromo-2-butanol is treated with KOH in methanol to obtain an optically inactive product having the formula C_4H_8O. What is the structure of this material?

16. Show how each of the following compounds may be prepared from an alkyl halide.
    (a) $CH_3CH_2CH_2SH$ (b) $(CH_3)_2CHCH_2CH_2CN$
    (c) $CH_3CH_2CH_2OCH_3$ (d) $CH_3CH_2CH_2OH$
    (e) CH_3ONO_2 (f) $CH_3CH_2CH_2CH_2N_3$

17. Suggest an explanation for each of the following observations.
    (a) Compound A reacts faster by the S_N2 mechanism than the compound B.

    (b) Compound C reacts faster by the S_N1 mechanism than compound D.

    (c) *t*-Butyl chloride reacts in methanol solution at 25°C 8 times faster than it does in ethanol solution.

Chapter 10

Alcohols and Ethers

10.1 Introduction: Structure

Alcohols are compounds in which an alkyl group replaces one of the hydrogens of water. They are organic compounds that contain the functional group OH. As we shall see, this functional group dominates the chemistry of alcohols. **Ethers** are analogs of water in which both hydrogens are replaced by alkyl groups.

$$CH_3-OH \qquad CH_3-O-CH_3$$

an alcohol   an ether
(methyl alcohol)   (dimethyl ether)

Methyl alcohol has been found by microwave spectroscopy to have the following geometry.

Bond Lengths, Å		Bond Angles, deg	
C—H	1.10	H—C—H	109
O—H	0.96	H—C—O	110
C—O	1.43	C—O—H	108.9

The hybridization of carbon is approximately sp^3, as shown by the H—C—H and H—C—O bond angles of 109° and 110°. The hybridization of oxygen may also be described as approximately sp^3. Oxygen makes one bond to carbon and one to hydrogen. The oxygen-hydrogen bond distance is precisely the same as the oxygen-hydrogen bond distance in water. The molecule exists in a conformation that has the oxygen-hydrogen bond staggered between two carbon-hydrogen bonds and the barrier to rotation about the carbon-oxygen bond is 1.1 kcal mole^{-1}. It is frequently useful to consider the oxygen lone-pair electrons to occupy orbitals that are each approximately sp^3; such lone-pair orbitals are each staggered between two adjacent carbon-hydrogen bonds.

The simple alcohols are important industrial materials. They are also used extensively as laboratory reagents and as solvents. The most important representative of the class is undoubtedly ethyl alcohol, which has been known as an intoxicant since the dawn of civilization. Indeed, it has been suggested that the discovery of alcohol fermentation and the physiological effects of its product provided a major incentive for agriculture and the *start* of civilization! Alcohols can be prepared readily from many other classes of compounds and can, in turn, be transformed into many others. For this reason, alcohols play a key role as synthetic intermediates.

10.2 Nomenclature of Alcohols

Like most other classes of organic compounds, alcohols can be named in several ways. Common names are useful only for the simpler members of a class. However, common names are widely used in colloquial conversation and in the scientific literature. In order to communicate freely, the student must know common names. Since the systematic IUPAC names are often used for indexing the scientific literature, the student must be thoroughly familiar with systematic names in order to retrieve data from the literature.

The common names of alcohols are derived by combining the name of the alkyl group with the word alcohol. The names are written as two words.

$$CH_3CH_2CH_2CH_2OH \qquad CH_3\overset{\overset{\textstyle CH_3}{|}}{C}HCH_2OH \qquad CH_3\overset{\overset{\textstyle CH_3}{|}}{\underset{\underset{\textstyle CH_3}{|}}{C}}{-}OH$$

n-butyl alcohol   isobutyl alcohol   *t*-butyl alcohol

In common names the position of an additional substituent is indicated by letters of the Greek alphabet rather than by numbers.

$$Cl\underset{\beta}{C}H_2\underset{\alpha}{C}H_2OH \qquad CH_3\underset{\gamma}{C}H\underset{\beta}{C}H_2\underset{\alpha}{C}H_2OH$$
$$\qquad\qquad\qquad\qquad\qquad\overset{\textstyle |}{\underset{}{Br}}$$

β-chloroethyl alcohol   γ-bromobutyl alcohol

EXERCISE 10.1 Give common names for each of the following alcohols:

In the IUPAC system of nomenclature alcohols are named by replacing the **-e** of the corresponding alkane name by the suffix **-ol**; that is, as **alkanols**.

$$CH_3OH \qquad CH_3CH_2OH$$

methanol   ethanol

The alkan- stem corresponds to the longest carbon chain in the molecule *which contains the OH group.* The chain is numbered so that the OH group gets the smaller of two possible numbers.

$$CH_3CH_2CH_2CH_2OH \qquad CH_3\overset{\overset{\textstyle OH}{|}}{C}HCH_2CH_3$$

1-butanol   2-butanol

or butan-1-ol   or butan-2-ol

Substituents are appended as prefixes and are numbered according to the numbering system established by the position of the OH group. Names are written as one word with no spaces.

Cl
|
CH_3CHCH_2OH ≡
2-chloro-1-propanol

CH_2Cl
|
$CH_3CH_2CHCH_2OH$ ≡
2-(chloromethyl)-1-butanol

$(CH_3)_2CH$
|
$CH_3CH_2CH_2CHCH_2OH$ ≡
2-isopropyl-1-pentanol
(not 3-methyl-2-propyl-1-butanol; pentanol
has a longer chain)

1-methylcyclopentanol

2-butyl-1-heptanol   4,6,6,-trimethyl-3-heptanol   cyclohexanol

The general rule in the IUPAC system of nomenclature is that a functional group
named as a suffix becomes a parent system that dominates the numbering scheme.
Prefix groups are considered to be substituents or appendages to the parent compound.

Some kinds of alcohols are too difficult or cumbersome to name as alkanols. For
such compounds it is preferable to use the appropriate hydroxyalkyl name as a prefix.

cis-4-(hydroxymethyl)cyclohexanol   (hydroxymethyl)cyclopropane

---

EXERCISE 10.2 Write structures corresponding to each of the following names.
(a) 2,4-dimethyl-3-pentanol   (b) 2-(2-bromoethyl)-3-methyl-1-pentanol
(c) *trans*-4-methylcyclohexanol

EXERCISE 10.3 Explain why each of the following names is incorrect.
(a) 2-isopropyl-1-butanol   (b) 2-ethyl-4-butanol
(c) 2,2-dichloro-5-hydroxymethylheptane

EXERCISE 10.4 Name each of the following compounds by the IUPAC system.

(a)

(b) $(CH_3)_3CCOH$
    with CH_3 above and CH_3 below

(c)

(d)

10.3 Physical Properties of Alcohols

The lower molecular weight alcohols are liquids with characteristic odors and sharp tastes. One striking feature is their relatively high boiling points (Table 10.1). The OH group is roughly equivalent to a methyl group in size and polarizability, but alcohols have much higher boiling points than an alkane of corresponding size. For example, compare ethanol (mol. wt. 46, b.p. 78.5°C) and propane (mol. wt. 44, b.p. −42°C). A plot of boiling point versus molecular weight for straight-chain alcohols and alkanes is shown in Figure 10.1.

The abnormally high boiling points of alcohols are the result of a special type of dipolar association that these molecules experience in the liquid phase. Because oxygen is more electronegative than carbon or hydrogen, both the carbon-oxygen and the oxygen-hydrogen bonds are polar. These polar bonds cause alcohols to have substantial dipole moments. However, dipole moments of alcohols are no greater than those of corresponding chlorides.

$$CH_3OH \qquad CH_3CH_2OH$$
$$\mu = 1.71 \text{ D} \qquad \mu = 1.70 \text{ D}$$

$$CH_3Cl \qquad CH_3CH_2Cl$$
$$\mu = 1.94 \text{ D} \qquad \mu = 2.04 \text{ D}$$

We would expect molecules with substantial dipole moments to have enhanced intermolecular interaction in the liquid phase because of electrostatic interaction between the dipoles. However, we have just seen that the dipole moments of alcohols are actually smaller than those of alkyl chlorides. In fact, alkyl chlorides differ very little in boiling point from alkanes of corresponding molecular weight (see Figure 8.2). Consequently, it would seem that dipolar attraction is not the cause of the elevated boiling points of alcohols. Or is it? The magnitudes of the individual dipole moments

TABLE 10.1 Physical Properties of Alcohols

Compound	Common Name	IUPAC Name	Melting Point, °C	Boiling Point, °C	Density d^{20}	Solubility, g/100 mL H_2O
CH_3OH	methyl alcohol	methanol	−97.8	65.0	0.7914	∞
CH_3CH_2OH	ethyl alcohol	ethanol	−114.7	78.5	0.7893	∞
$CH_3CH_2CH_2OH$	n-propyl alcohol	1-propanol	−126.5	97.4	0.8035	∞
$CH_3CHOHCH_3$	isopropyl alcohol	2-propanol	−89.5	82.4	0.7855	∞
$CH_3CH_2CH_2CH_2OH$	n-butyl alcohol	1-butanol	−89.5	117.3	0.8098	8.0
$CH_3CH_2CHOHCH_3$	sec-butyl alcohol	2-butanol	−114.7	99.5	0.8063	12.5
$(CH_3)_2CHCH_2OH$	isobutyl alcohol	2-methyl-1-propanol		107.9	0.8021	11.1
$(CH_3)_3COH$	tert-butyl alcohol	2-methyl-2-propanol	25.5	82.2	0.7887	∞
$CH_3(CH_2)_4OH$	n-pentyl alcohol	1-pentanol	−79	138	0.8144	2.2
$CH_3CH_2CH_2CHOHCH_3$	—	2-pentanol		119.3	0.809	4.9
$CH_3CH_2CHOHCH_2CH_3$	—	3-pentanol		115.6	0.815	5.6
$(CH_3)_3CCH_2OH$	neopentyl alcohol	2,2-dimethyl-1-propanol	53	114	0.812	∞
$CH_3(CH_2)_5OH$	n-hexyl alcohol	1-hexanol	−46.7	158	0.8136	0.7

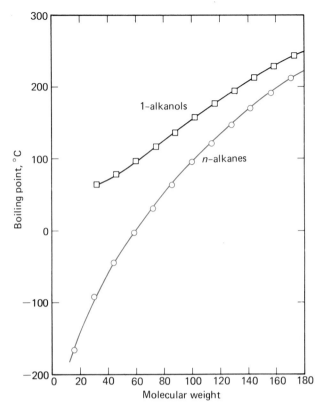

FIGURE 10.1 Boiling points of 1-alkanols as a function of molecular weight

are not the only important factor. How closely the negative and positive ends of the dipoles can approach one another is also important.

By Coulomb's law two opposite charges attract each other with an energy proportional to $1/r$, where r is the distance between the charges. The electrostatic energy of two dipoles is related to $1/r^3$ and therefore falls off sharply with distance. In alkyl halides the negative end of the dipoles is out at the lone-pair electrons, but the positive end is in the C—X bond close to carbon. Because of the van der Waals size of carbon, the positive and negative ends of adjacent dipoles cannot get close together and the electrostatic energy of dipole-dipole attraction is relatively small.

Consequently, such dipole association does not have much of an effect on the energy required to separate alkyl halide molecules.

For alcohols the negative end of the dipole is out at the oxygen lone pairs, and the positive end is close to the small hydrogen. For hydrogen atoms bonded to electronegative elements dipole-dipole interaction is uniquely important and is called a **hydrogen bond**. This proximity of approach is shown by bond-distance data. The oxygen-hydrogen bond length in alcohols is 0.96 Å. The hydrogen-bonded H—O distance is 2.07 Å, about twice as large. In fact, this distance is sufficiently small that some hydrogen bonds may have a significant amount of covalent or shared electron character. In condensed phases, alcohols are associated via a chain of hydrogen bonds.

A three-dimensional view of liquid methanol showing the hydrogen-bonding network is given in Figure 10.2. The figure is of a random cube of the liquid, showing only the C—O—H parts of the various molecules. Some of the oxygen atoms are colored in the figure. The six at the top of the cube are the oxygens of a "chain" of methanol molecules; the molecules are held in the chain by hydrogen bonds. At the bottom of the cube may be seen a cyclic tetramer of methanol molecules.

The oxygen-hydrogen bond in alcohols is stronger than most carbon-hydrogen bonds. It has a bond dissociation energy of 104 kcal mole^{-1}. The hydrogen bond is far weaker—only about 5 kcal mole^{-1}. Nevertheless, this additional heat term in the heat of vaporization results in relatively high boiling points. A bond strength of 5 kcal mole^{-1} does not sound like much; however, when there are many such bonds, as in polyhydroxy compounds such as carbohydrates, the total strength is sufficient to hold up tall redwoods.

Since alcohols and water both contain the OH group, they have many properties in common. We should emphasize that water is a remarkable substance. Its boiling point of 100°C is exceedingly high for a compound with a molecular weight of only 18. The extensive hydrogen-bond networks in liquid water make it a highly polar liquid with a dielectric constant of 78.5 at 25°C. In aqueous solution the interaction between ions is relatively small. Therefore, water is a good solvent for ionic compounds. The lower alcohols also have relatively high dielectric constants (Table 10.2). As the carbon chain gets longer, the importance of the OH group is reduced relative to that of the alkyl group and the dielectric constant approaches the alkane value of about 2.

FIGURE 10.2 Three-dimensional view (stereo plot) of a random cube of liquid methanol, showing the hydrogen-bonded networks. The large circles represent methyl groups, the small circles hydrogen, and the intermediate circles oxygen. Colored oxygens describe a chain and a cycle of molecules. [Courtesy of W. L. Jorgensen, Department of Chemistry, Purdue University.]

TABLE 10.2 Dielectric Constants of Alcohols

Compound	Dielectric Constant
H_2O	78.5
CH_3OH	32.6
CH_3CH_2OH	24.3
$CH_3(CH_2)_3OH$	17.1
$CH_3(CH_2)_4OH$	13.9
$CH_3(CH_2)_{11}OH$	6.5

Because of their high dielectric constants, methanol and ethanol are reasonably good solvents for salt-like compounds. Since they are also good solvents for organic compounds, they are used frequently for organic reactions such as S_N2 displacement reactions (Chapter 9).

The OH groups of alcohols can participate in the hydrogen-bond network of water. The smaller alcohols are completely soluble in water. As the hydrocarbon chain of an alcohol gets larger, the compound begins to look more like an alkane, and more of the hydrogen bonds in water must be broken to make room for the hydrocarbon chain. Since the hydrogen bonds that are lost are not completely compensated by bonding to the alcohol OH, solubility decreases as the hydrocarbon chain gets larger. A rough point of division is four carbons to one oxygen. Above this ratio, alcohols tend to have little solubility in water. This guideline is only approximate because the shape of the hydrocarbon portion is also important. *t*-Butyl alcohol is much more soluble than *n*-butyl alcohol because the *t*-butyl group is more compact and requires less room or broken water hydrogen bonds in an aqueous solution. A similar phenomenon is seen with the branched pentyl alcohols.

10.4 Acidity of Alcohols: Inductive Effects

One of the important properties of water is its self-ionization.

$$H_2O + H_2O \xrightleftharpoons{K_w} H_3O^+ + OH^-$$

In pure water, the concentrations of H_3O^+ and OH^- are low, only 10^{-7} mole L^{-1}. The ion product or self-dissociation constant K_w is defined as

$$K_w = [H_3O^+][OH^-] = 1.0 \times 10^{-14} \text{ mole}^2 \text{ L}^{-2} \text{ (or } M^2)$$

Remember that this is not a normal equilibrium constant, which includes the concentrations of reactants and products. For water, the concentration is 55.5 moles L^{-1}. The equilibrium constant for dissociation is therefore

$$K = \frac{(10^{-7})(10^{-7})}{(55.5)(55.5)} = 3.25 \times 10^{-18}$$

Note that K is unitless. The relationship between K and K_w is

$$K_w = K \times (55.5 \ M)^2$$

Alcohols also undergo self-dissociation, but to a much smaller extent than water.

$$2\ CH_3OH \rightleftharpoons CH_3OH_2^+ + CH_3O^-$$

For methanol the ion product $K_{[CH_3OH]} = 1.2 \times 10^{-17}\ M^2$, and for larger alcohols the value is even smaller.

$$K_{CH_3OH} = [CH_3OH_2^+][CH_3O^-] = 1.2 \times 10^{-17}\ M^2$$

The reduced value comes in large part from the lower dielectric constant of alcohols—it takes greater energy to separate charges. But the relative acidities and basicities of alcohols are also important.

The acidity of an alcohol in water is defined in the usual way.

$$ROH + H_2O \xrightarrow{K_a} H_3O^+ + RO^-$$

The acid dissociation constant K_a is defined as:

$$K_a = \frac{[H_3O^+][RO^-]}{[ROH]}$$

Since these equilibria refer to dilute solutions in water, the concentration of water is generally omitted in the expression for an equilibrium constant and K_a has units of mole L^{-1}, or molarity, M. Recall that the acid dissociation constant is generally such a small number that it is usually more convenient to refer to the negative logarithm (pK_a).

$$pK_a = -\log K_a$$

Values of pK_a for some alcohols are listed in Table 10.3. For comparison, the pK_a values of some common inorganic acids are also given. Note that the K_a for water is obtained by dividing K_w by the concentration of water, 55.5 moles L^{-1}. This change is necessary to put all of the ionizations on the same scale and in the same units. Recall that the ion product of water, K_w, has units of moles^2 L^{-2} or M^2, whereas K_a values are given in units of moles L^{-1} or M.

Methanol and ethanol are about as acidic as water itself. The larger alcohols are less acidic. Alcohols (and water) are generally much less acidic than other compounds commonly regarded as acids. "Strong" acids, such as HI, HBr, HCl and H_2SO_4, have negative pK_a values. Such compounds are completely dissociated in water and are 10^{15} to 10^{20} more acidic than alcohols. Typical "weak" acids such as acetic acid (to be discussed in Chapter 18), HF, H_2S, and HOCl are still 10^7 to 10^{10} stronger than alcohols. For a brief review of acidity, see Section 4.5.

TABLE 10.3 pK_a Values for Alcohols and Some Acids

Compound	pK_a	Compound	pK_a
H_2O	15.7	HCl	-2.2
CH_3OH	15.5	H_2SO_4	-5
C_2H_5OH	15.9	H_3PO_4	2.15
$(CH_3)_3COH$	$\cong 18$	HF	3.18
$ClCH_2CH_2OH$	14.3	H_2S	6.97
CF_3CH_2OH	12.4	HOCl	7.53
C_6H_5OH	10.0	H_2O_2	11.64
CH_3COOH	4.8		

The weakly acidic character of alcohols is seen primarily in their reactions with very strong bases. Alcohols, like water, react with alkali metals to liberate hydrogen and form the corresponding metal alkoxide.

$$CH_3OH + Na \longrightarrow CH_3O^- + Na^+ + \tfrac{1}{2} H_2$$

The reaction of sodium with an alcohol tends to be less vigorous than that with water. In fact, isopropyl alcohol is often used to decompose scraps of sodium in the laboratory because its reaction is relatively slow and moderate. When sodium reacts with water, the reaction is so rapid that the heat produced cannot be dissipated quickly enough; the evolved hydrogen catches fire, and an explosion results. Tertiary alcohols react so sluggishly with sodium that potassium must often be used to convert such an alcohol to the alkoxide.

Potassium has a relatively low m.p., 64°C. In laboratory use it is sometimes converted to a finely divided state in order to render it more reactive. Solid pieces of potassium are added to benzene (b.p. 80°C), and the mixture is heated to the boiling point of the benzene. The potassium melts, and the mixture is allowed to cool with vigorous stirring. The molten potassium solidifies as small particles of "potassium sand." The alcohol is added to this mixture with stirring and generally reacts readily because of the large surface area of the potassium sand. This procedure is especially useful with tertiary alcohols.

Another reagent commonly used to prepare the sodium salts of alcohols is sodium hydride, NaH. This compound is a nonvolatile, insoluble salt, Na^+H^-, and reacts readily with acidic hydrogens.

$$CH_3OH + Na^+ H^- \longrightarrow CH_3O^- + Na^+ + H_2$$

The reaction may be regarded as a combination of hydride ion with a proton.

$$H:^- + H^+ \longrightarrow H_2$$

The sodium salts of primary alcohols are common reagents in organic chemistry.

$$\underset{\text{sodium methoxide}}{Na^+ \ ^-OCH_3} \qquad \underset{\text{sodium ethoxide}}{Na^+ \ ^-OCH_2CH_3}$$

Because sodium and sodium hydride react so sluggishly with tertiary alcohols, the corresponding potassium salts are more commonly used as reagents.

$$K^+ \ ^-O\!-\!\overset{\overset{\displaystyle CH_3}{|}}{\underset{\underset{\displaystyle CH_3}{|}}{C}}\!-\!CH_3$$

potassium *t*-butoxide

Note in Table 10.3 that 2-chloroethanol is significantly more acidic than ethanol. This difference in acidity is best understood in terms of the electrostatic interaction of the C—Cl dipole with the negative charge of the alkoxide ion.

$$\overset{Cl}{\diagdown}\overset{}{CH_2\!-\!CH_2}\diagdown_{O^-}$$

The negative charge on oxygen is closer to the positive end of the dipole than it is the negative end. Thus, electrostatic attraction exceeds repulsion, and the result is a net stabilization of the anion. Stabilization of the anion increases its ease of formation and the conjugate acid, 2-chloroethanol, is more acidic than ethanol itself (Figure 10.3).

$$\Delta H^{\circ}_{ion.} (ClCH_2CH_2OH) < \Delta H^{\circ}_{ion.} (CH_3CH_2OH)$$

FIGURE 10.3 The effect of a dipolar substituent on the ionization energy of an alcohol. The stabilizing effect of the substituent is greater in the anion (charge-dipole interaction) than in the alcohol (dipole-dipole interaction).

This effect is generally called an **inductive field effect** or, more simply, an **inductive effect**. The magnitude of the effect falls off as the distance between the dipolar group and the charged group is increased. The effect increases with the number of dipolar groups. Note the relatively large effect of the three fluorines in 2,2,2-trifluoroethanol. Halogen groups are said to be **electron attracting** and to stabilize anions. The effect is present in inorganic systems as well: HOCl is a stronger acid than HOH. Conversely, alkyl groups are generally considered to be somewhat **electron donating** and, therefore, to weaken acids. We will make use of inductive effects frequently in our subsequent discussions of the effects of structure on reactivity.

Like water, alcohols are not only acids, but also bases. For example, when gaseous hydrogen chloride is passed into an alcohol it protonates the oxygen just as it does the oxygen of water.

$$H_2O + HCl \longrightarrow H_3O^+ + Cl^-$$

$$ROH + HCl \rightleftharpoons \underset{\text{alkyloxonium chloride}}{ROH_2^+ Cl^-} \rightleftharpoons ROH_2^+ + Cl^-$$

The initially formed species in such a protonation is an **ion pair** (two ions in close juxtaposition). In water and the smaller alcohols, the dielectric constant is sufficiently high that the initially formed ion pairs largely dissociate to free ions. However, as the dielectric constant becomes smaller, too much work is required to separate the ion pairs, and the oxonium chloride remains largely associated.

EXERCISE 10.5 For each of the following pairs of compounds, which is more acidic?

(a) $ClCH_2CH_2CH_2OH$ and $CH_3CHClCH_2OH$

(b) $CH_3CH_2CH_2CH_2OH$ and $CH_3OCH_2CH_2OH$

10.5 Preparation of Alcohols

The hydroxy group occupies a central role in organic chemistry. Alcohols can be prepared from many other classes of compounds, and they also serve as important starting materials for the synthesis of other materials. In this section, we will consider the preparation of alcohols from alkyl halides. In later sections, as we study the chemical reactions of other functional groups, we shall learn many other important ways of preparing alcohols.

Hydrolysis of alkyl halides in aqueous solvents may occur by either the S_N1 or S_N2 mechanism. With some halides, elimination is a major side reaction (Chapter 9). The hydrolysis of most primary halides occurs by the S_N2 path and is sufficiently clean that this reaction is a good preparative method.

$$CH_3CH_2CH_2CH_2Cl + OH^- \xrightarrow[100°C]{H_2O} CH_3CH_2CH_2CH_2OH + Cl^-$$

The reaction can be carried out in refluxing aqueous sodium hydroxide, especially with lower molecular weight halides. Although alkyl halides are only slightly soluble in water, a two-phase reaction takes place. If the alcohol is water-soluble, the end of the hydrolysis is marked by the formation of a homogeneous solution. Alternatively, the reaction can be carried out in a mixture of water and some inert organic cosolvent such as dioxane.

dioxane

Dioxane is a colorless liquid, b.p. 100°C, and is completely miscible with water. It is relatively inert to many reagents and is frequently used in mixtures with water to increase the solubility of organic compounds.

Remember that with secondary alkyl halides and primary halides with a β-branch, elimination is an important side reaction and may be the principal reaction.

$$(CH_3)_2CHCH_2Br \xrightarrow{OH^-} (CH_3)_2C{=}CH_2$$

An alternative procedure, which avoids the use of strong base, employs of acetate ion ($CH_3CO_2^-$) as the nucleophilic reagent (Section 9.2). Since acetate is much less basic than hydroxide (the pK_a of acetic acid, CH_3COOH, is 4.8, whereas that of water is 15.7), the E2 mechanism is suppressed, and alkene formation is minimized.

$$CH_3CH_2CH_2CH_2Br + CH_3\overset{O}{\overset{\|}{C}}O^- K^+ \xrightarrow[100°C]{DMF} CH_3CH_2CH_2CH_2O\overset{O}{\overset{\|}{C}}CH_3 + K^+ Br^-$$

The product, an ester, can be readily hydrolyzed to the desired alcohol (Section 18.6).

$$CH_3CH_2CH_2CH_2O\overset{O}{\overset{\|}{C}}CH_3 \xrightarrow[H_2O]{OH^-} CH_3CH_2CH_2CH_2OH + CH_3CO_2^-$$

Since displacement by acetate ion proceeds by the S_N2 mechanism, the alcohol product has an absolute configuration opposite that of the starting halide.

$$\underset{\substack{\text{(R)-1-chloro-1-deuteriobutane}\\ \text{(R)-chlorobutane-}1\text{-}d}}{CH_3CH_2CH_2-\overset{\overset{\displaystyle Cl}{|}}{\underset{\underset{\displaystyle D}{|}}{C}}-H} + CH_3CO_2^- \longrightarrow$$

$$\underset{\text{(S)-butyl-}1\text{-}d\text{ acetate}}{CH_3CH_2CH_2-\overset{\overset{\displaystyle H}{|}}{\underset{\underset{\displaystyle D}{|}}{C}}-O\overset{\overset{\displaystyle O}{\|}}{C}CH_3} \xrightarrow[\text{H}_2\text{O}]{\text{OH}^-} \underset{\text{(S)-butanol-}1\text{-}d}{CH_3CH_2CH_2-\overset{\overset{\displaystyle H}{|}}{\underset{\underset{\displaystyle D}{|}}{C}}-OH} + CH_3CO_2^-$$

Implicit in the foregoing statement is the assumption that the newly formed carbon-oxygen bond is not broken in the ester hydrolysis step. As we shall see in Section 18.6, the normal mechanism for this reaction involves cleavage of the other carbon-oxygen bond, as indicated below.

$$\text{This bond cleaves.} \searrow \quad \overset{\displaystyle O}{\underset{}{R-O-\overset{\|}{C}-R'}}$$

That is, ester hydrolysis *does not proceed by the S_N2 mechanism*, even when the ester group is attached to a primary carbon.

Tertiary halides also undergo hydrolysis, but this reaction occurs by the S_N1 rather than the S_N2 mechanism. The reaction is best carried out by shaking the halide with aqueous sodium carbonate. The carbonate neutralizes the acid formed by hydrolysis but avoids the high concentration of hydroxide ion that encourages elimination. Unimolecular elimination is more difficult to avoid. However, this side reaction may be minimized by using highly aqueous solvents and by operating at low temperature. Nevertheless, hydrolysis of tertiary halides involves carbocation intermediates, and such intermediates have several modes of reaction available besides reaction with water. As discussed in Section 10.6.B, rearrangements frequently occur.

The conversions of alkyl halides to alcohols discussed in this section are, by and large, *not important synthetic laboratory processes*. This is not due solely to deficiencies in the methods (although there obviously are some) but also to the practical fact that the halides are commonly obtained from alcohols in the first place. Hydrolysis of sulfonate esters is also a perfectly good reaction, but they are invariably prepared from alcohols. Hydrolysis of halides is an important industrial reaction for those halides obtained commercially by direct halogenation of hydrocarbons. More important laboratory syntheses of alcohols will be discussed in subsequent chapters as reactions of other functional groups.

EXERCISE 10.6 Write equations showing how each of the following alcohols can be prepared from an alkyl halide.
(a) (R)-1-butanol-1-^2H (b) 4-methyl-1-pentanol   (c) 1-methylcyclohexanol

---

Methanol at one time was prepared commercially by the dry distillation of wood and had the commercial name of "wood alcohol." It is now prepared on a large scale by catalytic hydrogenation of carbon monoxide. Methanol is toxic; ingestion of small amounts causes nausea and blindness, and death can result from ingestion of 100 mL or less. It is an important industrial solvent and reagent and is also used to denature ethanol.

Ethanol is prepared for consumption in beverages by fermentation of sugars, but industrial alcohol is prepared by other routes such as the hydration of ethylene (Section 11.6.B). Ethanol is toxic in large quantities but is a normal intermediate in metabolism and, unlike methanol, is metabolized by normal enzymatic body processes. It is an important solvent and reagent in industrial processes and in such use is often "denatured" by addition of toxic and unappetizing diluents. Alcohol for consumption is heavily taxed, but denatured alcohol is not (for example, the 1982 price of 100% ethanol was $1.85-1.97 per gal; the federal distilled spirits tax was $21.00 per gal).

t-Butyl alcohol has a much higher octane number than straight-run gasoline (108 versus 70). For some time, it has been used for increasing the octane rating in the production of unleaded gasoline. It has the advantage of being a "clean" octane booster, in contrast to tetraethyllead, which is converted to potentially dangerous lead oxides upon combustion. Unfortunately, the supply of *t*-butyl alcohol is sufficient to treat only a minute fraction of the gasoline produced in the United States.

10.6 Reactions of Alcohols

A. Reactions of Alkoxides with Alkyl Halides

The alkali alkoxides, produced by reaction of alcohols with alkali metals, are important reagents as bases in nonaqueous media and as nucleophilic reagents. An example of the latter use is the reaction of potassium *t*-butoxide and methyl iodide to form *t*-butyl methyl ether.

$$(C_2H_5)_3COH + K \longrightarrow \tfrac{1}{2} H_2 + (C_2H_5)_3CO^- K^+$$

$$(C_2H_5)_3CO^- K^+ + CH_3I \longrightarrow (C_2H_5)_3COCH_3 + KI$$

This is a typical example of a reaction that proceeds by the S_N2 mechanism. The reaction is a good method for preparing ethers from primary halides that have no β-substituents. Other kinds of halides give more or less elimination.

$$(C_2H_5)_3CCl + CH_3O^- K^+ \longrightarrow (C_2H_5)_2C{=}CHCH_3 + KCl + CH_3OH$$
$$\text{100\% elimination}$$

In those cases that give a large amount of elimination, the reaction may be used as a method for the synthesis of alkenes. Potassium *t*-butoxide is frequently used as a reagent for dehydrohalogenation because of its high basicity and because it is moderately soluble in nonpolar organic solvents such as benzene (C_6H_6).

EXERCISE 10.7 Which of the following ethers could be prepared from an alcohol and an alkyl halide?

      $\overset{\displaystyle OCH_3}{\underset{\displaystyle |}{}}$

(a) $CH_3CHCH_2CH_3$ (b) $(CH_3)_3COCH(CH_3)_2$ (c) $CH_3CH_2OCH_2C(CH_3)_3$

B. Conversion of Alcohols into Alkyl Halides

Sodium bromide is slightly soluble in ethanol. Such a solution can be refluxed indefinitely with no reaction; ethyl bromide and sodium hydroxide are *not* formed. Indeed, we have just seen that the reverse reaction, *hydrolysis* of ethyl bromide, can be carried out readily.

$$C_2H_5OH + Br^- \overset{K}{\rightleftharpoons} C_2H_5Br + OH^-$$

For this system, the thermodynamics is such that equilibrium lies far to the left (Section 4.2).

$$K = \frac{[C_2H_5Br][OH^-]}{[C_2H_5OH][Br^-]} \cong 10^{-19}$$

Consequently, the rate of reaction of ethanol with bromide ion is totally negligible compared to the reverse reaction. (Remember that $K = k_1/k_{-1}$; for the foregoing reaction, k_{-1} must be greater than k_1 by a factor of 10^{19}!)

However, if some sulfuric acid is added to our solution of sodium bromide in ethanol, reaction does occur (of course, the same result is obtained if a mixture of ethanol and hydrobromic acid is used from the start).

$$C_2H_5OH + HBr \longrightarrow C_2H_5Br + H_2O$$

Why this dramatic difference? For one thing, the equilibrium constant for the reaction of ethanol and hydrogen bromide to give ethyl bromide and sodium bromide must obviously be favorable, or net reaction would not be observed. Indeed, it has been estimated that the equilibrium constant for reaction of ethanol and hydrogen bromide is approximately 10^2.

$$K = \frac{[C_2H_5Br][H_2O]}{[C_2H_5OH][HBr]} \cong 10^2$$

This large change in equilibrium constant (more than 20 orders of magnitude) results from both an increase in rate constant of the forward reaction (k_1) and a decrease in the rate constant for the reverse reaction (k_{-1}). The rate constant for the reaction of ethyl bromide with water (k_{-1}) is less than that for reaction with hydroxide ion, because H_2O is a much weaker nucleophile than OH^-. In the forward reaction, the leaving group is now H_2O, which is a weaker base, and hence a better leaving group, than OH^-. The displacement reaction in this case actually occurs on the intermediate **alkyloxonium salt** which is formed when the strong acid protonates the oxygen of ethanol.

$$C_2H_5OH + HBr \rightleftharpoons C_2H_5OH_2^+ + Br^-$$

$$Br^- + CH_2-\overset{+}{O}H_2 \longrightarrow Br-CH_2 + OH_2$$
$$\qquad\quad |\qquad\qquad\qquad\quad |$$
$$\qquad\quad CH_3 \qquad\qquad\qquad CH_3$$

Protonation converts the substrate from one with a very poor leaving group (hydroxide ion) to one with a better leaving group (water).

The foregoing reaction is only another example of a nucleophilic displacement. For primary alcohols, the reaction proceeds by the S_N2 mechanism and can be a useful method for preparing primary alkyl halides. The reaction is carried out by refluxing the alcohol with a mixture of concentrated sulfuric acid and either sodium bromide or hydrobromic acid.

A mixture of 71 mL of 48% hydrobromic acid, 30.5 mL of concentrated sulfuric acid, and 37 g of *n*-butyl alcohol is refluxed for 2 hr. The product is separated, washed, and distilled to yield 50 g (95%) of *n*-butyl bromide.

For the preparation of primary alkyl chlorides, more vigorous conditions are required because chloride ion is a poorer nucleophile than bromide. A mixture of concentrated hydrochloric acid and zinc chloride, the so-called Lucas reagent, is frequently used. Zinc chloride is a powerful Lewis acid that serves the same purpose as does a proton in coordinating with the hydroxy oxygen.

$$\text{\textasciitilde\textasciitilde OH} + HCl \xrightarrow[150°C]{ZnCl_2} \text{\textasciitilde\textasciitilde Cl}$$
$$(76-78\%)$$

> A mixture of 371 g of *n*-butyl alcohol, 1.363 kg of anhydrous zinc chloride, and 864 mL of concentrated hydrochloric acid is heated in an oil bath at 150°C. The product *n*-butyl chloride, 352–361 g (76–78%), is distilled from the reaction mixture over a 1-hr period.

Secondary alcohols react more readily than primary alcohols under these conditions. For example, the foregoing HCl-ZnCl$_2$ procedure may also be applied for the conversion of 2-butanol to 2-chlorobutane. In this case, a reaction temperature of only 140°C is required, and the yield of alkyl halide is 85-88%.

$$\underset{OH}{\bigwedge\!\!\bigvee} + HCl \xrightarrow[140°C]{ZnCl_2} \underset{Cl}{\bigwedge\!\!\bigvee}$$
$$(85-88\%)$$

Tertiary alcohols react the most rapidly of all. For example, *t*-butyl alcohol is converted into *t*-butyl chloride simply by shaking with hydrochloric acid at room temperature.

$$(CH_3)_3COH + HCl \xrightarrow[25°C]{H_2O} (CH_3)_3CCl$$

> A mixture of 74 g of *t*-butyl alcohol and 247 mL of concentrated hydrochloric acid is shaken in a separatory funnel at room temperature. After 15–20 min, the upper layer is drawn off and washed with dilute sodium bicarbonate solution until neutral. The yield of *t*-butyl chloride is 72–82 g (78–88%).

There is ample evidence that, unlike primary alcohols, secondary and tertiary alcohols react with hydrohalic acids by the S$_N$1 mechanism; that is, the reactions involve carbocation intermediates. One strong piece of evidence in this regard is the observation of skeletal rearrangements, a phenomenon that we shall consider in detail in the next section.

> **EXERCISE 10.8** Write a mechanism for reaction of *t*-butyl alcohol with HBr. Be careful to show each step (there are three).

In summary, OH$^-$ is too basic to function as an effective leaving group in nucleophilic substitution reactions, either by the S$_N$1 or S$_N$2 mechanism. Protic acids can catalyze the substitution process by protonating the OH group of the alcohol, converting it to a much better leaving group, H$_2$O. The ensuing substitution reaction takes place by the S$_N$2 mechanism in primary systems and by the S$_N$1 mechanism in secondary and tertiary systems.

There are other ways in which the poor leaving group OH$^-$ may be converted into a better one. Thionyl chloride, SOCl$_2$, is a colorless liquid with b.p. 79°C. It reacts rapidly with water to give sulfur dioxide and HCl.

$$SOCl_2 + H_2O \longrightarrow 2\ HCl + SO_2$$

Thionyl chloride also reacts readily with primary and secondary alcohols, giving the corresponding alkyl chloride, sulfur dioxide, and HCl. An organic base is usually added to catalyze the substitution reaction and to neutralize the acid that is produced.

(85%)

Pyridine is a heterocyclic amine, b.p. 115°C. Like the nitrogen of ammonia, the pyridine nitrogen has a nonbonded electron pair that may accept a proton. Pyridine is a weak base (approximately 10^6 less basic than ammonia), and is soluble in water. Because of these properties, it is frequently used as an acid scavenger and mildly basic catalyst in organic reactions.

pyridine   pyridinium ion

In the reaction of an alcohol with thionyl chloride, the first step is formation of a **chlorosulfite ester**. In this intermediate, the hydroxy group of the alcohol has effectively been converted into a better leaving group, since displacement by a nucleophile produces SO_2 and Cl^-.

n-butyl chlorosulfite

EXERCISE 10.9 On the basis of the foregoing mechanism, explain how pyridine *promotes* the reaction of an alcohol with $SOCl_2$.

Another reagent that can be used to activate a hydroxy group so that it can function as a leaving group is phosphorus tribromide, PBr_3. This substance is a dense, colorless liquid with b.p. 173°C that is prepared by the direct reaction of phosphorus with bromine. It reacts with water to give phosphorous acid and HBr.

$$PBr_3 + 3\ H_2O \longrightarrow 3\ HBr + H_3PO_3$$

The reaction of PBr_3 with three mole-equivalents of an alcohol produces first a phosphite ester, which may be isolated if the reaction is conducted at low temperature and the reaction time is minimized.

$$3 \quad \underset{\text{OH}}{\bigwedge\!\!\!\!\!\bigwedge} + \text{PBr}_3 \longrightarrow \left(\underset{\text{O}}{\bigwedge\!\!\!\!\!\bigwedge} \right)_3 \!\! \text{P} + 3\ \text{HBr}$$

triisobutyl phosphite

However, the mixture of alcohol and PBr$_3$ is usually allowed to react further, until the initially formed phosphite has reacted with the HBr to give the alkyl bromide and phosphorous acid.

$$\left(\underset{\text{O}}{\bigwedge\!\!\!\!\!\bigwedge} \right)_3 \!\! \text{P} + 3\ \text{HBr} \longrightarrow 3\ \underset{\text{Br}}{\bigwedge\!\!\!\!\!\bigwedge} + \text{H}_3\text{PO}_3$$

The substitution reaction occurs by the S$_N$2 mechanism, with bromide being the attacking nucleophile and the protonated phosphite being the leaving group.

$$\text{Br}^- \quad \underset{\underset{\text{H}}{|}}{\overset{\text{O}^+ - \text{P(OR)}_2}{\bigwedge\!\!\!\!\!\bigwedge}} \longrightarrow \underset{\text{Br}}{\bigvee\!\!\!\bigwedge} + \text{(RO)}_2\text{POH}$$

Isobutyl alcohol is maintained at 0°C with PBr$_3$ for 4 hr. The product is washed, dried, and distilled to give 60% of isobutyl bromide.

The reaction also works well with most secondary alcohols, although with such compounds, the reaction temperature must be no higher than 0°C in order to avoid carbocation rearrangements.

Thionyl chloride and phosphorus tribromide are commercially available and are common laboratory chemicals. Phosphorus triiodide is a red solid that decomposes on heating. It is usually prepared *in situ* by heating red phosphorus, iodine, and the appropriate alcohol.

$$3\ \text{CH}_3\text{OH} + \tfrac{3}{2}\ \text{I}_2 + \text{P} \longrightarrow 3\ \text{CH}_3\text{I} + \text{H}_3\text{PO}_3$$

Iodine is added over a period of several hours to a refluxing mixture of red phosphorus and methanol. Methyl iodide is distilled, washed, dried, and redistilled: yield 94%.

> **EXERCISE 10.10** Write balanced equations showing how the following alkyl halides may be prepared from the corresponding alcohols. In each case carefully write out each step in the reaction mechanism, showing all reaction products, both organic and inorganic.
> (a) CH$_3$CH$_2$OCH$_2$CH$_2$Br   (b) 2-chloropentane   (c) 1-iodobutane

The foregoing inorganic reagents (SOCl$_2$, PBr$_3$, PI$_3$) are useful mainly for the conversion of primary and secondary alcohols to the corresponding halides. The major advantages of these reagents, compared to the hydrohalic acids, is that milder reaction conditions are required and carbocation rearrangements (Section 10.6.C) are less important. The ultimate way to minimize carbocation formation, and thus avoid the problems that are usually associated with reactions involving these intermediates, is to convert the alcohol first to the **sulfonate ester**, which is then allowed to react with halide ion under conditions favorable for the S$_N$2 mechanism.

Common reagents for the formation of sulfonate esters are benzenesulfonyl chloride, $C_6H_5SO_2Cl$, and p-toluenesulfonyl chloride, $CH_3C_6H_4SO_2Cl$ (Section 25.5). These compounds react with primary and secondary alcohols, generally in the presence of a tertiary amine such as pyridine, to produce sulfonate esters.

benzenesulfonyl   pyridine
chloride

4-chlorobutyl benzenesulfonate

We saw in Chapter 9 that sulfonate ions are good leaving groups in substitution reactions, since the sulfonate anion is the conjugate base of a strong acid (notice the similarity of benzenesulfonic acid to sulfuric acid). Such esters react with halide ion in inert solvents to give alkyl halides and the sulfonate ion.

Note that the benzenesulfonate ion is displaced selectively in this reaction, even though displacement of chloride ion might also have occurred. The benzenesulfonate ion is about 100 times more reactive as a leaving group than chloride.

Other common reagents of this type are lithium chloride in dimethylformamide or ethanol and sodium bromide in dimethylformamide (DMF) or dimethyl sulfoxide (DMSO).

3-pentyl p-toluenesulfonate   (85%)
3-bromopentane

Of course, the preceding method is useful only with primary and secondary alcohols. With tertiary alcohols, the S_N2 displacement reaction is so slow that side reactions (mainly elimination) dominate.

EXERCISE 10.11 What product is expected when each of the following alcohols is converted into the corresponding alkyl bromide by the sulfonate displacement method?
(a) (S)-2-pentanol   (b) cis-4-methylcyclohexanol

C. Carbocation Rearrangements

In the preceeding Section, we saw that the hydroxy group of an alcohol may be replaced by a halide nucleophile if it is converted into a better leaving group by reaction with a proton, an inorganic halide such as $SOCl_2$, or a sulfonyl chloride such as benzenesulfonyl chloride. Many of the examples given were primary alcohols, which react by the S_N2 mechanism. In these cases, the reactions are relatively uncomplicated by side reactions. Other examples given were for tertiary alcohols, which react by the S_N1 mechanism. Again, the transformation is relatively simple and the reaction conditions are mild; one simply treats the tertiary alcohol with either the aqueous hydrohalic acid or with the anhydrous HX at low temperature. Yields of alkyl halide are generally good, and there is little complication by side reactions. With secondary alcohols, the situation is often more complicated. With the sulfonate method, the actual substitution reaction can be carried out under conditions that are favorable for the S_N2 process, and the situation is relatively straightforward. However, when using HBr, $HCl-ZnCl_2$ ("Lucas Reagent"), or PBr_3, the substitution reaction usually occurs by the S_N1 process, by way of the intermediate carbocation.

$$R-OH + HBr \rightleftharpoons R-\overset{+}{O}H_2 + Br^-$$

$$R-\overset{+}{O}H_2 \rightleftharpoons R^+ + H_2O$$

$$R^+ + Br^- \longrightarrow R-Br$$

One important drawback in carbocation reactions is the alternative reaction pathways that are available. We have already discussed one such reaction, E1 elimination. The electron-deficient carbocation center tends to attract electron density from adjacent bonds, and these bonds become weaker. One result is the ready loss of a proton to a basic solvent molecule. In some systems, another important side reaction can occur—rearrangement. The hydrogen attached by the weakened bond *and its bonding electrons* can move to the cationic center, thus generating a new carbocation.

Note that in this process the positive charge moves to the carbon to which the hydrogen was originally attached. Such rearrangements are especially important when the new carbocation is more stable than the old, but the reaction can occur even when the two carbocations have comparable stability. Such reactions are common for secondary carbocations but almost never involve primary carbocations. For primary systems, the alternative S_N2 process is generally so favorable that the relatively energetic primary carbocation is never produced. Rearrangements are less common in tertiary systems because it is usually the case that any rearrangement would produce a *less stable* carbocation.

An example of a process involving carbocation rearrangement is seen in the reaction of 3-methyl-2-butanol with HBr; the sole product is 2-bromo-2-methylbutane. In this case, the intermediate secondary carbocation rearranges to the more stable tertiary carbocation much more rapidly than it reacts with bromide ion.

$$CH_3\overset{\overset{\displaystyle H}{|}}{\underset{\underset{\displaystyle CH_3}{|}}{C}}-CHOHCH_3 \underset{}{\overset{H^+}{\rightleftharpoons}} CH_3\overset{\overset{\displaystyle H}{|}}{\underset{\underset{\displaystyle CH_3}{|}}{C}}-\overset{\overset{\displaystyle \overset{+}{O}H_2}{}}{C}HCH_3 \underset{}{\overset{-H_2O}{\rightleftharpoons}}$$

$$CH_3\overset{\overset{\displaystyle H}{|}}{\underset{\underset{\displaystyle CH_3}{|}}{\overset{+}{C}}}-CHCH_3 \rightleftharpoons CH_3\overset{\overset{\displaystyle H}{|}}{\underset{\underset{\displaystyle CH_3}{|}}{C}}-\overset{+}{C}HCH_3 \overset{HBr}{\longrightarrow} (CH_3)_2\overset{\overset{\displaystyle Br}{|}}{C}CH_2CH_3$$

| secondary carbocation | tertiary carbocation (more stable) | actual product |

Another interesting example is seen in the reactions of 2-pentanol and 3-pentanol with hot hydrobromic acid; both alcohols give mixtures of 2- and 3-bromopentane.

$$CH_3CH_2CH_2CHOHCH_3 \overset{HBr}{\longrightarrow} CH_3CH_2CH_2CHBrCH_3 + CH_3CH_2CHBrCH_2CH_3$$
$$(86\%) \qquad\qquad\qquad (14\%)$$

$$CH_3CH_2CHOHCH_2CH_3 \overset{HBr}{\longrightarrow} CH_3CH_2CH_2CHBrCH_3 + CH_3CH_2CHBrCH_2CH_3$$
$$(20\%) \qquad\qquad\qquad (80\%)$$

The mechanism whereby these two products are formed is

$$CH_3CH_2CH_2\underset{\underset{\displaystyle +OH_2}{|}}{C}HCH_3 \rightleftharpoons CH_3CH_2CH_2\overset{+}{C}HCH_3 \overset{Br^-}{\longrightarrow} CH_3CH_2CH_2CHBrCH_3$$

$$\Big\Updownarrow$$

$$CH_3CH_2\underset{\underset{\displaystyle +OH_2}{|}}{C}HCH_2CH_3 \rightleftharpoons CH_3CH_2\overset{+}{C}HCH_2CH_3 \overset{Br^-}{\longrightarrow} CH_3CH_2CHBrCH_2CH_3$$

Note that equilibration of the carbocations is not complete. In this case, the rate of reaction of the carbocation with bromide ion is comparable to the rate of rearrangement.

> **EXERCISE 10.12** Suggest a reason why 3-methyl-2-butanol gives completely the rearranged bromide, while rearrangement is not complete in the 2-pentanol case.

It is important to remember that these rearrangements generally do not occur in primary systems. For example, the reaction of 1-butanol with HBr gives 1-bromobutane in good yield; reaction occurs by the S_N2 mechanism, and carbocations are not involved.

$$CH_3CH_2\underset{\underset{\displaystyle H}{|}}{C}HCH_2-\overset{+}{O}H_2 \overset{Br^-}{\longrightarrow} CH_3CH_2CH_2CH_2-Br$$

$$\not\Updownarrow$$

$$CH_3CH_2\overset{+}{\underset{\underset{\displaystyle H}{|}}{C}}HCH_2$$

Even isobutyl alcohol on heating with HBr and H_2SO_4 gives mainly isobutyl bromide.

The formation of the relatively stable *t*-butyl cation in this case *does* result in the formation of a little *t*-butyl bromide.

$$(CH_3)_2CHCH_2Br \xleftarrow{Br^-} CH_3\overset{\overset{\displaystyle H}{|}}{\underset{\underset{\displaystyle CH_3}{|}}{C}}CH_2\overset{+}{-}\overset{..}{O}H_2 \longrightarrow CH_3\overset{+}{\underset{\underset{\displaystyle CH_3}{|}}{C}}\overset{\overset{\displaystyle H}{|}}{CH_2} \xrightarrow{Br^-} (CH_3)_3CBr$$
(80%)   (20%)

However, primary alcohols that have a quaternary carbon (a carbon attached to four other carbons) next to the alcohol carbon react with complete rearrangement.

$$CH_3\overset{\overset{\displaystyle CH_3}{|}}{\underset{\underset{\displaystyle CH_3}{|}}{C}}CH_2\overset{+}{-}\overset{..}{O}H_2 \longrightarrow CH_3\overset{+}{\underset{\underset{\displaystyle CH_3}{|}}{C}}\overset{\overset{\displaystyle CH_3}{|}}{CH_2} \xrightarrow{Br^-} (CH_2)_2\overset{\overset{\displaystyle Br}{|}}{C}CH_2CH_3$$

Recall that S_N2 reactions of compounds such as this (neopentyl-type compounds) are very slow (Section 9.3). Consequently the alternative rearrangement reaction is able to compete and becomes the dominating reaction. This example shows also that alkyl groups can migrate as well as hydrogen.

Alcohols with a cycloalkyl group next to the alcohol carbon frequently undergo rearrangement with resultant **ring expansion**. Ring expansion is particularly prone to occur when there is a decrease in ring strain.

This reaction involves formation of an intermediate carbocation, which undergoes rearrangement of one of the ring bonds to give a cyclopentyl cation.

The driving force for this rearrangement is relief of ring strain—the cyclobutyl system has about 26 kcal mole^{-1} of strain, while the cyclopentyl cation has only about 6 kcal mole^{-1} (see Table 5.5). For this reason, ring expansion occurs even though it involves rearrangement of a tertiary to a secondary carbocation.

EXERCISE 10.13 Make a molecular model of 2-cyclobutyl-2-propanol. Remove the hydroxy group; the vacant valence on the propane chain represents the carbocation center. Now disconnect one of the C-1, C-2 bonds of the cyclobutane ring and reattach it to the carbocation center. Note that the product of these operations is a model of the 2,2-dimethylcyclopentyl cation. Repeat these operations until you are thoroughly at ease with the bond reorganization that occurs in the ring expansion.

In the last two sections, we have considered a number of reactions that may be used for accomplishing the important conversion ROH $\longrightarrow$ RX, and we have various complications to watch out for. The best overall methods may be summarized as follows.

1. **Primary alcohols with no β-branching**
   chloride: $SOCl_2$ + pyridine (generally better than $ZnCl_2$-HCl)
   bromide: PBr_3 or HBr-H_2SO_4
   iodide: $P + I_2$
2. **Primary alcohols with β-branching**
   chloride: $SOCl_2$ + pyridine
   bromide: PBr_3
3. **Secondary alcohols**
   chloride: $SOCl_2$ + pyridine
   bromide: PBr_3 (low temperature, less than 0°C)
   (The two-step sequence alcohol $\longrightarrow$ sulfonate ester $\longrightarrow$ halide gives
   a product of higher purity.)
4. **Tertiary alcohols**
   chloride: HCl at 0°C
   bromide: HBr at 0°C

EXERCISE 10.14 Suggest a method for preparation of each of the following alkyl halides
from an alcohol.
(a) 3-chloro-3-ethylpentane   (b) 1-chloropentane
(c) 1-bromo-2-ethylbutane   (d) (S)-2-bromooctane
(e) *trans*-1-chloro-3-methylcyclohexane

D. Dehydration of Alcohols: Formation of Ethers and Alkenes

When a primary alcohol is treated with sulfuric acid alone, the product is an **alkylsulfuric acid**. The reaction is an equilibrium process—the product alkylsulfuric acid is
readily hydrolyzed by excess water. If the transformation is carried out with excess
sulfuric acid at 0°C, the reaction proceeds to completion and the alkylsulfuric acid may
be isolated.

$$C_2H_5OH + H_2SO_4 \xrightarrow{0°C} C_2H_5OSO_2OH + H_2O$$

(excess)

However, if ethanol is *heated* with concentrated sulfuric acid, ethyl ether is produced
in high yield.

$$2\ C_2H_5OH \xrightarrow[140°C]{H_2SO_4} C_2H_5OC_2H_5 + H_2O$$

The detailed mechanism of the reaction under these conditions is not known. One
possibility is that the alkyloxonium ion formed by reaction of alcohol with sulfuric acid
is attacked by another alcohol molecule instead.

$$RCH_2-\overset{}{\underset{H}{O}} + \overset{+}{\underset{R}{CH_2-OH_2}} \longrightarrow RCH_2-\overset{+}{\underset{H}{O}}-CH_2R + OH_2$$

Alternatively the alkylsulfuric acid may be an intermediate.

$$RCH_2-\overset{}{\underset{H}{O}} + \overset{}{\underset{R}{CH_2-OSO_2OH}} \longrightarrow RCH_2-\overset{+}{\underset{H}{O}}-CH_2R + HSO_4^-$$

In the case of primary alcohols, the reaction is an acceptable way of preparing symmetrical ethers.

> *n*-Butyl alcohol and concentrated sulfuric acid are refluxed with provision to remove water as it is formed, either with a suitable trap or by a fractionating column. The reaction mixture is maintained at 130–140°C. The reaction mixture is allowed to cool and, after washing and drying, is distilled to give di-*n*-butyl ether.

At still higher temperature, elimination occurs to give the alkene.

$$C_2H_5OH \xrightarrow[170°C]{H_2SO_4} CH_2{=}CH_2 + H_2O$$

Secondary and tertiary alcohols generally give only the elimination products.

cyclohexanol   cyclohexene
(79–84%)

> A mixture of 1 kg of technical grade cyclohexanol and 200 g of 85% phosphoric acid is heated at 165–170°C for 4–5 hr and at 200°C for 30 min. The upper layer is separated, dried and distilled to obtain 660–690 g (79–84%) of cyclohexene, b.p. 81–83°C.

Tertiary alcohols eliminate water readily on heating with even traces of acid. If elimination is to be avoided, the alcohols should be distilled at low temperature (vacuum distillation) or in apparatus that has been rinsed with ammonia.

> **EXERCISE 10.15** Explain why acid-catalyzed dehydration of an alcohol is not a desirable method for the preparation of 1-butene.

E. Oxidation of Alcohols: Formation of Aldehydes and Ketones

Primary and secondary alcohols can be oxidized to carbonyl compounds.

$$RCH_2OH \xrightarrow[-2\,H]{[O]} \underset{\text{an aldehyde}}{R{-}\overset{\overset{\displaystyle O}{\|}}{C}{-}H}$$

$$\underset{}{R{-}\overset{\overset{\displaystyle OH}{|}}{C}H{-}R} \xrightarrow[-2\,H]{[O]} \underset{\text{a ketone}}{R{-}\overset{\overset{\displaystyle O}{\|}}{C}{-}R}$$

Many procedures are available for accomplishing these transformations, but the most common general oxidizing agent is some form of chromium(VI), which becomes reduced to chromium(III).

> Chromium trioxide, CrO_3, also known as chromic anhydride, forms red, deliquescent crystals. It is soluble in water and in sulfuric acid.

Sodium or potassium dichromate forms orange aqueous solutions that convert to the yellow chromate salt under basic conditions.

$$2\,CrO_4^{2-} + 2\,H^+ \rightleftharpoons Cr_2O_7^{2-} + H_2O$$

yellow   orange

Pyridinium chlorochromate (PCC) is produced by the reaction of equimolar amounts of pyridine (page 203), chromium trioxide, and HCl. It is a yellow-orange, crystalline material, m.p. 205°C, and is soluble in organic solvents such as methylene chloride and chloroform.

$$+ CrO_3 + HCl \longrightarrow$$

pyridine

pyridinium chlorochromate
(PCC)

Primary alcohols give aldehydes on warming with sodium dichromate and aqueous sulfuric acid. However, in aqueous solution, aldehydes are also readily oxidized to give carboxylic acids (Section 14.9.A). Thus, this method is only successful for the synthesis of an aldehyde if it is of sufficiently low molecular weight that it may be distilled from solution as formed. For example, *n*-butyl alcohol can be oxidized in this way to give a 50% yield of butyraldehyde.

$$CH_3CH_2CH_2CH_2OH + H_2Cr_2O_7 \longrightarrow CH_3CH_2CH_2CHO$$

(50%)
butyraldehyde

In practice, only aldehydes that boil significantly below 100°C can be conveniently prepared in this manner (since it would not be possible to distil a higher boiling aldehyde from an aqueous reaction mixture). This effectively limits the method to the production of a few simple aldehydes, and it is not an important synthetic method.

A virtue of pyridinium chlorochromate (PCC) is that it is soluble in organic solvents. Therefore, it may be used for the oxidation of primary alcohols to aldehydes under nonaqueous conditions. An example is seen in the preparation of oct-2-yn-1-al from oct-2-yn-1-ol.

$$\xrightarrow[\text{CH}_2\text{Cl}_2]{\text{PCC}}$$

oct-2-yn-l-ol

(84%)
oct-2-yn-l-al

Since ketones are more stable to general oxidation conditions than aldehydes, chromic acid oxidations are more important for secondary alcohols. In one common procedure a 20% excess of sodium dichromate is added to an aqueous mixture of the alcohol and a stoichiometric amount of acid.

4-ethylcyclohexanol   4-ethylcyclohexanone
(90%)

An especially convenient oxidizing agent is Jones reagent, a solution of chromic acid in dilute sulfuric acid. The secondary alcohol in acetone solution is "titrated" with the reagent with stirring at 15–20°C. Oxidation is rapid and efficient. The green chromium salts separate from the reaction mixture as a heavy sludge; the supernatant liquid consists mainly of an acetone solution of the product ketone.

cyclooctanol   cyclooctanone

Chromium(VI) oxidations are known to proceed by way of a chromate ester of the alcohol. If the alcohol has one or more hydrogens attached to the carbinol position, a base-catalyzed elimination occurs, yielding the aldehyde or ketone and a chromium(IV) species. The overall effect of these two consecutive reactions is oxidation of the alcohol and reduction of the chromium.

$$(1) \quad R_2CHOH + H_2CrO_4 \rightleftharpoons R_2CH-O-\overset{\overset{O}{\|}}{\underset{\underset{O}{\|}}{Cr}}-OH + H_2O$$

$$(2) \quad B: \overset{\frown}{R_2C}-O-\overset{\overset{O}{\|}}{\underset{\underset{O}{\|}}{Cr}}-OH \longrightarrow R_2C=O + HCrO_3^- + BH^+$$

The chromium(IV) produced in the elimination undergoes rapid reaction with a molecule containing chromium(VI) to produce two chromium(V) species. These chromium(V)-containing molecules function further as two-electron oxidants to produce more aldehyde or ketone and two chromium(III) species, the ultimate form of the chromium in such reactions.

Under conditions such as these, tertiary alcohols do not generally react, although under proper conditions the chromate ester can be isolated.

$$2\,(CH_3)_3COH + H_2CrO_4 \rightleftharpoons (CH_3)_3CO-\overset{\overset{O}{\|}}{\underset{\underset{O}{\|}}{Cr}}-OC(CH_3)_3 + 2\,H_2O$$

Since there is no carbinol proton to eliminate in the case of a tertiary alcohol, such esters are stable. If the chromate ester is treated with excess water, simple hydrolysis occurs with regeneration of the tertiary alcohol and chromic acid.

Balancing Oxidation-Reduction Reactions. Organic redox reactions may be balanced by the method of half-cells often taught in beginning chemistry courses for inorganic redox reactions. To use this method, first write an equation for the substance being oxidized, showing the hydrogens that are lost in the process as protons. Add enough electrons to the side of the equation showing the protons so that the equation is *balanced for electrons*. For oxidation of an alcohol, two hydrogens are lost, so we must add two electrons to the right side of the equation. (In other words, oxidation of an alcohol is a "two-electron" oxidation.)

$$RCH_2OH = RCHO + 2\,H^+ + 2\,e^-$$

Next, write an equation showing the change that the oxidizing agent undergoes. One side of this equation will contain the oxidizing agent and the other will contain its ultimate reduced form. In the case of chromium(VI), the reduced form is chromium(III). Add enough electrons to balance this equation.

$$3\,e^- + Cr^{6+} = Cr^{3+}$$

Now add the two half-reactions together, multiplying by the appropriate factor so that the electrons cancel.

$$\begin{array}{l} 3 \times [RCH_2OH = RCHO + 2\,H^+ + 2\,e^-] \\ \underline{2 \times [3\,e^- + Cr^{6+} = Cr^{3+}]} \\ 3\,RCH_2OH + 2\,Cr^{6+} = 3\,RCHO + 6\,H^+ + 2\,Cr^{3+} \end{array}$$

As shown by the foregoing procedure, 3 moles of alcohol are oxidized by 2 moles of chromium(VI) reagent.

EXERCISE 10.16 How many grams of sodium dichromate is required to convert 70 g of cyclohexanol to cyclohexanone?

10.7 Nomenclature of Ethers

The common names of ethers are derived by naming the two alkyl groups and adding the word ether.

$$CH_3OCH_2CH_3 \qquad CH_3OC(CH_3)_3$$
ethyl methyl ether *t*-butyl methyl ether

In symmetrical ethers the prefix di- is used. Although the prefix is often omitted, it should be included to avoid confusion.

$$CH_3CH_2OCH_2CH_3 \qquad (CH_3)_2CHOCH(CH_3)_2$$
diethyl ether diisopropyl ether
(or ethyl ether) (or isopropyl ether)

In the IUPAC system ethers are named as alkoxyalkanes. The larger alkyl group is chosen as the stem.

$$\underset{\text{2-ethoxypentane}}{CH_3CH_2O\overset{\overset{\displaystyle CH_3}{|}}{C}HCH_2CH_2CH_3} \qquad \underset{\text{1-methoxy-2,2-dimethylpropane}}{CH_3\overset{\overset{\displaystyle CH_3}{|}}{\underset{\underset{\displaystyle CH_3}{|}}{C}}CH_2OCH_3} \qquad \underset{\text{1,2-dimethoxyethane}}{CH_3OCH_2CH_2OCH_3}$$

EXERCISE 10.17 Write common and IUPAC names for the following ethers.

(a) (b) (c)

10.8 Physical Properties of Ethers

The physical properties of some ethers are listed in Table 10.4. Note that dimethyl ether is a gas at room temperature and that diethyl ether has a boiling point only about 10°C above normal room temperature. Diethyl ether is an important solvent and has a characteristic odor. It was once used as an anesthetic, but it has been largely replaced for this purpose by other compounds.

The rule of thumb that compounds having no more than four carbons per oxygen are water-soluble holds for ethers as well as for alcohols. Dimethyl ether is completely miscible with water. The solubility of diethyl ether in water is about 10 g per 100 g of H_2O at 25°C. Tetrahydrofuran (b.p. 67°C) is another important solvent. This cyclic ether, commonly abbreviated THF, has essentially the same molecular weight as diethyl ether, but it is much more soluble in water.

tetrahydrofuran (THF)
(b.p. 67°C; miscible with H_2O in all proportions at 25°C)

diethyl ether
(b.p. 34.5°C; 10 g dissolves in 100 g of H_2O at 25°C)

Because of its cyclic structure, THF has lone-pair electrons that are more accessible for hydrogen bonding than those of diethyl ether. The "floppy" ethyl groups in the acyclic compound interfere with hydrogen bonding and cause the water solubility of diethyl ether to be lower. Also note that the cyclic compound has a significantly higher boiling

TABLE 10.4 Physical Properties of Ethers

Compound	Name	Melting Point, °C	Boiling Point, °C
CH_3OCH_3	dimethyl ether	−138.5	−23
$CH_3OCH_2CH_3$	ethyl methyl ether		10.8
$(CH_3CH_2)_2O$	diethyl ether	−116.62	34.5
$CH_3CH_2OCH_2CH_2CH_3$	ethyl propyl ether	−79	63.6
$(CH_3CH_2CH_2)_2O$	dipropyl ether	−122	91
$(CH_3\overset{\underset{\displaystyle CH_3}{\mid}}{CH})_2O$	diisopropyl ether	−86	68
$(CH_3CH_2CH_2CH_2)_2O$	dibutyl ether	−95	142

point; its more compact structure allows for more efficient van der Waals attraction between molecules.

As we shall see, ethers are fairly inert to many reagents. Because of their unreactivity, they are not generally important as chemical reagents. However, their general lack of reactivity, combined with their favorable solvent properties, makes ethers useful solvents for many other reactions. Several ethers that are important as solvents are dioxane (page 198), methyl *t*-butyl ether (MBE), 1,2-dimethoxyethane (glyme), and bis-β-methoxyethyl ether (diglyme).

$$CH_3OCH_2CH_2OCH_3 \qquad CH_3OCH_2CH_2OCH_2CH_2OCH_3 \qquad (CH_3)_3COCH_3$$

1,2-dimethoxyethane   bis-β-methoxyethyl ether   methyl *t*-butyl ether
(glyme, DME)   (diglyme)   (MBE)

10.9 Preparation of Ethers

Ethers may be prepared by the **Williamson ether synthesis** or by the reaction of alcohols with sulfuric acid. The Williamson ether synthesis is simply an S_N2 displacement of a primary alkyl halide or sulfonate ester by an alkoxide ion. The alkoxide may be derived from a primary or secondary alcohol, but the substrate must be primary and have no β-branches.

Methyl and ethyl substrates may be used with tertiary alkoxides. Other halides and sulfonates give too much elimination (Section 11.5).

Since the reaction is a classic example of a an S_N2 reaction, one must keep in mind the principles of that mechanism (Chapter 9) when planning an ether synthesis by this route.

EXERCISE 10.18 Methyl neopentyl ether can be prepared readily from sodium neopentoxide and methyl benzenesulfonate, but not from sodium methoxide and neopentyl benzenesulfonate. Write equations for these two reactions and explain why one combination works and the other does not.

The alcohol-sulfuric acid reaction, which was discussed in Section 10.6.D, is most often used for the conversion of simple primary alcohols into symmetrical ethers.

$$ClCH_2CH_2OH \xrightarrow[\Delta]{H_2SO_4} ClCH_2CH_2OCH_2CH_2Cl$$

(75%)
bis-β-chloroethyl ether

Secondary and tertiary alcohols undergo predominant dehydration when subjected to these conditions. Occasionally some of the symmetrical ether is formed as a by-product in the case of secondary alcohols.

$$CH_3CHOH \xrightarrow{H_2SO_4} CH_3CH=CH_2 + CH_3CH-O-CHCH_3$$

with CH_3 group on the first carbon of the alcohol, and CH_3 and CH_3 groups on the ether.

major product   by-product

The method is generally useless for the preparation of unsymmetrical ethers because complex mixtures are formed.

$$ROH + R'OH \xrightarrow{H^+} ROR + ROR' + R'OR'$$

An exception is the case in which one alcohol is tertiary and the other alcohol is primary or secondary. Since tertiary carbocations form under mild conditions, this method is generally a satisfactory synthetic method.

$$CH_3\overset{CH_3}{\underset{CH_3}{\overset{|}{\underset{|}{C}}}}OH + CH_3\overset{CH_3}{\overset{|}{CHOH}} \xrightarrow[\substack{H_2O \\ 100°C}]{NaHSO_4} CH_3\overset{CH_3}{\underset{CH_3}{\overset{|}{\underset{|}{C}}}}-O-\overset{CH_3}{\overset{|}{CHCH_3}}$$

(82%)

EXERCISE 10.19 Show how the following ethers may be prepared.
(a) 1-methoxy-1-methylcyclohexane   (b) di-*n*-butyl ether

10.10 Reactions of Ethers

Ethers are relatively inert to most reagents. They are stable to base and to most reducing agents. They are also stable to dilute acid but do react with hot concentrated acids. Strong HBr or HI causes cleavage.

$$CH_3CH_2OCH_2CH_3 + 2\,HBr \xrightarrow{\Delta} 2\,CH_3CH_2Br + H_2O$$

The mechanism of this reaction involves an S_N2 displacement by bromide ion on the protonated ether. The alcohol produced reacts further with HBr to yield more alkyl bromide.

(1) $CH_3CH_2OCH_2CH_3 + HBr \rightleftharpoons CH_3CH_2\overset{+}{\underset{H}{O}}CH_2CH_3 + Br^-$

(2) $Br^-: + CH_2-\overset{H}{\overset{\diagup}{O^+}}_{CH_2CH_3} \longrightarrow CH_3CH_2Br + CH_3CH_2OH$
      with CH_3 group

(3) $CH_3CH_2OH + HBr \rightleftharpoons CH_3CH_2\overset{+}{O}H_2\ Br^-$

(4) $Br^-: + CH_2-\overset{+}{O}H_2 \longrightarrow CH_3CH_2Br + H_2O$
      with CH_3 group

With tertiary ethers, carbocations are involved and the reactions tend to be much more complex. Heating such ethers with strong acid generally leads to elimination as the major reaction.

$$CH_3\overset{\displaystyle CH_3}{\underset{\displaystyle CH_3}{\overset{|}{\underset{|}{C}}}}{-}OCH_3 \xrightarrow[\Delta]{H_2SO_4} CH_3\overset{\displaystyle CH_3}{\overset{|}{C}}{=}CH_2 + CH_3OH$$

t-butyl methyl ether   isobutylene

The reaction is not generally useful for preparations unless one of the alkyl groups of the ether is a small tertiary group. In such a case the alkene formed upon elimination volatilizes as it is produced.

EXERCISE 10.20 When methyl neopentyl ether is treated with anhydrous hydrogen bromide, an alcohol and an alkyl bromide are produced. What are they?

One of the most important reactions of ethers is an undesirable one—the reaction with atmospheric oxygen to form peroxides (**autoxidation**).

$$CH_3\overset{}{\underset{\displaystyle CH_3}{\overset{|}{CH}}}{-}O{-}\overset{}{\underset{\displaystyle CH_3}{\overset{|}{CHCH_3}}} + O_2 \longrightarrow CH_3\overset{\displaystyle OOH}{\underset{\displaystyle CH_3}{\overset{|}{\underset{|}{C}}}}{-}O{-}\overset{}{\underset{\displaystyle CH_3}{\overset{|}{CHCH_3}}}$$

a hydroperoxide

Autoxidation occurs by a free radical mechanism.

$$(1)\ RO{-}\overset{\displaystyle H}{\overset{|}{\underset{|}{C}}}{-} + R'\cdot \longrightarrow RO{-}\overset{\displaystyle \cdot}{\overset{}{\underset{|}{C}}}{-} + R'H$$

$$(2)\ RO{-}\overset{\displaystyle \cdot}{\overset{}{\underset{|}{C}}}{-} + O_2 \longrightarrow RO{-}\overset{\displaystyle OO\cdot}{\overset{|}{\underset{|}{C}}}{-}$$

$$(3)\ RO{-}\overset{\displaystyle OO\cdot}{\overset{|}{\underset{|}{C}}}{-} + RO{-}\overset{\displaystyle H}{\overset{|}{\underset{|}{C}}}{-} \longrightarrow RO{-}\overset{\displaystyle OOH}{\overset{|}{\underset{|}{C}}}{-} + RO{-}\overset{\displaystyle \cdot}{\overset{}{\underset{|}{C}}}{-}$$

or

$$RO{-}\overset{\displaystyle OO\cdot}{\overset{|}{\underset{|}{C}}}{-} + RO{-}\overset{\displaystyle \cdot}{\overset{}{\underset{|}{C}}}{-} \longrightarrow RO{-}\overset{}{\underset{|}{\overset{|}{C}}}{-}OO{-}\overset{}{\underset{|}{\overset{|}{C}}}{-}OR$$

a peroxide

Ethers of almost any type that have been exposed to the atmosphere for any length of time invariably contain peroxides. Isopropyl ether is especially treacherous in this regard, but ethyl ether and tetrahydrofuran are also dangerous. One virtue of using methyl *t*-butyl ether (MBE) as a laboratory solvent is the fact that it is not as prone to autoxidation as ethyl ether and THF. Peroxides and hydroperoxides are hazardous because they decompose violently at elevated temperatures, and serious explosions may result. When an ether that contains peroxides is distilled, the less volatile peroxides concentrate in the residue. At the end of the distillation, the temperature increases, and the residual peroxides may explode. For this reason, ethers should never be evaporated to dryness, unless care has been taken to exclude peroxides rigorously.

A simple test for peroxides is to shake a small volume of the ether with aqueous KI solution. If peroxides are present, they oxidize I^- to I_2. The characteristic purple-to-brown color of I_2 is diagnostic of the presence of peroxides. Contaminated ether may be purified by shaking with aqueous ferrous sulfate to reduce the peroxides.

Several years ago one of the authors had an impressive demonstration of the violence of a peroxide explosion. In a laboratory adjacent to his office, a laboratory technician was engaged in purifying about 2 L of old THF, later found to contain substantial amounts of peroxides. The material exploded, virtually demolishing the laboratory, and moving the wall several inches toward the author's desk. Several large bookshelves were knocked over and emptied their contents onto his desk and chair. Only by good fortune was no one injured.

10.11 Cyclic Ethers

A. Epoxides: Oxiranes

Heterocyclic compounds are cyclic structures in which one or more ring atoms are **hetero atoms**, a hetero atom being an element other than carbon. The three-membered ring containing oxygen is the first class of heterocyclic compounds whose chemistry we shall consider. Because they are readily prepared from alkenes (Section 11.6), they are commonly named as "olefin oxides." Hence, the parent member is often called ethylene oxide, although the formal IUPAC nomenclature is oxirane. Oxiranes are also called **epoxides**. Substituents on the oxirane ring require a numbering system. The general rule for heterocyclic rings is that the hetero atom gets the number 1.

ethylene oxide · oxirane   propylene oxide · 2-methyloxirane   isobutylene oxide · 2,2-dimethyloxirane

Ethylene oxide is a significant article of commerce and is prepared industrially by the catalyzed air oxidation of ethylene.

$$CH_2{=}CH_2 \xrightarrow[\underset{\Delta}{Ag}]{O_2} \overset{O}{\overbrace{CH_2{-}CH_2}}$$

Several general laboratory preparations are available. One reaction is an internal S_N2 displacement reaction starting with a β-halo alcohol.

As shown by the foregoing equation, the intramolecular displacement of a halide ion by a neighboring alkoxide group requires that the reacting groups have a specific relationship such that the alkoxide can attack the rear of the carbon-chlorine bond. As we shall see in Section 11.6.B, the required stereoisomer is readily available by the reaction of hypochlorous acid (HOCl) with an alkene.

(70–73%)

(70–73%)
cyclohexene oxide

EXERCISE 10.21 (2R,3R)-3-Chloro-2-butanol is treated with KOH in ethanol. Is the product *cis-* or *trans-*2,3-dimethyloxirane?

Like other ethers, oxiranes undergo carbon-oxygen bond cleavage under acidic conditions. However, because of the large ring strain associated with the three-membered ring (about 25 kcal mole^{-1}, see Section 5.6), they are much more reactive than normal ethers.

The product is a 1,2-diol. As a class, 1,2-diols are called "glycols." They are important industrial compounds. The simplest 1,2-diol, "ethylene glycol," is commonly used as antifreeze for automobile radiators.

As shown by the foregoing mechanism, ring opening of an epoxide is another example of the S_N2 mechanism (Chapter 9) in which the attacking nucleophile is H_2O and the leaving group is ROH. The "leaving group" is, of course, part of the molecule and doesn't leave completely.

The stereochemical outcome of the reaction is inversion at the reaction center. Thus, cyclohexene oxide reacts with aqueous acid to give exclusively *trans*-cyclohexane-1,2-diol.

The oxirane ring is so prone to undergo ring-opening reactions that it even reacts with aqueous base.

The base-catalyzed opening of an epoxide occurs by the S_N2 mechanism with an alkoxide ion as the leaving group and has no counterpart with normal ethers. It occurs with epoxides only because the relief of ring strain provides a potent driving force for reaction.

The two ring-opening reactions have different orientational preferences. The acid-catalyzed process is essentially a carbocation reaction, and reaction tends to occur at that ring carbon which corresponds to the more stable carbocation. That is, reaction with solvent occurs at the more highly substituted ring carbon. Like other reactions that occur by the S_N2 mechanism, the base-catalyzed reaction is subject to steric influences. Reaction occurs at the less hindered carbon. The difference is exemplified by the reactions of 2,2-dimethyloxirane in methanol under acidic and basic conditions.

Acidic conditions

Basic conditions

The product from the reaction of ethylene oxide with hydroxide ion is an alkoxide. Under the proper conditions this species can react with more ethylene oxide.

$$ HO^- \xrightarrow{\triangle} HOCH_2CH_2O^- \xrightarrow{\triangle} HOCH_2CH_2OCH_2CH_2O^- \longrightarrow \text{etc.} $$

The final products are ether alcohols, which are called diethylene glycol, triethylene glycol and so on. These diols are methylated to produce a series of polyethers that have useful solvent properties. These materials are known by the trivial names **glyme,** **diglyme, triglyme,** and so on.

$$HOCH_2CH_2OCH_2CH_2OH \longrightarrow CH_3OCH_2CH_2OCH_2CH_2OCH_3$$

diethylene glycol   diethylene glycol dimethyl ether
(diglyme)

EXERCISE 10.22 Write the equation for the reaction of *trans*-2,3-dimethyloxirane with sulfuric acid in methanol. What is the stereostructure of the product?

An important variation of the ring opening of epoxides with bases is the reaction with organometallic reagents. For example, the sodium salts of 1-alkynes react readily with oxirane itself to give alk-3-yn-1-ols.

The ring opening is an S_N2 reaction in which a carbanion is the nucleophile. This reaction does not occur with ordinary ethers because the RO^- group is normally a poor leaving group; indeed, diethyl ether and tetrahydrofuran are common solvents for these reactions.

A similar reaction occurs with Grignard reagents. The reaction of an organometallic reagent with oxirane is a useful synthetic transformation because *the carbon chain is extended by two carbons in one step*.

EXERCISE 10.23 Show how isobutyl alcohol can be converted into 1-bromo-4-methylpentane.

B. Higher Cyclic Ethers

One of the most important of the cyclic ethers is tetrahydrofuran, THF, a material we have encountered frequently as a solvent.

tetrahydrofuran
THF

Like many other ethers, tetrahydrofuran reacts with oxygen to form dangerous peroxides. The five-membered ring is stable to ring opening, but ring opening can be accomplished under conditions that cause ether-cleavage reactions of open-chain ethers.

A group of large-ring polyethers that has attracted a good deal of recent attention is the **crown ethers**. The compounds are cyclic polymers of ethylene glycol, $(OCH_2CH_2)_n$, and are named in the form *x*-crown-*y*, where *x* is the total number of atoms in the ring and *y* is the number of oxygens. An example is 18-crown-6, the cyclic hexamer of ethylene glycol.

18-crown-6

EXERCISE 10.24 Write the structure of 15-crown-5.

The crown ethers are important for their ability to solvate cations strongly. The six oxygens in 18-crown-6 are ideally situated to solvate a potassium cation, just as water molecules would normally do. In the resulting complex the cation is solvated by the polar oxygens, but the exterior has hydrocarbon properties. As a result, the complexed ion is soluble in nonpolar organic solvents. For example, the complex of 18-crown-6 and potassium permanganate is soluble in benzene.

K^+ MnO_4^-

18-crown-6–$KMnO_4$ complex
soluble in benzene

18-Crown-6 may be prepared by treating a mixture of triethylene glycol and the corresponding dichloride with aqueous KOH.

aq. KOH

triethylene
glycol

18-crown-6

The reaction mechanism involves two successive S_N2 displacements with chloride ion being the leaving group. Even though a large ring is being formed, the reaction need not be carried out at high dilution. After the initial alkylation, the potassium cation apparently acts as a "template" to bring the two reacting ends of the long chain close together for rapid reaction.

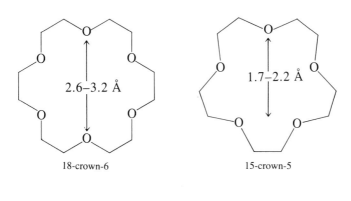

In the last 15 years, organic chemists have actively investigated the chemistry of synthetic crown ethers. Hundreds of different examples have been synthesized and their properties studied. A relationship has been discovered between the structure of a crown ether and its ability to complex various cations. For example, 18-crown-6 shows a high affinity for K^+, 15-crown-5 for Na^+, and 12-crown-4 for Li^+. Measurement of molecular models of these three molecules reveals that the "cavity size," is in each case a good match for the ionic diameter of the cation most strongly bound by the molecule.

18-crown-6   2.6–3.2 Å

15-crown-5   1.7–2.2 Å

12-crown-4   1.2–1.5 Å

Ionic Diameter, Å	
K^+	2.66
Na^+	1.80
Li^+	1.20

A number of naturally occurring cyclic compounds are now known with oxygens or nitrogens in the ring that coordinate with metal cations. Some of these compounds are involved in the transport of ions across biological membranes. An example is nonactin, an antibiotic that functions by transporting sodium ions into bacteria until the resulting osmotic pressure causes rupture of the cell wall.

nonactin

10.12 Multistep Synthesis

We have seen in our study so far that organic compounds may conveniently be classi-fied according to **functional groups**, and that such a classification aids in organizing a massive amount of information into a relatively few categories. One of the characteris-tic properties of a given functional group is its "qualitative chemical reactivity." By this we mean the *kinds* of reaction that are typical for molecules containing a given functional group. For example, two chemical properties of the class of compounds that we call alcohols are the replacement of the hydroxy group by halogen, to give alkyl halides, and the reaction with oxidizing agents, to give aldehydes and ketones. Of course, every chemical reaction is at the same time a characteristic property of one functional group and a **method of preparation** of another. For example, the reaction of a secondary alcohol with chromium(VI) is a property of secondary alcohols and a method of preparation of ketones.

Because of the ability of carbon to form chains and rings, and because of the differ-ent functional groups that exist, the number of possible organic structures that may exist is virtually limitless. Indeed, more than *four million* different organic compounds were known by 1983. Of course, only a relatively small number (about 10,000) of these compounds can be purchased from companies that sell chemicals. Most of the rest have been **synthesized** from other compounds.

One of the powerful aspects of organic chemistry is that the chemical reactions characteristic of various classes of compounds may be carried out in sequence to synthesize almost any desired structure, *whether or not that compound has ever existed before!* As a simple example, suppose that we wish to have a sample of the ketone 2-butanone, and that the only chemicals we have are alkanes and inorganic reagents. We saw in Section 10.6 that ketones are produced by the oxidation of secondary alcohols. Thus, if we had the secondary alcohol 2-butanol, we might oxidize it to prepare 2-butanone.

$$\underset{\text{2-butanone}}{CH_3\overset{\displaystyle O}{\overset{\|}{C}}CH_2CH_3} \xleftarrow{\;[O]\;} \underset{\text{2-butanol}}{CH_3\overset{\displaystyle OH}{\overset{|}{C}HCH_2CH_3}}$$

Now our problem changes to how to obtain 2-butanol. We have also learned, in Sec-tions 9.1 and 10.5, that alcohols may be prepared by the hydrolysis of alkyl halides. Thus, we might hydrolyze a 2-halobutane as a method of preparing 2-butanol.

$$\underset{\underset{\displaystyle CH_3CHCH_2CH_3}{|}}{OH} \xleftarrow{H_2O} \underset{\underset{\displaystyle CH_3CHCH_2CH_3}{|}}{X}$$

But where do we obtain the 2-halobutane? We saw in Chapter 6 that alkyl halides may be prepared by the free-radical halogenation of alkanes. Thus, a possible method of preparation of 2-halobutanes is by halogenation of butane itself.

$$\underset{\underset{\displaystyle CH_3CHCH_2CH_3}{|}}{X} \xleftarrow{X_2} CH_3CH_2CH_2CH_3$$

Since our storeroom contains butane, the foregoing **multistep synthesis** plan represents a possible way for us to obtain 2-butanone.

Of course, at this point, the plan has been sketched out in only rough form. To evaluate whether the plan is really workable, it is necessary to consider the details of the transformations we have proposed. The last step in our proposed multistep synthesis presents no problem, since the oxidation of secondary alcohols by chromium(VI) reagents is a reaction that is not subject to any real limitations.

$$\underset{\underset{\displaystyle CH_3CHCH_2CH_3}{|}}{OH} \xrightarrow{PCC} \underset{\overset{\displaystyle O}{\|}}{CH_3CCH_2CH_3}$$

However, the proposed hydrolysis of a 2-halobutane to 2-butanol may be tricky. We saw in Sections 9.6 and 10.5 that hydrolysis of secondary alkyl halides is accompanied by more or less elimination. In many cases, this competing elimination reaction is the main reaction.

$$\underset{\underset{\displaystyle CH_3CHCH_2CH_3}{|}}{X} \xrightarrow[H_2O]{OH^-} CH_2{=}CHCH_2CH_3 + CH_3CH{=}CHCH_2$$

However, we also learned that, by using the less basic nucleophile sodium acetate, elimination may be minimized. The initial product of this substitution is an ester, which can be hydrolyzed to obtain the alcohol.

$$\underset{\underset{\displaystyle CH_3CHCH_2CH_3}{|}}{X} \xrightarrow{CH_3CO_2{}^-} \underset{\underset{\displaystyle CH_3CHCH_2CH_3}{|}}{\overset{\displaystyle O}{\overset{\displaystyle \|}{OCCH_3}}} \xrightarrow[H_2O]{OH^-} \underset{\underset{\displaystyle CH_3CHCH_2CH_3}{|}}{OH}$$

Thus, 2-butanol is a viable intermediate, *if* we can obtain a 2-halobutane. Here we must consider the fine points of the free-radical halogenation process. We saw in Section 6.3 that chlorination is a rather indiscriminate reaction; the relative reactivity of secondary and primary carbon-hydrogen bonds is only 4:1. Since butane contains four secondary carbon-hydrogen bonds and six primary carbon-hydrogen bonds, we can expect that chlorination of butane would give something on the order of a 16:6 ratio of 2-chlorobutane and 1-chlorobutane. Thus, the maximum yield of 2-chlorobutane would be about 70%. In addition, we would be faced with the problem of *separating* the two isomers.

$$CH_3CH_2CH_2CH_3 \xrightarrow[h\nu]{Cl_2} \underset{\underset{\displaystyle \cong 73\%}{}}{\underset{\underset{\displaystyle CH_3CH_2CHCH_3}{|}}{Cl}} + \underset{\cong 27\%}{CH_3CH_2CH_2CH_2Cl}$$

A better solution would be to use bromine, rather than chlorine, as the halogenating agent. We saw in Section 6.3 that bromine is much more selective than chlorine, and we could expect the vapor phase bromination to give almost completely 2-bromobutane.

$$CH_3CH_2CH_2CH_3 \xrightarrow[h\nu]{Br_2} \overset{\overset{\displaystyle Br}{\displaystyle |}}{CH_3CHCH_2CH_3} + CH_3CH_2CH_2CH_2Br$$

$$>95\% \qquad\qquad <5\%$$

Thus, the multistep synthesis of 2-butanone that we have sketched out holds up to closer scrutiny. The full plan, complete with reagents, is summarized as follows.

$$CH_3CH_2CH_2CH_3 \xrightarrow[h\nu]{Br_2} \overset{\overset{\displaystyle Br}{\displaystyle |}}{CH_3CHCH_2CH_3} \xrightarrow{CH_3CO_2^-}$$

$$\overset{\overset{\displaystyle O}{\overset{\displaystyle \|}{\displaystyle OCCH_3}}}{CH_3CHCH_2CH_3} \xrightarrow[H_2O]{NaOH} \overset{\overset{\displaystyle OH}{\displaystyle |}}{CH_3CHCH_2CH_3} \xrightarrow{PCC} \overset{\overset{\displaystyle O}{\displaystyle \|}}{CH_3CCH_2CH_3}$$

Of course, this is a highly simplified and somewhat artificial example of a multistep synthesis. Actually, 2-butanone *is* available from chemical supply houses; in fact, it would be found in any well-stocked storeroom. Furthermore, it is not likely that a chemist would actually carry out a free-radical bromination reaction as part of a multistep synthesis, since this kind of reaction is relatively inconvenient for normal laboratory operation. However, the principle is illustrative of how real-life multistep syntheses are planned. Note that we began by *working backwards* from our desired final product toward the simpler starting materials we had in our storeroom. At first we sketched out the plan qualitatively. After we had a rough plan, we thought about the details of each step and made suitable modifications until we arrived at a plan that appeared practical.

EXERCISE 10.25 Plan a synthesis of each of the following compounds, starting with alkanes and employing any inorganic reagents necessary.

(a) [cyclohexanone structure]   (b) CH_3CH_2CN (c) [cyclopentene structure]

PROBLEMS

1. Give the structure corresponding to each of the following common names.
   (a) isobutyl methyl ether
   (b) neopentyl alcohol
   (c) tetrahydrofuran (THF)
   (d) dioxane
   (e) 18-crown-6
   (f) bis-β-bromopropyl ether
   (g) *sec*-butyl alcohol
   (h) isobutyl alcohol

2. Give the structure corresponding to each of the following IUPAC names.
   (a) 3-ethoxy-2-methylhexane
   (b) 4-methyl-2-pentanol

(c) 4-*t*-butyl-3-methoxyheptane   (d) (1*S*,3*R*)-3-methylcyclohexanol
(e) (2*R*,3*R*)-dimethyloxirane   (f) 1,6-hexanediol

3. Give the IUPAC name corresponding to each of the following structures.

(a)

(b)

(c)

(d)

(e)

(f)

(g)

(h)

4. Explain why each of the following is not a correct name.
   (a) 4-hexanol   (b) 2-hydroxy-3-methylhexane
   (c) 3-(hydroxymethyl)-1-hexanol   (d) 2-isopropyl-1-butanol

5. How many isomeric ethers correspond to the molecular formula $C_5H_{12}O$? Give common and IUPAC names for each structure. Which of these ethers is capable of optical activity? Write out the structures of the two mirror images and show that they are not superimposable.

6. There are 17 isomeric alcohols of the formula $C_6H_{13}OH$. Write out the structure and give the IUPAC name of each one. Identify the primary, secondary, and tertiary alcohols.

7. (a) In a popular handbook the compound $CH_3CH_2C(CH_3)_2OCH_3$ is listed as ether, *sec*-butylmethyl, 2-methyl-. Is this name consistent with any approved nomenclature you have studied? Give correct common and IUPAC names.
   (b) Note the resemblance in shape of this ether to 3,3-dimethylpentane. Compare the boiling points of the two compounds as given in a handbook.
   (c) 2,2-Dimethyl-3-pentanol and *t*-butyl isopropyl ether are isomers that are not listed in common handbooks. How would you expect their boiling points to compare?

8. Give the principal product(s) from each of the following reactions.

   (a) $CH_3CH_2CH_2OH \xrightarrow[130°C]{H_2SO_4}$

   (b) $CH_3CH_2CH_2O^- + (CH_3)_3CCl$

   (c) $(CH_3)_3CO^- + CH_3CH_2CH_2Br$

   (d) $CH_3CH_2CH_2OH + K_2Cr_2O_7 + H_2SO_4 \xrightarrow{50°C}$

   (e) $\xrightarrow[CH_3COOH]{CrO_3}$

(f) $CH_3CH_2CH_2OS$—⟨benzene ring⟩ (with two O on the S) $\xrightarrow[\text{acetone}]{\text{NaI}} \xrightarrow{\Delta}$

(g) $CH_3CH_2CH_2OH \xrightarrow[\substack{H_2SO_4 \\ \Delta}]{HBr}$

(h) $(CH_3CH_2)_3CCH_2OH \xrightarrow[\substack{H_2SO_4 \\ \Delta}]{HBr}$

(i) $(S)\text{-}CH_3\overset{\displaystyle OH}{\underset{\displaystyle |}{C}}HCH_2CH_3 + SOCl_2 \xrightarrow{\text{pyridine}}$

(j) $(CH_3CH_2)_2CHOH + KH \longrightarrow$

(k) $(CH_3CH_2CH_2)_2O + HI \text{ (excess)} \xrightarrow{\Delta}$

(l) $CH_3CH_2\overset{\displaystyle |}{\underset{\displaystyle OCH_3}{C}}HCH_2CH_3 + HBr \text{ (excess)} \xrightarrow{\Delta}$

9. Give the reagents and conditions for the best conversions of alcohol to alkyl halide as shown.

(a) $CH_3CH_2CH_2CH_2OH \longrightarrow CH_3CH_2CH_2CH_2Cl$

(b) $CH_3CH_2\overset{\displaystyle CH_3}{\underset{\displaystyle |}{C}}HCH_2OH \longrightarrow CH_3CH_2\overset{\displaystyle CH_3}{\underset{\displaystyle |}{C}}HCH_2Cl$

(c) $CH_3CH_2\overset{\displaystyle CH_3}{\underset{\displaystyle |}{C}}HCH_2OH \longrightarrow CH_3CH_2\overset{\displaystyle CH_3}{\underset{\displaystyle |}{\underset{\displaystyle |}{\underset{\displaystyle Cl}{C}}}}-CH_3$

(d) $CH_3CH_2CH_2CHOHCH_3 \longrightarrow CH_3CH_2CH_2CHICH_3$

(e) ⟨cyclopentane ring with CH_2OH and H⟩ $\longrightarrow$ ⟨cyclopentane ring with CH_2Br and H⟩

(f) ⟨cyclohexane ring with HO and CH_3⟩ $\longrightarrow$ ⟨cyclohexane ring with Cl and CH_3⟩

10. Show how to accomplish each of the following conversions in a practical manner.
    (a) $(CH_3)_3CCH_2OH \longrightarrow CH_3CH_2CCl(CH_3)_2$
    (b) $(CH_3)_2CHCHOHCH_3 \longrightarrow (CH_3)_2CHCHBrCH_3$
    (c) $(CH_3CH_2)_3COH \longrightarrow (CH_3CH_2)_2C\!=\!CHCH_3$
    (d) $CH_3CH_2CH_2CH_2OH \longrightarrow CH_3CH_2CH_2CH_2CN$
    (e) $(CH_3)_3CCl + CH_3I \longrightarrow (CH_3)_3COCH_3$
    (f) $(CH_3)_2CHCH_2OH \longrightarrow (CH_3)_2CHCH_2SCH_3$
    (g) $(CH_3)_3COH \longrightarrow (CH_3)_3CCH_2CH_2OH$

11. Outline multistep syntheses of the following compounds, starting with alkanes and using any necessary inorganic reagents.
    (a) methanol   (b) methyl cyclohexyl ether
    (c) propene, $CH_3CH\!=\!CH_2$ (d) ethanethiol, CH_3CH_2SH

12. A naive graduate student attempted the preparation of $CH_3CH_2CDBrCH_3$ from $CH_3CH_2CDOHCH_3$ by heating the deuterio alcohol with HBr and H_2SO_4. He obtained a

product having the correct boiling point, but a careful examination of the spectral properties by his research director showed that the product was a mixture of $CH_3CHDCHBrCH_3$ and $CH_3CH_2CDBrCH_3$. What happened?

13. Explain why 2-cyclopropyl-2-propanol reacts with HCl to give 2-chloro-2-cyclopropyl-propane instead of 1-chloro-2,2-dimethylcyclobutane.

14. Write balanced equations for the following reactions.

   (a) $(CH_3)_2CHOH + KMnO_4 + H^+ \longrightarrow (CH_3)_2C{=}O + MnO_2 + K^+ + H_2O$

   (b) $ClCH_2CH_2CH_2OH + HNO_3 \longrightarrow ClCH_2CH_2CO_2H + NO_2 + H_2O$

   (c) $+ K_2Cr_2O_7 + H^+ \longrightarrow HOC(CH_2)_4COH + Cr^{3+} + K^+ + H_2O$

15. (a) Although isobutyl alcohol reacts with HBr and H_2SO_4 to give isobutyl bromide, with little rearrangement, 3-methyl-2-butanol reacts on heating with conc. HBr to give only the rearranged product, 2-bromo-2-methylbutane. Explain this difference using the re-action mechanisms involved.

   (b) Unsymmetrical ethers are generally not prepared by heating two alcohols with sulfuric acid. Why not? Yet, when *t*-butyl alcohol is heated in methanol containing sulfuric acid, a good yield of *t*-butyl methyl ether results. Explain this result by means of the reaction mechanism.

   (c) Prolonged reaction of ethyl ether with HI gives ethyl iodide. Write out the reaction mechanism.

16. *n*-Butyl ethyl ether is cleaved by hot conc. HBr to give both ethyl bromide and *n*-butyl bromide. However, *t*-Butyl ethyl ether is cleaved readily by cold conc. HBr to give almost completely *t*-butyl bromide and ethyl alcohol. Write the reaction mechanisms of both reac-tions, showing all intermediates, and explain briefly how the reaction mechanisms relate to these experimental observations.

17. Triethyloxonium cation can be prepared as a crystalline tetrafluoroborate salt, $(C_2H_5)_3O^+$ BF_4^-, which is appreciably soluble in methylene chloride. Write the Lewis structure of this salt. The compound is a reactive ethylating reagent and reacts with alcohols, for example, to yield ethers.

$$ROH + (CH_3CH_2)_3O^+ BF_4^- \longrightarrow ROC_2H_5 + (C_2H_5)_2O + HBF_4$$

Write out the mechanism of the reaction. Why is the reagent so reactive in this process?

18. 1-Butanol-*1-d*, $CH_3CH_2CH_2CHDOH$, has a relatively small optical activity, $[\alpha]_D = 0.5°$, due solely to a difference between hydrogen isotopes. The $(-)$ enantiomer has been shown to have the R configuration. On treatment with thionyl chloride and pyridine, $(-)$-1-butanol-*1-d* gives $(+)$-1-chlorobutane-*1-d*. What is the configuration of the chloride? Draw perspective diagrams of the two compounds. Show how (R)-$CH_3CH_2CH_2CHDOH$ may be converted to (S)-$CH_3CH_2CH_2CHDOCH_3$.

19. Provide a mechanistic rationalization for the following reaction course.

20. Optically active (2R,3S)-3-chloro-2-butanol is allowed to react with sodium hydroxide in ethanol to give an optically active oxirane, which is treated with potassium hydroxide in water to obtain 2,3-butanediol. What is the stereostructure of the diol? What can you say about its optical rotation?

21. Optically active 5-chloro-2-hexanol is allowed to react with KOH in methanol. The product, $C_6H_{12}O$, is found to have $[\alpha]_D = 0$. What can you say about the stereochemistry of the reactant?

22. 18-Crown-6 is a useful catalyst for some reactions of potassium salts. For example, KF reacts with 1-bromooctane to give 1-fluorooctane much faster in the presence of 10 mole % 18-crown-6 than in its absence. However, the crown ether is ineffective as a catalyst if NaF is used. Explain.

23. Treatment of 1,2,2-trimethylcycloheptanol with sulfuric acid gives a mixture of 1,7,7-trimethylcycloheptene, 1-*t*-butylcyclohexene, and 1-isopropenyl-1-methylcyclohexane. Write a mechanism that accounts for the formation of these products.

24. The thermodynamics of reactions in a solution are often quite different from those in the gas phase because of the importance of solvation energies. However, thermodynamic data for solvents other than water are sparse, whereas many heats of formation are now available for the gas phase. If one considers reactions in which the number of ions or ion pairs remains the same, the relative gas-phase values can be instructive. Compare $\Delta H°$ for the following two reactions in the gas phase.

$$CH_3CH_2OH + Br^- \rightleftharpoons CH_3CH_2Br + OH^-$$
$$CH_3CH_2OH + HBr \rightleftharpoons CH_3CH_2Br + H_2O$$

25. By using a collection of point charges, show that the electrostatic energy between a charge and a dipole varies as $1/r^2$ and that between two dipoles varies as $1/r^3$, where r is the distance to the center of the dipole. The dipole can be treated as two point charges close together relative to r.

26. (a) One useful measure of the energy of hydrogen bonding derives from heats of vaporization, ΔH_v. The following table gives the vapor pressure of ethanol at different temperatures.

Temperature, °C	Vapor Pressure, mm
−31.3	1
−2.3	10
+19.0	40
34.9	100
64.5	400
78.4	760

From the equation

$$\frac{d \ln P}{dT} = -\frac{\Delta H_v}{RT^2} \quad \text{or} \quad \frac{d \ln P}{d(1/T)} = -\frac{\Delta H_v}{R}$$

plot ln P versus $1/T$ and calculate ΔH_v for ethanol. For comparison, ΔH_v of propane is 4.49 kcal mole^{-1}.

(b) This difference can be compared to an electrostatic model. The dipole moment of ethanol is 1.7 D. Consider the approximation that this dipole results from partial charges at oxygen and hydrogen. The oxygen-hydrogen bond distance is 0.96Å. What fraction of positive and negative electronic charges separated by 0.96×10^{-8} cm correspond to a dipole moment of 1.7×10^{-18} esu cm? The charge on an electron is 4.8×10^{-10} esu. Calculate the electrostatic energy of attraction of a pattern of such charges arranged as follows.

$$\underset{q^-}{O} \xleftrightarrow{0.96\,\text{Å}} \underset{q^+}{O} \xleftrightarrow{2.07\,\text{Å}} \underset{q^-}{O} \xleftrightarrow{0.96\,\text{Å}} \underset{q^+}{O}$$

An electron and a proton 1 Å apart have an electrostatic energy of attraction of 332 kcal mole^{-1}. This electrostatic energy calculation is only a crude model for a hydrogen bond

O—H···O—H but it does give a rough idea of the magnitude of the energy quantities
|　　　|　　　involved.
R　　　R

27. Propose a mechanism for the following reaction.

Chapter 11

Alkenes

Alkenes are hydrocarbons with a carbon-carbon double bond. The double bond is a stronger bond than a single bond, yet paradoxically the carbon-carbon double bond is much more reactive than a carbon-carbon single bond. Unlike alkanes, which generally show rather nonspecific reactions, the double bond is the site of many specific reactions and is a functional group.

11.1 Electronic Structure

The geometric structure of ethylene, the simplest alkene, is well known from spectroscopic and diffraction experiments and is shown in Figure 11.1. The entire molecule is planar. In the Lewis structure of ethylene, the double bond is characterized as a region with two pairs of electrons.

$$\begin{array}{ccc} \text{H} & & \text{H} \\ & \ddot{\text{C}} :: \ddot{\text{C}} & \\ \text{H} & & \text{H} \end{array}$$

In molecular orbital descriptions, we need one orbital for each pair of electrons. Hence, we need two orbitals between the carbons to accommodate the electrons. The orbital model of ethylene starts with the two sp^2-hybrids from each carbon to the hydrogens. A third sp^2-hybrid on each carbon is used to form a C_{sp^2}—C_{sp^3} single bond. So far, we have used the s-orbital and two of the p-orbitals of each carbon—each carbon has a p-orbital "left over." These p-orbitals are perpendicular to the plane of the six atoms. They are parallel to each other and have regions of overlap above and below the molecular plane. This type of bond, in which there are two bonding regions above and below a nodal plane, is called a π-bond. This notation is used in order to distinguish it from the type of bond formed by overlap of two carbon sp^2-orbitals. Such a bond has no node and is called a σ-bond (Figure 11.2). This orbital picture of ethylene is shown in Figure 11.3.

An interesting view of the electron density in the ethylene double bond is seen in Figure 11.4. Each contour diagram represents the electron density of a slice cut through the midpoint of the carbon-carbon bond (see plane in Figure 11.4a). Each line

FIGURE 11.1 Structure of ethylene.

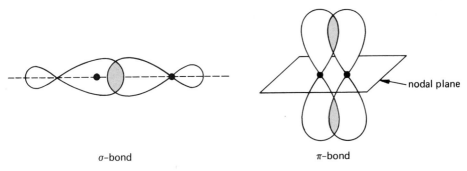

σ–bond   π–bond

FIGURE 11.2 σ- and π-bonds.

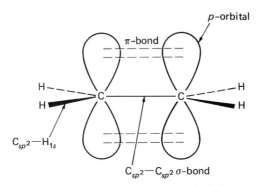

FIGURE 11.3 σ-π-bond model of ethylene.

in such a contour diagram represents a constant definite value of the electron density. For example, the innermost oval in Figure 11.4b represents a rather high value of the electron density, and the outermost oval has a rather low value. The σ-electron density is almost cylindrically symmetric but not quite. The outermost contours are oval rather than circular because of electron repulsion by the π-electrons. The π-electron density in Figure 11.4d is much less than the σ-density, and the total electron density in Figure 11.4b has a smooth oval character. This total electron distribution does not have the appearance one might expect from the simple representation in Figure 11.3.

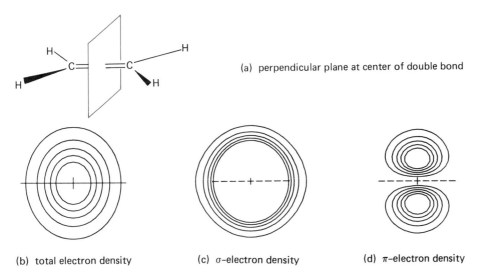

(a) perpendicular plane at center of double bond

(b) total electron density   (c) σ–electron density   (d) π–electron density

FIGURE 11.4 Electron-density distribution in center of ethylene double bond.

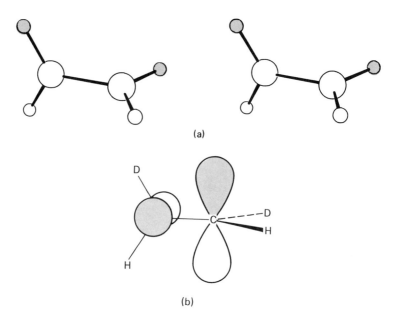

FIGURE 11.5 The half-twisted transition state for interconversions of dideuterioethylenes. (a) The structure is shown in the stereo plot. (b) The orbital representation shows one electron in each of the noninteracting π-orbitals, which are at right angles to each other.

One important consequence of the noncylindrically symmetric electron density about the carbon-carbon bond axis is that there is a barrier to rotation about this axis. For example, two dideuterioethylenes are known and can be distinguished by their different spectroscopic properties.

two different dideuterioethylenes

Interconversion of these isomers takes place only at high temperatures ($\cong 500°C$) and has an activation energy of 65 kcal mole^{-1}. The transition state for the reaction has a half-twisted structure in which the p-orbitals have zero overlap. This structure is represented in Figure 11.5.

The two forms of dideuterioethylene represent another case of stereoisomerism (Chapter 7). Recall that stereoisomers are compounds having the same sequence of covalently bonded atoms but differing in the orientation of the atoms in space. In older books, one often finds alkene isomers such as these classified as geometric isomers. However, since they are stereoisomers that *do not* have a mirror image relationship to one another, they are actually diastereomers.

The two dideuterioethylene stereoisomers may be interconverted by rotation about a bond, just as the anti and gauche stereoisomers of butane.

However, in one case the barrier to interconversion (the rotational barrier) is 65 kcal mole^{-1}, and in the other it is only 3.3 kcal mole^{-1}. The dideuterioethylene stereoisomers may be obtained separately, and each isomer is perfectly stable at normal temperatures. On the other hand, the anti and gauche butane stereoisomers interconvert easily at temperatures above about $-230°C$. This difference in the ease of interconversion has resulted in the two types of stereoisomers having different names. Stereoisomers that can be easily interconverted by rotation about a bond are called **conformational isomers**. Stereoisomers that are not easily interconverted are called **configurational isomers**. The dideuterioethylenes are two such configurational isomers.

EXERCISE 11.1 How many stereoisomers exist for each of the following compounds? Write their structures.
(a) 1,4-dideuterio-1,3-butadiene, $CHD{=}CH{-}CH{=}CHD$
(b) 3-chloro-1-butene, $CH_2{=}CHCHClCH_3$

11.2 Nomenclature

Historically, hydrocarbons with a double bond were known as **olefins**. This rather strange class name comes from the Latin words *oleum*, an oil, and *ficare*, to make. It arose because derivatives of such compounds often had an oily appearance.

As with other classes of organic compounds, two systems of nomenclature are used: common and systematic. In the common system, which is only used for fairly simple compounds, the final **-ane** of the alkane name is replaced by **-ylene**.

$$CH_2{=}CH_2 \qquad CH_3CH{=}CH_2 \qquad CH_3\overset{\displaystyle CH_3}{\underset{\displaystyle |}{C}}{=}CH_2$$

ethylene   propylene   isobutylene

A few simple molecules are named as derivatives of ethylene.

tetramethylethylene   trichloroethylene

Configurational isomers are distinguished by the use of the prefixes *cis*- (L., on this side) and *trans*- (L., across), as with disubstituted cycloalkanes (page 127).

cis-dibromoethylene   *trans*-dibromoethylene

Some monosubstituted ethylenes are named as radical combinations in which the $CH_2{=}CH{-}$ group is called **vinyl**.

$$CH_2{=}CHCl \qquad\qquad CH_2{=}CHOCH_3$$
vinyl chloride   methyl vinyl ether

In the IUPAC system alkenes are named as derivative of a parent alkane. The **alk-** stem specifies the number of carbons in the chain and the **-ene** suffix specifies a double bond. A number is used to indicate the position of the double bond along the chain.

Since the double bond joins one carbon to a carbon with the next higher number, only one number need be given. Finally, a prefix *cis-* or *trans-* is included where necessary.

$$CH_2{=}CH_2 \qquad CH_3CH{=}CH_2 \qquad CH_3CH_2CH{=}CH_2$$

ethene   propene   1-butene

trans-2-butene   *cis*-2-pentene   cyclohexene
(no number necessary)

Substituent groups are included as prefixes with appropriate numbers to specify position. Since the **-ene** stem is a suffix, it dominates the numbering. That is, the parent alkene chain is named first, including *cis-* or *trans-* where necessary, and then the substituents are appended as prefixes.

3-chloro-*trans*-3-hexene   2,4-dimethyl-1-pentene

2-ethyl-1-butene   4-methyl-*cis*-2-hexene
(parent is longest chain that   (not 3-methyl-*cis*-4-hexene)
includes double bond)

EXERCISE 11.2 Name the following alkenes.

(a)

(b)

(c)

(d) Cl

The cis-trans system for naming configurational isomers frequently leads to confusion. The Chemical Abstracts Service has proposed an unambiguous system. In this system, the two groups attached to each end of the double bond are assigned priority numbers as is done in naming enantiomers by the R-S system (Chapter 7). When the two groups of higher priority number are on the **same side** of the molecule, the compound is the **Z** isomer (Ger., *zusammen*, together). When the two groups of highest priority are on **opposite sides** of the molecule, the compound is the **E** form (Ger., *entgegen*, opposite).

$$CH_3CH_2 \qquad CH_2CH_3$$
$$\underset{CH_3}{\overset{}{C}}{=}\underset{H}{\overset{}{C}} \qquad \equiv$$

(Z)-3-methyl-3-hexene

(E)-1,4-dichloro-3-(2-chloroethyl)-2-methyl-2-pentene

The E-Z system for specifying stereoisomerism in alkenes been sanctioned by the IUPAC, although this body still recognizes the use of cis and trans in cases where there is no ambiguity. In normal use, most alkenes are named by the IUPAC system (using either cis-trans or E-Z to specify stereostructure), although several common compounds (ethylene, propylene, isobutylene) are invariably called by their common or trivial names.

EXERCISE 11.3 Name the following alkenes using the E-Z system to specify stereostructure.

In compounds that have both a double bond and a hydroxy group, two suffixes are used. The -ol suffix has priority, and the longest chain *containing both the double bond and the OH group* is numbered in such a way as to give the OH group the smaller number.

but-3-en-1-ol
(not but-1-en-3-ol)

3-ethylbut-3-en-1-ol

[Note that the final "e" of the alkene suffix -ene is dropped when it is followed by another suffix.]

EXERCISE 11.4 Explain why the following names are incorrect.
(a) 2-(chloromethyl)-2-pentene   (b) (E)-2-methyl-2-hexene   (c) *trans*-pent-2-en-4-ol

---

11.3 Physical Properties

Physical properties of some alkenes are summarized in Table 11.1. These properties are similar to those of the corresponding alkanes, as shown by the boiling point plot in Figure 11.6. The smaller alkenes are gases at room temperature. Starting with the C_5

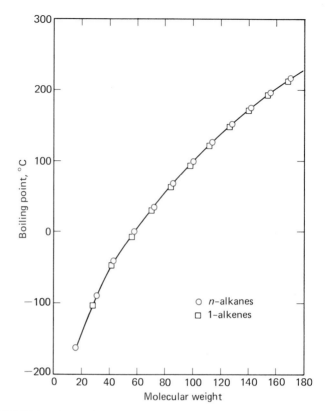

FIGURE 11.6 Boiling point relationships of alkenes and alkanes.

TABLE 11.1 Physical Properties of Alkenes

Name	Structure	Boiling Point, °C	Density d^{20}
ethylene	$CH_2{=}CH_2$	−103.7	
propene	$CH_3CH{=}CH_2$	−47.4	0.5193
1-butene	$CH_3CH_2CH{=}CH_2$	−6.3	0.5951
cis-2-butene	$\overset{\text{H}}{\underset{}{}}\ \overset{\text{H}}{\underset{}{}}$ $CH_3C{=}CCH_3$	3.7	0.6213
trans-2-butene	$\overset{\text{H}}{\underset{}{}}$ $CH_3C{=}CCH_3$ $\underset{\text{H}}{}$	0.9	0.6042
2-methyl-1-propene	$(CH_3)_2C{=}CH_2$	−6.9	0.5942
1-pentene	$CH_3CH_2CH_2CH{=}CH_2$	30.0	0.6405
cis-2-pentene	$\overset{\text{H}}{\underset{}{}}\ \overset{\text{H}}{\underset{}{}}$ $CH_3CH_2C{=}CCH_3$	36.9	0.6556
trans-2-pentene	$\overset{\text{H}}{\underset{}{}}$ $CH_3CH_2C{=}CCH_3$ $\underset{\text{H}}{}$	36.4	0.6482
2-methyl-2-butene	$(CH_3)_2C{=}CHCH_3$	38.6	0.6623

compounds, the alkenes are volatile liquids. Isomeric alkenes have similar boiling points, and mixtures can be separated only by careful fractional distillation with efficient columns. 1-Alkenes tend to boil a few degrees lower than internal olefins and can be separated readily by careful fractionation.

In an alkyl-substituted double bond the carbon orbitals making up the $=C$—C bond have different amounts of s-character. Such a bond may be approximated as C_{sp^2}—C_{sp^3}. The resulting change in electron density distribution gives such bonds an effective dipole moment with the negative end of the dipole the sp^2-hybridized carbon.

$$\overset{\longrightarrow}{C}\text{—}C=C$$

These dipole moments are small for hydrocarbons, but still permit a distinction between cis and trans isomers. For example, *cis*-2-butene has a small dipole moment, whereas *trans*-2-butene has a resultant dipole moment of zero because of its symmetry.

$\mu = 0.33$ D $\qquad\qquad \mu = 0$ D

With substituents such as halogens, the dipole moment differences are greater.

$\mu = 2.95$ D $\qquad\qquad \mu = 0$ D

11.4 Relative Stabilities of Alkenes: Heats of Formation

Heats of formation have been evaluated for a number of alkenes. Examination of these values shows that trans alkenes are generally more stable than the isomeric cis alkenes by about 1 kcal mole^{-1}. (Remember that a *more negative* heat of formation ΔH_f° corresponds to a *more stable* compound.)

$\Delta H^\circ = -1.1$ kcal mole^{-1}

ΔH_f°: $\quad -1.9 \qquad\qquad\qquad -3.0$

$\Delta H^\circ = -0.9$ kcal mole^{-1}

ΔH_f°: $\quad -7.0 \qquad\qquad\qquad -7.9$

$$H_3C \diagdown \atop H \diagup C{=}C \diagup ^{CH(CH_3)_2} _{\diagdown H} \quad \rightleftharpoons \quad H_3C \diagdown \atop H \diagup C{=}C \diagup ^{H} _{\diagdown CH(CH_3)_2} \qquad \Delta H° = -1.0 \text{ kcal mole}^{-1}$$

$\Delta H_f°:$ -13.7 -14.7

The distance between the adjacent methyl groups in *cis*-2-butene is about 3 Å. Since the sum of the van der Waals radii for two methyl groups is 4 Å, the hydrogens in these two groups are sufficiently close that there is a net repulsion not present in the trans compound (Figure 11.7). This effect of repulsion for sterically congested systems is another form of **steric hindrance** (Section 9.3).

Monosubstituted ethylenes are 2-3 kcal mole^{-1} less stable than disubstituted ethylenes. The examples in the following table may be compared with the corresponding isomers listed above.

Compound	$\Delta H_f°$, kcal mole^{-1}
$CH_3CH_2CH{=}CH_2$	-0.2
$CH_3CH_2CH_2CH{=}CH_2$	-5.3
$(CH_3)_2CHCH_2CH{=}CH_2$	-12.3

The stabilizing effect of substituents on the double bond continues with additional substituents, although the incremental effect is reduced because of cis interactions. For example, 2-methyl-2-butene, with $\Delta H_f° = -10.1$ kcal mole^{-1}, is the most stable five-carbon alkene. Similarly, 2,3-dimethyl-2-butene is the most stable six-carbon alkene.

These results are most simply interpreted on the basis of relative bond strengths. A C_{sp^2}—H bond is a stronger bond than a C_{sp^3}—H bond. If this were the only important factor, the least substituted alkenes would be the most stable. However, a C_{sp^2}—C_{sp^3}

FIGURE 11.7   Steric hindrance in *cis*-2-butene, relative to *trans*-2-butene.

TABLE 11.2 Equilibrium Concentrations as a Function of $\Delta G°$ at 25°C: A $\rightleftharpoons$ B

$\Delta G°$, kcal mole^{-1}	Percent A	Percent B
-5	0.02	99.98
-2	3.3	96.7
-1	15.6	84.4
-0.5	30.1	69.9
0	50.0	50.0
$+0.5$	69.9	30.1
$+1$	84.4	15.6
$+2$	96.7	3.3
$+5$	99.98	0.02

bond is also stronger than a C_{sp^3}—C_{sp^3} bond, and it seems that putting more s-character in a carbon-carbon bond has a greater effect than in a carbon-hydrogen bond. This hybridization effect may also be observed in the bond lengths because bond lengths are inversely related to bond strengths. We noted earlier that the carbon-hydrogen bond in ethylene is about 0.01 Å shorter than the carbon-hydrogen bond in ethane. The carbon-carbon single bond in propene (1.505 Å) is 0.03 Å shorter than the carbon-carbon bond in propane. The difference $r_{C_{sp^3}-C_{sp^3}} - r_{C_{sp^2}-C_{sp^3}}$, is greater than $r_{C_{sp^3}-H} - r_{C_{sp^2}-H}$.

The difference in stability of various alkene isomers is only a few kilocalories per mole, but this makes an important difference in equilibria. From the thermodynamic equation

$$\Delta G° = -RT \ln K$$

a free-energy difference of 1.4 kcal mole^{-1} at room temperature corresponds to an equilibrium constant of 10 (Table 11.2). Consequently, in an equilibrium mixture of alkenes, the more highly substituted isomers predominate. For example, the equilibrium composition of the butenes is

We will find that such equilibria can be established and that the relative stabilities of alkene isomers are important in some synthetic methods.

EXERCISE 11.5 Using the heats of formation for *cis*- and *trans*-2-pentene given on page 239, calculate the composition of an equilibrium mixture of these two isomers (ignore 1-pentene and assume $\Delta S° = 0$) at 25°C and at 300°C.

In principle, the double bond in a cyclic alkene can be either cis or trans. In a cis cycloalkene two carbons that are attached cis to each other on the double bond are also part of the ring. Several examples are shown below.

cyclohexene   1-methylcycloheptene   1,2-dimethylcyclobutene

In a trans cycloalkene the two ring carbons are trans with respect to the double bond. In practice, the trans isomers are too strained to exist at room temperature for three-through seven-membered rings. The smallest cycloalkene for which an isolable trans isomer is known is cyclooctene. Even in this case there is significant strain—*cis*-cyclooctene is 9.1 kcal mole^{-1} more stable than the trans isomer.

cis-cyclooctene   *trans*-cyclooctene

EXERCISE 11.6 Calculate the composition at 25°C for an equilibrium mixture of *cis*- and *trans*-cyclooctene. Construct molecular models of the stereoisomeric cyclooctenes. Note that it is much more difficult to construct a model of the trans isomer than of the cis. Demonstrate that the trans isomer is chiral, whereas the cis isomer is not.

11.5 Preparation

The important preparations of alkenes that we have discussed thus far have all been elimination reactions—dehydrohalogenation of alkyl halides and dehydration of alcohols. Other important procedures for creating the carbon-carbon double bond will be discussed in subsequent chapters.

A. Dehydrohalogenation of Alkyl Halides

Dehydrohalogenation was discussed previously (Section 9.6), but primarily as a complication of nucleophilic substitution. Elimination can often be made the principal reaction by using a suitably strong base. One common reagent used for this purpose is potassium hydroxide in refluxing ethanol. This solution is really a solution primarily of potassium ethoxide in ethanol because of the equilibrium

$$OH^- + C_2H_5OH \rightleftharpoons C_2H_5O^- + H_2O$$

EXERCISE 11.7 Assuming that ethanol and water have equal dissociation constants in ethanol solution, estimate the hydroxide/ethoxide ratio in a solution made by dissolving one mole of KOH in enough ethanol to make 1 L of solution. (Assume that entropy changes can be neglected.)

In such a solution, the elimination reaction shows second order kinetics, first order in alkyl halide and first order in base. As we have seen (Section 9.6), eliminations that occur under such conditions are classified mechanistically as E2, for bimolecular elimination. Later in this section, we shall consider some of the considerable amount of evidence upon which the E2 mechanism is based.

For secondary and tertiary alkyl halides, treatment with alcoholic potassium hydroxide gives the elimination products in good yield.

$$\underset{\underset{\text{I}}{|}}{CH_3CHCH_3} \xrightarrow[\text{EtOH}]{\text{EtOK}} CH_3CH=CH_2$$

(94%)

For primary halides, especially with no β-branches, nucleophilic substitution by the S_N2 mechanism is so facile that it dominates, and ethers are the principal products.

$$n\text{-}C_5H_{11}Br \xrightarrow[\underset{55°C}{\text{EtOH}}]{\text{EtONa}} CH_3CH_2CHCH=CH_2 + n\text{-}C_5H_{11}OC_2H_5$$
$$\qquad\qquad (12\%) \qquad\qquad (88\%)$$

Bimolecular elimination almost invariably gives a mixture of the possible alkene products. The mixture usually reflects the thermodynamic stabilities of the isomeric alkenes; the most stable isomers tend to predominate.

$$CH_3CH_2CH_2CHBrCH_3 \xrightarrow[\underset{\Delta}{\text{EtOH}}]{\text{EtOK}} CH_3CH_2CH=CHCH_3 +$$
$$(41\% \text{ trans})$$
$$(14\% \text{ cis})$$

$$CH_3CH_2CH_2CH=CH_2 + CH_3CH_2CH_2CH(OEt)CH_3$$
$$(25\%) \qquad\qquad (20\%)$$

In this example note that the trans isomer is produced in greater amount than is the cis and that the combined 2-pentenes are produced to a greater extent than is 1-pentene. However, the more basic and bulkier reagent potassium *t*-butoxide in the less polar solvent *t*-butyl alcohol tends to give more of the terminal olefin. A further increase in the fraction of terminal alkene is obtained by the use of the potassium alkoxide derived from 3-ethyl-3-pentanol.

2-methyl-2-butene   2-methyl-1-butene

	2-methyl-2-butene	2-methyl-1-butene
EtOK/EtOH	71%	29%
KOC(CH$_3$)$_3$/HOC(CH$_3$)$_3$	28%	72%
KOC(C$_2$H$_5$)$_3$/HOC(C$_2$H$_5$)$_3$	11%	89%

Potassium *t*-butoxide gives good yields of elimination product even with straight-chain primary halides.

$$n\text{-}C_{18}H_{37}Br \xrightarrow[\underset{40°C}{\text{HOC(CH}_3)_3}]{\text{KOC(CH}_3)_3} n\text{-}C_{16}H_{33}CH=CH_2 + n\text{-}C_{18}H_{37}OC(CH_3)_3$$
$$(88\%) \qquad\qquad (12\%)$$

These various effects of structure are best rationalized in the context of reaction mechanism. A correct mechanism needs to explain these facts as well as several other generalizations that can be made about such eliminations.

1. The rate of bimolecular elimination reactions depends on the concentration of both the alkyl halide and the base.
2. The rate of reaction depends on the nature of the leaving group. The general reactivity order for alkyl halides is iodides > bromides > chlorides.
3. The reaction has a high primary hydrogen isotope effect; that is, carbon-deuterium bonds are broken more slowly than carbon-hydrogen bonds.
4. The reaction is **stereospecific**. The leaving hydrogen must generally be conformationally **anti** to the leaving halide.

The first generalization has an obvious consequence for any proposed mechanism. Both the base and the alkyl halide must be involved in the rate-determining step. In fact, it is this observation that gives the mechanism its name—E2 or "elimination, bimolecular."

EXERCISE 11.8 We saw in Chapter 8 that elimination is often a complicating side reaction in nucleophilic substitution reactions. For a primary alkyl halide, how would you expect the substitution/elimination ratio to vary with nucleophile (base) concentration?

The second generalization also has an obvious consequence: The bond to the leaving halide must be partially broken in the transition state. Bonds that are broken more easily lead to a lower energy transition state and a faster reaction rate.

The third generalization establishes that the bond to the leaving hydrogen is also partially broken in the transition state. To a first approximation, it effectively takes more energy to break a carbon-deuterium bond than it does to break a carbon-hydrogen bond.

To be more precise, isotope effects originate in the nature of the vibrational energy levels of bonds. These quantum states were discussed previously in connection with bond dissociation energies of alkanes (Section 6.1), and we will encounter them again in studying infrared spectra (Section 14.2). For the present purpose, consider the two carbon-hydrogen bond motions in Figure 11.8. In the strong carbon-hydrogen bond the potential energy is very sensitive to the value of the carbon-hydrogen bond distance. Thus, in order to accommodate the Heisenberg uncertainty principle, the lowest vibrational energy state is relatively high above the potential minimum. That is, the zero point energy, ϵ_0, is relatively large. For the carbon-hydrogen bond in alkanes ϵ_0 is about 4 kcal mole^{-1}. For a weaker bond, as shown in Figure 11.8b, a given uncertainty in the position of the hydrogen corresponds to a smaller change in potential energy. Hence, ϵ_0 is smaller.

A deuterium atom is twice as heavy as hydrogen because its nucleus has a neutron as well as a proton. Because of its greater mass, the same momentum corresponds to a slower velocity. A given uncertainty in momentum corresponds to a smaller uncertainty in position compared to the hydrogen case. Accordingly, the zero point energy for C—D is less than that for C—H, as shown in Figure 11.8.

In a reaction in which a carbon-hydrogen bond is broken, the bond is weaker in the transition state. In the change from reactant to transition state, the carbon-hydrogen bond

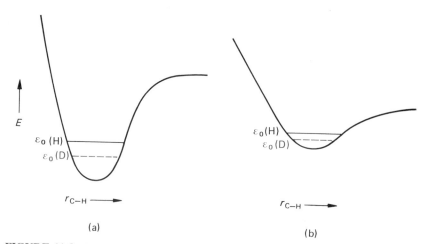

(a)

(b)

FIGURE 11.8 Potential energies for stretching motion of (*a*) a strong and (*b*) a weak carbon-hydrogen bond.

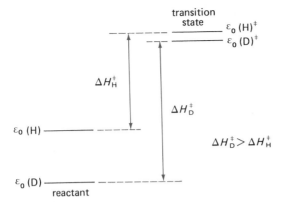

transition
state

$\epsilon_0 (H)^{\ddagger}$

$\epsilon_0 (D)^{\ddagger}$

$\Delta H_{H}^{\ddagger}$

$\Delta H_{D}^{\ddagger}$

$\epsilon_0 (H)$

$\Delta H_{D}^{\ddagger} > \Delta H_{H}^{\ddagger}$

$\epsilon_0 (D)$

reactant

FIGURE 11.9   Effect on the activation energy of loss of zero point energy in a reaction.

has lost some zero point energy. In the corresponding case of a carbon-deuterium bond the loss in zero point energy is lower because the heavier isotope had less zero point energy to begin with. As a result, as shown in Figure 11.9, the activation energy for breaking a carbon-deuterium bond is greater than that for a carbon-hydrogen bond. The difference in reaction rates can be substantial. For hydrogen isotopes, the effect on ϵ_0 is approximately the square root of the ratio of masses. If $\epsilon_0(H)$ is 4 kcal mole^{-1}, the corresponding $\epsilon_0(D)$ is 2.8 kcal mole^{-1}. If all of this zero point energy were lost in the transition state, the difference in activation energies would correspond to a reaction rate difference of a factor of about 9. In practice, primary isotope effects for E2 reactions have been observed commonly in the range of 4-8.

$$CD_3CHBrCD_3 \xrightarrow{\text{EtO}^-} CD_2{=}CHCD_3$$

$$\frac{k_{CH_3CHBrCH_3}}{k_{CD_3CHBrCD_3}} = 6.7$$

If no bond to hydrogen is broken at the transition state isotope effects are generally rather small. For example, in substitution reactions occuring by the S_N2 mechanism deuterium compounds react at virtually the same rates as the corresponding hydrogen compounds.

EXERCISE 11.9   Compare the substitution/elimination ratio for the reactions of ethyl bromide and 2,2,2-trideuterioethyl bromide (CD_3CH_2Br) with potassium *t*-butoxide in *t*-butyl alcohol?

The fourth generalization has been established by many examples. A particularly striking case is the behavior of the two diastereomeric 1,2-dibromo-1,2-diphenyl-ethanes upon treatment with base. (The phenyl group, C_6H_5, is derived from the benzene ring, and is analogous to an alkyl group. We shall consider the chemistry of benzene and other molecules containing the phenyl group in Chapter 20. In the current example, the phenyl group plays no role other than that of a stereochemical marker.) The two stereoisomers react by the E2 mechanism to give *totally different* products. From a knowledge of the configurations of the two reactant dibromides and the product that each gives, it may be deduced that each isomer reacts in a conformation that has H anti to Br. The staggered conformations of the two compounds are shown in Newman-projection form in Figure 11.10. Note that removal of H and Br from opposite sides of

(1R,2R)-1,2-dibromo-1,2-diphenylethane

(Z)-1-bromo-1,2-diphenylethene

meso-1,2-dibromo-1,2-diphenylethane

(E)-1-bromo-1,2-diphenylethene

the molecule results in conversion of the 1R,2R stereoisomer into the alkene having the two phenyl groups trans.

Similarly, anti elimination in the meso stereoisomer gives the alkene having the phenyl groups cis.

This example demonstrates that anti elimination can give either a cis or a trans alkene, depending on the structure of the starting halide.

The strict requirement for anti elimination may also be seen in the reactions of cyclic alkyl halides. For example, *trans*-1-bromo-4-*t*-butylcyclohexane reacts rapidly with sodium ethoxide in ethanol to give 4-*t*-butylcyclohexene. However, the cis isomer undergoes elimination extremely slowly.

In this example the *t*-butyl group is so sterically demanding that it determines which chair conformation is adopted by each molecule. *cis*-1-Bromo-4-*t*-butylcyclohexane exists almost entirely in the conformation shown, in which bromine is axial. To determine the relative energy of the axial-*t*-butyl, equatorial-bromo conformation, the energies in Table 7.1 may be used.

(a) staggered conformation of (1R,2R)-1,2-dibromo- 1,2-diphenylethane

(b) staggered conformations of *meso*-1,2 dibromo-1,2-diphenylethane

FIGURE 11.10 Newman Projections illustrating the staggered conformations of the stereoisomeric 1,2-dibromo-1,2-diphenylethanes.

relative energy: $0 + 0.5 = 0.5$ kcal mole^{-1} $\sim 5 + 0 = \sim 5$ kcal mole^{-1}

$$\Delta G° \cong 4.5 \text{ kcal mole}^{-1}$$

The corresponding equilibrium constant, $K \cong 10^{-3}$; that is, *cis*-1-bromo-4-*t*-butyl-cyclohexane exists at least 99.9% in the axial-bromo conformation.

Applying the same approach to the trans isomer reveals that the conformation with axial bromo is only about 0.01% of the total.

relative energy; $0 + 0 = 0$ $\sim 5 + 0.5 = \sim 5.5$ kcal mole^{-1}

$$\Delta G° \cong 5.5 \text{ kcal mole}^{-1}$$

Thus, only in the cis isomer is there any significant number of molecules in which the bromine has an anti relationship to a hydrogen.

hydrogens anti
to Br

no hydrogens anti
to Br

EXERCISE 11.10 Construct a molecular model of bromocyclohexane with the bromine in an axial position. Verify that the trans hydrogens at C-2 and C-6 are anti and coplanar with the carbon-bromine bond. Now flip the cyclohexane ring into the other chair conformation and note the relationship of the carbon-bromine and carbon-hydrogen bonds.

The mechanism that results from putting these facts together is one in which the attacking base removes a proton concurrently with loss of halide ion from the other side of the molecule. As the carbon-hydrogen bond lengthens and weakens, the carbon-halogen bond also lengthens and weakens. The remaining four groups on the two carbons start to move into coplanarity, and a carbon-carbon double bond starts to form. We may represent this reaction as follows:

reactants   transition state   products

Recall that each curved arrow represents the movement of one pair of electrons. The proton has been displaced in a typical acid-base proton-transfer reaction, and the leaving halide has been displaced by a pair of electrons at the rear of the carbon-halogen bond. The transition state for the E2 reaction is represented in stereo form in Figure 11.11.

In orbital terms the bonds on the alkyl halide all involve C_{sp^3} orbitals. In the product

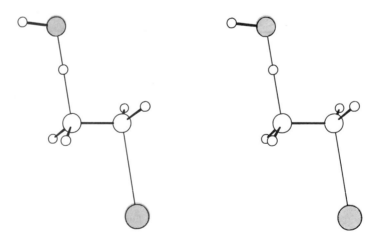

FIGURE 11.11 Stereo representation of the E2 transition state.

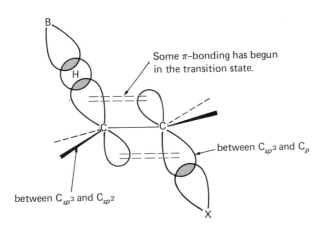

FIGURE 11.12 Orbital representations of the E2 transition state.

alkene some orbitals are C_{sp^2} and others are C_p. At the transition state the orbitals have an intermediate character, as illustrated in Figure 11.12. Because π-bonding is significant in the transition state, those effects that stabilize double bonds, such as added substituents, also stabilize the transition state. However, inasmuch as π-overlap is only partial, these stabilizing effects are not as important as they are in the product olefins.

It is clear that for π-bonding to be significant in the transition state, the carbon-hydrogen and carbon-halogen bonds to be broken must lie in the same plane, but we may well ask why this requires anti elimination. The answer is simply that in the corresponding syn elimination, groups are eclipsed to each other and represent a structure of higher energy.

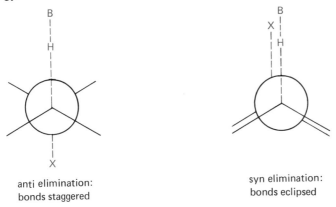

anti elimination:
bonds staggered

syn elimination:
bonds eclipsed

Finally, primary hydrogens are less sterically hindered and more open to attack than secondary or tertiary hydrogens. Refer back to the reaction of 2-bromopentane with potassium ethoxide in ethanol (page 243). 1-Pentene is formed in 25% yield although at equilibrium it would constitute only about 3% of a mixture of pentene isomers. With the larger bases this disparate amount of the 1-alkene is even greater (compare the examples on page 243).

EXERCISE 11.11 Treatment of *meso*-2,3-dibromobutane [the 2*R*,3*S* diastereomer] with KOH in ethanol gives a mixture of 3-bromo-1-butene and one of the isomeric 2-bromo-2-butenes. What is the stereostructure of the latter product? Use your molecular models in working out the answer to this exercise.

B. Dehydration of Alcohols

We saw in Section 10.6.D that alcohols undergo dehydration when heated with strong acids. In the case of ethyl alcohol, the reaction requires concentrated sulfuric acid at 170°C. At lower temperatures (140°C) diethyl ether is the major reaction product.

$$2\ CH_3CH_2OH \xrightarrow[140°C]{H_2SO_4} CH_3CH_2OCH_2CH_3 + H_2O$$

$$CH_3CH_2OH \xrightarrow[170°C]{H_2SO_4} CH_2{=}CH_2 + H_2O$$

n-Propyl alcohol may be similarly dehydrated to propene.

$$CH_3CH_2CH_2OH \xrightarrow[170°C]{H_2SO_4} CH_3CH{=}CH_2 + H_2O$$

With primary alcohols larger than propyl, mixtures of alkenes result.

$$CH_3(CH_2)_6CH_2OH \xrightarrow[\Delta]{H_3PO_4} CH_3(CH_2)_4CH{=}CHCH_3 + CH_3(CH_2)_3CH{=}CHCH_2CH_3$$

major products

Essentially no 1-octene is produced in this reaction. The problem in this case is that the initially-formed 1-octene undergoes acid-catalyzed isomerization to give the more stable internal octene isomers.

$$CH_3(CH_2)_6CH_2OH \longrightarrow CH_3(CH_2)_4CH_2CH{=}CH_2 \underset{-H^+}{\overset{+H^+}{\rightleftharpoons}}$$

$$CH_3(CH_2)_4CH_2\overset{+}{C}HCH_3 \underset{+H^+}{\overset{-H^+}{\rightleftharpoons}} CH_3(CH_2)_4CH{=}CHCH_3 \rightleftharpoons\ etc.$$

This type of isomerization is common under the conditions of acid-catalyzed dehydration. The intermediate secondary carbocations can also rearrange (see pages 206–208). (Note that isomerization of the double bond in propene does not lead to a new product.) As a result, acid-catalyzed dehydration is not a generally useful procedure for the conversion of primary alcohols to alkenes.

EXERCISE 11.12   Suppose you had a sample of 3,3,3-trideuterio-1-propanol, $CD_3CH_2CH_2OH$, and wished to convert it into 3,3,3-trideuteriopropene, $CD_3CH{=}CH_2$. Could dehydration with hot sulfuric acid be used? Explain.

In contrast, secondary and tertiary alcohols are more easily dehydrated.

OH

cyclohexanol $\xrightarrow[130°C]{95\%\ H_2SO_4}$ cyclohexene (83%) + H_2O

$$CH_3CH_2\underset{\underset{CH_3}{|}}{\overset{\overset{OH}{|}}{C}}CH_3 \xrightarrow[90°C]{46\%\ H_2SO_4} CH_3CH{=}C\overset{CH_3}{\underset{CH_3}{\diagdown}} + H_2O$$

2-methyl-2-butanol   2-methyl-2-butene
(84%)

$$CH_3CH_2CH_2\overset{\overset{\displaystyle OH}{|}}{C}HCH_3 \xrightarrow[95°C]{62\% \ H_2SO_4} CH_3CH_2CH=CHCH_3 + H_2O$$

(65–80%)

2-pentanol   cis- and trans-2-pentene

> 2-Pentanol, 214 mL, is heated with a mixture of 200 mL of sulfuric acid and 200 mL of water and the alkene produced is distilled as formed. The distillate is washed, dried, and redistilled; yield, 65–80%. This product is mostly a mixture of *cis-* and *trans*-2-pentenes. The small amount of 1-pentene also present can be removed by careful fractional distillation.

In these cases dehydration probably occurs by the E1 mechanism, by way of intermediate carbocations.

(1) + H⁺ ⇌

(2) ⇌ + H_2O

(3) ⇌ + + H⁺

Acid-catalyzed dehydration is especially suitable for relatively simple alcohols. In more complex cases, rearrangements may occur.

2,3-dimethyl-1-butene   2,3-dimethyl-2-butene
(minor product)   (major product)

> **EXERCISE 11.13** What major product would you expect from the acid-catalyzed dehydration of 3-methylcyclohexanol?

A simple and effective procedure for dehydration of many alcohols, including primary alcohols, involves passing the vapors over alumina at 350-400°C.

> Alumina is a common name for aluminum oxide, Al_2O_3. It occurs naturally in crystalline form as ruby, sapphire, and corundum. Commercial alumina for laboratory use is a white powder, which is available in many grades. It is highly insoluble in water and in organic solvents and has an extremely high melting point (over 2000°C). It is used as an adsorbent in liquid chromatography, as a catalyst for some reactions, and as a catalyst support in other cases.

Like many aluminum salts, alumina is a Lewis acid. The dehydration reaction probably occurs by some version of the E1 mechanism on the alumina surface.

$$\text{ROH} \quad \overset{R \quad H}{\underset{\overset{|}{\overset{\displaystyle O^{+}}{\underset{|}{-Al-}}}}{} } $$

ROH $\quad$ $\ce{R\overset{+}{O}H}$ / $-Al-$ $\longrightarrow$ $-Al^{--}$ $\longrightarrow$ $\underset{|}{\overset{OH}{-Al-}} + R^+$ $\longrightarrow$ $\underset{|}{\overset{^+OH_2}{-Al-}} + \text{alkene}\uparrow$ $\longrightarrow$ $-Al- + H_2O\uparrow$

Accordingly, isomerization of olefins and rearrangements are common. These reactions can be suppressed by first treating the alumina with a base such as ammonia.

EXERCISE 11.14 1-Cyclobutylethanol reacts with 60% aqueous sulfuric acid to give 1-methylcyclopentene. Write a mechanism, showing each step, for this rearrangement reaction. If the rearrangement step is not clear, construct a molecular model of the 1-cyclobutylethyl cation and perform the following operation: break the C-1—C-2 bond of the cyclobutane ring and attach C-2 to the former cationic carbon. What is the structure of the product?

C. Industrial Preparation of Alkenes

Ethylene is an important item of commerce. It is used in large quantities for the manufacture of polyethylene and as an intermediate in the preparation of a host of other chemicals. It is obtained primarily as a cracking product in petroleum refining (Section 6.2). Although any hydrocarbon may be cracked to yield mainly ethylene, in the United States the primary material used for this purpose is ethane.

$$\ce{CH3CH3} \xrightarrow[\text{1 atm}]{700-900\,°C} \ce{CH2=CH2 + H2}$$

When higher hydrocarbons are submitted to the cracking process, significant amounts of propene are produced.

$$n\text{-}\ce{C6H14} \xrightarrow{700-900\,°C} \underset{(15\%)}{\ce{CH4}} + \underset{(40\%)}{\ce{CH2=CH2}} + \underset{(20\%)}{\ce{CH3CH=CH2}} + \underset{(25\%)}{\text{other}}$$

A large amount of the propene produced in this country goes into the manufacture of polypropylene. Other important industrial alkenes are the butenes and 1,3-butadiene. The 1983 industrial production of various alkenes is summarized in Table 11.3.

TABLE 11.3 1983 Production of Alkenes

Compound	Production, tons
$\ce{CH2=CH2}$	14,245,000
$\ce{CH3CH=CH2}$	6,990,000
$\ce{C6H5CH=CH2}$	3,475,000
$\ce{CH2=CHCl}$	3,495,000
$\ce{CH2=CHCH=CH2}$	1,155,000
$\ce{CH2=CHCN}$	1,075,000
$\ce{CH2=CHOCOCH3}$	980,000

11.6 Reactions

In Appendix III, "Average Bond Energies", we find that the value for C=C is 146 kcal mole^{-1}. This value is 63 kcal mole^{-1} higher than the normal C—C strength of 83 kcal mole^{-1}. The difference is reminiscent of the 65 kcal mole^{-1} required for rotation about the double bond in ethylene (Section 11.1) and may be considered roughly as the bond strength of the second or π-bond in ethylene. That is, the "second" bond of a double bond is substantially weaker than the first.

The reaction of this "weak" π-bond with a normal single bond to produce a molecule containing two new single bonds is generally a thermodynamically favorable process. For example, in gas phase reactions at 25°C the reactions of ethylene with a number of inorganic compounds are exothermic processes.

$$CH_2{=}CH_2 + H_2 \longrightarrow CH_3CH_3 \qquad \Delta H° = -32.7 \text{ kcal mole}^{-1}$$
$$CH_2{=}CH_2 + Cl_2 \longrightarrow CH_2ClCH_2Cl \qquad \Delta H° = -43.2 \text{ kcal mole}^{-1}$$
$$CH_2{=}CH_2 + HBr \longrightarrow CH_3CH_2Br \qquad \Delta H° = -19.0 \text{ kcal mole}^{-1}$$
$$CH_2{=}CH_2 + H_2O \longrightarrow CH_3CH_2OH \qquad \Delta H° = -10.9 \text{ kcal mole}^{-1}$$

Not only do such *additions across a double bond* have favorable thermodynamics; many also have accessible pathways or reaction mechanisms. Such additions form an important part of the chemistry of alkenes.

A. Catalytic Hydrogenation

Even though the reaction is highly exothermic ($\Delta H° = -32.7$ kcal mole^{-1}), ethylene does not react with hydrogen at an appreciable rate without an appropriate catalyst. The following "four-center" mechanism, which is conceptually very simple, is apparently not energetically accessible for the reaction of ethylene with hydrogen.

cyclic four-membered
transition state

Such four-center mechanisms are rare because cyclic four-membered transition states, such as that shown, have unusually high energy. The high activation energy corresponds to an impractically slow reaction rate. The relatively high energies of such four-center transition states can be explained by molecular orbital concepts, and further discussion is deferred to Section 21.4.

The hydrogenation reaction does take place readily on the surface of some metals, particularly platinum, palladium, and nickel. These metals are known to coordinate with double bonds and to absorb hydrogen. The detailed reaction mechanism is complex and involves various types of metal-carbon bonds. A schematic representation that is suitable for our purposes is approximated as follows.

(catalyst surface)

Platinum is usually used as the black oxide known as "Adams' catalyst." The oxide is prepared by fusion of chloroplatinic acid, $H_2PtCl_6 \cdot 6H_2O$, hygroscopic red-brown crystals, or ammonium chloroplatinate, $(NH_4)_2PtCl_6$, yellow crystals, with sodium nitrate. It reacts readily with hydrogen gas even at low pressures to form a finely divided platinum metal catalyst. This transformation is usually accomplished by stirring with a suitably inert solvent, such as ethanol or acetic acid. The alkene is then added, and when the solution is stirred with the suspension of platinum under an atmosphere of hydrogen, hydrogen gas is absorbed rapidly. The hydrogen is usually contained in a gas buret so that the amount absorbed can be measured. The resulting mixture is filtered and the product is isolated from the filtrate. Only small amounts of platinum catalyst are required, but the filter paper residues are normally saved for recovery of the platinum, a rare and expensive material.

Palladium is usually used as a commercial preparation in which the finely divided metal is supported on an inert surface, frequently charcoal (Pd/C) or barium sulfate (Pd/BaSO₄). Alkenes are normally hydrogenated in ethanol solution by stirring with the supported palladium catalyst at room temperature under an atmosphere of hydrogen.

Nickel is usually used in a finely divided state called "Raney nickel." The catalyst is prepared by allowing nickel-aluminum alloy to react with aqueous sodium hydroxide. The aluminum dissolves and leaves the nickel as a finely divided suspension. Typical hydrogenations are conducted at moderately high pressures of hydrogen ($\cong 1000$ psi).

Other hydrogenation catalysts that are used for specific purposes are rhodium, ruthenium, and iridium, but platinum, palladium, and nickel in their various forms are the most common. They are subject to "poisoning" by some compounds, notably sulfur-containing compounds such as thiols and sulfides. These compounds bind firmly to the catalyst surface and destroy its catalytic activity.

Since the two hydrogens are added to the double bond from the surface of the metal, they are normally both added *to the same face of the double bond*. This type of addition is referred to as **syn** (Gk., *syn*, together). The other stereochemical possibility, addition of two "pieces" of a reagent to opposite faces of a double bond is called **anti** addition (Gk., *anti*, opposite). In the case of catalytic hydrogenation the alkene molecule is adsorbed to the catalyst surface with one face of the double bond coordinated to the surface; the two hydrogens are both added to this face.

Although syn addition is the general rule, anti addition is sometimes observed. For example, hydrogenation of 1,2-dimethylcyclohexene over palladium gives *trans*-1,2-dimethylcyclohexane as the major product.

Anti addition in this example results because double bond isomerization occurs more rapidly than hydrogenation. The isomerized alkene, 1,6-dimethylcyclohexene, reacts with hydrogen from both its faces, giving a mixture of the cis and trans products.

Palladium is particularly prone to catalyze double bond isomerization. Platinum, rhodium, or iridium should be used if such isomerization is a possible problem.

> **EXERCISE 11.15** Hydrogenation of optically active 3,7-dimethyl-1-octene using platinum as catalyst gives optically active 2,6-dimethyloctane. If Pd/C is used as a catalyst, the 2,6-dimethyloctane produced is racemic. Explain.

B. Addition of Halogens

An important general reaction of double bonds is the addition of chlorine and bromine.

$$\text{C=C} + X_2 \longrightarrow X\text{—C—C—}X \qquad X = Cl, Br$$

This reaction is rapid and can be regarded as a nucleophilic displacement reaction on a halogen. The alkene is the nucleophile and halide ion is the leaving group.

The resulting cation reacts with halide ion to give the observed product.

$$Br\text{—C—C} + Br^- \longrightarrow Br\text{—C—C—}Br$$

The intermediate cation contains an electron-deficient cationic carbon and a halogen atom with nonbonding electron pairs. Consequently there is a tendency for overlap to produce a **cyclic halonium ion** as in Figure 11.13.

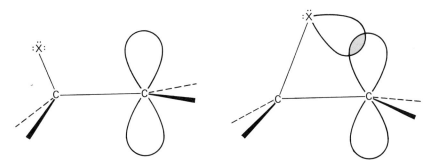

FIGURE 11.13 Formation of cyclic halonium ion.

The cyclic halonium ion may be written in Lewis form as follows:

$$\overset{\overset{\displaystyle \ddot{X}{}^+}{\diagup \diagdown}}{\underset{\diagup}{C}\!-\!\underset{\diagdown}{C}}$$

The advantage in terms of energy in forming such a structure is primarily the formation of an additional covalent bond. Furthermore, all of the atoms now have an octet electronic configuration. However, a price is paid for these gains. The bond angles in the three-membered ring structure are bent far from the desired tetrahedral geometry, and the positive charge is localized on the more electronegative halogen atom rather than on carbon.

In practice, the tendency of such a cation to exist in the cyclic form depends on the stability of the "open" carbocation. The intermediate formed from the addition of bromine to ethylene is best described as a symmetrical bromonium ion with relatively strong carbon-bromine bonds. The alternative open form would be a highly unstable primary carbocation.

$$\overset{\overset{\displaystyle Br^+}{\diagup \diagdown}}{CH_2\!-\!CH_2} \quad \text{better than} \quad \overset{\displaystyle Br}{\diagdown}{CH_2\!-\!\overset{+}{C}H_2}$$

The ion formed by addition of bromine to isobutylene is better described as a tertiary carbocation with a long and weak bond to bromine.

$$CH_3\!-\!\overset{\underset{\displaystyle \ddot{C}H_3}{|}}{\overset{\overset{\displaystyle \cdot\cdot Br}{\vdots}}{\overset{|}{C}}{}^+}\!-\!CH_2$$

Cations such as these may be described in terms of three resonance structures: The actual ion is a composite or hybrid of the three structures A, B, and C.

$$-\overset{|}{\underset{|}{\overset{+}{C}}}\!-\!\overset{\overset{\displaystyle \cdot X}{\diagup \diagdown}}{\underset{|}{C}}- \quad\longleftrightarrow\quad -\overset{\overset{\displaystyle \overset{+}{X}}{\diagup \diagdown}}{\underset{|}{C}}\!-\!\overset{|}{\underset{|}{C}}- \quad\longleftrightarrow\quad -\overset{|}{\underset{|}{C}}\!-\!\overset{\overset{\displaystyle X\cdot}{}}{\underset{|}{C}}{}^+-$$

$$\quad\quad A \quad\quad\quad\quad\quad B \quad\quad\quad\quad\quad C$$

If both A and C correspond to unstable carbocations, then structure B is a more important contributor to the actual structure of the ion. If either A or C corresponds to a relatively stable carbocation, then that structure contributes more and the ion has substantial carbocation character without as much halonium ion character.

The cyclic halonium ion intermediate has an important effect on the *stereochemistry* of halogen additions. When halide ion reacts with the cyclic ion, the reaction is a nucleophilic displacement reaction. Since the nucleophile Br⁻ must approach carbon to the rear of the leaving group, the net result is anti addition of Br_2 to the double bond.

As a result, addition of halogens to cycloalkenes having cis double bonds gives the trans product.

Cyclopentene

trans-1,2-dibromocyclopentane

In additions to cyclohexene the initial product is the diaxial dibromide, which immediately undergoes chair-chair conformational interconversion to give the more stable diequatorial conformer.

trans–1,2–dibromocyclohexane

Note the conformation of cyclohexene that is indicated in this equation. The double bond and the four atoms attached to it lie in one plane, as shown by the stereoscopic representation in Figure 11.14. The remaining two ring carbons lie above and below this plane in order to stagger the hydrogens. In the conventional symbol used in the foregoing equation, we are viewing the molecule *in the plane of the double bond*. We see the carbon-carbon double bond in front, with C-4 and C-5 above and below this plane, respectively. The hydrogens are usually omitted for clarity, although in the present example they are included to emphasize the stereochemistry of the addition reaction.

EXERCISE 11.16 Construct a molecular model of *trans*-1,2-dibromocyclohexane with the two bromine atoms in axial positions. Note that there is an anti-coplanar arrangement of the four-atom array Br—C—C—Br. Imagine that one bromine uses one of its nonbonding electron pairs to attack the other C—Br from the rear and displace bromide ion. What is the product of this internal S_N2 process? Now place your *trans*-1,2-dibromocyclohexane model in the conformation with the two bromines in equatorial positions. Can a similar S_N2 process occur in this conformation? Keeping in mind the principle of microscopic reversibility (page 98), what does this exercise tell you about the stereochemistry of the addition of bromine to cyclohexene?

When reaction of an alkene with bromine is carried out in an inert solvent such as carbon tetrachloride, the only nucleophilic reagent available for reaction with the inter-

FIGURE 11.14 Stereoscopic representation of cyclohexene.

mediate cation is bromide ion. In hydroxylic solvents, the solvent itself is nucleophilic and can react in competition with the bromide ion.

$$C_6H_5CH{=}CH_2 \xrightarrow[\text{Br}_2 \text{ in CH}_3\text{OH}]{\text{dilute solution of}} \underset{\text{minor}}{C_6H_5CHBrCH_2Br} + \underset{\text{major}}{C_6H_5\overset{\overset{\displaystyle OCH_3}{|}}{C}HCH_2Br}$$

The relative amounts of dibromide and bromo ether produced depend on the concentration. For dilute solutions the product is almost exclusively the bromo ether.

Similarly, aqueous or aqueous alkaline solutions of chlorine or bromine produce the corresponding halo alcohols.

trans-2-chlorocyclohexanol

> A solution of chlorine in aqueous sodium hydroxide cooled with ice is added in portions to cyclohexene keeping the temperature at 15–20°C. The mixture is saturated with salt and steam distilled. The distillate is saturated with salt and extracted with ether. Distillation of the dried ether solution gives 70–73% yield of product.

> Solutions of chlorine and bromine in water are in equilibrium with the corresponding hypohalous acids.
>
> $$X_2 + H_2O \rightleftharpoons H^+ + X^- + HOX$$
>
> A saturated solution of chlorine in water at 25°C is 0.09 M and is one-third converted to chloride ion and hypochlorous acid. In saturated bromine water (0.2 M) 0.5% of the bromine is converted to hypobromous acid. Thus, although the formation of halo alcohol may be formally regarded as an addition of HO—X across the double bond, the mechanism probably involves a reaction of an intermediate halonium ion with water or hydroxide ion.

The halo alcohols that result from these additions provide a useful route to epoxides (Section 9.11).

cyclohexene oxide

> **EXERCISE 11.17** Make a conformational drawing showing the chair conformation of *trans*-2-chlorocyclohexanol that results *immediately* from the reaction of hydroxide ion with the intermediate halonium ion. What is the relationship of the carbon-oxygen and carbon-chlorine bonds? What is the stable conformation of this molecule? Now write a mechanism for the conversion of *trans*-2-chlorocyclohexanol into cyclohexene oxide, taking care to indicate any conformational changes that must occur as separate steps.

The 1,2-dihalides produced by the addition of halogens to alkenes are called **vicinal** dihalides (L., *vicinus*, near). They have many chemical properties in common with simple alkyl halides. For example, 1,2-dibromoethane readily enters into nucleophilic displacement reactions.

$$BrCH_2CH_2Br + 2\,CN^- \longrightarrow NCCH_2CH_2CN + 2\,Br^-$$

As with the simple monohalides, nucleophilic displacement is usually accompanied by some elimination, particularly when one or both of the halogens is attached to a secondary carbon. With strong bases, elimination is the principal reaction.

$$\underset{\text{1,2-dichlorobutane}}{CH_3CH_2\overset{\displaystyle Cl}{\underset{\displaystyle |}{C}}HCH_2Cl} + CH_3O^- \longrightarrow \underset{\text{1-chloro-1-butene}}{CH_3CH_2CH=CHCl} + \underset{\text{2-chloro-1-butene}}{CH_3CH_2\overset{\displaystyle Cl}{\underset{\displaystyle |}{C}}=CH_2}$$

Such dehydrohalogenations are not generally useful ways to prepare haloalkenes because both isomers are usually produced.

EXERCISE 11.18 What products are expected to result from each of the following reactions? Show the complete stereostructure of the product where relevant.
(a) 1-methylcyclohexene + bromine
(b) *cis*-2-butene + chlorine + aqueous NaOH at 10°C
(c) the product of (b) + aqueous NaOH at 100°C

C. Addition of HX and Water

The region above and below a double bond is electron-rich because of the π-bond. Consequently, alkenes have a tendency to act as Lewis bases and react with electrophilic reagents. An example is the reaction of 2-methylpropene with HCl. In the first step the double bond reacts with a proton to give a carbocation intermediate, which combines with chloride ion to give *t*-butyl chloride.

Some further examples of this reaction are

4-methyl-1-pentene   2-bromo-4-methylpentane

1-methylcyclohexene   1-chloro-1-methylcyclohexane

Gaseous hydrogen chloride is bubbled slowly into a solution of 1-methylcyclohexene in methylene chloride at 0°C. The end of the reaction is marked by the appearance of HCl fumes over the surface of the reaction mixture. The methylene chloride solution is washed with aqueous sodium bicarbonate, dried, and evaporated to obtain 1-chloro-1-methylcyclohexane.

With unsymmetrical alkenes the initial protonation occurs so as to afford the *more stable carbocation*. Since alkyl substituents stabilize carbocations, the proton adds to the less substituted carbon of the double bond.

$$
\begin{array}{c}
CH_3 \\
\diagdown \\
C{=}CH_2 + HCl \\
\diagup \\
CH_3
\end{array}
\longrightarrow
\begin{array}{c}
CH_3 \\
\diagdown \\
\overset{+}{C}{-}CH_3 \\
\diagup \\
CH_3
\end{array}
\quad not \quad
\begin{array}{c}
CH_3 \\
| \\
CH_3{-}C{-}\overset{+}{C}H_2 \\
| \\
H
\end{array}
$$

This generalization is commonly referred to as **Markovnikov's rule**. It was formulated by Markovnikov long before the foregoing mechanistic interpretation was developed to explain it.

> **EXERCISE 11.19** Refer back to the examples given for the addition of HCl and HBr to unsymmetrical alkenes in this section. Note the operation of Markovnikov's rule. Write a reaction mechanism for each example, showing the intermediate carbocation in each case.

If two intermediate carbocations of comparable stability can be formed, a mixture of products results.

> **EXERCISE 11.20** Addition of HBr to *trans*-2-pentene gives a mixture of 2-bromopentane and 3-bromopentane. Write a mechanism, showing all intermediates, and explain this result.

The addition of HX to a double bond is a significant reaction because of what it reveals about the general chemistry of alkenes, but it is not an important method for preparing the simpler alkyl halides, which are prepared either by halogenation of alkanes or from the corresponding alcohols.

The **hydration** of alkenes is an important industrial method for the manufacture of alcohols. Hydration is usually accomplished by passing the alkene into a mixture of sulfuric acid and water. For example, gaseous isobutylene is absorbed in 60-65% aqueous sulfuric acid. The intermediate formed is undoubtedly the *t*-butyl cation, which reacts with water to give *t*-butyl alcohol.

$$(CH_3)_2C{=}CH_2 + H^+ \rightleftharpoons (CH_3)_3C^+ \xrightarrow{H_2O} (CH_3)_3C{-}\overset{+}{O}H_2 \rightleftharpoons (CH_3)_3COH + H^+$$

The reaction is the reverse of acid-catalyzed dehydration. Low temperatures and aqueous solution favor formation of the alcohol, whereas high temperatures and distillation of the alkene as it is formed shift the equilibrium toward the alkene. Under more vigorous conditions dimeric and polymeric products are produced.

Ethylene is also absorbed by sulfuric acid, but in this case 98% H_2SO_4 is required. The product is ethylsulfuric acid, which is hydrolyzed to ethyl alcohol in a separate step. This reaction may involve ethyl cation as an intermediate and is a rare example of the involvement of primary alkyl cations in solution.

$$H_2SO_4 + CH_2{=}CH_2 \longrightarrow CH_3CH_2^+ + HOSO_3^- \longrightarrow$$

$$CH_3CH_2OSO_2OH \xrightarrow{H_2O} CH_3CH_2OH + H_2SO_4$$

Although direct hydration is an important industrial process, it is seldom used as a laboratory procedure. Yields of alcohol are highly variable and depend strongly on the exact reaction conditions. A much more reliable procedure for small-scale work involves the use of mercuric ion, Hg^{2+}, as an electrophile. If an alkene is treated with an aqueous solution of mercuric acetate or mercuric perchlorate, a hydroxyalkylmercuric salt is formed.

$$CH_3CH=CHCH_3 + Hg(OAc)_2 \xrightarrow[25°C]{H_2O-THF} CH_3\overset{\overset{\displaystyle OH}{|}}{C}HCHCH_3$$
$$\underset{\displaystyle HgOAc}{|}$$

The mechanism of this reaction involves initial ionization of the mercuric acetate to provide the acetoxymercuric ion, $AcOHg^+$. This species reacts with the carbon-carbon double bond, in much the same manner as a proton. The carbocation so formed reacts with water to give the hydroxyalkylmercuric salt.

(1) $Hg(OAc)_2 \rightleftharpoons AcO^- + AcOHg^+$

(2) $AcOHg^+ + \overset{}{\underset{}{>}}C=C\overset{}{\underset{}{<}} \rightleftharpoons AcOHg-\overset{|}{\underset{|}{C}}-\overset{+}{C}\overset{}{<}$

(3) $AcOHg-\overset{|}{\underset{|}{C}}-\overset{+}{C}\overset{}{<} + H_2O \rightleftharpoons AcOHg-\overset{|}{\underset{|}{C}}-\overset{|}{\underset{|}{C}}-OH + H^+$

Mercuric acetate in methanol or ethanol readily yields the corresponding alkoxyalkyl-mercuric acetate.

$$CH_3CH=CH_2 + Hg(OAc)_2 \xrightarrow[25°C]{CH_3OH} CH_3\overset{\overset{\displaystyle OCH_3}{|}}{C}HCH_2HgOAc$$

These compounds are readily reduced with sodium borohydride, which replaces the carbon-mercury bond by C—H with liberation of free mercury. The intermediate orga-nomercury compounds need not be isolated. The net result of mercuration in alcohol or water, followed by sodium borohydride reduction, is addition of alcohol or water to the alkene. The reduction is an excellent method for the synthesis of alcohols and ethers. **Addition follows the Markovnikov rule**, Hg^{2+} becoming attached to the less substi-tuted carbon.

$$n\text{-}C_4H_9CH=CH_2 \xrightarrow[\text{aq. THF}]{Hg(OAc)_2} \xrightarrow[\text{NaOH}]{NaBH_4} n\text{-}C_4H_9CHOHCH_3 + Hg$$
$$(96\%)$$

1-hexene   2-hexanol

1-Hexene is added with stirring to an equivalent amount of mercuric acetate in 1:1 water-THF. After stirring for 10 min at 25°C, aqueous NaOH is added, followed by a 0.5 M solution of $NaBH_4$ in 3 M NaOH. The organic layer is separated, dried and distilled to yield 2-hexanol.

The sodium borohydride used in the foregoing reaction is an important reagent in organic chemistry.

Sodium borohydride, $NaBH_4$, is a salt containing the borohydride ion, BH_4^-. This anion has a tetrahedral structure and can be regarded as being derived from BH_3 and hydride ion, H^-. Sodium borohydride is a white powder and dissolves in water to form stable solutions at basic pH. In acidic medium, $NaBH_4$ reacts rapidly to form hydrogen and sodium borate. Sodium borohydride is soluble in methanol and ethanol, but decomposes slowly in these solvents. It is appreciably soluble in diglyme (5.5 g per 100 g of solvent), but is almost insoluble in glyme or tetrahydrofuran.

The reaction combination of mercuration and reduction is a useful laboratory alternative to acid-catalyzed hydration of olefins. Of course, it cannot compete with sulfuric acid in large-scale commercial productions.

EXERCISE 11.21 What products are expected from each of the following reactions?
(a) 1-methylcyclohexene + $Hg(OAc)_2$ in methanol, followed by $NaBH_4$
(b) 2-methyl-2-pentene + $Hg(OAc)_2$ in water-THF, followed by $NaBH_4$

D. Hydroboration

Although the reaction of alkenes with diborane was discovered less than forty years ago it has become one of the most important reactions in the repertoire of the synthetic chemist.

Diborane B_2H_6 is a colorless, toxic gas that is spontaneously flammable in air. It is usually prepared by the reaction of sodium borohydride with boron trifluoride.

$$3\,NaBH_4 + 4\,BF_3 \longrightarrow 2\,B_2H_6 + 3\,NaBF_4$$

Borane itself, BH_3, is not known. In this compound boron has a sextet of electrons and is a Lewis acid. In ethers such as tetrahydrofuran or diglyme, common solvents for hydroboration reactions, diborane dissolves readily to form an ether-monomer complex, $R_2O:BH_3$. Commercially, borane is often sold as the THF complex.

Diborane has an unusual bridged structure because it is an electron-deficient compound. The 12 valence electrons are too few to provide enough normal two-electron bonds for an ethane-like structure with six boron-hydrogen bonds. In the actual structure four hydrogens and the two borons define a plane with four two-electron boron-hydrogen bonds.

diborane

The other two hydrogens lie above and below this plane and involve three-center two-electron bonds symbolized by ⅄ (see p. 149).

Boron trifluoride is a colorless gas, b.p. $-100°C$, and is available commercially in cylinders. The compound has a planar structure. The Lewis structure shows that there are only six electrons around boron.

$$:\!\ddot{F}\!-\!B\!-\!\ddot{F}\!:$$
$$|$$
$$:\!\ddot{F}\!:$$

The tendency of boron to combine with an electron pair to form an octet is augmented by the electron-attracting character of the attached fluorines. Boron trifluoride is a strong Lewis acid. It reacts avidly with water to form a hydrate, $F_3\overset{-}{B}\!-\!\overset{+}{O}H_2$, which is itself a strong acid but slowly hydrolyzes in water to form boric acid and HF. In fact, BF_3 has a strong affinity generally for oxygen, nitrogen, and fluorine. With HF it forms fluoboric acid, HBF$_4$, a strong acid in aqueous solution. With ethyl ether it forms the complex (C$_2$H$_5$)$_2$O:BF$_3$, boron trifluoride etherate, which can be formulated as (C$_2$H$_5$)$_2$O$\overset{+}{}$—$\overset{-}{}$BF$_3$. This compound is a distillable liquid, b.p. 126°C, and is water-white when pure. We will encounter it often as a useful Lewis acid catalyst.

The boron-hydrogen bond adds rapidly and quantitatively to many multiple bonds including carbon-carbon double bonds. With simple alkenes the product is a tri-alkylborane.

$$3 \text{ CH}_3\text{CH}_2\text{CH}{=}\text{CH}_2 + \text{BH}_3 \xrightarrow{\text{THF}} (\text{CH}_3\text{CH}_2\text{CH}_2\text{CH}_2)_3\text{B}$$

tri-*n*-butylborane

The addition appears to be dominated by steric considerations. The boron generally becomes attached to the less substituted and less sterically congested carbon. With highly substituted or hindered olefins, addition may stop at the mono- or dialkylborane stage. The reaction appears to involve initial coordination of BH$_3$ with the π-electrons of the double bond followed by formation of the carbon-hydrogen bond.

In cases where stereochemistry may be defined, exclusive syn addition is observed.

The alkylborane products are generally not isolated but are converted by subsequent reactions directly into desired products. The most important general reaction of alkylboranes is that with alkaline hydrogen peroxide.

trans-2-methylcyclopentanol

Three separate processes are involved in the oxidation of alkylboranes to alcohols. In the first step, hydroperoxide anion adds to the electron-deficient boron atom.

$$\begin{array}{c} \text{R} \\ | \\ \text{R}{-}\text{B} \\ | \\ \text{R} \end{array} + {}^-\text{OOH} \longrightarrow \begin{array}{c} \text{R} \\ | \\ \text{R}{-}\text{B}{-}\text{O}{-}\text{OH} \\ | \\ \text{R} \end{array}$$

The resulting intermediate rearranges with loss of hydroxide ion. The driving force for the rearrangement is liberation of the stable anion OH$^-$ and formation of the strong boron-oxygen bond.

$$\begin{array}{c} \text{R} \\ | \\ \text{R}{-}\text{B}{-}\text{O}{\overset{\frown}{-}}\text{OH} \\ | \\ \text{R} \end{array} \longrightarrow \begin{array}{c} \text{R} \\ | \\ \text{R}{-}\text{B}{-}\text{OR} + \text{OH}^- \\ | \\ \text{R} \end{array}$$

The boron-oxygen bond is much stronger than a boron-carbon bond because of overlap of an oxygen *p*-orbital with its lone pair of electrons and the empty *p*-orbital on boron.

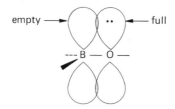

empty ⟶ ⟵ full

--- B — O —

The oxygen lone pair becomes polarized toward boron in the sense indicated by the resonance structures

$$\text{B}\overset{..}{\underset{..}{-}}\text{O}- \longleftrightarrow \text{B}\overset{-}{=}\overset{+}{\underset{..}{O}}-$$

Hydrogen peroxide is available as the anhydrous liquid, b.p. 152°C, or as aqueous solutions ranging from 3 to 90% in concentration. The compound is thermodynamically unstable with respect to water and oxygen, and high-strength solutions are explosively hazardous. The 3% solution is used medicinally as a topical antiseptic, but the 30% solution is commonly used in the organic laboratory. Even with the 30% reagent, experiments should be carried out behind safety shields and the material should be kept out of contact with skin and eyes.

The migration of an alkyl group, and its bonding electron pair, is analogous to the rearrangements of carbocations that we considered in Section 9.6.C.

$$\begin{array}{c}
\underset{\underset{R}{|}}{-\text{C}}-\overset{+}{\text{C}}- \longrightarrow \overset{+}{-\text{C}}-\underset{\underset{R}{|}}{\text{C}}-
\end{array}$$

$$\begin{array}{c}
\underset{\underset{R}{|}}{-\overset{-}{\text{B}}}-\text{O}-\text{OH} \longrightarrow \underset{\underset{R}{|}}{-\text{B}}-\text{O} + \text{OH}^-
\end{array}$$

The reaction of boranes with alkaline hydrogen peroxide is rapid and exothermic. The product R_2BOR reacts further by the same process to give a trialkyl borate ester.

$$R_2BOR + 2\,OOH^- \longrightarrow B(OR)_3 + 2\,OH^-$$

The borate ester is then hydrolyzed under the reaction conditions to the alcohol and sodium borate.

$$B(OR)_3 + OH^- + 3H_2O \longrightarrow 3\,ROH + B(OH)_4^-$$

EXERCISE 11.22 Write all of the steps in a reaction mechanism for the alkaline hydrolysis of trimethyl borate.

The net result of hydroboration and oxidation-hydrolysis is **anti-Markovnikov hydration** of a double bond. The reaction is a relatively simple and convenient laboratory procedure and has become an important synthetic reaction in organic chemistry.

1-methylcyclopentene   (85%)
trans-2-methylcyclopentanol

Diborane prepared by reaction of sodium borohydride and boron trifluoride etherate in diglyme is swept by a stream of nitrogen into a solution of 1-methylcyclopentene in THF at 0°C. The reaction is completed by addition of aqueous sodium hydroxide followed slowly by 30% hydrogen peroxide. After stirring for an additional period the layers are separated, the aqueous phase is extracted with ether and the combined organic layers are dried and distilled to give 85% of *trans*-2-methylcyclopentanol.

EXERCISE 11.23 Write the structure, paying attention to stereochemistry where pertinent, for the alcohol produced by hydroboration-oxidation of each of the following alkenes.
(a) 4-methyl-1-pentene
(b) (*E*)-3-methyl-2-pentene
(c) 1,2-dideuteriocyclohexene

E. Oxidation

Alkenes are oxidized readily by potassium permanganate, $KMnO_4$, but the products depend on the reaction conditions.

Potassium permanganate forms dark purple crystals that dissolve in water to give intense red solutions. In permanganate anion, MnO_4^-, manganese has an oxidation state of +7. As an oxidizing agent in basic solution, manganese is reduced to manganese dioxide, MnO_2, an insoluble brown compound that is frequently difficult to filter because it tends to form colloidal suspensions. Treatment with SO_2 at this point forms the soluble $MnSO_4$. In acid solution reduction of permanganate to Mn^{2+} occurs. The half-reactions for these two reactions are as follows.

$$3e^- + MnO_4^- + 2\,H_2O \longrightarrow MnO_2 + 4\,OH^-$$

$$5e^- + MnO_4^- + 8\,H^+ \longrightarrow Mn^{2+} + 4\,H_2O$$

In acid solution potassium permanganate is a strong reagent that attacks organic compounds almost indiscriminantly. It will even oxidize HCl to Cl_2. Hence, in organic reactions potassium permanganate is almost always used in neutral or alkaline solutions in which MnO_2 is produced.

Cold dilute potassium permanganate reacts with double bonds to give vicinal diols, which are commonly called glycols.

a glycol

Reaction conditions need to be carefully controlled. Yields are variable and often low. The reaction occurs with syn addition and is thought to involve an intermediate cyclic manganate ester that is rapidly hydrolyzed.

(30–33%)
cis-1,2-cyclohexanediol

The same overall reaction can be accomplished with osmium tetroxide, a reagent that forms isolable cyclic adducts with alkenes.

black precipitate

Osmium tetroxide, OsO_4, forms colorless or yellow crystals that are soluble in water and in organic solvents. The compound sublimes readily and is highly toxic. It is an expensive reagent (greater than \$10 per gram). Because of its cost, it is normally used only in relatively small-scale preparations. It is supplied commercially in small sealed tubes.

The cis diol can be isolated from the alkene-OsO_4 adduct by treatment with H_2S. A more convenient (and less expensive) procedure involves the combination of hydrogen peroxide with a *catalytic* amount of osmium tetroxide. The alkene-OsO_4 adduct is formed as ususal, but is converted by the peroxide directly to the cis diol. In this procedure, osmium tetroxide is constantly regenerated, so that only a small amount need be used.

(58%)

Oxidative cleavage of the double bond can be accomplished by reaction of an alkene with ozone.

Ozone, O_3, is an important constituent of the upper atmosphere, where it is produced by action of solar ultraviolet radiation on atmospheric oxygen. Ozone, in turn, absorbs in the ultraviolet region of the spectrum and provides an important screen that limits the amount of this radiation that reaches the earth's surface. Ozone is thermodynamically unstable with respect to oxygen.

$$O_3 \longrightarrow \tfrac{3}{2} O_2 \qquad \Delta H° = -34 \text{ kcal mole}^{-1}$$

Ozone is produced in the laboratory with an "ozonator," a special apparatus in which an electrodeless discharge is induced in dry air passing through an alternating electric field. Ozone concentrations as high as 4% in air can be produced. The gas has the characteristic odor usually associated with electric arcs.

Reactions of alkenes with ozone are normally carried out by passing ozone-containing air through a solution of the alkene in an inert solvent at a low temperature (usually

−78°C, the temperature of a dry ice-isopropyl alcohol cooling bath). Reaction is rapid and completion of reaction is determined by testing the effluent gas with aqueous potassium iodide. Unreacted ozone reacts to give iodine. Suitable solvents for ozonizations include methylene chloride, ethanol, and ethyl acetate. The first-formed addition product, which is called a molozonide, rearranges rapidly, even at low temperatures, to the ozonide structure.

molozonide   ozonide

In some cases polymeric structures are obtained. Some ozonides, especially the polymeric structures, decompose with explosive violence on heating; hence, the ozonides are generally not isolated but are decomposed directly to desired products.

Hydrolysis with water occurs readily to give carbonyl compounds and hydrogen peroxide.

Aldehydes are oxidized by hydrogen peroxide to carboxylic acids. Hence, reduction conditions are often used in decomposing the ozonides. Such conditions include zinc dust-acetic acid and H_2-Pd/C.

A solution of 6-methyl-1-heptene in methylene chloride at −78°C is treated with ozone and is then added to a stirred mixture of zinc dust and 50% aqueous acetic acid. The mixture is refluxed for 1 hr and extracted with ether. The last traces of peroxides are removed from the ether with aqueous potassium iodide and the washed and dried solution is distilled to give 5-methylhexanal, b.p. 144°C.

Treatment of the ozonide with sodium borohydride gives a mixture of the corresponding alcohols. In the case of a cyclic alkene, the ring is cleaved, and a diol is produced.

(63%)
1,6-hexanediol

EXERCISE 11.24 What products are produced by each of the following reactions. Indicate stereostructure where pertinent.
(a) 1-methylcyclohexene + O_3, followed by zinc-acetic acid
(b) *cis*-2-butene + 10 mole % OsO_4 + H_2O_2
(c) cyclopentene + aqueous $KMnO_4$ at 5°C

Alkenes may also be oxidized by peroxycarboxylic acids. The product is an oxirane (Section 10.11.A).

trans-3-hexene   peroxyacetic acid   *trans*-2,3-diethyloxirane

Peroxycarboxylic acids are related to hydrogen peroxide, in that they have an oxygen-oxygen single bond.

$$R-\overset{\overset{\displaystyle O}{\|}}{C}-O-OH$$

Like H_2O_2, peroxycarboxylic acids are oxidizing agents and are often used for that purpose. Peroxycarboxylic acids are generally unstable and must either be stored in the cold or prepared as needed. An important exception is 3-chloroperoxybenzoic acid, an exceptionally stable crystalline solid that is available commercially. This reagent provides a simple and convenient one-step route to oxiranes.

3-chloroperoxybenzoic   (60%)   3-chlorobenzoic
acid   1-butyloxirane   acid

The mechanism of the oxidation of alkenes by peroxycarboxylic acids is such that *both new carbon-oxygen bonds are formed at one time*. Thus, the oxidation is stereospecific, and may be considered as an addition reaction in which the two new bonds (which happen both to be to the same oxygen) are formed in a syn manner.

Recall that oxiranes may also be synthesized by addition of aqueous halogen to an alkene, followed by base-catalyzed cyclization (page 258).

1-methylcyclohexene oxide

EXERCISE 11.25 We saw in Section 10.11.A that oxiranes undergo ring-opening upon treatment with aqueous acid. What is the stereostructure of the product resulting from application of the following reaction sequence to *trans*-2-butene? (1) peroxyacetic acid, CH_2Cl_2; (2) 10% H_2SO_4, 100°C.

F. Addition of Carbenes and Carbenoids

Carbenes are reactive intermediates that have the general formula R_2C:, in which carbon has only a sextet of electrons. Although carbenes are neutral species, the electron-deficient carbon is still "hungry" for electrons, and hence carbenes behave as **electrophiles**. One way in which carbenes may be generated is by the reaction of chloroform with a strong base. Because of the strong electron-attracting effect of the three chlorines, chloroform is rather acidic ($pK_a \cong 25$). Thus, upon treatment of chloroform with hydroxide or alkoxide ion, the trichloromethyl anion is formed in a small equilibrium concentration. If the reaction is carried out in water, the $Cl_3C:^-$ is mainly protonated to regenerate chloroform. However, in less acidic solvents such as *t*-butyl alcohol, the trichloromethyl anion lives long enough to lose a chloride ion to give dichlorocarbene.

$$CHCl_3 + RO^- \rightleftharpoons ROH + \underset{\substack{\text{trichloromethyl} \\ \text{anion}}}{Cl_3C:^-} \longrightarrow Cl^- + \underset{\text{dichlorocarbene}}{Cl_2C:}$$

If dichlorocarbene is generated in the presence of an alkene, it adds to the double bond to give a 1,1-dichlorocyclopropane.

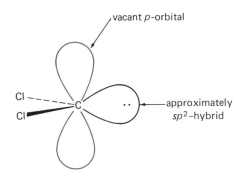

1,1-dichloro-2,2-dimethyl cyclopropane

The electronic structure of the intermediate dichlorocarbene has a pair of electrons in an orbital that has hybridization of approximately sp^2. In addition, the carbene carbon also has a vacant *p*-orbital (Figure 11.15). Thus, a carbene has both a carbanion lone pair and a carbocation vacancy on a single carbon.

As in the epoxidation of alkenes, the addition of dichlorocarbene is stereospecific—syn addition of the two new carbon-carbon bonds is observed.

no cis isomer is formed

This reaction can also be applied to bromoform, $CHBr_3$, to yield the corresponding dibromocyclopropanes.

Carbene itself, $:CH_2$, can be produced by photolysis or pyrolysis of a compound known as diazomethane, CH_2N_2. However, a better way to add $:CH_2$ to an alkene utilizes a mixture of diiodomethane and zinc dust (Simmons-Smith reaction). In practice, the zinc dust is usually activated by alloying it with a small amount of copper.

vacant *p*-orbital

approximately sp^2-hybrid

FIGURE 11.15 Electronic structure of dichlorocarbene.

$$\text{1-heptene} + CH_2I_2 \xrightarrow[\text{ether}]{Zn(Cu)} \text{pentylcyclopropane (30\%)}$$

The reaction is applicable to many kinds of double bonds. Yields are generally only fair (30-70%), but the products are often difficult to prepare by alternative routes. The method appears to involve the formation of an organometallic species, iodomethylzinc (Section 8.8.A). It is proposed that this species, which is sometimes termed a **carbenoid** because it behaves in some ways like a true carbene, adds to the double bond to give an adduct, which then eliminates zinc iodide.

(1) $CH_2I_2 + Zn \longrightarrow ICH_2ZnI$

(2) $\ce{C=C} + ICH_2ZnI \longrightarrow ICH_2\overset{|}{\underset{|}{C}}\overset{|}{\underset{|}{C}}ZnI$

(3) $ICH_2\overset{|}{\underset{|}{C}}\overset{|}{\underset{|}{C}}ZnI \longrightarrow$

EXERCISE 11.26 What is the stereostructure of the product of each of the following reactions.
(a) (E)-3-methyl-3-hexene + CHCl₃ + potassium t-butoxide
(b) *trans*-2-pentene + CH₂I₂ + Zn(Cu) in ether

G. Free Radical Additions

The early literature of organic chemistry contained considerable disagreement on the mode of addition of HBr to terminal olefins. In some cases Markovnikov's rule appeared to hold; in other cases it did not. Often two chemists would add HBr to the same alkene and obtain contradictory results.

$$RCH{=}CH_2 + HBr \longrightarrow RCH_2CH_2Br \quad \text{or} \quad R\overset{\overset{\displaystyle Br}{|}}{C}HCH_3$$

In the 1930s this apparent dilemma was resolved when it was discovered that HBr (but *not* HCl or HI) can add to alkenes by two different mechanisms. Pure materials and pure solvents encourage addition by the electrophilic mechanism discussed in Section 11.6.C, which leads to normal Markovnikov addition.

$$RCH{=}CH_2 + HBr \xrightarrow{\text{(ionic mechanism)}} R\overset{\overset{\displaystyle Br}{|}}{C}HCH_3$$

Impure materials, oxygen, and some other additives were found to promote "abnormal" addition by a mechanism involving free radical intermediates.

$$RCH{=}CH_2 + HBr \xrightarrow{\substack{\text{(free radical} \\ \text{mechanism)}}} RCH_2CH_2Br$$

The free radical mechanism starts with an initiation step that results in oxidation of HBr to bromine atoms.

$$\text{HBr} + \text{O}_2 \text{ (or other radical initiators)} \longrightarrow \text{Br} \cdot$$

The bromine atom then adds to the alkene to give a free radical that continues the chain by abstracting hydrogen from a molecule of HBr. Both of the propagation steps are exothermic and have low activation energies.

$$\text{RCH}{=}\text{CH}_2 + \text{Br} \cdot \longrightarrow \text{R}\overset{\cdot}{\text{C}}\text{HCH}_2\text{Br} \qquad\qquad \Delta H° = -9 \text{ kcal mole}^{-1}$$

$$\text{R}\overset{\cdot}{\text{C}}\text{HCH}_2\text{Br} + \text{HBr} \longrightarrow \text{RCH}_2\text{CH}_2\text{Br} + \text{Br} \cdot \qquad \Delta H° = -7 \text{ kcal mole}^{-1}$$

Note that the bromine atom adds to the alkene in such a way as to give the more highly substituted (more stable) free radical. The overall outcome is thus **anti-Markovnikov** orientation. This abnormal addition or ''peroxide effect'' is a useful reaction with HBr, but is not significant with HCl or HI. The carbon-iodine bond is so weak that the addition of iodine atoms to double bonds is endothermic. It becomes favorable only at elevated temperatures.

$$\text{RCH}{=}\text{CH}_2 + \text{I} \cdot \longrightarrow \text{R}\overset{\cdot}{\text{C}}\text{HCH}_2\text{I} \qquad\qquad \Delta H° = +5 \text{ kcal mole}^{-1}$$

$$\text{R}\overset{\cdot}{\text{C}}\text{HCH}_2\text{I} + \text{HI} \longrightarrow \text{RCH}_2\text{CH}_2\text{I} + \text{I} \cdot \qquad \Delta H° = -24 \text{ kcal mole}^{-1}$$

The hydrogen-chlorine bond is so strong that the second step in the sequence is endothermic and slow.

$$\text{RCH}{=}\text{CH}_2 + \text{Cl} \cdot \longrightarrow \text{R}\overset{\cdot}{\text{C}}\text{HCH}_2\text{Cl} \qquad\qquad \Delta H° = -22 \text{ kcal mole}^{-1}$$

$$\text{R}\overset{\cdot}{\text{C}}\text{HCH}_2\text{Cl} + \text{HCl} \longrightarrow \text{RCH}_2\text{CH}_2\text{Cl} + \text{Cl} \cdot \qquad \Delta H° = +8 \text{ kcal mole}^{-1}$$

Free radical chain reactions work best when both propagation steps are exothermic. An endothermic step corresponds to a slow and reversible reaction that breaks the chain.

Other compounds that have appropriate bond strengths can add to double bonds under free radical conditions. Examples include chlorine, bromine, hydrogen sulfide, thiols, and polyhaloalkanes.

$$\text{CH}_3\text{CH}_2\text{CH}{=}\text{CH}_2 + \text{H}_2\text{S} \xrightarrow[0°C]{h\nu} \text{CH}_3\text{CH}_2\text{CH}_2\text{CH}_2\text{SH} + (\text{CH}_3\text{CH}_2\text{CH}_2\text{CH}_2)_2\text{S}$$
$$\qquad\qquad\qquad\qquad\qquad\qquad (68\%) \qquad\qquad\qquad (12\%)$$

$$(\text{CH}_3)_2\text{C}{=}\text{CH}_2 + \text{CH}_3\text{CH}_2\text{SH} \xrightarrow[\text{O}_2]{100°C} (\text{CH}_3)_2\text{CHCH}_2\text{SCH}_2\text{CH}_3$$
$$\qquad\qquad\qquad\qquad\qquad\qquad\qquad (94\%)$$
$$\qquad\qquad\qquad\qquad\qquad\text{ethyl isobutyl sulfide}$$

Carbon tetrachloride and carbon tetrabromide react readily with olefins and free radical initiators to give 1:1 adducts. The propagation steps are addition of the trihalomethyl radical to C=C and reaction of the free radical so produced with CX_4 to regenerate the trihalomethyl radical.

$$\text{RCH}{=}\text{CH}_2 + \cdot\text{CX}_3 \longrightarrow \text{R}\overset{\cdot}{\text{C}}\text{HCH}_2\text{CX}_3$$

$$\overset{\cdot}{\text{R}}\text{CHCH}_2\text{CX}_3 + \text{CX}_4 \longrightarrow \text{R}\overset{\text{X}}{\overset{|}{\text{C}}}\text{HCH}_2\text{CX}_3 + \cdot\text{CX}_3$$

Again, the overall result is Markovnikov addition; the trihalomethyl group ends up bonded to the carbon bearing the smaller number of hydrogens.

$$\text{CH}_3(\text{CH}_2)_5\text{CH}{=}\text{CH}_2 + \text{CCl}_4 \xrightarrow[\Delta]{\text{peroxide}} \text{CH}_3(\text{CH}_2)_5\text{CHClCH}_2\text{CCl}_3$$
$$\qquad\qquad\qquad\qquad\qquad\qquad\qquad (75\%)$$
$$\qquad\qquad\qquad\qquad\qquad\text{1,1,1,3-tetrachlorononane}$$

$$CH_3(CH_2)_5CH{=}CH_2 + CBr_4 \xrightarrow[75°C]{h\nu} CH_3(CH_2)_5CHBrCH_2CBr_3$$

(88%)

1,1,1,3-tetrabromononane

At this point it is instructive to review the meanings of the terms ''Markovnikov addition'' and ''anti-Markovnikov addition.'' When first formulated, the Markovnikov rule simply stated that ''in the addition of HX to an alkene, the H goes to the carbon already having the greater number of hydrogens.''

Markovnikov addition

$$CH_3{-}CH{=}CH_2 + HX \longrightarrow CH_3\overset{\displaystyle X}{\underset{\displaystyle |}{-}}CH{\overset{\displaystyle H}{\underset{\displaystyle |}{-}}}CH_2$$

Anti-Markovnikov addition

$$CH_3{-}CH{=}CH_2 + HX \longrightarrow CH_3{-}CH{-}CH_2$$

We now recognize that electrophilic additions obey the Markovnikov rule simply because H^+ is the reagent that adds to the double bond first and *it always adds to the end that produces the more stable intermediate carbocation.*

$$CH_3CH{=}CH_2 + HX \longrightarrow CH_3\overset{+}{C}H{-}CH_2 \quad (\text{not } CH_3CH{-}\overset{+}{C}H_2)$$

Free radical additions ''disobey'' the Markovnikov rule because in this case it is X· that adds first and this species *adds so as to produce the more stable intermediate free radical.*

$$CH_3CH{=}CH_2 + X\cdot \longrightarrow CH_3\dot{C}H{-}CH_2 \quad (\text{not } CH_3CH{-}CH_2\cdot)$$

EXERCISE 11.27 Write the two propagation steps for addition of methanethiol, CH_3SH, to ethylene. Estimate $\Delta H°$ for each of these steps, using the following bond energies (all in kcal mole^{-1}): C=C, 150; C—C, 83; C—S, 65; S—H, 83; C—H, 104.

PROBLEMS

1. (a) Give the structure and IUPAC name of each of the isomeric pentenes. Which ones are stereoisomers? Which ones are capable of optical activity?
   (b) Answer part (a) for the methylcyclopentenes.

2. Write the structure corresponding to each of the following names:
   (a) *trans*-3,4-dimethyl-2-pentene   (b) 4-methyl-3-penten-1-ol
   (c) *cis*-3-ethyl-2-hexene   (d) vinyl fluoride
   (e) 1-bromocyclohexene   (f) (*R*)-3-methylcyclohexene
   (g) (*Z*)-2-bromo-2-pentene   (h) (*E*)-3-methyl-2-hexene
   (i) 3-methyl-*cis*-cyclooctene   (j) 3-methyl-*trans*-cyclooctene
   (k) *trans*-3,4-dimethylcyclobutene   (l) 2,3-dimethyl-2-butene

3. Explain why each of the following names is incorrect.
   (a) 2-methylcyclopentene   (b) 2-methyl-*cis*-3-pentene

(c) *trans*-1-butene
(e) 2-chlorocyclopentene
(g) *trans*-pent-2-en-4-ol

(d) 1-bromoisobutylene
(f) (*E*)-3-ethyl-3-pentene
(h) (*Z*)-3-isopropyl-3-heptene

4. Name each of the following compounds. For compounds capable of stereoisomers, use the E-Z and R-S nomenclature.

(a)

(b)

(c)

(d)

(e)

(f) Cl

(g) Cl

(h) Cl

(i) Cl

(j) HO

(k) OH

(l)

5. Give the structure of the principal organic product(s) produced from 3-ethyl-2-pentene under each of the following reaction conditions.
(a) H_2/Pd-C
(b) H_2O, Br_2
(c) Cl_2 in CCl_4 at 0°C
(d) cold dilute $KMnO_4$
(e) (i) B_2H_6; (ii) NaOH—H_2O_2
(f) (i) aq. $Hg(ClO_4)_2$; (ii) $NaBH_4$
(g) (i) O_3; (ii) Zn dust, aq. CH_3COOH
(h) HBr, free-radical inhibitor
(i) HBr, peroxides
(j) Br_2, dilute solution in CH_3OH
(k) peroxybenzoic acid in chloroform
(l) $CHBr_3$, *t*-BuOK, *t*-BuOH
(m) CH_2I_2, Zn(Cu), ether

6. Apply each of the reaction conditions in problem 5 to *cis*- and *trans*-3-hexene. For which reactions are the same products obtained from both stereoisomers? For which reactions do the products differ and how do they differ?

7. Apply each of the reaction conditions in problem 5 to cyclohexene. Specify stereochemistry where pertinent.

8. What is the principal organic product of each of the following reaction conditions? Specify stereochemistry where appropriate.

(a) $(CH_3)_3CO^-$ K^+

(b) $\xrightarrow[\text{THF}]{BH_3}$ $\xrightarrow[\text{NaOH}]{H_2O_2}$

(c) $\xrightarrow[\substack{CCl_4 \\ 0°C}]{Cl_2}$

(d) $\xrightarrow{(CH_3)_3CO^-\ K^+}$ $\xrightarrow{cold\ dil.\ KMnO_4}$

(e) $\xrightarrow[\substack{C_2H_5OH \\ \Delta}]{KOH}$

(f) $\xrightarrow[\substack{C_2H_5OH \\ \Delta}]{C_2H_5O^-\ K^+}$

(g) $\xrightarrow[H_2O]{Br_2}$ $\xrightarrow[\substack{C_2H_5OH \\ \Delta}]{C_2H_5O^-\ K^+}$

(h) $\xrightarrow[\substack{CH_3OH \\ -60°C}]{O_3}$ $\xrightarrow{Zn\text{-}HOAc}$

(i) $+ Br_2$ $\xrightarrow[0°C]{CCl_4}$

9. Show how one may accomplish each of the following transformations in a practical manner.

(a) $\longrightarrow$

(b) $\longrightarrow$

(c) $\longrightarrow$

(d) $\longrightarrow$

(e) $\longrightarrow$

(f) $\longrightarrow$

(g) $\longrightarrow$

10. Show how one may accomplish each of the following transformations in a practical manner.

(a)

(b)

(c)

(d)

(e)

(f)

(g)

11. Starting with alcohols, outline multistep syntheses of each of the following compounds.

(a)

(b)

(c) HO $\diagup\!\!\!\diagdown\!\!\!\diagup\!\!\!\diagdown$ OH

(d)

12. The potential function for rotation of the methyl group in propylene is approximately that of a threefold barrier with a barrier height of 2.0 kcal mole^{-1}. The most stable conformation is A in which a methyl hydrogen is eclipsed with the double bond. The least stable conformation is B in which H-2 is eclipsed to a methyl hydrogen. Plot the energy of the system as a function of a 360° rotation of the methyl group. Identify the points along this plot that correspond to conformations A and B.

A   B

13. Although the difference in energy between cis and trans olefins is generally about 1 kcal mole^{-1}, for 4,4-dimethyl-2-pentene the cis isomer is 3.8 kcal mole^{-1} less stable than the trans isomer. Explain.

14. In the acid-catalyzed dehydration of 6-methyl-1,6-heptanediol, it is easy to find conditions that give smooth loss of one molecule of water to yield 6-methyl-5-hepten-1-ol. Explain.

15. Explain why the disubstituted olefin 2,4,4-trimethyl-1-pentene predominates in the acid-catalyzed equilibrium with its trisubstituted isomer 2,4,4-trimethyl-2-pentene.

16. Compare the product of addition of bromine to *cis*-1,2-dideuterioethylene and to *trans*-1,2-dideuterioethylene. On treatment with base each of the dibromides gives predominantly a single different dideuteriovinyl bromide. Show the structure in each case. (Remember: HBr is eliminated faster than DBr.)

17. When isopropyl bromide is treated with sodium ethoxide in ethanol, propene and ethyl isopropyl ether are formed in a 3:1 ratio. If the hexadeuterioisopropyl bromide, $CD_3CHBrCD_3$, is used, $CD_3CH{=}CD_2$ and $(CD_3)_2CHOC_2H_5$ are formed in a ratio of 1:2. Explain.

18. The heat of hydrogenation, ΔH°_{hydrog}, is defined as the enthalpy of the reaction of an alkene with hydrogen to give the alkane.

$$CH_2{=}CH_2 + H_2 \longrightarrow CH_3CH_3 \qquad \Delta H^\circ_{hydrog.} = -32.7 \text{ kcal mole}^{-1}$$

From the heats of formation given in Appendix I calculate heats of hydrogenation for a number of simple alkenes. Note that all monoalkyl ethylenes have about the same ΔH°_{hydrog} which is more positive than that for ethylene. Explain. How would you expect ΔH°_{hydrog} to compare for isomeric cis and trans olefins?

19. Reaction of either 1-butene or 2-butene with HCl gives the same product, 2-chlorobutane, via the same carbocation, 2-butyl cation. Yet, the reaction of 1-butene is faster than that of 2-butene. Explain why, using simple energy diagrams. Using this explanation predict which is more reactive, *cis*-2-butene or *trans*-2-butene.

20. Treatment of $C_7H_{15}Br$ with strong base gave an alkene mixture that was shown by careful gas chromatographic analysis and separation to consist of three alkenes, C, D, and E each having the formula C_7H_{14}. Catalytic hydrogenation of each alkene gave 2-methylhexane. Reaction of C with B_2H_6 in ether, followed by H_2O_2 and OH^- gave mostly an alcohol, F. Similar reaction of D or E gave approximately equal amounts of F and an isomeric alcohol G. What structural assignments can be made for C through G on the basis of these observations? What structural element is left undetermined by these data alone?

21. Propose a mechanism for each of the following reactions.

(a) $HOCH_2CH_2CH_2CH{=}CH_2 \xrightarrow[\text{NaHCO}_3]{\text{I}_2}$ $\text{—CH}_2\text{I}$

(b) $CH_3CH_2\overset{\displaystyle CH_3}{\underset{}{C}}{=}CH_2 + INCO \longrightarrow CH_3CH_2\overset{\displaystyle CH_3}{\underset{\displaystyle NCO}{C}}CH_2I$

(c) $\overset{\displaystyle O}{CH_2{-}CH{-}CD_2Cl} + CH_3O^- \xrightarrow[\Delta]{\text{CH}_3\text{OH}} CH_3OCH_2{-}\overset{\displaystyle O}{CH{-}CD_2}$

22. 3,3,5-Trimethyl-1-methylenecyclohexane reacts with 3-chloroperoxybenzoic acid to give mainly the diastereomeric epoxide shown. However, when the same alkene is treated first with Br_2 in water and then with alcoholic base, the other diastereomer is the major product.

Explain.

23. Compound H, $C_{11}H_{24}O$, reacts with PBr_3 in ether at 0°C to give I, $C_{11}H_{23}Br$. Treatment of I with potassium ethoxide in ethanol gives a mixture of J (major) and K (minor), both $C_{11}H_{22}$. Each of these compounds was treated first with ozone in $CHCl_3$ at 0°C, and then with $NaBH_4$. In each case a mixture of 3-methyl-1-butanol and 4-methyl-1-pentanol was produced. What are compounds H through K?

24. Optically active 1-chloro-3-methylcyclopentane was treated with potassium *t*-butoxide in *t*-butyl alcohol. Two isomeric alkenes were obtained. The major product was optically active whereas the minor product was optically inactive. What are the structures of the major and minor products?

25. The propagation steps for the radical addition of HY to propylene are as follows.

(a) $\quad CH_3CH{=}CH_2 + Y\cdot \longrightarrow CH_3\overset{\cdot}{C}HCH_2Y$

(b) $\quad CH_3\overset{\cdot}{C}HCH_2Y + HY \longrightarrow CH_3CH_2CH_2Y + Y\cdot$

$\quad \overline{CH_3CH{=}CH_2 + HY \longrightarrow CH_3CH_2CH_2Y}$

The following table gives $\Delta H°$ values for steps (a) and (b) and for the net reaction with a number of reagents of the type HY in the gas phase. For which reagents is such a radical chain mechanism plausible?

Y:	F	Cl	Br	I	HS	HO	H_2N	CH_3	$(CH_3)_3C$
$\Delta H_a°$	-48	-22	-9	$+5$	-12	-32	-23	-27	-20
$\Delta H_b°$	$+41$	$+8$	-8	-24	-4	$+24$	$+12$	$+10$	-2
$\Delta H_{net}°$	-7	-14	-17	-18	-16	-8	-11	-17	-22

26. Consider a proposed free radical chain addition of HCN to $CH_3CH{=}CH_2$ to give *n*-propyl cyanide, $CH_3CH_2CH_2CN$. Use data in Appendix I and the following $DH°$ values:

$\quad$ H—CN $\qquad\qquad$ 125 kcal mole^{-1}

$\quad$ $CH_3\overset{\underset{|}{H}}{C}HCH_2CN$ $\qquad$ 95 kcal mole^{-1}

(a) Determine $\Delta H°$ for the net reaction, $CH_3CH{=}CH_2 + HCN = CH_3CH_2CH_2CN$.
(b) Write the two chain-propagation steps for the proposed reaction and calculate $\Delta H°$ for each.
(c) Is the proposed reaction feasible? Explain.

Chapter 12

Alkynes and Nitriles

12.1 Electronic Structure of the Triple Bond

Acetylene is known experimentally to have a linear structure. The C≡C distance of 1.20 Å is the shortest carbon-carbon bond length known. The carbon-hydrogen bond length of 1.06 Å is shorter than that in ethylene (1.08 Å) or in ethane (1.10 Å) (Figure 12.1). These structural details are readily interpreted by an extension of the σ-π electronic structure of double bonds. In acetylene the σ-framework consists of C_{sp}-hybrid orbitals as indicated in Figure 12.2.

In Section 11.1 we saw that sp^2-s σ-bonds are shorter than are sp^3-s σ-bonds. The trend also holds for the sp-s bonds in acetylene. The effect of the amount of s-character in the carbon-hydrogen bond distance is shown graphically in Figure 12.3. Superim-

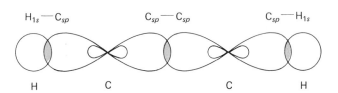

FIGURE 12.1 Structure of acetylene.

FIGURE 12.2 σ-electronic framework of acetylene.

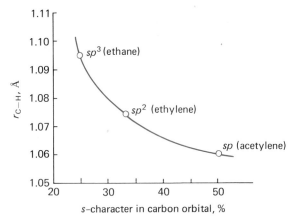

FIGURE 12.3 Relationship between carbon-hydrogen bond distance and the approximate amount of s-character in carbon orbital.

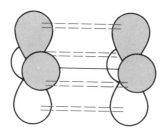

FIGURE 12.4 π-systems of acetylene.

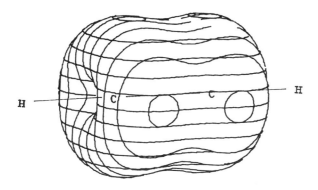

FIGURE 12.5 π-electron density in the acetylene triple bond.

posed on the σ-electrons are two orthogonal π-electron systems as shown in Figure 12.4.

The symbolic representations in Figure 12.4 are actually misleading because the electrons in two orthogonal p-orbitals form a cylindrically symmetrical torus or dough-nut-like electron density distribution. A perspective view of the total π-electron density is seen in Figure 12.5.

The structure of acetylene presented in Figures 12.1-5 is similar to that of the inorganic compound hydrogen cyanide (Figure 12.6). In the latter compound, the triple bond may be viewed as one C_{sp}—N_{sp} and two C_p—N_p bonds. The remaining electron pair on the nitrogen occupies the other N_{sp}-hybrid orbital.

In fact, a close examination of the nuclear and electronic structures of acetylene and hydrogen cyanide reveals that they differ in only two aspects:

1. In hydrogen cyanide, the two electrons in the sp-orbital not bonded to carbon are non-bonding, while in acetylene they form a σ-bond to a hydrogen.
2. In hydrogen cyanide, there are seven protons and seven neutrons in the nucleus of the nitrogen, whereas in acetylene the nucleus of the corresponding carbon contains only six protons and six neutrons.

When two compounds have equivalent electronic distributions, and only differ in their nuclei, they are said to be **isoelectronic**. In such cases, it is usually found that their

1.066 Å   1.153 Å

FIGURE 12.6 Structure of hydrogen cyanide.

chemical properties are qualitatively similar. We shall see that parallels do exist between the reactions of acetylene and hydrogen cyanide. Similar analogies are found in the reactions of alkyl substituted acetylenes, and the organic derivatives of hydrogen cyanide, which are called **nitriles**.

$$H—C\equiv C—CH_3 \qquad :N\equiv C—CH_3$$

a substituted acetylene   a nitrile

12.2 Nomenclature of Alkynes and Nitriles

The simple alkynes are readily named in the common system as derivatives of acetylene itself.

$$CH_3C\equiv CH \qquad CH_3C\equiv CCH_2CH_3 \qquad F_3CC\equiv CH$$

methylacetylene   ethylmethylacetylene   trifluoromethylacetylene

In the IUPAC system the compounds are named as alkynes, in which the final **-ane** of the parent alkane is replaced by the suffix **-yne**. The position of the triple bond is indicated by a number when necessary.

$$CH_3C\equiv CH \qquad (CH_3)_2CHC\equiv CH \qquad CH_3CH_2CH_2CHC\equiv CCH_3$$
$$\overset{|}{C}H_2CH_2CH_3$$

propyne   3-methyl-1-butyne   4-propyl-2-heptyne

If both -yne and -ol endings are used, the -ol is last and determines the numbering sequence.

$$HC\equiv CCH_2CH_2OH \qquad HOCH_2C\equiv CCH_2OH$$

3-butyn-1-ol   2-butyn-1,4-diol
(not but-4-ol-1-yne)

When both a double and triple bond are present, the hydrocarbon is named an **alkenyne** with numbers as low as possible given to the multiple bonds. In case of a choice, the *double bond gets the lower number*.

$$CH_3CH=CHC\equiv CH \qquad HC\equiv CCH_2CH=CH_2$$

3-penten-1-yne   1-penten-4-yne
(not 2-penten-4-yne)   (not 4-penten-1-yne)

In complex structures the alkynyl group is used as a modifying prefix.

ethynylcyclopentane

Nitriles are named in the IUPAC system by adding the suffix **-nitrile** to the name of the alkane corresponding to the longest carbon chain in the molecule (*including the nitrile carbon*).

$$\qquad\qquad\qquad \overset{CH_3}{\overset{|}{}}$$
$$CH_3CN \qquad CH_3CHCH_2CN \qquad BrCH_2CH_2CH_2CH_2CH_2CN$$

ethanenitrile   3-methylbutanenitrile   6-bromohexanenitrile
(acetonitrile)

The simplest nitrile, CH_3CN, is usually referred to by the common name of acetonitrile.

> **EXERCISE 12.1** Write the structures and name all ten isomeric pentynols (do not forget stereoisomerism).

> **EXERCISE 12.2** Write structures corresponding to each of the following names.
> (a) dimethylacetylene   (b) (*S*)-pent-3-yn-2-ol   (c) 2-chlorobutanenitrile

12.3 Physical Properties

The physical properties of alkynes are similar to those of the corresponding alkenes. The lower members are gases with boiling points somewhat higher than those of the corresponding alkenes. Terminal alkynes have lower boiling points than isomeric internal alkynes (Table 12.1) and can be separated by careful fractional distillation.

The CH_3—C bond in propyne is formed by overlap of a C_{sp^3}-hybrid orbital from the methyl carbon with a C_{sp}-hybrid from the acetylenic carbon. The bond is C_{sp^3}—C_{sp}. Since one orbital has more *s*-character than the other and is thereby more electronegative, the electron density in the resulting bond is not symmetrical. The unsymmetrical electron distribution results in a dipole moment larger than that observed for an alkene, but still relatively small.

$$CH_3CH_2C{\equiv}CH \qquad CH_3CH_2CH{=}CH_2 \qquad CH_3C{\equiv}CCH_3$$
$$\mu = 0.80\ D \qquad\quad \mu = 0.30\ D \qquad\quad \mu = 0\ D$$

Symmetrically disubstituted acetylenes, of course, have no net dipole moment.

In contrast, the boiling points for nitriles are markedly higher than those of analogous acetylenes. The difference may be readily seen in Figure 12.7, which shows a plot of molecular weight versus boiling point for 1-alkynes and straight-chain nitriles. Note that the nitrile line lies approximately 60°C above the alkyne line.

In contrast to the relatively small dipole moments of acetylenes, those of nitriles are substantial, and result from the greater electronegativity of nitrogen relative to carbon, as well as the lone electron pair at the nitrogen end of the molecule.

$$\overset{\longrightarrow}{CH_3C{\equiv}N:} \qquad \overset{\longrightarrow}{CH_3CH_2C{\equiv}N:}$$
$$\mu = 3.30\ D \qquad\quad \mu = 3.39\ D$$

It is the dipole moments of nitriles that are responsible for their abnormally high boiling points. In order for a nitrile molecule to be brought into the vapor state, it is necessary that rather strong polar intermolecular forces be disrupted.

TABLE 12.1 Physical Properties of Alkynes

Compound	Boiling Point, °C	Melting Point, °C	d^{20}
ethyne (acetylene)	−84.0[a]	−81.5[b]	
propyne	−23.2	−102.7	
1-butyne	8.1	−122.5	
2-butyne	27	−32.3	
1-pentyne	39.3	−90.0	
2-pentyne	55.5	−101	
1-hexyne	71	−132	0.7152
2-hexyne	84	−88	0.7317
3-hexyne	81	−105	0.7231

[a] Sublimation temperature.   [b] Under pressure.

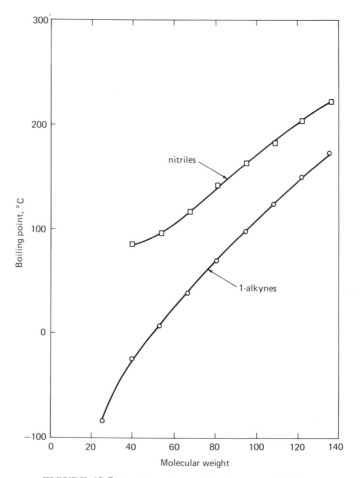

FIGURE 12.7 Boiling points of 1-alkynes and nitriles.

$$R—C\equiv N$$

$$:N\equiv C—R$$

12.4 Acidity of Alkynes

The hydrogens in terminal alkynes are relatively acidic. Acetylene itself has a pK_a of about 25. It is a far weaker acid than water (pK_a 15.7) or the alcohols (pK_a 16-19), but it is much more acidic than ammonia ($pK_a \cong 34$). A solution of sodium amide in liquid ammonia readily converts acetylene and other terminal alkynes into the corresponding carbanions.

$$RC\equiv CH + NH_2^- \rightleftharpoons RC\equiv C^- + NH_3$$

This reaction does not occur with alkenes or alkanes. Ethylene has a pK_a of about 44 and methane has a pK_a of about 50.

$$CH_2{=}CH_2 + NH_2^- \rightleftharpoons CH_2{=}CH^- + NH_3$$

$$CH_4 + NH_2^- \rightleftharpoons CH_3^- + NH_3$$

EXERCISE 12.3 Using the pK_a values given in the preceeding paragraph, estimate the equilibrium constants for the reactions of sodium amide with acetylene, ethylene, and methane.

From the foregoing pK_as we see that there is a vast difference in the stability of the carbanions $RC\equiv C^-$, $CH_2=CH^-$, and CH_3^-. This difference may readily be explained in terms of the character of the orbital occupied by the lone-pair electrons in the three anions. Methyl anion has a pyramidal structure with the lone-pair electrons in an orbital that is approximately sp^3 ($\frac{1}{4}$ s and $\frac{3}{4}$ p). In vinyl anion the lone-pair electrons are in an sp^2-orbital ($\frac{1}{3}$ s and $\frac{2}{3}$ p). In acetylide ion the lone pair is in an sp-orbital ($\frac{1}{2}$ s and $\frac{1}{2}$ p).

| methyl anion | vinyl anion | acetylide ion |

Electrons in s-orbitals are held, on the average, closer to the nucleus than they are in p-orbitals. This increased electrostatic attraction means that s-electrons have lower energy and greater stability than p-electrons. In general, *the greater the amount of s-character in a hybrid orbital containing a pair of electrons, the less basic is that pair of electrons, and the more acidic is the corresponding conjugate acid.*

$$\text{base strength} \uparrow \quad \begin{matrix} CH_3{:}^- \\ CH_2=CH{:}^- \\ HC\equiv C{:}^- \end{matrix} \qquad \begin{matrix} CH_4 \\ CH_2=CH_2 \\ HC\equiv CH \end{matrix} \quad \text{acid strength} \downarrow$$

Of course, the foregoing argument applies to hydrogen cyanide as well. In this case, the conjugate base, $N\equiv C^-$, is further stabilized by the presence of the electronegative nitrogen. Consequently, HCN is sufficiently acidic (pK_a 9.2) that it is converted to its salt with hydroxide ion in water.

$$HCN + OH^- \rightleftharpoons CN^- + H_2O$$

EXERCISE 12.4 Estimate the equilibrium constant for reaction of 1 M HCN with 1 M NaOH in water.

Alkynes are also quantitatively deprotonated by alkyllithium compounds, which may be viewed as the conjugate bases of alkanes (Section 8.9).

$$CH_3(CH_2)_3C\equiv CH + n\text{-}C_4H_9Li \longrightarrow CH_3(CH_2)_3C\equiv CLi + n\text{-}C_4H_{10}$$

The foregoing transformation is simply an acid-base reaction, with 1-hexyne being the acid and n-butyllithium being the base. Since the alkyne is a much stronger acid than the alkane (by over 20 pK units!), equilibrium lies essentially completely to the right.

Terminal alkynes give insoluble salts with a number of heavy metal cations such as Ag^+ and Cu^+. The alkyne can be regenerated from the salt, and the overall process serves as a method for purifying terminal alkynes. However, many of these salts are explosively sensitive when dry and should always be kept moist.

$$CH_3(CH_2)_3C\equiv CH + AgNO_3 \longrightarrow CH_3(CH_2)_3C\equiv CAg + HNO_3$$

Impure 1-hexyne is dissolved in 95% ethanol and aqueous silver nitrate is added. The resulting white precipitate is filtered and washed with alcohol. On refluxing with sodium cyanide solution, the alkyne is regenerated and distilled.

Cyanide ion regenerates the alkyne by converting silver cation to the stable complex $Ag(CN)_2^-$.

EXERCISE 12.5 Since 1-alkynes have substantially lower boiling points than internal alkynes, mixtures can be separated by careful fractional distillation. In practice, however, complete separation of such a mixture is difficult. Suggest a simple way in which the last traces of 1-pentyne might be removed from a sample of 2-pentyne.

12.5 Preparation of Alkynes and Nitriles

A. Acetylene

Acetylene itself is formed from the reaction of the inorganic compound calcium carbide with water.

$$CaC_2 + 2 H_2O \longrightarrow Ca(OH)_2 + HC\equiv CH$$

Calcium carbide is a high-melting (m.p. 2300°C) gray solid prepared by heating lime and coke in an electric furnace.

$$CaO + 3 C \longrightarrow CaC_2 + CO$$

This method was once an important industrial process for the manufacture of acetylene. However, the method has now been replaced by a process in which methane is pyrolyzed in a flow system with short contact time.

$$2 CH_4 \xrightarrow[\text{0.01-0.1 sec}]{1500°C} HC\equiv CH + 3 H_2$$

This reaction is endothermic at ordinary temperatures, but is thermodynamically favored at high temperatures.

At room temperature acetylene is thermodynamically unstable with respect to its elements, as shown by its large positive heat of formation ($\Delta H_f^\circ = +54.3$ kcal mole^{-1} at 25°C).

$$C_2H_2 = 2 C(s) + H_2 \qquad \Delta H° = -54.3 \text{ kcal mole}^{-1}$$

This instability causes certain problems in the handling and storage of the material. When under pressure or in the presence of copper, it can convert to carbon and hydrogen with explosive violence. Although acetylene gas can be condensed readily (b.p. −84°C), the liquid is similarly unstable. Since the gas is extremely soluble in acetone, commercial cylinders of acetylene contain pieces of pumice saturated with acetone. When the cylinder is filled, the acetylene mostly dissolves, giving a relatively stable solution. Acetylene is also appreciably soluble in water. A saturated aqueous solution at 25°C and 1 atm pressure has a concentration of 0.05 M (0.13 g C_2H_2 per 100 mL).

B. Nucleophilic Substitution Reactions

We saw in Section 9.1 that cyanide ion is an effective nucleophile and readily displaces halide ion from primary alkyl halides. In fact, the reaction represents a general method of preparation of nitriles.

(93%)
pentanenitrile

> A solution of 92.5 g of 1-chlorobutane and 53 g of sodium cyanide in 250 mL of dimethyl sulfoxide (DMSO) is heated at 140-150°C for 15 min. The reaction mixture is diluted with water and extracted with ether to obtain pentanenitrile in 93% yield.

Since the acetylide anion is isoelectronic with cyanide, it is no surprise to find that it is also highly nucleophilic and and that it participates readily in displacement reactions that occur by the S_N2 mechanism.

$$RC{\equiv}C{:}^- + R'X \longrightarrow RC{\equiv}CR' + X^-$$

This reaction is a useful general method for the preparation of certain types of alkynes. The reaction may be carried out in liquid ammonia solution or in an ether such as tetrahydrofuran (THF). The acetylide anion is formed with sodium amide or with *n*-butyllithium.

> Liquid ammonia is available commercially in cylinders. Although the compound boils at $-33°C$ it has a relatively high heat of vaporization, due to extensive hydrogen bonding in the liquid. Because of this high heat of vaporization, boiling is a relatively slow process at room temperature. When using liquid ammonia, the material is kept in a normal reaction flask, which is equipped with a type of trap or condenser containing dry ice ($-78°C$). The liquid ammonia in the flask refluxes gently and condenses on the dry ice condenser. The terminal alkyne is added to a solution of sodium amide in ammonia. After it has been converted into its salt, the alkyl halide is added. The mixture is stirred for a few hours, and water is then added. The hydrocarbon is separated from the aqueous ammonia layer and purified.

There is a fair amount of variety possible using this method. Acetylene itself may be alkylated either once to make a terminal alkyne or twice to make an internal alkyne.

$$HC{\equiv}CH + NaNH_2 \xrightarrow[-33°C]{\text{liq. } NH_3} HC{\equiv}C^-Na^+ \xrightarrow{n\text{-}C_4H_9Br} CH_3(CH_2)_3C{\equiv}CH$$

(89%)
1-hexyne

$$HC{\equiv}CH \xrightarrow[\substack{-33°C}]{\substack{2\,NaNH_2 \\ \text{liq. } NH_3}} \xrightarrow{2\,n\text{-}C_3H_7Br} CH_3CH_2CH_2C{\equiv}CCH_2CH_2CH_3$$

(60–66%)
4-octyne

In Section 9.6, we saw that elimination by the E2 mechanism competes with nucleophilic substitution, and that this side reaction is particularly competitive when the alkyl halide is secondary or tertiary. Furthermore, we saw that the elimination/substitution ratio is a function of the **basicity** of the nucleophile. Since acetylide ions are highly basic, competing elimination is a common side reaction. The products of such an elimination reaction are an alkene (from the alkyl halide) and an alkyne (from the acetylide ion).

$$RC\equiv C: \; + \; H-CH_2-CHR \longrightarrow RC\equiv C-H \; + \; CH_2=CHR \; + \; Br^-$$

In practice, the alkylation of acetylene or another terminal alkyne is only a good method for the synthesis of alkynes when applied to primary halides that do not have branches close to the reaction center. With secondary halides, and even with primary halides that have branches close to the reaction center, elimination is usually the major reaction.

$$CH_3(CH_2)_3C\equiv C^-Li^+ \; + \; CH_3\overset{\overset{\displaystyle Br}{|}}{CH}CH_3 \xrightarrow[25\,°C]{HMPT} \begin{cases} CH_3CH_2CH_2CH_2C\equiv CCH(CH_3)_2 \\ \qquad\qquad (6\%) \\ + \\ \{CH_3CH_2CH_2CH_2C\equiv CH \; + \; CH_2=CHCH_3\} \\ \qquad\qquad (85\%) \end{cases}$$

$$CH_3(CH_2)_3C\equiv C^-Li^+ \; + \; CH_3\overset{\overset{\displaystyle CH_3}{|}}{CH}CH_2Br \xrightarrow[25\,°C]{HMPT} \begin{cases} CH_3CH_2CH_2CH_2C\equiv CCH_2CH(CH_3)_2 \\ \qquad\qquad (32\%) \\ + \\ \{CH_3CH_2CH_2CH_2C\equiv CH \; + \; (CH_3)_2C=CH_2\} \\ \qquad\qquad (68\%) \end{cases}$$

EXERCISE 12.6 The nucleophilic substitution of alkyl halides by cyanide ion is not nearly as subject to competing elimination as is acetylene alkylation. For example, isobutyl chloride and isopropyl chloride may both be converted into the corresponding nitriles in excellent yield by treatment with sodium cyanide in DMSO. Explain.

EXERCISE 12.7 Outline syntheses of each of the following compounds from alkyl halides.
(a) 1-octyne   (b) 2-octyne   (c) 4-methylpentanenitrile

C. Elimination Reactions

A triple bond can be introduced into a molecule by elimination of two molecules of HX from either a **geminal** (L., *geminus*, twin) or a **vicinal** (L., *vicinus*, near) dihalide.

$$-CBr_2-CH_2- \xrightarrow{-2\,HBr} -C\equiv C-$$

a *gem*-dibromide

$$-CHBr-CHBr- \xrightarrow{-2\,HBr} -C\equiv C-$$

a *vic*-dibromide

Both kinds of dehydrohalogenation are known. The reactions proceed in stages, with the second molecule of HX being removed with greater difficulty than the first.

$$\left.\begin{array}{c} -CX_2CH_2- \\ \text{or} \\ -CHXCHX- \end{array}\right\} \xrightarrow{\text{faster}} -CX=CH- \xrightarrow{\text{slower}} -C\equiv C-$$

Typical reaction conditions involve the use of molten KOH, solid KOH moistened with alcohol, or concentrated alcoholic KOH solutions at temperatures of 150-200°C. In practice, these conditions are so drastic that the method is only useful for the preparation of certain kinds of alkynes. Under these highly basic conditions the triple bond can **migrate** along a chain. Since disubstituted alkynes are thermodynamically more stable than terminal alkynes, the triple bond will migrate from the end of a chain to an internal position. For example, treatment of 1-butyne with hot alcoholic KOH affords 2-butyne.

$$CH_3CH_2C\equiv CH \xrightarrow[\Delta]{\text{alc. KOH}} CH_3C\equiv CCH_3$$

EXERCISE 12.8 Using the heats of formation in Appendix I, estimate the equilibrium constant for the foregoing reaction at 100°C.

In more complex cases, complex mixtures result, since there are generally several isomeric internal alkynes of comparable stability. For example, application of the foregoing conditions to 1-hexyne gives an equimolar mixture of 2-hexyne and 3-hexyne. Consequently, the dehydrohalogenation of a dihalide by KOH or NaOH is *not a* generally useful procedure for the preparation of alkynes.

Sodium amide is an effective strong base that is particularly useful for the preparation of 1-alkynes.

Sodium amide, $NaNH_2$, is a white solid prepared by the reaction of sodium with ammonia. Sodium actually dissolves in liquid ammonia to give a blue solution of "solvated electrons" and sodium cations.

$$Na \xrightarrow{NH_3} Na^+ + e^-(NH_3)$$

These solutions are relatively stable. However, in the presence of small amounts of ferric ion, a rapid reaction takes place with the liberation of hydrogen.

$$e^- + NH_3 \xrightarrow{Fe^{3+}} NH_2^- + \tfrac{1}{2}H_2$$

The overall equation for the ferric ion-catalyzed reaction of sodium with ammonia is as follows:

$$2\,Na + 2\,NH_3 \xrightarrow{Fe^{3+}} 2\,NaNH_2 + H_2$$

In liquid ammonia sodium amide is a strong base just as sodium hydroxide is in water.
Since NH_3 is much less acidic than water, sodium amide reacts quantitatively with water. Solutions of $NaNH_2$ in NH_3 readily absorb moisture from the atmosphere.

$$NH_2^- + H_2O \longrightarrow NH_3 + OH^-$$

In the organic laboratory, sodium amide is generally prepared and used as a solution in liquid ammonia. However, for some applications, suspensions of solid $NaNH_2$ in an inert medium such as benzene or mineral oil are used.

In one classical procedure for the dehydrohalogenation of a dihalide, a suspension of sodium amide in mineral oil is heated to 150-165°C. The dihalide is added slowly and a vigorous reaction ensues. Ammonia is evolved, and the sodium salt of the alkyne is formed. After cooling, the hydrocarbon is liberated by the addition of water.

$$CH_3(CH_2)_3CH_2CHCl_2 + NaNH_2 \xrightarrow{160°C} CH_3(CH_2)_3C{\equiv}C^- \, Na^+ + NH_3$$

$$CH_3(CH_2)_3C{\equiv}C^-Na^+ + H_2O \longrightarrow CH_3(CH_2)_3C{\equiv}CH + Na^+ \, OH^-$$

Since the reaction product is the salt of an alkyne, this method is useful for preparing terminal alkynes even when migration of the triple bond is possible.

$$n\text{-}C_{14}H_{29}CHBrCH_2Br \xrightarrow{\text{NaNH}_2} n\text{-}C_{14}H_{29}C{\equiv}CH$$
$$(65\%)$$

In fact, internal alkynes may even be isomerized to terminal alkynes by the use of sodium amide or alkali metal salts of amines. A particularly useful reagent for this type of reaction is potassium 3-aminopropylamide ("KAPA"), which is used in 1,3-diamionpropane as solvent. This reagent causes rapid reaction even at room temperature.

$$CH_3(CH_2)_2C{\equiv}CCH_3 \xrightarrow[\substack{H_2N(CH_2)NH_2 \\ (1,3\text{-propanediamine}) \\ 20°C}]{\substack{H_2NCH_2CH_2CH_2NH^- \, K^+ \\ (KAPA)}} CH_3(CH_2)_3C{\equiv}C^- \, K^+ \xrightarrow{H_2O} CH_3(CH_2)_3C{\equiv}CH$$

2-hexyne   1-hexyne
                                                                          (100%)

EXERCISE 12.9 Suggest a way in which 2-pentene can be converted into
(a) 2-pentyne and (b) 1-pentyne.

EXERCISE 12.10 With 1-bromobutane as the only source of carbon, show how each of the following compounds may be synthesized.
(a) 1-butyne   (b) 2-butyne   (c) 3-octyne   (d) 1-octyne

12.6 Reactions of Alkynes and Nitriles

Many of the reactions of alkynes involve the triple bond in a manner analogous to comparable reactions of alkenes. However, just as a double bond is weaker than two single bonds, a triple bond is weaker still than three single bonds. This comparison is apparent in the average bond energies tabulated in Table 12.2. As a result the carbon-carbon triple bond enters into some reactions not generally seen with alkenes.

**TABLE 12.2 Average Bond
Energies of C—C Bonds**

Bond	Average Bond Energy, kcal mole^{-1}
C—C	83
C=C	146
C≡C	200

A. Reduction

Hydrogenation of an alkyne to an alkane occurs readily with the same general catalysts that are used for the reduction of alkenes.

$$R-C{\equiv}C-R' + 2\ H_2 \xrightarrow{\text{Pt, Pd, Ni}} R-CH_2CH_2-R'$$

The first step in the reduction is a more exothermic reaction than is the second.

$$HC{\equiv}CH + H_2 \longrightarrow CH_2{=}CH_2 \qquad \Delta H° = -41.9\ \text{kcal mole}^{-1}$$

$$CH_2{=}CH_2 + H_2 \longrightarrow CH_3CH_3 \qquad \Delta H° = -32.7\ \text{kcal mole}^{-1}$$

The second reaction is so facile that, with many catalysts, it is not possible to stop the reduction at the alkene stage. However, with palladium or nickel, alkynes undergo hydrogenation extremely readily—faster than any other functional group. By taking advantage of this catalytic effect, one may accomplish the **partial hydrogenation** of an alkyne to an alkene. In practice, specially deactivated or "poisoned" catalysts are usually used. An effective catalyst for this purpose is palladium metal that has been deposited in a finely divided state on solid $BaSO_4$ and then treated with quinoline (the actual poison).

The function of the poison is to moderate the catalyst's activity to a point where triple bonds are still reduced at a reasonable rate but double bonds react only slowly. One can then readily stop the reduction after absorption of 1 mole of hydrogen and isolate the alkene in excellent yield.

Quinoline is a heterocyclic amine and is discussed in Section 31.7.

quinoline

It is isolated commercially from coal tar, but the commercial material contains trace amounts of sulfur compounds that are difficult to remove. Divalent sulfur compounds are such exceedingly powerful catalyst poisons that they completely inhibit the catalytic activity. For this reason, only pure synthetic quinoline may be used for this purpose.

For the reduction, 10 g of alkyne in 75-100 mL of methanol is treated with 0.2 g of 5% palladium on barium sulfate and 5-6 drops of pure, synthetic quinoline is added. The reaction mixture is stirred under an atmosphere of hydrogen until hydrogen absorption ceases.

As in the hydrogenation of alkenes, the hydrogenation of acetylenes is a syn process. That is, the disubstituted alkene product has predominantly the cis stereostructure. In fact, alkyne hydrogenation is even more stereoselective than alkene hydrogenation, although small amounts (5-10%) of the trans isomer are often formed.

$$C_2H_5C{\equiv}CC_2H_5 + H_2 \xrightarrow[\text{quinoline}]{\text{Pd/BaSO}_4} \begin{array}{c} C_2H_5 \\ \diagdown \\ \end{array} C{=}C \begin{array}{c} C_2H_5 \\ \diagup \\ \end{array}$$

Reduction of triple bonds can also be accomplished by treating the alkyne with sodium in liquid ammonia at $-33°C$. This reduction produces exclusively the trans alkene.

$$C_4H_9C\equiv CC_4H_9 \xrightarrow[\text{liq. NH}_3]{\text{Na}} \xrightarrow{\text{NH}_4\text{OH}} \underset{\substack{(80\text{-}90\%) \\ \textit{trans-5-decene}}}{\overset{C_4H_9}{\underset{H}{}}\diagdown}C=C\underset{\substack{}}{\overset{H}{\diagup}}\overset{\diagup}{\underset{C_4H_9}{}}$$

The mechanism of this reaction involves the reduction of the triple bond by two electrons from sodium atoms. The first electron goes into an antibonding π-orbital to give a radical anion. This strongly basic species is protonated by ammonia to give a vinyl radical, which is reduced by another electron to give a vinyl anion. Final protonation of the vinyl anion by ammonia (acting as an acid) yields the trans alkene and amide ion.

Step 1. $R-C\equiv C-R + Na \longrightarrow Na^+ + \left[R-\ddot{C}=\dot{C}-R\right]^-$

radical anion

Step 2. $\left[R-\ddot{C}=\dot{C}-R\right]^- + NH_3 \longrightarrow NH_2^- + \underset{H}{\overset{R}{\diagdown}}C=C\overset{\diagup}{\underset{R}{}}$

vinyl radical

Step 3. $\underset{H}{\overset{R}{\diagdown}}C=C\overset{}{\underset{R}{\diagup}} + Na \longrightarrow Na^+ + \underset{H}{\overset{R}{\diagdown}}C=C\overset{}{\underset{R}{\diagup}}$

vinyl anion

Step 4. $\underset{H}{\overset{R}{\diagdown}}C=C\overset{}{\underset{R}{\diagup}} + NH_3 \longrightarrow NH_2^- + \underset{H}{\overset{R}{\diagdown}}C=C\overset{H}{\underset{R}{\diagup}}$

The stereochemistry of the final product is probably established in the reduction of the vinyl radical (step 3). The two vinyl radicals with the R groups trans or cis interconvert rapidly, but the trans form is preferred because of nonbonded interactions in the cis form. Since reduction of the two vinyl radicals probably proceeds at comparable rates and the trans form is present in much greater amount, the vinyl anion formed is mostly trans. The vinyl anion interconverts between cis and trans forms only relatively slowly and appears to protonate before it has a chance to isomerize.

Note that we have used the term **vinyl** in two different senses. It refers to the common name for the specific organic function, $-CH=CH_2$ (for example, vinyl chloride, $CH_2=CHCl$) but it is also used generically to refer to substitution at a carbon that is part of an alkene double bond (e.g., $CH_3CCl=CH_2$, a vinyl or vinylic chloride).

Simple alkenes are not reduced by sodium in liquid ammonia, so it is easy to perform the partial reduction of an alkyne to an alkene by this method. It is important not to confuse a solution of Na in liquid NH_3 (which is actually a solution containing Na^+ ions and solvated electrons, e^-) with a solution of $NaNH_2$ in liquid NH_3 (which is a solution containing Na^+ ions and NH_2^- ions). The former solution reduces alkynes. The latter solution does not reduce alkynes, but does deprotonate terminal alkynes.

Disubstituted alkynes may also be reduced to trans alkenes by lithium aluminum hydride, $LiAlH_4$.

$$CH_3CH_2C{\equiv}CCH_2CH_2CH_3 \xrightarrow[\substack{\text{THF}\\ \text{diglyme}\\ 138°C}]{LiAlH_4}$$

3-hexyne

(96%)

trans-3-hexene

A solution of 85 mmol of $LiAlH_4$ in 50 mL each of THF and diglyme is heated with the removal of some solvent until the internal temperature reaches 138°C. 3-Hexyne (50 mmol) is added, and the solution is refluxed for 4.5 hr. Distillation of the product gives 96% yield of *trans*-3-hexene, contaminated with 4% of the cis isomer.

Lithium aluminum hydride, $LiAlH_4$, is a white, salt-like compound that is prepared by the reaction of lithium hydride with aluminum chloride.

$$4\ LiH + AlCl_3 \longrightarrow LiAlH_4 + 3\ LiCl$$

It is easily soluble in ethers such as diethyl ether, tetrahydrofuran (THF), glyme, and diglyme. It has a clear structural relationship to sodium borohydride, $NaBH_4$ (page 261), and is a salt of the cation Li^+ and the anion AlH_4^-. It reacts avidly with traces of moisture to liberate hydrogen.

$$LiAlH_4 + 4\ H_2O \longrightarrow LiOH + Al(OH)_3 + 4\ H_2$$

All hydroxylic compounds (alcohols, carboxylic acids, and so on) react similarly. The dry crystalline powder must be used with care. It produces dust particles that are highly irritating to mucous membranes. It may also inflame spontaneously while being crushed with a mortar and pestle and explodes violently when heated to about 120°C.

By means of these several reactions it is possible to construct larger chains from smaller ones and to prepare either cis or trans alkenes with little contamination from the other. For example, acetylene can be converted into propyne, which can, in turn, be alkylated with *n*-propyl bromide to give 2-hexyne. This disubstituted acetylene can be reduced by sodium in ammonia to yield *trans*-2-hexene, or with hydrogen in the presence of a poisoned palladium catalyst to produce the cis isomer.

$$HC{\equiv}CH \xrightarrow[]{NaNH_2} \xrightarrow[]{CH_3I} HC{\equiv}CCH_3 \xrightarrow[]{NaNH_2} \xrightarrow[]{\textit{n}-C_3H_7Br} \textit{n}-C_3H_7C{\equiv}CCH_3$$

trans-2-hexene

cis-2-hexene

We begin to see the sensitivity and power of organic syntheses and we have only barely scratched the surface of the many and varied reactions known and used in the organic laboratory.

> **EXERCISE 12.11** Using 1-chlorobutane as the only source of carbon, show how the following compounds may be prepared.
> (a) *cis*-3-octene   (b) *trans*-3-octene   (c) 1-octyne

The carbon-nitrogen triple bond in nitriles is also readily reduced. However, in this case, it is the completely reduced product that is usually desired. Catalytic hydrogenation can be employed, as shown in the following example.

$$\text{CN} + H_2 \xrightarrow[\substack{C_2H_5OH \\ HCl}]{PtO_2} \overset{+}{N}H_3 \; Cl^-$$

(95%)

The product of this reaction is an example of an amine, an organic analog of ammonia. Since the hydrogenation is carried out in the presence of slightly more than one equivalent of hydrochloric acid, the amine is isolated in the form of its ammonium salt. We will go into the chemistry of amines in detail in Chapter 23.

Nitriles may also be reduced to amines by lithium aluminum hydride. Because the carbon-nitrogen triple bond is more polar than the carbon-carbon triple bond, the reduction can be accomplished under considerably milder conditions.

$$\text{CN} + LiAlH_4 \xrightarrow[70°C]{diglyme} \xrightarrow{ROH} NH_2$$

(86%)

> 2,2-Dideuteriobutanenitrile (71 g) is added slowly to a solution of 38 g of lithium aluminum hydride in 500 mL of diglyme heated at 70°C. The solution is cooled and treated with 2-butoxyethanol to destroy excess LiAlH$_4$. Distillation of the product affords 65 g (86%) of 3,3-dideuteriobutanamine.

> **EXERCISE 12.12** Starting with 1-chlorobutane, and using any necessary inorganic reagents, show how 1-pentanamine, $CH_3CH_2CH_2CH_2CH_2NH_2$, can be prepared.

B. Electrophilic Additions

The triple bond reacts with HCl and HBr in much the same manner as does the double bond. The addition goes in stages, and Markovnikov's rule is followed.

$$RC{\equiv}CH \xrightarrow{HCl} RC{=}CH_2 \xrightarrow{HCl} R\underset{\underset{Cl}{|}}{\overset{\overset{Cl}{|}}{C}}CH_3$$

Although alkynes are only about 10^{-2} to 10^{-3} as reactive as comparable alkenes, it is sometimes possible to stop the reaction of an alkyne with HX at the monoadduct stage, since the presence of a halogen in the initial product reduces its reactivity. However, yields of 1:1 adducts are usually poor.

$$CH_3(CH_2)_3C\equiv CH + HBr \xrightarrow[\substack{FeBr_3 \\ 15°C}]{inhibitor} CH_3(CH_2)_3\overset{\overset{\displaystyle Br}{|}}{C}=CH_2$$

$$(40\%)$$
2-bromo-1-hexene

Although addition across a triple bond is a more exothermic process than comparable addition across a double bond, alkynes are generally less reactive than alkenes toward electrophilic reagents. This apparent anomaly is rationalized by comparison of the intermediate carbocations produced from alkynes and alkenes.

$$RC\equiv CH + H^+ \longrightarrow R\overset{+}{C}=CH_2$$

a vinyl cation

$$RCH=CH_2 + H^+ \longrightarrow R\overset{+}{C}H-CH_3$$

an alkyl cation

The carbocation produced from the alkyne is a vinyl cation, $R\overset{+}{C}=CH_2$, whose electronic structure is shown in Figure 12.8. This type of carbocation is substantially less stable than an ordinary alkyl cation such as $R\overset{+}{C}HCH_3$, since the vacant *p*-orbital belongs to an *sp*-hybridized carbon rather than to an sp^2-hybridized carbon. Since a carbon that has *sp*-hybridization is more electronegative than one having sp^2-hybridization, it is less tolerant of the positive charge. We shall return to the subject of vinyl cations in Section 12.7.

Once formed, the vinyl cation reacts with whatever nucleophiles are present. For example, the overall reaction with HCl involves initial formation of the vinyl cation, followed by its reaction with chloride ion.

$$(1) \quad RC\equiv CH + H^+ \longrightarrow R\overset{+}{C}=CH_2$$

$$(2) \quad R\overset{+}{C}=CH_2 + Cl^- \longrightarrow R\overset{\overset{\displaystyle Cl}{|}}{C}=CH_2$$

Addition of a second HX to the initially formed vinyl halide gives a product in which the two halogens are attached to the same carbon, a *gem*-dihaloalkane.

$$R\overset{\overset{\displaystyle Cl}{|}}{C}=CH_2 + HCl \longrightarrow R\overset{\overset{\displaystyle Cl}{|}}{\underset{\underset{\displaystyle Cl}{|}}{C}}CH_3$$

a *gem*-dichloroalkane

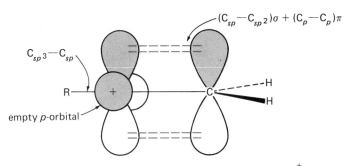

FIGURE 12.8 Electronic structure of a vinyl cation, $R\overset{+}{C}=CH_2$.

In reactions with aqueous sulfuric acid the intermediate carbocation reacts with water to produce an intermediate vinyl alcohol, $RC(OH)\!\!=\!\!CHR$. This reaction is poor with sulfuric acid alone, but is catalyzed by mercuric salts. Vinyl alcohols are unstable and rearrange immediately under the reaction conditions to give ketones (Section 14.6).

$$\underset{\text{4-hexyne}}{\text{—}\!\!\diagdown\!\!\diagup\!\!\equiv\!\!\diagdown\!\!\diagup\!\!\text{—}} \xrightarrow[\substack{\text{H}_2\text{O}\\ \text{HOAc}}]{\substack{\text{H}_2\text{SO}_4\\ \text{HgSO}_4}} \underset{\substack{\text{4-octanone}\\ (89\%)}}{\text{—}\!\!\diagup\!\!\diagdown\!\!\overset{\text{O}}{\overset{\|}{\text{C}}}\!\!\diagdown\!\!\diagup\!\!\text{—}}$$

As shown in this example, hydration of *symmetrical* internal alkynes can be a good method for the preparation of ketones. This is only true if the alkyne is symmetrical, since for an unsymmetrical internal alkyne, there are two possible secondary vinyl carbocations that can be formed. Since these have comparable stabilities, they both form, and a mixture of ketones results.

EXERCISE 12.13 Consider the hydration of 2-pentyne. Write a complete mechanism for the reaction, assuming that the electrophile that initiates carbocation formation is H^+. Note that H^+ may be added either to C-2 or to C-3. Are the two resulting carbocations different? Can you think of any reason why they should be very different in stability?

EXERCISE 12.14 Hydration of *terminal* alkynes is a general method for the preparation of methyl ketones:

$$RC\!\!\equiv\!\!CH \xrightarrow[\substack{\text{H}_2\text{O}\\ \text{HOAc}}]{\substack{\text{H}_2\text{SO}_4\\ \text{HgSO}_4}} \underset{\text{a methyl ketone}}{R\overset{\text{O}}{\overset{\|}{C}}CH_3}$$

Explain the observed selectivity with a reaction mechanism.

The carbon-nitrogen triple bond also undergoes acid-catalyzed hydration. Since they have nonbonding electron pairs on nitrogen, nitriles are Lewis bases in the same way that ammonia is a Lewis base. However, the nitrile nonbonding pair is in a N_{sp}-orbital, and it is therefore not very basic; the pK_a of protonated acetonitrile is -10.1.

$$CH_3C\!\!\equiv\!\!\overset{+}{N}\!\!-\!\!H \;\rightleftharpoons\; CH_3C\!\!\equiv\!\!N\!: + H^+$$

Nevertheless, in acidic medium, the nitrile nitrogen is reversibly protonated. The protonated form is much more receptive to nucleophiles than the neutral nitrile, and adds water slowly. The initial product rearranges to give an amide.

$$RC\!\!\equiv\!\!N\!: + H^+ \rightleftharpoons \left[RC\!\!\equiv\!\!\overset{+}{N}H \longleftrightarrow R\overset{+}{C}\!\!=\!\!\overset{..}{N}H \right] \xrightarrow{\text{H}_2\text{O}} R\overset{\overset{+}{O}H_2}{\underset{|}{C}}\!\!=\!\!NH \xrightarrow{-H^+} R\overset{OH}{\underset{|}{C}}\!\!=\!\!NH \rightleftharpoons R\overset{O}{\overset{\|}{C}}NH_2$$

Typical catalysts are aqueous hydrochloric acid and concentrated sulfuric acid.

$$C_6H_5CH_2CN \xrightarrow[\substack{\text{H}_2\text{O}\\ 50°\text{C}}]{\text{HCl}} \underset{(82-86\%)}{C_6H_5CH_2\overset{O}{\overset{\|}{C}}NH_2}$$

A mixture of 200 g of phenylacetonitrile and 800 mL of concentrated hydrochloric acid is stirred at 50°C for 20-30 min. At the end of this time, ice-cold water is added and the crystalline phenylacetamide isolated by filtration. The yield is 190-200 g (82-86%).

EXERCISE 12.15 Show how 1-chlorobutane may be converted into the following compounds.

(a) [structure: butanamide with NH₂ and O]   (b) [structure: pentan-2-one]

C. Nucleophilic Additions

Unlike simple alkenes, alkynes undergo nucleophilic addition reactions. For example, acetylene reacts with alkoxides in alcoholic solution to yield vinyl ethers. The reaction usually requires conditions of high temperature and pressure.

$$HC\equiv CH + RO^- \xrightarrow[\substack{150°C \\ pressure}]{ROH} ROCH=CH^- \xrightarrow{ROH} ROCH=CH_2 + RO^-$$

The reaction of a stable alkoxide ion to produce a less stable and more basic vinyl anion may seem surprising. However, the addition also involves the formation of a strong carbon-oxygen bond at the expense of the relatively weak "third bond" of a triple bond. The net effect of stronger bonding is more than enough to compensate for the creation of a stronger base. The intermediate vinyl anion is immediately protonated by the alcohol solvent to regenerate the alkoxide ion.

As might be expected, the more polar carbon-nitrogen triple bond in nitriles is more susceptible to nucleophilic addition. A common procedure is the base-catalyzed hydration, which is a good method for the synthesis of amides from nitriles.

$$\text{[structure: }CH_3CH_2CH_2CH_2CN] + KOH \xrightarrow[80°C]{t\text{-BuOH}} \text{[structure: pentanamide with }NH_2, O]$$

(84%)

To a solution of 5 g of pentanenitrile in 50 mL of *t*-butyl alcohol is added 10 g of powdered KOH. The mixture is refluxed for 20 min, poured into aqueous sodium chloride solution, and extracted to obtain 5.1 g (84%) of pentanamide.

D. Hydroboration

Hydroboration of alkynes is a useful laboratory process for the synthesis of several types of compounds. Diborane reacts with alkynes at 0°C to produce the intermediate trivinylborane. The reaction is generally useful for terminal alkynes. As with alkenes, the boron adds to the terminal carbon. The reaction is also useful with symmetrical disubstituted alkynes. Unsymmetrical disubstituted alkynes generally give a mixture of products. The net reaction is syn addition of H—BR₂ to the triple bond.

$$3 \ RC{\equiv}CR + BH_3 \longrightarrow \left(R \underset{H}{\diagup\!\!\diagdown} \overset{R}{\diagdown\!\!\diagup} \right)_3 B$$

$$3 \ RC{\equiv}CH + BH_3 \longrightarrow \left(R \underset{H}{\diagup\!\!\diagdown} \overset{H}{\diagdown\!\!\diagup} \right)_3 B$$

The resulting vinylboranes, like alkylboranes (Section 11.6.D), enter into a number of reactions, the most useful of which is oxidative cleavage with alkaline hydrogen peroxide. The initial product is a vinyl alcohol, which rearranges quantitatively to the corresponding aldehyde or ketone (Section 14.6.A).

$$\diagup\!\!\diagdown\!\!\diagup\!\!\diagdown\!\!{\equiv} \xrightarrow[\text{THF}]{\text{BH}_3} \xrightarrow[\text{NaOH}]{\text{H}_2\text{O}_2} \left[\diagup\!\!\diagdown\!\!\diagup\!\!\diagdown\!\!\diagup\!\!\overset{\text{H}}{\underset{\text{H}}{\diagdown}}\text{OH} \right] \longrightarrow \diagup\!\!\diagdown\!\!\diagup\!\!\diagdown\!\!\diagup\!\!\overset{\text{O}}{\diagdown}\text{H}$$

The overall effect of hydroboration-oxidation is that of hydration of the triple bond. Note that with terminal alkynes the aldehyde is formed (anti-Markovnikov hydration), whereas with direct H_2SO_4-$HgSO_4$ hydration the ketone is produced.

EXERCISE 12.16 What are the principal organic products of the reaction of borane in THF followed by alkaline hydrogen peroxide with (a) 1-butyne, (b) 2-butyne, and (c) 2-pentyne?

12.7 Vinyl Halides

We saw in the last section that alkenyl halides may be prepared by addition of 1 mole of hydrogen halide to an alkyne, often with the aid of a mild Lewis-acid catalyst.

$$CH_3C{\equiv}CH + HCl \xrightarrow{\text{CuCl}} CH_3CCl{=}CH_2$$

Alcoholic dehydrohalogenation of 1 mole of HX from a vicinal dihalide generally gives a mixture of the possible haloalkenes.

$$CH_3CHClCH_2Cl \xrightarrow[\text{alcohol}]{\text{KOH}} CH_3CCl{=}CH_2 + \underset{H}{\overset{CH_3}{\diagdown}}C{=}C\underset{H}{\overset{Cl}{\diagup}} + \underset{H}{\overset{CH_3}{\diagdown}}C{=}C\underset{Cl}{\overset{H}{\diagup}}$$

However the *vic*-dichlorides obtained from symmetrical olefins give good yields of single products.

$$\underset{H}{\overset{C_2H_5}{\diagdown}}C{=}C\underset{C_2H_5}{\overset{H}{\diagup}} \xrightarrow{\text{Cl}_2} \underset{C_2H_5}{\overset{Cl}{\diagdown}}C{-}C\underset{\underset{Cl}{H}}{\overset{H \ C_2H_5}{\diagup}} \xrightarrow[\text{80°C}]{\overset{t\text{-BuOK}}{t\text{-BuOH}}} \underset{H}{\overset{C_2H_5}{\diagdown}}C{=}C\underset{Cl}{\overset{C_2H_5}{\diagup}}$$

(*E*)-3-chloro-3-hexene

Haloalkenes in which the halogen is attached directly on the double bond have exceptionally low reactivity in nucleophilic substitution reactions, either by the S_N1 or

S_N2 mechanism. For example, 1-chloropropene is inert to potassium iodide in acetone under conditions where *n*-propyl chloride undergoes rapid substitution.

$$CH_3CH_2CH_2Cl + I^- \longrightarrow CH_3CH_2CH_2I + Cl^- \qquad \text{fairly fast}$$

$$CH_3CH=CHCl + I^- \longrightarrow \text{no reaction}$$

Similarly, simple alkenyl halides do not readily form carbocations. For such halides, reaction by the S_N1 mechanism is exceedingly slow. Consequently, other reactions, such as addition to the double bond, occur instead. The relative difficulty of ionizing a vinylic carbon-chlorine bond is shown by the following gas phase enthalpies.

$$\Delta H°, \text{ kcal mole}^{-1}$$

$CH_3Cl \longrightarrow CH_3^+ + Cl^-$	228
$CH_3CH_2Cl \longrightarrow CH_3CH_2^+ + Cl^-$	191
$CH_2=CHCl \longrightarrow CH_2=CH^+ + Cl^-$	223
$(CH_3)_2CHCl \longrightarrow (CH_3)_2CH^+ + Cl^-$	166

The difference between the energy required to form a vinyl cation and that needed for a simple primary carbocation is comparable to the difference between primary and secondary carbocations. Recall that secondary carbocations are common intermediates in many reactions but that simple primary carbocations are virtually unknown in solution. Primary vinyl cations are similarly unknown in S_N1 reactions; however, secondary vinyl cations of the type $R\overset{+}{C}=CH_2$ have been detected under special conditions. They are not important in most organic reactions of the simple vinyl halides.

This lack of reactivity is explained most simply as an increased difficulty in removing an atom with its pair of electrons from a bond to a vinyl orbital with its higher *s*-character than from a simple primary sp^3-orbital. The increased strength of the vinyl-halogen bond compared to the ethyl-halogen bond is manifest also in the relative bond lengths and bond-dissociation energies as shown in the following examples.

	r_{C-X}, Å	$DH°$, kcal mole^{-1}
CH_3CH_2-Cl	1.78	80
$CH_2=CH-Cl$	1.72	90
CH_3CH_2-Br	1.94	68
$CH_2=CH-Br$	1.89	78

The sp^2-carbon orbital involved in the vinyl halide bond is expected to produce a shorter and stronger bond than the ethyl sp^3-orbital. However, an additional component leading to a still shorter and stronger bond is π-overlap between the π-orbital of the double bond and a lone-pair orbital of the halogen, as depicted in Figure 12.9.

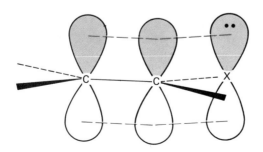

FIGURE 12.9 π-orbital overlap in a vinyl halide.

Such π-overlap can also be represented by resonance involving Lewis structures.

$$\left[CH_2{=}CH{-}\ddot{\underset{\cdot\cdot}{X}}: \;\longleftrightarrow\; \bar{C}H_2{-}CH{=}\overset{+}{\underset{\cdot\cdot}{X}}: \right]$$

As a result of such overlap the carbon-halogen bond in a vinyl halide has partial double bond character. The amount of double bond character (that is, the contribution of resonance structure $^-CH_2{-}CH{=}X^+$) is relatively small, but has a significant effect on reactivity.

EXERCISE 12.17   Using your molecular models, construct a model of $(3R,4S)$-3,4-dichlorohexane. Convince yourself that if elimination of HCl occurs in an anti fashion, the product will be (E)-3-chloro-3-hexene, regardless of which chlorine is lost. Suggest a way in which 3-hexyne can be converted into (Z)-3-chloro-3-hexene (three steps are necessary).

PROBLEMS

1. Write the structure corresponding to each of the following common names.
   (a) methylisopropylacetylene   (b) acetonitrile
   (c) vinylacetylene   (d) di-*t*-butylacetylene
   (e) vinyl bromide   (f) isobutylacetylene
   (g) methyl ethynyl ether

2. Write the structure corresponding to each of the following IUPAC names.
   (a) cyclodecyne   (b) (R)-3-methyl-1-pentyne
   (c) 1-ethynylcyclohexanol   (d) 1-methoxyethyne
   (e) 3-methoxy-1-pentyne   (f) pent-2-yn-1-ol
   (g) (S)-2-chlorobutanenitrile (h) pent-1-en-3-yne
   (i) 2,2,5,5-tetramethyl-3-hexyne (j) 4-methyl-2-pentyne

3. Give an acceptable name for each of the following structures.

   (a) $BrCH_2CH_2CH_2CH_2C{\equiv}CH$ (b) $(CH_3)_3CC{\equiv}CCH_2CH_3$

   (c) CH_3CH_2CN (d) ▷$-C{\equiv}CH$

   (e) $CH_2{=}CH{-}\overset{\overset{\displaystyle OH}{|}}{\underset{\underset{\displaystyle H}{|}}{C}}{-}C{\equiv}CH$ (f) $HOCH_2C{\equiv}CCH_2OH$

   (g) $CH_2{=}CHCH_2CH_2C{\equiv}CH$ (h) $\underset{Cl}{\overset{CH_3}{\diagdown}}C{=}C\underset{CH_3}{\overset{H}{\diagup}}$

4. Give the principal reaction product(s) for the reaction of 1-butyne with each of the following reagents. If no reaction is expected, so indicate.
   (a) *n*-butyllithium, THF   (b) H_2/Pt
   (c) Na, liquid NH_3 (d) aq. NaCl
   (e) aq. $AgNO_3$ (f) (i) B_2H_6; (ii) H_2O_2, NaOH
   (g) H_2SO_4, H_2O, $HgSO_4$ (h) H_2 (1 mole), Pd(BaSO$_4$)-quinoline

5. Answer problem 4 for 2-butyne.

6. Give the principal reaction product for reaction of butanenitrile with each of the following reagents.

   (a) H_2, Pd/C, ethanol, HCl
   (b) conc. HCl, 50°C
   (c) KOH, *t*-butyl alcohol, reflux
   (d) (i) LiAlH$_4$, ether; (ii) water

7. Using propyne or sodium cyanide as the only sources of carbon, devise practical syntheses for the following compounds.

   (a) $(CH_3)_2CHBr$
   (b) CH_3COCH_3

   (c) CH_3CH_2CHO
   (d) $CH_3(CH_2)_4CH_3$

   (e)
   $$\underset{H}{\overset{CH_3}{\diagdown}}C=C\underset{CH_2CH_2CH_3}{\overset{H}{\diagup}}$$
   (f) $CH_3CCl=CH_2$

   (g) $CH_3CH_2CH_2CN$
   (h) $CH_3CH_2CH_2CH_2NH_2$

8. Show how each of the following conversions may be accomplished in good yield. In each case, use only the indicated starting material as a source of carbon.

   (a) $CH_3CH_2CH_2CH_3 \longrightarrow CH_3CH_2\overset{\overset{\displaystyle Cl}{|}}{C}HCH_3$ (containing *no* 1-chlorobutane)

   (b) $CH_3CH_2CH_2CH=CH_2 \longrightarrow CH_3CH_2CH_2C\equiv CH$

   (c) $CH_3CH_2CH_2Br \longrightarrow CH_3CH_2CH_2C\equiv CCH_3$

   (d) $HC\equiv CH \longrightarrow CH_3CH_2CH_2CH_2OH$

   (e) $HC\equiv CH \longrightarrow CH_3CH_2\overset{\overset{\displaystyle OCH_3}{|}}{C}HCH_2CH_2CH_3$

   (f)
   $$\underset{H}{\overset{(CH_3)_3C}{\diagdown}}C=C\underset{C(CH_3)_3}{\overset{H}{\diagup}} \longrightarrow \underset{H}{\overset{(CH_3)_3C}{\diagdown}}C=C\underset{H}{\overset{C(CH_3)_3}{\diagup}}$$

   (g) $CH_3CH_2CH_2OH \longrightarrow CH_3COCH_3$

   (h) $CH_3CH_2C\equiv CH \longrightarrow \underset{H}{\overset{CH_3CH_2}{\diagdown}}C=C\underset{H}{\overset{D}{\diagup}}$

   (i) $HC\equiv CH \longrightarrow CH_3CH_2CH_2CH_3$

9. Assume that you are shipwrecked on a desert island and that you find the ship pharmacist's trunk, which turns out to be well-stocked with inorganic chemicals and also contains bottles of ethyl iodide, isopropyl bromide, *n*-butyl chloride, DMSO, diethyl ether, and *t*-butyl alcohol. How might these materials be used to prepare the following compounds, and thereby start a chemical industry in your new homeland?

   (a)
   (b)

   (c)
   (d)

10. Show how each of the following conversions may be accomplished in good yield. In addition to the indicated starting material, other organic compounds may be used as necessary.

(a) $HC\equiv CH \longrightarrow CH_3CH_2\overset{\displaystyle O}{\overset{\displaystyle \|}{C}}CH_3$

(b) $CH_3OCH_2CH_2C\equiv CH \longrightarrow CH_3OCH_2CH_2CH_2CH_2CN$

(c) $HC\equiv CH \longrightarrow CH_3CH_2C\equiv CCH_2CH_2CH_3$

(d) $(CH_3)_2\overset{\displaystyle OH}{\overset{\displaystyle |}{C}}CH_2CH_3 \longrightarrow (CH_3)_2CHC\equiv CCH_3$

11. From 3-methyl-1-butanol, acetylene, and any required straight-chain primary alcohols, derive a practical synthesis for 2-methylheptadecane, the sex attractant for the Tiger moth (page 89).

12. Muscalure, *cis*-9-tricosene, is the sex-attractant insect pheromone of the common housefly. Give a practical synthesis of this compound from acetylene and straight-chain alcohols.

13. The pK_as of ethane, ethylene, and acetylene are approximately 50, 44, and 25, respectively.
    (a) If each hydrocarbon is treated with sodium amide in liquid ammonia and the resulting solution then treated with methyl iodide, different results are obtained. There is no reaction with ethane or ethylene, but acetylene gives a good yield of propyne. Explain this observation using the results in (a).
    (b) The bond-dissociation energies, $DH°$, for the carbon-hydrogen bonds are ethane, 98; ethylene, 110; acetylene, 132 kcal mole^{-1}. The carbon-hydrogen bonds are progressively harder to break along this series, yet the compounds are increasingly acidic. Explain this apparent paradox.

14. Alkenyl chlorides react with a solution of sodium in liquid ammonia to replace the Cl by H with *retention of configuration*. That is, reduction of (*E*)-2-chloro-2-pentene gives (*Z*)-2-pentene. The reaction may be regarded as a reduction with solvated electrons to produce a vinyl anion which is protonated to give the observed product.

$$\underset{}{\overset{Cl}{C=C}} \xrightarrow{2\,e^-} \overset{}{C=C^-} + Cl^- \xrightarrow{NH_3} \underset{}{\overset{H}{C=C}} + NH_2^-$$

    (a) What does the stereochemistry of the reaction reveal concerning the geometrical structure and configurational stability of the intermediate vinyl anion?
    (b) This reaction is used in a sequence to invert the configuration of internal olefins. Show how *trans*-3-hexene may be converted to *cis*-3-hexene by use of this reaction as the final step.

15. The hydration of alkynes is catalyzed by Hg^{2+}. Write a mechanism for the hydration that accounts for this catalysis. (Hint: The mercuric ion adds to the triple bond to give a mercuricarbocation).

16. Compound A has the formula C_8H_{12} and is optically active. It reacts with hydrogen in the presence of platinum metal to give B, which has the formula C_8H_{18} and is optically inactive. Careful hydrogenation of A using H$_2$ and a poisoned palladium catalyst gives C, which has the formula C_8H_{14} and is optically active. Compound A reacts with sodium in ammonia to give D, which also has the formula C_8H_{14} and is optically inactive. What are compounds A through D?

17. Compound E has the formula C_7H_{12}. It reacts with dry HCl at $-20°C$ to give F, $C_7H_{13}Cl$. Compound F reacts with potassium *t*-butoxide in *t*-butyl alcohol to give a small amount of

E and mainly G, which has the formula C_7H_{12}. Ozonization of G gives cyclohexanone and formaldehyde. What are compounds E through G?

cyclohexanone   formaldehyde

18. The reaction of (Z)-1,5-dibromo-1-pentene with ethanolic $NaOC_2H_5$ can give principally (Z)-1-bromo-5-ethoxy-1-pentene, 5-ethoxy-1-pentyne, or 2,5-diethoxy-1-pentene, depending on the reaction conditions. Explain. Why is 1,5-diethoxy-1-pentene not a principal product under any of these conditions?

19. Appendix II, "Bond-Dissociation Energies," gives values of DH° for the carbon-halogen bonds in CH_2=CH—Cl and CH_2=CH—Br. Compare with the corresponding values for ethyl halides and explain any difference. Estimate DH° for vinyl fluoride and vinyl iodide.

Chapter 13

Nuclear Magnetic Resonance Spectroscopy

13.1 Structure Determination

Structure determination is one of the fundamental operations in chemistry. How does the chemist determine the structure of a compound? In order to answer this question, let us consider a simple, hypothetical situation. Imagine that we carry out a reaction between propane (C_3H_8) and chlorine, both of which are gases at room temperature. After the reaction is completed, we obtain a liquid product. We distill this liquid and obtain two main fractions, one boiling at 36°C and one at 47°C. These two liquids are obviously not the reactants, which are both gases. Therefore, they must be reaction products. What are they?

As a first step, we might perform an elemental analysis (Section 3.4) and determine their empirical formulas. When we do this, we find that they both have the formula C_3H_7Cl. We conclude that a reaction has occurred in which a hydrogen has been replaced by a chlorine and that two isomeric products have been produced in the reaction. Since there are only two types of hydrogen in propane, we can write structures for the two products. One is 1-chloropropane and the other is 2-chloropropane. Therefore, the reaction that has occurred is substitution of hydrogen by chlorine and the two possible substitution products have been formed.

$$CH_3CH_2CH_3 + Cl_2 \longrightarrow CH_3CH_2CH_2Cl + CH_3\overset{\displaystyle Cl}{\overset{|}{C}}HCH_3$$

But which is which? Is the product that boils at 36°C 1-chloropropane or 2-chloropropane?

One way to answer this question is to look up the boiling points of 1-chloropropane and 2-chloropropane in a handbook. But suppose for a moment that the two compounds have never been prepared before and their boiling points are not known. [Remember, this is a *hypothetical* exercise.] Another way to answer our question would be to convert the two isomers into compounds that *are* known. For example, suppose we have samples of 1-propanol and 2-propanol and that we know which is which. We can treat each of our two C_3H_7Cl isomers with aqueous KOH. Under these conditions, each alkyl halide is converted into the structurally analogous alcohol, by the S_N2 reaction. The isomer that boils at 47°C gives 1-propanol and the isomer that boils at 36°C gives 2-propanol. (In addition, both isomers give some propene.) Because we know that the OH group in 1-propanol is attached to the end of the propane chain, it follows that the C_3H_7Cl isomer with b.p. 47°C also has its chlorine attached to the end of the chain. In this simple example, we have assigned structures to the two isomers on the basis of their conversion to products of known structure.

$$CH_3CH_2CH_2Cl + OH^- \longrightarrow CH_3CH_2CH_2OH + CH_3CH{=}CH_2$$

1-chloropropane   1-propanol
b.p. 47°C

$$\underset{\substack{\text{2-chloropropane}\\\text{b.p. 36°C}}}{CH_3\overset{\displaystyle Cl}{\underset{|}{C}}HCH_3} + OH^- \longrightarrow \underset{\text{2-propanol}}{CH_3\overset{\displaystyle OH}{\underset{|}{C}}HCH_3} + CH_3CH{=}CH_2$$

A more direct method of structure determination involves the careful examination of certain physical properties of the compound of unknown structure. The most useful properties for this purpose are spectra. Spectroscopy is a powerful tool for structure determination. There are many different types of spectroscopy. In the following section we shall have a brief introduction to spectroscopy generally, and then we shall take up one specific type of spectroscopy, nuclear magnetic resonance spectroscopy, in detail.

13.2 Introduction to Spectroscopy

Molecules, and parts of molecules, are constantly in **motion**. The entire molecule rotates, the bonds vibrate, and even the electrons move—albeit so rapidly that we generally deal only with electron density distributions. It is a fundamental law of nature that each of these kinds of motion is **quantized.** That is, the molecule can exist only in distinct states (**quantum states**) that correspond to discrete energy contents. Each state is characterized by one or more quantum numbers.

> The quantum nature of molecules conflicts with our day-to-day experience, which leads us to assume that there is a continuous range of velocities and energies. For example, we are used to the idea that we can drive our automobile at 55, 56, ... 60 mph, or even at $57\frac{1}{3}$ mph. However, even though it is not intuitive, the student must get used to the idea that on the molecular level, velocities and energies *are* restricted to certain specific values. It is just as though there were a law of nature that restricted the velocity of a Volkswagen only to the speeds 40 mph, 48 mph, 55 mph, and 61 mph.

The energy difference, ΔE, between two quantum states is related to a light frequency ν by Planck's constant h (Figure 13.1).

$$\Delta E = h\nu \tag{13-1}$$

Spectroscopy is an experimental process in which the energy differences between allowed states of a system are measured by determining the frequencies of the corresponding light absorbed.

The energy difference between the different quantum states depends on the type of motion involved. The general wavelength of light required to bring about a transition is

$$E_2 \rule{2cm}{0.4pt}$$
$$h\nu = \Delta E$$
$$E_1 \rule{2cm}{0.4pt}$$

FIGURE 13.1 Light of frequency ν corresponds to an energy difference ΔE between states corresponding to energies E_1 and E_2.

304

Chap. 13

*Nuclear
Magnetic
Resonance
Spectroscopy*

different for the different types of motion. That is, each type of motion corresponds to the absorption of light in a different part of the electromagnetic spectrum. Because the wavelengths required are so vastly different, different instrumentation is required for each spectral region. For example, the energy differences between molecular rotational states are rather small, on the order of 1 cal mole^{-1}. Light having this energy has a wavelength of about 3 cm and is called microwave radiation. The energy spacings of molecular rotational states depend on bond distances and angles and the atomic masses of the bonded atoms (moments of inertia). Hence, **microwave spectroscopy** is a powerful tool for precise structure determination. However, the technique must be applied in the vapor phase and it is restricted to rather simple molecules. Although it is an important technique in the hands of a specialist, it is not commonly used by organic chemists.

Energy differences between different states of bond vibration are of the order 1-10 kcal mole^{-1} and correspond to light having wavelengths of 30-3 μ (1 $\mu \equiv 10^{-3}$ mm). This is the **infrared** region of the spectrum. Infrared spectrometers are relatively inexpensive and easy to use, and infrared spectroscopy is an important technique in organic chemistry. It is used mainly to determine which functional groups are present in a compound. We will study its use in more detail in Chapter 15.

Different electronic states of organic compounds correspond to energies in the visible (4000-7500 Å; 1 Å $\equiv 10^{-8}$ cm; 70-40 kcal mole^{-1}) and ultraviolet (1000-4000 Å; 300-70 kcal mole^{-1}) regions of the electromagnetic spectrum. Spectrometers for this region are also common, and ultraviolet-visible spectroscopy is an important technique in organic chemistry, especially for conjugated systems. Such compounds will be discussed in detail later, and our study of this spectroscopy will be deferred to Chapter 21.

13.3 Nuclear Magnetic Resonance

Nuclear magnetic resonance (NMR) spectroscopy has only been important in organic chemistry since the mid-1950s, yet in this relatively brief time it has taken its place as one of our most important spectroscopic tools. In NMR spectroscopy, a solution of the sample is placed in the instrument—actually the sample tube is fitted precisely between the poles of a powerful magnet—and the spectrum is recorded as a curve. A typical example is the NMR spectrum of 1-chloropropane shown in Figure 13.2. Some appreciation of the usefulness of this technique can be sensed by comparing the spectrum of the isomeric compound, 2-chloropropane, shown in Figure 13.3. In this chapter we will develop the rules for interpreting such spectra. We will find it rather simple, for example, to *deduce* the structures of 1-chloropropane and 2-chloropropane from their NMR spectra. It is possible to treat the NMR spectrometer as a ''magic box'' and simply memorize a few rules that suffice for deducing the structure of a compound from its spectrum. In this chapter we will also go into some of the theoretical background of NMR spectroscopy to show why the rules take the form they do.

Nuclear magnetic resonance spectroscopy differs from the spectroscopic techniques discussed in the previous section in that the states being examined have different energies in a magnetic field. That is, the molecules are placed in a powerful magnetic field to create a difference in energy between two states, which is then detected by absorption of light of the appropriate energy. In the absence of the magnetic field, these different states all have nearly the same energy.

The motion involved in NMR spectroscopy is that of **nuclear spin**. The nuclei of many atoms behave as though they are spinning on an axis. Since they are positively

FIGURE 13.2 NMR spectrum of 1-chloropropane, $CH_3CH_2CH_2Cl$.

charged, such nuclei must obey the physical laws of spinning charged particles. A moving charge, positive or negative, is associated with a magnetic field. Consequently, the spinning nuclei behave as tiny bar magnets; that is, such nuclei have **magnetic moments**. In field-free space these magnetic moments are oriented in random fashion, but they have the important quantization property that in a magnetic field only certain discrete orientations are allowed. For some important nuclei, ^1H (but not ^2H), ^{13}C (but not ^{12}C), and ^{19}F (the only common fluorine isotope), the nuclear spin can have only two alternative values associated with the quantum numbers, $+\frac{1}{2}$ ($= \alpha$) and $-\frac{1}{2}$ ($= \beta$). When these nuclei are placed in a magnetic field, their magnetic moments tend either to align with the field (corresponding to α-spin) or against the field (corresponding to β-spin) (Figure 13.4).

In an applied field, a magnetic moment tends to align with the field (for example, a compass needle in the earth's magnetic field). A magnet aligned against the magnetic

FIGURE 13.3 NMR spectrum of 2-chloropropane, $CH_3CHClCH_3$.

306

Chap. 13

*Nuclear
Magnetic
Resonance
Spectroscopy*

nuclear magnetic moments with no magnetic field

nuclear magnetic moments in a magnetic field
Nuclei with α-spin are aligned with the field;
those with β-spin are aligned against the field.

FIGURE 13.4 Orientation of nuclear magnetic moments.

field is in a higher energy state than one aligned with the field. For ^{1}H, ^{13}C, and ^{19}F the β-spin state (magnetic moment aligned against the field) corresponds to a higher energy state than the α-spin state. If the system is irradiated with light of the proper frequency or wavelength, a nucleus with α-spin can absorb a light quantum and be converted to the higher-energy β-spin state, a process colloquially described as "flipping the spin" (Figure 13.5).

To recapitulate, the nuclei of ^{1}H, ^{13}C, and ^{19}F have spinning nuclei with spins of $\pm\frac{1}{2}$. Because of the restrictions imposed by quantization, only two orientations are permitted for these nuclei in a magnetic field:

$(+\frac{1}{2})$ **α-spin** (nuclear magnetic moment aligned **with** the applied magnetic field, lower energy).

$(-\frac{1}{2})$ **β-spin** (nuclear magnetic moment aligned **against** the applied magnetic field, higher energy).

Many nuclei have no spin. All even-even nuclei (those having an even number of protons and an even number of neutrons) are in this class. In this important class, which includes ^{12}C and ^{16}O, individual pairs of protons and neutrons have opposed spins so that the net spin of the nucleus as a whole is zero. Other nuclei, such as ^{14}N, have three or more possible spin states in a magnetic field. We will not consider such cases, but will restrict our attention primarily to those nuclei that have spin of $\pm\frac{1}{2}$: ^{1}H, ^{13}C, and ^{19}F. The energy difference between the two states is given by the relationship

$$\nu = \frac{\gamma \mathbf{H}}{2\pi} \qquad (13\text{-}2)$$

in which $\mathbf{H}$ is the magnetic field strength *at the nucleus* and γ is the magnetogyric ratio of the nucleus. This quantity is the ratio of the angular momentum (from the rotating nuclear mass) and the magnetic moment (from the rotating nuclear charge) and is characteristic and different for each nucleus. That is, the energy difference between the α- and β-spin states in a magnetic field is proportional to the strength of the magnetic field with a proportionality constant that is characteristic of the nucleus (Figure 13.6). In other words, the difference in energy between the α- and β-spin states is greater the

magnetic
field $\xrightarrow{\quad h\nu \quad}$

FIGURE 13.5 Absorption of light of proper frequency changes the nuclear spin state.

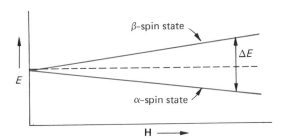

FIGURE 13.6 The energy difference ΔE between the α- and β-spin states is a function of the magnetic field at the nucleus.

greater the strength of the magnetic field; when there is no field, the two spin states have the same energy.

For ^{1}H γ has the value 2.6753×10^4 radians sec^{-1} gauss^{-1}. When **H** is given in units of gauss, the frequency ν is given in units of cycles per second or Hertz, Hz. This energy unit is used commonly in NMR, and it may be converted to the more familiar units of cal mole^{-1} by the following equation.

$$E \text{ (cal mole}^{-1}) = 9.54 \times 10^{-11} \, \nu \text{ (Hz)} \tag{13-3}$$

According to equation (13-2), the energy differences involved are proportional to the magnetic field and are exceedingly small. For example, for an isolated hydrogen atom in a magnetic field of 42,276 gauss (the field strength of the magnet used to obtain the spectra shown in Figures 13.2 and 13.3), the energy difference between α- and β-spin states is given by $\Delta E = (26,753)(42,276)/2\pi = 180 \times 10^6$ Hz $= 180$ MHz (mega-Hertz). From equation (13-3) this energy value is equivalent to only 0.0171 cal mole^{-1} (not kcal!). The frequency of 180 MHz corresponds to a wavelength of about 170 cm and is in the radio region of the electromagnetic spectrum. A field of 42,000 gauss is a rather strong magnetic field but one that is readily accessible with modern technology. NMR spectrometers with field strengths of 20,000-80,000 gauss are now relatively common, and commercial instruments are also available with field strengths in which the proton "flip" corresponds to 400 and 500 MHz.

13.4 Chemical Shift

If NMR spectroscopy related only to free protons floating in a magnetic field, we would hardly expect to find the thousands of NMR spectrometers now spread in laboratories throughout the world. It is when we look at magnetic phenomena in bonds to protons in molecules that we find why NMR is such an invaluable asset to the organic chemist. A proton in a molecule is surrounded by a cloud of electronic charge. In a magnetic field these electrons move in such a way that their motion induces their own small magnetic field, characterized by a magnetic moment that is **opposed** to the field applied by the external magnet. Consequently, the *net* magnetic field at the hydrogen nucleus is slightly *less* than the applied field (Figure 13.7).

A frequent source of confusion is the difference between electron flow and electrical current. By a convention established before the discovery of electrons, *current* flows from anode (+) to cathode (−), which turns out to be exactly the opposite of the actual *movement of electrons*. The figures in this book (e.g., Figure 13.7) represent the actual flow of electrons and are the reverse of the direction of a positive electrical current.

308

Chap. 13

Nuclear
Magnetic
Resonance
Spectroscopy

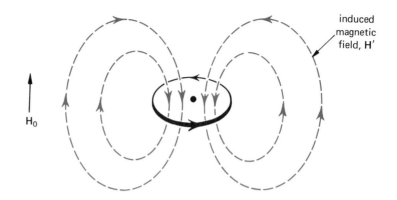

FIGURE 13.7 An external magnetic field induces an electron flow in an electron cloud that, in turn, induces a magnetic field. At the nucleus the induced field opposes the external field.

The magnetic field **H** experienced by the nucleus is therefore

$$\mathbf{H} = \mathbf{H}_0 - \mathbf{H}'$$
(13-4)

where $\mathbf{H}_0$ is the applied field and $\mathbf{H}'$ is the induced field. Because the nucleus experiences a smaller magnetic field than that applied externally, it is said to be **shielded**. This particular type of shielding is called **diamagnetic shielding**. If we are irradiating the proton with radio waves of exactly 180 MHz frequency, the change of $\alpha \rightarrow \beta$ energy states of "spin flipping" requires a field of 42,276 gauss *at the proton*. However, since the nucleus is shielded by electrons, *the applied field* must be made somewhat higher than 42,276 gauss in order for the field at the nucleus to have the **resonance** value of 42,276 gauss, the field strength that corresponds to the radio frequency required to produce "spin flipping." Protons in different electronic environments experience different amounts of shielding, and the resonance absorption of light energy will occur at different values for the applied field or irradiating light frequency. These changes are referred to as **chemical shifts**.

A nuclear magnetic resonance spectrometer is arranged schematically as shown in Figure 13.8. A liquid sample or solution contained in a narrow glass tube is put between the poles of the powerful magnet. The magnetic field creates the two energy states for various hydrogen nuclei in the sample. The sample is irradiated with radio

FIGURE 13.8 Schematic of an NMR spectrometer.

waves from a simple coil. In one mode of operation we fix the radio frequency at, say, 180 MHz. We then vary the magnetic field, and as the field at each kind of proton reaches the **resonance** value, energy is absorbed from the radio waves as the nuclear spins "flip," and this absorption is measured and recorded on a graph.

For example, 1,2,2-trichloropropane, $CH_3CCl_2CH_2Cl$, gives the spectrum shown in Figure 13.9. This spectrum consists of two sharp peaks corresponding to the methylene group and the methyl group. The CH_2 group is attached to chlorine, an electronegative element, which withdraws electrons from carbon and hydrogen. Since there is less electron density around the methylene protons, the diamagnetic shielding of these protons is less than it is for the methyl protons. The induced magnetic field is therefore lower at CH_2 than at CH_3, and the applied field must be increased less in order to achieve resonance. Consequently, the methylene protons appear to the left or **downfield** compared to the methyl protons. Note that the difference is exceedingly minute— about 0.012 gauss compared to a total applied field of about 42,000 gauss.

Alternatively, we can keep the magnetic field constant and vary the frequency of the radio electromagnetic irradiation. The lower the electronic shielding of the nucleus, the higher the effective magnetic field at a proton and the higher the frequency required to reach the resonance condition. If we plot the frequency increasing from right to left, the resulting spectrum looks exactly like Figure 13.9. The methylene hydrogens now appear at higher frequency than the methyl hydrogens, the frequency difference being 318 Hz. Frequency differences can be measured more precisely than differences in magnetic field strength. Consequently, the difference in peaks is always given in frequency units, regardless of the specific mode of operation of the NMR spectrometer. In practice, most spectrometers today operate at constant field and vary the frequency. Nevertheless, the kind of language in common use is illustrated by the statement that in Figure 13.9 the methylene group appears *downfield* with a frequency difference of 318 Hz. Note again that this is a small difference between large numbers; if the methyl group resonates at 180,000,000 Hz, the methylene is at 180,000,318 Hz! Since these *absolute numbers* are difficult to reproduce, in practice we compare differences relative to a standard.

The standard compound used for most proton NMR spectra is tetramethylsilane, $(CH_3)_4Si$, commonly abbreviated **TMS**, a volatile liquid, b.p. 26.5°C (Sections 8.5,

FIGURE 13.9 NMR spectrum of $CH_3CCl_2CH_2Cl$ at 180 MHz.

310

Chap. 13

Nuclear
Magnetic
Resonance
Spectroscopy

8.6). This useful compound is inert to most reagents and is soluble in most organic liquids. A small amount has been added to our sample of 1,2,2-trichloropropane, and it gives rise to the peak at the far right in Figure 13.9. All of the hydrogens in TMS are equivalent and give rise to the single sharp line 402 Hz upfield from the methyl of the trichloropropane. Furthermore, silicon is electropositive relative to carbon and tends to donate electron density to the methyl groups, thereby increasing their shielding. The relatively high shielding of the protons in TMS causes them to resonate upfield from most other protons commonly encountered in organic compounds.

When the spectrum is recorded with a spectrometer operating at 70,460 gauss, the resonance frequency of hydrogen is 300 MHz. The larger magnetic field induces a larger electron current, which causes a larger diamagnetic shielding at the nucleus. The difference in diamagnetic shielding is proportionally larger and the peaks spread apart, as shown in Figure 13.10. The chemical shift of the methyl group is now 669 Hz downfield from TMS instead of 402 Hz. Because different NMR instruments are in common use, it is convenient to define a unitless measure that is independent of field strength. The unit used is δ. It is simply the ratio of the chemical shift of the resonance in question, in Hertz, to the total light frequency used. Since the resulting number is small, it is multiplied by 10^6 so as to be convenient to handle. Thus, δ has the units of parts per million (ppm) and represents a chemical shift downfield (higher frequency) from TMS.

$$\delta_i = \frac{\nu_i - \nu_{TMS}}{\nu_0} \times 10^6 \text{ ppm} \tag{13-5}$$

In equation (13-5) δ_i is the chemical shift of proton i, ν_i is the resonance frequency of that proton, ν_{TMS} is the resonance frequency of TMS, and ν_0 is the operating frequency of the instrument. Thus, for $CH_3CCl_2CH_2Cl$, $\delta(CH_3) = 402/180$ (or 531/300) = 2.23 ppm, and $\delta(CH_2) = 720/180$ (or 1200/300) = 4.00 ppm. If a resonance is upfield from TMS, its δ value has a negative sign.

EXERCISE 13.1 Sketch the NMR spectrum of 1,2,2-trichloropropane as it would appear if measured with a spectrometer operating at 250 MHz. What would be the difference in Hz between the TMS and CH_3 resonances? Between the CH_3 and CH_2 resonances?

FIGURE 13.10 NMR spectrum of $CH_3CCl_2CH_2Cl$ at 300 MHz.

13.5 Relative Peak Areas

We saw in the previous section that we can obtain a valuable piece of information from an NMR spectrum—the number of magnetically different hydrogens in the compound. The amount of energy absorbed at each resonance frequency is proportional to the number of nuclei that are absorbing energy at that frequency. By measuring the **areas** of each of the resonance lines, we may determine the relative number of each different kind of hydrogen. In practice, this is accomplished with an electronic integrator. After the NMR spectrum has been recorded, the instrument is switched to an "integrator mode" of operation and the spectrum is recorded again. The recorder output in this mode of operation is illustrated in Figure 13.11. The integral line for each of the two peaks in the spectrum of 1,2,2-trichloropropane is shown superimposed on the appropriate peak. The ratio of the heights of the two integral lines is equal to the ratio of the number of protons giving rise to the two peaks, in this case 3:2. In the remaining sample spectra in this book, integral lines are shown in a separate color. Measurement of the heights of the separate "steps" on the integral line will give the relative numbers of hydrogens that are responsible for the corresponding resonances.

We should note that the NMR experiment does not measure all of the protons, but just those that have α-spin and absorb energy in "flipping" to β-spin. The difference in the population of α- and β-spins is rather small. We learned above that the energy difference between the proton α- and β-spin states in the magnetic field of a 180-MHz NMR instrument is only 0.018 cal mole^{-1}. At equilibrium, the population difference is given by the Boltzmann distribution as

$$\frac{N_\alpha}{N_\beta} = e^{0.017/RT} = 1.00003$$

When we now turn on the applied radio frequency field, we excite the slight excess of α nuclei to β. Of course, those nuclei with β-spin can also *give up* energy to the applied field, and **relax** back to the α-spin state. If there were no other mechanism for converting β back to α, we would quickly have exactly equal populations in both spin states and

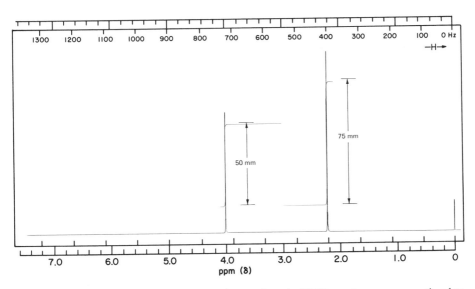

FIGURE 13.11 Integrated intensities superimposed on the NMR spectrum are proportional to the relative numbers of hydrogens.

312

Chap. 13

*Nuclear
Magnetic
Resonance
Spectroscopy*

would no longer observe a net absorption of energy; there would be no spectrum. With a sufficiently strong radio frequency field this can generally be done and the system is then said to be **saturated**. However, in normal operation, hydrogens in the β-spin state continually relax back to the α-state because of local fields, and equilibrium imbalance is maintained. These local fields are associated with other spinning nuclei. That is, even in the absence of the applied radio frequency field, individual protons convert from one state to another quite readily because, in moving about the liquid, they experience the magnetic fields of other nearby nuclear magnetic moments. Occasionally, such moving and changing fields happen to have the resonance value, and energy interchange can occur resulting in spin flipping. In the NMR experiment the net result of all this activity is the conversion of our measuring radio waves into heat within the sample. In normal operation the distribution of α- and β-spins remains close to the equilibrium value and the amount of energy absorbed is proportional to the number of protons.

EXERCISE 13.2 What are the relative peak areas of the different resonances in the NMR spectra of the following compounds?
(a) 1,1,3-trichloro-2,2-dimethylpropane (b) 1,1,3,3-tetramethylcyclobutane
(c) 1,2-dimethoxyethane (glyme) (d) (*E*)-1-chloropropene

13.6 Spin-Spin Splitting

We have seen that the NMR spectrum of 1,2,2-trichloropropane shows two sharp peaks that are easy to interpret. From the fact that there are two peaks, we deduce that the compound has two types of hydrogen that are magnetically nonequivalent, and, from the relative areas of the two peaks, we conclude that they are present in a ratio of 3:2. Let us now consider the NMR spectrum of a related trihaloalkane, 1,1,2-tribromo-3,3-dimethylbutane, $(CH_3)_3CCHBrCHBr_2$ (Figure 13.12).

We recognize the small peak at $\delta = 0.0$ as that of TMS added as a standard to define the zero on our scale. The large peak at $\delta = 1.2$ ppm comes from the nine equivalent

FIGURE 13.12 NMR spectrum of $(CH_3)_3CCHBrCHBr_2$. The scale expansion shows the doublets more clearly.

methyl protons. The other two protons are responsible for the downfield resonances; the downfield shifts are explained by their proximity to one and two electronegative bromines, respectively. But these two resonances are not single lines, as are the CH_3 and CH_2 resonances in 1,2,2-trichloropropane. Instead, each resonance appears as a **doublet.** This "splitting" of peaks is common in NMR spectra. The phenomenon has its origin in the magnetic field associated with each individual spinning proton. These small magnetic fields affect the total magnetic field experienced by another proton. For convenience we will label these hydrogens as H_a and H_b.

$$Br-\overset{\overset{\displaystyle Br}{|}}{\underset{\underset{\displaystyle H_a}{|}}{C}}-\overset{\overset{\displaystyle Br}{|}}{\underset{\underset{\displaystyle H_b}{|}}{C}}-C(CH_3)_3$$

In the applied magnetic field of the NMR spectrometer we would expect H_a normally to show up as a single peak. However, the magnetic field associated with the spin of the nearby proton, H_b, contributes to the effective field experienced by H_a. This is not a through-space effect of the magnetic field associated with the spinning nucleus H_b but results instead from interaction between each H nucleus and electron spins. That is, the spin of H_b is relayed to H_a by way of shared electrons. For most cases, if H_b has α-spin, the effect is as if the total magnetic field at H_a were slightly greater than that provided by the NMR instrument's applied field alone. Consequently, a slightly higher frequency is required to achieve resonance than in the absence of H_b, and we find a slight "downfield" shift (Figure 13.13). But only half of the H_b nuclei have α-spin.

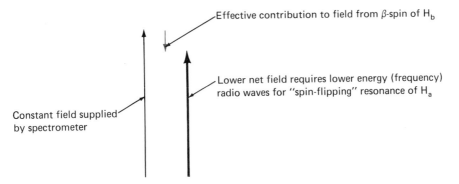

FIGURE 13.13 Source of spin-spin splitting.

314

Chap. 13

Nuclear
Magnetic
Resonance
Spectroscopy

The rest have β-spin, in which the opposite effect results. For these molecules the effect is as if the effective magnetic field at H_a were slightly *weaker* than that given by the applied field alone. The NMR spectrometer must then provide a slightly smaller frequency in order to achieve the "spin-flipping" resonance condition with H_a. Now the result is an upfield shift (Figure 13.13). In such a case, H_a and H_b are said to be "coupled."

Let us recapitulate the conditions of the experiment. We apply a constant magnetic field in the NMR instrument and irradiate our sample with a high frequency radio signal. As we slowly decrease the frequency, we reach a point where the energy of the irradiating radio waves matches the effective magnetic field at the half of the H_a protons which are in molecules where the H_b protons have α-spin. At this frequency, H_a protons of α-spin absorb photons and "flip" to β-spins. Motion in the liquid sample provides a mechanism for the β-spins to change to α with the excess energy given up as heat. The absorption of radio waves is recorded by the NMR instrument as a "peak." As the frequency of the radio waves is decreased still more, the resonance condition is destroyed and the recorder pen returns to the base line. At a still lower frequency, we reach a point where the other half of the H_a protons absorb radio energy. These H_a protons are in molecules where H_b has β-spin; in this case the coupling effect subtracts from the applied field, and a lower frequency must therefore be applied to achieve resonance.

These relationships are summarized in Figure 13.14. Note that only one kind of hydrogen is in resonance at any given point in the spectrum. Both lines in the low-field doublet in Figure 13.14 correspond to transitions of H_a. If there were no coupling to H_b, the resonance position of H_a would be at the point marked δ_a. However, since H_b *is* there, and since its spin *does* affect the magnetic field experienced by H_a, we see two lines, one at slightly lower field (higher frequency) for the one half of the molecules having H_b nuclei with α-spin and one at slightly higher field (lower frequency) for the one half of the molecules having H_b nuclei with β-spin. At these frequencies H_b, with its different chemical shift, is not in resonance even though its presence is "felt" by H_a, and it produces two resonance positions instead of one. As the frequency is decreased still further, the H_b nuclei eventually come into resonance. However, now we must reckon with the effect of α- or β-spin of H_a on the effective magnetic field experienced by H_b. The effect is an exact reciprocity—the effect of H_a on H_b is exactly the same as the effect of H_b on H_a. Consequently, the splitting of the H_b peaks has the same magnitude as that of the H_a peaks. The spacing between the peaks in a resonance multiplet is called the **coupling constant** between the two protons. The coupling constant is conventionally labeled J, and is given in units of cycles per second or Hertz. For the case under discussion, $J_{ab} = 1.6$ Hz.

In the foregoing example, we note that there is no coupling to the nine methyl protons, which appear as a sharp singlet. Because the coupling effects of proton spin are relayed by way of shared electrons, the effect is attenuated rapidly with the number

increasing radiofrequency

FIGURE 13.14 J_{ab} causes equal spin-spin splitting in H_a and H_b.

of bonds and is usually quite small if more than two atoms intervene between the protons. Thus, the methyl protons do indeed couple to the other two protons in our example, but the magnitude of each such J is so small as to be unobservable with normal spectrometers. As a further example, in the spectrum of 1,2,2-trichloropropane, which was discussed in Section 13.4, the protons on C-1 and C-3 do not noticeably split each other.

$$\underset{}{\overset{\text{H}_a\ \text{H}_b}{\text{C}-\text{C}}}$$ spin-spin splitting normally observed

$$\underset{}{\overset{\text{H}_a\qquad\ \text{H}_b}{\text{C}-\text{C}-\text{C}}}$$ spin-spin splitting normally not observed

Now let us consider a slightly more complex spectrum, that of 1,1,2-trichloroethane. In this compound, there are also two types of hydrogen, H_a and H_b.

$$\text{Cl}-\underset{\underset{\text{H}_a}{|}}{\overset{\overset{\text{Cl}}{|}}{\text{C}}}-\underset{\underset{\text{H}_b}{|}}{\overset{\overset{\text{H}_b}{|}}{\text{C}}}-\text{Cl}$$

The spectrum of 1,1,2-trichloroethane (Figure 13.15) shows two resonances, a triplet of relative area 1 centered at $\delta = 5.8$ ppm and a doublet of relative area 2 centered at $\delta = 3.9$ ppm. The triplet is associated with H_a, which is more deshielded because it is bonded to a carbon that also has two chlorines. The two equivalent H_b hydrogens are less deshielded because their carbon has only one attached chlorine.

The spectrum of 1,1,2-trichloroethane is shown in diagramatic form in Figure 13.16. If there were no spin-spin coupling, the resonance positions of H_a and H_b would be at the points marked δ_a and δ_b, respectively. However, in any given molecule, the two H_b nuclei may have their spins as $\alpha\alpha$, $\alpha\beta$, $\beta\alpha$, or $\beta\beta$. If both H_b nuclei have α-spin, the effect of coupling is to augment the applied field and a higher frequency is required for H_a to be in resonance. Thus, H_a in molecules with this arrangement of H_b spins comes into resonance at slightly higher frequency than if there was no coupling to

FIGURE 13.15 NMR spectrum of $CHCl_2CH_2Cl$.

316

Chap. 13

Nuclear
Magnetic
Resonance
Spectroscopy

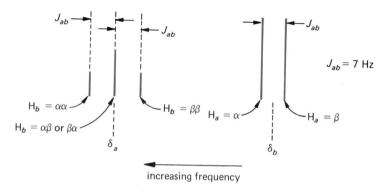

FIGURE 13.16 Spin-spin splitting analysis of 1,1,2-trichloroethane.

H_b. If the H_b spins are $\alpha\beta$ or $\beta\alpha$, there is no effect on the field experienced by H_a because the opposed spins of the two H_b nuclei cancel. If both H_b nuclei have β-spin, the magnetic field associated with their coupling subtracts from H_0 and a lower frequency is necessary to achieve resonance at H_a. Statistically, the probability of the two H_b nuclei being $\alpha\alpha$, $\alpha\beta$, $\beta\alpha$, and $\beta\beta$ is 1:1:1:1. Since $\alpha\beta$ and $\beta\alpha$ are energetically equivalent, the H_a resonance appears as three lines with relative intensities of 1:2:1. At the resonance frequency of the two H_b hydrogens we find two lines because H_a can have either α- or β-spin. In this case the coupling constant J has the value 7 Hz.

Extension to different numbers of equivalent neighboring hydrogens is straightforward. Three hydrogens, as in a methyl group, can have the possible spin states $\alpha\alpha\alpha$, $\alpha\alpha\beta$, $\alpha\beta\alpha$, $\beta\alpha\alpha$; $\alpha\beta\beta$, $\beta\alpha\beta$, $\beta\beta\alpha$, and $\beta\beta\beta$. An adjacent proton would therefore give four peaks with area ratios of approximately 1:3:3:1. These numbers are simply the polynomial coefficients and are summarized in Table 13.1. In general, n neighboring equivalent hydrogens cause splitting into $n + 1$ peaks.

TABLE 13.1 Number of Peaks and Area Ratios for NMR Multiplets

Number of Equivalent Adjacent Hydrogens	Total Number of Peaks	Area Ratios
0	1	1
1	2	1:1
2	3	1:2:1
3	4	1:3:3:1
4	5	1:4:6:4:1
5	6	1:5:10:10:5:1
6	7	1:6:15:20:15:6:1

EXERCISE 13.3 Sketch the NMR spectra of the following compounds. Show the relative resonance positions (not the precise values of δ) and the expected appearance of each resonance multiplet. Finally, indicate the expected *relative heights* of the various peaks.
(a) (*E*)-1-chloro-3,3-dimethyl-1-butene   (b) 1,1-dimethoxyethane
(c) diethyl ether   (d) 1-methoxy-3,3-dimethylbutane

EXERCISE 13.4 Sketch the NMR spectra that you would expect for 1-chloropropane and 2-chloropropane. Compare your sketches with Figures 13.1 and 13.2.

Since *J* has its origin in the magnetic spin of the proton, its magnitude is not dependent on the strength of the applied magnetic field. That is, the same *J* value applies for spectra determined at 60 MHz, 180 MHz, 300 MHz, and so on. Because *J* is field-independent, and the resonance position of a multiplet does vary with field-strength, spectra of the same compound that are measured with different instruments can sometimes have rather different appearance. An example is seen in the 60-MHz and 180-MHz spectra of 1-bromo-3-chloropropane (Figures 13.17 and 13.18). In this compound, the protons attached to C-3 are slightly more deshielded than those attached to C-1, because chlorine is more electronegative than bromine. Thus, in the 180-MHz spectrum (Figure 13.18), we see two downfield triplets (δ = 3.67 and 3.54, respectively). In this spectrum, the two triplets are readily apparent, since the magnitudes of the coupling constants ($\cong$ 7 Hz) are considerably less than the difference in resonance frequencies (661 − 637 = 24 Hz). However, in the 60-MHz spectrum (Figure 13.17),

FIGURE 13.17 60-MHz NMR spectrum of $BrCH_2CH_2CH_2Cl$.

FIGURE 13.18 180-MHz NMR spectrum of $BrCH_2CH_2CH_2Cl$.

318

Chap. 13

Nuclear
Magnetic
Resonance
Spectroscopy

the two coupling constants are still the same, but the difference in resonance frequencies is now only 8 Hz. Therefore, the two triplets *overlap*, making the spectrum rather difficult to decipher at first examination. Note that, even though CH_2Br and CH_2Cl are not magnetically equivalent, the two Js are accidentally equal. Therefore, the center CH_2 appears as a 1:4:6:4:1 quintet with $\delta = 2.15$ ppm.

EXERCISE 13.5 Sketch the expected appearance of the NMR spectrum of each of the following compounds. Indicate the approximate resonance positions, the multiplicity of each resonance, and the relative area of the resonance.
(a) 1,3-dichloropropane   (b) 1,2-dimethoxypropane

13.7 More Complex Splitting

Our simple splitting rules, with peak numbers and intensities that follow the polynomial coefficients as given in Table 13.1, apply for cases where splitting is small compared to the difference in chemical shift between the neighboring hydrogens; that is, $J << \Delta\nu$. As $\Delta\nu$ is reduced (as the peaks for two nonequivalent hydrogens approach each other), the inner peaks increase in intensity and the outer ones diminish. In practice, such perturbations are almost always apparent. This effect may be seen in the spectra in Figures 13.12, 13.15, 13.17, and 13.18.

If $\Delta\nu$ is too small compared to J, the simple rules do not apply at all. Such spectra are often rather complex and require a detailed analysis beyond the scope of this book. One especially simple case, however, is the extreme one for which $\Delta\nu = 0$. Such hydrogens are *magnetically equivalent and do not split each other*. In the cases discussed previously, for example, a methylene group was treated as a unit—because the two hydrogens are magnetically equivalent, they have no effect on each other. This effect is a direct and exact outcome of the quantum mechanics of magnetic resonance and the detailed reason is not important for our purposes.

The following simple explanation may be helpful. Because the NMR experiment does not distinguish magnetically equivalent hydrogens, different spin properties cannot be assigned to individual protons. For example, in a methylene group in which the protons have α- and β-spin, we cannot assign one spin to one proton and the other spin to the remaining proton. Instead, the $\alpha\beta$-spin property belongs to the methylene protons *as a unit*. Since we cannot assign individual spins to individual equivalent protons, it follows that we should not observe the splitting or J-coupling normally associated with such assignments.

The effect of the relative magnitudes of J and $\Delta\nu$ is illustrated in Figure 13.19 for a two-proton system, H_a—C—C—H_b. The first spectrum, for $\Delta\nu >> J$, is close to the "first-order" analysis that we outlined above. As $\Delta\nu$ and J become of comparable magnitude, the inner peaks increase in intensity and the outer ones fade until, in the limit where $\Delta\nu = 0$, the two inner peaks have merged and the outer peaks have vanished.

The spectra of 1-methoxybutane in Figures 13.20 and 13.21 illustrate the complications of small $\Delta\nu/J$ ratios. In the 180-MHz spectrum of this ether (Figure 13.20), the C-4 methyl resonance at $\delta = 0.95$ ppm is only barely discernible as a triplet, and the resonances of the C-2 and C-3 methylene hydrogens appear as an ill-defined lump centered at about $\delta = 1.5$ ppm. Furthermore, the methoxy singlet at $\delta = 3.32$ ppm

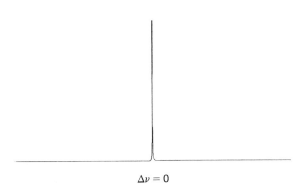

FIGURE 13.19 NMR spectra of the system H_a—C—C—H_b for various values of J and $\Delta\nu$.

overlaps and partially obscures the C-1 triplet. However, the 300-MHz spectrum of this same compound (Figure 13.21) is readily interpretable in terms of the simple rules we have discussed.

Splitting can become more complex if coupling occurs to more than one type of hydrogen. Consider the case of H_a coupled to two different hydrogens, H_b and H_c, with $J_{ab} > J_{ac}$.

$$\begin{array}{ccc} H_b & H_a & H_c \\ | & | & | \\ C & - C & - C \end{array}$$

320

Chap. 13

*Nuclear
Magnetic
Resonance
Spectroscopy*

FIGURE 13.20 NMR spectrum of 1-methoxybutane (180 MHz).

FIGURE 13.21 NMR spectrum of 1-methoxybutane (300 MHz).

In this case, H_a is split into a doublet by H_b, and each of the lines of the doublet is split into a further doublet to give a total of four lines, as shown in Figure 13.22. The four lines will have approximately the same intensity and correspond to transitions of H_a when the H_b and H_c nuclei have the following spin states.

Line	Spin of H_b	Spin of H_c
1	α	α
2	α	β
3	β	α
4	β	β

In this example, $J_{ab} > J_{ac}$. This means that the effect of nucleus H_b on H_a is greater than the effect of nucleus H_c on H_a. Thus, line 2 appears at higher frequency than the

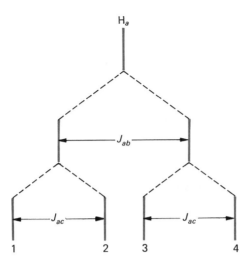

FIGURE 13.22 Effect of two coupling constants, $J_{ab} > J_{ac}$, on the resonance frequency of H_a.

resonance position of H_a in the absence of H_b and H_c because the α- and β-spins of the two nuclei do not cancel. Similarly, line 3, which corresponds to a transition of H_a when H_b is β and H_c is α, is at slightly lower frequency than the resonance position of H_a in the absence of the other nuclei. The remainder of the spectrum will show H_b and H_c each as doublets due to their respective couplings to H_a (Figure 13.23).

Note what happens if $J_{ab} = J_{ac}$. This will occur if H_b and H_c are magnetically equivalent (that is, if they have the same chemical shift) or if the two Js accidentally have the same value. In such a case the two inner lines of the quartet occur at the same point and appear as a single line of double the intensity. The net result is a triplet with intensity ratios of 1:2:1 (Figure 13.24).

The spectrum of 1-bromo-3-chloropropane (Figure 13.18) is a relevant example. The CH_2Cl hydrogens and the CH_2Br hydrogens are not magnetically equivalent, and therefore they do not have the same chemical shift. Each is adjacent to two hydrogens (the center CH_2 group) and each appears as a 1:2:1 triplet. Even though CH_2Cl and CH_2Br are not magnetically equivalent, the two Js are accidentally equal. Therefore, the center CH_2 still appears as a 1:4:6:4:1 quintet with $\delta = 2.15$ ppm.

Figure 13.25 shows the spectrum of 1,1,2-trichloropropane, a compound in which there are two different coupling constants. There are three different types of hydrogen, which we may label H_a, H_b, and H_c.

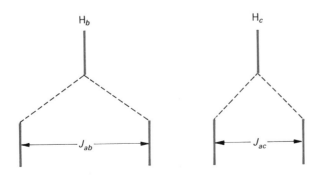

FIGURE 13.23 The H_b and H_c resonances of the system H_b—H_a—H_c when $J_{ab} > J_{ac}$.

322

Chap. 13

Nuclear
Magnetic
Resonance
Spectroscopy

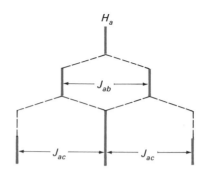

FIGURE 13.24 Effect of equal coupling constants, $J_{ab} = J_{ac}$, on the resonance frequency of H_a.

$$
\begin{array}{ccc}
& \overset{\text{Cl}}{\underset{|}{}} & \overset{\text{Cl}}{\underset{|}{}} \\
\text{Cl} - & \overset{|}{\underset{|}{\text{C}}} - & \overset{|}{\underset{|}{\text{C}}} - \text{CH}_{3(c)} \\
& \underset{\text{H}_a}{} & \underset{\text{H}_b}{}
\end{array}
$$

The H_a hydrogen is most deshielded and appears as a low-field (high-frequency) resonance with relative area of unity. It is a doublet due to coupling with H_b, and the separation between the two lines, J_{ab}, is 3.6 Hz. The three equivalent CH_3 hydrogens, H_c, are least deshielded and appear as a high-field (low-frequency) resonance of area 3. They are also coupled to H_b and appear as a doublet. In this case the separation between the lines, J_{bc}, is 6.8 Hz. The two coupling constants in this case are unequal. The resonance for H_b is in between those of H_a and H_b, and it has a relative area of unity. Because of the two unequal Js, it appears as a "doubled quartet" and may be analyzed as shown on the insert in Figure 13.25. The chemical shift for H_b is $\delta = 4.30$ ppm, the midpoint of the multiplet.

Finally, remember that J is independent of applied field, whereas the normal shielding by electrons $\Delta\nu$ results from an induced field and is proportional to the applied field. One of the incentives for seeking larger magnetic fields for NMR instruments is

FIGURE 13.25 NMR spectrum of 1,1,2-trichloropropane, $CH_3CHClCHCl_2$. The center multiplet ($\delta = 4.30$ ppm) is expanded in the insert.

323

Sec. 13.8

*The Effect of
Conformation on
Coupling
Constants*

the spreading of $\Delta\nu$ relative to J. At a sufficiently high field strength, all spectra reduce to the simple "first-order" type ($\Delta\nu \gg J$) we have treated.

EXERCISE 13.6 Consider the following three-spin system, with resonance frequencies $\delta_a = 6.0$ ppm, $\delta_b = 4.0$ ppm, $\delta_c = 7.0$ ppm

$$
\begin{array}{ccc}
\text{H}_b & \text{H}_a & \text{H}_c \\
| & | & | \\
-\text{C}-\text{C}-\text{C}- \\
| & | & | \\
& \text{H}_b &
\end{array}
$$

Sketch the expected NMR spectrum for each of the following situations. [The use of graph paper will greatly facilitate working this exercise.]

(a) $J_{ab} = 6$ Hz, $J_{ac} = 4$ Hz, $J_{bc} = 0$ (b) $J_{ab} = 6$ Hz, $J_{ac} = 3$ Hz, $J_{bc} = 0$
(c) $J_{ab} = 4$ Hz, $J_{ac} = 6$ Hz, $J_{bc} = 0$ (d) $J_{ab} = 3$ Hz, $J_{ac} = 6$ Hz, $J_{bc} = 0$

13.8 The Effect of Conformation on Coupling Constants

Although spin-spin coupling works through the bonding electrons, the magnitude of J *is* related to the relative orientation of the coupled nuclei in space. For example, the J value between adjacent axial hydrogens in cyclohexanes is 10-13 Hz, whereas J between axial and equatorial or between two equatorial hydrogens is 3-5 Hz.

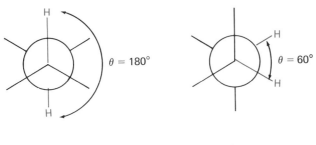

$$J_{aa'} = 11.1 \text{ Hz}$$
$$J_{ae} = 4.3 \text{ Hz}$$

$$J_{ee'} = 2.7 \text{ Hz}$$
$$J_{ae} = 3.0 \text{ Hz}$$

The dihedral angle (the solid angle between the C—C—H_a and C—C—H_b planes) between two axial hydrogens is 180°, whereas the axial-equatorial and equatorial-equatorial dihedral angles are both 60° (Figure 13.26).

The relation between J and the dihedral angle between hydrogens has been established theoretically and may be depicted in a familiar graphic form known as the **Karplus curve** (Figure 13.27). The coupling constant between two hydrogens reaches

$$\theta = 180°$$
$$\theta = 60°$$

$$J \cong 10-13 \text{ Hz}$$
$$J \cong 3-5 \text{ Hz}$$

FIGURE 13.26 J_{HH} and conformation. The angle θ is the dihedral angle between the carbon-hydrogen bonds.

324

Chap. 13

Nuclear
Magnetic
Resonance
Spectroscopy

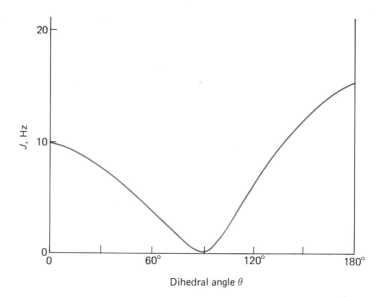

FIGURE 13.27   Karplus curve.

a minimum when the dihedral angle between them is 90°. The curve can be expressed analytically by two equations.

$$J_{HH'} = 10 \cos^2 \theta \quad (0° \leq \theta \leq 90°)$$
$$J_{HH'} = 16 \cos^2 \theta \quad (90° \leq \theta \leq 180°)$$

> **EXERCISE 13.7**   Use a sheet of graph paper and your calculator to plot the magnitude of J_{HH} as a function of dihedral angle, from $\theta = 0°$ to 180°.

The Karplus relationship also applies to hydrogens attached to the carbon-carbon double bond. Figures 13.28 and 13.29 show the NMR spectra of (*E*)- and (*Z*)-3-chloropropenenitrile. Note that the coupling constant for the trans hydrogens, in which the dihedral angle is 180°, is 14.0 Hz, while that for the cis hydrogens, with dihedral angle of 0°, is 7.7 Hz.

As shown by the foregoing example, the value of the vicinal coupling constant is an excellent criterion for stereostructure of alkenes. In general, J is greater for trans hydrogens than for cis; J_{trans} is usually in the range 11-19 Hz and J_{cis} is in the range 5-14 Hz. Although the two ranges overlap, J_{trans} is invariably greater than J_{cis} for a pair of isomeric cis and trans alkenes. Thus, when one has only one isomer of an alkene, stereochemistry may be assigned with confidence if the vicinal coupling constant is quite small (<10 Hz) or quite large (>14 Hz). If the coupling constant is in the overlap range (10-14 Hz), it is necessary to have both isomers before a reliable assignment of structure can be made.

In a monosubstituted alkene, $H_2C=CHX$, all three vinyl hydrogens are nonequivalent. In such a case, we see a fully-coupled three-spin system, with $J_{ab} \neq J_{ac} \neq J_{bc}$. Such an example is shown in Figure 13.30. In this case, $J_{trans} = 18.0$ Hz and $J_{cis} = 10.0$ Hz. The third coupling constant, between the two non-equivalent C-1 hydrogens, is 2.0 Hz. This value is a typical value for the geminal coupling constant for two alkene hydrogens.

In summary, the *magnitude* of J is related to the spatial orientation of two coupled hydrogens relative to one another. With the aid of the Karplus relationship, useful

325

Sec. 13.8

*The Effect of
Conformation on
Coupling
Constants*

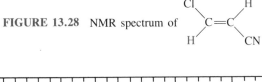

FIGURE 13.28 NMR spectrum of

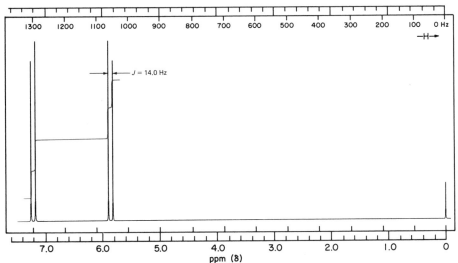

FIGURE 13.29 NMR spectrum of

structural information may be garnered from an examination of these absolute values of
J. The effect is most easily seen in conformationally-locked cyclohexanes and in alkenes. In cyclohexanes, $J_{\text{axial-axial}}$ is generally large, in the range 10-13 Hz, with
$J_{\text{axial-equatorial}}$ and $J_{\text{equatorial-equatorial}}$ being smaller, in the range 3–5 Hz. In alkenes,
J_{trans} is large (11–19 Hz) and J_{cis} is small (5–14 Hz).

EXERCISE 13.8 What is the expected appearance of the resonance of the C-1 hydrogen in
trans-4-*t*-butyl-1-methoxycyclohexane?

326

Chap. 13

Nuclear
Magnetic
Resonance
Spectroscopy

FIGURE 13.30 NMR spectrum of 3,3-dimethyl-1-butene, $(CH_3)_3CCH{=}CH_2$.

13.9 Remote Shielding of Multiple Bonds: Magnetic Anisotropy

In the previous section, we discussed the effect of stereochemistry on the magnitude of J and illustrated our discussion with the NMR spectra of several alkenes (Figures 13.28–13.30). We saw that, because of the dependence of J on the dihedral angle of the system H—C—C—H, NMR is an excellent tool for assigning stereochemistry to disubstituted alkenes. However, the NMR spectra of alkenes are also distinguished by the fact that the hydrogens attached to the carbon-carbon double bond (vinyl hydrogens) are found to resonate far downfield of normal alkane resonances, in the region $\delta \cong 4.5$–5.5 ppm. The actual values vary from about $\delta = 4.7$ ppm when the vinyl hydrogen is at the end of a chain to about $\delta = 5.3$ ppm when it is at some other position along the chain.

These values may appear to be rather far downfield for a C—H function. It is true that the increased *s*-character of the carbon orbital makes the carbon effectively more electronegative, but the observed change is too large to be a simple electronegativity effect.

The effect has its origin in the induced motion of bond electrons, just as discussed earlier in the diamagnetic shielding (Section 13.4) by electrons around the hydrogen nucleus. In a double bond the π-electrons are more polarizable than σ-electrons and are freer to move in response to a magnetic field. Such an electron cloud is said to be magnetically **anisotropic**. Thus when the molecule is oriented so that the plane of the double bond is perpendicular to the applied magnetic field, the π-electrons tend to circulate about the direction of the applied field. As shown in Figure 13.31, the circular motion of the π-electrons produces an induced magnetic field opposed to the applied field *at the middle of the double bond*. Out by the vinyl hydrogens, the magnetic lines of force are in the same direction as the applied field. Hence, a higher frequency is

327

Sec. 13.9

*Remote Shielding
of Multiple
Bonds: Magnetic
Anisotropy*

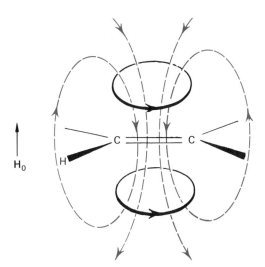

FIGURE 13.31 Induced motion of π-electrons of a double bond in a magnetic field; the induced field has the same direction as the applied field at a vinyl proton. Recall our convention of representing circulating electrons rather than positive current.

necessary for resonance at the total field at the hydrogen nucleus. For double bonds with orientations other than that shown, the effect will be smaller and the actual effect will be the average for all orientations because the tumbling and rotation of molecules is so rapid that only an "time-averaged state" is observed.

It should be emphasized that vinyl hydrogens are still subject to the normal diamagnetic shielding effects of the electron clouds that envelope them. The net effect is still a chemical shift far upfield from a bare proton. However, the effect of the **π-electron circulation** partially opposes the normal effect of local electrons in such a way that resonance occurs downfield from that observed for a saturated C—H by a significant amount. The resulting chemical shift of vinyl hydrogens provides an important analytical method for establishing both their presence and number.

The applied magnetic field also induces electron currents in carbon-carbon and carbon-hydrogen single bonds, and it is these induced currents rather than electronegativity effects that give rise to the characteristic pattern of chemical shifts for differently substituted alkyl hydrogens.

$$\delta_{(-\overset{|}{\underset{|}{C}}-H)} > \delta_{(>CH_2)} > \delta_{(-CH_3)}$$

The NMR resonance for a hydrogen attached to the carbon *next to a double bond* is shifted downfield by about 0.8 ppm. This effect is due partly to the weak inductive effect of the sp^2-hybridized carbon of the double bond and partly to the anisotropy of the π-system of the double bond.

In contrast to alkene protons, the hydrogens attached to carbon-carbon triple bonds resonate at rather high field, $\delta \cong 2$ ppm. In fact, the alkyne C—H resonates at approximately the same place as does a comparable alkane proton. The observed position results from a deshielding effect of the electronegative triple bond superimposed on the effect of the magnetic anisotropy of the triple bond π-electrons. Recall that a triple bond has a cylindrically symmetric sheath of π-electrons. The electrons in this torus can circulate in a magnetic field, just as the electrons in the π-system of the carbon-car-

328

Chap. 13

*Nuclear
Magnetic
Resonance
Spectroscopy*

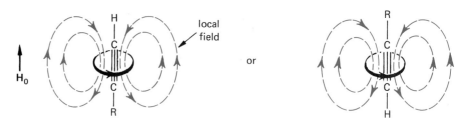

FIGURE 13.32 Shielding of acetylenic protons by a triple bond in parallel orientation to the applied field.

bon double bond. As shown in Figure 13.32, the alkyne π-electrons are most free to circulate *around the symmetry axis of the triple bond*. When the molecule finds itself in an orientation that has the triple bond aligned with the external magnetic field, this induced electronic motion in turn induces a local field (dashed lines in Figure 13.32). At the acetylenic proton the induced field opposes the applied field. Thus, a lower frequency is required to bring this proton into resonance. In this case, the result of the induced field is additional shielding of the alkyne proton.

Actually, the diamagnetic shielding of acetylenic protons is a result of two factors. When the molecule is aligned perpendicular to H_0, the acetylenic proton is deshielded, just as in the case of alkene hydrogens (Figure 13.33). This deshielding component is smaller than the shielding component diagrammed in Figure 13.32, because the electrons are not as free to move in this direction. When averaged over all possible orientations, the effect is a net diamagnetic shielding.

FIGURE 13.33 Shielding of acetylenic protons by a triple bond perpendicular to the applied field.

In the alkene case, the long-range effect of the anisotropic C=C π-electrons has the effect of deshielding the vinyl hydrogens. It therefore *augments* the inductive effect of the somewhat electronegative sp^2-hybridized alkene carbon. In the alkyne case, the long-range effect of the C≡C π-electrons *diminishes* the normal inductive effect. As a result of these two opposing effects, the resonance positions of acetylenic protons are similar to those of alkane protons. Similar effects operate on hydrogens bound to carbons adjacent to triple bonds, causing them to resonate about 1 ppm downfield from the corresponding alkane position.

The NMR spectra of 3,3-dimethyl-1-butyne and 1-hexyne are shown in Figures 13.34 and 13.35. Note that in the spectrum of 1-hexyne, the alkyne proton ($\delta = 1.7$ ppm) appears as a triplet with $J = 2.5$ Hz. This small splitting is the result of **long-range coupling** through the triple bond. Although coupling through more than three bonds is not usually observed in alkanes, small four-bond and five-bond coupling is frequently seen in alkenes and alkynes. In these cases, the coupling occurs through the π-electrons of the multiple bond.

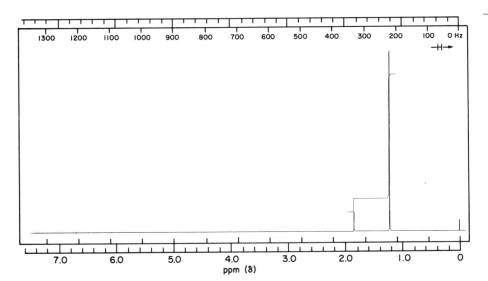

FIGURE 13.34 NMR spectrum of 3,3-dimethyl-1-butyne.

FIGURE 13.35 NMR spectrum of 1-hexyne.

EXERCISE 13.9 An unknown hydrocarbon is found to have the formula C_6H_{10}. Its NMR spectrum shows a three-proton triplet ($J = 6.5$ Hz) at 0.9 ppm, a three-proton doublet ($J = 6.6$ Hz) at 1.1 ppm, a two-proton multiplet at 1.5 ppm, a one-proton doublet ($J = 2.3$ Hz) at 1.8 ppm, and a one-proton multiplet at 2.3 ppm. Suggest a structure for the compound.

13.10 Dynamical Systems

In our discussion of the NMR spectrum of 1,2,2-trichloropropane (Section 13.4) it seemed quite natural to expect both hydrogens in the methylene group to absorb in the same place because they appear to be equivalent. However, if we examine the structure

330

Chap. 13

*Nuclear
Magnetic
Resonance
Spectroscopy*

in more detail, this equivalence is not so apparent. The compound actually exists as an equilibrium mixture of three conformations, symbolized by the following Newman projections.

In structure A hydrogens H_a and H_b are clearly equivalent, but this is not the case in B and C. For example, in conformation B H_b is flanked by two chlorines and would be expected to be deshielded relative to H_a. Why, then, do we not see two or more peaks for these hydrogens?

The answer comes from the Heisenberg uncertainty principle of quantum mechanics. One expression of this principle is

$$\Delta E \, \Delta t \cong h/2\pi \qquad \text{or} \qquad \Delta \nu \, \Delta t \cong 1/2\pi \quad \text{(since } \Delta E = h\Delta\nu)$$

where $\Delta\nu$ and Δt are the uncertainties in energy and time in units of Hertz and seconds, respectively. That is, we cannot know precisely both the energy and the lifetime of a given state. The longer-lived the state, the more precisely can its energy content be evaluated. In NMR, as in the case of 1,2,2-trichloropropane, suppose that $\delta(H_a)$ and $\delta(H_b)$ differ by 1 ppm. This amount in a 180-MHz instrument corresponds to an energy difference of 180 Hz or 18×10^{-9} cal mole^{-1}, an exceedingly small energy quantity. In order to measure this small difference for H_a and H_b as separate states, they would have to have lifetimes in each conformation of at least

$$\Delta t \cong 1/(2\pi \, \Delta E) = 1/(2\pi \cdot 180) = 0.00088 \text{ sec}$$

But with an energy barrier of only 3-4 kcal mole^{-1} between one conformer and another, the average lifetime of a given conformation is only about 10^{-10} to 10^{-11} sec! (See Section 5.2.) In other words, the lifetime of a given methylene hydrogen in the magnetic environment of a given conformation is too short to permit us to distinguish it from the other methylene hydrogen. The "state" measured in a NMR spectrometer is a weighted average of all of the rotational conformations. The energy differences measured in NMR are so small that one frequently refers to the "NMR time scale," a time period ranging from milliseconds to seconds.

To summarize, a consequence of the Heisenberg uncertainty principle and the small energy changes characteristic of NMR spectroscopy is that two hydrogen states that are interconvertible but have separate lifetimes of more than about 1 sec can be seen as two sharp peaks whose separation can be measured accurately. If the lifetimes are less than about 1 msec, they can be seen only as a combined single sharp peak; that is, on the "NMR time scale" the two hydrogens are **magnetically equivalent**. If the lifetimes are in an intermediate region, a broad peak results.

The foregoing discussion shows why the NMR sample tube is spun rapidly between the magnet faces. It is difficult to prevent slight changes in a magnetic field at different places. In a tube placed between the pole faces of even high-quality magnets, different protons would experience slightly different fields at different points. The result would be a rather broad NMR signal. Rapid spinning of the tube causes all of the protons to experience the same average field *on the NMR time scale*. It is also clear why the normal tumbling and rotation of molecules results in our seeing only a time-averaged spectrum (page 327), since such molecular motions are exceedingly rapid relative to the NMR time scale.

Reactions that have half-lives of the order of minutes or hours can generally be determined without difficulty. Faster reactions, with half-lives of the order of seconds, can frequently be measured with careful work. Nuclear magnetic resonance spectroscopy provides an excellent extension for determining rates of reactions having half-lives in the NMR time scale of about 0.001 to 1 sec. The chair-chair interconversion of cyclohexane provides an example of the type of techniques used. At room temperature cyclohexane gives a sharp singlet. The rate of chair-chair interconversion is so fast that NMR measures only the average state of the axial and equatorial hydrogens. However, at sufficiently low temperature, $< -70°C$, the rate of interconversion is so slow that the molecular state measured by NMR is a single conformation.

In one chair conformation, all equatorial hydrogens are equivalent but different from the axial hydrogens. The two sets of hydrogens have different chemical shifts and give rise to two broad bands separated by $\delta = 0.5$ ppm with $\delta_{equatorial} > \delta_{axial}$. The bands are broad because of J-splittings between the two sets of protons. The NMR spectrum of cyclohexane-d_{11} is a simpler case to interpret because the J-coupling between the proton nucleus and a deuteron is rather small (on the order of 15% of the corresponding H-H coupling), and each cyclohexane molecule now has only a single proton. The NMR spectrum is reproduced in Figure 13.36 as a function of temperature. At the

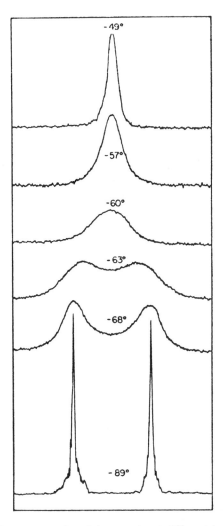

FIGURE 13.36 NMR spectrum of cyclohexane-d_{11} at different temperatures. [Reproduced with permission from F. A. Bovey, *Nuclear Magnetic Resonance Spectroscopy*, Academic Press, New York, 1969.]

332

Chap. 13

Nuclear
Magnetic
Resonance
Spectroscopy

lowest temperature (−89°C) half of the deuteriated cyclohexane molecules have their lone proton in an axial position and the other half have the proton equatorial. Interconversion of the two isomers is slow, and since the chemical shifts differ, we see two sharp singlets. At the highest temperature (−49°C) the ring interconversions are rapid, and the NMR spectrometer "sees" only a time-average position, a singlet with δ midway between δ_{axial} and $\delta_{equatorial}$. At intermediate temperatures, the rate of interconversion of the conformations is comparable to the frequency difference between the states, and a broad signal results. The results can be analyzed completely to give rate constants as a function of temperature and an enthalpy of activation, $\Delta H^{\ddagger}$, of 10.8 kcal mole^{-1}. This value is relatively high compared to other conformational interchanges we have studied. The transition state involves a partially planar cyclohexane that has both bond angle strain and eclipsed hydrogen strain.

EXERCISE 13.10   1,3,5-Trioxane exists in a chair conformation similar to that of cyclohexane.

$$H_2C \overset{\displaystyle O}{\underset{\displaystyle O \overset{\displaystyle C}{\underset{\displaystyle H_2}{}} O}{}} CH_2$$

What is the expected appearance of its NMR spectrum at room temperature and −100°C?

13.11 Chemical Exchange of Hydrogens Bonded to Oxygen

Alcohols and ethers often have hydrogens attached to a carbon bearing an electronegative atom (oxygen). Thus, we expect to find resonance of such protons downfield from normal alkane protons, as in the case of alkyl halides. Indeed, we have already seen an example of such a spectrum (Figures 13.20 and 13.21). A further example is seen in the spectrum of diisopropyl ether (Figure 13.37).

FIGURE 13.37   NMR spectrum of diisopropyl ether, $(CH_3)_2CHOCH(CH_3)_2$.

333

Sec. 13.11

*Chemical
Exchange of
Hydrogens
Bonded to
Oxygen*

EXERCISE 13.11 Using the simplified prescription that you learned in Section 13.6 for predicting the multiplicity of NMR resonances, predict the number of peaks and relative intensities expected for the C—H resonance in diisopropyl ether. Assuming $J = 6$ Hz, plot the expected appearance of the multiplet on graph paper. Compare your predicted spectrum with Figure 13.37.

The hydroxy proton itself shows more complex behavior. In dilute solutions of rigorously purified alcohols, the hydroxy proton shows normal splitting by adjacent carbinol protons. Under these conditions, the proton exchange caused by autoprotolysis is sufficiently slow that a given proton is associated with a given oxygen on the NMR time scale. However, the protons are still hydrogen bonded, and this leads to deshielding. The spectrum of pure ethyl alcohol in Figure 13.38 is illustrative. Note that the H—C—C—H and the H—C—O—H couplings have different magnitudes. The CH$_2$ resonance appears as a complex multiplet rather than a simple quartet.

FIGURE 13.38 NMR spectrum of pure ethyl alcohol.

FIGURE 13.39 NMR spectrum of ethyl alcohol containing 1% formic acid.

334

Chap. 13

Nuclear
Magnetic
Resonance
Spectroscopy

Traces of acid or base cause the resonance of the hydroxy proton to collapse to a sharp singlet (see Figure 13.39). In such cases proton exchange is rapid on the NMR time scale, and the "state" observed is that of a proton in a weighted average of a number of environments. The situation may be thought of in the following way. Imagine that the proton jumps rapidly from one oxygen to another during the time that the NMR measurement is carried out. In its first environment, the spins of the adjacent CH_2 may be $\alpha\alpha$, in the second they may be $\beta\beta$, in the third $\beta\alpha$, in the fourth $\alpha\beta$, and so on. Thus, the average environment will be one in which the effects of the spins of CH_2 cancel, and no spin-spin splitting is observed.

When an alcohol is diluted by an inert solvent, its hydroxy proton resonance shifts to higher field because hydrogen bonding becomes less important (Figure 13.40). In very dilute solutions the hydroxy proton may resonate as high as 0.5 ppm. However, because of a combination of hydrogen bonding and some exchange, the hydroxy proton is often observed as a broad featureless peak at a position varying from 2 to 4.5 ppm. The

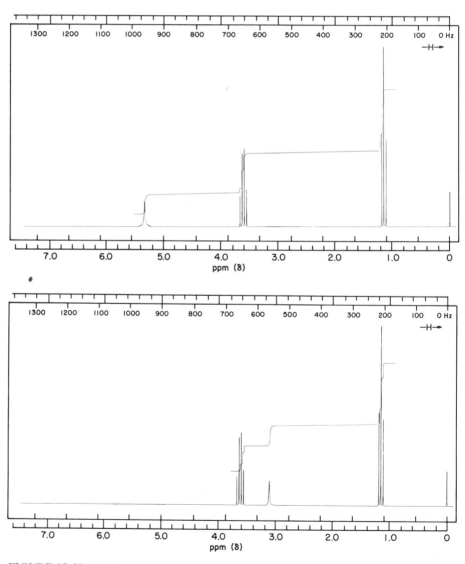

FIGURE 13.40 NMR spectra of ethyl alcohol in carbon tetrachloride. The ethyl alcohol concentration in the top spectrum is 1.0 M; in the bottom 0.1 M.

FIGURE 13.41 NMR spectrum of ethyl alcohol in carbon tetrachloride. The solution was shaken with D_2O and the layers were separated before the spectrum was measured.

exact appearance and position depend on the solvent, purity, temperature, and structure. One simple diagnosis for an OH group is the addition of D_2O to the NMR solution. Rapid exchange replaces the OH groups by OD and the NMR signal for OH vanishes or becomes less intense (Figure 13.41).

EXERCISE 13.12 The CH_2 resonance of ethyl alcohol is a double quartet with coupling constants of $J = 5$ and 7 Hz. Using graph paper, plot the expected appearance of such a double quartet. Remember that a simple doublet has relative intensities of 1:1 and a simple quartet has relative intensities of 1:3:3:1. What would be the appearance of the CH_2 resonance if the two Js were equal?

EXERCISE 13.13 Plot the expected appearance of the NMR spectrum of pure isopropyl alcohol. Assume that the coupling constants are 5 and 7 Hz, as they are in ethyl alcohol.

13.12 Carbon NMR Spectroscopy

Up until now, we only have discussed proton NMR. However, nuclear magnetic resonance experiments may be done with any element whose nuclei have a net magnetic spin. A few examples are given in Table 13.2. In addition to ${}^{1}H$ NMR, ${}^{19}F$ NMR and ${}^{13}C$ NMR are used extensively. Carbon NMR (CMR) is of particular value in organic chemistry. While proton NMR allows us to "see" the protons attached to the carbon framework of an organic compound, CMR allows us to see the carbons themselves. Therefore, CMR is a perfect complement to proton NMR in solving structural problems.

There is one important difference between proton NMR and CMR. In proton NMR, we are observing the most abundant isotope, ${}^{1}H$. For carbon, the most abundant isotope, ${}^{12}C$, has an even-even nucleus that has no net nuclear spin or magnetic moment. Therefore, we must observe the isotope ${}^{13}C$, which has a natural abundance of only

336

Chap. 13

*Nuclear
Magnetic
Resonance
Spectroscopy*

TABLE 13.2 The Magnetic Properties of Some Nuclei

Isotope	Natural Abundance, %	Spin States	Resonance Frequency at 42,276 Gauss, MHz
^1H	99.88	$\pm\frac{1}{2}$	180
^{13}C	1.1	$\pm\frac{1}{2}$	45.3
^{19}F	100	$\pm\frac{1}{2}$	169.2
^{31}P	100	$\pm\frac{1}{2}$	73.2

about 1%. This low abundance is both a blessing and a curse. A simplifying feature is that since the natural abundance of ^{13}C is so low, the chance that we will find two ^{13}C nuclei adjacent to each other in the same molecule is very small ($10^{-2} \times 10^{-2} = 10^{-4}$). Therefore, *we do not observe spin-spin splitting between the carbon nuclei.* However, the low abundance means that we must use a larger sample than is normally required for proton NMR. Whereas an excellent proton NMR spectrum can usually be obtained with 0.1–1 mg of sample, something on the order of 5–10 mg is required to obtain a CMR spectrum of comparable quality.

Figure 13.42 shows the CMR spectrum of 2-butanol. The spectrum was measured with a spectrometer operating at a field strength of 58,717 gauss, which corresponds to a frequency of 62.5 MHz for ^{13}C. The spectrum was determined by a method called "proton off-resonance decoupling." In this mode of operation one observes only one-bond couplings, that is, ^{13}C—H, and these are reduced in magnitude by a considerable factor. Two-bond couplings, ^{13}C—C—H, are not observed.

In the spectrum in Figure 13.42 note that we see four signals corresponding to the four carbon atoms. The 1:1:1 triplet at $\delta = 76$ ppm is due to the carbon of $CDCl_3$, the solvent. Deuterium, ^2H, has three spin states, -1, 0, and $+1$. Thus, it splits a coupled resonance into a 1:1:1 triplet. The four carbon atoms in 2-butanol appear as a doublet, triplet, and two quartets due to spin-spin splitting by their attached hydrogens (one, two, and three, respectively). As in proton NMR, the electronegative oxygen causes C-2 to resonate downfield from the other carbons. Note that the chemical shifts in

FIGURE 13.42 CMR spectrum of 2-butanol.

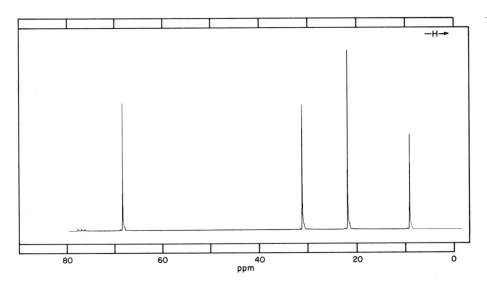

FIGURE 13.43 Proton-decoupled CMR spectrum of 2-butanol.

CMR are much greater than in proton NMR; in this example, they range from $\delta = 10.2$ ppm for C-4 to $\delta = 69.0$ for C-2.

The spectrum in Figure 13.43 is also of 2-butanol, but in this case the spectrum was measured while simultaneously applying a strong radio frequency field of 250 MHz. The irradiating field is not a sharp signal, but has a sufficient bandwidth that it covers the resonance frequencies of all of the protons in the molecule, which resonate at about 250 MHz at 58,727 gauss. Since the hydrogen nuclei are being constantly excited, they do not spend sufficient time in either the α- or β-spin state to couple with the ^{13}C nuclei. That is, on the NMR time scale each hydrogen is in an average or effectively constant state, and the result is that no coupling is observed. This process is called **decoupling,** and the spectrum in Figure 13.43 is said to be **proton-decoupled.** Each carbon nucleus now appears as a sharp singlet and the entire spectrum is greatly simplified.

For structure work, it is convenient to obtain both types of spectra. For complex molecules the proton-decoupled spectrum often allows one to "see" each carbon resonance and to measure its chemical shift accurately. This type of spectrum is especially useful for *counting the number of different carbons in a molecule*. The proton-coupled spectrum then allows the analyst to determine the number of hydrogens attached to each carbon. By using these data together with the proton NMR spectrum, even complex structures may be solved.

Because of their simplicity, proton-decoupled CMR spectra are particularly suited for detecting symmetry in fairly complicated molecules. For example, Figures 13.44 and 13.45 are the proton-decoupled spectra of the two diastereomers of 1,3,5-trimethylcyclohexane.

1-*cis*,3-*cis*,5-trimethylcyclohexane   1-*cis*,3-*trans*,5-trimethylcyclohexane

338

Chap. 13

*Nuclear
Magnetic
Resonance
Spectroscopy*

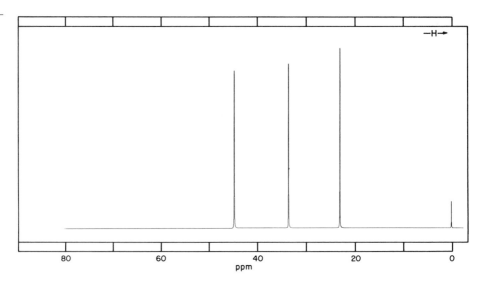

FIGURE 13.44 CMR spectrum of 1-*cis*,3-*cis*,5-trimethylcyclohexane.

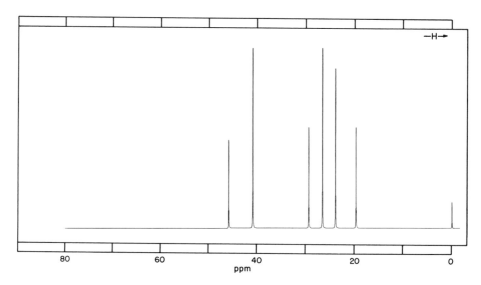

FIGURE 13.45 CMR spectrum of 1-*cis*,3-*trans*,5-trimethylcyclohexane.

Note that the CMR spectrum of one of the isomers shows only three resonances. This must be the isomer in which all methyl groups are cis. Since all of the methyl groups occupy equatorial positions, there is only one kind of CH_3 resonance. Likewise, there are only one kind of CH_2 and only one kind of CH. In the other diastereomer the two equatorial methyls are equivalent, but the axial one gives rise to a different resonance. Similarly, this isomer has two different kinds of CH_2 resonance and two different kinds of CH resonance. Note that the six resonances of this molecule occur in three sets with the relative intensities being 2:1 in each set.

EXERCISE 13.14 A compound known to be one of the stereoisomeric 1,5-dichloro-2,4-dimethyl-3-pentanols is found to have a four-signal CMR spectrum. Write the structures of the four stereoisomers and indicate which are eliminated by the CMR spectrum.

As in proton NMR spectra, the resonance frequencies in CMR spectra are influenced by the nature and number of substituents attached to the carbon under observation. However, simple alkyl substitution has a much greater effect on CMR resonance than it does on proton NMR resonances. Notice the chemical shifts of the simple alkanes tabulated in the first four lines of Table 13.3. The chemical shift of methane is −2.1 ppm (that is, CH_4 resonates 2.1 ppm *upfield* from the reference compound TMS). In ethane, the chemical shift of the two equivalent CH_3 carbons is 5.9 ppm. Thus, replacement of a hydrogen by a methyl group causes a *downfield* shift of 8.0 ppm. Further replacement of hydrogens by methyl groups, as in the central carbons of propane and isobutane, results in further downfield shifts of 10.2 and 9.1 ppm. This regular substituent effect is called an "α-effect" and is usually taken to have the value +9 ppm. This empirical value carries over to other classes of compounds as well, and can be of great use in *predicting* the approximate resonance positions of carbons in compounds for which data are not available.

EXERCISE 13.15 Methanol resonates at 49.3 ppm. Estimate the chemical shift of the alcohol carbon in ethanol, 2-propanol, and 2-methyl-2-propanol. Compare your estimates with the values given in Table 13.4. Note that your estimates are only approximate.

Another difference between CMR and proton NMR chemical shifts is the rather large effect that results from substitution at the adjacent carbon and at the position one carbon removed from that under observation. For example, compare the chemical shifts of the methyl resonances in ethane (5.9 ppm) and propane (15.6 ppm). There is a downfield shift of 9.7 ppm as a result of replacing a hydrogen *on an adjacent carbon* by a methyl group. This "β-effect" may also be seen in the shift of the methyl resonance of isobutane (24.3 ppm). Thus, replacement of a second hydrogen by a methyl group results in a further downfield shift of 8.7 ppm. The β-effect is usually taken to have the value +9.5 ppm.

Finally, examination of the chemical shifts tabulated in Table 13.3 reveals that there is a γ-effect that results in an *upfield* shift of 2-3 ppm. It may be seen clearly in the C-1 resonance of propane and butane and the C-4 resonance of isopentane. The γ-effect is usually taken to have the value −2.5 ppm.

TABLE 13.3 CMR Chemical Shifts for Alkanes

	C-1	C-2	C-3	C-4	C-5	C-6	Other
methane	−2.1						
ethane	5.9	5.9					
propane	15.6	16.1	15.6				
isobutane	24.3	25.2	24.3				
neopentane	31.5	27.9	31.5				
n-butane	13.2	25.0	25.0	13.2			
2-methylbutane	22.0	29.9	31.8	11.5			
2,3-dimethylbutane	19.3	34.1	34.1	19.3			
2,2,3-trimethylbutane	27.2	32.9	38.1	15.9			
n-pentane	13.7	22.6	34.5	22.6	13.7		
2-methylpentane	22.5	27.8	41.8	20.7	14.1		
3-methylpentane	11.3	29.3	36.7	29.3	11.3		18.6[a]
3,3-dimethylpentane	6.8	25.1	36.1	25.1	6.8		4.4[a]
n-hexane	13.9	22.9	32.0	32.0	22.9	13.9	

[a] C-3 methyl carbon(s).

340

Chap. 13

Nuclear
Magnetic
Resonance
Spectroscopy

Let us see how these empirical substituent effects might be useful. Suppose we want to predict the chemical shifts of the various carbon resonances in the CMR spectrum of 2-methylhexane. We may do this by adding the appropriate substituent corrections (α-, β-, and γ-effects) to the known chemical shifts of the various carbons of *n*-hexane (Table 13.3). The calculation is illustrated below.

Estimation of CMR Chemical Shifts for 2-Methylhexane

Carbon	Chemical Shift in *n*-Hexane	Correction	Estimated Chemical Shift in 2-Methylhexane	Actual Chemical Shift in 2-Methylhexane
1	13.9	β, +9.5	23.4	22.4
2	22.9	α, +9.0	31.9	28.1
3	32.0	β, +9.5	41.5	38.9
4	32.0	γ, −2.5	29.5	29.7
5	22.9	none	22.9	23.0
6	13.9	none	13.9	13.6

Although such estimates are admittedly crude, they are useful in assigning observed resonances to the proper carbons, and in some cases they may be useful in assigning a structure to a compound from its CMR spectrum.

> **EXERCISE 13.16** Predict the resonance frequencies of the seven carbons in 3-methylhexane.

Table 13.4 summarizes the CMR chemical shifts for some simple alcohols. By comparing these data with those given for alkanes in Table 13.3, it may be seen that the hydroxy group causes a large downfield shift of the carbon to which it is attached. This OH α-effect is generally taken to be +48 ppm. The β- and γ-effects are about the same as for a methyl group, +9.5 ppm and −2.5 ppm, respectively.

Carbon NMR is also a useful tool for the analysis of alkenes. Chemical shifts for some simple alkenes are collected in Table 13.5. Comparison of this table with Table 13.3 shows that sp^2-hybridized carbons resonate 90-120 ppm downfield from sp^3-hybridized carbons having the same degree of substitution. Substituent effects are about the same as for alkanes, with one significant exception. The γ-effect is highly dependent on the steric relationship between the carbon being observed and the substituent. For example, the CH_3 resonances in *cis*- and *trans*-2-butene occur at 11.4 and 16.8

TABLE 13.4 CMR Chemical Shifts for Some Alcohols

	C-1	C-2	C-3	C-4	C-5
methanol	49.3				
ethanol	57.3	17.9			
1-propanol	63.9	26.1	10.3		
2-propanol	25.4	63.7	25.4		
1-butanol	61.7	35.3	19.4	13.9	
2-butanol	22.9	69.0	32.3	10.2	
2-methyl-1-propanol	69.2	31.1	19.2		
2-methyl-2-propanol	31.6	68.7	31.6		
1-pentanol	62.1	32.8	28.5	22.9	14.1
2-pentanol	23.6	67.3	41.9	19.4	14.3
3-pentanol	10.1	30.0	74.1	30.0	10.1

TABLE 13.5 CMR Chemical Shifts for Alkenes

	C-1	C-2	C-3	C-4	C-5	C-6
propene	115.4	135.7	18.7			
1-butene	112.8	140.2	23.8	9.3		
cis-2-butene	11.4	124.2	124.2	11.4		
trans-2-butene	16.8	125.4	125.4	16.8		
1-pentene	114.3	138.9	36.0	22.1	13.6	
cis-2-pentene	12.0	122.8	132.4	20.3	13.8	
trans-2-pentene	17.3	123.6	133.2	25.8	13.6	
1-hexene	114.1	139.1	33.6	31.2	22.2	13.9
cis-2-hexene	12.3	123.7	130.6	29.3	23.0	13.5
trans-2-hexene	17.5	124.7	131.5	35.1	23.1	13.4
cis-3-hexene	14.3	20.6	131.0	131.0	20.6	14.3
trans-3-hexene	13.9	25.8	131.2	131.2	25.8	13.9

ppm, respectively. In essence, each methyl in the cis isomer is exerting a γ-effect of
−5.4 on the other.

The appearance of alkene CMR spectra is shown in Figures 13.46 (1-octene) and 13.47
(*trans*-4-octene). Note that *trans*-4-octene shows only four resonances because of the
symmetry of the molecule. In both spectra the small 1:1:1 triplet at about 76 ppm is
caused by $CDCl_3$, the solvent.

Proton NMR and CMR are the preferred techniques for detecting the presence of a
carbon-carbon double bond in a molecule and for deducing something about its nature.
The low-field resonances of vinyl hydrogens in the NMR spectrum ($\delta \cong 5$ ppm) and of
olefinic carbons in the CMR spectrum ($\delta \cong 110\text{-}140$ ppm) are used to deduce the

FIGURE 13.46 CMR spectrum of 1-octene.

342

Chap. 13

_Nuclear
Magnetic
Resonance
Spectroscopy_

FIGURE 13.47 CMR spectrum of _trans_-4-octene.

presence of a double bond. The magnitudes of the NMR coupling constants and of the
γ-effects in the CMR spectra are diagnostic of the stereostructure of the alkene.

> **EXERCISE 13.17** Explain how CMR spectroscopy can be used to distinguish between
> (_E_)- and (_Z_)-3-methyl-3-pentene.

> **EXERCISE 13.18** Sketch the expected CMR spectrum of cycloheptene.

13.13 Solving Spectral Problems

We can now apply our knowledge to interpret the spectra of the propyl chlorides
introduced in Section 13.2. In the NMR spectrum of _n_-propyl chloride (Figure 13.2),
for example, the methyl group is clearly distinguished as the group furthest upfield
($\delta = 1.2$), split into a triplet by its neighboring methylene group. The chlorine-bearing
methylene group is furthest downfield ($\delta = 3.6$), also split into a triplet by its neighboring methylene group. The center methylene group is expected to be split into a
quartet by the adjacent methyl and into a triplet by the adjacent methylene. If these two
interactions had different _J_ values, we would indeed see a total of twelve lines under
sufficient resolution. However, because the two _J_ values are approximately the same
(note that the CH_3 quartet and the CH_2Cl triplet have approximately equal splittings),
the splitting in the middle CH_2 group is that expected for five magnetically equivalent
hydrogens, namely six peaks.

The spectrum of 2-chloropropane in Figure 13.3 is simpler. The two methyl groups
are equivalent and appear as a pair of superimposed doublets because of coupling to the
C-2 hydrogen. They have a combined area six times that of the downfield resonance of
the single C-2 hydrogen. The downfield position of $\delta = 4.05$ ppm results from the
deshielding effect of the neighboring electronegative chlorine. This peak is split into
seven peaks by the six adjacent methyl hydrogens. The theoretical relative intensities
of such a septet are 1:6:15:20:15:6:1 (Table 13.1). Thus, it is difficult to see the two
weak outer lines.

Proton and carbon NMR spectroscopy are now the primary methods whereby the structures of organic compounds are determined. Spectra are deduced from a consideration of several important spectral features. From the CMR spectrum, we can usually determine the number of carbons in the molecule. In addition, from the general resonance positions, we can often deduce the presence of functional groups. Furthermore, when we know the number of carbons from some other piece of data (such as elemental analysis), the appearance of fewer than the expected number of lines in the CMR spectrum often allows us to infer molecular symmetry.

A simple example will illustrate the use of CMR spectroscopy in solving a structure problem. Let us assume that we subject 3-hexanol to boiling sulfuric acid and isolate a mixture of isomeric alkenes.

The isomers are separated by preparative gas chromatography and the CMR spectra are measured. The data are as follows:

isomer A: 12.3, 13.5, 23.0, 29.3, 123.7, 130.6
isomer B: 13.4, 17.5, 23.1, 35.1, 124.7, 131.5
isomer C: 14.3, 20.6, 131.0
isomer D: 13.9, 25.8, 131.2

We can immediately deduce that isomers C and D are the two 3-hexenes, from the fact that each shows only three resonances. In these spectra, the resonances at about 131 ppm are clearly the double bond carbons and the resonances at about 14 ppm are probably the methyl carbons. However, note that the C-2 carbon resonances differ by about 5 ppm. This is exactly what we expect for the γ-effect in a pair of cis-trans isomers; we can confidently deduce that isomer C (with the upfield C-2) must be the cis isomer. Similar arguments can be used to deduce that isomer A is *cis*-2-hexene and isomer B is *trans*-2-hexene. Note in isomer A, two of the resonances are about 5 ppm upfield of their counterparts in isomer B (35.1 compared to 29.3, 17.5 compared to 12.3).

It is important to reiterate that it is not necessary to memorize a lot of chemical shift information to use CMR spectroscopy. It is only necessary to remember that double-bonded carbons resonate far downfield and that carbons bonded to halogen or oxygen resonate moderately far downfield. When we know enough about the possible structure of the unknown sample, as in the example just given, it is often possible to determine the structure completely from the CMR spectrum. However, in other cases we only derive partial information—pertaining to the carbon skeleton and the functional groups that are present.

In proton NMR we look at the resonance positions (chemical shifts) and spin-spin splitting patterns for structural information. Again, it is not recommended that the student try to memorize a lot of precise chemical shift information. Rather, the practicing chemist usually thinks of the NMR spectral chart as a sort of football field. We remember that alkanes tend to resonate around the 10 or 20 yard line on the right side,

344

Chap. 13

Nuclear
Magnetic
Resonance
Spectroscopy

while protons attached to carbons that also bear an electronegative group (Cl, Br, OH) and vinyl protons resonate near midfield. It is also useful to remember that inductive deshielding effects are cumulative—when there are more halogens or oxygens, the C—H resonance can move over midfield into the other end of the field. If more precise chemical shift information is desirable, the practicing chemist refers to compilations of data.

The most useful aspect of proton NMR is undoubtedly spin-spin splitting. From this complication, we are often able to deduce the relative placements of most or all of the hydrogens in the molecule. It is important to remember that, when we look at a multiplet, we are not evaluating the hydrogens that actually give rise to the resonance, but rather *the neighboring hydrogens*. For example, the student should learn to associate a triplet with a proton (or protons) that has two neighboring hydrogens. A few common multiplets, with the types of structures that give rise to them, are shown in Figure 13.48.

An example of the way in which proton NMR data are frequently presented and a structural problem is solved is shown in the following example. Assume that an unknown compound is found to have the formula $C_4H_7Cl_3$ and the following proton NMR spectrum.

$$\delta, \text{ppm: } 0.9 \text{ (t, 3H); } 1.7 \text{ (m, 2H); } 4.3 \text{ (m, 1H); } 5.8 \text{ (d, 1H)}$$

In this shorthand the δ value in ppm is given for the center of a multiplet. The number of peaks in the multiplet is indicated by the code: s = singlet, d = doublet, t = triplet.

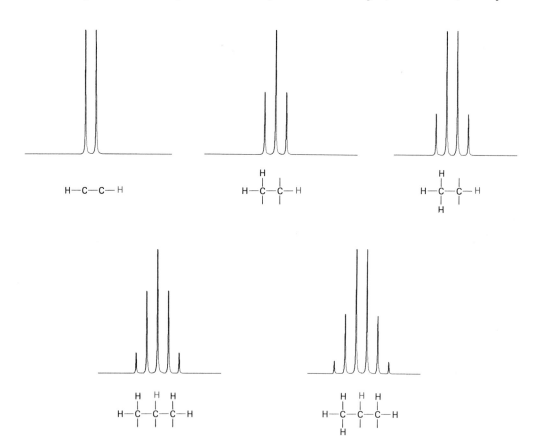

FIGURE 13.48 Common NMR multiplets.

Quartet and quintet are obvious, but it may not always be possible to resolve all of these peaks, and such multiple peak groups are frequently recorded as m = multiplet. Finally, the number of hydrogens represented by each multiplet as determined from the integral line is indicated.

To solve the problem shown, we generate hypotheses of structural units from the information given about δ values and put the units together with the help of the splitting information. The three-proton triplet with $\delta = 0.9$ ppm clearly corresponds to a methyl group; both the number of hydrogens and the upfield resonance position fit this hypothesis. The one-proton doublet at $\delta = 5.8$ ppm is so far downfield it must correspond to $CHCl_2$. Its multiplicity tells us that it has only one neighboring H. The one-proton multiplet with $\delta = 4.3$ ppm is probably H—C—Cl. We are left with a two-proton multiplet at rather high field ($\delta = 1.7$ ppm); this must be from a CH_2 group. Our structural units are therefore CH_3, CH_2, CHCl, and $CHCl_2$. Since the methyl group is a triplet, it must be attached to the CH_2 group. Since $CHCl_2$ is a doublet, it must be attached to CHCl. The entire structure then becomes

CH_3—CH_2—CHCl—$CHCl_2$

the compound is 1,1,2-trichlorobutane. The CH_2 and CHCl protons give rise to complex multiplets because of the unequal coupling constants to their adjacent neighbors (see Figure 13.25).

The foregoing example illustrates the power of NMR spectroscopy in deducing structure and exemplifies the general approach to be used. In working actual problems look first for methyl groups—they are common in organic structures and are frequently readily recognizable since they are generally the furthest upfield and often occur as sharp peaks even when the compound contains several types of methylene groups and complex multiplets in the 1–2 ppm region. Downfield peaks next help to identify protons on double bonds or near electronegative functions. The molecular formula as given by combustion analysis tells us whether multiple bonds are likely to be present and which electronegative elements to account for. When these resonances are identified and their splittings are analyzed many structural problems are essentially solved.

EXERCISE 13.19 The proton NMR spectra of several $C_5H_{10}Br_2$ isomers are summarized below. Deduce the structure of each compound.

(a) δ, 1.0 (s, 6H); 3.4 (s, 4H)

(b) δ, 1.0 (t, 6H); 2.4 (quart, 4H)

(c) δ, 0.9 (d, 6H); 1.5 (m, 1H); 1.85 (t, 2H); 5.3 (t, 1H)

(d) δ, 1.0 (s, 9H); 5.3 (s, 1H)

(e) δ, 1.0 (d, 6H); 1.75 (m, 1H); 3.95 (d, 2H); 4.7 (quart, 1H)

(f) δ, 1.3 (m, 2H); 1.85 (m, 4H); 3.35 (t, 4H)

PROBLEMS

1. Fill in the blank spaces in the following statement

In the NMR spectrum of ethyl bromide, the methyl hydrogens have $\delta = 1.7$ ppm, the methylene hydrogens have $\delta = 3.3$ ppm, and J = 7 Hz. The number of peaks given by the methyl hydrogens is _____ with the approximate area ratio: _____. These peaks are separated from one another by _____ Hz. The number of peaks given by the methylene hydrogens is _____ with the approximate area ratio: _____. These peaks are separated by _____ Hz. The total area of the methyl peaks compared to the methylene peaks is in the ratio: _____. Of these two groups of peaks, the _____ peaks are further downfield. The chemical shift differ-

346

Chap. 13

*Nuclear
Magnetic
Resonance
Spectroscopy*

ence between these peaks of 1.6 ppm corresponds in a 180-MHz instrument to _____ Hz and in a 250-MHz instrument to _____ Hz.

2. The NMR spectra for some isomers having the formula $C_4H_{10}O$ are summarized as follows. Deduce the structure of each compound.
   (a) δ, 0.95 (t, 3H); 1.52 (sextet, 2H); 3.30 (s, 3H); 3.40 (t, 2H)
   (b) δ, 1.15 (s, 1H); 1.28 (s, 9H)
   (c) δ, 1.20 (t, 3H); 3.45 (quartet, 2H)
   (d) δ, 0.90 (d, 6H); 1.78 (m, 1H); 2.45 (t, 1H); 3.30 (t, 2H)
   (e) δ, 1.13 (d, 6H); 3.30 (s, 3H); 3.65 (septet, 1H)
   (f) δ, 0.95 (t, 3H); 1.50 (m, 4H); 2.20 (t, 1H); 3.70 (dt, 2H)
   (g) δ, 0.92 (t, 3H); 1.18 (d, 3H); 1.45 (m, 2H); 1.80 (d, 1H); 3.75 (multiplet, 1H)

3. Free radical chlorination of propane using 1 mole of C_3H_8 and 2 moles of Cl_2 gives a complex mixture of chlorination products. By careful fractional distillation of the product mixture, one may isolate four dichloropropanes, A, B, C, and D. From the NMR spectra of the four isomers, deduce their structures.

   isomer A: (b.p. 69°C) δ 2.4 (s, 6H)
   isomer B: (b.p. 88°C) δ 1.2 (t, 3H), 1.9 (quintet, 2H), 5.8 (t, 1H)
   isomer C: (b.p. 96°C) δ 1.4 (d, 3H), 3.8 (d, 2H), 4.3 (sextet, 1H)
   isomer D: (b.p. 120°C) δ 2.2 (quintet, 2H), 3.7 (t, 4H)

4. There are nine possible isomers (not counting stereoisomers) of $C_4H_8Br_2$. Two of them have the following NMR spectra. Deduce the structures of each and indicate the logic used in your assignment.
   (a) δ 1.7 (d, 6H), 4.4 (quart, 2H)
   (b) δ 1.7 (d, 3H), 2.3 (quart, 2H), 3.5 (t, 2H), 4.2 (m, 1H)

5. Sketch the expected NMR spectra of the following compounds. Be sure to represent the approximate δ expected for each group of peaks, the relative areas, and the splittings.
   (a) $CH_3CBr_2CH_3$ (b) CH_3CH_2Br
   (c) $CH_3CHBrCHBrCH_3$ (d) $CH_3CBr_2CH_2CH_3$
   (e) $CH_3CHClCH_2CH_2Cl$

6. A compound having the formula $C_5H_{10}Br_2$ has a proton-coupled CMR spectrum consisting of a doublet, a triplet, and a quartet. What is its structure?

7. Free radical chlorination of (R)-2-chlorobutane gives a mixture of isomeric products that is subjected to careful fractional distillation. Five different dichlorobutanes are obtained. For each compound, the optical rotation and the CMR spectrum are measured. The following results are obtained.

   isomers E and F: optically active; CMR, 4 resonances
   isomer G: optically active; CMR, 2 resonances
   isomer H: optically inactive; CMR, 4 resonances
   isomer I: optically inactive; CMR, 2 resonances

   From these data, make whatever structural assignments are possible.

8. Deduce the structure corresponding to each of the following NMR spectra.

(a) C₂H₃Cl₃

(b) C₅H₁₂O

(c) C₂H₅I

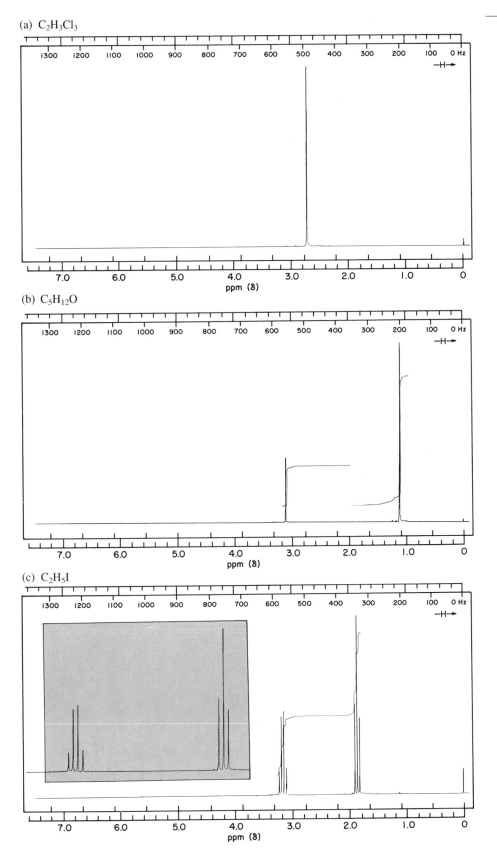

(d) $C_3H_6Cl_2$

(e) C_3H_8O

(f) C_3H_3Cl

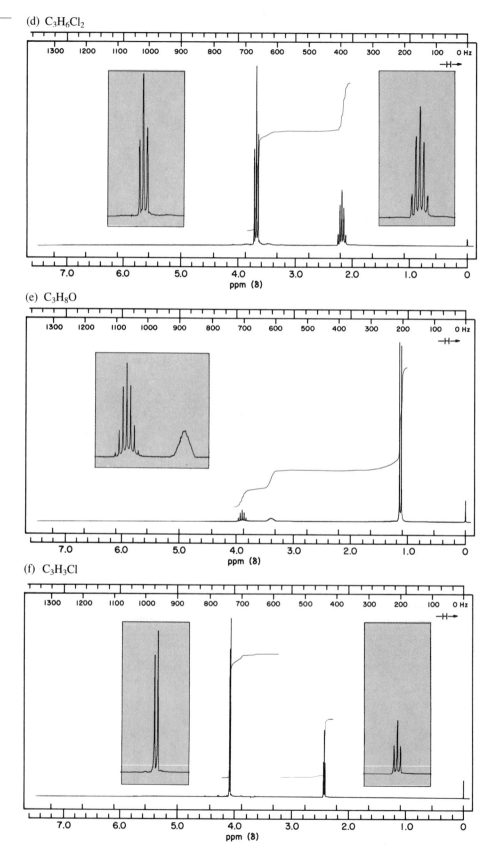

9. While in the process of writing this chapter, the authors ordered a sample of 1,2,2-trichloro-propane from a chemical supplier in order to obtain its proton NMR and CMR spectra. The proton-coupled and -decoupled CMR spectra of the commercial sample were determined first and are reproduced below. The bottle was obviously mislabeled. What is the actual structure of this compound?

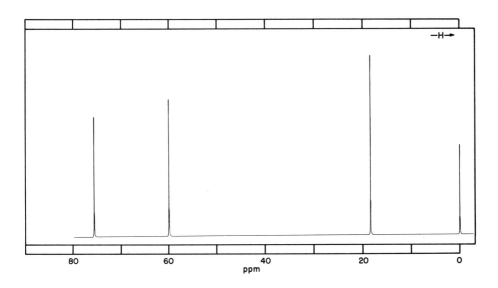

10. The proton NMR spectrum of chloroform shows a single intense peak at $\delta = 7.27$ ppm. However, careful examination shows a small peak -104.5 Hz above and below the main peak. These peaks are associated with $^{13}CHCl_3$. Explain. What CMR spectrum would you expect for $^{13}CHCl_3$?

11. Deduce the structure of each of the following compounds from the NMR and proton-decoupled CMR spectra.

(a) C_8H_8O

(b) $C_3H_5Cl_3$

(c) C$_4$H$_8$O

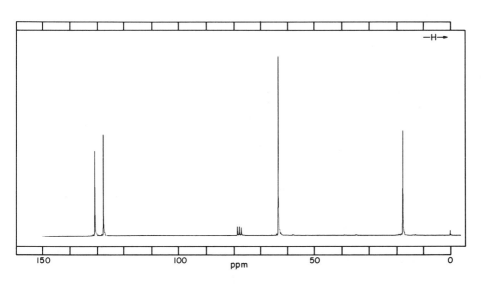

352

Chap. 13

*Nuclear
Magnetic
Resonance
Spectroscopy*

12. Deduce the structure corresponding to each of the following NMR spectra.
    (a) C_4H_9Cl

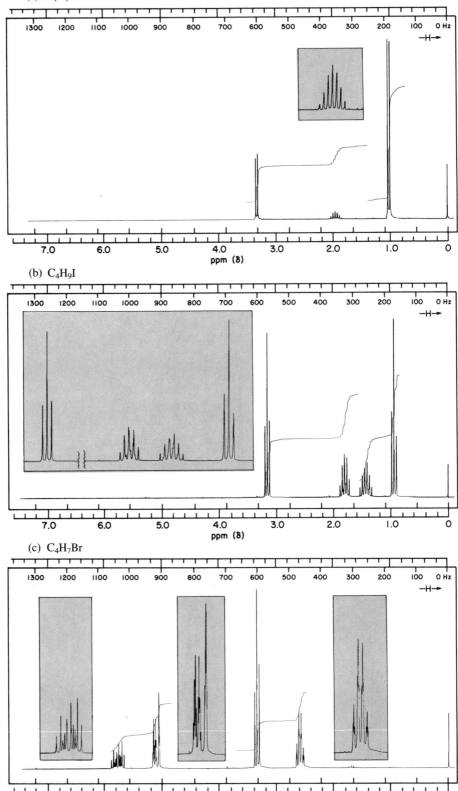

(b) C_4H_9I

(c) C_4H_7Br

(d) C$_5$H$_8$O

(e) C$_4$H$_8$O

(f) C$_{11}$H$_{24}$O$_4$

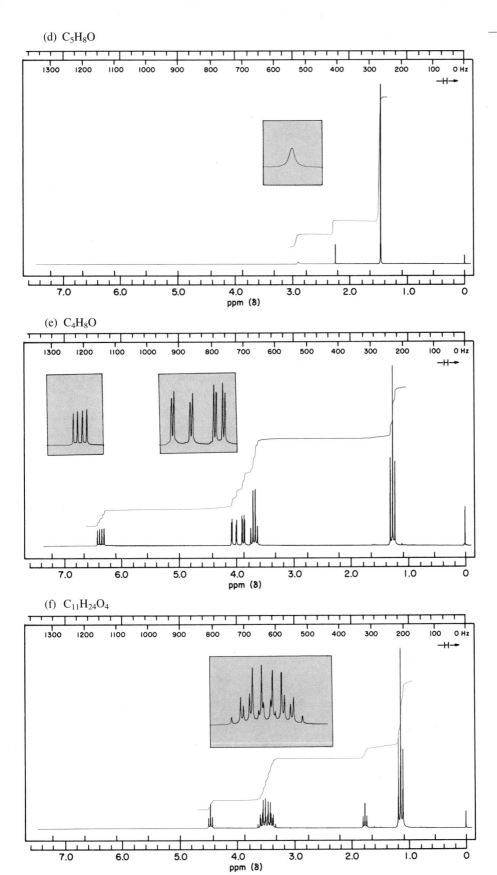

354

Chap. 13

Nuclear
Magnetic
Resonance
Spectroscopy

13. Deduce the structure of the following compound (C_4H_9Br) from its proton-decoupled CMR spectrum. What will its proton NMR spectrum look like?

14. There are four compounds with the formula C_4H_9Cl. The proton-decoupled CMR spectrum of one of the isomers is shown below. Which isomers are eliminated by the spectrum? Which isomers might give such a spectrum? Describe how the proton-coupled CMR spectrum can be used to decide which C_4H_9Cl isomer the compound is.

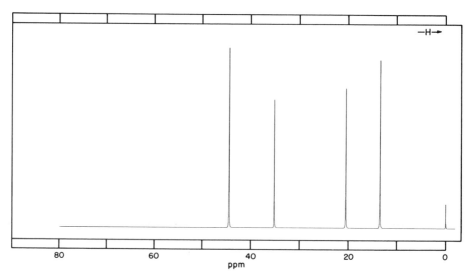

15. Explain why the CMR spectrum of *cis*-1,2-dimethylcyclohexane shows only one methyl resonance, even though one methyl is axial and the other is equatorial. How would you expect the spectrum to change on cooling below $-70°C$?

16. Identify each of the following compounds from the CMR data presented [resonance position (multiplicity of proton-coupled resonance)].

(a) $C_5H_{11}ClO$; 62.2(t), 45.4(t), 32.9(t), 32.1(t), 23.7(t)
(b) $C_8H_{18}O$; 71.2(t), 33.1(t), 20.3(t), 14.6(quartet)
(c) $C_6H_{14}O$; 75.1(d), 35.3(s), 25.8(quartet), 18.2(quartet); the resonance at 25.8 ppm is much more intense than the others
(d) $C_6H_{14}O$; 65.5(d), 49.2(t), 25.1(d), 24.3(quartet), 22.7(quartet)
(e) $C_6H_{12}O_2$; 71.1(d), 33.9(t)

17. 3-Bromo-2,3-dimethylpentane was treated with KOH in refluxing ethanol. The resulting alkene mixture was separated by preparative gas chromatography into four fractions. The principal product was found by proton NMR to be 2,3-dimethyl-2-pentene (no vinyl hydrogens). A second product was found to be 2-ethyl-3-methyl-1-butene (two vinyl hydrogens). The other two products have the following CMR chemical shifts.

   isomer J: 12.4, 17.8, 20.6, 28.5, 117.9, 141.0
   isomer K: 13.0, 13.1, 21.6, 37.4, 116.2, 141.5

   What are the structures of these two isomers?

18. Three compounds, all having the formula C_6H_{10}, are found to have the following CMR spectra. Propose structures for the three compounds.

   isomer L: 12.9, 124.9, 125.3
   isomer M: 17.6, 125.8, 132.3
   isomer N: 13.0, 18.0, 123.1, 127.4, 128.3, 130.2

19. 1-Chloro-3-methylcyclopentane was treated with potassium *t*-butoxide in *t*-butyl alcohol. Two isomeric alkenes were formed. The CMR spectrum of the major product has only four resonances and that of the minor product has six. What are the structures of the two products?

20. The CMR spectrum of *n*-butanol, $CH_3CH_2CH_2CH_2OH$, shows four resonances with chemical shifts of 61.7, 35.3, 19.4, and 13.9 ppm. Using these data and the chemical shifts of butane (Table 13.3), calculate α-, β-, and γ-effects for the OH group. Chlorination of *n*-butanol gives several products, one of which shows the CMR resonances 62.0, 29.7, 30.0, and 45.4 ppm. What is the structure of this chlorination product?

21. Triply-bonded carbons have CMR resonances in the range $\delta = 60\text{-}80$ ppm. For example, in 1-butyne, the C-1 resonance is at 67.3 ppm and the C-2 resonance is at 85.0 ppm. These resonance positions are in between those of the corresponding carbons in butane (C-1 = 13.2 ppm, C-2 = 25.0 ppm) and 1-butene (C-1 = 112.8 ppm, C-2 = 140.2 ppm). Explain.

22. Treatment of *trans*-3-methylcyclohexanol with concentrated sulfuric acid gave a mixture of three alkenes, having the following CMR spectra.

   isomer O: 23.8, 24.4, 26.7, 31.5, 122.3, 134.3
   isomer P: 22.4, 26.1, 30.9, 32.6, 126.6, 134.0
   isomer Q: 23.0, 26.0, 29.6, 32.2, 34.9, 127.1

   [Note that, in each case, there is an accidental coincidence of a pair of resonances.] In the proton NMR spectra, isomer O shows one vinyl proton and isomers P and Q show two each. Assign structures to the three isomers.

23. Several simple compounds containing only ^{13}C at one or more positions are available commercially. These compounds may be used to synthesize more complex molecules in which one or more positions are *labeled* with [13]C. Such materials are useful for elucidating reaction mechanisms. In one such experiment, a sample of 2-pentanol containing only ^{13}C at C-2 and C-3 was prepared and treated with hot H_2SO_4. From the reaction mixture, *trans*-2-pentene was isolated.
   (a) What is the expected appearance of the CMR spectrum of the dilabelled 2-pentanol? (Remember that the natural abundance of ^{13}C is only 1%, so the synthetic material has 1% [13]C at C-3 and C-4 and 100% at C-1 and C-2.)
   (b) The isolated *trans*-2-pentene has a CMR spectrum that consists of doublets at 25.8 ppm ($J = 44$ Hz) and 123.6 ppm ($J = 70$ Hz); at 133.2 ppm there are two superimposed doublets ($J = 44$ Hz and 70 Hz). Explain.

356

Chap. 13

*Nuclear
Magnetic
Resonance
Spectroscopy*

24. The NMR spectrum of difluoromethane measured as a dilute solution in carbon tetrachloride is shown below. Provide an interpretation of the spectrum. (*Hint*: Recall that the fluorine nucleus, ^{19}F, also has spin of $\pm\frac{1}{2}$.)

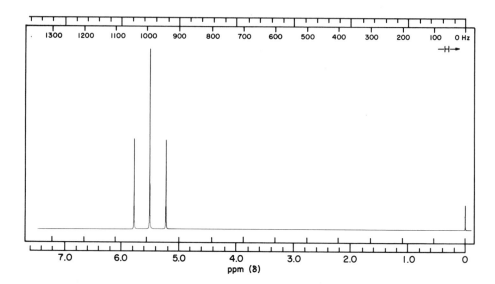

25. The proton-decoupled CMR spectrum of ethyl fluoride consists of two doublets with chemical shifts of 79.3 and 13.6 ppm. Explain.

26. The radio waves used to irradiate the NMR sample are absorbed in converting α-spin states to β and are converted ultimately to heat. To see how much heat is involved, calculate approximately the temperature increase produced in 1 mL of an NMR solution containing 0.01 mole of protons in a 180-MHz NMR instrument. For the purpose of this calculation consider that the entire excess population of α-spins is converted to β and that the heat capacity of the solution is 1 cal deg^{-1} mL^{-1}.

Chapter 14

Aldehydes and Ketones

14.1 Structure

Aldehydes and ketones are compounds containing the **carbonyl group**, C=O. When two alkyl groups are attached to the carbonyl, the compound is a **ketone**. When two hydrogens, or one hydrogen and one alkyl group, are attached to the carbonyl, the compound is an **aldehyde**.

| Lewis structure | Kekulé structure | Condensed structure |

The structure of formaldehyde, the simplest member of the class, is depicted below, along with its experimental bond lengths and bond angles.

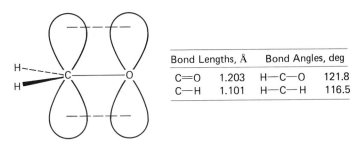

Bond Lengths, Å		Bond Angles, deg	
C=O	1.203	H—C—O	121.8
C—H	1.101	H—C—H	116.5

The carbon atom is approximately sp^2-hybridized and forms σ-bonds to two hydrogens and one oxygen. The molecule is planar and the H—C—O and H—C—H angles are close to 120°, the idealized sp^2-angles. The remaining carbon p-orbital overlaps with the oxygen p-orbital, giving rise to a π-bond between these atoms. The oxygen atom also has two nonbonding electron pairs (the lone pairs) that occupy the remaining orbitals. A stereo representation of acetaldehyde is shown in Figure 14.1. Note the planarity of the carbonyl group. Also note that one carbon-hydrogen bond of the

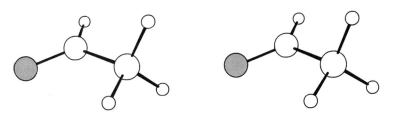

FIGURE 14.1 Stereo representation of acetaldehyde.

357

methyl group is eclipsed with the C=O and that the carbonyl C—H is staggered with respect to the other two carbon-hydrogen bonds.

Oxygen is more electronegative than carbon and attracts the bonding electrons more strongly; that is, the higher nuclear charge on oxygen provides a greater attractive force than carbon. Accordingly, the carbon-oxygen bond is polarized in the direction C^+—O^-. This effect is especially pronounced for the π-electrons and can be represented by the following resonance structures for formaldehyde.

The actual structure is a composite of the normal octet structure, CH_2=O, and the polarized structure, $^+CH_2$—O^-, which corresponds to a carbocation oxide. The composite structure may be represented with dotted line symbolism that shows the partial charges in carbon and oxygen and the partial single-bond character of the carbon-oxygen bond.

One physical consequence of this bond polarity is that carbonyl compounds generally have rather high dipole moments. The experimental dipole moments of formaldehyde and acetone are 2.27 D and 2.85 D, respectively.

formaldehyde
dipole moment, 2.27 D

acetone
dipole moment, 2.85 D

The chemical consequences of this bond polarity will become apparent during our discussions of the reactions of carbonyl groups. We shall find that the positive carbon can react with bases and that much of the chemistry of the carbonyl function corresponds to that of a relatively stable carbocation.

The lone-pair electrons in the carbonyl oxygen have weakly basic properties. In acidic solution acetone acts as a Lewis base and is protonated to a small but significant extent.

$$CH_3-\overset{\overset{\displaystyle :O:}{\|}}{C}-CH_3 + H^+ \rightleftharpoons CH_3-\overset{\overset{\displaystyle :\overset{+}{O}H}{\|}}{C}-CH_3$$

In fact, acetone is a much weaker Lewis base than is water. An acid strength corresponding to 82% sulfuric acid is required to give 50% protonation of acetone. This corresponds to an approximate pK_a for the conjugate acid of acetone of -7.2 (the approximate pK_a of H_3O^+ is -1.7). Even though the carbonyl group has only weakly basic properties, we shall find that this basicity plays an important role in the chemistry of aldehydes, ketones, and related compounds.

14.2 Nomenclature

Traditionally, aldehyde names were derived from the name of the corresponding carboxylic acids (Section 17.2) by dropping the suffix -**ic** (or -**oic**) and adding in its place the suffix -**aldehyde**. These common names are still widely used for simpler aldehydes.

$$H-\overset{\overset{\displaystyle O}{\|}}{C}-OH$$

formic acid

$$H-\overset{\overset{\displaystyle O}{\|}}{C}-H$$

formaldehyde

$$CH_3-\overset{\overset{\displaystyle O}{\|}}{C}-OH$$

acetic acid

$$CH_3-\overset{\overset{\displaystyle O}{\|}}{C}-H$$

acetaldehyde

benzoic acid

benzaldehyde

> Because of their characteristic acidic properties, which rendered them relatively easy to purify and characterize, the carboxylic acids were among the first well-known organic compounds. As they were found, they were given names stemming from their natural sources. Thus, formic (L., *formica*, ant); acetic (L., *acetum*, vinegar); benzoic (from gum benzoin, *Styrax benzoin*). As the "type theory" developed, and functional group interconversions were discovered, the carboxylic acid names were translated, with appropriate modification, to related compounds.

In the common names of aldehydes, appendage groups are traditionally designated by the appropriate Greek letters as prefixes. The chain is labeled by using α, β, γ, and so on, beginning with the carbon *next to the carbonyl group*.

$$\overset{\overset{\displaystyle Cl}{|}}{CH_3CHCHO}$$

α-chloropropionaldehyde

$$\overset{\overset{\displaystyle Br}{|}}{CH_3CHCH_2CHO}$$

β-bromobutyraldehyde

The common names of ketones are derived by prefixing the word **ketone** by the names of the two alkyl radical groups; the separate parts are separate words. Dimethyl ketone has the additional trivial name acetone, which is universally used.

$$CH_3\overset{\overset{\displaystyle O}{\|}}{C}CH_3$$

dimethyl ketone
(acetone)

$$CH_3\overset{\overset{\displaystyle O}{\|}}{C}CH_2CH_3$$

ethyl methyl ketone

$$(CH_3)_2CH\overset{\overset{\displaystyle O}{\|}}{C}CH(CH_3)_2$$

diisopropyl ketone

EXERCISE 14.1 Write structures for each of the following common names.
(a) isopropyl *n*-propyl ketone
(b) isobutyl neopentyl ketone
(c) γ-methoxybutyraldehyde (butyric acid is the four-carbon carboxylic acid; its name derives from L., *butyrum*, butter).
(d) *t*-butyl cyclohexyl ketone

In the IUPAC system aldehyde names are derived from the name of the alkane of the same carbon number. The final -e of the alkane is replaced by the suffix -**al**. Since the carbonyl group is necessarily at the end of a chain, it is not necessary to designate its position by a number, but as a suffix group it determines the direction in which the chain is numbered; the carbonyl carbon in an aldehyde is *always C-1*. [Note that the carbonyl carbon is C-1 in the IUPAC system, but it is given no designation in the common system.]

$$CH_3CH_2\overset{\overset{\displaystyle O}{\|}}{C}H \qquad CH_3\overset{\overset{\displaystyle CH_3}{|}}{C}HCH_2CH_2CH_2\overset{\overset{\displaystyle O}{\|}}{C}H$$

propanal   5-methylhexanal

More complicated aldehydes may be named using the suffix **-carbaldehyde**. When it is necessary to name a compound as another functional group, the aldehyde grouping is designated with the prefix **formyl-**.

3,3-dimethylcyclohexanecarbaldehyde   3-formylcyclohexanone

The IUPAC names of ketones are derived from the name of corresponding alkane by replacing the final *-e* by *-one*. In acyclic ketones it is necessary to prefix the name by a number indicating which carbon along the longest chain is the carbonyl carbon. The longest chain containing the carbonyl group is numbered from the end that gives the carbonyl carbon the lower number. In cyclic ketones it is understood that the carbonyl carbon is number 1.

$$CH_3CH_2\overset{\overset{\displaystyle CH_3CH_2}{|}}{C}H\overset{\overset{\displaystyle O}{\|}}{C}CH_2CH_3$$

5-ethyl-3-heptanone   3-methylcyclohexanone

Occasionally it is necessary to name a molecule containing a carbonyl group as a derivative of a more important function. In such a case, the prefix **oxo-** is used, along with a number, to indicate the position and nature of the group. One such example is shown below.

$$CH_3CH_2\overset{\overset{\displaystyle O}{\|}}{C}CH_2\overset{\overset{\displaystyle CH_3}{|}}{C}HCHO$$

2-methyl-4-oxohexanal

It is generally desirable that the common and IUPAC nomenclature systems not be mixed. Ambiguity can result because counting by Greek letters in the common system starts from the carbon next to the carbonyl group, whereas the numbers in the IUPAC system always include the carbonyl group.

$$ClCH_2CH_2CHO$$

correct:	β-chloropropionaldehyde or 3-chloropropanal
incorrect:	β-chloropropanal
allowed but not recommended:	3-chloropropionaldehyde

EXERCISE 14.2 Give IUPAC names for each of the compounds in Exercise 14.1.

14.3 Physical Properties

Physical data for a number of aldehydes and ketones are collected in Tables 14.1 and 14.2. As in other homologous series, there is a smooth increase in boiling point with increasing molecular weight. Aldehydes and ketones boil higher than alkanes of comparable molecular weights. This boiling-point elevation results from the interaction between dipoles.

$$\begin{array}{ccc} R & \longleftrightarrow & R & \longleftrightarrow \\ & C{=}O & & C{=}O \\ R & & R & \end{array}$$

The discrepancy is largest with the simplest aldehyde, formaldehyde (mol. wt. 30, b.p. −21°C), which boils 68° higher than ethane (mol. wt. 30, b.p. −89°C). With higher members of the series, as the polar functional group becomes a smaller and smaller part

TABLE 14.1 Physical Properties of Some Aldehydes

Compound	Structure	Molecular Weight	Boiling Point, °C	Melting Point, °C
formaldehyde	HCHO	30	−21	−92
acetaldehyde	CH_3CHO	44	21	−121
propionaldehyde	CH_3CH_2CHO	58	49	−81
butyraldehyde	$CH_3(CH_2)_2CHO$	72	76	−99
pentanal	$CH_3(CH_2)_3CHO$	86	103	−92
hexanal	$CH_3(CH_2)_4CHO$	100	128	−56
heptanal	$CH_3(CH_2)_5CHO$	114	153	−43
octanal	$CH_3(CH_2)_6CHO$	128	171	
nonanal	$CH_3(CH_2)_7CHO$	142	192	
decanal	$CH_3(CH_2)_8CHO$	156	209	−5

TABLE 14.2 Physical Properties of Some Ketones

Compound	Structure	Molecular Weight	Boiling Point, °C	Melting Point, °C	H_2O Solubility, wt. % (25°C)
acetone	CH_3COCH_3	58	56	−95	∞
2-butanone	$CH_3CH_2COCH_3$	72	80	−86	25.6
2-pentanone	$CH_3(CH_2)_2COCH_3$	86	102	−78	5.5
3-pentanone	$CH_3CH_2COCH_2CH_3$	86	102	−40	4.8
2-hexanone	$CH_3(CH_2)_3COCH_3$	100	128	−57	1.6
3-hexanone	$CH_3(CH_2)_2COCH_2CH_3$	100	125		1.5
2-heptanone	$CH_3(CH_2)_4COCH_3$	114	151	−36	0.4
2-octanone	$CH_3(CH_2)_5COCH_3$	128	173	−16	
2-nonanone	$CH_3(CH_2)_6COCH_3$	142	195	−7	
2-decanone	$CH_3(CH_2)_7COCH_3$	156	210	14	

of the molecule, the boiling point tends to come closer and closer to that of a corresponding alkane (see 2-decanone, mol. wt. 156, b.p. 210°C; *n*-undecane, mol. wt. 155, b.p. 196°C).

14.4 Nuclear Magnetic Resonance Spectra

Nuclear magnetic resonance spectroscopy is an important technique for identifying aldehydes. The hydrogen attached to the carbonyl carbon gives rise to a characteristic band at very low field, usually around $\delta = 9.5$ ppm. In a magnetic field the circulating π-electrons produce an induced field that effectively deshields the aldehyde proton (Figure 14.2). That is, the induced field adds to the applied field in such a way that a smaller applied field is required to achieve resonance. The same phenomenon was discussed earlier with alkenes and accounts for the substantial downfield shift of vinyl protons (Section 13.9). In aldehydes the effect is greater and, in addition, the positive character of the carbonyl carbon provides a further downfield shift. The net result is a relatively large downfield resonance position for the aldehyde proton. Few other kinds of protons appear in this region; thus a peak at $\delta = 9.5$ is strongly indicative of the presence of a CHO function.

The same induced field that causes deshielding of a proton attached directly to a carbonyl group also produces significant deshielding of protons somewhat farther away at the α-carbon atoms. Typical chemical shifts for these protons are summarized in Table 14.3.

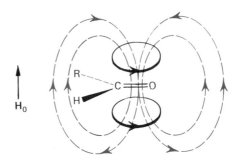

FIGURE 14.2 The diamagnetic anisotropy of the carbonyl group.

TABLE 14.3 Chemical Shifts for Aldehyde and Ketone Hydrogens

Hydrogen	Approximate Chemical Shift δ, ppm
$R-\overset{\overset{\text{O}}{\|\|}}{C}-H$	9.5
$R-\overset{\overset{\text{O}}{\|\|}}{C}-CH_3$	2.0
$R-\overset{\overset{\text{O}}{\|\|}}{C}-CH_2R$	2.2
$R-\overset{\overset{\text{O}}{\|\|}}{C}-CHR_2$	2.4

The spectra of acetaldehyde and 3-methyl-2-butanone shown in Figures 14.3 and 14.4 are characteristic. Note that the vicinal coupling constant in acetaldehyde is quite small, only 3 Hz.

The CMR chemical shifts for a few simple aldehydes and ketones are collected in Table 14.4. Note the extreme downfield shift of the carbonyl resonance—about 200 ppm from TMS. Carbonyl groups resonate further downfield than any other type of carbon. There are two main reasons for this effect. First, there is the fact that sp^2-hybridized carbons resonate downfield from sp^3-hybridized carbons. However, comparison of the shifts in Table 14.4 with those given for alkenes in Table 13.5 shows that aldehyde carbons resonate about 70 ppm downfield from alkene carbons of comparable substitution (compare propanal with 1-butene and butanal with 1-pentene). The reason

FIGURE 14.3   NMR spectrum of acetaldehyde, CH_3CHO.

FIGURE 14.4   NMR spectrum of isopropyl methyl ketone, $CH_3COCH(CH_3)_2$.

TABLE 14.4 CMR Chemical Shifts of Aldehydes and Ketones

	C-1	C-2	C-3	C-4	C-5
ethanal	199.6	31.2			
propanal	201.8	36.7	5.2		
butanal	201.6	45.7	15.7	13.3	
propanone	30.2	205.1	30.2		
butanone	28.8	206.3	36.4	7.6	
2-pentanone	29.3	206.6	45.2	17.5	13.5
3-pentanone	7.3	35.3	209.3	35.3	7.3

FIGURE 14.5 CMR spectrum of 2-octanone.

for this additional shift is the polar nature of the carbonyl bond, which *deshields* the carbon nucleus even more. Because the carbonyl carbon has a long relaxation time, carbonyl resonances are normally much weaker than the resonances of other carbons, as shown in the CMR spectrum of 2-octanone (Figure 14.5).

On page 311 we discussed the "relaxation" of excited spin states to lower energy spin states. The dominant relaxation mechanisms are different for different nuclei. For protons a major mechanism involves motion of the molecule relative to other molecules in the sample. Although this mechanism also contributes to relaxation of carbon nuclei, a more important one involves interaction with hydrogens that are *bonded directly to the nucleus undergoing relaxation*. As a consequence, carbons that have no attached hydrogens have long relaxation times. This is true for the carbonyl carbons of ketones (but not of aldehydes) and for other carbons that are fully substituted by alkyl groups ("quaternary carbons").

EXERCISE 14.3 Write the structure for a compound having the formula $C_5H_{10}O$, that shows four signals in its CMR spectrum and has a triplet with $\delta = 9.7$ ppm and $J = 3$ Hz in its NMR spectrum.

14.5 Synthesis of Aldehydes and Ketones

The carbonyl group in aldehydes and ketones is one of the most important functional groups. In this section we shall review several reactions that are good methods for the synthesis of aldehydes and ketones.

We saw in Section 10.6.E that aldehydes and ketones may be obtained by the oxidation of primary and secondary alcohols, respectively.

$$R-CH_2OH \xrightarrow{[O]} R-\overset{\overset{\displaystyle O}{\|}}{C}-H$$

$$R-\overset{\overset{\displaystyle OH}{|}}{CH}-R' \xrightarrow{[O]} R-\overset{\overset{\displaystyle O}{\|}}{C}-R'$$

In the latter case the product is not easily oxidized further, so there is no special problem in controlling the reaction to obtain the ketone in good yield. Although many oxidants have been used, the most commonly employed ones are chromium(VI) compounds.

menthol

(84%)
menthone

A mixture of 120 g of $Na_2Cr_2O_7$, 100 g of conc. H_2SO_4, and 600 mL of water is prepared. To this solution is added 90 g of menthol (2-isopropyl-5-methylcyclohexanol). Heat is evolved, the temperature of the mixture rising to 55°C. As soon as the reaction is complete, the oily product layer is removed by ether extraction and distilled to obtain 75 g (84%) of menthone.

In the case of primary alcohols, this simple picture is clouded by the fact that the product aldehyde may be further oxidized to a carboxylic acid. In most cases, the primary alcohol undergoes oxidation *more rapidly* than the corresponding aldehyde. However, in aqueous solution the product aldehyde forms a **hydrate**, which is oxidized even more rapidly than the primary alcohol. Aldehyde hydrates are discussed thoroughly in Section 14.7.A.

We mentioned previously (Section 10.6.E) that the preparation of aldehydes by oxidation of primary alcohols with aqueous chromic acid is limited to compounds of low molecular weight that can be removed from the reaction mixture by distillation as they are formed. However, in nonhydroxylic solvents, selective oxidation may be accomplished, and several oxidants that may be used in organic solvents have been developed for this purpose. One such oxidant is the complex formed between chromium trioxide, pyridine, and HCl (pyridinium chlorochromate, PCC, page 211). This material is soluble in chloroform and dichloromethane and may therefore be used to oxidize primary alcohols to aldehydes under anhydrous conditions.

$$n\text{-}C_9H_{19}CH_2OH + C_5H_5\overset{+}{N}H\ CrO_3Cl^- \xrightarrow[\substack{25°C \\ 1\ hr}]{CH_2Cl_2} n\text{-}C_9H_{19}CHO$$

(92%)

Aldehydes and ketones may also be prepared by oxidative cleavage of carbon-carbon double bonds. A particularly useful reagent for this purpose is ozone (Section 11.6.E). Hydrolysis of the ozonide, usually under reductive conditions, results in the production of two carbonyl compounds.

5-methylhexanal (62%)

In our study of the carbon-carbon triple bond (Section 12.6), we found that alkynes undergo hydration to yield an unstable vinyl alcohol that immediately rearranges to the corresponding ketone. The hydration reaction is usually catalyzed by mercuric ion and sulfuric acid.

$$R-C\equiv C-R + H_2O \xrightarrow[H_2SO_4]{Hg^{2+}} \left[R-\overset{\overset{\displaystyle OH}{|}}{C}=CH-R \right] \rightleftharpoons R-\overset{\overset{\displaystyle O}{\|}}{C}-CH_2R$$

The reaction is generally useful as a preparative method only when the alkyne is terminal, in which case a methyl alkyl ketone is always formed, or in cases where the molecule is symmetrical.

(84%)

(80%)

Since the direct addition of water to a terminal alkyne always occurs in such a way that the hydroxy group becomes attached to the carbon bearing the alkyl group, the only alkyne that will yield an aldehyde upon hydration is acetylene itself. Indirect hydration of the triple bond, by the hydroboration route, yields the opposite result—terminal alkynes yield aldehydes (Section 12.6.D).

$$n\text{-}C_5H_{11}C\equiv CH \xrightarrow{B_2H_6} \xrightarrow[OH^-]{H_2O_2} n\text{-}C_5H_{11}CH_2CHO$$

14.6 Enolization

A. Keto-Enol Equilibria

Aldehydes and ketones exist in solution as equilibrium mixtures of two isomeric forms, the keto form and the **enol** (from -**ene** + -**ol**, unsaturated alcohol) form. For simple aliphatic ketones there is very little of the enol form present at equilibrium, as shown by the following examples.

$$K = \frac{[\text{enol form}]}{[\text{keto form}]}$$

$$CH_3-\overset{\overset{\displaystyle O}{\|}}{CH} \; \rightleftharpoons \; CH_2{=}CHOH \qquad 2 \times 10^{-5}$$

$$CH_3-\overset{\overset{\displaystyle O}{\|}}{C}-CH_3 \; \rightleftharpoons \; CH_2{=}\overset{\overset{\displaystyle OH}{|}}{C}-CH_3 \qquad 1.5 \times 10^{-7}$$

$$5 \times 10^{-5}$$

Even though the percentage of enol isomer at equilibrium is quite small, enols are important in many reactions. As we shall soon see, many reactions of aldehydes and ketones occur by way of the unstable enol form.

Enolization is subject to both acid and base catalysis. In aqueous solutions the base is hydroxide ion. The base attacks the molecule, forming a bond to a proton α to the carbonyl group as the carbon-hydrogen bond breaks to give an anion that is called an **enolate** ion. The enolate ion may be protonated on carbon, which regenerates the keto form, or on oxygen, which yields the enol form.

$$(1) \quad HO{:}^- + H{-}CH_2{-}\overset{\overset{\displaystyle O}{\|}}{C}CH_3 \; \rightleftharpoons \; \left[CH_2{=}\overset{\overset{\displaystyle O^-}{|}}{C}CH_3 \longleftrightarrow {}^-CH_2{-}\overset{\overset{\displaystyle O}{\|}}{C}CH_3 \right] + H_2O$$

$$(2) \quad \left[CH_2{=}\overset{\overset{\displaystyle O^-}{|}}{C}CH_3 \longleftrightarrow {}^-CH_2{-}\overset{\overset{\displaystyle O}{\|}}{C}CH_3 \right] + H_2O \; \rightleftharpoons \; CH_2{=}\overset{\overset{\displaystyle OH}{|}}{C}CH_3 + OH^-$$

Note that the first step in base-catalyzed enolization is formally analogous to the E2 mechanism. The "leaving group" may be considered to be the π-bond electron pair.

The first step of base-catalyzed enolization is simply an acid-base reaction, with the ketone acting as a protic acid. The pK_a for acetone is approximately 19. Although this makes it an extremely weak acid compared to such familiar acids as HCl (pK_a -2.2), HF (pK_a $+3$), acetic acid (pK_a $+5$) or water (pK_a $+15.7$), we must remember that acidity is relative. In all of these acids, the acidic proton is bonded to an electronegative hetero atom (Cl, F, O), whereas acetone is a **carbon acid**. If we compare acetone to ethane (pK_a estimated to be approximately $+50$), we see that the carbon-hydrogen bonds in acetone are enormously more acidic than those in an alkane.

$$CH_3CH_3 \rightleftharpoons CH_3CH_2^- + H^+ \qquad K_a \cong 10^{-50} M$$

The reason for this enhanced acidity is apparent from a consideration of the conjugate bases produced by ionization of the two carbon acids. The anion produced from ethane has its negative charge localized on carbon. Since carbon is a fairly electropositive element, a carbanion is a high-energy species and the ionization that produces it is highly endothermic. On the other hand, the enolate ion produced by ionization of acetone is not a localized carbanion but a resonance hybrid of two structures.

$$CH_3\overset{\overset{\displaystyle O}{\|}}{C}CH_3 \rightleftharpoons H^+ + \left[\ddot{C}H_2-\overset{\overset{\displaystyle O}{\|}}{C}CH_3 \longleftrightarrow CH_2{=}\overset{\overset{\displaystyle O^-}{|}}{C}CH_3\right] \qquad K_a \cong 10^{-19} M$$

In one of the resonance structures the negative charge is borne by carbon, as in the ethyl anion. In the other the negative charge is on the more electronegative oxygen. Although the resonance hybrid has the character of both structures, it is more like the structure in which the negative charge is on oxygen. It is important to point out once again that the two structures connected by the double-headed arrow are *not isomers, but resonance structures*. The anion derived from acetone is neither one nor the other of the two indicated structures; it has the character of both. An alternative symbol that gives a somewhat more accurate picture of the electronic distribution is

$$CH_3-C\overset{\diagup O^{\delta-}}{\underset{\diagdown CH_2{}^{\delta-}}{}}$$

wherein we see that the negative charge is divided between the carbon and the oxygen. When this anion reacts with water, it can undergo protonation either on carbon, in which case the keto form results, or on oxygen, in which case the enol form is produced. The rate-limiting step for base-catalyzed enolization is usually the deprotonation step.

EXERCISE 14.5 What is the kinetic rate law for base-catalyzed enolization? (Remember that, for most aldehydes and ketones, enolization is an *endothermic* process. In order actually to measure the rate of enolization, you would have to devise some indirect method to determine that the reaction had actually occurred.)

In neutral solution enolization is much slower than it is in basic medium. At pH 7 the principal base present is H_2O. Since H_2O is a much weaker base than OH^-, proton transfer from an aldehyde or ketone is not as rapid, and consequently enolization is slower.

However, below pH 7, the rate of enolization is proportional to the acid concentration. In acidic solution some of the weakly basic carbonyl groups are protonated. The protonated aldehyde or ketone loses a proton from carbon with much greater ease, even to such a weak base as H_2O. A carbonyl group is not very basic, and only a small amount of the protonated structure is present at equilibrium. The presence of the positive charge, however, greatly increases the rate of proton loss from carbon to solvent.

(1) $H{-}CH_2{-}\overset{\overset{\displaystyle O}{\|}}{C}CH_3 + H_3O^+ \rightleftharpoons \left[H{-}CH_2{-}\overset{\overset{\displaystyle {}^+OH}{\|}}{C}CH_3 \longleftrightarrow H{-}CH_2{-}\overset{\overset{\displaystyle OH}{|}}{\underset{+}{C}}CH_3 \right] + H_2O$

(2) $\left[H{-}CH_2{-}\overset{\overset{\displaystyle {}^+OH}{\|}}{C}CH_3 \longleftrightarrow H{-}CH_2{-}\overset{\overset{\displaystyle OH}{|}}{\underset{+}{C}}CH_3 \right] + H_2O \rightleftharpoons CH_2{=}\overset{\overset{\displaystyle OH}{|}}{C}CH_3 + H_3O^+$

In fact, deprotonation of the protonated ketone (step 2) is analogous to the E1 reaction, deprotonation of a carbocation.

$$H_2O \overset{\frown}{\quad} H{-}CH_2{\overset{\curvearrowright}{-}}\underset{+}{C}(CH_3)_2 \longrightarrow H_3O^+ + CH_2{=}C(CH_3)_2$$

In acid-catalyzed enolization the first step is a rapid equilibrium. Loss of a proton from carbon (step 2) is slower and is rate-determining.

Let us summarize. In aqueous solution aldehydes and ketones are in equilibrium with their corresponding enol forms. Interconversion of the enol and keto forms is catalyzed by either acid or base. At any given moment the vast majority of molecules are present as the more stable keto form. However, as we shall see, the small amount of enol form present is involved as an important *intermediate* in many of the reactions of aldehydes and ketones.

One way in which the intermediate enols and enolates can be detected is by **deuterium exchange**. If one dissolves a ketone in D_2O containing DCl or Na^+OD^-, all of the α-hydrogens are exchanged for deuterium.

$$CH_3CH_2\overset{\overset{\displaystyle O}{\|}}{C}CH_2CH_3 + D_2O \xrightarrow[OD^-]{D^+ \text{ or}} CH_3CD_2\overset{\overset{\displaystyle O}{\|}}{C}CD_2CH_3 + H_2O$$

3-pentanone   3-pentanone-*2,2,4,4-d₄*

The amount of deuterium incorporation at equilibrium is related to the initial concentrations of the ketone and D_2O. In dilute solution the D_2O is present in large excess, and replacement of the α-hydrogens by deuterium is essentially complete.

EXERCISE 14.6 For a 1 M solution of 3-pentanone in D_2O in the presence of a catalytic amount of DCl, calculate how many deuterium atoms will be present in each 3-pentanone molecule (on the average) at equilibrium. (Remember that there is a statistical factor; each 3-pentanone molecule starts with four exchangeable Hs, whereas each D_2O molecule starts with two exchangeable Ds. Also remember that the molarity of pure, liquid water is 55.5.)

The *rate* of deuterium incorporation is proportional to the concentration of ketone and the catalyst, either D^+ or OD^-.

$$\text{rate}_{ex} = k[\text{ketone}][D^+] \quad \text{or} \quad k'[\text{ketone}][OD^-]$$

Such exchange reactions may be applied even when the aldehyde or ketone is not very soluble in water. Shaking such a compound with NaOD or DCl in D_2O for several hours results in virtually complete exchange.

2-methylcyclohexanone   2-methylcyclohexanone-*2,6,6-d₃*

Since the number of deuteriums is easily determined by mass spectrometry or by NMR, this reaction is a useful technique for *counting* the number of α-hydrogens in an aldehyde or ketone.

EXERCISE 14.7 How many hydrogens are replaced by deuterium when each of the following compounds is treated with NaOD in D_2O?
(a) 2,2,4-trimethyl-3-pentanone   (b) 2-ethylbutanal
(c) 3-methylcyclopentanone   (d) *trans*-2-pentene

B. Enolate Ions

From the pK_a of acetone, $+19$, it is clear that in aqueous solution where the strongest base is OH^- the amount of enolate ion present is small.

$$\underset{pK_a\ 19}{CH_3\overset{O}{\overset{\|}{C}}CH_3} + OH^- \ \rightleftharpoons\ \underset{pK_a\ 15.7}{CH_2\!\!=\!\!\overset{O^-}{\overset{|}{C}}CH_3} + H_2O$$

$$K = \frac{[\text{enolate}][H^+]}{[\text{acetone}]} \cdot \frac{[H_2O]}{[OH^-][H^+]} = \frac{10^{-19}}{10^{-15.7}} \cong 10^{-3}\ M$$

However, if a ketone is treated with a much stronger base, it can be converted completely into the corresponding enolate ion.

$$\underset{pK_a\ 19}{CH_3\overset{O}{\overset{\|}{C}}CH_3} + (i\text{-}C_3H_7)_2N^-\ Li^+ \ \overset{THF}{\rightleftharpoons}\ \underset{pK_a\ \cong\ 40}{CH_3\overset{O^-\ Li^+}{\overset{|}{C}}\!\!=\!\!CH_2} + (i\text{-}C_3H_7)_2NH$$

$$K = \frac{[\text{enolate}]}{[\text{acetone}]} \times \frac{[(i\text{-}C_3H_7)_2NH]}{[(i\text{-}C_3H_7)_2N^-\ Li^+]} = \frac{10^{-19}}{10^{-40}} \cong 10^{21}$$

Lithium diisopropylamide, $(i\text{-}C_3H_7)_2N^-\ Li^+$, is commonly abbreviated as LDA. It is prepared by treating a solution of diisopropylamine in ether, THF, or 1,2-dimethoxyethane with *n*-butyllithium.

$$(i\text{-}C_3H_7)_2NH + n\text{-}BuLi \longrightarrow (i\text{-}C_3H_7)_2N^-\ Li^+ + C_4H_{10}$$

Since diisopropylamine has $pK_a \cong 40$, while *n*-butyllithium may be regarded as the conjugate base of butane ($pK_a \cong 50$), proton transfer is virtually quantitative. Because of its highly basic nature, and because it is relatively soluble in common ether solvents, LDA is widely used for converting ketones quantitatively into their corresponding lithium enolates.

Solutions of enolate ions may be prepared by the use of strong bases such as LDA.

They are quite stable if air and moisture are rigorously excluded. Spectroscopic measurements have shown that lithium enolates exist as tetrameric aggregates in ether solvents. In fact, crystalline lithium enolates have been isolated and found by x-ray analysis to have dimeric and tetrameric structures. One such example is the lithium enolate of 3,3-dimethyl-2-butanone (Figure 14.6). In this structure, note that each lithium cation is surrounded by four oxygens, three from neighboring enolates and one from a tetrahydrofuran molecule.

Enolate ions have significant nucleophilic properties and are readily alkylated by primary alkyl halides.

(98%)

> Potassium hydride, KH, is commercially available as a grey microcrystalline material dispersed in white mineral oil. Potassium hydride is insoluble in hydrocarbons, ethers, ammonia, and amines. For use, the mineral oil is washed away with an appropriate solvent and the hydride is used as a slurry. It is much more reactive than sodium hydride (page 196). It converts ketones to the potassium enolates in minutes at room temperature.

The alkylation of ketone enolates is a significant synthetic method, since it allows one to construct larger molecules from small, readily available ketones and alkyl halides.

FIGURE 14.6 Structure of the crystalline lithium enolate of 3,3-dimethyl-2-butanone. The hydrogens are omitted. Each lithium is at the center of a tetrahedron of oxygen atoms, three from neighboring enolate ions and one from a tetrahydrofuran molecule. The four tetrahydrofuran molecules are shown as simple pentagons. [Courtesy of D. Seebach and J. Dunitz, Eidgenössische Technische Hochschule, Zürich, Switzerland.]

2,2-dimethyl-3-pentanone

(57%)
2,2,4-trimethyl-3-octanone

However, there are significant limitations to the alkylation of enolate ions. The most serious limitation is the fact that *only primary alkyl halides may be used*. In this regard, enolate alkylation is just like the alkylation of alkyne anions (Section 12.5.B). Because the enolate ion is derived from a relatively weak acid ($pK_a \cong 19$), it is very basic and therefore prone to enter into the E2 reaction with secondary and tertiary alkyl halides.

Another limitation is the fact that *aldehydes may not generally be alkylated in this manner*. The problem with aldehydes is not that their enolate ions cannot be formed, but that the aldehyde carbonyl is itself so reactive to enolate ions that it reacts with the enolate as fast as it is formed. We shall return to a consideration of this reaction in Section 14.8.C.

Enolate ions are ambident anions (Section 9.4.D). Just as they may undergo protonation on either carbon or oxygen, they may also react with other electrophilic species at either of these two centers. An example that illustrates this ambident character is the reaction with chlorotrimethylsilane.

Chlorotrimethylsilane, $(CH_3)_3SiCl$, is a clear liquid, b.p. 57°C, that has a number of uses in organic synthesis. The chemistry of organosilicon compounds is discussed in Sections 25.9–25.11.

Whether or not the oxygen or the carbon of an enolate ion is the site of reaction with an electrophile is determined by a number of factors. One important factor, which is illustrated by the examples just given, is the nature of the electrophile. In general, alkylation of an enolate always occurs on carbon. However, some electrophiles, including silyl halides, react predominantly on oxygen. In the latter case it is the great strength of the silicon-oxygen bond that governs the course of reaction. In Table 25.4, we see that the bond dissociation energy for the silicon-oxygen bond is approximately 127 kcal mole^{-1}, whereas that for the silicon-carbon bond is only 89 kcal mole^{-1}. This large difference in the heats of reaction for the two competing processes is already evident in the two transition states. On the other hand, the carbon-carbon and carbon-oxygen single bonds have comparable $DH°$'s, 83 and 86 kcal mole^{-1}, respectively. In the absence of a strong bias for the formation of C—C or C—O, alkylation of an enolate tends to produce the more stable product. We have seen in the previous section that the keto form is much more stable than the enol form.

EXERCISE 14.8 From the pK_a of acetone, 19, and the equilibrium constant for formation of the enol form (page 367), derive the pK_a of the enol. How does this value compare with the pK_a values for alcohols?

EXERCISE 14.9 Show how the following compounds may be synthesized from cyclohexanone.

(a)   (b)

C. Racemization

When (R)-3-phenyl-2-butanone is dissolved in aqueous ethanol that contains NaOH or HCl, the optical rotation of the solution gradually drops to zero. Reisolation from the reaction mixture yields a racemate, an equimolar mixture of the R and S enantiomers. Such a process, in which an enantiomerically homogeneous compound changes into a racemate, is called **racemization**. In this case, the rate of racemization is proportional to the concentration of the ketone and also to the concentration of NaOH or HCl. Clearly, racemization occurs by way of the intermediate enol form in which the former stereocenter is planar and hence achiral.

(R)-3-phenyl-2-butanone   (achiral)   (S)-3-phenyl-2-butanone

Since racemization involves the formation of the enol form, the rate of racemization is exactly equal to the rate of enolization.

$$\text{rate} = k[\text{ketone}][\text{H}^+] \quad \text{or} \quad k'[\text{ketone}][\text{OH}^-]$$

Furthermore, the rate of racemization is equal to the rate of deuterium incorporation because both reactions involve the same intermediate enol.

Note that racemization of an optically active ketone will occur *only* when the stereocenter is α to the carbonyl group. If the aldehyde or ketone is chiral because some other carbon is a stereocenter, the enol form is also chiral, and enolization does not result in racemization.

(S)-4-methyl-2-hexanone   (still chiral)

EXERCISE 14.10 Which of the following compounds will racemize in basic solution (sodium ethoxide in ethanol)?
(a) (R)-2-methylbutanal   (b) (S)-3-methylcyclohexanone
(c) (S)-3-methyl-2-heptanone   (d) (S)-2-methyl-1-pentanol

D. Halogenation

Aldehydes and ketones undergo acid- and base-catalyzed halogenation. The reaction occurs with chlorine, bromine, and iodine.

(61–66%)

(70%)

Halogenation is often carried out without added catalyst. In this case the reaction is **autocatalytic** (catalyzed by one of the reaction products). There usually is no apparent reaction when bromine and the ketone are first mixed. However, there is a slow uncatalyzed reaction that produces some HBr. As HBr is produced in the reaction, it catalyzes the bromination, producing more HBr, which makes the reaction proceed even faster. In practice, autocatalytic reactions often have an **induction period** (a time when no apparent reaction is occurring), after which a rapid and vigorous reaction sets in and is soon over. In base-catalyzed halogenation, a full equivalent of base must be used because an equivalent of HX is formed in the reaction.

The actual species that reacts with the halogen is the enol form of the aldehyde or ketone; the purpose of the acid or base is simply to catalyze enolization. Acid-catalyzed halogenation is simply the normal electrophilic reaction of halogen with a double bond. The probable mechanism of the acid-catalyzed reaction is as follows.

There is considerable evidence for this mechanism. First, the rate of halogenation depends *only* upon the concentration of the ketone and the acid; it is independent of halogen concentration. Second, chlorination and bromination occur at the same rate. Finally, acid-catalyzed halogenation occurs at the same rate as does acid-catalyzed exchange of an α-proton for deuterium, strongly suggesting that these two reactions proceed by way of the same intermediate.

375

Sec. 14.7

*Addition of
Oxygen and
Nitrogen
Nucleophiles*

In the base-catalyzed reaction, the enolate ion is the probable intermediate.

(1) $-\overset{\text{H}}{\underset{|}{\text{C}}}-\overset{\text{O}}{\overset{\|}{\text{C}}}- + \text{OH}^- \rightleftharpoons \text{\char`\>C=C<}\overset{\text{O}^-}{} + \text{H}_2\text{O}$

(2) $\left[\text{\char`\>C=C<}\overset{\text{O}^-}{} \longleftrightarrow \text{\char`\>}\overset{-}{\text{C}}-\text{C<}\overset{\text{O}}{} \right] + \text{X}_2 \rightleftharpoons -\overset{\text{X}}{\underset{|}{\text{C}}}-\overset{\text{O}}{\overset{\|}{\text{C}}}- + \text{X}$

The acid- and base-catalyzed halogenation reactions differ in several important aspects. In acid-catalyzed halogenation each successive halogenation step is normally slower than the previous one. Therefore it is usually possible to prepare a monohalo ketone in good yield by carrying out the halogenation under conditions of acid catalysis using one equivalent of halogen, as shown by the examples on page 374. In the base-catalyzed reaction, each successive halogenation step is faster than the previous one, since the electron-attracting halogens increase the acidity of halogenated ketones; consequently base-catalyzed halogenation is not a generally useful method for preparation of a monohalo ketone.

EXERCISE 14.11 Show how acetone can be converted into each of the following compounds.

(a) [structure: CH₃-C(=O)-CH₂-Br]   (b) [structure: epoxide with O]

14.7 Addition of Oxygen and Nitrogen Nucleophiles

A. Carbonyl Hydrates: *gem*-Diols

Aldehydes and ketones react with water to give an equilibrium concentration of the hydrate, a *gem*-diol.

$$\text{\char`\>C=O} + \text{H}_2\text{O} \overset{K}{\rightleftharpoons} \text{\char`\>C}\overset{\text{OH}}{\underset{\text{OH}}{}}$$

The reaction is not a significant synthetic transformation, but it points up many of the important principles of reactions of carbonyl groups. The equilibrium constant for hydration, K, is sensitive to the nature of the carbonyl group. In aqueous solution, the equilibrium constant is

$$K = \frac{[\text{C(OH)}_2]}{[\text{C=O}][\text{H}_2\text{O}]}$$

The equilibrium constant has a value of about 18 for formaldehyde, roughly 0.01 for other aldehydes such as propionaldehyde, and about 10^{-5} for ketones. Thus a solution of formaldehyde in water is almost all $\text{CH}_2(\text{OH})_2$. Aqueous solutions of other aldehydes contain comparable amounts of the hydrated and nonhydrated forms, and ketones are present almost wholly in their carbonyl forms.

$$CH_2{=}O + H_2O \xrightarrow{K} HOCH_2OH \qquad K \cong 18$$

$$CH_3CH_2\overset{O}{\overset{\|}{C}}H + H_2O \xrightarrow{K} CH_3CH_2{-}\underset{OH}{\overset{OH}{\overset{|}{C}H}} \qquad K \cong 10^{-2}$$

$$CH_3COCH_3 + H_2O \xrightarrow{K} CH_3{-}\underset{OH}{\overset{OH}{\overset{|}{\underset{|}{C}}}}{-}CH_3 \qquad K \cong 4 \times 10^{-5}$$

> **EXERCISE 14.12** Using the approximate values given above for K, estimate the ratio of hydrated and nonhydrated forms of formaldehyde, acetaldehyde, and acetone in aqueous solutions nominally 1 M in carbonyl compound.

The relative tendency for various carbonyl compounds to undergo hydration can be explained with concepts that come from our knowledge of carbocation chemistry. Two important resonance structures can be written for a carbonyl group.

$$\left[{-}\overset{O}{\overset{\|}{C}}{-} \longleftrightarrow {-}\underset{+}{\overset{O^-}{\overset{|}{C}}}{-} \right]$$

The structure with the double bond is the more important because in it all atoms have complete octets. However, the other structure contributes to a significant extent. This dipolar structure has the character of a carbocation. Recall that the order of carbocation stability is secondary > primary > methyl.

The dipolar resonance structure of formaldehyde is analogous to a methyl cation, that for propionaldehyde is analogous to a primary carbocation, and that for a ketone is analogous to a secondary carbocation.

$$\left[H{-}\overset{O}{\overset{\|}{C}}{-}H \longleftrightarrow H{-}\underset{+}{\overset{O^-}{\overset{|}{C}}}{-}H \right] \qquad H{-}\underset{+}{\overset{H}{\overset{|}{C}}}{-}H$$

formaldehyde   methyl cation

$$\left[CH_3CH_2{-}\overset{O}{\overset{\|}{C}}{-}H \longleftrightarrow CH_3CH_2{-}\underset{+}{\overset{O^-}{\overset{|}{C}}}{-}H \right] \qquad CH_3CH_2{-}\underset{+}{\overset{H}{\overset{|}{C}}}{-}H$$

propionaldehyde n-propyl cation

$$\left[CH_3{-}\overset{O}{\overset{\|}{C}}{-}CH_3 \longleftrightarrow CH_3{-}\underset{+}{\overset{O^-}{\overset{|}{C}}}{-}CH_3 \right] \qquad CH_3{-}\underset{+}{\overset{H}{\overset{|}{C}}}{-}CH_3$$

acetone   isopropyl cation

Just as isopropyl cation is more stable than n-propyl cation, acetone is more stable than propionaldehyde owing to the extra stabilization imparted by the dipolar resonance structure.

We can see this effect by an examination of heats of formation of isomeric aldehydes and ketones. Some of these comparisons are summarized in Table 14.5. The data show that ketones are about 7 kcal mole^{-1} more stable than the isomeric aldehydes.

TABLE 14.5 Heats of Formation of Some Aldehydes and Ketones

Aldehydes	ΔH_f°, kcal mole^{-1} 25°C, gas	Ketones	ΔH_f°, kcal mole^{-1} 25°C, gas
HCHO	−26.0		
CH$_3$CHO	−39.7		
CH$_3$CH$_2$CHO	−45.5	CH$_3$COCH$_3$	−51.9
CH$_3$CH$_2$CH$_2$CHO	−48.9	CH$_3$CH$_2$COCH$_3$	−57.0
CH$_3$CH$_2$CH$_2$CH$_2$CHO	−54.5	CH$_3$CH$_2$CH$_2$COCH$_3$	−61.8
		CH$_3$CH$_2$COCH$_2$CH$_3$	−61.8

Consideration of the carbocation character of a carbonyl group has other corollaries as well. Consider the effect of a nearby polar substituent such as a chlorine, as in chloroacetaldehyde. The C—Cl dipole acts to destabilize the carbocation resonance structure. Hence, this structure contributes less to the overall resonance hybrid and the resonance hybrid is less stable as a result.

contributes less

No comparable effect operates on the corresponding hydrate. Thus, the chlorine substituent destabilizes the nonhydrated form, relative to the hydrated form, and as a result the aldehyde is more hydrated at equilibrium. For trichloroacetaldehyde, "chloral," the equilibrium constant is about 500. This compound exists almost wholly as the hydrate.

Chloral hydrate, CCl$_3$CH(OH)$_2$, is a crystalline solid, m.p. 57°C, having a distinctive odor. Its narcotic effect has led to its illegal use as "knockout drops."

The equilibrium between a carbonyl compound and its hydrate can also be described as the resultant of two rate constants.

The equilibrium constant is given by the ratio, $K = k_1/k_{-1}$. In the case of a ketone, such as acetone, the amount of hydrate present is so small that its rate of formation cannot be determined directly. The rate constant k_1 can be determined indirectly by an isotope exchange reaction. Water consists mostly of H$_2{}^{16}$O, but it also contains 0.20% of the heavy oxygen isotope, H$_2{}^{18}$O. Water enriched in the heavy isotope is available, and the rate of hydration can be followed by measuring the rate of incorporation of ^{18}O into acetone. The ^{18}O content of the ketone can be determined by mass spectrometry (Chapter 32).

This exchange reaction is slow in pure water, but is much faster in the presence of small amounts of either acid or base. In the uncatalyzed reaction a molecule of water attacks the electron-deficient carbonyl carbon to produce an intermediate that undergoes rapid proton exchange to give the *gem*-diol.

$$H_2O \quad {}^{\delta+}\underset{CH_3}{\overset{CH_3}{C}}=O^{\delta-} \rightleftharpoons H_2\overset{+}{O}-\underset{CH_3}{\overset{CH_3}{C}}-O^- \rightleftharpoons HO-\underset{CH_3}{\overset{CH_3}{C}}-OH$$

The *gem*-diol decomposes to give back the ketone by an exact reversal of this sequence. If one of the oxygens in the diol is heavy oxygen, the dehydration process has an equal probability of expelling the labeled oxygen in the leaving water or of retaining it in the ketone. However, water is a rather weakly basic reagent, and the carbonyl carbon is only slightly positive. Furthermore, the product of this addition has a charge-separated structure, as shown in the foregoing equation. Consequently, the direct attack by water on the carbonyl carbon is a slow process.

Hydroxide ion is a much more basic reagent and its reaction with a carbonyl group is much faster than that of water.

$$HO^-\underset{CH_3}{\overset{CH_3}{C}}=O \rightleftharpoons HO-\underset{CH_3}{\overset{CH_3}{C}}-O^- \underset{HO^-}{\overset{H_2O}{\rightleftharpoons}} HO-\underset{CH_3}{\overset{CH_3}{C}}-OH$$

Note that the presence of hydroxide ion does not affect the *position* of equilibrium in the hydration reaction. Hydroxide ion catalyzes the reverse reaction exactly as much as the forward reaction.

In the acid-catalyzed reaction the ketone oxygen is first protonated in a rapid equilibrium process.

$$\underset{CH_3}{\overset{CH_3}{C}}=O + H^+ \rightleftharpoons \left[\underset{CH_3}{\overset{CH_3}{C}}=\overset{+}{O}H \longleftrightarrow {}^+\underset{CH_3}{\overset{CH_3}{C}}-OH \right]$$

In the protonated compound the carbonyl carbon has more positive charge than in the neutral ketone. One resonance structure is that of a hydroxycarbocation.

A carbonyl group has dipolar character because oxygen is more electronegative than carbon and has greater attraction for electrons than carbon. The π-bond of the carbonyl group is relatively polarizable, and the electron density in this bond is displaced toward oxygen. In a protonated carbonyl group the oxonium ion oxygen is even more electronegative, and the electron density is displaced even more toward oxygen, leaving a more positive carbon.

The hydroxycarbocation reacts rapidly with water to give a protonated form of the ketone hydrate.

$$H_2O + \left[{}^+\underset{CH_3}{\overset{CH_3}{C}}-OH \longleftrightarrow \underset{CH_3}{\overset{CH_3}{C}}=\overset{+}{O}H \right] \rightleftharpoons H_2\overset{+}{O}-\underset{CH_3}{\overset{CH_3}{C}}-OH \rightleftharpoons HO-\underset{CH_3}{\overset{CH_3}{C}}-OH + H^+$$

Note that this reaction is closely analogous to the S_N1 reaction involving carbocations (Section 9.7).

$$H_2O + {}^+\underset{\underset{CH_3}{|}}{\overset{\overset{CH_3}{|}}{C}}-CH_3 \rightleftharpoons H_2\overset{+}{O}-\underset{\underset{CH_3}{|}}{\overset{\overset{CH_3}{|}}{C}}-CH_3 \rightleftharpoons HO-\underset{\underset{CH_3}{|}}{\overset{\overset{CH_3}{|}}{C}}-CH_3 + H^+$$

Furthermore, the reverse reaction, dehydration of the ketone hydrate, is analogous to unimolecular elimination of an alcohol (E1 reaction).

EXERCISE 14.13 The NMR spectrum of a solution of chloroacetaldehyde in tetra-deuteriomethanol, CD_3OD, shows no signals in the region δ 9–10 ppm. Explain.

B. Acetals and Ketals

The equilibrium between carbonyl compounds and water is not a significant synthetic reaction because *gem*-diols are generally unstable and readily dehydrate. However, the analogous reaction of aldehydes and ketones with alcohols does have significant utility. The addition of one mole of an alcohol to the carbonyl group of an aldehyde or ketone yields a **hemiacetal** or a **hemiketal**, respectively.

$$CH_3CH_2CHO + CH_3OH \rightleftharpoons CH_3CH_2\overset{\overset{OH}{|}}{C}H-OCH_3$$
a hemiacetal

$$CH_3\overset{\overset{O}{\|}}{C}CH_3 + CH_3OH \rightleftharpoons CH_3\underset{\underset{OCH_3}{|}}{\overset{\overset{OH}{|}}{C}}CH_3$$
a hemiketal

Addition of 2 moles of an alcohol, with the consequent formation of 1 mole of water, yields an **acetal** or a **ketal**.

$$CH_3CH_2CHO + 2\ CH_3OH \rightleftharpoons CH_3CH_2\underset{\underset{OCH_3}{|}}{\overset{\overset{OCH_3}{|}}{C}}H + H_2O$$
an acetal

$$CH_3\overset{\overset{O}{\|}}{C}CH_3 + 2\ CH_3OH \rightleftharpoons CH_3\underset{\underset{OCH_3}{|}}{\overset{\overset{OCH_3}{|}}{C}}CH_3 + H_2O$$
a ketal

Formation of the hemiacetal or hemiketal is directly analogous to addition of water and is also subject to both acid and base catalysis. As with hydration, aldehydes give more of the addition product at equilibrium than do ketones.

Acid-catalyzed hemiacetal formation

$$(1)\ CH_3\overset{\overset{O}{\|}}{C}H + H^+ \rightleftharpoons CH_3\overset{\overset{{}^+OH}{\|}}{C}H$$

$$\underset{\substack{\text{+OH}\\ \parallel}}{\text{(2) }CH_3CH} + CH_3OH \rightleftharpoons \underset{\substack{\text{OH}\\ \mid \\ +\\ \mid\\ H}}{CH_3CHOCH_3}$$

$$\underset{\substack{\text{OH}\\ \mid\\ +\\ \mid\\ H}}{\text{(3) }CH_3CHOCH_3} \rightleftharpoons \underset{\substack{\text{OH}\\ \mid}}{CH_3CHOCH_3} + H^+$$

Base-catalyzed hemiacetal formation

$$\underset{\substack{O\\ \parallel}}{\text{(1) }CH_3CH} + CH_3O^- \rightleftharpoons \underset{\substack{O^-\\ \mid}}{CH_3CHOCH_3}$$

$$\underset{\substack{O^-\\ \mid}}{\text{(2) }CH_3CHOCH_3} + CH_3OH \rightleftharpoons \underset{\substack{OH\\ \mid}}{CH_3CHOCH_3} + CH_3O^-$$

Like hydrates, simple hemiacetals and hemiketals are generally not sufficiently stable for isolation.

Acetals and ketals are formed by way of the intermediate hemiacetal or hemiketal. *However, replacement of the OH group by OR is only brought about by acid catalysis.*

Acid-catalyzed acetal formation

$$\underset{\substack{OH\\ \mid}}{\text{(1) }CH_3CHOCH_3} + H^+ \rightleftharpoons \underset{\substack{\text{+OH}_2\\ \mid}}{CH_3CHOCH_3}$$

$$\underset{\substack{\text{+OH}_2\\ \mid}}{\text{(2) }CH_3CHOCH_3} \rightleftharpoons \left[\underset{\substack{+\\ \mid\\ H}}{CH_3C-OCH_3} \longleftrightarrow \underset{\substack{+\\ \mid\\ H}}{CH_3C=OCH_3}\right] + H_2O$$

$$\text{(3) }\left[\underset{\substack{+\\ \mid\\ H}}{CH_3C-OCH_3} \longleftrightarrow \underset{\substack{+\\ \mid\\ H}}{CH_3C=OCH_3}\right] + CH_3OH \rightleftharpoons \underset{\substack{+\\ HOCH_3\\ \mid\\ H}}{CH_3C-OCH_3}$$

$$\text{(4) }\underset{\substack{+\\ HOCH_3\\ \mid\\ H}}{CH_3C-OCH_3} \rightleftharpoons \underset{\substack{OCH_3\\ \mid\\ H}}{CH_3C-OCH_3} + H^+$$

The net equilibrium that occurs when an aldehyde or ketone is treated with an alcohol and an acid catalyst is as follows.

$$\underset{\substack{O\\ \parallel}}{CH_3CCH_3} + 2\,CH_3OH \underset{}{\overset{H^+}{\rightleftharpoons}} \underset{\substack{OCH_3\\ \mid\\ \mid\\ OCH_3}}{CH_3CCH_3} + H_2O$$

For simple aldehydes the overall equilibrium constant is favorable, and the acetal may be prepared simply by treating the aldehyde with two equivalents of alcohol and an acid catalyst.

381

Sec. 14.7

Addition of
Oxygen and
Nitrogen
Nucleophiles

$$CH_3CHO + 2\ CH_3CH_2OH \underset{}{\overset{H^+}{\rightleftharpoons}} CH_3CH(OCH_2CH_3)_2 + H_2O$$

A mixture of 1305 mL of ethanol (21.7 moles), 500 g of acetaldehyde (11.4 moles) and 200 g of anhydrous $CaCl_2$ is placed in a 4 L bottle and kept at 25°C for 1–2 days. At the end of this time the upper layer is washed with water and distilled to yield 790–815 g of 1,1-diethoxyethane, b.p. 101–103°C. Note that $CaCl_2$ serves as a catalyst by hydrolyzing to give a small amount of HCl.

With larger aldehydes and with ketones, the equilibrium constant for acetalization or ketalization is generally unfavorable, more so for ketalization than for acetalization. For this reason the reaction is usually carried out with the alcohol as solvent in order to drive the equilibrium to the right. With aldehydes this usually allows the acetal to be produced in good yield.

3-nitrobenzaldehyde

$+ CH_3OH \xrightarrow{HCl}$

(76–85%)
3-nitrobenzaldehyde
dimethyl acetal

For ketones the equilibrium lies even further to the left, and special techniques are used to remove water as it is formed and thus drive the equilibrium to the right.

The acetal and ketal equilibria provide an illustration of the role of entropy in equilibria. In the formation of an acetal or ketal, three reactant molecules combine to form two product molecules. The resulting loss of the freedom of motion of one molecule corresponds to a negative entropy change. As in the hydration reaction (page 375), the formation of acetals from aldehydes is so exothermic that the equilibrium lies far to the right despite the unfavorable entropy change. However, in the case of ketones, the equilibrium constant for ketal formation is unfavorable, both as a result of ΔH and ΔS. This unfavorable entropy effect is avoided by the use of a 1,2- or 1,3-diol to form a cyclic ketal.

$+ HOCH_2CH_2OH \rightleftharpoons H_2O +$

(80%)

Note in this case that two reactant molecules produce two product molecules. The overall entropy change is approximately zero, resulting in less unfavorable equilibria for ketones. However, for most cases, $\Delta G°$ is still positive, and it is necessary to drive the reaction to completion by removing the water produced.

Acetals and ketals are generally stable to basic conditions and are hydrolyzed back to carbonyl compounds in acidic solution. They play an important role in carbohydrate chemistry (Chapter 28). They are also used to **protect** a carbonyl group during a synthetic scheme. The following synthesis of 4-heptynal from 3-bromopropanal illustrates the use of an acetal as a **protecting group**.

In this case it is desired to replace Br by the 1-butynyl group. As we saw in Section 12.5.B, alkynyllithium compounds undergo ready alkylation by primary alkyl bromides. However, we shall see in Section 14.8 that organolithium reagents also react readily with the carbonyl group. Thus, direct replacement of bromine in the bromoaldehyde is not possible. Therefore the aldehyde is temporarily "protected" by conversion to the acetal, which is an ether and does not react with the organolithium reagent. After the displacement reaction has been carried out, the aldehyde functional group is regenerated by treatment of the acetal with aqueous acid. Since an excess of water is used in the regeneration step, the equilibrium is shifted back onto the side of the aldehyde and the diol.

A group of compounds that are related to acetals and ketals are the **enol ethers**, produced by the nucleophilic addition of alcohols to alkynes (Section 12.6.D).

$$HC{\equiv}CH + C_2H_5OH \xrightarrow{C_2H_5O^-} C_2H_5OCH{=}CH_2$$
ethyl vinyl ether

Like other ethers, enol ethers are stable to basic conditions and to basic reagents such as organolithium reagents. However, under acidic conditions they undergo rapid hydrolysis to give the aldehyde or ketone and alcohol.

$$C_2H_5OCH{=}CH_2 + H_2O \xrightarrow{H^+} C_2H_5OH + CH_3CHO$$

The mechanism of this ready hydrolysis starts with the addition of a proton to the carbon-carbon double bond. The resulting cation is completely analogous in structure to a protonated aldehyde or ketone. From this point on, the hydrolysis mechanism involves the same type of intermediates as are involved in the formation and hydrolysis of acetals and ketals.

(1) $C_2H_5O{-}CH{=}CH_2 + H^+ \rightleftharpoons [C_2H_5O{-}\overset{+}{C}H{-}CH_3 \longleftrightarrow C_2H_5\overset{+}{O}{=}CH{-}CH_3]$

(2) $[C_2H_5O{-}\overset{+}{C}H{-}CH_3 \longleftrightarrow C_2H_5\overset{+}{O}{=}CH{-}CH_3] + H_2O \rightleftharpoons C_2H_5O{-}\overset{\overset{+}{O}H_2}{\underset{}{C}H}{-}CH_3$

(3) $C_2H_5O{-}\overset{\overset{+}{O}H_2}{\underset{}{C}H}{-}CH_3 \rightleftharpoons C_2H_5O{-}\overset{OH}{\underset{}{C}H}{-}CH_3 + H^+$

(4) $C_2H_5O{-}\overset{OH}{\underset{}{C}H}{-}CH_3 + H^+ \rightleftharpoons C_2H_5\overset{OH}{\underset{H}{\overset{+}{O}}}{-}\overset{}{C}HCH_3$

(5) $C_2H_5\overset{OH}{\underset{H}{\overset{+}{O}}}{-}CHCH_3 \rightleftharpoons C_2H_5OH + [HO{-}\overset{+}{C}HCH_3 \longleftrightarrow H\overset{+}{O}{=}CHCH_3]$

382   (6) $[HO{-}\overset{+}{C}HCH_3 \longleftrightarrow H\overset{+}{O}{=}CHCH_3] \rightleftharpoons \overset{O}{\overset{\|}{HCCH_3}} + H^+$

383

Sec. 14.7

*Addition of
Oxygen and
Nitrogen
Nucleophiles*

EXERCISE 14.14 Write the steps in the mechanism for acid-catalyzed hydration of propene (Section 11.6.C) and compare with the steps in the foregoing mechanism for hydrolysis of ethyl vinyl ether. Note that there is a parallel between the steps of the alkene hydration mechanism and the first three steps of the mechanism for enol ether hydrolysis. Can you offer an explanation for the observation that enol ether hydrolysis is *much* more facile than is alkene hydration?

Acetals and ketals are ethers and will form dangerous peroxides on exposure to air. Appropriate precaution should be taken when heating acetals and ketals that have had long exposure to oxygen.

There is a final important consequence to be discussed relative to the tendency of aldehydes to form acetals. On standing, aldehydes tend to form cyclic or polymeric acetals that are isomeric with several molecules of aldehyde. Formaldehyde itself is a gas that is available commercially as a 37% aqueous solution called formalin, or as a solid polymer, paraformaldehyde. For use in syntheses, formaldehyde is normally obtained by heating the dry polymer.

The linear polymer, $HO-(CH_2-O)_n-H$, forms the basis of several commercial plastics such as Delrin and Celcon. In these cases the terminal OH groups are "capped" with ester groups to prevent depolymerization or "unzipping" upon heating.

Formaldehyde also forms a cyclic trimer, trioxane, a solid having m.p. 64°C, which can be sublimed unchanged. Paraldehyde, from acetaldehyde, is a liquid, b.p. 128°C, that regenerates acetaldehyde on heating with a trace of acid.

trioxane   paraldehyde

Acetaldehyde also forms a cyclic tetramer, metaldehyde, a solid that sublimes readily. Other low molecular weight aldehydes form cyclic trimers related to paraldehyde. This kind of behavior is not shown by ketones.

EXERCISE 14.15 Careful purification of paraldehyde yields two isomeric substances. The CMR spectrum of one isomer has only two signals, whereas that of the other isomer shows four signals. What are the structures of these two isomers?

C. Imines and Related Compounds

Ammonia reacts with aldehydes and ketones to form compounds called **imines**. These compounds contain the functional group $C=N$, which may be considered to be the nitrogen analog of a carbonyl group.

Imines derived from ammonia are not an important class of compounds. They hydrolyze rapidly even with water to generate carbonyl compounds.

However, the substituted imines that are produced from the reactions of aldehydes and ketones with primary amines (amines having only one alkyl group attached to nitrogen) are much more stable. These compounds are sometimes referred to as **Schiff bases**.

$$RCHO + R'NH_2 \rightleftharpoons RCH{=}NR' + H_2O$$

substituted imine,
a Schiff base

Even though N-substituted imines are more stable than their N—H relatives, they are still fairly reactive compounds. They readily undergo hydrolysis back to the amine and carbonyl compound and are often prone to polymerization. However, if either the carbon or the nitrogen is substituted by a phenyl group, the resulting imine is generally rather stable.

(84–87%)

Imines prepared from aliphatic aldehydes and ketones and aliphatic amines are more reactive than aromatic analogs and are somewhat more difficult to prepare. Since the equilibrium constant in this case is not as large as when there is a phenyl group attached to the carbon-nitrogen double bond, it is usually necessary to drive the reaction to completion by removal of water from the reaction mixture as it is formed, as in the formation of ketals. An example of such a case is the condensation of cyclohexanone with *t*-butylamine.

t-butylamine   (85%)

Aldehydes and ketones also react with other ammonia derivatives to give analogous adducts. Common reagents are hydroxylamine (H_2NOH), hydrazine (H_2NNH_2), and phenylhydrazine ($H_2NNHC_6H_5$). Examples of such reactions follow. Unlike imines, the products of these reactions are generally quite stable.

hydroxylamine   an oxime

hydrazine   a hydrazone

385

Sec. 14.7

*Addition of
Oxygen and
Nitrogen
Nucleophiles*

phenylhydrazine   a phenylhydrazone

EXERCISE 14.16 The reaction of acetaldehyde with hydroxylamine gives a product that shows *two* CH_3 doublets in its NMR spectrum. Explain.

The reactions of carbonyl compounds with substituted ammonia compounds are generally catalyzed by mild acid. The mechanism is directly analogous to the reactions discussed previously with water and alcohols.

The first step is a nucleophilic addition to the carbonyl group. Rapid proton transfer gives the product of net addition of RNH_2 to C=O, a **hemiaminal**, also sometimes called a carbinolamine. This substance is generally so reactive that it cannot normally be isolated. A second acid-catalyzed reaction occurs in which water is eliminated from the hemiaminal. The resulting product is the imine, oxime, or hydrazone, and so on.

In the foregoing mechanism, steps (1)–(3) are rapid equilibria. The rate-limiting step is generally step (4), the elimination of water from the protonated hemiaminal. The overall reaction obeys the following rate law.

$$\text{rate} = k[\text{ketone}][H^+][RNH_2]$$

EXERCISE 14.17 Assuming that steps (1)–(3) are rapid equilibria, characterized by equilibrium constants K_1, K_2, and K_3, and that step (4) is the rate-limiting step, characterized by rate constant k_1, derive the expected rate law. What rate law would be observed if the first step was rate limiting?

Although the reaction is catalyzed by acid at moderate pH, at higher acid concentration the rate actually diminishes with increasing acid concentration because the nitrogen base is itself protonated by acid. Therefore the concentration of free nucleophile is inversely related to the acid concentration. In solutions having high acid concentrations (low pH) the concentration of unprotonated nitrogen base is so low that step (1) becomes rate limiting. At moderate acid concentrations enough free nitrogen base is available that step (1) is a rapid equilibrium, yet enough acid is also available to catalyze step (4). For this reason the reaction is often carried out in the presence of a buffer such as sodium acetate. In some cases, particularly in the formation of simple imines, the reaction proceeds satisfactorily without acid catalysis.

14.8 Addition of Carbon Nucleophiles

A. Addition of Organometallic Reagents: Synthesis of Alcohols

One of the most useful techniques in organic chemistry for building up more complex molecules from simple ones involves the reaction of Grignard reagents and organolithium compounds with carbonyl compounds. We have seen previously (Section 8.6) that the carbon-metal bonds in these highly reactive organometallic compounds are polarized in the sense $C^- M^+$. The negative carbon (carbanion) of Grignard reagents reacts readily and rapidly with the positive carbon of the carbonyl group of aldehydes and ketones. Some examples show the scope of this important reaction.

(64–69%)
cyclohexylmethanol

The Grignard reagent is prepared from 26.7 g of magnesium turnings and 118.5 of cyclohexyl chloride in 450 mL of dry ether. In a separate flask 50 g of dry paraformaldehyde (page 383) is heated to 180–200°C, and the formaldehyde formed by depolymerization is carried by a stream of nitrogen gas into the solution of the Grignard reagent. When the reaction is complete, ice and dilute sulfuric acid are added, and the mixture is steam distilled. The distillate is extracted with ether and distilled at reduced pressure to yield 72.5–78.5 g of cyclohexylmethanol.

(53–54%)
3-methyl-2-butanol

A solution of 600 g of isopropyl bromide in ether is slowly added to a mixture of 146 g of dry magnesium turnings in ether. The Grignard solution is then cooled to −5°C, and a solution of 200 g of acetaldehyde in ether is added. Ice and dilute sulfuric acid are added, and the mixture is extracted with ether. The dried extract is distilled to give 210–215 g of 3-methyl-2-butanol, b.p. 110–111.5°C.

3,5-dimethyl-3-hexanol

As shown by these examples, the reaction is useful for preparation of primary, secondary, and tertiary alcohols. Reaction of a Grignard reagent with formaldehyde gives a primary alcohol, other aldehydes yield secondary alcohols, and ketones lead to tertiary alcohols. Note that secondary and tertiary alcohols may generally be prepared by more than one combination of Grignard reagent and carbonyl component.

$$CH_3MgBr + CH_3CH_2\overset{\overset{\displaystyle O}{\|}}{C}CH_2CH_2CH_3 \longrightarrow CH_3CH_2\underset{\underset{\displaystyle CH_3}{|}}{\overset{\overset{\displaystyle OH}{|}}{C}}CH_2CH_2CH_3$$

$$CH_3CH_2MgBr + CH_3\overset{\overset{\displaystyle O}{\|}}{C}CH_2CH_2CH_3 \longrightarrow CH_3CH_2\underset{\underset{\displaystyle CH_3}{|}}{\overset{\overset{\displaystyle OH}{|}}{C}}CH_2CH_2CH_3$$

$$CH_3CH_2CH_2MgBr + CH_3\overset{\overset{\displaystyle O}{\|}}{C}CH_2CH_3 \longrightarrow CH_3CH_2\underset{\underset{\displaystyle CH_3}{|}}{\overset{\overset{\displaystyle OH}{|}}{C}}CH_2CH_2CH_3$$

The particular combination used is governed by such practical matters as cost and availability of reagents and ease of handling reactants.

For the preparation of many alcohols the Grignard reaction is a simple and straightforward process. However, side reactions are important and can dominate in sterically congested cases in which the normal addition reaction is retarded. One such side reaction is enolization.

In this reaction, the organomagnesium reagent acts as a *base*, rather than as a nucleophile, and abstracts an α-proton from the ketone to give the enolate ion. When water is added during normal work-up, the enolate is hydrolyzed to give back the starting ketone.

Another side reaction is important in hindered cases when the Grignard reagent has a β-hydrogen. In this reaction the carbonyl group is *reduced* and an alkene is formed.

The initial product is the magnesium alkoxide, which is hydrolyzed to the secondary alcohol upon workup.

This reaction can be formulated as an alternative mode of reaction of a Grignard reagent coordinated to a carbonyl group.

In situations such as the foregoing, alkyllithium reagents are especially useful because they are more reactive than Grignard reagents and can be used at low temperature where the alternative reduction and enolization reactions are less important. A spectacular example of a hindered system prepared by an organolithium reaction is

$$(t\text{-Bu})_2C{=}O \ + \ t\text{-BuLi} \ \xrightarrow[-78°C]{\text{ether}} \ \xrightarrow{H_3O^+} \ (t\text{-Bu})_3COH$$

di-*t*-butyl ketone   *t*-butyllithium   (81%)
3-*t*-butyl-2,2,4,4-tetra-
methyl-3-pentanol

EXERCISE 14.18 Show how 1-bromobutane may be converted into each of the following compounds.
(a) 1-pentanol   (b) 2-methyl-2-pentanol
(c) 2-methyl-2-hexanol   (d) 3-heptanol (see section 10.11.A)

EXERCISE 14.19 Outline three different combinations of alkyl halide and ketone that can be used to prepare each of the following tertiary alcohols.
(a) 3-methyl-3-nonanol   (b) 3,4,5-trimethyl-3-heptanol
(c) 4-ethyl-2-methyl-4-octanol

The organometallic derivatives of alkynes (Sections 12.4 and 12.5.B) also undergo ready addition to the carbonyl group of aldehydes and ketones. For example, the sodium salt of a terminal alkyne, prepared in the normal manner by treatment of the alkyne with a solution of sodium amide in liquid ammonia, readily adds to aldehydes and ketones. As in the Grignard and alkyllithium reactions we just discussed, the initial product is the salt of the alcohol. The neutral alcohol is obtained by the addition of acid.

(65–75%)
1-ethynylcyclohexanol

A stream of dry acetylene is passed into a solution of 23 g of sodium in 1 L of liquid ammonia. After the sodium has been consumed, 98 g of cyclohexanone is added dropwise. The ammonia is allowed to evaporate, and the residue is treated with 400 mL of ice water and acidified with 50% H_2SO_4. The product is extracted with ether and distilled. The yield of 1-ethynylcyclohexanol is 81–93 g (65–75%).

EXERCISE 14.20 Show the principal products from reaction of 1-ethynylcyclohexanol with the following reagents.
(a) H_2SO_4, H_2O, $HgSO_4$ (b) H_2, poisoned Pd catalyst
(c) (i) BH_3, THF; (ii) NaOH, H_2O_2

B. Addition of HCN

Because of the analogy that exists between the chemical reactivity of acetylide and cyanide ions (Chapter 12), we might expect that cyanide would also add to aldehydes and ketones. Such addition does occur, but the equilibrium constant for the reaction is often unfavorable, and net reaction is generally not observed.

$$\text{(acetone)} + CN^- \rightleftharpoons \text{(O, CN adduct)}$$

The relatively unfavorable equilibrium constant in this reaction is primarily the result of trading in the salt of HCN ($pK_a = 9.2$) for the salt of an alcohol ($pK_a \cong 16$).

Although the addition of Na^+CN^- to ketones is a generally poor reaction, the addition of HCN itself usually proceeds in good yield. For example, acetone reacts readily with HCN to give the 1:1 adduct, which is called a **cyanohydrin**.

$$\text{(acetone)} + HCN \rightleftharpoons \text{(HO, CN adduct)}$$

acetone cyanohydrin

Although most acids will add to the carbonyl group to some extent, usually the adducts are not stable. For example, with HCl the equilibrium lies far to the left and α-chloro alcohols cannot be isolated.

$$\text{(acetone)} + HCl \rightleftharpoons \text{(HO, Cl adduct)}$$

Furthermore, if such an α-chloro alcohol is produced by some other process, it immediately decomposes to give HCl and the corresponding aldehyde or ketone.

The relative stabilities of 1-chloro alcohols and cyanohydrins can be appreciated by comparing bond energies.

$$RCH{=}O + HY \rightleftharpoons \underset{\underset{Y}{|}}{RCH{-}OH}$$

$$\Delta H^\circ = E(C{=}O) + E(H{-}Y) - E(O{-}H) - E(C{-}O) - E(C{-}Y)$$

The differences for ΔH° from one Y group to another are in the comparisons of $E(H{-}Y) - E(C{-}Y)$. To evaluate these bond-strength differences, compare the DH° values of H—Y and CH_3—Y for Y = Cl and CN.

Y = Cl: $DH^\circ(H{-}Cl) - DH^\circ(CH_3{-}Cl) = 103 - 85 = 18 \text{ kcal mole}^{-1}$
Y = CN: $DH^\circ(H{-}CN) - DH^\circ(CH_3{-}CN) = 124 - 122 = 2 \text{ kcal mole}^{-1}$

The difference in bond strengths between H—Cl and C—Cl is much greater than between H—CN and C—CN; hence, formation of the cyanohydrin has a more favorable energy change than formation of a 1-chloroalkanol.

For aldehydes and most aliphatic ketones the equilibrium favors the adduct. For some aliphatic ketones the equilibrium constant is small, and the reaction is not a useful one. The reaction is a typical nucleophilic addition with the attacking nucleophile being CN^-. Addition is therefore catalyzed by base, which increases the cyanide concentration. The reaction can be carried out using liquid hydrogen cyanide (b.p. 26°C) as the solvent.

$$ClCH_2CHO + HCN \longrightarrow \underset{\underset{(95\%)}{}}{ClCH_2\overset{\overset{OH}{|}}{C}HCN}$$

Because of the high toxicity of HCN, procedures such as the foregoing are seldom used. A more common procedure is to generate the HCN *in situ* by the addition of HCl or H_2SO_4 to a mixture of the carbonyl compound and sodium or potassium cyanide.

$$CH_2O + KCN \xrightarrow[H_2O]{H_2SO_4} HOCH_2CN$$
$$(76-80\%)$$

A mixture of 130 g of potassium cyanide in 250 mL of H_2O and 170 mL of 37% formaldehyde solution (formalin) is prepared. To this solution is added a mixture of 57 mL of conc. H_2SO_4 and 173 mL of H_2O. The product, obtained by exhaustive extraction with ether, weighs 87–91 g (76-80%).

Under strongly basic conditions cyanohydrin formation may be reversed. The equilibrium is shifted by transformation of HCN into its conjugate base.

$$+ \ HCN \xrightarrow{NaOH} Na^+CN^- + H_2O$$

EXERCISE 14.21 By combining the chemistry you have learned in this section with reactions you have learned previously, show how to convert acetone into each of the following compounds.

(a)   (b)   (c)

C. The Aldol Addition Reaction

When acetaldehyde is treated with aqueous sodium hydroxide solution, 3-hydroxybutanal is formed in 50% yield. When this reaction was first discovered, in the early nineteenth century, the product was known as "aldol," from "*ald*ehyde-alcoh*ol*."

$$2 \ CH_3CHO \xrightarrow[5°C, 4-5 \ hr]{OH^-, \ H_2O} \overset{\overset{\displaystyle OH}{|}}{CH_3CHCH_2CHO}$$
$$(50\%)$$
$$aldol$$

The reaction is a general one for aldehydes that have a hydrogen α to the carbonyl group. Consequently, the term "aldol" addition reaction has come to be a generic term for the addition of the enol or enolate of one aldehyde or ketone to the carbonyl group of another. Under more vigorous conditions (base concentration, temperature), elimination of the β-hydroxy group occurs and an α,β-unsaturated aldehyde is produced.

$$2 \ CH_3CH_2CH_2CHO \xrightarrow[\substack{80-100°C \\ 3 \ hr}]{1 \ M \ NaOH, \ H_2O} \left[\overset{\overset{\displaystyle OH}{|}}{CH_3CH_2CH_2CHCHCHO} \atop \overset{\displaystyle |}{\underset{\displaystyle CH_3}{CH_2}} \right] \xrightarrow{-H_2O}$$

$$\overset{\overset{\displaystyle CHO}{|}}{CH_3CH_2CH_2CH{=}CCH_2CH_3}$$
$$(86\%)$$
$$2\text{-ethylhex-2-enal}$$

Mechanistically, the addition reaction is simply the nucleophilic addition of an enolate ion onto the carbonyl group of another, nonionized molecule. Thus, in one reaction, both of the important chemical properties of the carbonyl group are expressed. The mechanism for the dimerization of acetaldehyde consists of the following three simple steps.

(1) $CH_3CHO + OH^- \rightleftharpoons [CH_2{=}CHO^- \longleftrightarrow \bar{C}H_2{-}CH{=}O] + H_2O$

(2) $CH_3\overset{\overset{\displaystyle O}{\|}}{C}H + \, ^-CH_2{-}CH{=}O \rightleftharpoons CH_3\overset{\overset{\displaystyle O^-}{|}}{C}HCH_2CHO$

(3) $CH_3\overset{\overset{\displaystyle O^-}{|}}{C}HCH_2CHO + H_2O \rightleftharpoons CH_3\overset{\overset{\displaystyle OH}{|}}{C}HCH_2CHO + OH^-$

The slow, rate-limiting step is usually the addition step. The dehydration of the β-hydroxy aldehyde or ketone mechanism to produce an α,β-unsaturated carbonyl compound involves the enolate ion of the aldol product.

(4) $CH_3\overset{\overset{\displaystyle OH}{|}}{C}HCH_2CHO + OH^- \rightleftharpoons CH_3\overset{\overset{\displaystyle OH}{|}}{C}H{-}\bar{C}HCHO + H_2O$

(5) $CH_3\overset{\overset{\displaystyle OH}{|}}{C}H{-}\bar{C}HCHO \rightleftharpoons CH_3CH{=}CHCHO + OH^-$

When a mixture of two different aldehydes is treated with base, four aldol products are possible.

$$RCH_2CHO + R'CH_2CHO \longrightarrow \begin{cases} RCH_2\overset{\overset{\displaystyle OH}{|}}{C}H{-}\overset{\overset{\displaystyle R}{|}}{C}HCHO \\[8pt] RCH_2\overset{\overset{\displaystyle OH}{|}}{C}H{-}\overset{\overset{\displaystyle R'}{|}}{C}HCHO \\[8pt] R'CH_2\overset{\overset{\displaystyle OH}{|}}{C}H{-}\overset{\overset{\displaystyle R}{|}}{C}HCHO \\[8pt] R'CH_2\overset{\overset{\displaystyle OH}{|}}{C}H{-}\overset{\overset{\displaystyle R'}{|}}{C}HCHO \end{cases}$$

In practice, a complex mixture usually results in such a situation. However, when one of the aldehydes cannot form an enolate ion or when one has an unusually unreactive carbonyl group, such a "mixed aldol reaction" is often feasible.

furfural $+ CH_3CH_2CHO \xrightarrow{NaOH, \, H_2O}$ (72%)

Although ketones also undergo aldol addition, the reaction in this case often requires rather special conditions. The overall reaction is an equilibrium process, and it appears that the equilibrium constant in most ketone aldol reactions is unfavorable. For example, acetone and its aldol product (4-hydroxy-4-methyl-2-pentanone) are in rapid equilibrium in the presence of base catalysts. The amount of the aldol product in the equilibrium is only a few percent. However, if the product is removed from the basic catalyst as it is formed, the conversion can be accomplished in 80% yield.

4-hydroxy-4-methyl-2-pentanone

Intramolecular aldol addition of diketones is an important method for the synthesis of cyclic compounds. In this case, the dehydrated product is usually desired, and such reactions are carried out under conditions of base concentration and temperature that lead to the α,β-unsaturated ketone.

Although intramolecular aldol addition is exceedingly useful for the synthesis of cyclic compounds, the method has an important limitation in that *it is only generally applicable for the synthesis of five- six-, and seven-membered ring systems.*

The intermolecular aldol addition of one ketone to another is slightly *endothermic*. In part this is due to the fact that the bonds formed in the product are about the same strength as those broken in the reactants and in part it is due to the unfavorable entropy resulting from combining two molecules into one. In the intramolecular version of the reaction, the entropy of reaction is not unfavorable, since one reactant molecule gives one product molecule. Consequently, intramolecular aldol additions of one ketone to another are generally successful.

However, the $\Delta G°$ of reaction is not very negative in most cases, and as a result, the addition reaction is easily reversible. Cyclopropane and cyclobutane rings are not produced by intramolecular aldol addition because it is necessary to create approximately 25 kcal mole^{-1} of ring strain in the formation of these rings. Rings larger than seven members are not formed, both because of ring strain in the product (unfavorable $\Delta H°$, see Table 5.5) and the improbability of bringing the two ends of the chain into proximity (unfavorable $\Delta S°$).

Since ketones undergo self-addition much more slowly than aldehydes, mixed aldol additions between a ketone and a nonenolizable aldehyde are usually clean. In order to ensure the formation of a 1:1 adduct, an excess of ketone is often used, and the reaction is carried out under fairly mild conditions.

EXERCISE 14.22 Write the structure of the diketone that would give each of the following cyclic α,β-unsaturated ketones upon treatment with KOH in ethanol.

(a)   (b)

The aldol reactions discussed up to this point are carried out with a base such as hydroxide ion or ethoxide ion in a protic solvent such as water or ethanol. Since aldehydes and ketones are a good deal less acidic than these solvents, the enolate ions are formed reversibly and in only small amounts (see Section 14.6.B). However, the reaction may also be carried out in another manner. Recall that the strong base lithium diisopropylamide (LDA) converts a ketone completely into the corresponding enolate ion (see page 370). Since all of the ketone is consumed in this essentially irreversible reaction, self-addition of the ketone to itself does not occur. However, if an aldehyde is subsequently added to the cold enolate solution, a rapid and efficient mixed aldol reaction occurs. The initial product is the lithium salt of the β-hydroxy ketone. Aqueous work-up affords the aldol.

With unsymmetrical ketones, the strong base LDA always removes a proton from the *least sterically hindered position*; that is, from the position having the larger number of α-hydrogens. Thus, in such a case the mixed aldol reaction occurs specifically at one of the two α-positions.

This method of preforming the lithium enolate and subsequently adding the carbonyl receptor compound is the best way of carrying out a mixed aldol reaction.

EXERCISE 14.23 Show how each of the following compounds may be prepared from simple aldehydes and ketones utilizing the aldol addition reaction.

(a)

(b)

(c)

(d)

D. Diastereomeric Transition States

In Section 7.8, we saw that reactions which involve achiral reactants and media but which produce a new stereocenter must give racemic products. This truth stems from the fact that, under such circumstances, the transition states leading to the two stereoisomeric products are enantiomeric. Since the competing reactions start from the same point and pass through enantiomeric transition states that must necessarily have identical energies, their energies of activation must be equal. A further example is seen in the addition of methylmagnesium bromide to pentanal, which gives racemic 2-hexanol.

$$\text{CHO} + \text{CH}_3\text{MgBr} \xrightarrow{\text{H}_3\text{O}^+}$$

(R)-2-hexanol (S)-2-hexanol

When one of the reactants is chiral, and a new stereocenter is created in the reaction, the two products bear a diastereomeric relationship to one another. In such a case, the two competing transition states are also diastereomeric, and therefore have *different* energies. For example, in addition of methyllithium to 2-methylcyclopentanone, the two diastereomeric products are produced in unequal amounts.

(ca. 90%)
(1R,2S)-1,2-dimethyl-cyclopentanol

(ca. 10%)
(1S,2S)-1,2-dimethyl-cyclopentanol

It is intuitive that the two isomers should be produced in unequal amount in this example. To form the 1R,2S compound, the organometallic reagent may approach the face of the cyclopentanone C=O from the side of the ring *opposite the C-2 methyl substituent*. However, in order to form the 1S,2S compound, it must attack *from the same side of the ring as the C-2 methyl group*. There will obviously be more steric repulsion in the latter case than in the former.

It is perhaps *not* so obvious that the foregoing situation holds even for additions to carbonyl groups that are in noncyclic structures. For example, consider the addition of methylmagnesium bromide to the chiral aldehyde 2-cyclohexylpropanal. Again, a new stereocenter is produced in the reaction, and the two products have a diastereomeric relationship. In this case, just as in the 2-methylcyclopentanone case, the two diastereomers are formed in unequal amounts.

(65%)
(2R,3R)-3-cyclohexyl-
2-butanol

(35%)
(2S,3R)-3-cyclohexyl-
2-butanol

The relationship that holds in both the cyclic and noncyclic cases is illustrated in Figure 14.7. Since the two competing reactions start at the same point, and since they proceed through diastereomeric transition states (which have different energies), it follows that the two reactions *must* have different activation energies, and therefore the two diastereomers must be formed in unequal amounts.

While the foregoing analysis assures us that the two diastereomers must be formed in unequal amounts, it does not help us to decide which will be the major product. In the 2-methylcyclopentanone case, it is relatively easy to predict that the reagent will prefer to attack the face of the C=O from the less-hindered side of the cyclopentanone ring.

FIGURE 14.7 Nucleophilic addition to a chiral aldehyde gives diastereomeric products in unequal amounts.

In the acyclic case, it is not obvious which face is more reactive, since the molecule is free to rotate about the C-1—C-2 bond.

Be careful not to fall into the trap of neglecting this free rotation. For example, some students will look at the following depiction of the reaction and assume that the $2R,3R$ isomer predominates because "the methyl group is on top and the hydrogen is on the bottom."

This is a completely falacious argument, since we could just as well have written the structure of (R)-2-cyclohexylpropanal in the following way. Application of the foregoing argument to this depiction of the molecule would lead one to expect the reagent to attack the top face of the C=O, since "hydrogen is on top and cyclohexyl is on the bottom."

This way of looking at the question leads to *exactly the opposite prediction.*

Several useful models have been developed for predicting the relative stereochemistry of the major and minor products in reactions such as these. However, they are beyond the scope of an introductory textbook.

EXERCISE 14.24 Predict the product, including stereochemistry, of the acid-catalyzed bromination of 3-methylcyclobutanone.

E. The Wittig Reaction

Alkyl halides react with triphenylphosphine, $(C_6H_5)_3P$, by the S_N2 mechanism to give crystalline phosphonium salts.

ethyltriphenylphosphonium bromide

Phosphine, PH_3, is the phosphorus analog of ammonia (Section 25.6). It is a poisonous gas and is usually spontaneously flammable because of the presence of impurities. Triphenylphosphine, Ph_3P, is a commercially available crystalline solid, m.p. 80°C. Note that the abbreviation Ph is used to represent the phenyl group, C_6H_5. Triphenylphosphine is insoluble in water, but is soluble in most organic solvents.

Since phosphines are good nucleophiles and weak bases, competing elimination is not as important here as in other bimolecular substitutions (Section 9.6). Consequently, most primary and secondary alkyl halides give good yields of phosphonium salts.

cyclohexyltriphenylphosphonium iodide

The alkyl proton adjacent to the positive phosphorus is moderately acidic ($pK_a \cong 35$) and may be removed by strong bases such as *n*-butyllithium or sodium hydride to give a neutral phosphorus compound called an **ylide** or **phosphorane**.

> The formula $Ph_3P=CHCH_2CH_3$ implies an expansion of the phosphorus octet and orbital overlap with phosphorus $3d$-atomic orbitals, Detailed quantum-mechanical studies show that the actual participation of such *d*-orbitals in bonding in phosphorus ylides is minor. Instead, the dipolar structure is stabilized by polarization of the electrons around phosphorus. Such polarization can be represented in terms of an induced dipole on phosphorus.
>
>
> Nevertheless, we will frequently use the simple pentacoordinate formula for convenience.

Ylides react rapidly with aldehydes and ketones, even at $-80°C$, to give neutral products called **oxaphosphetanes**. The carbon-carbon and phosphorus-oxygen bonds may form simultaneously or the mechanism may involve initial nucleophilic addition of the ylide carbon to the carbonyl group, giving a dipolar intermediate called a **betaine** (pronounced "bay-ta-ene"), which then reacts further to give the oxaphosphetane. At $-80°C$ the oxaphosphetane is stable in solution. Upon warming the solution to $0°C$, it decomposes to give an alkene and triphenylphosphine oxide. The overall process, illustrated by the following equations for the reaction of acetone and the ylide derived from ethyl bromide, is called the **Wittig reaction**, in honor of the German organic chemist Georg Wittig, who developed the process and subsequently received a share of the 1980 Nobel Prize in chemistry for the achievement.

a betaine

an oxaphosphetane

triphenylphosphine
oxide

The Wittig reaction is an exceedingly useful method for the synthesis of alkenes. Although a mixture of cis and trans isomers usually results, *only a single positional isomer is produced*. Consider, as an example, the synthesis of methylenecyclohexane. Dehydration of 1-methylcyclohexanol gives mainly 1-methylcyclohexene, since this isomer is more stable.

1-methylcyclohexene

The less stable isomer may be readily prepared from cyclohexanone by the Wittig reaction.

EXERCISE 14.25 Starting with triphenylphosphine and any desired alkyl halides, aldehydes, and ketones, show how the following alkenes can be prepared.
(a) 2-methyl-2-pentene   (b) 2,2-dimethyl-3-heptene   (c) 3-methyl-2-hexene

---

14.9 Oxidation and Reduction

A. Oxidation of Aldehydes and Ketones

Aldehydes are oxidized to carboxylic acids with ease. Oxidizing agents that have been used are Ag_2O, H_2O_2, $KMnO_4$, CrO_3, and peroxy acids.

(97%)

peroxyacetic acid

(88%)

This oxidation is so facile that even atmospheric oxygen will bring it about. Most aldehyde samples that have been stored for some time before use are found to be contaminated with variable amounts of the corresponding carboxylic acid. In the case of oxidation by air (**autoxidation**) the initial oxidation product is a **peroxycarboxylic acid** (page 268). The peroxycarboxylic acid reacts with another molecule of aldehyde to give two carboxylic acid molecules.

$$RCHO + O_2 \longrightarrow RC\overset{O}{\overset{\|}{}}OOH$$

a peroxycarboxylic
acid

$$RC\overset{O}{\overset{\|}{}}OOH + RCHO \longrightarrow 2 RC\overset{O}{\overset{\|}{}}OH$$

The initial oxidation (to the peroxycarboxylic acid stage) is a free radical chain process. The second stage oxidation of the aldehyde by the initially formed peroxycarboxylic acid, is an example of the **Baeyer-Villiger oxidation**. The probable course of this oxidation follows.

$$
R-\overset{\overset{\displaystyle O}{\|}}{C}-H + R-\overset{\overset{\displaystyle O}{\|}}{C}-OOH \rightleftharpoons R-\underset{\underset{\displaystyle H}{|}}{\overset{\overset{\displaystyle OH}{|}}{C}}-O-O-\overset{\overset{\displaystyle O}{\|}}{C}-R
$$

$$
R-\underset{\underset{\displaystyle H}{|}}{\overset{\overset{\displaystyle OH}{|}}{C}}-O-O-\overset{\overset{\displaystyle O}{\|}}{C}-R \rightleftharpoons R-\overset{\overset{\displaystyle {}^{+}OH}{\|}}{C}-OH + {}^{-}O-\overset{\overset{\displaystyle O}{\|}}{C}-R
$$

$$
R-\overset{\overset{\displaystyle {}^{+}OH}{\|}}{C}-OH + {}^{-}O-\overset{\overset{\displaystyle O}{\|}}{C}-R \longrightarrow 2\,R-\overset{\overset{\displaystyle O}{\|}}{C}-OH
$$

In contrast to aldehydes, ketones are oxidized only under rather special conditions. The Baeyer-Villiger oxidation is one reaction in which a ketone undergoes oxidation. In this case the product is an ester.

$$
\xrightarrow[\text{CH}_2\text{Cl}_2]{\text{CF}_3\text{CO}_3\text{H}}
$$

(78%)

The mechanism of the reaction is believed to be similar to that outlined for the oxidation of an aldehyde, except that the migrating group is an alkyl group rather than a hydrogen.

$$
C_2H_5-\underset{\underset{\displaystyle C_2H_5}{|}}{\overset{\overset{\displaystyle OH}{|}}{C}}-O-O-\overset{\overset{\displaystyle O}{\|}}{C}-CF_3 \longrightarrow C_2H_5-\overset{\overset{\displaystyle {}^{+}OH}{\|}}{C}-OC_2H_5 + CF_3CO_2^{-} \longrightarrow
$$

$$
C_2H_5\overset{\overset{\displaystyle O}{\|}}{C}OC_2H_5 + CF_3COOH
$$

The overall result of the Baeyer-Villiger oxidation is *insertion of an oxygen atom into one of the bonds to the carbonyl group*; consequently, the ketone is converted into an ester. The reaction is a preparatively useful one for the oxidation of certain ketones to esters. Cyclic ketones give cyclic esters, which are called lactones (Section 27.5.C).

$$
+ CH_3CO_3H \xrightarrow[\substack{40°C \\ 6.5\ \text{hr}}]{CH_3COOEt}
$$

(90%)

Symmetrical ketones can give only one product in the Baeyer-Villiger oxidation. However, unsymmetrical ketones can give two oxidation products, and this is sometimes observed. When the two alkyl groups differ substantially, a clear selectivity can often be observed. The approximate order of decreasing ease of migration (the migratory aptitude) for various groups is hydrogen > tertiary alkyl > secondary alkyl > phenyl > primary alkyl > methyl. The following examples illustrate this selectivity.

(67%)

(62%)

Although ketones may be oxidized by other reagents, oxidative cleavage is seldom a useful preparative method. The conditions required for the oxidation of most ketones are sufficiently vigorous that complex mixtures result. The chief exception to this generalization is in symmetrical cyclic ketones, where the reaction can be useful. The oxidation of cyclohexanone by nitric acid is catalyzed by vanadium pentoxide. The product, adipic acid, is an important industrial chemical because it is one of the constituents of nylon 66 (Section 34.5).

adipic acid

EXERCISE 14.26 Give the principal expected product of Baeyer-Villiger oxidation of the following compounds.
(a) $C_6H_5COCH_3$ (b) cyclopentanone
(c) 3,3-dimethyl-2-butanone   (d) ethyl cyclohexyl ketone

B. Metal Hydride Reduction

Aldehydes and ketones are easily reduced to the corresponding primary and secondary alcohols, respectively.

$$R{-}CHO \xrightarrow{[H]} R{-}CH_2OH.$$

$$\underset{\displaystyle O}{R{-}\overset{\displaystyle O}{\overset{\|}{C}}{-}R'} \xrightarrow{[H]} \underset{\displaystyle OH}{R{-}\overset{\displaystyle OH}{\overset{|}{C}H}{-}R'}$$

Many different reducing agents may be used. For laboratory applications the complex metal hydrides are particularly effective. Lithium aluminum hydride ($LiAlH_4$, page 291) is a powerful reducing agent that has been used for this purpose. Reductions are normally carried out by adding an ether solution of the aldehyde or ketone to an ether solution of $LiAlH_4$. Reduction is rapid even at $-78°C$ (dry ice temperature). At the end of the reaction the alcohol is present as a mixture of lithium and aluminum salts and is liberated by hydrolysis.

$$\langle\!\!\rangle\!=\!O + LiAlH_4 \xrightarrow[30°C, 1\ hr]{ether} \xrightarrow[H_2O]{H_2SO_4}$$

(90%)

cyclobutanol

The reagent also reduces many other oxygen- and nitrogen-containing functional groups, as illustrated in Table 14.5. The chief drawbacks of the reagent are its cost, which renders it useful only for fairly small-scale laboratory applications, and the hazards involved in handling it.

Sodium borohydride, $NaBH_4$ (page 261), offers certain advantages. This hydride is much less reactive than $LiAlH_4$ and is consequently more selective. Of the functional groups in Table 14.6 that are reduced by $LiAlH_4$, only aldehydes and ketones are reduced at a reasonable rate by $NaBH_4$. The reagent is moderately stable in aqueous and in alcoholic solution, especially at basic pHs. The following example illustrates the selectivity that may be achieved with the reagent.

The carbonyl group is also reduced rapidly and quantitatively by diborane in ether or THF (page 262). The initial product is the ester of boric acid and an alcohol, a trialkyl borate. This material is rapidly hydrolyzed upon treatment with water.

$$(CH_3)_2CHCHO + B_2H_6 \xrightarrow{THF} [(CH_3)_2CHCH_2O]_3B \xrightarrow{H_2O} (CH_3)_2CHCH_2OH$$

(100%)   (100%)

EXERCISE 14.27 Suggest reaction sequences for carrying out the following transformations.
(a) 1-octyne to 2-octanol   (b) cyclopentanone to 1,5-pentanediol

---

TABLE 14.6 Functional Groups Reduced by LiAlH$_4$

Functional Group	Product	Moles of LiAlH$_4$ Required
RCHO	RCH$_2$OH	0.25
R$_2$C=O	R$_2$CHOH	0.25
RCOOR′	RCH$_2$OH + R′OH	0.5
RCOOH	RCH$_2$OH	0.75
$\overset{\overset{O}{\|\|}}{R}CNH_2$	RCH$_2$NH$_2$	1
RC≡N	RCH$_2$NH$_2$	0.5
RNO$_2$	RNH$_2$	1.5
RCl(Br, I)	RH	0.25

C. Catalytic Hydrogenation

Aldehydes and ketones may also be reduced to alcohols by hydrogen gas in the presence of a metal catalyst (catalytic hydrogenation; Section 11.6.A). The chief advantages of this method are that it is relatively simple to accomplish and usually affords a quantitative yield of product because no complicated work-up procedure is required. However, it suffers from the disadvantages that many of the catalysts used (Pd, Pt, Ru, Rh) are relatively expensive and that other functional groups (C=C, C≡C, NO_2, C≡N) also react.

(96%)

D. Deoxygenation Reactions

Several methods are known whereby the oxygen of an aldehyde or ketone is replaced by two hydrogens; this process is known as **deoxygenation**.

$$R\!-\!\overset{\overset{\displaystyle O}{\|}}{C}\!-\!R' \longrightarrow R\!-\!CH_2\!-\!R'$$

One such method is the **Wolff-Kishner reduction**. The method involves first the formation of the hydrazone by reaction with hydrazine. At elevated temperatures with base the hydrazone loses nitrogen to give the hydrocarbon. The reaction is normally carried out by heating the ketone with hydrazine hydrate (Section 14.7.C) and sodium hydroxide in diethylene glycol, $HOCH_2CH_2OCH_2CH_2OH$, which has a b.p. of 245°C. Alternatively, the reduction may be carried out in the polar aprotic solvent DMSO at 100°C. The hydrazone forms, and water distills out of the mixture. On refluxing, nitrogen is evolved, and the product is isolated.

cyclononanone   (47%)
cyclononane

The decomposition of the hydrazone involves an intermediate carbanion. In the presence of base the hydrazone is in equilibrium with a double bond isomer. This isomer forms an anion with base, which loses nitrogen to produce the alkyl anion. The carbanion is exceedingly basic and rapidly abstracts a proton from the solvent. Alkyl anions are rarely encountered in reactions because of the low acidity of hydrocarbons. In the present case they are formed only because the nitrogen also produced is an extremely stable molecule and its production provides the driving force for the reaction.

(1) R_2C=$N\ddot{N}H_2$ + B^- $\rightleftharpoons$ BH + $[R_2C$=N—$\ddot{N}H^-$ $\longleftrightarrow$ $R_2\ddot{C}^-$—N=$NH]$

(2) $[R_2C$=N—$\ddot{N}H^-\longleftrightarrow$ $R_2\ddot{C}^-$—N=$NH]$ + BH $\rightleftharpoons$ $R_2\overset{\overset{\textstyle H}{\textstyle |}}{C}$—$N$=$NH$ + B^-

(3) R_2CH—N=$\ddot{N}H$ + B^- $\rightleftharpoons$ R_2CH—N=$\ddot{N}^-$ + BH

(4) $R_2\ddot{C}H$—N=$\ddot{N}^-$ $\xrightarrow{slow}$ $R_2\ddot{C}H^-$ + N_2

(5) $R_2\ddot{C}H^-$ + BH $\xrightarrow{fast}$ R_2CH_2 + B^-

An alternative procedure for the direct reduction of a carbonyl group to a methylene group involves refluxing the aldehyde or ketone with amalgamated zinc and hydrochloric acid (**Clemmensen reduction**).

Amalgamated zinc is zinc with a surface layer of mercury. It is prepared by treating zinc with an aqueous solution of a mercuric salt. Since zinc is higher on the electromotive force scale than mercury, it displaces mercury from its salts.

$$Zn + Hg^{2+} \longrightarrow Zn^{2+} + Hg$$

The mercury then alloys with the surface of zinc to produce an amalgam.

Reduction of the carbonyl compound occurs on the surface of the zinc, and, like many heterogeneous reactions, this reaction does not have a simple mechanism. The Clemmensen reduction is suitable for compounds that can withstand treatment with hot acid. Many ketones are reduced in satisfactory yields.

$$C_6H_5COCH_3 \xrightarrow[\substack{HCl \\ \Delta}]{Zn(Hg)} C_6H_5CH_2CH_3$$

acetophenone   (80%)
ethylbenzene

EXERCISE 14.28 Which method is preferable for deoxygenation of each of the following aldehydes or ketones? If neither the Wolff-Kishner nor the Clemmensen method is expected to be suitable, so indicate.

(a) Br⌒⌒⌒CHO

(b) [structure with OH and O groups]

(c) [structure with O and epoxide ring]

(d) [cyclohexanone with propyl substituent]

PROBLEMS

1. Provide common names for the following ketones and aldehydes.

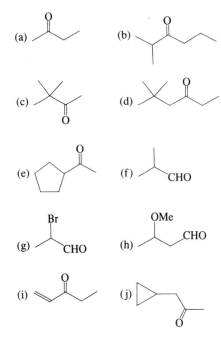

(a)   (b)

(c)   (d)

(e)   (f)   CHO

(g)   Br   CHO   (h)   OMe   CHO

(i)   (j)

2. Provide IUPAC names for the compounds in Problem 1.

3. Write the structure corresponding to each of the following names.
   (a) methyl isobutyl ketone   (b) propionaldehyde diethyl acetal
   (c) β-chlorobutyraldehyde   (d) 2,2-dimethylcyclopentanone
   (e) cyclododecanone   (f) formaldehyde phenylhydrazone
   (g) cyclohexanone oxime   (h) acetone hydrazone

4. What is the product of the reaction of 4,4-dimethylcyclohexanone with each of the following reagents?
   (a) (i) Lithium diisopropylamide (LDA) in THF; (ii) CH_3CH_2Br
   (b) bromine in acetic acid
   (c) peroxyacetic acid
   (d) (i) $LiAlH_4$ in ether; (ii) H_2O
   (e) $NaBH_4$ in ethanol
   (f) (i) $CH_3C{\equiv}C^-$ Na^+ in liq. NH_3; (ii) H_2O
   (g) KCN and aqueous sulfuric acid
   (h) H_2NOH + sodium acetate in acetic acid
   (i) 0.5 mole of H_2NNH_2 + sodium acetate in acetic acid

   (j) ⟨benzene ring⟩—CHO + aqueous NaOH

   (k) H_2NNH_2 + $HOCH_2CH_2OCH_2CH_2O^-$ Na^+, 200°C
   (l) zinc amalgam + hot conc. hydrochloric acid
   (m) NaOD in D_2O at 25°C
   (n) $Ph_3P{=}CHCH_2CH_3$

5. Answer Problem 4 for 2-methylpentanal. In this case, some of the reactions will not work. Give products for those reactions that are expected to be successful and indicate those that are expected to fail.

6. Show how each of the following compounds can be prepared from alkyl halides and alcohols containing four or fewer carbons.

(a)

(b)

(c)

(d)

(e)

(f)

(g)

(h)

7. Show how each of the following compounds may be prepared from pentanal. Any other reagents, organic or inorganic, may be used.

(a)

(b)

(c)

(d)

(e)

(f)

(g)

(h)

8. Show how one may accomplish each of the following conversions in a practical manner using any necessary organic or inorganic reagents.

(a)

(b)

(c)

(d)

(e)

(f)

9. Show how each of the following compounds can be prepared from aldehydes, ketones, and alkyl halides containing four carbons or less using the Grignard synthesis as a key step in each case.
   (a) 1-bromopentane
   (b) 3-hexanone
   (c) 4-propyl-3-heptene
   (d) 2,5-dimethyl-3-ethyl-3-hexanol

10. Show how each of the following isotopically labeled compounds can be synthesized. You may use any necessary organic starting materials, as long as they are unlabelled at the start of your synthesis. You may use any necessary inorganic reagents, labelled or otherwise.

(a)

(b)

(c)

(d)

11. Explain why each of the following syntheses cannot be accomplished in the specified manner.
    (a) 2,2,5,5-tetramethyl-3-hexene by the Wittig reaction.
    (b) 2,2-dimethyl-3-hydroxycyclobutanone by an intramolecular aldol addition
    (c) 2-ethyl-3-hydroxybutanal by a mixed aldol addition reaction
    (d) 3-methyl-2-hexanol by Clemmensen reduction of 4-methyl-5-hydroxy-3-hexanone

12. Outline a sequence of reactions that can be used to convert hept-6-en-2-one into 7-hydroxyheptan-2-one. [*Caution:* Remember that ketones are reduced by diborane.]

13. In reactions of protonated acetone, why does reaction with a base always occur at carbon rather than at the positive oxygen?

14. If the acid-catalyzed bromination of bromoacetone is analyzed immediately after the bromine has all reacted, the major product present is 1,1-dibromoacetone. If the reaction mixture is allowed to stir at room temperature for several hours and then analyzed, the sole product is found to be 1,3-dibromoacetone. Explain these observations with a reasonable mechanism for each step.

15. Acetaldehyde reacts with (*R*)-1,2-propanediol to give *two* isomeric acetals. What are the structures of these two compounds?

16. Propose a mechanism for the following reaction.

$$+ Br_2 \xrightarrow{\text{trace } H^+}$$

17. 1,1-Diethoxyethane hydrolyzes readily to acetaldehyde and ethanol in water containing some sulfuric acid. Write a complete reaction mechanism for this transformation including each significant intermediate and reaction step.

18. Is the equilibrium constant for the following equilibrium greater than, less than, or equal to unity? Explain briefly.

$$CF_3CHO + CH_3CH(OCH_3)_2 \rightleftharpoons CH_3CHO + CF_3CH(OCH_3)_2$$

19. When 4-hydroxybutanal is dissolved in methanol containing HCl, the following reaction occurs.

$$HOCH_2CH_2CH_2CHO + CH_3OH \xrightarrow{HCl} \underset{OCH_3}{\overset{O \quad H}{\diamond}} + H_2O$$

(a) What type of compound is the product?
(b) Propose a mechanism for this reaction.
Actually, 4-hydroxybutanal exists in solution mostly in the cyclic form.

$$HOCH_2CH_2CH_2CHO \rightleftharpoons \underset{OH}{\overset{O \quad H}{\diamond}}$$

(c) What type of compound is this product?
(d) Propose a mechanism for the equilibrium.

20. Write a plausible reaction mechanism for the trimerization of acetaldehyde to paraldehyde with a trace of acid. How does this mechanism compare to the acid-catalyzed depolymerization of paraldehyde?

21. Undecanal is a sex attractant for the greater wax moth (*Galleria mellonella*). Show how to synthesize this compound efficiently from (a) 1-decanol and (b) 1-dodecanol.

22. Compound A, $C_7H_{16}O$, reacts with sodium dichromate in aqueous H_2SO_4 to give B, $C_7H_{14}O$. When B is treated with NaOD at 25°C for several hours analysis shows that it has incorporated two deuteriums. Compound B is not oxidized by Ag_2O. What are A and B?

23. Compound C has the formula $C_{12}H_{20}$ and is optically active. It reacts with H_2 and Pt to give two isomers, D_1 and D_2, $C_{12}H_{22}$. Ozonolysis of C gives only E, $C_6H_{10}O$, which is optically active. Compound E reacts with hydroxylamine to give F, $C_6H_{11}NO$. When E is treated with DCl in D_2O for several hours and then analyzed by mass spectrometry, it is found to have a molecular weight of 101. The NMR spectrum of E shows that it has only one methyl group, which appears as a doublet with $J = 6.5$ Hz. What are compounds C through F?

24. An unknown compound, G, has the formula C_6H_8O and shows a singlet methyl in its NMR spectrum. When treated with hydrogen gas and palladium it absorbs one equivalent of H_2 to give a product, H, with the formula $C_6H_{10}O$. The infrared spectrum of compound H shows that it has a carbonyl group. Compound H reacts with NaOD in D_2O to give a product shown by mass spectrometry to have the formula $C_6H_7D_3O$. Compound H reacts with peroxyacetic acid, CH_3CO_3H, to give I, which has the formula $C_6H_{10}O_2$. The NMR spectrum of I contains one and only one absorption due to a CH_3 group, a doublet with $J = 8$ Hz at $\delta = 1.2$ ppm. Propose structures for compounds G, H, and I.

25. *trans*-3-Isopropyl-6-methylcycloheptanone has the following proton-coupled CMR spectrum (letters in parentheses after each chemical shift indicate multiplicity of the resonance: s = singlet, d = doublet, t = triplet, q = quartet): 18.5(q), 18.9(q), 23.9(q), 32.0(d), 32.5(t), 34.9(d), 38.5(t), 41.9(d), 47.0(t), 51.6(t), and 213.4(s). A certain reaction provided samples of the cis and trans isomers of 3,6-dimethylcycloheptanone. However, it was not known which isomer had which stereostructure. The isomers have the following CMR spectra.

isomer J: 20.9(q), 29.2(d), 33.9(t), 50.8(t), 212.1(s)
somer K: 23.7(q), 31.1(d), 37.9(t), 51.7(t), 212.1(s)

Which isomer has the cis structure, and which the trans?

26. Cyclopropanones undergo a reaction that is not common for other ketones—cleavage of one of the carbon-to-carbonyl bonds. Thus, cyclopropanone itself reacts with NaOH in water to give sodium propionate. Propose a mechanism for this unusual reaction. Predict the product that will result when 2-methylcyclopropanone is treated in the same manner. Treatment of 2-bromo-3-pentanone with NaOH in water yields, after acidification of the reaction mixture, 2-methylbutanoic acid. Propose a mechanism for this reaction (the **Favorskii reaction**).

27. Unsymmetrical alkynes normally undergo hydration to give a mixture of the two possible ketones. For example, hydration of 2-heptyne gives both 2-heptanone and 3-heptanone. However, treatment of hept-5-yn-2-one with aqueous sulfuric and a small amount of mercuric sulfate gives *only* heptan-2,5-dione. Suggest a mechanism that might account for this behavior.

28. Ethyl vinyl ether, CH_2=$CHOCH_2CH_3$, reacts with *n*-butanol and a trace of sulfuric acid in ether to give 1-*n*-butoxy-1-ethoxyethane. Treatment of this product with aqueous sulfuric acid affords a mixture of ethanol, *n*-butanol, and acetaldehyde. Propose a mechanism for each reaction. How might this chemistry be used to advantage in accomplishing the following conversion?

29. Each of the following compounds may be obtained by an intramolecular aldol condensation. Show the precursor in each case.

(a)   (b)

(c)   (d)

30. Bromination of 7-cholestanone gives 6-bromo-7-cholestanone with $J_{5H,6H} = 2.8$ Hz. This initial product slowly converts to the more stable 6-bromo stereoisomer that has $J_{5H,6H} = 11.8$ Hz. Assign stereostructures to the two isomers and explain their relative stabilities.

7-cholestanone

31. When a mixture of an aldehyde or ketone and an α-halo ester is treated with a strong base, an α,β-epoxy ester is obtained.

Propose a mechanism for this reaction (**Darzen's condensation**).

32. Treatment of an aldehyde or ketone with a mixture of ammonium chloride and sodium cyanide yields an α-amino nitrile (**Strecker synthesis**).

$$\text{CHO} + NH_4Cl + NaCN \longrightarrow \underset{\text{an } \alpha\text{-amino nitrile}}{\overset{NH_2}{\text{CN}}}$$

Propose a mechanism for the reaction. What product is expected when 2,6-heptanedione is subjected to the Strecker synthesis?

Chapter 15

Infrared Spectroscopy

15.1 The Electromagnetic Spectrum

There are many different forms of radiant energy that display wave properties. Examples are cosmic rays, x-rays, visible light and radio waves. These apparently different types of radiation are known collectively as **electromagnetic radiation**. They are all considered as waves that travel at a constant velocity (the "speed of light," $c = 3.0 \times 10^{10}$ cm sec^{-1}) and differ in wavelength or frequency. The **electromagnetic spectrum** is diagrammed in Figure 15.1 along with the wavelength in centimeters of its various regions. The divisions between regions are arbitrary and are established in

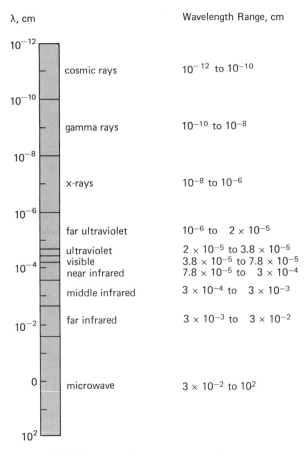

FIGURE 15.1 The electromagnetic spectrum.

practice by the different instrumentation required to produce and record electromagnetic radiation in the different regions. As pointed out in Section 13.2, compounds may absorb radiant energy in various regions of the electromagnetic spectrum and thereby become excited from their ground state to a more energetic state. **Spectroscopy** is a technique whereby we measure the amount of radiation a substance absorbs at various wavelengths. From the spectrum of a compound we may often obtain useful information about the structure of the compound.

The relationship between the wavelength and frequency of radiation is given by the relationship

$$\nu = \frac{c}{\lambda}$$

where λ = wavelength in centimeters, ν = frequency in Hertz (Hz), and c = the velocity of light (2.998×10^{10} cm sec^{-1}). The relationship between energy and frequency is

$$\epsilon = h\nu$$

where ϵ = the energy of a photon and h = Planck's constant (6.6242×10^{-27} erg sec), or

$$E = Nh\nu$$

where E = the energy of an Avogadro number N of photons ($E = \epsilon \times 6.023 \times 10^{23}$). Thus, when a compound absorbs radiation of a given wavelength, each molecule absorbs an amount of energy ϵ, and each mole of the compound absorbs an amount of energy E. In organic chemistry energy is traditionally expressed in units of kilocalories per mole.

$$E \, (\text{kcal mole}^{-1}) = \frac{2.857 \times 10^{-3}}{\lambda \, (\text{cm})}$$

In this chapter, we are concerned with absorption of light in the infrared region of the electromagnetic spectrum. Wavelengths in this region are traditionally expressed in microns (μ), where $10^4 \, \mu = 1$ cm. More commonly, another unit of measurement, the wavenumber, is used to describe infrared spectra. The wavenumber ($\tilde{\nu}$) is defined as the number of waves per centimeter and is expressed in units of cm^{-1} (reciprocal centimeters).

$$\tilde{\nu} = \frac{1}{\lambda}$$

By definition, the infrared region is split up into three parts (Figure 15.2): the near infrared ($\lambda = 0.78$–$3.0 \, \mu$; $\tilde{\nu} = 12{,}820$–3333 cm^{-1}), the middle infrared ($\lambda = 3$–30μ; $\tilde{\nu} = 3333$–333 cm^{-1}), and the far infrared ($\lambda = 30$–$300 \, \mu$; $\tilde{\nu} = 333$–33 cm^{-1}). The near infrared region corresponds to energies in the range 37–10 kcal mole^{-1}. Since there are few absorptions of organic molecules in this range, it is seldom used for spectroscopic purposes. Radiation in the middle infrared region has $E = 10$–1 kcal mole^{-1}, which corresponds to the differences commonly encountered between vibrational states. Spectroscopy in this region is useful to the organic chemist. The far infrared region has $E = 1.0$–0.1 kcal mole^{-1}. This region is little used for organic spectroscopy, again because few useful absorptions occur here.

An infrared spectrometer may be designed on either the single-beam or the double-beam principle. In a single-beam spectrophotometer light from the radiation source (usually an oxide-coated ceramic rod that is heated electrically to about 1500°C) is

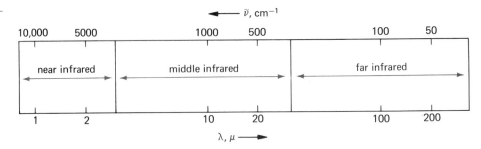

FIGURE 15.2 Regions of the infrared spectrum. Notice that the scales are logarithmic.

focused and passed through the sample, contained in a special cell. After passing through the sample, the emergent light beam is dispersed by a monochromater (either a prism or a diffraction grating) into its component wavelengths. The spectrum is scanned by slowly rotating the prism or grating. A double-beam spectrophotometer operates on a similar principle except that the original light is split into two beams, one of which passes through the sample while the other passes through a reference cell. The instrument records the difference in intensity of these two beams. This type of instrument is especially useful when spectra are to be measured in solution. In such a case the reference cell contains pure solvent. Thus, if the solvent absorbs weakly in a given region of the spectrum, its absorption may be "canceled out." Since glass absorbs strongly in the useful infrared region, it cannot be used for the optical parts of a spectrophotometer. The prism and sample cell walls are usually fabricated from large NaCl or KBr crystals.

15.2 Molecular Vibration

As discussed previously (Section 6.1), atoms in a molecule do not maintain fixed positions with respect to each other, but actually vibrate back and forth about an average value of the interatomic distance. This vibrational motion is quantized, as shown in the accompanying familiar diagram for a diatomic molecule (Figure 15.3). At room temperature most of the molecules in a given sample are in the lowest vibrational state. Absorption of light of the appropriate energy allows the molecule to become "excited" to the second vibrational level. In this level the amplitude of the molecular vibration is greater. In general, such absorption of an infrared light quantum can occur only if the dipole moment of the molecule is different in the two vibrational levels. The variation of the dipole moment with the change in interatomic distance during the vibration corresponds to an oscillating electric field that can interact with the oscillating electric field associated with electromagnetic radiation. The requirement that absorption of a vibrational quantum be accompanied by a change in dipole moment is known as a **selection rule**. Such a vibrational transition is said to be **infrared-active**. Furthermore, the greater the change in dipole moment, the more intense is the absorption. Vibrational transitions that do not result in a change of dipole moment of the molecule are not observed directly and are referred to as infrared-inactive transitions. Thus, carbon monoxide and iodine chloride absorb infrared light, but hydrogen, nitrogen, chlorine, and other symmetrical diatomics do not.

$$C{\equiv}O, \ I{-}Cl \qquad\qquad H_2, \ N_2, \ Cl_2$$

absorb in infrared   *do not absorb in infrared*

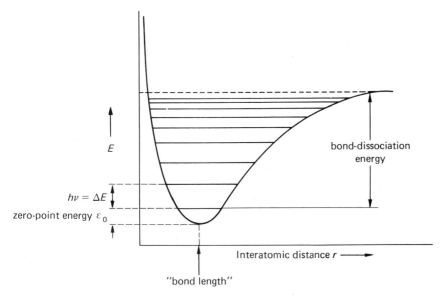

FIGURE 15.3 Vibrational levels for a vibrating bond.

For more complex molecules, there are more possible vibrations. A nonlinear molecule containing n atoms has $3n - 6$ possible fundamental vibrational modes. Polyatomic molecules exhibit two distinct types of molecular vibration, stretching and bending. Vibrations of bonds involving hydrogens are especially significant because atoms of low mass tend to do a lot of moving compared to atoms of higher mass. The stretching and bending motions in a methylene group are diagrammed in Figure 15.4.

For polyatomic molecules of the size of typical organic compounds, the possible number of infrared absorption bands becomes very large. For example, pentane has 45 possible infrared absorption bands, decane has 90, and triacontane has 270. Many of these vibrations occur at the same frequency (that is, some vibrations are "degenerate"), and not all of the possible bands are generally seen as independent absorptions.

Stretching Vibrations

(a) symmetric   (b) asymmetric

Bending Vibrations

(a) scissoring (in-plane)   (b) rocking (in-plane)   (c) wagging (out-of-plane)   (d) twisting (out-of-plane)

FIGURE 15.4 Some vibrational modes for the methylene group.

However, additional bands, usually of low intensity, may occur as overtones (at approximately $\frac{1}{2}$, $\frac{1}{3}$, $\frac{1}{4}$, . . . , and so on, the wavelength of the fundamental mode).

> Overtones may arise in two ways. If a molecule in the lowest or first vibrational state is excited to the third vibrational level, the energy required is almost twice that required for excitation to the second vibrational level. It is not exactly twice as much because the higher levels tend to lie closer together than the lower levels (see Figure 15.3).
>
> Another type of overtone, commonly referred to as a "combination band," occurs when a single photon has precisely the correct energy to excite two vibrations at once. For this to happen, the energy of the combination band must be the exact sum of the two independent absorptions.

As a result, the infrared spectrum of an organic compound is usually rather complex.

The spectrum of octane; shown in Figure 15.5, illustrates several features of an infrared spectrum. Note that the wavelength is plotted against the percent transmittance of the sample. An absorption band is therefore represented by a "trough" in the curve; zero transmittance corresponds to 100% absorption of light of that wavelength.

The curve in Figure 15.5 is a spectrum of pure octane. The spectrum was measured with a Perkin-Elmer Model 735 Spectrometer using a cell 0.016 mm in length. Only four major absorption bands are apparent, at 2925, 1465, 1380, and 720 cm^{-1}. These four bands correspond to the C—H stretching vibrations, the CH_2 and CH_3 scissoring mode, the CH_3 rocking mode, and the CH_2 rocking mode, respectively. Figure 15.6 is a spectrum of the same sample measured in a cell 0.20 mm long. Since the amount of light absorbed is proportional to the number of molecules encountered by the beam as it passes through the sample, the longer cell allows absorption bands of low intensity to be observed. Many more bands can now be seen, especially in the region from 700 to 1300 cm^{-1}.

Because of its complexity, the spectrum cannot be analyzed completely. However, a peak-by-peak correspondence in the infrared spectra of two different samples is an excellent criterion of identity, as a comparison of the octane spectrum in Figure 15.6 with the heptane spectrum in Figure 15.7 readily shows. That is, the IR spectrum of heptane is similar to, but differs in significant respects from, that of octane.

Molecular vibrations are actually rather complex. Generally, all of the atoms in a molecule contribute to a vibration. Fortunately, however, some molecular vibrations can be treated by considering the motion of a few atoms relative to one another and

FIGURE 15.5 Infrared spectrum of octane, 0.016-mm cell.

FIGURE 15.6 Infrared spectrum of octane, 0.2-mm cell.

ignoring the rest of the atoms in the molecule. For example, it is convenient to refer to the vibration of individual bonds. To a useful approximation (the harmonic oscillator approximation), the vibration frequency of a bond is related to the masses of the vibrating atoms and the force constant, f, of the vibrating bond by the following equation.

$$\tilde{\nu} = \frac{1}{2\pi c} \sqrt{\frac{f(m_1 + m_2)}{m_1 m_2}}$$

In this relationship $\tilde{\nu}$ = vibrational frequency in cm^{-1} (wavenumber), c = velocity of light in $cm\ sec^{-1}$, m_1 = mass of atom 1 in g, m_2 = mass of atom 2 in g, and f = force constant in dyne cm^{-1} ($g\ sec^{-2}$). The equation corresponds to a simple Hooke's law model of two units coupled by a spring in which the force constant is the restoring force provided by the spring.

The larger the force constant, the higher the vibration frequency and the greater the energy spacings between vibrational quantum levels. The force constants for single, double, and triple bonds are approximately 5×10^5, 10×10^5, and 15×10^5 dynes cm^{-1}, respectively.

FIGURE 15.7 Infrared spectrum of heptane, 0.2-mm cell.

Recall that 1 dyne is the force required to accelerate a 1 g mass 1 cm sec^{-2}. Therefore 1 dyne = 1 g cm sec^{-2}. The units of f, the force constant, are thus g sec^{-2}.

Force constants provide another measure of bond strength and generally are roughly proportional to bond-dissociation energies. On the other hand, vibration frequencies relate inversely to the masses of the vibrating atoms. Bonds to hydrogen occur at relatively high frequencies compared to bonds between heavier atoms—a light weight on a spring oscillates faster than a heavy weight.

In spite of its gross assumptions, the Hooke's law approximation is useful because it helps us to identify the general region in which a vibration will occur. For example, we may easily estimate the ^{12}C—^{1}H stretching frequency by

$$\bar{\nu} = \frac{1}{2\pi \, 2.998 \times 10^{10} \text{ cm sec}^{-1}} \sqrt{\frac{5 \times 10^5 \text{ g sec}^{-2} \left(\dfrac{12}{6.023} + \dfrac{1}{6.023}\right) \times 10^{-23} \text{ g}}{\left(\dfrac{12}{6.023} \times 10^{-23} \text{ g}\right)\left(\dfrac{1}{6.023} \times 10^{-23} \text{ g}\right)}}$$

$$\bar{\nu} = 3032 \text{ cm}^{-1}$$

The actual range for C—H absorptions is 2850-3000 cm^{-1}.

The regions of the infrared spectrum where various bond stretching vibrations are observed depend primarily on whether the bonds are single, double, or triple or bonds to hydrogen. These regions are summarized in Table 15.1.

EXERCISE 15.1 Using the Hooke's law approximation, estimate $\bar{\nu}$ for each of the following stretching vibrations.

(a) O—H   (b) O—D   (c) C=C   (d) C≡C
(e) C—O   (f) C=O   (g) C≡N   (h) C—F

15.3 Characteristic Group Vibrations

As was pointed out in the previous section, the infrared spectrum of a polyatomic molecule is so complex that it is usually inconvenient to analyze it completely. However, valuable information may nevertheless be gleaned from the infrared spectrum of an organic compound. Consider the infrared spectra of 1-octene and 1-octadecene shown in Figures 15.8 and 15.9. Aside from the C—H stretching and bending vibrations at 2925, 1450, and 1370 cm^{-1}, we see several distinctive bands that do not appear in the spectra of typical alkanes (compare Figure 15.5). These new bands occur in the following general positions: 3080, 1640, 995, and 915 cm^{-1}. The Hooke's law approximation tells us that the band in the 3080 cm^{-1} region is the C—H stretch of the

TABLE 15.1 Approximate Values for Infrared Absorptions

Bond	General Absorption Region, cm^{-1}
C—C, C—N, C—O	800–1300
C=C, C=N, C=O	1500–1900
C≡C, C≡N	2000–2300
C—H, N—H, O—H	2850–3650

FIGURE 15.8 Infrared spectrum of 1-octene.

FIGURE 15.9 Infrared spectrum of 1-octadecene.

olefinic carbon-hydrogen bonds, and the 1640 cm^{-1} band is the carbon-carbon double bond stretching vibration. Other theoretical considerations suggest that the 995 cm^{-1} and 915 cm^{-1} bands are from out-of-plane bending of the olefinic C—H bonds. The weak band near 1820 cm^{-1} is an overtone of the fundamental band at 915 cm^{-1}.

The absorption bands mentioned in the foregoing discussion are characteristic of compounds containing a carbon-carbon double bond and may be used to determine unsaturation in an organic compound. Organic chemists use infrared spectroscopy in this semiempirical way. Most of the common functional groups give rise to characteristic absorption bands in defined regions of the infrared range. The chemist uses the presence or absence of a band in that region of the infrared spectrum as a diagnosis for the presence or absence of the corresponding functional group in the compound. One example will illustrate this point. The spectrum of 4-bromo-1-butene is shown in Figure 15.10. The spectrum is a fairly complex one, with a number of bands not characteristic of simple alkanes. The highlighted bands in Figure 15.10 are all due to vibrational transitions associated with the double bond. The occurrence of these bands in the spectrum is taken as evidence for the presence of such a functional group in the molecule. In the next few sections, we shall consider the characteristic group vibrations for various classes of compounds we have encountered.

FIGURE 15.10 Infrared spectrum of 4-bromo-1-butene, $CH_2=CHCH_2CH_2Br$.

15.4 Alkanes

As we saw previously, the major bands that appear in the infrared spectra of alkanes are those due to C—H stretching in the $2850–3000 \text{ cm}^{-1}$ region, those due to CH_2 and CH_3 scissoring in the $1450–1470 \text{ cm}^{-1}$ region, the band due to CH_3 rocking at about $1370–1380 \text{ cm}^{-1}$, and the CH_2 rocking bands at $720–725 \text{ cm}^{-1}$. These bands are of essentially no diagnostic value because most alkanes contain all of these groupings.

15.5 Alkenes

The alkene C—H stretching vibration occurs at higher wavenumber (shorter wavelength) than that due to an alkane C—H. Recall that alkene carbon-hydrogen bonds have greater s-character and are stronger than alkane carbon-hydrogen bonds. Stronger bonds are more difficult to stretch (higher force constant) and require greater energy or higher light frequency. Thus alkenes that have at least one hydrogen attached to the double bond normally absorb in the region $3050–3150 \text{ cm}^{-1}$. The relative intensity of this band, compared with the band for saturated C—H stretch, is roughly proportional to the relative numbers of the two types of hydrogens in the molecule.

The alkene C=C stretching mode occurs in the region $1645–1670 \text{ cm}^{-1}$. This band is most intense when there is only one alkyl group attached to the double bond. As more alkyl groups are added, the intensity of the absorption diminishes because the vibration now results in a smaller change of dipole moment. For trisubstituted, tetrasubstituted, and relatively symmetrical disubstituted alkenes, the C=C stretching band is often of such low intensity that it is not observable.

Alkene C—H out-of-plane bending vibrations occur between 650 and 1000 cm^{-1}. For terminal alkenes, these vibrations are particularly intense and appear between 890 and 990 cm^{-1}

EXERCISE 15.2 The infrared spectrum for an unknown hydrocarbon is reproduced in Figure 15.11. What structural information can be gleaned from the highlighted absorption bands in this spectrum?

FIGURE 15.11 Infrared spectrum of an unknown hydrocarbon (Exercise 15.2).

EXERCISE 15.3 Explain why *trans*-4-octene shows no infrared absorption for its carbon-carbon double bond.

15.6 Alkynes and Nitriles

Terminal alkynes show a sharp C—H stretching band at 3300–3320 cm^{-1} and an intense C—H bending mode at 600–700 cm^{-1}. The C≡C stretch for terminal alkynes appears as a sharp absorption of moderate intensity at 2100–2140 cm^{-1} (Figure 15.12). For internal alkynes the C≡C stretch is a weak band occurring at 2200–2260 cm^{-1}. In hydrocarbons, there is little change in dipole moment when C≡C is stretched; consequently, this band is so weak that it is usually not observed. The C≡N stretch occurs in the 2210–2260 cm^{-1} region.

EXERCISE 15.4 1-Octyne is treated with butyllithium and the resulting 1-lithio-1-octyne is hydrolyzed with D_2O. Using the simple Hooke's law relationship, predict the position of the C—D stretch in the resulting product.

FIGURE 15.12 Infrared spectrum of 1-octyne.

15.7 Alkyl Halides

The characteristic absorption of alkyl halides is the band due to the C—X stretch. Typical positions for these bands are 1000–1350 cm^{-1} for C—F, 750–850 cm^{-1} for C—Cl, 500–680 cm^{-1} for C—Br, and 200–500 cm^{-1} for C—I. None of these absorptions is particularly useful for diagnosis.

15.8 Alcohols and Ethers

Alcohols and ethers have a characteristic infrared absorption associated with the C—O stretch (1050–1200 cm^{-1}). Since these bands occur in a region of the spectrum where there are usually many other bands, they are not of great diagnostic value. However, the O—H stretch of alcohols, which occurs in the 3200–3600 cm^{-1} region, is of more use. The infrared spectrum of *t*-butyl alcohol shown in Figure 15.13 is illustrative. Note the very intense O—H stretch, which is centered at about 3360 cm^{-1}.

In Figure 15.14 are plotted the spectra of the O—H and C—H regions of *t*-butyl alcohol dissolved in carbon tetrachloride. (Carbon tetrachloride is a frequently used solvent for infrared studies because it is relatively inert chemically and is "transparent" to infrared light in most of the useful spectral regions.) Notice that in the first spectrum the 3440 cm^{-1} O—H absorption is accompanied by a sharp peak at 3620 cm^{-1}. In more dilute solutions, the 3620 cm^{-1} band is more intense relative to the 3440 cm^{-1} band. These two bands are both due to O—H stretch. The band at shorter wavelength (higher energy) is due to the stretching mode of the "free" hydroxy. The stretching mode of hydrogen-bonded or "associated" O—H occurs at lower energy.

free hydroxy	[O—H]	3620–3640 cm^{-1}
associated hydroxy	[O—H···O]	3250–3450 cm^{-1}

As the solution is made progressively more dilute, it is more likely that a molecule will exist in an unassociated state. Consequently, the relative intensity of the "bonded" O—H absorption is less in dilute solutions.

FIGURE 15.13 Infrared spectrum of 2-methyl-2-propanol (*t*-butyl alcohol).

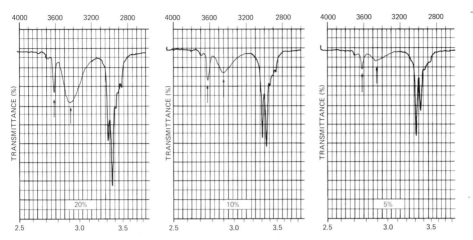

FIGURE 15.14 Infrared spectra of various solutions of *t*-butyl alcohol in carbon tetrachloride.

15.9 Aldehydes and Ketones

The characteristic infrared absorption for aldehydes and ketones is the band due to the C=O stretching vibration. Since the carbonyl group is highly polar, stretching of this bond results in a relatively large change in dipole moment. Consequently the carbonyl stretching band is an intense spectral feature. Because of its intensity, and also because it occurs in a region of the infrared spectrum commonly devoid of other absorptions, the carbonyl stretch is a reliable method for deducing the presence of such a functional group in a compound.

For simple saturated aldehydes the band occurs at about 1725 cm^{-1}. For saturated acyclic ketones the band occurs at about 1715 cm^{-1}. The distinctive nature of the C=O stretch is apparent in the spectrum of 2-heptanone shown in Figure 15.15. Since the carbonyl stretch is such an intense absorption, it often gives rise to a noticeable overtone in the 3400–3500 cm^{-1} region. In 2-heptanone the carbonyl overtone occurs at 3440 cm^{-1} and may be seen in Figure 15.15. One must be cautious not to mistake this overtone for an OH absorption.

FIGURE 15.15 Infrared spectrum of 2-heptanone.

**TABLE 15.2 Carbonyl
Stretching Frequencies**

Type of Ketone	Frequency, cm^{-1}
normal open chain	1715
cyclic	
three-membered	1850
four-membered	1780
five-membered	1745
six-membered	1715
seven-membered	1705

In cyclic ketones the exact stretching frequency depends on the size of the ring containing the carbonyl carbon. The magnitude of the effect is shown in Table 15.2. The observed relationship between C=O stretching frequency and C—C=O angle has its origin in a "coupling" of the C=O stretch with that of the carbon-carbon bonds. For example, consider the hypothetical molecule depicted in Figure 15.16a in which the C—C=O angle is 90°. When the carbon-oxygen double bond is stretched, the carbon and oxygen move apart from one another. As shown in Figure 15.16b, this motion may occur without seriously affecting the carbon-carbon bond length. However, the situation is different in the hypothetical ketone shown in Figure 15.16c, where the C—C=O angle is 180°. When the carbon-oxygen double bond is stretched in this case, the carbon-carbon bond must be simultaneously shortened (Figure 15.16d). In a way, the carbon-carbon bond acts as a kind of "ballast" that resists stretching of the adjacent carbon-oxygen double bond. It is obvious from these simple extremes that the magnitude of coupling between the two bonds will relate to the C—C=O angle. Cyclohexanone and normal acyclic ketones have C—C=O angles of about 112°, which is close to the normal angle for sp^2-hybridization (120°). Smaller ring size is associated with smaller internal bond angles and hence a larger C—C=O angle.

The characteristic stretching frequencies of cyclic carbonyl groups apply to polycyclic systems as well. For example, the carbonyl group of camphor is part of a five-membered ring and the stretching frequency of 1740 cm^{-1} is characteristic of a cyclopentanone. The fact that the CO group in the bicyclic camphor is also part of a six-membered ring is not relevant—it is the character of ring strain that shows up in the

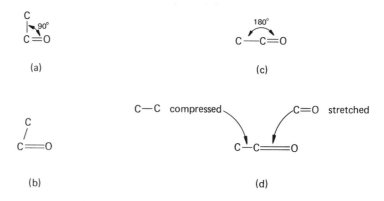

FIGURE 15.16 Illustrating the coupling of C=O and C—C stretching in ketones.

423

Sec. 15.10

*Use of Infrared
Spectroscopy in
Solving
Structural
Problems*

spectrum. However, since ring-strain effects do depend somewhat on the detailed structure, variations of a few cm^{-1} from the values in Table 15.3 are to be expected.

ν(CO) = 1740 cm^{-1}
camphor

ν(CO) = 1751 cm^{-1}
norbornanone

The following bicyclic ketone is an apparent exception. Its C=O stretching band at 1731 cm^{-1} is far higher than expected for a cyclohexanone ring. A second look at the structure of this bicyclic ketone reveals, however, that its six-membered ring is that of a boat conformation rather than a chair.

ν(CO) = 1731 cm^{-1}
bicyclo[2.2.2]octan-2-one

EXERCISE 15.5 The carbonyl stretching frequency of ketene, H$_2$C=C=O, is 2150 cm^{-1}. Is this value consistent with the argument advanced to account for the magnitude of C=O stretching frequencies?

15.10 Use of Infrared Spectroscopy in Solving Structural Problems

In this chapter we have considered the infrared spectra of the classes of organic compounds taken up so far in this book. We have seen that the infrared spectra of organic compounds are so complex that it is impractical to analyze a spectrum completely and assign each absorption to a given vibration. However, for each functional group there are characteristic absorptions that may be used empirically as a diagnosis for that particular functional group. Table 15.3 summarizes the infrared characteristics of alkanes, alkenes, alkynes, alkyl halides, alcohols, ethers, aldehydes, and ketones. The most useful bands are those printed in boldface type. As we consider other classes of compounds, we shall point out their characteristic infrared absorption bands.

It is important that the student recognize that it is not necessary to memorize all of the absorption ranges in Table 15.3. However, it *is* useful to commit a few numbers to memory. For the time being, it is sufficient if you remember that the O—H stretch is in the region 3400–3600 cm^{-1}, that the C=O stretch is an intense absorption in the region around 1700 cm^{-1}, that terminal alkynes are characterized by a relatively sharp and distinct C—H stretch at about 3300 cm^{-1}, and that the C=C stretch is at around 1650 cm^{-1}. Further values can be obtained by reference to tables of data, such as Table 15.3.

In modern practice, infrared spectroscopy is used as an adjunct to NMR and CMR spectroscopy—mainly for the identification of the functional groups in a molecule. For example, suppose that an unknown compound shows NMR resonances at δ 2.42 (quartet) and 1.05 (triplet) and has a strong band in its IR spectrum at 1710 cm^{-1}. The NMR splitting pattern tells us immediately that the compound has an ethyl group, CH_3CH_2,

TABLE 15.3 Principal Infrared Absorption

Class	Frequency, cm^{-1}	Intensity[a]	Assignment
1. Alkanes	2850–3000	s	C—H stretch
	1450–1470	s	
	1370–1380	s	CH$_2$ and CH$_3$ bend
	720–725	m	
2. Alkenes			
(a) RCH=CH$_2$	**3080–3140**	m	=C—H stretch
	1800–1860	m	overtone
	1645	m	C=C stretch
	990	s	C—H out-of-plane bend
	910	s	
(b) R$_2$C=CH$_2$	**3080–3140**	m	=C—H stretch
	1750–1800	m	overtone
	1650	m	C=C stretch
	890	s	C—H out-of-plane bend
(c) *cis*-RCH=CHR	3020	w	=C—H stretch
	1660	w	C=C stretch
	675–725	m	C—H out-of-plane bend
(d) *trans*-RCH=CHR	3020	w	=C—H stretch
	1675	vw	C=C stretch
	970	s	C—H out-of-plane bend
(e) R$_2$C=CHR	3020	w	=C—H stretch
	1670	w	C=C stretch
	790–840	s	C—H out-of-plane bend
(f) R$_2$C=CR$_2$	1670	vw	C=C stretch
3. Alkynes			
(a) RC≡CH	**3300**	s	≡C—H stretch
	2100–2140	m	C≡C stretch
	600–700	s	≡C—H bend
(b) RC≡CR	2190–2260	vw	C≡C stretch
4. Alkyl Halides			
(a) R—F	1000–1350	vs	C—F stretch
(b) R—Cl	750–850	s	C—Cl stretch
(c) R—Br	500–680	s	C—Br stretch
(d) R—I	200–500	s	C—I stretch
5. Alcohols			
(a) RCH$_2$OH	**3600**	var	free O—H stretch
	3400	s	bonded O—H stretch
	1050	s	C—O stretch
(b) R$_2$CHOH	**3600**	var	free O—H stretch
	3400	s	bonded O—H stretch
	1150	s	C—O stretch

TABLE 15.3 (continued)

Class	Frequency, cm^{-1}	Intensity[a]	Assignment
(c) R$_3$COH	**3600**	var	free O—H stretch
	3400	s	bonded O—H stretch
	1200	s	C—O stretch
6. Ethers	1070–1150	s	C—O stretch
7. Aldehydes	**1725**	s	C=O stretch
	2720, 2820	m	C—H stretch
8. Ketones			
(a) acyclic	**1715**	s	C=O stretch
(b) three-membered	**1850**	s	C=O stretch
(c) four-membered	**1780**	s	C=O stretch
(d) five-membered	**1745**	s	C=O stretch
(e) six-membered	**1715**	s	C=O stretch
(f) seven-membered	**1705**	s	C=O stretch

[a] vs = very strong, s = strong, m = medium, w = weak, vw = very weak, v = variable.

and the chemical shift of the quartet tells us that this group is attached to a relatively electronegative atom. The 1710 cm^{-1} band in the IR spectrum tells us that the compound has a carbonyl group. Putting these two facts together, we conclude that the unknown compound is 3-pentanone.

As CMR spectrometers have become more available, the importance of IR spectroscopy has diminished somewhat, since CMR is actually superior to IR for the identification of many functions. For example, the characteristic CMR resonances of alkenes (δ 110–140) are observed whether or not the double bond bears hydrogens. Indeed, the exact resonance position is highly characteristic of the substitution pattern of the double bond. In a similar manner, the carbonyl carbons of aldehydes and ketones give rise to characteristic CMR resonances in unique positions (δ 200–220). However, CMR spectroscopy has the drawback that relatively large amounts of sample are necessary (on the order of 15–25 mg for a normal spectrum), whereas IR spectra may be measured with a milligram or less of material.

EXERCISE 15.6 A compound with the formula C$_8$H$_{14}$O has a strong infrared absorption at 1710 cm^{-1}. The NMR spectrum shows a sharp, six-proton singlet at δ 1.0 ppm and a four-proton multiplet centered at δ 2.3 ppm. The other four protons are seen as a complex multiplet centered at δ 1.6 ppm. What structural information may be gained from these data?

PROBLEMS

1. Identify the functional groups in each compound from the following infrared spectra. Note that the spectra in parts (f) and (g) were obtained using a different instrument than that used for the spectra in parts (a)-(e). This is a common situation. Although the spectra obtained with the two instruments have a different appearance, the characteristic absorptions are independent of the spectrometer used.

(a)

(b)

(c)

(d)

(e)

(f)

(g)

2. Identify the following compound from its IR and NMR spectra.

3. Identify the following compound from its IR and NMR spectra.

4. Identify the following compound from its IR and NMR spectra.

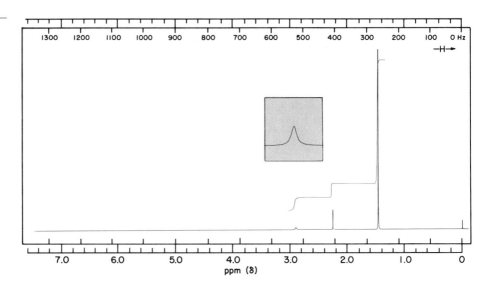

5. Identify the following compound from its IR and NMR spectra.

6. A compound gives the following IR spectrum. Its CMR spectrum has absorptions at 7.1, 8.5, 26.4, 30.7, 76.8, 212.7 ppm. Suggest a structure for the compound.

7. Identify the following isomeric compounds from their IR and CMR spectra.
   (a) CMR: 7.9, 25.5, 33.5, 72.6 ppm.

(b) CMR: 22.7, 23.5, 24.3, 25.1, 49.2, 65.5 ppm.

8. (a) For the heavier methyl halides one infrared frequency can be treated to an excellent approximation as a C—X stretching vibration. The position of this band is CH_3Cl, 732 cm^{-1}; CH_3Br, 611 cm^{-1}; CH_3I, 533 cm^{-1}. Find the corresponding C—X force constants and determine whether they are proportional to the corresponding $DH°$ (CH$_3$—X) values (see Appendix II).

(b) Astatine, element no. 85, is a halogen with no stable isotopes. The longest-lived isotope is ^{210}At with a half-life of 8.3 hr. At what value of $\bar{\nu}$ would you expect to find the CH$_3$—At stretching band of methyl astatide?

(c) Methanethiol has a corresponding vibration (C—S stretch) at 705 cm^{-1}. Use your results from (a) to calculate the corresponding $DH°$ value. The experimental value for $DH°$ (CH$_3$—SH) is about 76 kcal mole^{-1}.

9. Identify the following compound from its IR and proton-decoupled CMR spectra.

10. Dialkyl peroxides, ROOR, have an absorption in the region 820–1000 cm^{-1}, but this band is extremely weak and difficult to detect. Explain. Using the Hooke's law approximation, find the force constant for an O—O stretch of 900 cm^{-1}. How does it compare with the normal single bond f of 5×10^5? Explain.

11. For a harmonic oscillator the potential energy $E = f(r - r_0)^2$. In calculus form the radius of curvature is expressed as d^2E/dr^2. What is the relationship between the radius of curvature and the force constant f for a harmonic oscillator?

Chapter 16

Organic Synthesis

16.1 Introduction

Organic synthesis is the preparation of a desired organic compound from a commercially available material, usually by some multistep procedure. It is an important element of organic chemistry and the cornerstone upon which the organic chemical industry is based. A scientist who wishes to study the physical, chemical, or physiological properties of a compound obviously must have a sample of it. Since relatively few organic compounds are commercially available from chemical suppliers, the scientist often must synthesize the desired material. In Section 10.12 we had a brief look at multistep synthesis. In this chapter we shall go into the topic in somewhat greater detail using the chemistry previously learned.

16.2 Considerations in Synthesis Design

The goal in any synthesis is to obtain a pure sample of the desired product by the most efficient and convenient procedure possible. For this reason one usually strives to use reactions that can reliably be expected to give only a single product and avoids reactions that will give a mixture of products. It is also important to plan a synthesis that entails the fewest possible steps. This is necessary both in terms of the amount of time consumed in an overly long route and in the ultimate yield that may be realized. A ten-step synthesis averaging 80% yield per step will give an overall yield of only 10.7%.

In planning a synthesis, three interrelated factors are involved.

1. Construction of the Proper Carbon Skeleton. In a sense, reactions that result in formation of a new carbon-carbon bond are the most important reactions in organic chemistry because these reactions allow us to build up more complicated structures. A brief summary of the carbon-carbon bond-forming reactions that we have encountered follows.

(a) Reaction of primary alkyl halides with cyanide ion (Section 9.1).

$$RCH_2X + CN^- \longrightarrow RCH_2CN$$

(b) Reaction of primary alkyl halides with acetylide ions (Section 12.5.B).

$$RCH_2X + {}^-C\equiv CR' \longrightarrow RCH_2C\equiv CR'$$

(c) Addition of HCN to aldehydes and ketones (Section 14.8.B).

$$R_2C=O + HCN \longrightarrow R_2\overset{\overset{\displaystyle OH}{|}}{C}CN$$

(d) Addition of acetylide ions to aldehydes and ketones (Section 14.8.A).

$$R_2C=O + \ ^-C\equiv CR' \longrightarrow \overset{H^+}{\longrightarrow} R_2\overset{\overset{\displaystyle OH}{|}}{C}C\equiv CR'$$

(e) Reaction of Grignard reagents with oxirane (Section 10.11.A).

$$R\,MgX + H_2\overset{\displaystyle O}{\overset{/\backslash}{C}-CH_2} \longrightarrow \overset{H^+}{\longrightarrow} R\,CH_2CH_2OH$$

(f) Reactions of Grignard reagents and alkyllithium compounds with aldehydes and ketones (Section 14.8.A).

$$R\,MgX + R'CHO \longrightarrow \overset{H^+}{\longrightarrow} R-\overset{\overset{\displaystyle OH}{|}}{C}H-R'$$

$$R\,MgX + R'_2C=O \longrightarrow \overset{H^+}{\longrightarrow} R-\overset{\overset{\displaystyle OH}{|}}{\underset{\underset{\displaystyle R'}{|}}{C}}-R'$$

$$R\,MgX + CH_2O \longrightarrow \overset{H^+}{\longrightarrow} R\,CH_2OH$$

(g) Alkylation of enolate ions with primary alkyl halides (Section 14.6.B).

$$R_2CH\overset{\overset{\displaystyle O}{\|}}{C}R' \xrightarrow{base} R_2C=\overset{\overset{\displaystyle O^-}{|}}{C}R' \xrightarrow{R''CH_2X} R_2\overset{\overset{\displaystyle O}{\|}}{C}\underset{\underset{\displaystyle CH_2R''}{|}}{C}R'$$

(h) The Wittig reaction (Section 14.8.E).

$$R_2C=O + R'CH=P(C_6H_5)_3 \longrightarrow R_2C=CHR'$$

(i) The aldol addition reaction (14.8.C).

$$2\,RCH_2CHO \longrightarrow RCH_2\overset{\overset{\displaystyle HO}{|}}{C}H\overset{\overset{\displaystyle R}{|}}{C}HCHO \longrightarrow RCH_2CH=\overset{\overset{\displaystyle R}{|}}{C}CHO$$

$$R\overset{\overset{\displaystyle O}{\|}}{C}CH_3 \xrightarrow{LDA} R\overset{\overset{\displaystyle O^-}{|}}{C}=CH_2 \xrightarrow{R'CHO} R\overset{\overset{\displaystyle O}{\|}}{C}CH_2\overset{\overset{\displaystyle OH}{|}}{C}HR'$$

A more complete summary of carbon-carbon bond-forming reactions is given in Appendix II of the Study Guide.

2. Placement of Desired Functional Groups in Their Proper Place. This aspect of a synthesis involves the introduction, removal, or interconversion of functional groups. We have encountered a great many such reactions. Rather than summarize them all, we shall only give a few illustrative examples.

(a) Introduction of a functional group.

$$R-\overset{\overset{\displaystyle R'}{|}}{C}H-R'' + Br_2 \xrightarrow{h\nu} R-\overset{\overset{\displaystyle R'}{|}}{\underset{\underset{\displaystyle Br}{|}}{C}}-R''$$

(b) Removal of a functional group.

$$R-\overset{\overset{\displaystyle O}{\|}}{C}-R' + H_2NNH_2 \xrightarrow[\underset{\Delta}{(HOCH_2CH_2)_2O}]{NaOH} RCH_2R'$$

$$-\overset{\overset{\displaystyle H}{|}}{\underset{|}{C}}-\overset{\overset{\displaystyle OH}{|}}{\underset{|}{C}}- \xrightarrow[(-H_2O)]{H^+} \;\; \overset{}{\underset{}{}}C{=}C\overset{}{\underset{}{}} \xrightarrow[Pd]{H_2} -\overset{\overset{\displaystyle H}{|}}{\underset{|}{C}}-\overset{\overset{\displaystyle H}{|}}{\underset{|}{C}}-$$

(c) Interconversion of functional groups.

$$-\overset{\overset{\displaystyle OH}{|}}{C}H- \underset{\text{reduction}}{\overset{\text{oxidation}}{\rightleftarrows}} -\overset{\overset{\displaystyle O}{\|}}{C}-$$

$$-CH_2Br \underset{PBr_3}{\overset{OH^-}{\rightleftarrows}} -CH_2OH$$

Insofar as possible, one should choose reactions for building up the carbon skeleton so that the least amount of subsequent functional group manipulation is necessary. A complete summary of functional group interconversions is included in Appendix II of the Study Guide.

3. Control of Stereochemistry Where Relevant. When more than one stereoisomer of the desired product is possible, it is necessary to design a synthesis that will yield only that isomer. In such cases it is important to use reactions that are stereoselective—that is, reactions yielding largely or completely one stereoisomer when two or more might result. The stereoselective reactions we have encountered are summarized as follows.

(a) S_N2 displacement reactions of secondary halides (Chapter 9).

$$\overset{R}{\underset{H\;\;R'}{}}C-X + Y^- \longrightarrow Y-C\overset{R}{\underset{R'\;H}{}} + X^-$$

(b) Catalytic hydrogenation of alkynes (Section 12.6.A).

$$R-C{\equiv}C-R' \xrightarrow[cat.]{H_2} \overset{H\qquad H}{\underset{R\qquad R'}{}}C{=}C$$

(c) Metal ammonia reduction of alkynes (Section 12.6.A).

$$R-C{\equiv}C-R' \xrightarrow[NH_3]{Na} \overset{H\qquad R'}{\underset{R\qquad H}{}}C{=}C$$

(d) Oxidation of alkenes with osmium tetroxide (Section 11.6.E).

$$\bigcirc\!\!=\;\; + H_2O_2 \xrightarrow{OsO_4} \text{(cyclohexane-1,2-diol)}$$

(e) Addition of halogens to alkenes (Section 11.6.B).

(f) Bimolecular elimination of alkyl halides (Section 11.5.A)

(g) Hydroboration (Section 11.6.D).

(h) Epoxidation of alkenes (Section 11.6.E).

(i) Ring opening of epoxides (Section 10.11.A).

(k) Cyclopropanation (Section 11.6.F).

Sometimes it will not be possible to control a synthesis so that only the desired stereoisomer is produced because a method that will accomplish that goal is lacking. In such a case the next best solution is to prepare the mixture of isomers and separate the desired isomer. At this point in our study of organic synthesis we shall only touch on this subject of stereoselectivity, but the topic will come up frequently in our subsequent discussions.

EXERCISE 16.1 Consider the methods available for the general conversion of RY to RZ in which Y and Z are the seven groups given below. Set up a 7×7 matrix with Y down the side and Z across the top. Mark with a minus sign those conversions for which no *general* reaction sequence is presently known to you. Mark with a 1 those interconversions of functional groups that can usually be accomplished by a simple reaction process we have studied. Finally, mark with a + those interconversions that can be accomplished in a sequence of two or more reaction steps. Y and Z: H, Br, OH, CH_2OH, CHO, $COCH_3$, CN.

16.3 Planning a Synthesis

In planning a synthesis, one works from the product backward. Remember that the goal is to connect the desired product with some commercially available starting material by a series of reactions each of which will, insofar as possible, give a single product in high yield. For this reason, the practicing chemist usually acquires a fairly good working knowledge of what types of starting materials are available from chemical suppliers. Of course, if the chemist is not sure whether or not a possible starting material is available, he or she checks for its availability in the catalogs of various suppliers. A good rule of thumb is that most monofunctional aliphatic compounds containing five or fewer carbons may be purchased. A great many others are also available, but this type of information is acquired only by experience. For the purpose of learning how to design a synthesis, we shall assume that the only available starting materials are those monofunctional compounds containing five or fewer carbons.

For relatively simple synthetic problems, one may reason backward and soon arrive at possible starting materials that are known to be available. The process is called **retrosynthesis** and the result of such an analysis has been called a **synthetic tree**.

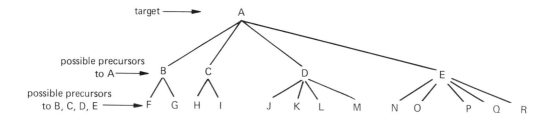

For more complex problems the synthetic tree soon becomes unwieldy and current research is being directed toward the application of computers to synthetic design. In most cases the practicing chemist solves such problems by a combination of logical analysis and intuition. The synthetic tree is built until the chemist recognizes, by insight or intuition, a complete path from one of the possible intermediates to an available starting material.

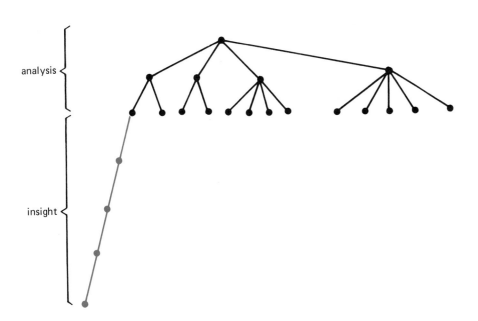

The importance of insight and intuition, relative to analytical reasoning, should not be underestimated for science in general and synthetic design in particular. Nevertheless, insight and intuition cannot function in the absence of a body of facts—in the present case, a thorough knowledge of organic reactions.

The best way to illustrate synthesis design is to demonstrate with a few specific simple examples.

Example 16.1 Plan a synthesis of 4-methyl-1-pentanol.

$$\underset{\displaystyle CH_3}{\overset{\displaystyle CH_3}{\mid}}$$
$$CH_3CHCH_2CH_2CH_2OH$$

Since the product contains six carbons, we must build up the skeleton from a simpler starting material. In principle, there are a number of ways in which this may be done.

1. $\overset{\displaystyle C}{\underset{\displaystyle |}{}}$ C—C—C—C—C*

2. C—$\overset{\displaystyle C}{\underset{\displaystyle |}{C}}$—C—C—C*

3. C—$\overset{\displaystyle C}{\underset{\displaystyle |}{C}}$—C—C—C*

4. C—$\overset{\displaystyle C}{\underset{\displaystyle |}{C}}$—C—C—C*

The carbon marked with an asterisk indicates the desired point of functionality, in this case, a hydroxy group. Of the various approaches, the fourth is most attractive, since the carbon-carbon bond to be created is adjacent to the functional group in the final product. In planning a synthesis, *it is generally most productive to look first at combinations in which the functional group is close to the carbon-carbon bonds that will be formed in the synthesis.* We immediately recognize that 4-methyl-1-pentanol is readily available by reaction of the Grignard reagent derived from 1-chloro-3-methylbutane with formaldehyde.

$$CH_3CH\!\!\underset{\underset{\displaystyle CH_3}{|}}{}\!\!CH_2CH_2Cl \xrightarrow[\text{ether}]{Mg} \xrightarrow{CH_2O} \xrightarrow{H_3O^+} CH_3CH\!\!\underset{\underset{\displaystyle CH_3}{|}}{}\!\!CH_2CH_2CH_2OH$$

EXERCISE 16.2 Plan a synthesis of 4-methylpentanenitrile, $(CH_3)_2CHCH_2CH_2CN$.

Example 16.2 Plan a synthesis of 4-methyl-1-hexanol.

$$CH_3CH_2CH\!\!\underset{\underset{\displaystyle CH_3}{|}}{}\!\!CH_2CH_2CH_2OH$$

In this example, the desired product contains seven carbons. Analysis of the carbon skeleton gives the following combinations.

$$1.\quad C-C-\overset{\displaystyle C}{\overset{|}{C}}-C-C-C^*$$

$$2.\quad C-C-\overset{\displaystyle C}{\overset{|}{C}}-C-C-C^*$$

$$3.\quad C-C-\overset{\displaystyle C}{\overset{|}{C}}-C-C-C^*$$

$$4.\quad C-C-\overset{\displaystyle C}{\overset{|}{C}}-C-C-C^*$$

$$5.\quad C-C-\overset{\displaystyle C}{\overset{|}{C}}-C-C-C^*$$

$$6.\quad C-C-\overset{\displaystyle C}{\overset{|}{C}}-C-C-C^*$$

In approach number 6 the functional group is nearest the bond to be formed. We might consider solving this synthetic problem in the same way we solved Example 16.1, by application of the Grignard synthesis to 1-chloro-3-methylpentane.

$$CH_3CH_2CH\!\!\underset{\underset{\displaystyle CH_3}{|}}{}\!\!CH_2CH_2Cl \xrightarrow[\text{ether}]{Mg} \xrightarrow{CH_2O} \xrightarrow{H_3O^+} CH_3CH_2CH\!\!\underset{\underset{\displaystyle CH_3}{|}}{}\!\!CH_2CH_2CH_2OH$$

However, this starting material contains six carbons and, by our ground rules, is not readily available. Thus we would have to synthesize it. Of course, this is easily accomplished as follows.

$$CH_3CH_2CH\!\!\underset{\underset{\displaystyle CH_3}{|}}{}\!\!CH_2Cl \xrightarrow[\text{ether}]{Mg} \xrightarrow{CH_2O} \xrightarrow{H_3O^+}$$

$$CH_3CH_2CH\!\!\underset{\underset{\displaystyle CH_3}{|}}{}\!\!CH_2CH_2OH \xrightarrow[\text{pyridine}]{SOCl_2} CH_3CH_2CH\!\!\underset{\underset{\displaystyle CH_3}{|}}{}\!\!CH_2CH_2Cl$$

The overall synthesis of 4-methyl-1-hexanol would therefore require three separate operations beginning with 1-chloro-2-methylbutane.

Although this route will provide the desired product, note that approach number 5 could afford it in only one operation, since this combination employs a five-carbon starting material. If we search through our repertoire of reactions for one in which the unit CH_2CH_2OH may be joined to another molecule, we recall that Grignard reagents react with ethylene oxide to produce exactly this result. Thus we can prepare the Grignard reagent of 1-chloro-2-methylbutane and allow it to react with ethylene oxide to obtain 4-methyl-1-hexanol.

$$CH_3CH_2\overset{\overset{\displaystyle CH_3}{|}}{C}HCH_2Cl \xrightarrow[\text{ether}]{Mg} \xrightarrow{CH_2-CH_2 \,(O)} \xrightarrow{H_3O^+} CH_3CH_2\overset{\overset{\displaystyle CH_3}{|}}{C}HCH_2CH_2CH_2OH$$

This example illustrates a second rule that should be observed when planning a synthesis. *It is more productive to add a large fragment in a single reaction than to add several smaller fragments sequentially.* One should therefore examine all of the various carbon-carbon bonds that might be formed, even though they are not immediately adjacent to the desired functional group. In some cases a reaction may exist that allows the formation of such a remote bond.

This example illustrates another concept of synthesis design, that of **synthetic equivalents**, or **synthons**. A synthon is defined as a part of a molecule that is related to some other structural unit by a reliable reaction or sequence of reactions. In the foregoing example, the molecule oxirane is a synthon for the structural unit CH_2CH_2OH. That is, the reaction of a Grignard reagent (RMgX) with oxirane to give RCH_2CH_2OH is a general process that can be relied upon.

EXERCISE 16.3 What synthons exist for each of the following structural units?
(a) —$COCH_3$ (b) —CH_2NH_2 (c) —CH_2OH (d) —$CH=CHCH_3$

Example 16.3 Plan a synthesis of 3-methyl-1-pentene.

$$CH_3CH_2\overset{\overset{\displaystyle CH_3}{|}}{C}HCH=CH_2$$

First, we might note that $HC\equiv CH$ is a synthon for the structural unit $CH=CH_2$. Thus, at first glance, partial hydrogenation of 3-methyl-1-pentyne is attractive, since the necessary alkyne appears to be available by alkylation of acetylene with 2-bromobutane.

$$CH_3CH_2\overset{\overset{\displaystyle Br}{|}}{C}HCH_3 + NaC\equiv CH \longrightarrow CH_3CH_2\overset{\overset{\displaystyle CH_3}{|}}{C}HC\equiv CH \longrightarrow CH_3CH_2\overset{\overset{\displaystyle CH_3}{|}}{C}HCH=CH_2$$

However, recall that acetylide ions cause *elimination* of secondary alkyl halides (Section 12.5.B).

$$CH_3CH_2\overset{\overset{\displaystyle Br}{|}}{C}HCH_3 + NaC\equiv CH \longrightarrow CH_3CH_2CH=CH_2 + HC\equiv CH + NaBr$$
$$\text{(plus other isomers)}$$

Therefore, this direct two-step synthesis of 3-methyl-1-pentene is not applicable. This example illustrates an important aspect of synthesis design. After writing out a possible route to a desired product, *carefully review the chemistry that would be involved to see if there are any subtle structural features that render the route inoperable for the specific carbon skeleton under consideration.*

The functional group in our desired product is a carbon-carbon double bond. We should now review the other methods whereby this functional group can be introduced into a molecule.

(a) Dehydration of an alcohol (Sections 10.6.D and 11.5.B)

$$\underset{\underset{\displaystyle R}{|}}{\overset{\displaystyle OH}{|}}$$

$$R\overset{|}{C}HCH_3 \xrightarrow{H^+} RCH{=}CH_2 + H_2O$$

(b) Elimination of an alkyl halide (Section 11.5.A).

$$RCH_2CH_2X + R'O^- \longrightarrow RCH{=}CH_2 + X^- + R'OH$$

(c) Wittig reaction (Section 14.8.E).

$$RCHO + (C_6H_5)_3P{=}CH_2 \longrightarrow RCH{=}CH_2 + (C_6H_5)_3P{=}O$$

For the problem under consideration, alcohol dehydration is not suitable, since carbocation rearrangements could result in a mixture of products (Section 10.6.C). Base-catalyzed elimination of an alkyl halide is a possibility. The required halide would be 1-chloro-3-methylpentane, which could be prepared as discussed in Example 16.2. This would provide a three-step synthesis of the desired alkene.

$$\underset{\displaystyle CH_3CH_2\overset{|}{C}HCH_2Cl}{\overset{\displaystyle \overset{CH_3}{|}}{}} \longrightarrow \underset{\displaystyle CH_3CH_2\overset{|}{C}HCH_2CH_2OH}{\overset{\displaystyle \overset{CH_3}{|}}{}} \longrightarrow$$

$$\underset{\displaystyle CH_3CH_2\overset{|}{C}HCH_2CH_2Cl}{\overset{\displaystyle \overset{CH_3}{|}}{}} \longrightarrow \underset{\displaystyle CH_3CH_2\overset{|}{C}HCH{=}CH_2}{\overset{\displaystyle \overset{CH_3}{|}}{}}$$

The final method for creation of a carbon-carbon double bond is the Wittig reaction. In this case the reaction of 2-methylbutanal with methylenetriphenylphosphorane would yield the desired alkene in one step.

$$\underset{\displaystyle CH_3CH_2\overset{|}{C}HCHO}{\overset{\displaystyle \overset{CH_3}{|}}{}} \longrightarrow \underset{\displaystyle CH_3CH_2\overset{|}{C}HCH{=}CH_2}{\overset{\displaystyle \overset{CH_3}{|}}{}}$$

This is clearly a more efficient synthesis of 3-methyl-1-pentene than either of the two routes considered heretofore, since only one step is involved. Even so, the practicing chemist might not choose this method, for practical reasons. The required reagent is prepared by reaction of methyltriphenylphosphonium bromide with a strong base such as *n*-butyllithium.

$$(C_6H_5)_3\overset{+}{P}{-}CH_3\ Br^- \xrightarrow{n\text{-}C_4H_9Li} (C_6H_5)_3P{=}CH_2$$

Both of these reactants are rather expensive. Furthermore, the molecular weight of the phosphonium salt is 357. Thus, to carry out the reaction on a 1-mole scale (which would provide a maximum of 82 g of alkene), one must employ 357 g of phosphonium salt. Consequently, for preparation of a large quantity of 3-methyl-1-pentene, the chemist would probably use the longer Grignard route rather than the one-step Wittig reaction. For preparation of only a small amount of material, where cost is of less importance, one might well use the Wittig procedure.

EXERCISE 16.4 Plan a synthesis of 1-heptene.

Example 16.4 Plan a synthesis of *cis*-2-methyl-5-decene.

$$\underset{CH_3CHCH_2CH_2}{\overset{\overset{\displaystyle CH_3}{|}}{}}\underset{}{\overset{\overset{\displaystyle H}{\diagdown}}{C}}=\underset{CH_2CH_2CH_2CH_3}{\overset{\overset{\displaystyle H}{\diagup}}{C}}$$

Here stereochemistry is important because only the cis isomer is desired. This consideration dominates the planning, since we have at this point only one method available for the stereospecific production of a cis alkene, partial catalytic hydrogenation of an internal alkyne.

$$RC\equiv CR \xrightarrow{H_2\text{-cat}} \underset{R}{\overset{H}{\diagdown}}C=\underset{R}{\overset{H}{\diagup}}C$$

Furthermore, we recognize that acetylene is a synthon for internal alkynes of many types, since it can be successively alkylated with two alkyl halides (page 285).

$$HC\equiv CH \xrightarrow[NH_3]{NaNH_2} \xrightarrow{CH_3\overset{\overset{\displaystyle CH_3}{|}}{CH}CH_2CH_2Br} CH_3\overset{\overset{\displaystyle CH_3}{|}}{CH}CH_2CH_2C\equiv CH \xrightarrow[NH_3]{NaNH_2}$$

$$\xrightarrow{BrCH_2CH_2CH_2CH_3} CH_3\overset{\overset{\displaystyle CH_3}{|}}{CH}CH_2CH_2C\equiv CCH_2CH_2CH_2CH_3$$

EXERCISE 16.5 Plan a synthesis of non-3-yn-1-ol, $CH_3(CH_2)_4C\equiv C(CH_2)_2OH$. [*Hint:* Look for two synthons.]

Example 16.5 Plan a synthesis of 2-ethylhexanol.

$$CH_3CH_2CH_2CH_2\overset{\overset{\displaystyle CH_3CH_2}{|}}{CH}CH_2OH$$

To simplify the problem, consider only the combinations involving five carbons or smaller fragments.

1. $C-C-C-C-\overset{\overset{\displaystyle C-C}{|}}{C}-\overset{*}{C}$

2. $C-C-C-C-\overset{\overset{\displaystyle C-C}{|}}{C}-\overset{*}{C}$

Combination number 1 is not practical, since we know no simple methods for making a bond so far from a functional group. However, the second possible approach has an interesting feature—it requires joining two similar four-carbon units *at the position adjacent to the position where functionality appears in the desired final product.* Thus, a simple solution to the synthetic problem would be in hand if we had a way to join two $CH_3CH_2CH_2CH_2X$ synthons, provided CH_2X can be converted readily into CH_2OH. We can accomplish this end with the aldol condensation (Section 14.8.C).

$$2\ CH_3CH_2CH_2CHO \xrightarrow[\Delta]{KOH,\ H_2O} CH_3CH_2CH_2CH=\overset{\overset{\displaystyle CH_3CH_2}{|}}{C}CHO$$

With this realization, we recognize a very efficient synthesis of 2-ethylhexanol, since catalytic hydrogenation will saturate both double bonds.

$$CH_3CH_2CH_2CH\!\!=\!\!\overset{\overset{\displaystyle CH_3CH_2}{|}}{C}CHO \xrightarrow{\text{H}_2\text{-Pt}} CH_3CH_2CH_2CH_2\overset{\overset{\displaystyle CH_3CH_2}{|}}{C}HCH_2OH$$

This example illustrates yet another aspect of synthesis design. Look for "hidden functionality." In this case it is important to notice that although the carbon-carbon double bond does not appear in the ultimate product, the most effective synthesis proceeds through an intermediate containing this functional group. This example also demonstrates the economy that results when a synthetic target can be dissected into two identical synthons.

EXERCISE 16.6 Plan a synthesis of 2,9-dimethyldecan-5-ol.

Example 16.6 Plan a synthesis of 4-methylnonane.

$$CH_3CH_2CH_2CH_2CH_2\overset{\overset{\displaystyle CH_3}{|}}{C}HCH_2CH_2CH_3$$

Here we have a compound with no functional group. Since it has ten carbons, we would like to assemble it from two five-carbon building blocks. Thus the questions are how to accomplish the following combination and how to get rid of any functional groups that might be present in our intermediates.

$$C\!-\!C\!-\!C\!-\!C\!-\!C\!-\!\overset{\overset{\displaystyle C}{|}}{C}\!-\!C\!-\!C\!-\!C$$

First, let us review the methods at our disposal for removal of a functional group. We have learned three such methods—hydrogenation of a multiple bond, removal of the oxygen from an aldehyde or ketone, and removal of halogen by formation and hydrolysis of a Grignard reagent.

(a) Hydrogenation of alkenes or alkynes (Sections 11.6.A and 12.6.A).

$$\diagup C\!\!=\!\!C\diagup + H_2 \xrightarrow{\text{cat.}} -\overset{\overset{\displaystyle H}{|}}{C}\!-\!\overset{\overset{\displaystyle H}{|}}{C}-$$

$$-C\!\!\equiv\!\!C- + 2\,H_2 \xrightarrow{\text{cat.}} -\overset{\overset{\displaystyle H}{|}}{\underset{\underset{\displaystyle H}{|}}{C}}\!-\!\overset{\overset{\displaystyle H}{|}}{\underset{\underset{\displaystyle H}{|}}{C}}-$$

(b) Deoxygenation of aldehydes and ketones (Section 14.9.D).

$$-\overset{\overset{\displaystyle O}{\|}}{C}- \xrightarrow[\text{Wolff–Kishner reduction}]{\text{Clemmensen or}} -\overset{\overset{\displaystyle H}{|}}{\underset{\underset{\displaystyle H}{|}}{C}}-$$

(c) Hydrolysis of organometallic compounds (Section 8.9.A).

$$-\overset{|}{\underset{|}{C}}\!-\!Cl \xrightarrow[\text{ether}]{\text{Mg}} -\overset{|}{\underset{|}{C}}\!-\!MgCl \xrightarrow{\text{H}_2\text{O}} -\overset{|}{\underset{|}{C}}\!-\!H$$

There are a number of ways by which we might use these reactions in a synthesis of 4-methylnonane. For example, we could make the Grignard reagent from 1-chloropentane, add it to 2-pentanone, and dehydrate the resulting tertiary alcohol. A mixture of $C_{10}H_{20}$ isomers is expected to result, but this is of no consequence, since all of the isomers will give 4-methylnonane upon hydrogenation.

$$\text{CH}_3\text{CH}_2\text{CH}_2\text{CH}_2\text{CH}_2\text{Cl} \xrightarrow[\text{ether}]{\text{Mg}} \xrightarrow{\text{CH}_3\overset{\text{O}}{\overset{\|}{\text{C}}}\text{CH}_2\text{CH}_2\text{CH}_3} \text{CH}_3\text{CH}_2\text{CH}_2\text{CH}_2\text{CH}_2\underset{\underset{\text{OH}}{|}}{\overset{\overset{\text{CH}_3}{|}}{\text{C}}}\text{CH}_2\text{CH}_2\text{CH}_3 \xrightarrow[\Delta]{\text{H}_2\text{SO}_4}$$

$$\left\{ \begin{array}{c} \overset{\overset{\text{CH}_3}{|}}{} \\ \text{CH}_3\text{CH}_2\text{CH}_2\text{CH}_2\text{CH}=\text{CCH}_2\text{CH}_2\text{CH}_3 \\ \text{(cis and trans)} \\ + \\ \overset{\overset{\text{CH}_3}{|}}{} \\ \text{CH}_3\text{CH}_2\text{CH}_2\text{CH}_2\text{CH}_2\text{C}=\text{CHCH}_2\text{CH}_3 \\ \text{(cis and trans)} \\ + \\ \overset{\overset{\text{CH}_2}{\|}}{} \\ \text{CH}_3\text{CH}_2\text{CH}_2\text{CH}_2\text{CH}_2\text{CCH}_2\text{CH}_2\text{CH}_3 \end{array} \right\} \xrightarrow[\text{Pd/C}]{\text{H}_2} \text{CH}_3\text{CH}_2\text{CH}_2\text{CH}_2\text{CH}_2\underset{}{\overset{\overset{\text{CH}_3}{|}}{\text{C}}}\text{HCH}_2\text{CH}_2\text{CH}_3$$

EXERCISE 16.7 Suppose that the compound needed in the foregoing example were actually 4-(deuteriomethyl)nonane. Plan an efficient synthesis for this labelled compound.

16.4 Protecting Groups

In the design of a synthesis that one wishes to carry out, often the reagent that produces a desired transformation on one functional group will also react with some other functional group present in the same molecule. The reagent may still be used by temporarily **protecting** one of the functional groups by changing it into another functional group that is unreactive to the reagent in question. For example, suppose it is desirable to carry out the following conversion.

The method for reducing a ketone to a secondary alcohol is reduction with sodium borohydride or lithium aluminum hydride (Section 14.9.B). However, there is a problem, since the aldehyde would react with either of these reagents *more rapidly than the ketone*. The problem can be circumvented by first transforming the aldehyde into an acetal. In principle, the ketone can also be converted into a ketal. However, the same factors that cause the aldehyde carbonyl to be reduced more rapidly than the ketone carbonyl also cause it to be transformed more readily into the corresponding acetal.

Since an acetal is an ether and ethers do not react with either NaBH$_4$ or LiAlH$_4$, the ketone reduction may now be carried out. After the reduction, the acetal is hydrolyzed by treatment with acid and excess water in order to regenerate the aldehyde function.

In this example the acetal group is a protecting group. It is a good protecting group for aldehydes because it is easily introduced and removed and, since it is an ether, is stable to many reagents. In a similar manner, ketals are sometimes useful as protecting groups for the ketone carbonyl.

EXERCISE 16.8 Suggest a strategy for conversion of 5-bromo-2-pentanone into 7-hydroxy-2-heptanone.

A method often used for the protection of primary alcohols is to convert them into *t*-butyl ethers. For example, suppose it is desired to convert 3-bromopropanol into 3-deuterio-1-propanol. Hydrolysis of a Grignard reagent with D$_2$O is often an effective method for introducing deuterium into a molecule. However, in this case the hydroxy function would interfere (Section 8.8.A). What is needed is a protecting group for OH. The group must be easily installed, it must be stable to the conditions of formation and reaction of Grignard reagents, and it must be conveniently removed. We saw in Section 10.9 that primary and secondary alcohols may be transformed into *t*-butyl ethers by treatment with isobutylene and acid.

$$\text{BrCH}_2\text{CH}_2\text{CH}_2\text{OH} + \text{CH}_3\overset{\text{CH}_3}{\underset{}{\text{C}}}=\text{CH}_2 \xrightarrow{\text{H}_2\text{SO}_4} \text{BrCH}_2\text{CH}_2\text{CH}_2\text{O}\overset{\text{CH}_3}{\underset{\text{CH}_3}{\text{C}}}-\text{CH}_3$$

The hydroxy group has now been protected by conversion into an ether function, which is stable to Grignard reagents. The Grignard reagent is prepared and hydrolyzed with D$_2$O, and the product is hydrolyzed with aqueous sulfuric acid to obtain the deuteriated propanol.

$$\text{BrCH}_2\text{CH}_2\text{CH}_2\text{O}\overset{\text{CH}_3}{\underset{\text{CH}_3}{\text{C}}}-\text{CH}_3 \xrightarrow[\text{ether}]{\text{Mg}} \text{BrMgCH}_2\text{CH}_2\text{CH}_2\text{O}\overset{\text{CH}_3}{\underset{\text{CH}_3}{\text{C}}}-\text{CH}_3 \xrightarrow{\text{D}_2\text{O}}$$

$$\text{DCH}_2\text{CH}_2\text{CH}_2\text{O}\overset{\text{CH}_3}{\underset{\text{CH}_3}{\text{C}}}-\text{CH}_3 \xrightarrow[\text{H}_2\text{O}]{\text{H}_2\text{SO}_4} \text{DCH}_2\text{CH}_2\text{CH}_2\text{OH} + \text{CH}_3\overset{\text{CH}_3}{\underset{}{\text{C}}}=\text{CH}_2$$
$$\qquad\qquad\qquad\qquad\qquad\qquad \text{3-deuterio-1-propanol}$$

Another protecting group commonly used for alcohols is the trimethylsilyl ether, which is formed by treating the alcohol with trimethylchlorosilane and an organic base such as triethylamine.

$$-\overset{|}{\underset{|}{C}}-OH + (CH_3)_3SiCl \xrightarrow{(C_2H_5)_3N} -\overset{|}{\underset{|}{C}}-O-Si(CH_3)_3$$

The silyl ether grouping is stable to most neutral and basic conditions. Upon treatment with mild aqueous acid, the alcohol is regenerated.

$$-\overset{|}{\underset{|}{C}}-O-Si(CH_3)_3 \xrightarrow[25°C]{H_3O^+} -\overset{|}{\underset{|}{C}}-OH + (CH_3)_3SiOH$$

EXERCISE 16.9 Suggest a strategy for the following conversion.

16.5 Industrial Syntheses

Organic compounds are synthesized for two fundamentally different kinds of reasons. On the one hand, we may need a specific compound in order to study its properties or to use it for further research purposes. For such purposes relatively small amounts generally suffice, and cost is not an important criterion—within limits. On the other hand, a compound may have commercial significance, and for such purposes economic factors take on a vital importance. The cost of a medicinal used in small quantity where no other product will work is clearly of a different magnitude than that of a polymeric building material that must compete with wood and steel.

Most of the reactions and syntheses we have studied are useful for understanding the chemistry of different kinds of functional groups and for the laboratory preparation of various compounds. Few of these reactions, however, are suitable for the industrial preparation of compounds, some of which are produced in the amount of millions of pounds a year. An important distinction is the following: the reactions and laboratory preparations that we study have generality. These methods, with minor modifications, are suitable for the preparation of whole classes of compounds. On the other hand, many industrial preparations are specific. They apply for making one and only one compound. Many such reactions are gas-phase catalytic processes with the precise catalysts and reaction conditions carefully worked out. An important advantage of such processes is that they are continuous rather than batch processes. Ideally, in a continuous process the reactants are fed into one end of a chemical plant and the product comes out at the other end without stopping, ready for marketing or for the next step. In practice, this ideal is rarely achieved. Catalysts lose their efficiency with time and need to be replaced. By-products build up and need to be cleaned out.

Much research in the chemical industry is devoted to discovering new products with useful properties. But much other research is devoted to existing products, improving processes to obtain these products cheaper and more efficiently, and, in many cases, purer. Research in process development is a fascinating area of its own that requires special talents of creativity, patience, and chemical knowledge. Close attention in process development is also given to the environment and to energy conservation. A suitable industrial process must involve a minimum of waste products that require disposal.

PROBLEMS

1. Plan a synthesis for each of the following compounds from starting materials containing five or fewer carbons.
   (a) 1-hexanol
   (b) 2-hexanol
   (c) 3-hexanol
   (d) 1-heptyne
   (e) *trans*-3-heptene
   (f) 5-methyl-5-nonanol
   (g) 2,6-dimethyl-2-heptanol
   (h) 1-cyclopentyl-2-methylpropene

2. Plan a synthesis for each of the following compounds from starting materials containing five or fewer carbons. For these compounds, the most efficient synthesis will involve removal of a functional group from an intermediate.
   (a) 2-methylnonane
   (b) cyclopentylcyclopentane
   (c) 2,9-dimethyldecane
   (d) 2,3,6-trimethylheptane
   (e) 4-methyl-1-heptene
   (f) 5-(3-methylbutyl)-2,8-dimethylnonane

3. Plan a synthesis for each of the following compounds from monofunctional starting materials containing five or fewer carbons. In each case, the final product may be racemic; it is not necessary to plan the synthesis using optically active reactants. Relative stereochemistry is important.
   (a) *trans*-2-hexene
   (b) *trans*-2-butylcyclopentanol
   (c) *cis*-4-octene
   (d) (3R,4R)-hexane-3,4-diol
   (e) (2R,3S)-3-methyl-2-heptanol
   (f)

   (g) *trans*-1,2-diethylcyclopropane

4. Show how each of the following *optically active* compounds may be prepared from optically active starting materials containing five or fewer carbons.
   (a) (S)-4-methyl-1-hexanol
   (b) (R)-2-methylpentanenitrile
   (c) (R)-4,4-dimethyl-2-pentanol
   (d) (S)-3-deuterio-4-octyne

5. Show how one may carry out each of the following conversions in good yield. In each case a protecting group will be necessary.
   (a) $BrCH_2CH_2CH_2CH_2CHO \longrightarrow CH_2{=}CHCH_2CH_2CHO$
   (b) 4-bromo-1-butanol $\longrightarrow$ 1,5,9-nonanetriol
   (c) $BrCH_2CH_2CHO \longrightarrow NCCH_2CH_2CHO$

6. Plan a synthesis for each of the following compounds from starting materials containing five or fewer carbons. Difunctional starting materials may be used if necessary.
   (a) *cis*-2,2-dimethyl-3-octene
   (b) $CH_3CH_2CH_2CH_2\overset{\overset{\displaystyle O}{\|}}{C}CH_2CH_2CHO$
   (c) 5-hydroxy-2-hexanone
   (d) 4-ethyl-2-methyl-2,4-octadiene
   (e) 2-methyloct-2-en-5-yn-4-ol
   (f) 3-ethylhept-6-en-4-yn-3-ol
   (g) 6-methylheptan-1,4-diol

Chapter 17

Carboxylic Acids

17.1 Structure

Carboxylic acids are distinguished by the functional group COOH, referred to as the **carboxy group**. Four ways of depicting the carboxy group are shown below.

$$R:\overset{\displaystyle :O:}{\underset{..}{C}}:\overset{..}{O}:H \qquad R-\overset{\displaystyle O}{\overset{\|}{C}}-O-H \qquad RCOOH \quad RCO_2H$$

Lewis structure   Kekulé structure   condensed structures

The R group can be either an organic group or a hydrogen.

The carbon atom in a carboxy group uses three hybrid orbitals to bond to the oxygen of the OH group, to the carboxy oxygen and to hydrogen or an organic group. These three orbitals are approximately sp^2-hybrids that lie in one plane. The remaining p-orbital on the carbon forms a π-bond to a p-orbital on the carboxy oxygen. There are two distinct carbon-oxygen bond distances, corresponding to C=O and C—O. The bond angles and bond lengths of formic acid, as determined by microwave spectroscopy, are shown in Figure 17.1. Note that the bond angles around the carboxy carbon are only approximately those expected for sp^2-hybridization. The array HCOO is planar, and the hydroxy hydrogen lies outside of this plane.

In the solid and liquid phases, as well as in the vapor phase at moderately high pressure, carboxylic acids exist largely in a dimeric form in which there is mutual hydrogen bonding from the OH of one molecule to the carbonyl oxygen of another.

$$2\ RCOOH \rightleftharpoons R-C\underset{O-H\cdots O}{\overset{O\cdots H-O}{\diagdown\hspace{1em}\diagup}}C-R$$

For formic acid in the vapor phase, $\Delta H°$ for the dimerization has been determined to be -14 kcal mole^{-1}.

Bond Lengths, Å		Bond Angles, deg	
C=O	1.202	H—C=O	124.1
C—O	1.343	O—C=O	124.9
C—H	1.097	H—C—O	111.0
O—H	0.972	H—O—C	106.3

FIGURE 17.1 Structure of formic acid.

17.2 Nomenclature

Two systems of nomenclature are currently in use for carboxylic acids, and the student should be acquainted with both. Since many of the simpler acids are naturally occurring and were discovered early in the history of organic chemistry, they have well-entrenched common names. At the 1892 Geneva Congress it was agreed to derive the name of a carboxylic acid systematically from that of the normal alkane having the same number of carbon atoms by dropping the ending -**e** and adding the suffix -**oic acid**. The common and IUPAC names for the first ten straight-chain acids, as well as other selected examples, are given in Table 17.1. The name used by *Chemical Abstracts* in indexing is printed in bold type.

Past caproic acid, the even-numbered carboxylic acids are the more important because it is only the even-numbered acids that occur in nature. Carboxylic acids are biosynthesized (built up by living organisms) by the combination of acetic acid units. Since acetic acid is a two-carbon building block, most of the naturally occurring acids have an even number of carbon atoms in the chain.

When naming a substituted carboxylic acid in the IUPAC system, the longest carbon chain *containing the carboxy group* is numbered from 1 to n, beginning with the carboxy carbon. The name of this parent straight-chain carboxylic acid is then prefixed by the names of the various substituents.

$$\underset{\substack{6 \quad 5 \quad\; 4 \quad\; 3 \quad\; 2 \quad 1}}{CH_3\overset{\displaystyle CH_3}{\overset{|}{C}}HCH_2CH_2CH_2\overset{\displaystyle OH}{\overset{|}{C}}HCOOH}$$

2-hydroxy-6-methylheptanoic acid

$$\underset{\substack{6 \quad\quad\; 5 \quad\; 4 \quad\; 3 \quad\; 2 \quad 1}}{CH_3(CH_2)_{11}\overset{\displaystyle CH_3}{\overset{|}{C}}HCH_2CH_2CH_2\overset{\displaystyle CH_3CH_2CH_2}{\overset{|}{C}}HCOOH}$$

6-methyl-2-propyloctadecanoic acid

When using common names, the chain is labeled α, β, γ, δ, and so on, *beginning with the carbon adjacent to the carboxy carbon* (see table of Greek letters inside the front cover).

TABLE 17.1 Nomenclature of Carboxylic Acids

Compound	Common Name	IUPAC Name
HCOOH	**formic acid**	methanoic acid
CH_3COOH	**acetic acid**	ethanoic acid
CH_3CH_2COOH	propionic acid	**propanoic acid**
$CH_3(CH_2)_2COOH$	butyric acid	**butanoic acid**
$CH_3(CH_2)_3COOH$	valeric acid	**pentanoic acid**
$CH_3(CH_2)_4COOH$	caproic acid	**hexanoic acid**
$CH_3(CH_2)_5COOH$	enanthic acid	**heptanoic acid**
$CH_3(CH_2)_6COOH$	caprylic acid	**octanoic acid**
$CH_3(CH_2)_7COOH$	pelargonic acid	**nonanoic acid**
$CH_3(CH_2)_8COOH$	capric acid	**decanoic acid**
$CH_3(CH_2)_{10}COOH$	lauric acid	**dodecanoic acid**
$CH_3(CH_2)_{12}COOH$	myristic acid	**tetradecanoic acid**
$CH_3(CH_2)_{14}COOH$	palmitic acid	**hexadecanoic acid**
$CH_3(CH_2)_{16}COOH$	stearic acid	**octadecanoic acid**

As in the case of aldehydes and ketones, it is desirable not to mix IUPAC and common nomenclature (page 360).

α-bromobutyric acid
2-bromobutanoic acid
(not 2-bromobutyric acid)

δ-hydroxyvaleric acid
5-hydroxypentanoic acid
(not δ-hydroxypentanoic acid)

It is not always possible or convenient to name a carboxylic acid in the foregoing way. This is the case with cyclic acids.

cyclopentane carboxylic acid   1-methylcyclohexane carboxylic acid

In rare cases it may be necessary to name a compound containing a carboxy group as a derivative of some other function. In such a case the COOH group is designated by the prefix **carboxy-**.

1-carboxycyclohexyl hydroperoxide

EXERCISE 17.1   What is the IUPAC name of each of the following carboxylic acids?

(a) $ClCH_2CH_2CH_2CH_2COOH$ (b) $(CH_3)_3CCH_2CH_2CH_2COOH$

(c) $CH_3CH_2\overset{\overset{\displaystyle CH_3}{|}}{C}HCH_2\overset{\overset{\displaystyle I}{|}}{C}HCOOH$ (d) $CH_2{=}CHCH{=}CHCOOH$

17.3 Physical Properties

Table 17.2 lists the melting point, boiling point, and water solubility of a number of straight-chain carboxylic acids. The boiling points of carboxylic acids are higher than expected for their molecular weights because of hydrogen bonding. The lower molecular weight acids are liquids at room temperature. The first four acids are fully miscible with water in all proportions. As the chain length is increased, the water solubility steadily decreases.

EXERCISE 17.2   Make a graph of the colligative properties presented in Table 17.2 versus molecular weight. Use your graph to estimate the boiling point and water solubility of undecanoic acid? (The actual values are 280°C and 0.0093 g/100 mL.)

TABLE 17.2 Physical Properties of Carboxylic Acids

Acid	Melting Point, °C	Boiling Point, °C (760 mm)	Solubility in H_2O g/100 ml, 20°C
formic	8.4	101	∞
acetic	16.6	118	∞
propanoic	−21	141	∞
butanoic	−5	164	∞
pentanoic	−34	186	4.97
hexanoic	−3	205	0.968
heptanoic	−8	223	0.244
octanoic	17	239	0.068
nonanoic	15	255	0.026
decanoic	32	270	0.015
dodecanoic	44	299	0.0055
tetradecanoic	54	251 (100 mm)	0.0020
hexadecanoic	63	267 (100 mm)	0.00072
octadecanoic	72	—	0.00029

17.4 Acidity

A. Ionization

We saw in Section 4.5 that compounds containing the carboxy group are weakly acidic. In fact, it is this property from which the class derives its name. When acetic acid is dissolved in water, the equilibrium shown in equation (17-1) exists.

$$CH_3-\overset{O}{\overset{\|}{C}}-OH + H_2O \rightleftharpoons CH_3-\overset{O}{\overset{\|}{C}}-O^- + H_3O^+ \qquad (17\text{-}1)$$

The equilibrium constant for this reaction, denoted as K_a or the "acid dissociation constant," has the magnitude

$$K_a = \frac{[CH_3CO_2^-][H^+]}{[CH_3COOH]} = 1.8 \times 10^{-5}\ M \qquad (17\text{-}2)$$

Remember that the concentration of H_2O, which remains essentially invariant for dilute solutions (at 55.5 M), is not carried in the denominator of the expression for K_a. More correctly, equation (17-2) is an expression for the equilibrium

$$CH_3COOH \rightleftharpoons CH_3CO_2^- + H^+$$

The exact equilibrium expression for equation (17-1) is

$$K = \frac{[CH_3CO_2^-][H_3O^+]}{[CH_3COOH][H_2O]} = 3.25 \times 10^{-7}$$

It follows that $K_a = [H_2O] \times K = 1.8 \times 10^{-5}\ M$.

The corresponding $pK_a = -\log (1.8 \times 10^{-5}) = 5 - \log (1.8) = 4.74$.

Dissociation constants of this magnitude put the carboxylic acids in the class of relatively weak acids. For example, a 0.1 M aqueous solution of acetic acid is only 1.3% dissociated into ions. Strong acids, such as HCl and H_2SO_4, are completely dissociated in dilute aqueous solution. Nevertheless, the carboxylic acids are distinctly acidic—their aqueous solutions have the characteristic sour taste of hydronium ion. Although the carboxylic acids are weak acids compared with mineral acids, they are much stronger than alcohols. Recall that ethanol has a dissociation constant of about 10^{-16}; ethanol is only 10^{-11} as strong an acid as acetic acid.

The question immediately arises, "Why is acetic acid more acidic than ethanol?" The answer lies mostly in the relative stability of the negative charge of the anion. In ethoxide ion the negative charge is concentrated on a single oxygen atom; ethoxide ion is basic because this concentrated charge provides strong attraction for a proton. In acetate ion, however, the charge on the carboxy group is divided between two oxygens. Acetate ion is not adequately represented by a single Lewis structure. A second and equivalent structure may be written that differs only in the position of electrons.

$$\left[CH_3-C\overset{\ddot{\ddot{O}}:}{\underset{\ddot{\ddot{O}}:^-}{\diagup}} \quad \longleftrightarrow \quad CH_3-C\overset{\ddot{O}:^-}{\underset{\ddot{O}:}{\diagup}} \right]$$

Acetate ion is described as a resonance hybrid of these two principal structures (Section 2.4). The hybrid structure may also be written as

$$CH_3-C\overset{O\frac{1}{2}-}{\underset{O\frac{1}{2}-}{\diagup}}$$

This symbol emphasizes that only half of a negative charge resides on each oxygen. The attraction for a proton is therefore reduced.

Another way of describing this phenomenon is wholly in terms of energy. The energies required to remove a proton from ethanol and acetic acid in the dilute gas phase are

$$CH_3CH_2OH \rightleftharpoons CH_3CH_2O^- + H^+ \qquad \Delta H° = 378 \text{ kcal mole}^{-1}$$
$$CH_3COOH \rightleftharpoons CH_3CO_2^- + H^+ \qquad \Delta H° = 349 \text{ kcal mole}^{-1}$$

It takes a large amount of energy to separate charges because of their Coulombic attraction. The energy required for dissociation of acetic acid is substantially less than that for ethanol because in acetate ion the negative charge is attracted by two oxygen nuclei, but since it is spread over a larger volume of space, there is less electron-electron repulsion. This energy effect in acetate ion is sometimes referred to as **resonance stabilization** or as a **resonance energy** (Chapter 19).

An alternative description can be given in terms of the overlap of atomic orbitals. Each oxygen contributes a p-orbital that can overlap in π-bonding to a p-orbital of the carboxy carbon, as illustrated in Figure 17.2. The resulting three-center π-molecular orbital system has four electrons with excess electron density on the two oxygens. Such multicenter π-molecular orbital systems are characteristic of conjugated systems and are discussed in more detail in Chapter 21.

In either representation, the two carbon-oxygen bonds in a carboxylate ion are equivalent. The carbon-oxygen bond length is 1.26 Å, which is between the bond length of 1.20 Å for C=O and 1.34 Å for C—O in formic acid (see Figure 17.1).

EXERCISE 17.3 Formic acid has a dissociation constant, $K_a = 1.77 \times 10^{-4}$. What is its pK_a? Calculate the approximate concentration of formate ions in a solution nominally 0.1 M in formic acid.

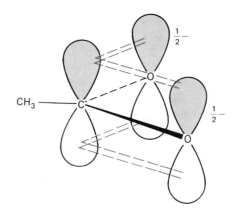

FIGURE 17.2 π-orbital interactions in acetate ion.

B. Inductive Effects

In Section 10.4 we found that electronegative groups whose bonds to carbon are highly polar have important effects on the acidity of alcohols. We saw that this effect could be interpreted in terms of the electrostatic interaction of a bond dipole with the negative charge on oxygen in the alkoxide ion. Substituent groups also affect the acidity of carboxylic acids. Because carboxylic acids are more acidic than alcohols, it is easier to determine their dissociation constants. Consequently, a wealth of such quantitative acidity data is available. Some of these results are summarized in Table 17.3.

Highly electronegative atoms tend to withdraw electron density from carbon and have a marked acid-strengthening effect. Chloroacetic acid is 1.9 pK_a units more acidic than acetic acid. The C—Cl dipole is oriented in such a way that the positive end

**TABLE 17.3 Acidity of Some Substituted
Acetic Acids**

Acid	K_a, M	pK_a
CH_3COOH	1.8×10^{-5}	4.74
FCH_2COOH	2.6×10^{-3}	2.59
F_3CCOOH	0.59	0.23
$ClCH_2COOH$	1.4×10^{-3}	2.86
$Cl_2CHCOOH$	5.5×10^{-2}	1.26
Cl_3CCOOH	0.23	0.64
$BrCH_2COOH$	1.3×10^{-3}	2.90
ICH_2COOH	6.7×10^{-4}	3.18
$HOCH_2COOH$	1.5×10^{-4}	3.83
CH_3OCH_2COOH	2.9×10^{-4}	3.54
$CH_2{=}CHCH_2COOH$	4.5×10^{-5}	4.35
$HC{\equiv}CCH_2COOH$	4.8×10^{-4}	3.32
CH_3CH_2COOH	1.3×10^{-5}	4.87
$NCCH_2COOH$	3.4×10^{-3}	2.46

is closer to the negative charge on the carboxy group than is the negative end. Electrostatic attraction exceeds the repulsion and the negative charge of the anion is therefore stabilized by the chlorine.

$$Cl{\diagdown}CH_2{-}CO_2{}^-$$

We used the same explanation to interpret the effect of a chlorine substituent on the acidity of ethanol (page 196).

$$Cl{\diagdown}CH_2{-}CH_2O^-$$

The acid-strengthening effect, in this case of 1.6 pK_a units, is similar to that in chloroacetic acid. In both anions the negative charge is two atoms away from the carbon-chlorine bond.

Carbon-carbon double and triple bonds have a significant electron-attracting effect that is reflected in the enhanced acidity of vinylacetic and ethynylacetic acids. An sp^2-hybridized carbon orbital with its greater s-character is effectively more electronegative than an sp^3-orbital. Recall that alkenes and alkynes have small but significant dipole moments (Sections 11.3 and 12.3).

The higher alkanoic acids are somewhat less acidic than acetic acid. Alkyl groups show a small but significant electron-donating inductive effect in appropriate systems in solution.

The inductive effect or remote substituents falls off dramatically with increased distance from the charged center. This effect is expected because electrostatic interactions between charges are inversely proportional to the distance between them. An example is seen in the acidity constants for butanoic acid and its three monochloro derivatives (Table 17.4). Beyond a few methylene groups, the effect becomes negligible.

EXERCISE 17.4 Plot the pK_as of chloroacetic acid and trichloroacetic acid versus the pK_as or the corresponding fluoroacetic acids. Note that the pK_a of acetic acid falls on the line. What is the predicted pK_a of difluoroacetic acid?

C. Salt Formation

There is one more aspect of acidity of carboxylic acids that we should consider. In Section 17.3 we saw that carboxylic acids of more than five carbons are essentially insoluble in water. Beyond this point, the polar portion of the molecule (COOH)

TABLE 17.4 Acidity of Butanoic Acids

Acid	K_a, M	pK_a
2-chlorobutanoic acid	139×10^{-5}	2.86
3-chlorobutanoic acid	8.9×10^{-5}	4.05
4-chlorobutanoic acid	3.0×10^{-5}	4.52
butanoic acid	1.5×10^{-5}	4.82

becomes less important than the nonpolar hydrocarbon tail (R). Consider the reaction of a carboxylic acid such as dodecanoic acid with hydroxide ion.

$$CH_3(CH_2)_{10}COOH + OH^- \overset{K}{\rightleftharpoons} H_2O + CH_3(CH_2)_{10}CO_2^- \qquad (17\text{-}3)$$

The equilibrium constant for reaction (17-3) may be derived as follows.

$$K_a = \frac{[CH_3(CH_2)_{10}CO_2^-][H^+]}{[CH_3(CH_2)_{10}COOH]} = 1.3 \times 10^{-5} \, M \qquad (17\text{-}4)$$

$$K_w = [H^+][OH^-] = 10^{-14} \, M^2 \qquad (17\text{-}5)$$

Rearranging (17-5), we have

$$[H^+] = \frac{10^{-14}}{[OH^-]} \, M \qquad (17\text{-}6)$$

Substituting (17-6) into (17-4) and expanding, we have

$$K = \frac{[CH_3(CH_2)_{10}CO_2^-]}{[CH_3(CH_2)_{10}COOH][OH^-]} = 1.3 \times 10^9 \, M^{-1} \qquad (17\text{-}7)$$

Equation (17-7) is merely the equilibrium expression for reaction (17-3). The large value of K shows that the reaction proceeds to completion; dodecanoic acid is converted by aqueous sodium hydroxide completely into the salt, sodium dodecanoate. Note that the anions of carboxylic acids are named by dropping -ic from the name of the parent acid and adding the suffix -**ate**. Although dodecanoic acid is a neutral molecule, sodium dodecanoate is a salt. Dissolution of this salt gives an anion and a cation, which can be solvated by water. It is not surprising that the solubility of sodium dodecanoate (1.2 g per 100 mL) is much greater than that of dodecanoic acid itself (0.0055 g per 100 mL).

EXERCISE 17.5 Equation (17-7) can be used to calculate the ratio of ionized and nonionized dodecanoic acid at a given pH, by inserting the proper value for $[OH^-]$. Calculate this ratio for pH = 2, 4, 6, and 8.

D. Soaps

The sodium and potassium salts of long-chain carboxylic acids ("fatty acids") are obtained by the reaction of natural fats with sodium or potassium hydroxide. These salts, referred to as soaps, have the interesting and useful ability to solubilize nonpolar organic substances. This phenomenon can easily be understood if one considers the structure of such a salt.

$$CH_3CH_2CH_2CH_2CH_2CH_2CH_2CH_2CH_2CH_2CH_2CH_2CH_2CH_2CH_2CO_2^- \, K^+$$

The molecule has a polar ionic region and a large nonpolar hydrocarbon region. In aqueous solution a number of carboxylate ions tend to cluster together so that the hydrocarbon tails are close to each other, thus reducing their energy by the attractive van der Waals forces enjoyed by normal hydrocarbons. The surface of the sphere-like cluster is then occupied by the highly polar CO_2^- groups. These polar groups face the medium, where they may be solvated by H_2O or paired with a cation. The resulting spherical structure, called a **micelle**, is depicted in cross section in Figure 17.3. The wavy lines in the figure represent the long hydrocarbon chains of the salt molecules.

Organic material such as butter or motor oil that is not normally soluble in water may "dissolve" in the hydrocarbon interior of a micelle. The overall process of soap solubilization is diagrammed schematically in Figure 17.4.

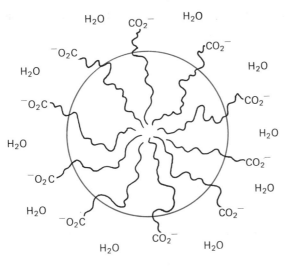

FIGURE 17.3 Cross section of a micelle.

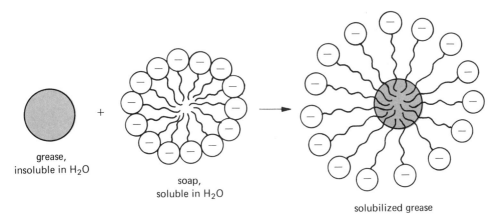

grease,
insoluble in H_2O

soap,
soluble in H_2O

solubilized grease

FIGURE 17.4 Schematic diagram of soap solubilization.

Certain bacteria can metabolize soaps. This degradation is most rapid when there are no branches in the hydrocarbon chain of the soap molecule. Since the naturally occurring fatty acids are all unbranched compounds, soaps derived from natural fats are said to be **biodegradable**. Before 1933 all cleaning materials were soaps. In that year the first synthetic detergents were marketed. Detergents have the useful property of not forming the hard ''scum'' that often results from the use of a soap with hard water. This scum is actually the insoluble magnesium and calcium salts of the fatty acid. The first detergents were alkylbenzenesulfonates. Like soaps, they had a large nonpolar hydrocarbon tail and a polar end.

$$R—\!\!\left\langle\!\!\bigcirc\!\!\right\rangle\!\!—SO_3^-\ K^+$$

R = branched alkyl chain

However, being branched compounds, these early detergents were not rapidly biodegradable. Since the materials could not be completely metabolized by the bacteria that operate in sewage treatment plants, they were passed into natural waterways with the treated sewage and often reappeared as foam or suds on the surface of lakes and rivers. After an

intensive research project, the detergent industry in 1965 introduced **linear alkanesul-
fonate detergents** (Section 25.5.B).

$$CH_3(CH_2)_nCH_2SO_3^- K^+$$

Since the new detergents are straight-chain compounds, they can be metabolized by
bacteria.

17.5 Spectroscopy

A. Nuclear Magnetic Resonance

The resonance positions for various types of hydrogens in carboxylic acids are summarized in Table 17.5. Hydrogens attached to C-2 of a carboxylic acid resonate at roughly
the same place as do the analogous hydrogens in aldehydes and ketones. The very
low-field resonance of the carboxy proton is associated with the dimeric hydrogen-
bonded structure discussed in Section 17.1. The spectrum of 2-methylpropanoic acid is
shown in Figure 17.5.

The CMR chemical shifts of carboxylic acids are similar to those seen with aldehydes (Table 14.4), except that the carbonyl carbon itself resonates at much lower
field. Representative data are summarized in Table 17.6.

**TABLE 17.5 Chemical Shifts of
Carboxylic Acid Hydrogens**

Type of Hydrogen	Chemical Shift, δ, ppm
C**H**₃COOH	2.0
RC**H**₂COOH	2.36
R₂C**H**COOH	2.52
RCOO**H**	about 10–13

FIGURE 17.5 NMR spectrum of 2-methylpropanoic acid, $(CH_3)_2CHCOOH$.

TABLE 17.6 CMR Chemical Shifts of Carboxylic Acids

	C-1	C-2	C-3	C-4	C-5
formic acid	166.3				
acetic acid	177.2	21.1			
propanoic acid	180.4	27.8	9.0		
butanoic acid	179.6	36.3	18.5	13.4	
pentanoic acid	179.7	34.1	27.0	22.0	13.5

EXERCISE 17.6 An unknown carboxylic acid shows NMR peaks at δ 12.5 (1H, s), 1.25 (6H, s), 0.95 (3H, t, J = 6) and 1.50 (2H, q, J = 6) ppm. The CMR spectrum shows signals at δ 9.5, 24.8, 33.7, 43.0, and 182.2 ppm. What is the structure of the compound?

B. Infrared

One of the characteristic absorptions of acids is the C=O stretch, which occurs in the region 1710-1760 cm^{-1}. The exact position and appearance of this absorption depends on the physical state in which the measurement is made. In pure liquids or in the solid state the C=O stretch occurs as a broad band at about 1710 cm^{-1}. In dilute solution (CCl$_4$, CHCl$_3$) the absorption band is narrower and is seen at about 1760 cm^{-1}. The O—H stretch occurs as a broad, relatively intense absorption that usually extends from 2400 to 3400 cm^{-1}. The spectrum of hexanoic acid in Figure 17.6 illustrates these bands.

17.6 Synthesis

A. Hydrolysis of Nitriles

We have seen that nitriles undergo acid-catalyzed and base-catalyzed hydration (Sections 12.6.B, 12.6.C). Under more drastic conditions, the product of such a hydration, called an **amide**, undergoes hydrolysis to give a mole of carboxylic acid and a mole of ammonia.

FIGURE 17.6 Infrared spectrum of hexanoic acid.

$$RC{\equiv}N \xrightarrow{\text{H}_2\text{O}} R\overset{\overset{\displaystyle O}{\|}}{C}NH_2 \xrightarrow{\text{H}_2\text{O}} RCOOH + NH_3$$

nitrile   amide   carboxylic acid

For the preparation of a carboxylic acid from a nitrile, it is not necessary to isolate the intermediate amide. Either acidic or basic hydrolysis may be employed. In acidic medium, the ammonia produced is protonated as ammonium ion. Under basic conditions, gaseous ammonia is evolved as the hydrolysis reaction proceeds.

$$\text{phenylacetonitrile} \quad \langle\!\!\rangle-CH_2CN + 2\,H_2O \xrightarrow[\substack{100\,°C \\ 3\,hr}]{H_2SO_4} \langle\!\!\rangle-CH_2COOH + NH_4{}^+\,HSO_4{}^-$$

phenylacetonitrile   phenylacetic acid

> A mixture of 1150 mL of water, 840 mL of conc. H_2SO_4, and 700 g of phenylacetonitrile is heated at reflux for 3 hr. Phenylacetic acid (630 g, 78% yield) is obtained when the reaction mixture is poured into cold water.

$$CH_3(CH_2)_9CN + 2\,H_2O \xrightarrow[\substack{C_2H_5OH \\ reflux \\ 77\,hr}]{KOH} \xrightarrow{HCl} CH_3(CH_2)_9COOH + NH_3$$

undecanenitrile   undecanoic acid

> A mixture of 27 g of undecanenitrile, 200 g of 20% ethanolic KOH, and 50 mL of water is refluxed for 77 hr, during which time ammonia is evolved. The solvent is evaporated, and the residue is treated with conc. HCl. After washing with water, 24 g of undecanoic acid (80%), m.p. 29° C, is obtained.

As we saw in Chapters 9 and 12, nitriles are conveniently prepared from primary alkyl halides by treatment with cyanide ion. Thus, cyanide ion is a synthon for the carboxy group.

$$\text{1-bromobutane} \qquad \diagdown\!\diagup\!\diagdown Br + NaCN \xrightarrow{DMSO} \diagup\!\diagdown\!\diagup CN \xrightarrow[\substack{H_2O \\ \Delta}]{KOH}$$

1-bromobutane   (92%)
                                pentanenitrile

$$\diagup\!\diagdown\!\diagup CO_2{}^-\,K^+ \xrightarrow{H^+} \diagup\!\diagdown\!\diagup COOH$$

                                      (90%)
                                pentanoic acid

The mechanism of the hydrolysis reaction will be discussed in Section 18.6.

> **EXERCISE 17.7** Which of the following carboxylic acids can be prepared from an alkyl halide by formation and hydrolysis of a nitrile?
> (a) 2,2-dimethylpropanoic acid   (b) 2-methylpentanoic acid
> (c) 1-methylcyclohexanecarboxylic acid   (d) 7-methyloctanoic acid

B. Carbonation of Organometallic Reagents

Alkyl halides may also be converted into carboxylic acids by formation of an organometallic reagent, which is then allowed to react with carbon dioxide. The product is the salt of a carboxylic acid. Treatment of this salt with aqueous mineral acid liberates the free acid. Grignard reagents are commonly used (Section 8.8).

Carbon dioxide gas is bubbled through a solution of *sec*-butylmagnesium chloride (prepared from 46 g of 2-chlorobutane and 13.4 g of magnesium in 400 mL of ether) at $-10°C$. When CO_2 is no longer absorbed, the mixture is hydrolyzed with 25% aqueous H_2SO_4. Distillation of the crude product gives 40 g (80%) of 2-methylbutanoic acid.

A similar reaction occurs between carbon dioxide and organolithium compounds.

phenyllithium   benzoic acid

The Grignard method of converting an alkyl halide to the corresponding carboxylic acid must be used when the alkyl halide is unreactive in S_N2 reactions. With primary and unbranched secondary alkyl halides the nitrile displacement method discussed in the previous section may also be used.

EXERCISE 17.8   Show how the following conversions may be accomplished.
(a) cyclohexanone $\longrightarrow$ 1-methylcyclohexanecarboxylic acid
(b) 2-methylbutane $\longrightarrow$ 2,2-dimethylbutanoic acid
(c) 2-methyl-1-propanol $\longrightarrow$ 3-methylbutanoic acid

---

C. Oxidation of Primary Alcohols or Aldehydes

The third generally useful method for preparing carboxylic acids involves oxidation of aldehydes (obtained in the aldol reaction, Section 14.8.C) or primary alcohols (obtained, for example, by hydroboration of terminal alkenes; Section 11.6.D). A useful oxidizing agent for this purpose is potassium permanganate.

2-ethyl-1-hexanol

2-ethylhexanal

2-ethylhexanoic acid

same as above
(78%)

The initial product in oxidation of a primary alcohol is the corresponding aldehyde. However, with aqueous permanganate the aldehyde undergoes subsequent oxidation more rapidly than the primary alcohol, so it is normally not observed in the reaction mixture.

A mild and selective reagent for the oxidation of aldehydes to carboxylic acids is silver oxide suspended in aqueous base. Although the method usually affords the desired acid in good yield, it is expensive to carry out on a large scale owing to the cost of silver oxide, unless one reclaims and recycles the silver metal.

$$
\begin{array}{c}
\underset{CH_3CH_2}{H}\!\!\diagdown C\!\!=\!\!C\!\!\diagup\overset{CHO}{CH_3} + Ag_2O \xrightarrow[NaOH]{H_2O} \xrightarrow{HCl} \underset{CH_3CH_2}{H}\!\!\diagdown C\!\!=\!\!C\!\!\diagup\overset{COOH}{CH_3} + Ag \\
(95\text{–}98\%)
\end{array}
$$

The foregoing example illustrates the virtue of a mild oxidant, since the double bond is sensitive to stronger oxidizing agents.

> Silver oxide is a brown solid that has only slight solubility in water. It is usually prepared as needed by mixing a solution of silver nitrate with sodium hydroxide. The precipitate may be filtered, washed with water, and used as an aqueous suspension.

> **EXERCISE 17.9** Write the balanced equation for oxidation of ethanol to acetic acid by $KMnO_4$ (see page 265).

17.7 Reactions

A. Reactions Involving the OH Bond

We have already seen one important reaction of carboxylic acids involving the OH bond—the reaction with bases to give salts.

$$CH_3CH_2CH_2COOH + Na^+\,OH^- \longrightarrow CH_3CH_2CH_2CO_2^-\,Na^+ + H_2O$$

The resulting carboxylate salts enter into the S_N2 reaction with alkyl halides to give carboxylic acid **esters**.

$$CH_3CH_2CH_2CH_2Br + CH_3CO_2^-\,Na^+ \xrightarrow[95°C]{DMF} CH_3CH_2CH_2CH_2O\overset{\overset{\displaystyle O}{\|}}{C}CH_3$$

1-bromobutane

(95–98%)
butyl acetate

Of course, dehydrohalogenation is an important competing reaction, especially with tertiary halides (Sections 9.6, 11.5.A). However, because carboxylate ions are rather weak bases, even secondary halides may often be converted into the corresponding esters with little competing elimination.

Another important reaction involving the OH bond is the reaction of carboxylic acids with diazomethane. The products of this reaction are the methyl ester and nitrogen.

$$RCOOH + CH_2N_2 \longrightarrow RCOOCH_3 + N_2$$

> Diazomethane is a yellow gas boiling at about 0°C. It is highly toxic and, under certain conditions, explosive. Diazomethane is another example of a compound for which multi-

ple Kekulé or Lewis structures can be written. The molecule is considered to be a resonance hybrid of the following forms.

$$[:\overset{-}{C}H_2-\overset{+}{N}\equiv N: \longleftrightarrow CH_2=\overset{+}{N}=\overset{..}{\overset{..}{N}}:^-]$$

The reaction of diazomethane with carboxylic acids probably involves the following steps.

(1) $R-\overset{\overset{\displaystyle O}{\|}}{C}-\overset{\frown}{O}-H + :\overset{-}{C}H_2-\overset{+}{N}\equiv N: \longrightarrow R-\overset{\overset{\displaystyle O}{\|}}{C}-\overset{..}{\overset{..}{O}}:^- + CH_3-\overset{+}{N}\equiv N:$

(2) $R-\overset{\overset{\displaystyle O}{\|}}{C}-\overset{..}{\overset{..}{O}}:^- + {}^+CH_3-\overset{\frown}{N}\equiv N: \longrightarrow R-\overset{\overset{\displaystyle O}{\|}}{C}-OCH_3 + :N\equiv N:$

The first step is a simple acid-base reaction; the moderately acidic carboxylic acid transfers a proton to the basic carbon atom of diazomethane. The pair of ions thus formed immediately reacts by the S_N2 mechanism; carboxylate ion is the entering nucleophile and nitrogen is the leaving group.

Because of the toxicity and danger of explosion, diazomethane reactions are rarely carried out on a large scale. However, because of the convenience of the procedure (yields are usually quantitative and the only by-product is a gas), it is frequently used for the small-scale conversion of an acid into its methyl ester, especially when the acid is a relatively precious one.

(100%)

EXERCISE 17.10 Write the structure of the product of the reaction of (R)-1-deuterio-1-iodobutane with sodium propanoate.

B. Reactions Involving the Hydrocarbon Side Chain

Carboxylic acids undergo the normal reactions of alkanes, as modified by the presence of the carboxy group, in the hydrocarbon chain of the molecule. For example, butanoic acid undergoes combustion and free radical chlorination.

$$CH_3CH_2CH_2COOH \begin{cases} \xrightarrow{O_2} CO_2 + H_2O \\ \xrightarrow[\substack{\text{heat or}\\\text{light}}]{Cl_2} \text{mixture of mono- and polychlorobutanoic acids} \end{cases}$$

Since these reactions are not selective for any particular position along the chain they generally have no preparative utility.

The indiscriminate nature of such free radical reactions is demonstrated by the light-initiated chlorination of butanoic acid in CCl_4 at 25°C.

$$CH_3CH_2CH_2COOH \xrightarrow[h\nu]{Cl_2} \begin{cases} ClCH_2CH_2CH_2COOH \\ \quad\quad (31\%) \\[1em] \underset{\substack{| \\ Cl}}{CH_3}CHCH_2COOH \\ \quad\quad (64\%) \\[1em] CH_3CH_2\underset{\substack{| \\ Cl}}{C}HCOOH \\ \quad\quad (5\%) \end{cases}$$

One reaction of the aliphatic chain that does have utility is the reaction of carboxylic acids with phosphorus tribromide and bromine.

$$3\ CH_3CH_2CH_2COOH + PBr_3 + 3\ Br_2 \longrightarrow 3\ CH_3CH_2\overset{Br}{\underset{|}{C}}H\overset{O}{\overset{||}{C}}Br + H_3PO_3 + 3\ HBr$$

Note that the reaction is *positionally selective*—only the hydrogen at C-2 is replaced. The reaction is not a free radical halogenation process. The overall result, α-bromination, is accomplished by a sequence of steps. The key step involves the reaction of bromine with the **enol form** of the corresponding **acyl bromide**. Phosphorus tribromide facilitates the reaction by reacting with the carboxylic acid to yield the acyl bromide (Section 17.7.D), which undergoes enolization more readily than the acid itself.

(1) $3\ RCH_2COOH + PBr_3 \longrightarrow 3\ RCH_2\overset{O}{\overset{||}{C}}Br + H_3PO_3$

(2) $RCH_2\overset{O}{\overset{||}{C}}Br \underset{}{\overset{H^+}{\rightleftharpoons}} RCH{=}\overset{OH}{\overset{|}{C}}Br$

      keto form   enol form

(3) $RCH{=}\overset{OH}{\overset{|}{C}}Br + Br_2 \longrightarrow R\underset{\substack{| \\ Br}}{C}H\overset{O}{\overset{||}{C}}Br + HBr$

The reaction is analogous to the acid-catalyzed bromination of ketones (Section 14.6.D). Only a catalytic amount of PBr_3 is needed because the product acyl bromide enters into the following equilibrium with the starting acid.

$$R\underset{\substack{| \\ Br}}{C}H\overset{O}{\overset{||}{C}}Br + RCH_2\overset{O}{\overset{||}{C}}OH \rightleftharpoons R\underset{\substack{| \\ Br}}{C}H\overset{O}{\overset{||}{C}}OH + RCH_2\overset{O}{\overset{||}{C}}Br$$

Under these conditions the product that is isolated is the α-bromo carboxylic acid rather than the α-bromo acyl bromide.

$$CH_3CH_2CH_2COOH + Br_2 \xrightarrow{PBr_3} CH_3CH_2\underset{\substack{| \\ Br}}{C}HCOOH + HBr$$

$$(82\%)$$

Since phosphorus reacts rapidly with bromine to give PBr_3, the reaction is often carried out by simply heating the carboxylic acid with a mixture of phosphorus and bromine. In the bromination reaction one normally begins with a carboxylic acid and ends up with the α-bromo carboxylic acid, as illustrated in the last example. However, it is important to remember that the crucial reaction, introduction of the bromine into the molecule, is actually a reaction of the intermediate acyl bromide.

EXERCISE 17.11 Show how hex-2-enoic acid ($CH_3CH_2CH_2CH{=}CHCOOH$) can be synthesized starting with 1-chloropentane.

C. Formation of Esters

Carboxylic acids react readily with alcohols in the presence of catalytic amounts of mineral acids to yield compounds called **esters** (Chapter 18). The process is called **esterification**.

$$CH_3COOH + C_2H_5OH \overset{H^+}{\rightleftharpoons} CH_3COOC_2H_5 + H_2O \qquad (17\text{-}8)$$

Unlike most of the reactions we have encountered, this one has an equilibrium constant of relatively low magnitude. The experimental equilibrium constant for the reaction of acetic acid with ethanol is

$$K_{eq} = \frac{[CH_3COOC_2H_5][H_2O]}{[CH_3COOH][C_2H_5OH]} = 3.38$$

As in any equilibrium process, the reaction may be driven in one direction by controlling the concentration of either the reactants or products (Le Châtelier's principle). For reaction (17-8) the equilibrium constant tells us that an equimolar mixture of acetic acid and ethanol will eventually reach equilibrium to give a mixture containing 0.35 mole each of acetic acid and ethanol and 0.65 mole each of ethyl acetate and water. Of course, the same equilibrium mixture is obtained if one starts with equimolar quantities of ethyl acetate and water.

If we increase the concentration of either reactant relative to the other, the reaction will be driven to the right and the equilibrium mixture will contain proportionately more ethyl acetate and water. Table 17.7 shows the equilibrium compositions that will be achieved starting with various mixtures of acetic acid and ethanol.

Similar results will obviously be obtained by increasing the acetic acid concentration rather than the ethanol concentration. In a practical situation, when one wants to prepare an ester, it is desirable to obtain the maximum yield of pure product. It is often done as suggested in the preceding paragraph—by using a large excess of one of the

TABLE 17.7 Equilibrium Compositions

	CH_3COOH	$+ \; C_2H_5OH$	$\rightleftharpoons \; CH_3COOC_2H_5$	$+ \; H_2O$
at start	1	1	0	0
at equilibrium	0.35	0.35	0.65	0.65
at start	1	10	0	0
at equilibrium	0.03	9.03	0.97	0.97
at start	1	100	0	0
at equilibrium	0.007	99.007	0.993	0.993

reactants. For economic reasons, the reactant chosen is usually the less expensive of the two.

The mechanism of the acid-catalyzed esterification reaction has been studied thoroughly. All of the experimental facts are consistent with a mechanism involving the following steps (illustrated for acetic acid and methanol).

$$(1)\quad CH_3-\overset{\overset{\displaystyle O}{\|}}{C}-OH + H^+ \rightleftharpoons CH_3-\overset{\overset{\displaystyle OH^+}{\|}}{C}-OH$$

$$(2)\quad CH_3-\overset{\overset{\displaystyle OH^+}{\|}}{C}-OH + CH_3\ddot{O}H \rightleftharpoons CH_3-\overset{\overset{\displaystyle OH}{|}}{\underset{\underset{\displaystyle H\overset{+}{O}CH_3}{|}}{C}}-OH$$

$$(3)\quad CH_3-\overset{\overset{\displaystyle OH}{|}}{\underset{\underset{\displaystyle H\overset{+}{O}CH_3}{|}}{C}}-OH \rightleftharpoons CH_3-\overset{\overset{\displaystyle OH}{|}}{\underset{\underset{\displaystyle OCH_3}{|}}{C}}-OH + H^+$$

$$(4)\quad CH_3-\overset{\overset{\displaystyle OH}{|}}{\underset{\underset{\displaystyle OCH_3}{|}}{C}}-OH + H^+ \rightleftharpoons CH_3-\overset{\overset{\displaystyle OH}{|}}{\underset{\underset{\displaystyle OCH_3}{|}}{C}}-OH_2{}^+$$

$$(5)\quad CH_3-\overset{\overset{\displaystyle :\ddot{O}H}{|}}{\underset{\underset{\displaystyle OCH_3}{|}}{C}}-OH_2{}^+ \rightleftharpoons CH_3-\overset{\overset{\displaystyle \ddot{O}H^+}{\|}}{C}-OCH_3 + H_2O$$

$$(6)\quad CH_3-\overset{\overset{\displaystyle OH^+}{\|}}{C}-OCH_3 \rightleftharpoons CH_3-\overset{\overset{\displaystyle O}{\|}}{C}-OCH_3 + H^+$$

Steps (1), (3), (4), and (6) are rapid proton-transfer steps—simple acid-base reactions. Although we show "bare" protons in each case, they are actually solvated by some Lewis base, which may be methanol, water, or any of the other oxygenated species present. In steps (2) and (5), carbon-oxygen bonds are formed or broken. These steps have higher activation energies than the proton-transfer steps.

The foregoing mechanism is an important one in organic chemistry. As mentioned previously, it is based on a large amount of experimental data. Two of the more definitive experiments involved the use of ^{18}O-labeled materials. The first of these interesting experiments demonstrated that the oxygen-carbonyl bond is broken during the esterification process. Benzoic acid was treated in the presence of HCl with methanol enriched in ^{18}O. The water produced in the reaction was isolated and shown to be normal $H_2{}^{16}O$.

$$C_6H_5\overset{\overset{\displaystyle O}{\|}}{C}-OH + CH_3{}^{18}OH \overset{H^+}{\rightleftharpoons} C_6H_5\overset{\overset{\displaystyle O}{\|}}{C}-{}^{18}OCH_3 + H_2{}^{16}O$$

This experiment rules out mechanisms such as the following, in which the oxygen in the water produced comes from the alcohol.

$$C_6H_5\overset{\overset{\displaystyle O}{\|}}{C}-\ddot{O}H + CH_3-\overset{+}{\ddot{O}H_2} \overset{}{\nrightarrow} C_6H_5\overset{\overset{\displaystyle O}{\|}}{C}-\underset{\underset{\displaystyle H}{|}}{\overset{+}{O}}CH_3 + H_2O$$

The second important labeling experiment showed that a symmetrical **intermediate** intervenes in the process. Ethyl benzoate enriched in ^{18}O in the carbonyl oxygen was hydrolyzed with HCl and normal water. The reaction was stopped short of completion, and the recovered ethyl benzoate was analyzed. It was found that exchange of ^{18}O in the ester by ^{16}O had occurred. Although hydrolysis occurs approximately five times faster than exchange, this experiment demonstrates that an intermediate is formed that can go on to give acid or reverse to give exchanged ester. Mechanisms such as the following, which is analogous to the S_N2 displacement in saturated systems, are ruled out.

$$\left\{ \begin{array}{c} \underset{H}{\overset{\displaystyle O}{\underset{|}{\overset{\parallel}{R-C-\overset{+}{O}R}}}} + H_2O \longrightarrow \left[\overset{\ddagger}{\underset{R}{\overset{\displaystyle O}{\overset{\parallel}{H_2\overset{\delta+}{O}\cdots\underset{|}{C}\cdots\overset{\delta+}{O}R}}}} \right] \longrightarrow \overset{\displaystyle O}{\overset{\parallel}{H_2\overset{+}{O}-C-R}} + ROH \right\} \quad \text{not observed}$$

Note that the accepted mechanism involves simply an acid-catalyzed addition of an alcohol to the carbonyl group and is analogous to the similar reactions with aldehydes and ketones to form intermediate hemiacetals (Section 14.7.B). Also note that the overall process of esterification amounts to no more than **nucleophilic substitution**— the nucleophile OR substitutes for the nucleophile OH.

EXERCISE 17.12 In the mechanism for acid-catalyzed esterification (page 466), step (1) is a rapid equilibrium and step (2) is usually the rate-determining step. Derive the rate law for acid-catalyzed esterification as a function of K, the equilibrium constant for step (1), and k, the rate constant for the forward reaction of step (2).

D. Formation of Acyl Halides

Carboxylic acids react with thionyl chloride, phosphorus pentachloride, and phosphorus tribromide in the same way that alcohols do (Section 10.6.B). The products are **acyl halides** (Chapter 18).

pentanoic acid   pentanoyl chloride

2-methylpropanoic acid   2-methylpropanoyl chloride

butanoic acid   butanoyl bromide

Mechanistically, these reactions are related to the acid-catalyzed esterification mechanism. In each case, the inorganic chloride reacts with the carboxylic acid to give an intermediate in which the OH group has been converted into a relatively good leaving group. The ensuing reaction is nucleophilic substitution, which occurs by the "addition-elimination" mechanism. For example, in the formation of acyl chlorides with $SOCl_2$ the leaving group in the nucleophilic substitution process is the chlorosulfite ion.

$$
\text{(1)} \quad CH_3\overset{\overset{O}{\|}}{C}OH + SOCl_2 \longrightarrow CH_3\overset{\overset{O}{\|}}{C}-O-\overset{\overset{O}{\|}}{S}Cl + HCl
$$

$$
\text{(2)} \quad CH_3\overset{\overset{O}{\|}}{C}-O-\overset{\overset{O}{\|}}{S}Cl + Cl^- \longrightarrow CH_3\overset{\overset{O^-}{|}}{\underset{\overset{|}{Cl}}{C}}-O-\overset{\overset{O}{\|}}{S}Cl
$$

$$
\text{(3)} \quad CH_3\overset{\overset{O^-}{|}}{\underset{\overset{|}{Cl}}{C}}{-}O{-}\overset{\overset{O}{\|}}{S}Cl \longrightarrow CH_3\overset{\overset{O}{\|}}{C}Cl + {}^-OSCl
$$

We shall see in the next chapter that acyl halides are important intermediates for the conversion of carboxylic acids into other derivatives.

E. Reaction with Ammonia: Formation of Amides

As in aldehydes and ketones, the carbonyl group in carboxylic acids is polarized. That is, the bonding electrons have higher density in the neighborhood of the oxygen than at the carbon.

$$
\left[R-\overset{\overset{O}{\|}}{C}-OH \longleftrightarrow R-\overset{\overset{O^-}{|}}{\underset{+}{C}}-OH \right]
$$

With aldehydes and ketones, we found that, in addition to acid-catalyzed nucleophilic addition, base-catalyzed addition is also observed. With carboxylic acids base-catalyzed nucleophilic additions are rare, and with good reason. Consider the reaction of acetic acid with sodium methoxide. Since methoxide ion is a strong base (the pK_a of methanol is about 16) and acetic acid is a moderately strong acid (pK_a about 5), the following simple acid-base equilibrium lies strongly to the right ($K \cong 10^{11}$) and is established very rapidly.

$$
CH_3-\overset{\overset{O}{\|}}{C}-OH + CH_3O^- \overset{K}{\rightleftharpoons} CH_3-\overset{\overset{O}{\|}}{C}-O^- + CH_3OH
$$

In other words, the acetic acid is converted immediately and quantitatively into acetate ion and the methoxide into methanol. Even in the presence of excess methoxide ion no further reaction occurs, since the acetate carbonyl is less electrophilic. That is, nucleophilic addition to the carbonyl would require that two anions combine to give a dianion. Since like charges repel one another, this reaction is unlikely.

$$
CH_3-\overset{\overset{O}{\|}}{C}-O^- + CH_3O^- \overset{}{\nrightarrow} CH_3-\overset{\overset{O^-}{|}}{\underset{\overset{|}{O^-}}{C}}-OCH_3
$$

Even so, several base-catalyzed nucleophilic additions of carboxylic acids are known. As we shall see, each involves rather special conditions.

The most common reaction of this type is the reaction of carboxylic acids with ammonia or amines to give amides. When ammonia is bubbled through butanoic acid at 185°C, butanamide is obtained in 85% yield. The reaction involves two stages. At room temperature, or even below, butanoic acid reacts with the weak base ammonia to give the salt ammonium butanoate.

$$CH_3CH_2CH_2COOH + NH_3 \xrightarrow{25°C} CH_3CH_2CH_2CO_2^- \ NH_4^+$$

This salt is perfectly stable at normal temperatures. However, pyrolysis of the salt results in the elimination of water and formation of the amide.

$$CH_3CH_2CH_2CO_2^- \ NH_4^+ \xrightarrow{185°C} CH_3CH_2CH_2\overset{\overset{\displaystyle O}{\|}}{C}NH_2 + H_2O$$

ammonium butanoate   butanamide

The reaction occurs only because ammonium butanoate, being the salt of a weak acid and a weak base, is in equilibrium with a significant amount of ammonia and butanoic acid. The actual dehydration step is probably the result of nucleophilic addition of ammonia to the carbonyl group of butanoic acid itself.

EXERCISE 17.13 From the pK_as of butanoic acid and ammonium ion, 4.82 and 9.24, respectively, calculate K for the following equilibrium.

$$CH_3CH_2CH_2CO_2^- + NH_4^+ \rightleftharpoons CH_3CH_2CH_2COOH + NH_3$$

F. Reduction of the Carboxy Group

Another nucleophilic addition to the carboxylate group that is of some interest is in the reduction of carboxylic acids by lithium aluminum hydride.

(93%)

The first step in this reaction is an acid-base reaction, giving the lithium salt of the acid, hydrogen gas, and aluminum hydride.

$$RCOOH + LiAlH_4 \longrightarrow RCOOLi + H_2 + AlH_3$$

The lithium carboxylate is then reduced further, eventually to the salt of the corresponding primary alcohol. Tetrahydroaluminate ion, AlH_4^-, is so reactive that it reduces even a carboxylate ion.

$$RCO_2^- + AlH_4^- \longrightarrow R-\overset{\overset{\displaystyle O^-}{|}}{\underset{\underset{\displaystyle H}{|}}{C}}-O^- + AlH_3$$

The reaction is undoubtedly assisted by the Lewis-acid character of aluminum salts, which reduces the effective negative charge on oxygen. The remaining steps in the reduction are still more complex, but undoubtedly also involve lithium and aluminum salts. For example, further reaction of the bis-alkoxide dianion could involve expulsion of O^{2-} as an aluminum oxide with formation of an intermediate aldehyde. The aldehyde is then rapidly reduced to the alcohol with lithium aluminum hydride.

EXERCISE 17.14 Show how pentanenitrile might be converted into 1-pentanol.

G. One-Carbon Degradation of Carboxylic Acids

Carboxylic acids undergo several reactions in which the carboxy group is replaced by halogen.

$$RCOOH \longrightarrow RX$$

Such reactions, in which carbons are lost from a molecule, are called "degradations."

In the **Hunsdiecker reaction** the silver salt of a carboxylic acid, prepared by treating the acid with silver oxide, is treated with a halogen. Bromine is the usual reagent, but iodine may also be used. Carbon dioxide is evolved and the corresponding alkyl halide is obtained, usually in fair to good yield.

(65–68%)

The reaction appears to proceed by a free radical path and may be formulated as follows.

$$(1) \quad R-\overset{\overset{\displaystyle O}{\|}}{C}-O^- \; Ag^+ + Br_2 \longrightarrow R-\overset{\overset{\displaystyle O}{\|}}{C}-OBr + AgBr$$

(2) $R-\overset{\overset{\displaystyle O}{\|}}{C}-OBr \longrightarrow R-\overset{\overset{\displaystyle O}{\|}}{C}-O\cdot + Br\cdot$ initiation step

(3) $R-\overset{\overset{\displaystyle O}{\|}}{C}-O\cdot \longrightarrow R\cdot + CO_2$

(4) $R\cdot + R-\overset{\overset{\displaystyle O}{\|}}{C}-OBr \longrightarrow RBr + R-\overset{\overset{\displaystyle O}{\|}}{C}-O\cdot$

propagation steps

In a useful modification of the Hunsdiecker reaction the carboxylic acid is treated with mercuric oxide and bromine.

$$2\underset{COOH}{\overset{H}{\triangleright\!\!\!<}} + HgO + 2\,Br_2 \longrightarrow 2\underset{Br}{\overset{H}{\triangleright\!\!\!<}} + HgBr_2 + 2\,CO_2 + H_2O$$

(41–46%)

In the **Kochi reaction** the carboxylic acid is treated with lead tetraacetate and lithium chloride; the product is an alkyl chloride.

$$\square{-}COOH + Pb(O\overset{\overset{\displaystyle O}{\|}}{C}CH_3)_4 + LiCl \longrightarrow \square{-}Cl + CO_2 + LiPb(O\overset{\overset{\displaystyle O}{\|}}{C}CH_3)_3 + CH_3COOH$$

(100%)

The Hunsdiecker and Kochi reactions complement each other, the former giving best results with primary alkyl carboxylic acids and the latter being preferred for secondary and tertiary alkyl carboxylic acids.

EXERCISE 17.15 Show how 2,2-dimethylpentanoic acid could be converted into 2-methyl-1-pentene.

17.8 Natural Occurrence of Carboxylic Acids

Carboxylic acids are widespread in nature, both as such and in the form of esters. Partly because they are easily isolated as salts, they were among the earliest known organic compounds.

Formic acid was first discovered in 1670 by the distillation of ants. Its name comes from the Latin word for ant, *formica*. Formic acid is partially responsible for the irritation resulting from the sting of the red ant and the stinging nettle.

Acetic acid is a product of fermentation. The characteristic taste of sour wine is due to the oxidation of ethanol to acetic acid. Vinegar is a dilute solution of acetic acid. Although the acid has been known in the form of vinegar since antiquity, it was first isolated in pure form by Stahl in 1700. Pure acetic acid is known as glacial acetic acid. This term arises from the relatively high melting point of the compound (17°C, 63°F). In earlier times, when buildings were not heated as they are now, pure acetic acid was commonly observed to be a solid at "room temperature." Acetic acid is also one of the products of pyrolysis of wood (destructive distillation).

Butyric acid is responsible for the sharp odor of rancid butter. It was first isolated from this source. Caproic acid also has a penetrating unpleasant odor described as "goat-like." Indeed, its name, as well as those of caprylic acid and capric acid, is derived from the Latin word for goat, *caper*. These acids and their esters are widespread in nature.

Juvenile hormone and juvabione are examples of carboxylic acids that occur in nature in the form of their methyl esters.

juvenile hormone

juvabione

These compounds are associated with the pupal development of various insects. Such compounds offer some promise as insect-control agents. Since they are highly species-specific and leave no residues, they have obvious advantages over other commonly used pesticides.

PROBLEMS

1. Give the IUPAC name for each of the following compounds.

(a) $CH_3CH_2CHCH_2COOH$ with CH_3 substituent   (b) $(CH_3)_3CCOOH$

(c) $BrCH_2CH_2CH_2COOH$ (d) ICH_2COOH

(e) $CH_3CH_2CHCOOH$ with OH substituent   (f) $CH_3(CH_2)_8COOH$

(g) 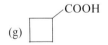 cyclobutane with $COOH$ (h) CH_3CHCH_2COOH with OCH_3 substituent

(i) $(CH_3)_2CHCHCH_2COOH$ with CH_3 substituent   (j) $NCCH_2COOH$

2. Write the correct structure for each of the following names.
   (a) β-chlorobutyric acid   (b) hexanoic acid
   (c) γ-methoxyvaleric acid   (d) cyclopentanecarboxylic acid
   (e) 3-bromopropanoic acid   (f) cis-2-pentenoic acid
   (g) (E,R)-4-hydroxypent-2-enoic acid   (h) α-chloro-β-bromopropionic acid

3. Give the products in each of the following reactions of cyclohexanecarboxylic acid.
   (a) LiAlH₄ in ether, then dilute hydrochloric acid
   (b) P + Br₂, heat, then water
   (c) diazomethane in ether
   (d) isopropyl alcohol (excess) and a trace of sulfuric acid
   (e) ammonia, 200°C
   (f) methylamine (CH₃NH₂), 200°C
   (g) SOCl₂
   (h) PBr₃
   (i) Pt/H₂, room temperature

(j) dilute aqueous sodium hydroxide at room temperature
(k) silver hydroxide, followed by bromine in carbon tetrachloride
(l) $Pb(OAc)_4 + LiCl$

4. Two general methods for converting alkyl halides to carboxylic acids are displacement by cyanide ion, followed by hydrolysis, and conversion to the Grignard reagent, followed by carbonation with carbon dioxide. Which method is superior for each of the following transformations? In which cases would a protecting group facilitate the conversion? Explain why.
   (a) $(CH_3)_3CCl \longrightarrow (CH_3)_3CCOOH$
   (b) $BrCH_2CH_2CH_2Br \longrightarrow HOOCCH_2CH_2CH_2COOH$
   (c) $CH_3COCH_2CH_2CH_2Br \longrightarrow CH_3COCH_2CH_2CH_2COOH$
   (d) $(CH_3)_3CCH_2Br \longrightarrow (CH_3)_3CCH_2COOH$
   (e) $CH_3CH_2CH_2CH_2Br \longrightarrow CH_3CH_2CH_2CH_2COOH$
   (f) $HOCH_2CH_2CH_2CH_2Br \longrightarrow HOCH_2CH_2CH_2CH_2COOH$

5. Show how neopentane may be converted into each of the following compounds.
   (a) $(CH_3)_3CCH_2COOH$ (b) $(CH_3)_3CCHBrCOOH$
   (c) $(CH_3)_3CCH_2CH_2OH$ (d) $(CH_3)_3CCH_2COCl$

6. Show how butanal may be converted into each of the following compounds.

$$COOH$$

   (a) $CH_3CH_2CH_2COOH$ (b) $CH_3CH_2CH_2CH{=}\overset{\mid}{C}CH_2CH_3$

$$OH$$

   (c) $CH_3CH_2CH_2\overset{\mid}{C}HCOOH$ (d) $CH_3CH_2CH_2CH_2COOH$

7. Show how 3-methylbutanoic acid may be converted into each of the following compounds.
   (a) $(CH_3)_2CHCH_2CH_2OH$ (b) $(CH_3)_2CHCH_2CH_2COOH$

$$Br$$

   (c) $(CH_3)_2CHCH_2CH_2\overset{\mid}{C}HCH_2Br$ (d) $(CH_3)_2C{=}CHCOOCH_3$

$$O$$
$$\parallel$$

   (e) $(CH_3)_2CHCH_2\overset{}{C}CH_3$ (f) $(CH_3)_2CHCH_2\overset{}{C}NH_2$

   (g) $(CH_3)_2CHCH_2Br$

8. Show how each of the following transformations may be accomplished in a practical manner.

   (a) $=CH_2 \longrightarrow$ $-CH_2COOH$

   (b) $(CH_3)_3CCH{=}CH_2 \longrightarrow (CH_3)_3CCOOH$

$$CH_3 \qquad\qquad\qquad CH_3$$

   (c) $CH_3COCH_2CH_2CH_2\overset{\mid}{\underset{\mid}{C}}Br \longrightarrow CH_3COCH_2CH_2CH_2\overset{\mid}{\underset{\mid}{C}}COOH$
   $\qquad\qquad\qquad\quad CH_3 \qquad\qquad\qquad\qquad\qquad\quad CH_3$

   (d) $CH_3CH_2COOH \longrightarrow CH_3CH_2CH_2COOH$
   (e) $CH_3CH_2CH_2COOH \longrightarrow CH_3CH_2COOH$
   (f) $CH_3CH_2CH_2COOH \longrightarrow CH_3CH_2CH_2N_3$

9. The dissociation constant of acetic acid is $1.8 \times 10^{-5}\,M$. Calculate the percent dissociation when the following amounts of acetic acid are made up to 1 L with water at 25°C.
   (a) 0.1 mole   (b) 0.01 mole   (c) 0.001 mole

10. The following dissociation constants are given. Calculate the corresponding pK_a values.

    (a) $(CH_3)_2CHCH_2CH_2COOH$; $K_a = 1.4 \times 10^{-5}\,M$

    (b) —COOH; $K_a = 6.3 \times 10^{-5}\,M$

    (c) $Cl_2CHCOOH$; $K_a = 5.5 \times 10^{-2}\,M$

    (d) Cl_3CCOOH; $K_a = 0.23\,M$

    (e) $CH_3CONHCH_2COOH$; $K_a = 2.1 \times 10^{-4}\,M$

11. In each of the following pairs, which is the stronger *base*? Explain briefly.
    (a) $CH_3CH_2O^-$; $CH_3CO_2^-$ (b) $ClCH_2CH_2CO_2^-$; $CH_3CH_2CH_2CO_2^-$
    (c) $ClCH_2CH_2CO_2^-$; $CH_3CHClCO_2^-$ (d) $FCH_2CO_2^-$; $F_2CHCO_2^-$
    (e) $HC\equiv CCH_2CO_2^-$; $CH_3CH_2CH_2CO_2^-$ (f) Cl^-, $CH_3CO_2^-$

12. The two carboxy groups in 3-chlorohexanedioic acid are not equivalent and have different dissociation constants. Which carboxy group is the more acidic?

13. From the progression of acidity constants for chlorobutanoic acids in Table 17.4 and the pK_a of 3-cyanobutanoic acid, 4.44, estimate the pK_a of 2-cyanobutanoic acid.

14. When propanoic acid is refluxed with some sulfuric acid in water enriched with $H_2{}^{18}O$, ^{18}O gradually appears in the carboxylic acid group. Write the mechanism for this reaction, showing each intermediate in the reaction pathway.

15. When 5-hydroxyhexanoic acid is treated with a trace of sulfuric acid in benzene solution, the following reaction occurs.

    (a) Propose a mechanism for the reaction.
    (b) The equilibrium constant for this process is much larger than that normally observed for an esterification reaction. Explain.

16. On refluxing with D_2O containing a strong acid, propanoic acid is slowly converted to CH_3CD_2COOD. Write a plausible mechanism for this reaction.

17. Values of heats of formation, ΔH_f°, for the ideal gas state at 25°C are given in the table that follows for several compounds. Calculate ΔH° for the following equilibrium in the gas phase.

$$CH_3COOH + C_2H_5OH \rightleftharpoons CH_3COOC_2H_5 + H_2O$$

In the liquid phase, ΔH° for this equilibrium is -0.9 kcal mole^{-1}. Why is there such a difference between the two values?

Compound	ΔH_f° at 25°C, kcal mole^{-1}
CH_3COOH	-103.3
C_2H_5OH	-56.2
$CH_3COOC_2H_5$	-106.3
H_2O	-57.8

18. The following reaction is exothermic in the gas phase.

$$CH_3CO_2^- + ClCH_2COOH \rightleftharpoons CH_3COOH + ClCH_2CO_2^- \qquad \Delta H^\circ = -13 \text{ kcal mole}^{-1}$$

(a) Explain briefly why this reaction is exothermic.

(b) Perform a simple calculation to determine whether the electrostatic interaction of a C—Cl dipole with a carboxylate anion has the proper magnitude to account for this energy difference. For this purpose treat $ClCH_2CO_2^-$ as having the following structure in which the CCCl plane is perpendicular to the OCO plane.

in which θ is the angle between the dipole and the charge. For a charge q of one electron, $\mu = 1$ D, $r = 1$ Å, and $\theta = 0°$, the energy E is 69 kcal mole^{-1}. Consider the effect of the chlorine to be that of a point dipole of 1.9 D. The electrostatic energy for a point dipole and a charge is given by

$$E = \frac{q\mu \cos \theta}{r^2}$$

Chapter 18

Derivatives of Carboxylic Acids

18.1 Structure

Functional group derivatives of carboxylic acids are those compounds that are transformed into carboxylic acids by simple hydrolysis. The most common such derivatives are **esters**, in which the hydroxy group is replaced by an alkoxy group.

$$R-\overset{\overset{\displaystyle O}{\|}}{C}-OCH_3$$

an ester

Amides are compounds in which the hydroxy group is replaced by an amino group. The nitrogen of the amino group may bear zero, one, or two alkyl groups.

$$R-\overset{\overset{\displaystyle O}{\|}}{C}-NH_2 \qquad R-\overset{\overset{\displaystyle O}{\|}}{C}-N\overset{H}{\underset{CH_3}{}} \qquad R-\overset{\overset{\displaystyle O}{\|}}{C}-N\overset{CH_3}{\underset{CH_3}{}}$$

amides

Acyl halides are derivatives in which the carboxy OH is replaced by a halogen atom; acyl chlorides and acyl bromides are the most commonly encountered acyl halides.

$$R-\overset{\overset{\displaystyle O}{\|}}{C}-Cl \qquad R-\overset{\overset{\displaystyle O}{\|}}{C}-Br$$

an acyl chloride   an acyl bromide

Acid anhydrides are molecules in which one molecule of water has been removed from two molecules of a carboxylic acid. The only acyclic anhydride of general importance is acetic anhydride.

$$CH_3-\overset{\overset{\displaystyle O}{\|}}{C}-O-\overset{\overset{\displaystyle O}{\|}}{C}-CH_3$$

acetic anhydride

In a strict sense, nitriles are functional derivatives of carboxylic acids because they may be hydrolyzed to carboxylic acids (Section 17.6.A). The chemistry of nitriles has been discussed in Chapter 12.

$$R-CN$$

a nitrile

The simplest ester, methyl formate, may be considered a derivative of formic acid in which the OH group is replaced by the OCH_3 group. Correspondingly, the molecular

Bond Lengths, Å		Bond Angles, deg	
C=O	1.200	H—C=O	124.95
C(=O)—O	1.334	O—C=O	125.87
C(H₃)—O	1.437	H—C—O	109.18
C(=O)—H	1.101	CH₃—O—C	114.78

FIGURE 18.1 Structure of methyl formate.

geometry of methyl formate is similar to that of formic acid. Experimental bond lengths and bond angles, determined by microwave spectroscopy, are given in Figure 18.1.

Note that the C_{sp^2}—O σ-bond is considerably shorter than the C_{sp^3}—O σ-bond. Two factors are apparently important in accounting for this bond shortening. In Section 11.1 we saw that because of the difference in "length" of various hybrid orbitals, C_{sp^3}—C_{sp^3} σ-bonds are longer than C_{sp^3}—C_{sp^2} σ-bonds. This factor is probably also important in methyl formate. Another factor involves the dipolar resonance form (18-1) as a contributor to the structure of methyl formate.

$$\left[H-C\begin{matrix} :O: \\ \\ \ddot{O}CH_3 \end{matrix} \longleftrightarrow H-C\begin{matrix} :\ddot{O}:^- \\ \\ \overset{+}{O}-CH_3 \end{matrix} \right] \qquad (18\text{-}1)$$

To the extent that this form contributes to the actual structure of the molecule, the C_{sp^2}—O σ-bond will be shorter because it has some double bond character. This latter factor is especially important in amides.

Microwave measurements on formamide indicate the structure shown in Figure 18.2. The entire molecule is planar. Note that the two hydrogens attached to nitrogen are distinguishable. The barrier to rotation about the carbon-nitrogen bond has been measured experimentally and is found to be 18 kcal mole⁻¹. A high degree of **double-bond character** in this bond, as indicated in the dipolar resonance form (18-2), has been invoked to explain this relatively high rotational barrier. Because of the high barrier to rotation about the carbon-nitrogen bond, amides have a relatively rigid structure.

$$\left[\begin{matrix} :O: \\ \| \\ C \\ \diagup \quad \diagdown \\ H \qquad N \\ \qquad | \\ \qquad H \end{matrix} \, H \longleftrightarrow \begin{matrix} :\ddot{O}:^- \\ | \\ C \\ \diagup \quad \diagup\!\!\diagdown \\ H \qquad \overset{+}{N} \\ \qquad | \\ \qquad H \end{matrix} \, H \right] \qquad (18\text{-}2)$$

Bond Lengths, Å		Bond Angles, deg	
C=O	1.193	H—C=O	122.97
C—N	1.376	H—C—N	113.23
C—H	1.102	N—C=O	123.80
N—H(a)	1.014	C—N—H(a)	117.15
N—H(b)	1.002	C—N—H(b)	120.62
		H—N—H	118.88

FIGURE 18.2 Structure of formamide.

Bond Lengths, Å		Bond Angles, deg	
C=O	1.192	C—C=O	127.08
C—C	1.499	C—C—Cl	112.66
C—Cl	1.789	O=C—Cl	120.26
C—H	1.083		

FIGURE 18.3   Structure of acetyl chloride.

Since the simplest acyl chloride, formyl chloride, is not stable at temperatures above −60°C, its structural parameters have not been measured. However, the bond lengths and bond angles have been determined for acetyl chloride (Figure 18.3). The carbon-chlorine bond is not appreciably shorter than the analogous bond in methyl chloride (1.784 Å), suggesting that dipolar resonance structures are not particularly important in the case of acyl halides.

EXERCISE 18.1   For methylamine, dimethyl ether, and methyl fluoride, the CH_3—X distances are 1.47 Å, 1.42 Å, and 1.38 Å, respectively. For acetamide, methyl acetate, and acetyl fluoride, the analogous distances are 1.36 Å, 1.36 Å, and 1.37 Å, respectively. Use the differences in C—X distances to evaluate the relative importance of dipolar resonance structures in the three carboxylic acid derivatives. Is there a correlation between the importance of the dipolar resonance structure and the relative basicity of F^-, OH^-, and NH_2^-?

18.2 Nomenclature

Esters are named in the following way. The first word of the name is the stem name of the alkyl group attached to oxygen. The second word of the name is the name of the parent acid with the suffix -**ic** replaced by -**ate**. This nomenclature applies for both common and IUPAC names of acids.

H—C(=O)—OCH₃   CH₃—C(=O)—OCH₂CH₃   CH₃CH(CH₃)—C(=O)—OCH(CH₃)₂

methyl form*ate*   ethyl acet*ate*   isopropyl isobutyr*ate*
                                                 isopropyl 2-methylpropano*ate*

Amides are named by dropping the suffix -**ic** or -**oic** from the name of the parent acid and adding the suffix -**amide**.

H—C(=O)—NH₂   CH₃C(=O)—NH₂   CH₃CH₂CH₂C(=O)—NH₂

form*amide*   acet*amide*   butan*amide*

A substituted nitrogen is indicated by prefixing the name of the simple amide by N-, followed by the name of the substituent group.

$$CH_3CH_2\overset{\overset{\displaystyle O}{\|}}{C}-N\overset{H}{\underset{CH_3}{\diagdown}}$$

N-methylpropanamide

$$CH_3\overset{CH_3}{\underset{|}{CH}}CH_2\overset{\overset{\displaystyle O}{\|}}{C}-N\overset{CH_3}{\underset{CH_3}{\diagup}}$$

N,N,3-trimethylbutanamide

Acyl halides are named in a similar manner. In this case the suffix -**ic** is replaced by the suffix -**yl**, and the halide name is added as a second word. (Note that for acyl halides, the ''o'' of the ending -**oic** is retained.)

$$CH_3\overset{\overset{\displaystyle O}{\|}}{C}-Cl$$

acetyl chloride

$$CH_3CH_2\overset{CH_3}{\underset{|}{CH}}CH_2\overset{\overset{\displaystyle O}{\|}}{C}-Br$$

3-methylpentanoyl bromide

$$CH_3CH_2\overset{\overset{\displaystyle O}{\|}}{C}-F$$

propanoyl fluoride

Anhydrides are named by adding **anhydride** to the name of the corresponding carboxylic acid.

$$CH_3-\overset{\overset{\displaystyle O}{\|}}{C}-O-\overset{\overset{\displaystyle O}{\|}}{C}-CH_3$$

acetic anhydride

$$CH_3CH_2\overset{CH_3}{\underset{|}{CH}}CH_2-\overset{\overset{\displaystyle O}{\|}}{C}-O-\overset{\overset{\displaystyle O}{\|}}{C}-CH_2\overset{CH_3}{\underset{|}{CH}}CH_2CH_3$$

3-methylpentanoic anhydride

For mixed anhydrides, the parent name of each acid is given, followed by the word **anhydride**.

$$H-\overset{\overset{\displaystyle O}{\|}}{C}-O-\overset{\overset{\displaystyle O}{\|}}{C}-CH_3$$

acetic formic anhydride

For functional derivatives of carboxylic acids that are named as alkanecarboxylic acids (page 451) the suffix -**carboxylic acid** is replaced by -**carboxamide** or -**carbonyl halide**.

▷—COOH   ▷—CONH₂   ◇—COCl

cyclopropane carboxylic acid   cyclopropane carboxamide   cyclobutane carbonyl chloride

Occasionally it is necessary to name an acid derivative function as a derivative of some other functional stem. The group names for the various radicals as prefixes are given in Table 18.1.

It is important to remember that *Chemical Abstracts* does not always follow the IUPAC nomenclature conventions. For example, recent indices of *Chemical Abstracts*

TABLE 18.1 Functional Group Names

Radical	Group Name as Prefix
—COOCH₃	methoxycarbonyl
—COOCH₂CH₃	ethoxycarbonyl
—CONH₂	carbamoyl
—COCl	chloroformyl
—COBr	bromoformyl
—CN	cyano

use the IUPAC prefix methoxycarbonyl- for —COOCH₃, but use chlorocarbonyl-instead of chloroformyl- for —COCl. A user should always consult the Index Guide before searching a recent *Chemical Abstracts* index for a compound by name.

EXERCISE 18.2 What are the IUPAC names for the methyl ester, amide, acyl chloride and anhydride corresponding to each of the following carboxylic acids?
(a) $CH_3CH_2CH_2CH_2CH_2COOH$ (b) $(CH_3)_2CHCH_2CH_2COOH$
(c) $CH_2{=}CHCH_2CH_2COOH$ (d) $BrCH_2CH_2COOH$
What are the IUPAC names for the following ester and amide?
(e) $(CH_3)_2CHCH_2CH_2COOCH_2CH(CH_3)_2$ (f) $(CH_3)_3CCH_2CH_2CON(CH_2CH_3)_2$

18.3 Physical Properties

In Figure 18.4 the boiling points of straight-chain acids, methyl esters, and acyl chlorides are plotted against molecular weight. For comparison the boiling point curve for *n*-alkanes is also given. It can readily be seen that esters and acyl halides have approxi-

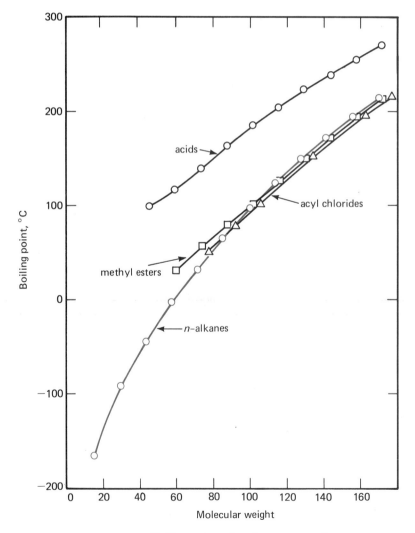

FIGURE 18.4 Boiling points of various compounds.

TABLE 18.2 Physical Properties for Acetamide Derivatives

	Molecular Weight	Melting Point, °C	Boiling Point, °C
$CH_3-\overset{\displaystyle O}{\overset{\|}{C}}-NH_2$	59	82	221
$CH_3-\overset{\displaystyle O}{\overset{\|}{C}}-NHCH_3$	73	28	204
$CH_3-\overset{\displaystyle O}{\overset{\|}{C}}-N(CH_3)_2$	87	-20	165

mately the boiling points expected for hydrocarbons of the same molecular weight. This correspondence indicates that the main attractive forces in the condensed phase for these compounds are the relatively weak van der Waals forces. On the other hand, carboxylic acids boil much higher than hydrocarbons of equivalent weight, a consequence of strong intermolecular hydrogen bonds (page 449). In addition to supplying enough energy to overcome the normal van der Waals attractive forces, additional energy must be supplied to overcome the "extra" polar attractive forces. The result is a higher boiling point.

All methyl and ethyl esters and acyl chlorides for the straight-chain acids lower than tetradecanoic are liquids at room temperature. Simple anhydrides above nonanoic anhydride are solid at room temperature.

The melting points and boiling points of acetamide, N-methylacetamide, and N,N-dimethylacetamide are tabulated in Table 18.2. Note that acetamide boils 215°C higher than a comparable alkane. Dimethylacetamide still boils 95°C higher than a comparable alkane, but it has a boiling point almost exactly the same as that for an acid of comparable weight. A similar downward trend is seen in the melting points of the three compounds.

The explanation of these interesting trends lies in the phenomenon of hydrogen bonding. Acetamide, with two hydrogens attached to nitrogen, is extensively hydrogen bonded in both the solid and liquid phases. In methylacetamide there is only one N—H, and therefore the hydrogen bonding is less extensive. Finally, dimethyl-acetamide cannot engage in hydrogen bonding at all, since it has no hydrogens attached to nitrogen.

Esters, amides, acyl halides, and anhydrides are generally soluble in common organic solvents (ether, chloroform, benzene, and so on). Dimethylformamide and dimethylacetamide are miscible with water in all proportions. Because of their polar, aprotic nature, these compounds are excellent solvents. Ethyl acetate, which is only sparingly soluble in water, is also a common solvent. Because of its excellent solvent properties, ethyl acetate is a common constituent of many brands of paint remover and is also used as a fingernail polish remover. It may easily be recognized by its characteristic "fruity" odor.

18.4 Spectroscopy

A. Nuclear Magnetic Resonance

Protons in the vicinity of the carbonyl group have similar NMR resonance positions regardless of the exact nature of the compound. Typical values are summarized in

**TABLE 18.3 Chemical Shifts in Compounds of
the Type R—Y**

Y	Chemical Shift in δ		
	CH_3Y	RCH_2Y	CH_3CH_2Y
—CHO	2.20	2.40	1.08
—COOH	2.10	2.36	1.16
—COOCH$_3$	2.03	2.13	1.12
—COCl	2.67		
—CONH$_2$	2.08	2.23	1.13
—CN	2.00	2.28	1.14

Table 18.3. A typical example is the spectrum of methyl propanoate, shown in Figure 18.5.

We saw in Section 14.4 that the CMR resonance position of the carbonyl carbon in aldehydes and ketones is in the region δ 190–200 ppm. The carbonyl resonances of carboxylic acids and of acid derivatives also appear at relatively low field, as shown in Table 18.4. However, in the case of RCOX compounds, the carbonyl resonances are in the range δ 168–178 ppm. Thus, CMR spectroscopy is an excellent tool for distinguishing certain types of carbonyl-containing compounds.

B. Infrared

In Chapter 15 we saw that the characteristic absorption of aldehydes and ketones is the C=O stretch that occurs in the 1710–1825 cm^{-1} region. Other compounds containing the carbonyl group also absorb in this general region. The exact position of the absorp-

FIGURE 18.5 NMR spectrum of methyl propanoate, $CH_3CH_2COOCH_3$.

TABLE 18.4 CMR Chemical Shifts in Carbonyl Derivatives, RCOX

X	δ, ppm
CH_3	205.1
H	199.6
OH	177.3
OCH_2CH_3	169.5
$N(CH_3)_2$	169.6
Cl	168.6

tion depends on the nature of the functional group. Typical values are listed in Table 18.5.

Amides that have one or two hydrogens on nitrogen show a characteristic N—H stretch. For compounds of the type $RCONH_2$ the N—H absorption occurs as two peaks at 3400 and 3500 cm^{-1}. For RCONHR compounds the N—H stretch comes at 3440 cm^{-1}.

Recall that the exact stretching frequency for cyclic ketones is related to ring size. This same effect is seen with cyclic esters, which are called **lactones** (Section 27.5.B), and with cyclic amides, which are called **lactams**.

$$CH_3\overset{O}{\overset{\|}{C}}OCH_3$$
1736 cm^{-1}

1735 cm^{-1}

1770 cm^{-1}

1800 cm^{-1}

$$CH_3\overset{O}{\overset{\|}{C}}NH_2$$
1680 cm^{-1}

1670 cm^{-1}

1700 cm^{-1}

1745 cm^{-1}

TABLE 18.5 Carbonyl Stretching Bands of Carboxylic Acid Derivatives in Solution

Functional Group	C=O Stretch, cm^{-1}
$-\overset{O}{\overset{\|}{C}}-OR$	1735
$-\overset{O}{\overset{\|}{C}}-Cl$	1800
$-\overset{O}{\overset{\|}{C}}-O-\overset{O}{\overset{\|}{C}}-$	1820 and 1760 (two peaks)
$-\overset{O}{\overset{\|}{C}}-NR_2$	1650–1690

EXERCISE 18.3 An unknown compound has the following spectral properties:

IR: 1740 cm^{-1}

NMR: δ 0.9 (3H, t, $J = 7$), 1.2-1.9 (6H, m), 1.25 (6H, d, $J = 7$), 2.3 (2H, t, $J = 7$), 5.0 (1H, septet, $J = 7$) ppm

CMR: δ 14.3, 20.2, 23.4, 25.5, 32.2, 33.9, 65.6, 172.0 ppm (the resonance at δ 20.2 ppm is approximately twice as strong as the other resonances in that region of the spectrum.)

18.5 Basicity of the Carbonyl Oxygen

As in the cases of aldehydes, ketones (Section 14.7), and carboxylic acids (Section 17.7.C), the carbonyl oxygen of carboxylic acid derivatives has basic properties. The conjugate acid, an oxonium salt, plays an important role as an intermediate in acid-catalyzed reactions of all of these types of compounds. The actual basicity of the lone-pair electrons of the carbonyl oxygen depends markedly on the nature of the group attached to the carbonyl. This basicity is expressed quantitatively in terms of the acidity or pK_a of the conjugate acid.

$$\underset{\text{RCY}}{\overset{\overset{+\text{OH}}{\|}}{}} \rightleftharpoons \underset{\text{RCY}}{\overset{\overset{\text{O}}{\|}}{}} + \text{H}^+$$

$$K_a = \frac{[\text{RCOY}][\text{H}^+]}{\left[\underset{\text{RCY}}{\overset{\overset{+\text{OH}}{\|}}{}}\right]}$$

$$\text{p}K_a = -\log K_a$$

Some pK_a values are summarized in Table 18.6. Most protonated carbonyl compounds are strong acids, stronger than H_3O^+ and comparable in acidity to sulfuric acid (p$K_a = -5.2$). That is, the carbonyl compounds themselves are weak bases in water, in a class with bisulfate ion. Some of the individual structural effects warrant comment.

Alcohols are generally a little weaker as bases than water itself, and ethers are weaker bases still. These variations are probably the result of solvation differences. The fewer the number of protons on an oxonium oxygen, the less the amount of solvation stabilization by hydrogen bonds to water. If the acid structure is less stable for whatever reason, the conjugate base has lower basicity.

The carbonyl oxygen of aldehydes and ketones is less basic than an alcohol or ether oxygen by several powers of ten. The lone-pair electrons of the carbonyl oxygen may be considered to be approximately sp^2 in character. These electrons have greater s-character than the lone pairs of alcohol oxygens. Hence, the lone-pair electrons of carbonyl oxygens are more tightly held. As a result, the carbonyl group as a conjugate base is more stable, and the corresponding protonated carbonyl is more acidic. This system is analogous to the corresponding hydrocarbon cases. Recall that ethylene is more acidic than ethane (Section 12.4). In a protonated carbonyl group the oxygen-hydrogen bond is described approximately as O_{sp^3}—H. In a protonated alcohol or ether the oxygen-hydrogen bond involves an oxygen orbital that has greater p-character.

TABLE 18.6 Acidities of Protonated Compounds

Compound	Conjugate Acid	pK_a of Conjugate Acid
CH_3CONH_2	$CH_3\overset{+OH}{\underset{\|}{C}}NH_2$	0.0
H_2O	H_3O^+	-1.7
CH_3OH	$CH_3\overset{+}{O}H_2$	-2.2
$(CH_3CH_2)_2O$	$(CH_3CH_2)_2\overset{+}{O}H$	-3.6
CH_3COOH	$CH_3\overset{+OH}{\underset{\|}{C}}OH$	-6
$CH_3COOC_2H_5$	$CH_3\overset{+OH}{\underset{\|}{C}}OC_2H_5$	-6.5
CH_3COCH_3	$CH_3\overset{+OH}{\underset{\|}{C}}CH_3$	-7.2
CH_3CHO	$CH_3\overset{+OH}{\underset{\|}{C}}H$	~ -8
CH_3COCl	$CH_3\overset{+OH}{\underset{\|}{C}}Cl$	~ -9
CH_3CN	$CH_3C\equiv\overset{+}{N}H$	-10.1

The structure of protonated carboxylic acids and esters is shown in Table 18.6 with the proton on the carbonyl oxygen rather than on the OR oxygen, despite the argument just presented that carbonyl oxygens are generally less basic than singly bonded oxygens. This result is a manifestation of conjugation. If the carbonyl group and hydroxy or alkoxy group are separated by one or more carbons (for example, in hydroxyacetone), we would anticipate the carbonyl group to be the less basic. That is, in an acidic medium the hydroxy or alkoxy group is protonated to a greater degree than is the carbonyl group.

$$CH_3\overset{O}{\overset{\|}{C}}CH_2\overset{+}{O}H_2$$
acetonyloxonium ion (more)

$$CH_3\overset{O}{\overset{\|}{C}}CH_2OH + H^+ \rightleftarrows$$
hydroxyacetone

$$\overset{+}{O}H \\ \overset{\|}{} \\ CH_3\overset{}{C}CH_2OH$$
hydroxyacetonium ion (less)

Note that both protonated isomers are more acidic than their monofunctional counterparts: acetonyloxonium ion is more acidic than propyloxonium ion, $CH_3CH_2CH_2OH_2^+$, and hydroxyacetonium ion is more acidic than acetonium ion. In both cases the substituent has an electron-attracting inductive effect that results in an increase in acidity, just as in the case of substituted acetic acids (Section 17.4.B).

When the OH or OR group is attached directly to the carbonyl group, electron density on the singly bonded oxygen can "leak over" to the electron-attracting carbonyl group, as symbolized by the following resonance structures.

$$\left[R-\overset{O}{\overset{\|}{C}}-OR' \longleftrightarrow R-\overset{O^-}{\overset{|}{C}}=\overset{+}{O}R' \right]$$

The actual electronic structure of the carboxylic acid or ester group may be represented as

$$R-\overset{O^{\delta-}}{\overset{\vdots}{C}}\overset{\delta+}{\cdots}OR'$$

The partial positive charge or oxonium character of the OR group makes this oxygen less basic than an ether oxygen. The partial negative charge on the carbonyl oxygen makes it more basic than a ketone oxygen. This argument does not mean that the alternative protonated compound cannot exist. It does say that this protonated compound, an acyloxonium ion, is much more acidic than a simple oxonium ion.

$$R-\overset{O}{\overset{\|}{C}}-\overset{+}{O}\overset{\diagup H}{\diagdown H} \qquad \text{more acidic than} \qquad RCH_2-\overset{+}{O}\overset{\diagup H}{\diagdown H}$$
acyloxonium ion   alkyloxonium ion

On the other hand, the carbonyl-protonated carboxylic grouping is stabilized by conjugation; the positive charge is distributed between the two oxygens, much as the negative charge is distributed in acetate ion (Section 17.4.A).

$$\left[R-\overset{+OH}{\overset{\|}{C}}-OH \longleftrightarrow R-\overset{OH}{\overset{|}{C}}=\overset{}{\underset{+}{O}}H \longleftrightarrow R-\overset{OH}{\overset{|}{\underset{+}{C}}}-OH \right] \quad \text{less acidic than} \quad R-\overset{+OH}{\overset{\|}{C}}-R'$$

These same considerations apply to an even greater extent in the case of amides. Ammonia is much more basic than water: $pK_a(NH_4^+) = 9.2$; $pK_a(H_3O^+) = -1.7$. The nitrogen in an amide is far less basic than that in ammonia because of the important contribution of the dipolar resonance structure.

487

Sec. 18.6

Hydrolysis:
Nucleophilic
Addition-
Elimination

$$\left[\underset{\text{R—C—NH}_2}{\overset{\text{O}}{\|}} \longleftrightarrow \underset{\text{R—C=}\overset{+}{\text{N}}\text{H}_2}{\overset{\text{O}^-}{|}} \right] \equiv \underset{\text{R—C}^{\cdots}\text{NH}_2}{\overset{\text{O}^{\delta-}}{\vdots}} {}^{\delta+}$$

That is, the nitrogen in an amide already has some of the character of an ammonium ion. If this nitrogen becomes protonated, the resonance stabilization of the amide is lost.

$$\underset{\text{R—C—}\overset{+}{\text{N}}\text{H}_3}{\overset{\text{O}}{\|}}$$

(no lone pair for conjugation with carbonyl group)

However, the O-protonated amide is greatly stabilized by resonance.

$$\left[\underset{\text{R—C—NH}_2}{\overset{{}^+\text{OH}}{\|}} \longleftrightarrow \underset{\text{R—}\overset{+}{\text{C}}\text{—NH}_2}{\overset{\text{OH}}{|}} \longleftrightarrow \underset{\text{R—C=}\overset{+}{\text{N}}\text{H}_2}{\overset{\text{OH}}{|}} \right]$$

In fact, as shown in Table 18.6, the O-protonated amide is almost 100 times less acidic than H_3O^+.

EXERCISE 18.4 In Exercise 18.1 we gave the lengths of a number of C—X bonds in compounds of the types R—XCH$_3$ and RCO—XCH$_3$. How do these bond lengths correlate with the carbonyl basicity of amides, esters and acyl halides as given in Table 18.6?

18.6 Hydrolysis: Nucleophilic Addition-Elimination

The most characteristic reaction of the functional derivatives of carboxylic acids is **hydrolysis**, the reaction with water to give the carboxylic acid itself.

$$\underset{\text{R—C—X}}{\overset{\text{O}}{\|}} + H_2O \longrightarrow \underset{\text{R—C—OH}}{\overset{\text{O}}{\|}} + HX$$

X = halogen, OR, NR$_2$, OOCR

Esters react with water to yield the corresponding carboxylic acid and alcohol.

$$\underset{\text{CH}_3\text{C—OCH}_3}{\overset{\text{O}}{\|}} + H_2O \rightleftharpoons \underset{\text{CH}_3\text{C—OH}}{\overset{\text{O}}{\|}} + CH_3OH$$

The reaction is generally slow, but is strongly catalyzed by acid. The acid-catalyzed hydrolysis of esters of primary and secondary alcohols is simply the reverse of the acid-catalyzed esterification reaction (Section 17.7.C). The reaction is an equilibrium process, but can be driven practically to completion by using a large excess of water (page 465). The probable mechanism involves the following steps.

(1) $\underset{\text{CH}_3\text{—C—OCH}_3}{\overset{\text{O}}{\|}} + H^+ \rightleftharpoons \underset{\text{CH}_3\text{—C—OCH}_3}{\overset{{}^+\text{OH}}{\|}}$

(2) $\underset{\text{CH}_3\text{—C—OCH}_3}{\overset{{}^+\text{OH}}{\|}} + H_2O \rightleftharpoons \underset{\underset{{}_+\text{OH}_2}{\overset{|}{\text{CH}_3\text{—C—OCH}_3}}}{\overset{\text{OH}}{|}}$

$$(3) \quad CH_3-\overset{\overset{\displaystyle OH}{|}}{\underset{\underset{\displaystyle +OH_2}{|}}{C}}-OCH_3 \rightleftharpoons CH_3-\overset{\overset{\displaystyle OH}{|}}{\underset{\underset{\displaystyle OH}{|}}{C}}-OCH_3 + H^+$$

$$(4) \quad CH_3-\overset{\overset{\displaystyle OH}{|}}{\underset{\underset{\displaystyle OH}{|}}{C}}-OCH_3 + H^+ \rightleftharpoons CH_3-\overset{\overset{\displaystyle OH}{|}}{\underset{\underset{\displaystyle OH}{|}}{C}}-\overset{\overset{\displaystyle H}{|}}{\underset{+}{O}}CH_3$$

$$(5) \quad CH_3-\overset{\overset{\displaystyle OH}{|}}{\underset{\underset{\displaystyle OH}{|}}{C}}-\overset{\overset{\displaystyle H}{|}}{\underset{+}{O}}CH_3 \rightleftharpoons CH_3-\overset{\overset{\displaystyle +OH}{\|}}{C}-OH + CH_3OH$$

$$(6) \quad CH_3-\overset{\overset{\displaystyle +OH}{\|}}{C}-OH \rightleftharpoons CH_3-\overset{\overset{\displaystyle O}{\|}}{C}-OH + H^+$$

Let us examine the role of the acid catalyst in the preceding reaction. In neutral water the preponderant nucleophile present is water. Even though the carbonyl double bond is polarized, water is not a sufficiently strong nucleophile to add to it at a reasonable rate. Furthermore, addition of water to methyl acetate would produce an intermediate bearing both a positive and a negative charge. Since charge separation requires electrostatic energy, this type of addition is exceptionally slow.

$$CH_3-\overset{\overset{\displaystyle O}{\|}}{C}-OCH_3 + H_2O \rightleftharpoons CH_3-\overset{\overset{\displaystyle O^-}{|}}{\underset{\underset{\displaystyle +OH_2}{|}}{C}}-OCH_3$$

In the presence of mineral acids, the ester may be protonated (Section 18.5).

$$CH_3-\overset{\overset{\displaystyle O}{\|}}{C}-OCH_3 + H^+ \rightleftharpoons \left[CH_3-\overset{\overset{\displaystyle +OH}{\|}}{C}-OCH_3 \longleftrightarrow CH_3-\overset{\overset{\displaystyle OH}{|}}{C}=\overset{+}{O}CH_3 \right]$$

resonance-stabilized cation

Since there is a very large excess of water molecules, and since the ester carbonyl is actually less basic than water (Table 18.6), only a small percentage of the ester is protonated at moderate acid concentration. However, the carbonyl carbon in the protonated species is much more electrophilic and reacts much faster with the weak nucleophile water than does the unprotonated ester. Furthermore, addition now involves no charge separation.

$$CH_3-\overset{\overset{\displaystyle OH^+}{\|}}{C}-OCH_3 + H_2\overset{..}{\underset{..}{O}} \rightleftharpoons CH_3-\overset{\overset{\displaystyle OH}{|}}{\underset{\underset{\displaystyle +OH_2}{|}}{C}}-OCH_3$$

In some cases acid-catalyzed ester hydrolysis involves cleavage of the *alkyl-oxygen* bond rather than the *acyl-oxygen* bond. Such is the case with *t*-butyl acetate (18-3).

$$CH_3\overset{\overset{\displaystyle O}{\|}}{C}-O-\overset{\overset{\displaystyle CH_3}{|}}{\underset{\underset{\displaystyle CH_3}{|}}{C}}CH_3 + H_2O \overset{H^+}{\rightleftharpoons} CH_3COOH + CH_3\overset{\overset{\displaystyle CH_3}{|}}{\underset{\underset{\displaystyle CH_3}{|}}{C}}-OH \qquad (18\text{-}3)$$

489

Sec. 18.6

Hydrolysis:
Nucleophilic
Addition-
Elimination

Although the products are the same in both cases, the different mechanisms may be demonstrated by the labeling experiments (18-4) and (18-5).

$$CH_3\overset{O}{\overset{\|}{C}}-^{18}OCH_3 + H_2O \longrightarrow CH_3\overset{O}{\overset{\|}{C}}-OH + CH_3{}^{18}OH \qquad (18\text{-}4)$$

$$CH_3\overset{O}{\overset{\|}{C}}-^{18}O-\overset{CH_3}{\underset{CH_3}{\overset{|}{\underset{|}{C}}}}CH_3 + H_2O \longrightarrow CH_3\overset{O}{\overset{\|}{C}}-^{18}OH + CH_3\overset{CH_3}{\underset{CH_3}{\overset{|}{\underset{|}{C}}}}-OH \quad (18\text{-}5)$$

The probable mechanism for this reaction involves the following steps.

$$(1)\ CH_3\overset{O}{\overset{\|}{C}}-O-\overset{CH_3}{\underset{CH_3}{\overset{|}{\underset{|}{C}}}}CH_3 + H^+ \rightleftharpoons CH_3\overset{+OH}{\overset{\|}{C}}-O-\overset{CH_3}{\underset{CH_3}{\overset{|}{\underset{|}{C}}}}CH_3$$

$$(2)\ CH_3\overset{+OH}{\overset{\|}{C}}-O-\overset{CH_3}{\underset{CH_3}{\overset{|}{\underset{|}{C}}}}CH_3 \rightleftharpoons CH_3\overset{OH}{\overset{\|}{C}}=O + CH_3\overset{CH_3}{\underset{CH_3}{\overset{|}{\underset{|}{C}}}}{}^+$$

$$(3)\ CH_3\overset{CH_3}{\underset{CH_3}{\overset{|}{\underset{|}{C}}}}{}^+ + H_2O \rightleftharpoons CH_3\overset{CH_3}{\underset{CH_3}{\overset{|}{\underset{|}{C}}}}-\overset{+}{O}H_2$$

$$(4)\ CH_3\overset{CH_3}{\underset{CH_3}{\overset{|}{\underset{|}{C}}}}-\overset{+}{O}H_2 \rightleftharpoons CH_3\overset{CH_3}{\underset{CH_3}{\overset{|}{\underset{|}{C}}}}-OH + H^+$$

It is reasonable that *t*-butyl acetate should react by this mechanism whereas methyl acetate does not. The reaction is simply an acid-catalyzed S_N1 process in which the nucleophile water replaces the nucleophile acetic acid. The reactive intermediate is the *t*-butyl cation. Esters of other alcohols that give rise to relatively stable carbocations also undergo hydrolysis by this mechanism.

Ester hydrolysis is also strongly catalyzed by hydroxide ion. Since the carboxylic acid product neutralizes one equivalent of hydroxide, it is actually necessary to employ a stoichiometric amount of base. That is, hydroxide ion is actually a reagent instead of just a catalyst. The products are the salt of the carboxylic acid and the corresponding alcohol.

$$CH_3(CH_2)_8CH=\overset{CH_3}{\overset{|}{C}}COOCH_3 + KOH \xrightarrow[\underset{\Delta}{H_2O}]{C_2H_5OH}$$

$$CH_3(CH_2)_8CH=\overset{CH_3}{\overset{|}{C}}CO_2{}^-\ K^+ \xrightarrow{H_2SO_4} CH_3(CH_2)_8CH=\overset{CH_3}{\overset{|}{C}}COOH$$

$$(68\text{-}83\%)$$

To a solution of 20 g of methyl (*E*)-2-methyl-2-dodecenoate in 100 mL of 95% aqueous ethanol is added 8.8 g of potassium hydroxide. The solution is refluxed for 1.5 hr, concentrated to 40 mL, and acidified by the addition of 5 *N* sulfuric acid. The product is

isolated by extraction with petroleum ether. After removal of the petroleum ether, the
crude product is distilled to yield 18 g of pure acid, m.p. 29.5–32.5°C.

The probable mechanism for base-catalyzed hydrolysis is illustrated below with methyl
acetate.

$$(1) \quad CH_3\overset{\displaystyle O}{\overset{\|}{C}}-OCH_3 + OH^- \rightleftharpoons CH_3\overset{\displaystyle O^-}{\underset{OH}{\overset{|}{C}}}-OCH_3$$

$$(2) \quad CH_3\overset{\displaystyle O^-}{\underset{OH}{\overset{|}{C}}}-OCH_3 \rightleftharpoons CH_3\overset{\displaystyle O}{\overset{\|}{C}}-OH + CH_3O^-$$

$$(3) \quad CH_3\overset{\displaystyle O}{\overset{\|}{C}}-OH + CH_3O^- \longrightarrow CH_3\overset{\displaystyle O}{\overset{\|}{C}}-O^- + CH_3OH$$

In basic aqueous solution two nucleophiles are present, H_2O and OH^-. As we have
seen, H_2O is a poor nucleophile and therefore reacts slowly with the carbonyl carbon.
On the other hand, OH^- is a much stronger nucleophile and adds more rapidly to the
carbonyl carbon.

After addition has taken place, elimination of a nucleophile from the tetrahedral
intermediate can occur. Elimination of hydroxide ion merely reverses the initial addition step. However, elimination of methoxide ion gives a new species—acetic acid.
Since acetic acid is a weak acid and methoxide ion is a strong base, a rapid acid-base
reaction then occurs, yielding acetate ion and methanol. Because of the great difference in acidity between acetic acid ($pK \cong 5$) and methanol ($pK_a \cong 16$), this last step is
essentially irreversible (K for the last reaction $\cong 10^{11}$). Thus basic hydrolysis of esters
differs from acid-catalyzed hydrolysis in that the equilibrium constant for the overall
reaction is very large, and it is sufficient to use only one equivalent of water in order
for the reaction to proceed to completion.

It is interesting to compare the carbon-oxygen bond-forming step in the acid-catalyzed and base-catalyzed mechanisms. In the former case the "weak" nucleophile
H_2O adds to the "strongly" electrophilic bond $C{=}OH^+$.

$$CH_3\overset{\displaystyle \overset{+}{O}H}{\overset{\|}{C}}-OCH_3 + \overset{..}{O}H_2 \rightleftharpoons CH_3\overset{\displaystyle OH}{\underset{\underset{+}{O}H_2}{\overset{|}{C}}}-OCH_3$$

In the latter case the "strong" nucleophile OH^- adds to the "weakly" electrophilic
bond $C{=}O$.

$$CH_3\overset{\displaystyle O}{\overset{\|}{C}}-OCH_3 + :\overset{..}{O}H^- \rightleftharpoons CH_3\overset{\displaystyle O^-}{\underset{OH}{\overset{|}{C}}}-OCH_3$$

Either case is better than the case where the "weak" nucleophile H_2O adds to the
"weakly" electrophilic bond $C{=}O$.

The most rapid hydrolysis would involve *both* acid and base catalysis.

491

Sec. 18.6
Hydrolysis:
Nucleophilic
Addition-
Elimination

$$CH_3\overset{\overset{+}{O}H}{\underset{\|}{C}}-OCH_3 + \overset{..}{O}H^- \longrightarrow CH_3\underset{\underset{OH}{|}}{\overset{\overset{OH}{|}}{C}}-OCH_3$$

In aqueous solution this mechanism is not observed for a simple reason. In acidic solution, where the concentration of $C=OH^+$ species is appreciable, the concentration of OH^- is very small. In basic solution, where the concentration of OH^- is appreciable, the concentration of $C=OH^+$ is low.

Amides undergo hydrolysis to 1 mole of carboxylic acid and 1 mole of ammonia or amine. The reaction is catalyzed by acid or base. The hydrolysis of amides is more difficult than the hydrolysis of esters, and more vigorous conditions are normally required.

$$\text{C}_6\text{H}_5\text{-CHCONH}_2 \xrightarrow[\text{H}_2\text{O}]{\text{H}_2\text{SO}_4} \text{C}_6\text{H}_5\text{-CHCOOH}$$

(with CH$_2$CH$_3$ groups on the CH)

(88–90%)

A mixture of 600 g of 2-phenylbutanamide, 1 L of water, and 400 mL of conc. sulfuric acid is refluxed for 2 hr. After cooling the mixture and diluting with 1 L of water, the oily organic layer is separated and distilled to yield 530–554 g of 2-phenylbutanoic acid, m.p. 42°C.

Both the acid- and base-catalyzed reactions are essentially irreversible. In the former case ammonium ion is produced; in the latter case a carboxylate ion is formed.

$$\underset{\|}{\overset{\overset{O}{\|}}{RC}}-NH_2 + H_2O \underset{}{\overset{H^+}{\rightleftharpoons}} \underset{\|}{\overset{\overset{O}{\|}}{RC}}-OH + NH_3 \xrightarrow{H^+} NH_4^+$$

$$\underset{\|}{\overset{\overset{O}{\|}}{RC}}-NH_2 + H_2O \underset{}{\overset{OH^-}{\rightleftharpoons}} \underset{\|}{\overset{\overset{O}{\|}}{RC}}-OH + NH_3 \xrightarrow{OH^-} RCO_2^-$$

Acyl halides and anhydrides undergo hydrolysis with ease. Acetyl chloride reacts with water to give acetic acid and hydrogen chloride, whereas acetic anhydride gives two equivalents of acetic acid.

$$CH_3\overset{\overset{O}{\|}}{C}-Cl + H_2O \longrightarrow CH_3\overset{\overset{O}{\|}}{C}-OH + HCl$$

$$CH_3\overset{\overset{O}{\|}}{C}-O-\overset{\overset{O}{\|}}{C}CH_3 + H_2O \longrightarrow 2\, CH_3\overset{\overset{O}{\|}}{C}-OH$$

As with esters and amides, hydrolysis of acyl halides and anhydrides is subject to acid or base catalysis. However, both acyl halides and anhydrides react much more rapidly than esters, and uncatalyzed hydrolysis occurs readily, provided the reaction mixture is homogeneous. Since most acyl halides and anhydrides are only sparingly soluble in water, hydrolysis often appears to be slow. However, if a solvent is used that dissolves both water and the organic reactant, hydrolysis is rapid.

$$n\text{-}C_9H_{19}\overset{\overset{O}{\|}}{C}-Cl + H_2O \xrightarrow[25°C]{\text{dioxane}} n\text{-}C_9H_{19}COOH + HCl$$

In hydrolysis of an ester, acyl halide, or anhydride the overall result is replacement of the nucleophile HO^- for one of the nucleophiles RO^-, X^-, or RCO_2^-. Thus hydrolyses of these compounds, as well as some of the reactions of carboxylic acids themselves (Section 17.7.D–F), are but further examples of **nucleophilic substitution** (Chapter 9). However, as we have seen in this section, the mechanism for these nucleophilic substitution reactions is different from the substitution mechanisms we have previously encountered (S_N1, S_N2). At this point it is instructive to examine the three distinct ways in which the bond-breaking and bond-making operations of a nucleophilic substitution process may be timed.

1. Bond breaking may occur first, followed in a subsequent step by bond making.

$$R\!-\!Y \rightleftharpoons R^+ + Y^-$$
$$R^+ + :N^- \longrightarrow R\!-\!N$$

This sequence of steps is involved in the S_N1 process for substitution in alkyl halides (Section 9.7). In the case of carboxylic acid derivatives, the intermediate carbocation is called an **acylium ion**.

$$R\!-\!\overset{\overset{\displaystyle O}{\|}}{C}\!-\!Y \rightleftharpoons :Y^- + \left[R\!-\!\overset{+}{C}\!=\!\overset{\cdot\cdot}{O}: \longleftrightarrow R\!-\!C\!\equiv\!\overset{+}{O}:\right]$$

acylium ion

$$R\!-\!\overset{+}{C}\!=\!\overset{\cdot\cdot}{O}: + :N^- \longrightarrow R\!-\!\overset{\overset{\displaystyle O}{\|}}{C}\!-\!N$$

Only relatively few reactions of carboxylic acids and their derivatives occur by this mechanism.

2. Bond breaking and bond making may occur more or less synchronously.

$$R\!-\!Y + :N^- \longrightarrow \left[\overset{\delta-}{N}\cdots R\cdots\overset{\delta-}{Y}\right]^{\ddagger} \longrightarrow N\!-\!R + :Y^-$$

This is the familiar S_N2 mechanism (Sections 9.1-9.5). The synchronous mechanism is rare in the chemistry of carboxylic acid derivatives. It has been suggested by a few workers that some reactions of acyl halides may occur by this path, but actual evidence for the mechanism is sparse.

3. Bond making may occur first, followed in a subsequent step by bond breaking. This mechanism is not possible in the case of simple alkyl halides, since it would require the intervention of a pentacoordinate carbon. However, the mechanism is the most common one in the chemistry of carboxylic acids and their derivatives.

$$R\!-\!\overset{\overset{\displaystyle O}{\|}}{C}\!-\!Y + :N^- \rightleftharpoons R\!-\!\overset{\overset{\displaystyle O^-}{|}}{\underset{\underset{\displaystyle N}{|}}{C}}\!-\!Y$$

$$R\!-\!\overset{\overset{\displaystyle O^-}{|}}{\underset{\underset{\displaystyle N}{|}}{C}}\!-\!Y \rightleftharpoons R\!-\!\overset{\overset{\displaystyle O}{\|}}{C}\!-\!N + :Y^-$$

In this case *addition* to the carbonyl group occurs first, giving an intermediate in which the former carbonyl carbon now has sp^3-hybridization. This intermediate then decomposes by ejection of a nucleophile, restoring the carbonyl group.

493

Sec. 18.7
Other
Nucleophilic
Substitution
Reactions

Almost all nucleophilic substitution reactions of carboxylic acids and their derivatives occur by this pathway, the so-called **nucleophilic addition-elimination** mechanism.

EXERCISE 18.5 Write the steps involved in the acid- and base-promoted hydrolysis of acetyl azide, CH_3CON_3.

18.7 Other Nucleophilic Substitution Reactions

The nucleophilic substitution mechanism discussed in the previous section is general. Carboxylic acids and their derivatives react with nucleophiles other than water in the same manner. In this section we shall consider some of these other reactions.

A. Reaction with Alcohols

Acyl halides react with alcohols to yield esters and the corresponding hydrohalic acid.

$$CH_3\overset{\overset{\displaystyle O}{\|}}{C}{-}Cl + CH_3\overset{\overset{\displaystyle CH_3}{|}}{C}HCH_2OH \longrightarrow CH_3\overset{\overset{\displaystyle O}{\|}}{C}{-}OCH_2\overset{\overset{\displaystyle CH_3}{|}}{C}HCH_3 + HCl$$

acetyl chloride   isobutyl alcohol   isobutyl acetate

Such reactions are usually carried out in the presence of a weak base that serves to neutralize the HX formed in the reaction.

To a refluxing solution of 114 g of *t*-butyl alcohol and 202 g of N,N-dimethylaniline in 200 mL of dry ether is added dropwise 124 g of acetyl chloride. After addition of all the acyl chloride, the mixture is cooled in an ice bath, and the solid N,N-dimethylaniline hydrochloride is removed by filtration. The ether layer is extracted with aqueous sulfuric acid to remove excess amine and worked up to yield 110–119 g of *t*-butyl acetate, b.p. 95–98°C.

Other bases commonly used for this purpose are triethylamine and pyridine (page 203).

Since acyl halides are readily available from the corresponding carboxylic acids (Section 17.7.D), the following sequence is often used for the preparation of esters.

$$RCOOH \xrightarrow[\text{PCl}_3]{\overset{\text{SOCl}_2}{\text{or}}} R\overset{\overset{\displaystyle O}{\|}}{C}{-}Cl \xrightarrow{R'OH} R\overset{\overset{\displaystyle O}{\|}}{C}{-}OR'$$

Anhydrides also react readily with alcohols. The product is 1 mole of ester and 1 mole of the carboxylic acid corresponding to the anhydride used.

cholesterol

$$+ \; CH_3\overset{\overset{\displaystyle O}{\|}}{C}O\overset{\overset{\displaystyle O}{\|}}{C}CH_3 \longrightarrow$$

acetic anhydride

$$+ \; CH_3COOH$$

cholesteryl acetate

A mixture of 5 g of cholesterol and 7.5 mL of acetic anhydride is boiled for 1 hr. The mixture is cooled and filtered to yield 5 g of cholesteryl acetate, m.p. 114–115°C.

The mechanism of the reaction is the same as that for the reaction of an alcohol with an acyl halide; the leaving group in this case is the carboxylate anion rather than a halide ion. This reaction is an important method for the preparation of acetates, since acetic anhydride is an inexpensive reagent and the reaction is convenient to carry out.

Esters undergo reaction with alcohols to give a new ester and a new alcohol. The reaction is catalyzed by either acid or base and is called **transesterification**.

$$CH_3\overset{\overset{\displaystyle O}{\|}}{C}-OCH_2CH_3 + CH_3OH \; \underset{}{\overset{H^+ \; or \; OCH_3^-}{\rightleftharpoons}} \; CH_3\overset{\overset{\displaystyle O}{\|}}{C}-OCH_3 + C_2H_5OH$$

The mechanism for the transesterification process involves steps identical to those given for acid-catalyzed and base-catalyzed ester hydrolysis, with one significant exception. In base-catalyzed transesterification, step (3) of the mechanism on page 490 cannot occur because the free carboxylic acid is never formed. Thus, base-catalyzed transesterification is subject to the same equilibrium conditions that apply to the acid-catalyzed reaction.

EXERCISE 18.6 What products are produced when a solution of 1.0 mole of cholesteryl acetate and 0.05 mole of sodium methoxide in 1 L of methanol is refluxed for 30 min? Write a stepwise mechanism for the reaction.

B. Reaction with Amines and Ammonia

Acyl halides react with ammonia or amines that have at least one hydrogen bound to nitrogen to give amides. Since one equivalent of hydrogen chloride is formed in the reaction, two equivalents of ammonia or the amine must be used.

$$CH_3CH_2\overset{\overset{\displaystyle O}{\|}}{C}-Cl + 2 \; HNR_2 \longrightarrow CH_3CH_2\overset{\overset{\displaystyle O}{\|}}{C}-NR_2 + R_2\overset{+}{N}H_2 \; Cl^-$$

(R = H or alkyl)

The reaction of ammonia and amines with anhydrides follows a similar course; the products are 1 mole of amide and 1 mole of carboxylic acid. Since the liberated acid reacts to form a salt with the ammonia or the amine, it is necessary to employ an excess of that reactant.

$$2\ CH_3CH_2NH_2 + CH_3\overset{\overset{\displaystyle O}{\|}}{C}-O-\overset{\overset{\displaystyle O}{\|}}{C}CH_3 \longrightarrow CH_3CH_2NH-\overset{\overset{\displaystyle O}{\|}}{C}CH_3 + CH_3CH_2NH_3^+\ CH_3CO_2^-$$

As in the analogous reaction of amines with acyl halides, one may carry out the reaction in the presence of one equivalent of tertiary amine.

Esters also react with ammonia and amines to yield the corresponding amide and the alcohol of the ester. The reaction is synthetically useful in cases where the corresponding acyl halide or anhydride is unstable or not easily available. An interesting example of such a case is

$$\underset{}{CH_3}\overset{\overset{\displaystyle OH}{|}}{C}HCOOC_2H_5 + NH_3 \xrightarrow[24\ hr]{25°C} CH_3\overset{\overset{\displaystyle OH}{|}}{C}H-\overset{\overset{\displaystyle O}{\|}}{C}NH_2 + C_2H_5OH$$
$$(70\text{--}74\%)$$

In this case the acyl halide method for preparing the amide may not be used, since the molecule contains an OH group, which will react rapidly with an acyl halide.

> **EXERCISE 18.7** Treatment of 2-hydroxypropanoic acid (lactic acid) with thionyl chloride gives a product having the formula $C_6H_8O_4$. Propose a structure for this material.

C. Reaction of Acyl Halides and Anhydrides with Carboxylic Acids and Carboxylate Salts. Synthesis of Anhydrides

A mixture of an acid anhydride and a carboxylic acid undergoes equilibration when heated.

$$\overset{\overset{\displaystyle O\ \ \ O}{\| \ \ \|}}{RCOCR} + 2\ R'COOH \underset{}{\overset{\Delta}{\rightleftharpoons}} \overset{\overset{\displaystyle O\ \ \ O}{\| \ \ \|}}{R'COCR'} + 2\ RCOOH$$

The reaction is preparatively useful when the anhydride is acetic anhydride. In this case, acetic acid can be removed by distillation as it is formed because it is the most volatile component in the equilibrium mixture.

| b.p. 142°C | benzoic acid | benzoic anhydride | b.p. 117°C |

The only carboxylic acid derivatives that undergo a useful reaction with carboxylate salts are acyl halides. The product is an anhydride.

$$C_6H_{13}\overset{\overset{\displaystyle O}{\|}}{C}Cl + C_6H_{13}\overset{\overset{\displaystyle O}{\|}}{C}O^-\ Na^+ \xrightarrow{H_2O} \left(C_6H_{13}\overset{\overset{\displaystyle O}{\|}}{C}\right)_2 O + Na^+\ Cl^-$$

heptanoyl   sodium   heptanoic
chloride   heptanoate   anhydride

(60%)

D. Reaction with Organometallic Compounds

Acyl halides react with various organometallic reagents to give ketones. When using a Grignard reagent, best results are obtained if the reaction is carried out at low temperature. Anhydrous ferric chloride is often added as a catalyst.

(71%)

$$CH_3\overset{\overset{\displaystyle O}{\|}}{C}Cl + CH_3CH_2CH_2CH_2MgCl \xrightarrow[-70°C]{\underset{FeCl_3}{ether}} CH_3\overset{\overset{\displaystyle O}{\|}}{C}CH_2CH_2CH_2CH_3$$

(72%)

When using the foregoing reaction as a way of preparing a ketone from a carboxylic acid, it is important that only one equivalent of Grignard reagent be used. If excess Grignard reagent is used the product ketone reacts further, giving a tertiary alcohol.

$$R\!-\!\overset{\overset{\displaystyle O}{\|}}{C}Cl \xrightarrow{R'MgX} R\!-\!\overset{\overset{\displaystyle O}{\|}}{C}\!-\!R' \xrightarrow{R'MgX} R\!-\!\overset{\overset{\displaystyle O^-\ ^+MgX}{|}}{\underset{\underset{\displaystyle R'}{|}}{C}}\!-\!R' \xrightarrow{H_2O} R\!-\!\overset{\overset{\displaystyle OH}{|}}{\underset{\underset{\displaystyle R'}{|}}{C}}\!-\!R'$$

Some of the less reactive organometallic compounds still react rapidly with acyl halides, but react with ketones only sluggishly or not at all. Such is the case with lithium organocuprates, which are obtained by treating an organolithium compound with cuprous iodide.

$$2\ CH_3Li + CuI \xrightarrow{ether} LiCu(CH_3)_2 + LiI$$

The cuprate reacts rapidly with acyl halides and aldehydes, slowly with ketones, and not at all with esters, amides, and nitriles.

3-methylbutanoyl   2,6-dimethylhept-2-en-4-one
chloride

(70%)

497

Sec. 18.7

*Other
Nucleophilic
Substitution
Reactions*

Since esters are generally less reactive than ketones, the preparation of ketones by nucleophilic substitution on an ester is usually unsatisfactory; in most cases the only isolable product is the tertiary alcohol. In fact, the reaction of esters with two equivalents of a Grignard reagent or an alkyllithium is probably the best general method for the synthesis of tertiary alcohols in which two of the alkyl groups are equivalent.

$$2 \; C_6H_5MgBr + CH_3\overset{\overset{\displaystyle O}{\|}}{C}OC_2H_5 \longrightarrow \overset{H_2O}{\longrightarrow} C_6H_5\!-\!\overset{\overset{\displaystyle OH}{|}}{\underset{\underset{\displaystyle CH_3}{|}}{C}}\!-\!C_6H_5$$

1,1-diphenylethanol

methyl cyclohexanecarboxylate   2-cyclohexyl-2-propanol

In this reaction, the initially formed ketone reacts with the second equivalent of Grignard reagent to give the tertiary alcohol. If an ester of formic acid is used, the product is a secondary alcohol.

$$2 \; CH_3CH_2CH_2CH_2MgBr + H\overset{\overset{\displaystyle O}{\|}}{C}OC_2H_5 \xrightarrow{\text{ether}} \overset{H_3O^+}{\longrightarrow} CH_3CH_2CH_2CH_2\overset{\overset{\displaystyle OH}{|}}{C}HCH_2CH_2CH_2CH_3$$

(85%)

5-nonanol

Carbonate esters yield tertiary alcohols in which all three of the carbinol alkyl groups come from the organometallic reagent.

$$3 \; C_2H_5MgBr + CH_3O\overset{\overset{\displaystyle O}{\|}}{C}OCH_3 \longrightarrow \overset{H_3O^+}{\longrightarrow} C_2H_5\!-\!\overset{\overset{\displaystyle OH}{|}}{\underset{\underset{\displaystyle C_2H_5}{|}}{C}}\!-\!C_2H_5$$

(85%)

dimethyl carbonate   3-ethyl-3-pentanol

Carbonic acid diesters, dialkyl carbonates, are generally prepared by the reaction of alcohols with phosgene, $COCl_2$.

$$COCl_2 + 2 \; CH_3CH_2OH \longrightarrow CH_3CH_2O\overset{\overset{\displaystyle O}{\|}}{C}OCH_2CH_3 + 2 \; HCl$$

Phosgene is a highly toxic colorless gas, b.p. 7.6°C, having a distinctive odor. It was used in World War I as a war gas. This compound is the diacyl chloride of carbonic acid and reacts accordingly. It is hydrolyzed by water to give carbon dioxide and HCl.

$$COCl_2 + 2 \; H_2O \longrightarrow 2 \; HCl + [CO(OH)_2] \longrightarrow CO_2 + H_2O$$

Dimethyl carbonate is a commercially available, colorless liquid, b.p. 90°C.

EXERCISE 18.8 Show how 2-chlorobutane can be converted into each of the following compounds.
(a) 3-methyl-2-pentanone   (b) 3,4,5-trimethyl-4-heptanol   (c) 3,5-dimethyl-4-heptanol

18.8 Reduction

Acyl halides may be reduced to aldehydes or to primary alcohols.

$$\underset{\displaystyle R-\overset{\displaystyle O}{\overset{\|}{C}}Cl}{} \xrightarrow{[H]} \underset{\displaystyle R-\overset{\displaystyle O}{\overset{\|}{C}}H}{} \xrightarrow{[H]} RCH_2OH$$

The selective reduction of an acyl halide is one of the most useful ways of preparing aldehydes. Such selective reduction is possible because acyl halides are generally more reactive than the product aldehydes. One procedure for accomplishing the selective reduction is catalytic hydrogenation; the method is called a **Rosenmund reduction**. The acyl halide is hydrogenated in the presence of a catalyst such as palladium deposited on barium sulfate. As in the reduction of alkynes to alkenes, a "regulator" or "catalyst poison" (page 289) is frequently added in order to moderate the effectiveness of the catalyst and thereby inhibit subsequent reduction of the product aldehyde.

$$CH_3O\overset{O}{\overset{\|}{C}}CH_2CH_2\overset{O}{\overset{\|}{C}}Cl + H_2 \xrightarrow[\substack{quinoline\\ sulfur\\ xylene,\ 110°C}]{Pd/BaSO_4} CH_3O\overset{O}{\overset{\|}{C}}CH_2CH_2\overset{O}{\overset{\|}{C}}H$$
$$(65\%)$$

Another reagent that has found use for the selective reduction of an acyl halide to an aldehyde is lithium tri-*t*-butoxyaluminohydride, $Li(t\text{-}C_4H_9O)_3AlH$.

$$+ Li(t\text{-}C_4H_9O)_3AlH \xrightarrow{ether} \xrightarrow{H_2O}$$

$$(60\%)$$

In general, acyl halides are reduced more rapidly than aldehydes. However, lithium aluminum hydride is so extremely reactive that a selective reduction is difficult to accomplish. The tri-*t*-butoxy derivative, prepared by treating the hydride with three equivalents of *t*-butyl alcohol in ether, is less reactive and therefore more selective.

$$LiAlH_4 + 3\ t\text{-}C_4H_9OH \longrightarrow Li(t\text{-}C_4H_9O)_3AlH + 3\ H_2$$

If excess reducing agent is used, the product aldehyde is reduced further to a primary alcohol.

$$(1)\ R-\overset{O}{\overset{\|}{C}}-Cl + Li(t\text{-}C_4H_9O)_3AlH \xrightarrow{faster} R-\overset{O^-}{\underset{H}{\overset{|}{C}}}-Cl + Li^+ + (t\text{-}C_4H_9O)_3Al$$

(2) $R-\overset{\underset{|}{O^-}}{\underset{H}{C}}-Cl \rightleftharpoons R-\overset{O}{\overset{||}{C}}-H + Cl^-$

(3) $R-\overset{O}{\overset{||}{C}}-H + Li(t\text{-}C_4H_9O)_3AlH \xrightarrow{\text{slower}} RCH_2O^- + Li^+ + (t\text{-}C_4H_9O)_3Al$

With the more reactive lithium aluminum hydride, it is difficult to achieve selectivity.

Since esters are generally less reactive than aldehydes, they cannot be selectively reduced to the aldehyde stage. However, the reduction of an ester to a primary alcohol is an important preparative method. The most generally used reducing agents are lithium aluminum hydride and lithium borohydride.

$$\text{C}_6\text{H}_5-\overset{O}{\overset{||}{C}}\text{OC}_2\text{H}_5 + \text{LiAlH}_4 \longrightarrow \xrightarrow{\text{H}_2\text{O}} \text{C}_6\text{H}_5-\text{CH}_2\text{OH} + \text{C}_2\text{H}_5\text{OH}$$
$$(90\%)$$

$$\text{CH}_3(\text{CH}_2)_{14}\text{COOCH}_2\text{CH}_2\text{CH}_2\text{CH}_3 + \text{LiBH}_4 \xrightarrow[\Delta]{\text{THF}} \xrightarrow{\text{H}_2\text{O}} \text{CH}_3(\text{CH}_2)_{14}\text{CH}_2\text{OH} + \text{CH}_3\text{CH}_2\text{CH}_2\text{CH}_2\text{OH}$$
$$(95\%)$$

Lithium borohydride LiBH_4 is a hygroscopic white solid, m.p. 284°C. It is prepared by the reaction of sodium borohydride (page 261) with lithium chloride in ethanol.

$$\text{NaBH}_4 + \text{LiCl} \longrightarrow \text{LiBH}_4 + \text{NaCl}$$

It is a more reactive reducing agent than sodium borohydride, but is less reactive than lithium aluminum hydride. It is much more soluble in ether (4 g per 100 mL) than is sodium borohydride.

Esters are also reduced by sodium in ethanol (the **Bouveault-Blanc reaction**). Before the discovery of lithium aluminum hydride, this was the most common laboratory method for reducing esters, and it is still an important method for large-scale preparations where reagent cost is a concern.

$$n\text{-}C_{11}\text{H}_{23}\text{COOC}_2\text{H}_5 + \text{Na} \xrightarrow[\Delta]{C_2H_5OH} n\text{-}C_{11}\text{H}_{23}\text{CH}_2\text{OH} + \text{C}_2\text{H}_5\text{OH}$$
$$(65\text{-}75\%)$$

    ethyl dodecanoate   1-dodecanol

The reaction mechanism is not known in detail, but undoubtedly involves electron transfer from sodium to the carbonyl group as a first step. The reaction is *not* a reduction by hydrogen liberated from the reaction of sodium with ethanol.

Reduction of amides having at least one hydrogen on nitrogen with lithium aluminum hydride in ether or THF provides the corresponding primary or secondary amines.

$$\text{C}_6\text{H}_5-\text{OCH}_2\overset{O}{\overset{||}{C}}\text{NH}_2 + \text{LiAlH}_4 \xrightarrow[\Delta]{\text{ether}} \xrightarrow{\text{H}_2\text{O}} \text{C}_6\text{H}_5-\text{OCH}_2\text{CH}_2\text{NH}_2$$
$$(80\%)$$

$$\text{CH}_3(\text{CH}_2)_{10}\overset{O}{\overset{||}{C}}\text{NHCH}_3 + \text{LiAlH}_4 \xrightarrow[\Delta]{\text{ether}} \xrightarrow{\text{H}_2\text{O}} \text{CH}_3(\text{CH}_2)_{10}\text{CH}_2\text{NHCH}_3$$
$$(81\text{-}95\%)$$

A solution of 38 g of lithium aluminum hydride in 1800 mL of dry ether is placed in a 5-L three-necked flask equipped with a condenser and a mechanical stirrer. The solution is gently refluxed while 160 g of N-methyldodecanamide is slowly added over a period of 3 hr. The mixture is refluxed an additional 2 hr, then stirred overnight. The reaction mixture is worked up by the addition of 82 mL of water. After filtration to remove the solid aluminum and lithium salts, the ether is evaporated, and the residue is distilled to yield 121–142 g of N-methyldodecylamine.

The first step in this reduction is probably reaction of the strongly basic $LiAlH_4$ with the weakly acidic NH bond, giving the lithium salt of the amide.

$$R-\overset{\overset{O}{\|}}{C}-NH_2 + LiAlH_4 \longrightarrow R-\overset{\overset{O}{\|}}{C}-NH^- \; Li^+ + AlH_3 + H_2$$

Aluminum hydride may then add to the carbonyl group.

$$R-\overset{\overset{O}{\|}}{C}-NH^- \; Li^+ + AlH_3 \longrightarrow R-\overset{\overset{O-AlH_2}{|}}{\underset{\underset{H}{|}}{C}}-NH^- \; Li^+$$

This tetrahedral intermediate may decompose by elimination of H_2AlO^-, which is a reasonably good leaving group (recall that aluminum is an amphoteric metal; H_3AlO_3 is a protonic acid).

$$R-\overset{\overset{OAlH_2}{|}}{\underset{\underset{H}{|}}{C}}-NH^- \; Li^+ \longrightarrow R-\overset{}{\underset{\underset{H}{|}}{C}}=NH + H_2AlO^- \; Li^+$$

The resulting imine is now reduced by another hydride (from AlH_4^- or H_2AlO^-).

$$R-\overset{\overset{NH}{\|}}{C}H + AlH_4^- \; (or \; H_2AlO^-) \longrightarrow R-\overset{\overset{NH-Al\diagdown}{|}}{\underset{\underset{H}{|}}{C}}-H$$

Upon aqueous work-up, the N—Al bond is hydrolyzed to liberate the amine.

$$RCH_2-NH-Al\diagdown + H_2O \longrightarrow RCH_2NH_2 + HO-Al\diagdown$$

N,N-Dialkylamides may also be reduced to amines by lithium aluminum hydride.

$$\underset{\text{N,N-diethylacetamide}}{CH_3\overset{\overset{O}{\|}}{C}N(CH_2CH_3)_2} + LiAlH_4 \xrightarrow[\text{reflux}]{\text{ether}} \xrightarrow{H_2O} \underset{\underset{\text{triethylamine}}{(50\%)}}{CH_3CH_2N(CH_2CH_3)_2}$$

With disubstituted amides the reduction may generally be controlled so that the aldehyde may be obtained. This occurs when the initial tetrahedral intermediate is sufficiently stable so that it survives until all of the hydride has been consumed. If one wishes to prepare an aldehyde in this manner, it is necessary to keep the amide in excess by slowly adding the reducing agent to it. Several modified hydrides have been used for this purpose. One reagent that is particularly useful with simple dimethylamides is lithium triethoxyaluminohydride, prepared *in situ* by the reaction of three moles of ethanol with one molar equivalent of lithium aluminum hydride.

$$\text{LiAlH}_4 + 3\,\text{C}_2\text{H}_5\text{OH} \xrightarrow{\text{ether}} \text{LiAlH(OC}_2\text{H}_5)_3 + 3\,\text{H}_2$$

$$(\text{CH}_3)_3\overset{\overset{\displaystyle O}{\|}}{\text{C}}\text{CN(CH}_3)_2 + \text{LiAlH(OC}_2\text{H}_5)_3 \xrightarrow[]{\text{ether}} \xrightarrow{\text{H}_2\text{O}} (\text{CH}_3)_3\overset{\overset{\displaystyle O}{\|}}{\text{C}}\text{CH}$$

(88%)

2,2-dimethylpropanal
pivalaldehyde

EXERCISE 18.9 Show how each of the following transformations may be accomplished.
(a) $CH_3CH_2CH_2COCl \longrightarrow CH_3CH_2CH_2CHO$
(b) $CH_3CH_2CH_2COOCH_3 \longrightarrow CH_3CH_2CH_2CH_2OH$
(c) $CH_3CH_2CH_2CONH_2 \longrightarrow CH_3CH_2CH_2CH_2NH_2$
(d) $CH_3CH_2CH_2CON(CH_3)_2 \longrightarrow CH_3CH_2CH_2CHO$

18.9 Acidity of the α-Protons

Like the α-protons of aldehydes and ketones (Section 14.6), protons adjacent to the carbonyl group in carboxylic acid derivatives are weakly acidic. Table 18.7 lists the pK_a values for some representative compounds. Recall that the main reason for the acidity of aldehydes and ketones relative to the alkanes is the fact that the resulting anion is resonance stabilized. In fact, the resonance contributor with the negative charge on oxygen (the enolate ion) is the more important structure because of the greater electronegativity of oxygen. This stabilization of the anion greatly reduces the $\Delta H°$ for the ionization process and is responsible for the fact that acetone is approximately 30 powers of ten more acidic than ethane.

TABLE 18.7 Acidity of
Carboxylic Acid Derivatives

Compound	pK_a of H
$CH_3\overset{\overset{\displaystyle O}{\|}}{C}Cl$	~16
$CH_3\overset{\overset{\displaystyle O}{\|}}{C}H$	17
$CH_3\overset{\overset{\displaystyle O}{\|}}{C}CH_3$	19
$CH_3\overset{\overset{\displaystyle O}{\|}}{C}OCH_3$	25
CH_3CN	25
$CH_3\overset{\overset{\displaystyle O}{\|}}{C}N(CH_3)_2$	~30
CH_3CH_3	~50

$$CH_3CH_3 \rightleftharpoons H^+ + CH_3CH_2^-$$

charge localized
on carbon

$$CH_3\overset{\overset{\displaystyle O}{\|}}{C}CH_3 \rightleftharpoons H^+ + \left[CH_3\overset{\overset{\displaystyle O}{\|}}{C}CH_2^- \longleftrightarrow CH_3\overset{\overset{\displaystyle O^-}{|}}{C}{=}CH_2 \right]$$

charge delocalized—mainly on oxygen

The anions obtained upon deprotonation of carboxylic acid derivatives are also stabilized by delocalization of the negative charge onto the carbonyl oxygen. Consequently these compounds also act as weak acids; representative pK_as are summarized in Table 18.7.

The α-proton acidity manifests itself in the chemistry of carboxylic acid derivatives in several ways. For example, if ethyl acetate is dissolved in deuterioethanol that contains a catalytic amount of sodium ethoxide, exchange of the α-protons by deuterium occurs.

$$CH_3\overset{\overset{\displaystyle O}{\|}}{C}OC_2H_5 + C_2H_5OD \underset{C_2H_5O^-}{\overset{C_2H_5O^-}{\rightleftharpoons}} CD_3\overset{\overset{\displaystyle O}{\|}}{C}OC_2H_5 + C_2H_5OH$$

Ethyl acetate is a much weaker acid than ethanol (pK_a 15.9), so that the foregoing equilibrium is established relatively slowly. For example, a solution of ethyl acetate in deuterioethanol containing 0.1 M sodium ethoxide is only 50% exchanged after 2 weeks at 25°C. For this reason, if one wishes to exchange the α-protons of an ester, it is necessary to reflux the solution for several hours.

If an ester is treated with a sufficiently strong base, it can be completely converted to the corresponding anion. For example, t-butyl acetate reacts with lithium isopropyl-cyclohexylamide in THF at $-78°C$ to give t-butyl lithioacetate, which may be isolated as a white crystalline solid.

$CH_3\overset{\overset{\displaystyle O}{\|}}{C}OC(CH_3)_3$ + lithium isopropyl-cyclohexylamide $\xrightarrow[-78°C]{THF}$ t-butyl lithioacetate +

p$K_a \cong 25$ p$K_a \cong 40$

Such ester anions are strong bases and are also good nucleophiles. They undergo reactions similar to those of the corresponding enolate ions derived from ketones. Examples are S$_N$2 displacements with primary alkyl halides and additions to aldehyde and ketone carbonyl groups.

methyl hexanoate $\xrightarrow[-78°C]{LDA \quad CH_3I}{THF}$ (83%) methyl 2-methylhexanoate

$CH_3COOC(CH_3)_3 \xrightarrow[-78°C]{LDA \quad THF} \quad \xrightarrow{H_2O}$

(93%)
t-butyl (1-hydroxycyclopentyl)acetate

A related reaction results when an aldehyde or ketone is treated with an α-halo ester and zinc in an inert solvent.

(70%)
ethyl (1-hydroxycyclohexyl)acetate

This reaction, which is known as the **Reformatsky reaction**, involves the formation of an intermediate organozinc compound. The intermediate has been isolated and examined spectroscopically. It crystallizes as a dimer, with each zinc partially bonded to both an oxygen and a carbon.

The virtue of the Reformatsky reaction, relative to the simple reaction of an aldehyde or ketone with the preformed lithium enolate of an ester, is convenience.

Ester anions also undergo another reaction that is an important synthetic procedure, the **Claisen condensation**. In this reaction the ester anion condenses with an nonionized ester molecule to give a β-keto ester.

(75%)

A mixture of 1.2 moles of ethyl acetate and 0.2 mole of alcohol-free sodium ethoxide is heated at 78°C for 8 hr. The mixture is then cooled to 10°C, and 36 g of 33% aqueous acetic acid is slowly added. The aqueous layer is washed with ether, and the combined organic layers are dried and distilled to give ethyl acetoacetate, b.p. 78–80°C (16 mm), in 75–76% yield.

The product in this example, ethyl 3-oxobutanoate, is known by the trivial name ethyl acetoacetate, or simply acetoacetic ester. For this reason the self-condensation of esters is sometimes called the **acetoacetic ester condensation**, even when other esters are involved.

The reaction is mechanistically similar to the aldol addition reaction (Section 14.8.C) in that the conjugate base of the ester is a reactive intermediate.

(3) $CH_3\overset{\underset{\displaystyle OC_2H_5}{|}}{\underset{\displaystyle O^-}{C}}CH_2\overset{\overset{\displaystyle O}{||}}{C}OC_2H_5 \rightleftharpoons CH_3\overset{\overset{\displaystyle O}{||}}{C}CH_2\overset{\overset{\displaystyle O}{||}}{C}OC_2H_5 + C_2H_5O^-$

(4) $CH_3\overset{\overset{\displaystyle O}{||}}{C}CH_2\overset{\overset{\displaystyle O}{||}}{C}OC_2H_5 + C_2H_5O^- \rightleftharpoons CH_3\overset{\overset{\displaystyle O^-}{|}}{C}=CH\overset{\overset{\displaystyle O}{||}}{C}OC_2H_5 + C_2H_5OH$

As we shall see in Section 27.7.C, 1,3-dicarbonyl compounds are fairly strong carbon acids; the pK_a of acetoacetic ester itself is about 11. Thus the equilibrium for the last step in this mechanism lies far to the right. Since the pK_a of ethanol is about 16, K for step (4) is about 10^5. This final, essentially irreversible, step provides the driving force for the Claisen condensation. A dramatic illustration is provided by attempted Claisen condensation with ethyl 2-methylpropanoate.

$$2\ (CH_3)_2CH\overset{\overset{\displaystyle O}{||}}{C}OC_2H_5 \xrightarrow[C_2H_5OH]{NaOC_2H_5} \!\!\!/\!\!/\!\!\longrightarrow (CH_3)_2CH\overset{\overset{\displaystyle O}{||}}{C}-\overset{\overset{\displaystyle CH_3}{|}}{\underset{\underset{\displaystyle CH_3}{|}}{C}}-\overset{\overset{\displaystyle O}{||}}{C}OC_2H_5$$

In this case there are no protons in the normally acidic position between the two carbonyl groups; hence, the final step in the mechanism cannot occur. The overall equilibrium constant for steps (1) through (3) in the mechanism is apparently too small for condensation to be observed in the absence of step (4). The most acidic proton available in the hypothetical product is the proton at C-4, which is a normal proton α to a ketone carbonyl; its pK_a is therefore about 20. If a much stronger base is used to catalyze the reaction, this proton can be removed and reaction can now be observed.

$$(CH_3)_2CHCOOC_2H_5 + (C_6H_5)_3C^-\ Na^+ \longrightarrow \xrightarrow[(work\text{-}up)]{H_3O^+} (CH_3)_2CH\overset{\overset{\displaystyle O}{||}}{C}-\overset{\overset{\displaystyle CH_3}{|}}{\underset{\underset{\displaystyle CH_3}{|}}{C}}-COOC_2H_5$$

$$(45\text{--}60\%)$$

The base in the foregoing example, sodium triphenylmethide, is much more basic than ethoxide ion. It is the conjugate base of the weak carbon acid triphenylmethane ($pK_a = 31.5$), and it will be discussed in detail in Section 20.5.D. Since it is such a strong base, K for the last step in the Claisen condensation is large (10^{11}), even though a normal ketone is being deprotonated.

$$(CH_3)_2CH\overset{\overset{\displaystyle O}{||}}{C}-\overset{\overset{\displaystyle CH_3}{|}}{\underset{\underset{\displaystyle CH_3}{|}}{C}}-COOC_2H_5 + (C_6H_5)_3C^- \overset{K}{\rightleftharpoons}$$

$$pK_a \cong 20$$

$$(CH_3)_2C=\overset{\overset{\displaystyle O^-}{|}}{C}-\overset{\overset{\displaystyle CH_3}{|}}{\underset{\underset{\displaystyle CH_3}{|}}{C}}-COOC_2H_5 + (C_6H_5)_3CH$$

$$pK_a = 31.5$$

Mixed Claisen condensations between two esters are successful when one of the esters has no α-hydrogens, as shown by the following examples.

$$CH_3\overset{O}{\underset{||}{C}}OC_2H_5 + H\overset{O}{\underset{||}{C}}OC_2H_5 \xrightarrow[C_2H_5OH]{NaOC_2H_5} \xrightarrow{H_3O^+} H\overset{O}{\underset{||}{C}}CH_2\overset{O}{\underset{||}{C}}OC_2H_5$$

(79%)

ethyl formylacetate

The overall result of a mixed Claisen condensation is given by the general equation

$$RCOOC_2H_5 + H-\overset{R'}{\underset{R''}{\overset{|}{\underset{|}{C}}}}-COOC_2H_5 \longrightarrow RC-\overset{O \quad R'}{\underset{R''}{\overset{||}{\underset{|}{C}}}}-COOC_2H_5$$

Best results are obtained when R has no α-hydrogens and either R' or R'' is hydrogen.

The Claisen condensation is used extensively in biological reactions to build up and degrade chains. Instead of a normal ester, the biochemical processes make use of a thioester together with enzyme catalysts specific for each step. The key ingredient is coenzyme A or CoA in the form of the thioacetate ester of acetyl CoA.

$$HSCH_2CH_2NHCOCH_2CH_2NHCOCHOH\overset{CH_3}{\underset{CH_3}{\overset{|}{\underset{|}{C}}}}CH_2O-\overset{O}{\underset{OH}{\overset{||}{P}}}-O-\overset{O}{\underset{OH}{\overset{||}{P}}}-OCH_2$$

NH_2

adenine

coenzyme A

H_2O_3PO

$$2\ CH_3CO-CoA \rightleftharpoons CH_3COCH_2CO-CoA\ +\ CoA$$

$$\Updownarrow$$

$$CH_3CHOHCH_2CO-CoA$$

$$\Updownarrow$$

$$CH_3CH=CHCO-CoA$$

$$\Updownarrow$$

$$CH_3CH_2CH_2CO-CoA \rightleftharpoons higher\ fatty\ acids$$

The initial condensation is of the Claisen type and is followed by reduction and dehydration reactions to give a butyrate ester that can react with acetyl CoA to build up higher fatty acids. Note that these acids are built up and degraded two carbons at a time. A consequence of this mechanism is that fatty acids almost always have an even number of carbons in the chain.

EXERCISE 18.10 Show how ethyl acetate may be converted into each of the following compounds.
(a) ethyl hexanoate
(b) ethyl 3-hydroxyhexanoate
(c) ethyl 3-hydroxy-3-methylbutanoate
(d) ethyl 2,2,2-trideuterioacetate
(e) 3-methylpentane-1,3-diol
(f) $CH_3CH_2OOCCH_2CHO$

18.10 Reactions of Amides That Occur on Nitrogen

The nitrogen-hydrogen bonds of amides are also acidic. In fact, since the negative charge in the resulting **amidate** anion is shared between oxygen and nitrogen, rather than oxygen and carbon, they are substantially more acidic than ketones; acetamide has $pK_a \cong 15$.

$$R-\overset{\overset{O}{\|}}{C}-NH_2 \rightleftharpoons H^+ + \left[R-\overset{\overset{O}{\|}}{C}-NH^- \longleftrightarrow R-\overset{\overset{O^-}{|}}{C}=NH \right]$$

an **amidate** anion

The lability of the amide N—H is reflected in many of the reactions of amides. One of these is dehydration. A primary amide may be converted into the corresponding nitrile by treatment with an efficient dehydrating agent such as P_2O_5, $POCl_3$, $SOCl_2$, or acetic anhydride.

2,3-dimethylhexanamide → 2,3-dimethylhexanenitrile (90%)

SOCl₂, benzene, 80°C

EXERCISE 18.11 Consider the four compounds ethyl bromide, propanoic acid, propanamide, and propanenitrile. Make a 4 × 4 matrix with the four compounds on each side of the matrix. There are twelve intersections of the matrix representing conversion of one compound to another (ignore the four that connect a compound with itself). We have learned reactions that correspond to eight of these twelve possibilities. Review these eight reactions.

18.11 Pyrolytic Eliminations: Syn Elimination

Several types of organic compounds undergo elimination to give alkenes when heated to relatively high temperatures. Such **pyrolytic eliminations** are often preparatively useful. In this section we shall discuss the pyrolytic elimination of esters and xanthates.

$$R-\overset{\overset{O}{\|}}{C}-OCH_2CHR_2' \overset{\Delta}{\longrightarrow} RCOOH + CH_2=CR_2'$$

an ester

$$RS-\overset{\overset{S}{\|}}{C}-OCH_2CHR_2' \overset{\Delta}{\longrightarrow} RSH + COS + CH_2=CR_2'$$

a xanthate

When a carboxylic ester is heated to 300–500°C, elimination occurs to give the carboxylic acid and an alkene. The elimination may be accomplished by heating the ester in the liquid phase or by passing the gaseous ester through a hot vapor-phase reactor.

$$CH_3\overset{\displaystyle O}{\overset{\|}{C}}OCH_2CH_2CH_2CH_3 \xrightarrow{500°C} CH_2{=}CHCH_2CH_3 + CH_3COOH$$
$$(100\%)$$

The elimination is believed to occur by a concerted mechanism involving a six-center transition state.

When the alkyl group of the ester has two or more β-hydrogens that may be lost mixtures are obtained. For simple esters the elimination is nearly statistical.

$$CH_3{-}\underset{\displaystyle \underset{\underset{\displaystyle CH_3}{|}}{O}\overset{\displaystyle O}{\overset{\|}{C}}CH_3}{\overset{|}{C}H}{-}CH_2CH_3 \xrightarrow{500°C} CH_2{=}CHCH_2CH_3 + CH_3CH{=}CHCH_3$$

$$\text{observed ratio: } 57\% \qquad\qquad 43\%$$
$$\text{(statistical: } 60\% \qquad\qquad 40\%)$$

Xanthate salts are prepared by treating an alcohol with carbon disulfide and sodium hydroxide.

$$ROH + CS_2 + NaOH \longrightarrow RO\overset{\displaystyle S}{\overset{\|}{C}}S^-\,Na^+$$

When the xanthate salt is treated with methyl iodide, S_N2 displacement occurs and a **xanthate ester** is formed.

$$RO\overset{\displaystyle S}{\overset{\|}{C}}S^-\,Na^+ + CH_3I \longrightarrow RO\overset{\displaystyle S}{\overset{\|}{C}}SCH_3 + Na^+I^-$$

Xanthates undergo pyrolytic elimination at somewhat lower temperatures than esters. The method, called the **Chugaev reaction**, has been widely used as method of dehydrating alcohols.

$$(71\%)$$

methyl 3,3-dimethyl-2-butylxanthate   3,3-dimethyl-1-butene

Recall that the E2 mechanism for dehydrohalogenation of alkyl halides is an **anti** elimination (Section 11.5.A). That is, the hydrogen and halogen depart from opposite sides of the molecule.

In contrast, ester and xanthate pyrolyses are **syn** eliminations; the leaving groups depart from the same side of the molecule. This stereochemistry was first demonstrated with an elegant labeling experiment by Curtin and Kellom in 1953. It was shown that 1,2-diphenylethyl acetate undergoes pyrolysis to give only *trans*-1,2-diphenylethylene (*trans*-stilbene).

1,2-diphenylethyl acetate   *trans*-stilbene

The two deuterium-labeled analogs shown in (18-6) and (18-7) were then prepared and pyrolyzed. The *R,R* compound gives *trans*-stilbene, which contains one deuterium atom per molecule, and the *R,S* compound gives a product that has no deuterium.

(18-6)

(*R,R*)

(18-7)

(*R,S*)

EXERCISE 18.12 Write the stereostructure of the alkene produced from each of the following reaction sequences.

18.12 Waxes and Fats

A. Waxes

Waxes are naturally occurring esters of long-chain carboxylic acids (C_{16} or greater) with long-chain alcohols (C_{16} or greater). They are low-melting solids that have a characteristic "waxy" feel. We present three examples. **Spermaceti** is a wax that separates from the oil of the sperm whale on cooling. It is mainly cetyl palmitate (cetyl alcohol is the common name for 1-hexadecanol) and melts at 42-47°C.

$$C_{15}H_{31}\overset{\displaystyle O}{\overset{\|}{C}}OC_{16}H_{33}$$

spermaceti
cetyl palmitate
1-hexadecyl hexadecanoate

Beeswax is the material from which bees build honeycomb cells. It melts at 60–82°C and is a mixture of esters. Hydrolysis yields mainly the C_{26} and C_{28} straight-chain carboxylic acids and the C_{30} and C_{32} straight-chain primary alcohols.

$$C_{25\text{-}27}H_{51\text{-}55}\overset{\displaystyle O}{\overset{\|}{C}}OC_{30\text{-}32}H_{61\text{-}65}$$

beeswax

Carnauba wax occurs as the coating on Brazilian palm leaves. It has a high melting point (80-87°C) and is impervious to water. It is widely used as an ingredient in automobile and floor polish. It is a mixture of esters of the C_{24} and C_{28} carboxylic acids and the C_{32} and C_{34} straight-chain primary alcohols. Other components are present in smaller amounts.

B. Fats

Fats are naturally occurring esters of long-chain carboxylic acids and the triol glycerol (propane-1,2,3-triol). They are also called **glycerides**.

$$
\begin{array}{ll}
CH_2OH & CH_2OCOR \\
| & | \\
CHOH & CHOCOR' \\
| & | \\
CH_2OH & CH_2OCOR''
\end{array}
$$

glycerol   a fat or glyceride
propane-1,2,3-triol

Hydrolysis of fats yields glycerol and the component carboxylic acids. The straight-chain carboxylic acids that may be obtained from fats are frequently called **fat acids** or **fatty acids**. Fatty acids may be saturated or unsaturated. The most common saturated fatty acids are lauric acid, myristic acid, palmitic acid, and stearic acid.

$$CH_3(CH_2)_{10}COOH \quad CH_3(CH_2)_{12}COOH \quad CH_3(CH_2)_{14}COOH \quad CH_3(CH_2)_{16}COOH$$

lauric acid	myristic acid	palmitic acid	stearic acid
dodecanoic acid	tetradecanoic acid	hexadecanoic acid	octadecanoic acid

The most important unsaturated fatty acids have 18 carbon atoms, with one or more double bonds. Examples are oleic acid, linoleic acid, and linolenic acid.

oleic acid
(Z)-9-octadecenoic acid

linoleic acid
(Z,Z)-9,12-octadecadienoic acid

linolenic acid
(Z,Z,Z)-9,12,15-octadecatrienoic acid

Almost invariably, the double bonds have the cis or Z configuration. A significant exception is eleostearic acid, which has one cis and two trans double bonds.

eleostearic acid
(Z,E,E)-9,11,13-octadecatrienoic acid

Arachidonic acid is a C_{20} tetraenoic acid that is important as the biological precursor to the prostaglandins and leukotrienes, natural substances that play important roles in the immune system.

arachidonic acid
(Z,Z,Z,Z)-5,8,11,14-docosatetraenoic acid

prostaglandin $F_{2\alpha}$

leukotriene-B

Natural fats are generally complex mixtures of triesters of glycerol (**triglycerides**). In general, the secondary hydroxy group is esterified with C_{18} acids, and the primary hydroxy groups are esterified with either C_{18} or other fatty acids. For example, hydrolysis of palm oil yields 1–3% myristic acid, 34–43% palmitic acid, 3–6% stearic acid, 38–40% oleic acid, and 5–11% linoleic acid. Some natural fats yield large amounts of a single fatty acid on hydrolysis; tung oil yields 2–6% stearic acid, 4–16% oleic acid, 1–10% linoleic acid, and 74–91% eleostearic acid.

Fats undergo the typical reactions of esters. An important commercial reaction of fats is alkaline hydrolysis. The product fatty acid salts are used as soaps (Section 17.4.D).

$$\begin{array}{l} CH_2OCOR \\ | \\ CH_2OCOR + 3\ NaOH \xrightarrow{H_2O} \\ | \\ CH_2OCOR \end{array} \quad \begin{array}{l} CH_2OH \\ | \\ CHOH + 3\ RCO_2^-\ Na^+ \\ | \\ CH_2OH \end{array}$$

The alkaline hydrolysis of an ester is often referred to as **saponification**, from this process.

The melting point of a fat depends on the amount of unsaturation in the fatty acids. Fats with a preponderance of unsaturated fatty acids have melting points below room temperature and are called **oils**. Fats with little unsaturation are solid at normal temperatures. For the manufacture of soaps and for certain food uses, solid fats are preferable to oils. The melting point of a natural fat may be increased by hydrogenation. Industrially, the process is called **hardening**. Vegetable oils, such as cottonseed and peanut, are often hardened to the consistency of lard by partial hydrogenation.

Phosphoglycerides are fats in which glycerol is esterified to two fatty acids and to phosphoric acid. Such monophosphate esters are called **phosphatidic acids**. Most phosphatidic acids contain one saturated and one unsaturated fatty acid. Because different acids are esterified at the C-1 and C-3 hydroxy groups of glycerol, phosphatidic acids are chiral; the absolute configuration at the C-2 ester link is *R*.

a phosphatidic acid

Free phosphatidic acids are rare in nature. Usually the phosphoric acid moiety is esterified to a second alcohol component. Important examples are phosphatidyl ethanolamine and phosphatidyl choline.

phosphatidyl ethanolamine

phosphatidyl choline

Phosphoglycerides are important biomolecules and occur widely in plants and animals. They are often referred to collectively as ''phospholipids.''

Lipid is a term that has been used to describe the group of natural substances which are soluble in hydrocarbons and insoluble in water. It includes fats, waxes, phosphoglycerides, natural hydrocarbons, and so on. Most biochemists reserve the term lipid for natural compounds that yield fatty acids upon hydrolysis.

Phosphoglycerides have long nonpolar "tails" and a small, highly polar "head."

$$OCH_2CH_2NH_3^+$$

$$O=P-O^-$$

$$O$$

⎫ polar head

$$CH_2-CH-CH_2$$

$$O \qquad O$$

$$O=C \qquad C=O$$

CH_2	CH_2
CH_2	CH_2
CH_2	CH_2
CH_2	CH_2
CH_2	CH_2
CH_2	CH_2
CH_2	CH_2
CH_2	CH_2
CH_2	CH_2
CH_2	CH_2
CH_2	CH_2
CH_2	CH_2
CH_2	CH_2
CH_2	CH_2
CH_3	CH_3

nonpolar tail

In aqueous solution, they disperse to form micelles in the same way soaps do (Section 17.4.D). The nonpolar tails cluster together in the middle of the micelle, leaving the polar heads exposed to the aqueous environment (Figure 18.6). Phospholipids also

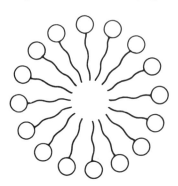

FIGURE 18.6 Cross section of a phospholipid micelle.

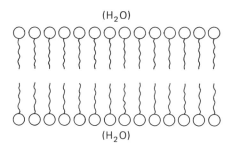

(H$_2$O)

FIGURE 18.7 Cross section of a phospholipid bilayer.

form **bilayers**, particularly at the interface between two aqueous surfaces. In such bilayers the hydrocarbon tails cluster toward one another, leaving a layer of polar heads on either side of the bilayer exposed to the aqueous phases (Figure 18.7). Such bilayers appear to form the fundamental framework of natural membranes.

PROBLEMS

1. Write the IUPAC name for each compound.

(a) $(CH_3CH_2)_2CHCH_2COOCH_2CH_2CH_3$

(b)
$$\bigcirc\!\!-COOCH_2CH_3$$

(c)
$$\square\!\!-COOCH_2CH_3$$

(d) $CH_3CH_2\overset{O}{\underset{\|}{C}}Cl$

(e) $\left(CH_3CH_2CH_2\overset{O}{\underset{\|}{C}}\right)_2 O$

(f) $CH_3CH_2\overset{O}{\underset{\|}{C}}NHCH_3$

(g)
$$\bigcirc\!\!-NH\overset{O}{\underset{\|}{C}}CH(CH_3)_2$$

(h) $CH_3CH_2\overset{Cl}{\underset{|}{C}}HCOOCH_3$

(i) $CH_3CH_2\overset{CH_3}{\underset{|}{C}}HCH_2\overset{O}{\underset{\|}{C}}Br$

(j)
$$\bigcirc\!\!-O\overset{O}{\underset{\|}{C}}CH_3$$

2. Write a structure that corresponds to each name.
   (a) N,3-diethylhexanamide
   (b) N,N-dimethylformamide
   (c) ethyl butanoate
   (d) methyl 3-chloropropanoate
   (e) propanoic anhydride
   (f) acetic formic anhydride
   (g) cyclohexanecarboxamide
   (h) butanoyl bromide
   (i) cyclobutyl formate
   (j) 3-formylhexanoic acid
   (k) ethyl acetoacetate
   (l) N-bromoacetamide

3. In a dilute solution of acetic acid in 0.1 M aqueous HCl, what percentage of the acetic acid is present as $CH_3CO_2{}^-$ and what percentage is present as $CH_3C(OH)_2{}^+$?

4. The pK_a of $CH_3\overset{\overset{\displaystyle O}{\|}}{C}OH_2^+$ may be estimated to be approximately -12. Calculate the ratio of $CH_3\overset{\overset{\displaystyle OH^+}{\|}}{C}OH$ to $CH_3\overset{\overset{\displaystyle O}{\|}}{C}OH_2^+$ in an acidic solution of acetic acid.

5. A neutral compound, $C_7H_{13}O_2Br$, shows bands in its infrared spectrum at 1740 cm^{-1} and 2850–2950 cm^{-1} but none above 3000 cm^{-1}. The NMR spectrum shows the following pattern: δ 1.0 ppm (3H, t), 1.3 ppm (6H, d), 2.1 ppm (2H, m), 4.2 ppm (1H, t) and 4.6 ppm (1H, m). The CMR spectrum has a resonance at δ 168 ppm. Deduce the structure and indicate the origin of the foregoing spectral features.

6. Identify the compound having the following IR and NMR spectra and the formula $C_6H_{11}BrO_2$.

7. What are the organic products of each of the following reactions or sequences of reactions?

(a) $CH_3CH_2CH_2OH + CH_3\overset{\overset{\displaystyle O}{\|}}{C}Cl \xrightarrow{500°C}$

(b)

$\xrightarrow[\text{NaOH}]{CS_2} \xrightarrow{CH_3I} \xrightarrow{200°C}$

(c) $\xrightarrow[\text{NaOH}]{\text{CS}_2}$ $\xrightarrow{\text{CH}_3\text{I}}$ $\xrightarrow{200°\text{C}}$

(d) $CH_3CH_2CH_2Cl$ $\xrightarrow[\substack{\text{ethanol}\\75°\text{C}}]{\text{NaCN}}$ $\xrightarrow[\substack{\text{H}_2\text{O}\\100°\text{C}}]{\text{NaOH}}$

(e) $\xrightarrow{\text{SOCl}_2}$ $\xrightarrow{\text{NH}_3}$ $\xrightarrow{\text{LiAlH}_4}$

(f) $\xrightarrow[\Delta]{\text{P}_2\text{O}_5}$

8. What are the organic products of each of the following reactions or sequences of reactions?

(a) $(CH_3)_3CCNH_2$ $\xrightarrow[\substack{\text{D}_2\text{O}\\25°\text{C, 5 min}}]{0.1\ M\ \text{NaOD}}$

(b) $\xrightarrow[\text{CH}_3\text{OH}]{\text{CH}_3\text{O}^-\text{Na}^+}$

(c) $\xrightarrow[\text{ether}]{\text{LiAlH}_4}$ $\xrightarrow[25°\text{C}]{\text{H}_3\text{O}^+}$

(d) $CH_3CH_2COOCH_2CH_3$ $\xrightarrow[\text{EtOH}]{\text{NaOEt}}$ $\xrightarrow{\text{H}_3\text{O}^+}$

(e) $BrCH_2COOCH_3 + CH_3CH_2CHO + Zn \xrightarrow{\text{benzene}}$

(f) $CH_3CH_2COOCH_2CH_3$ $\xrightarrow[\text{THF, }-78°\text{C}]{\text{LDA}}$ $\xrightarrow{\text{CH}_3\text{CH}_2\text{CHO}}$ $\xrightarrow{\text{H}_2\text{O}}$

9. Show how butanoic acid can be converted into each of the following compounds. More than one step may be required in some cases.

(a) $CH_3CH_2CH_2CCl$ (with $\overset{O}{\|}$ above C)

(b) $\left(CH_3CH_2CH_2C\right)_2O$ (with $\overset{O}{\|}$ above C)

(c) $CH_3CH_2CH_2CH_2OCCH_2CH_2CH_3$ (with $\overset{O}{\|}$)

(d) $CH_3CH_2CH_2CN(CH_3)_2$ (with $\overset{O}{\|}$)

(e) $CH_3CH_2CH_2C{\equiv}N$

(f) $CH_3CH_2CH_2CH_2NH_2$

(g) $CH_3CH_2CH_2Br$

(h) $CH_3CH_2CH_2CH_2N(CH_2CH_3)_2$

10. Show how butanoic acid can be converted into each of the following compounds. More than one step may be required in some cases.

(a) $CH_3CH_2CH_2CCH_2CHCH_3$ (with $\overset{O}{\|}$ over first C and $\overset{CH_3}{|}$ over CH)

(b) $CH_3CH_2CH_2COH$ with $\overset{CH_3}{|}$ above and $\underset{CH_3}{|}$ below

(c) $CH_3CH_2CH_2CHO$

(d) $CH_3CH_2CH_2CH_2OH$

(e) $CH_3CH_2CH_2\overset{\overset{\displaystyle OH}{|}}{C}HCHCH_2OH$
$\underset{CH_3CH_2}{|}$

(f) $CH_3CH_2CH_2\overset{\overset{\displaystyle OH}{|}}{C}HCHCOOC_2H_5$
$\underset{CH_2CH_3}{|}$

(g) $CH_3CH_2CH_2CO\overset{|}{C}HCOOC_2H_5$
$\underset{CH_2CH_3}{|}$

11. Predict the product of each of the following reactions. Rationalize your predictions.

(a) $H_2N\overset{\overset{\displaystyle O}{||}}{-}C-Cl + CH_3O^- \longrightarrow$

(b) $CH_3O\overset{\overset{\displaystyle O}{||}}{-}C-Cl + H_2N^- \longrightarrow$

12. How may each of the following compounds be prepared from monofunctional compounds containing five or fewer carbons.

(a) $(CH_3)_2CHCH_2CH_2CH_2COOCH_3$ (b) $CH_3CH_2CH_2CH(OH)CH_2COOCH_2CH_3$

(c) $(CH_3)_3C\overset{\overset{\displaystyle O}{||}}{C}CH_2COOCH_2CH_3$ (d) ⬡$\overset{OH}{\underset{CH_2COOH}{}}$

13. N-Methylacetamide reacts with triethyloxonium tetrafluoroborate to give a salt, $C_5H_{12}NO^+$ BF_4^-. When this salt is treated with sodium bicarbonate, a compound $C_5H_{11}NO$ is produced.

$$CH_3\overset{\overset{\displaystyle O}{||}}{C}NHCH_3 + (C_2H_5)_3O^+\,BF_4^- \longrightarrow C_5H_{12}NO^+\,BF_4^- \xrightarrow{\text{NaHCO}_3} C_5H_{11}NO$$

(a) What are the structures of the two compounds?
(b) Rationalize the formation of the salt in mechanistic terms.
(c) Predict the product that will be obtained if the salt is treated with aqueous acid.

14. Write a mechanism that explains the following reaction (the Ritter reaction).

$$CH_3\underset{\underset{CH_3}{|}}{\overset{\overset{CH_3}{|}}{C}}-OH + CH_3CN \xrightarrow[\Delta]{H_2O-H_2SO_4} CH_3\underset{\underset{CH_3}{|}}{\overset{\overset{CH_3}{|}}{C}}-NH\overset{\overset{\displaystyle O}{||}}{C}CH_3$$

What product is expected when 2-methyl-2,4-pentanediol is treated with acetonitrile and aqueous sulfuric acid?

15. Explain why the pyrolysis of *cis*-2-methylcyclohexyl acetate gives only 3-methylcyclohexene, whereas *trans*-2-methylcyclohexyl acetate gives a mixture of 1-methylcyclohexene and 3-methylcyclohexene.

16. The elimination of a carboxylic acid from an ester is generally an endothermic process, for example,

$$CH_3CH_2CH_2CH_2OCOCH_3 \longrightarrow CH_3CH_2CH{=}CH_2 + CH_3COOH$$

$$\Delta H° = +12.6 \text{ kcal mole}^{-1}$$

Yet the pyrolytic elimination is a useful preparative reaction. How do you account for this? Why is the pyrolytic elimination carried out at high temperature (300–500°C)?

17. Orthoesters are compounds that have three alkoxy groups attached to the same carbon, for example, ethyl orthoacetate, $CH_3C(OC_2H_5)_3$. When ethyl orthoacetate is treated with dilute aqueous acid, ethyl acetate is obtained. Explain with a mechanism.

$$CH_3C(OC_2H_5)_3 + H_2O \xrightarrow{H^+} CH_3COOC_2H_5 + 2\ C_2H_5OH$$

18. Treatment of diethyl adipate, $C_2H_5OOC(CH_2)_4COOC_2H_5$, with sodium ethoxide in ethanol, followed by neutralization with aqueous acid, yields a compound having the formula $C_8H_{12}O_3$. Propose a structure for this product, and write a mechanism that accounts for its formation. This reaction is a general reaction of certain diesters (the Dieckmann condensation) and will be discussed in Section 27.6.C.

19. A solution of methyl cyclohexyl ketone in chloroform is treated with peroxybenzoic acid for 16 hr at 25°C. The reaction mixture is worked up to obtain A, which has infrared absorption at 1740 cm^{-1}. The NMR spectrum of A shows a sharp three-proton singlet at $\delta = 2.0$ ppm and a one-proton multiplet at $\delta = 4.8$ ppm. Elemental analysis of A shows that it has the formula $C_8H_{14}O_2$. What is A and how is it formed?

20. (R)-2-Butanol, $[\alpha]_D = -13.5°$, reacts with methanesulfonyl chloride to give a methanesulfonate. Treatment of the methanesulfonate with aqueous sodium hydroxide affords 2-butanol having $[\alpha]_D = +13.5°$.
    (a) From this result, what conclusions may you draw regarding the mechanism of the hydrolysis?
    (b) How may (S)-2-octanol be converted into (R)-2-methoxyoctane?

21. Reduction of *trans*-2,3-dimethyloxirane with lithium aluminum deuteride (LiAlH$_4$) gives one of the diasteromeric 3-deuterio-2-butanols. The acetate of this alcohol is pyrolyzed at 500°C. What is the expected deuterium content of each of the three olefinic products?

Chapter 19

Conjugation

19.1 Allylic Systems

A. Allylic Cations

When 2-buten-1-ol is treated with hydrogen bromide at 0°C, a 3:1 mixture of 1-bromo-2-butene and 3-bromo-1-butene is produced. A comparable mixture is produced when 3-buten-2-ol is treated with HBr under the same conditions.

$$CH_3CH=CHCH_2OH$$
$$\xrightarrow[0°C]{HBr} CH_3CH=CHCH_2Br + CH_3CHBrCH=CH_2$$
$$CH_3CHOHCH=CH_2$$
$$3:1$$

Similarly, when 1-chloro-3-methyl-2-butene is hydrolyzed in water containing silver oxide at room temperature, a mixture of alcohols consisting of 15% of 3-methyl-2-buten-1-ol and 85% of 2-methyl-3-buten-2-ol is produced. Essentially the same mixture is obtained by the reaction of 3-chloro-3-methyl-1-butene with silver oxide in water.

$$(CH_3)_2C=CHCH_2Cl$$

$$\underset{\substack{Cl \\ | \\ (CH_3)_2CCH=CH_2}}{} \xrightarrow[\substack{H_2O \\ 25°C}]{Ag_2O} (CH_3)_2C=CHCH_2OH + (CH_3)_2\overset{OH}{\underset{|}{C}}CH=CH_2 + AgCl$$
$$(15\%) \qquad\qquad (85\%)$$

Silver cation catalyzes the formation of carbocations from alkyl halides. The Ag^+ tends to coordinate with the leaving halide group; that is, it provides a potent "pull" that contributes to the driving force of the reaction.

$$RX + Ag^+ \longrightarrow [R\cdots X\cdots Ag]^+ \longrightarrow R^+ + AgX\downarrow$$
$$\text{(transition state)}$$

Furthermore, silver chloride, bromide, and iodide are highly insoluble salts and remove the halide ion from further equilibration reactions. The net reaction of an alkyl halide with silver oxide is generally written as follows:

$$2\,RX + Ag_2O + H_2O \longrightarrow 2\,ROH + 2\,AgX\downarrow$$

However, since these reactions often involve carbocation intermediates, other reactions such as rearrangements and eliminations frequently occur. Because of these reaction possibilities and the high cost of the reagent, the reaction of silver oxide with alkyl halides has little preparative significance and is used mainly to study the properties of carbocation intermediates.

518

These observations are explained by the formation of an intermediate cation in which the positive charge is delocalized over two carbons.

$$CH_3CH=CHCH_2\overset{+}{O}H_2$$

$$\begin{array}{c} +OH_2 \\ | \\ CH_3\overset{}{C}HCH=CH_2 \end{array}$$

$$\xrightarrow{-H_2O} [CH_3CH=CH\overset{+}{C}H_2 \longleftrightarrow CH_3\overset{+}{C}HCH=CH_2] \xrightarrow{Br^-}$$

$$CH_3CH=CHCH_2Br + CH_3\overset{Br}{\underset{|}{C}}HCH=CH_2$$

$$(CH_3)_2C=CHCH_2Cl$$

$$\begin{array}{c} Cl \\ | \\ (CH_3)_2\overset{}{C}CH=CH_2 \end{array}$$

$$\xrightarrow{-Cl^-} [(CH_3)_2C=CH\overset{+}{C}H_2 \longleftrightarrow (CH_3)_2\overset{+}{C}CH=CH_2] \xrightarrow{H_2O}$$

$$(CH_3)_2C=CHCH_2\overset{+}{O}H_2 + (CH_3)_2\overset{\overset{+}{O}H_2}{\underset{|}{C}}CH=CH_2$$

The intermediate carbocations in the foregoing reactions are described as resonance hybrids of two important structures. The simplest such cation is the 2-propen-1-yl or **allyl cation**.

$$[CH_2=CH-\overset{+}{C}H_2 \longleftrightarrow \overset{+}{C}H_2-CH=CH_2] \equiv \overset{\frac{1}{2}+}{CH_2}\cdots CH\cdots\overset{\frac{1}{2}+}{CH_2}$$

allyl cation

Various symbols may be used to describe the hybrid electronic structure of the allyl cation. The two resonance structures in brackets show that the positive charge in the cation is divided equally between the two indicated positions. The alternative structure with dotted bonds shows that each carbon-carbon bond has an order of $1\frac{1}{2}$ and that each end carbon has $\frac{1}{2}$ of a positive charge.

The grouping $CH_2=CHCH_2-$ is called the **allyl group**, just as CH_3CH_2- is called the ethyl group. The group name is used in naming many compounds containing the allyl group.

$$CH_2=CHCH_2Cl \qquad CH_2=CHCH_2OH \qquad CH_2=CHCH_2O\overset{\overset{O}{\|}}{C}CH_3$$

allyl chloride allyl alcohol allyl acetate

Substituents may be indicated by the use of Greek letters.

$$\underset{\gamma}{CH_2}=\underset{\beta}{CH}\underset{\alpha}{\overset{\overset{CH_3}{|}}{C}HCl} \qquad \overset{CH_3}{\underset{CH_3}{\diagdown}}C\underset{\gamma}{=}\underset{\beta}{CH}\underset{\alpha}{CH_2OH}$$

α-methylallyl chloride γ,γ-dimethylallyl alcohol
3-chloro-1-butene   3-methyl-2-buten-1-ol

One important structural feature of allyl cation is that all of the atoms lie in one plane in such a way that the empty p-orbital of the carbocation can overlap with the π-orbital of the double bond. The electron density in the double bond is shared in the manner indicated by the following symbols.

$$[CH_2=CH-\overset{+}{C}H_2 \longleftrightarrow \overset{+}{C}H_2-CH=CH_2]$$

It is important to recall that resonance structures are used to symbolize alternative configurations of electron density. The geometry of the nuclei remains precisely the same in all resonance structures. The symbol $CH_2{=}CH{-}CH_2^+$ would normally indicate a carbon-carbon double bond having a short distance and a carbon-carbon single bond having a longer distance. However, the alternative structure $^+CH_2{-}CH{=}CH_2$ contributes equally to the actual structure, which may be symbolized by dotted lines as $(CH_2 {\cdots} CH {\cdots} CH_2)^+$. Allyl cation has two equivalent carbon-carbon bonds of equal length. The parent ion has been detected in the gas phase and is inferred as an intermediate in some solution reactions. The structure has not been determined experimentally, but sophisticated quantum mechanical calculations show the carbon-carbon bond length to be in between those for single and double bonds. Similarly, the two terminal carbon atoms share the positive charge equally.

A stereo representation of the planar structure of allyl cation and the corresponding orbital description are shown in Figure 19.1. The two electrons in the π-orbital are in a molecular orbital extending over all three carbon atoms (Section 21.1).

Since the positive charge is spread over a larger volume, we expect allyl cation to be more stable than a simple primary alkyl cation. This expectation is confirmed by a comparison of gas phase enthalpies of ionization of alkyl chlorides.

$$RCl \longrightarrow R^+ + Cl^-$$

R	$\Delta H°$, kcal mole^{-1}
CH_3CH_2Cl	191
$CH_2{=}CHCH_2Cl$	171
$(CH_3)_2CHCl$	166

In fact, *allyl cation is roughly comparable in relative stability to a secondary alkyl cation.* Similarly, methylallyl cation has the positive charge spread between a secondary and primary position, and the net stabilization is comparable to that of a tertiary alkyl cation.

$$[CH_3\overset{+}{C}H{-}CH{=}CH_2 \longleftrightarrow CH_3CH{=}CH{-}\overset{+}{C}H_2] \equiv CH_3\overset{\delta+}{C}H{\cdots}CH{\cdots}\overset{\delta+}{C}H_2$$

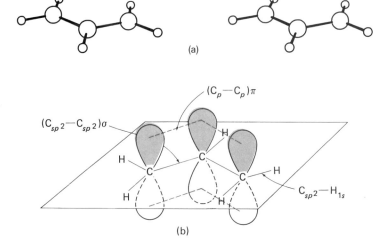

FIGURE 19.1   Allyl cation: (a) stereo structure; (b) orbital description.

When an allylic cation reacts with a nucleophilic reagent, it can react at either positive center and a mixture of products is generally produced. As a result, reactions that proceed by way of allyl cations often appear to give "rearranged" products. Such reactions are called **allylic rearrangements**. For example, in the first reaction we encountered in this chapter, 2-buten-1-ol reacts with HBr to give 1-bromo-2-butene, a "normal" product. However, the reaction also gives 3-bromo-1-butene, a product of allylic rearrangement. Allylic rearrangement can be observed even with the parent system by labeling one carbon with radioactive ^{14}C.

$$CH_2{=}CH^{14}CH_2OH \xrightarrow{SOCl_2} CH_2{=}CH^{14}CH_2Cl + {}^{14}CH_2{=}CHCH_2Cl$$

(ratio depends on reaction conditions)

EXERCISE 19.1 Write the structures for all of the isomeric products expected from the reaction of (R)-2-chloro-(E)-3-hexene with silver oxide in aqueous dioxane at 25°C.

B. S$_N$2 Reactions

In addition to forming carbocations relatively easily, allylic halides and alcohols also undergo substitution by the S$_N$2 mechanism more readily than analogous saturated systems. For example, allyl bromide undergoes bimolecular substitution about 40 times more rapidly than does ethyl bromide. This enhanced reactivity results from stabilization of the transition state for substitution by the double bond with consequent lowering of the activation energy for the reaction (Figure 19.2). Recall (Figure 9.3) that the S$_N$2 transition state can be viewed as a *p*-orbital on the central carbon that simultaneously overlaps with orbitals from the entering and leaving nucleophiles. In an allylic system this *p*-orbital also participates in π-overlap with the adjacent double bond. Thus, even though allylic systems are prone to react by the S$_N$1 mechanism because they form carbocations easily, it is possible by a careful choice of reaction conditions to cause them to react without allylic rearrangement by way of the S$_N$2 mechanism.

$$CH_3CH{=}CHCH_2OH \xrightarrow[\text{pyridine}]{C_6H_5SO_2Cl} CH_3CH{=}CHCH_2OSO_2C_6H_5 \xrightarrow{Cl^-} CH_3CH{=}CHCH_2Cl$$

but-2-en-1-ol   1-chloro-2-butene

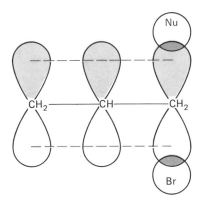

FIGURE 19.2 Transition state of an S$_N$2 reaction of allyl bromide with a nucleophile, Nu, showing interaction of the reacting center with the double bond.

In the foregoing example, the allylic hydroxy group is first converted into a good leaving group by reaction with benzenesulfonyl chloride in pyridine (page 205). This leaving group is then displaced by treatment with sodium chloride. Since substitution occurs by the S_N2 mechanism, only 1-chloro-2-butene is obtained. If substitution is accomplished by treatment of the alcohol with HCl, a mixture of 1-chloro-2-butene and 3-chloro-1-butene is obtained, analogously to the reaction with HBr shown on page 518.

The reactivity of allylic compounds in displacement reactions is sufficiently high that they even react with Grignard reagents.

$$CH_2\text{=}CHCH_2Br + \langle\text{cyclopentyl}\rangle\text{—}MgBr \longrightarrow \langle\text{cyclopentyl}\rangle\text{—}CH_2CH\text{=}CH_2 + MgBr_2$$

(70%)

> Cyclopentylmagnesium bromide is prepared from 745 g of bromocyclopentane and 125 g of magnesium in 3 L of anhydrous ether. The mixture is refluxed while 605 g of allyl bromide is added slowly. After 2 hr, cold 6N HCl is added and the ether layer is separated, washed, dried, and distilled to obtain 70% of allylcyclopentane, b.p. 121-125°C.

The reaction of Grignard reagents with allyl bromide is a good method for preparing 1-alkenes. The corresponding reaction with normal saturated alkyl halides does not occur.

> **EXERCISE 19.2** Show how 4,4-dimethyl-1-pentene and 4-methyl-1-hexene can be synthesized from allyl chloride.

C. Allylic Anions

The allyl Grignard reagent may be prepared by treating an allyl halide with magnesium.

$$CH_2\text{=}CHCH_2X + Mg \xrightarrow{\text{ether}} CH_2\text{=}CHCH_2MgX$$

However, since allyl halides react with Grignard reagents to give 1-alkenes, care must be taken in preparing the allyl Grignard reagent. If the allyl halide concentration is too great, a large amount of the coupling product, 1,5-hexadiene or "biallyl," is formed.

$$CH_2\text{=}CHCH_2MgX + CH_2\text{=}CHCH_2X \longrightarrow CH_2\text{=}CHCH_2CH_2CH\text{=}CH_2 + MgX_2$$

1,5-hexadiene
biallyl

The allyl Grignard reagent can be prepared in good yield by minimizing the further S_N2 reaction of the Grignard reagent with allyl halide. This result may be accomplished by slow addition of a dilute solution of the allyl halide in ether to a large excess of a vigorously stirred suspension of magnesium. This technique is an example of the **dilution principle**. The rate of reaction of an alkyl halide with magnesium depends on the concentration of the alkyl halide and the surface area of the magnesium.

$$\text{rate}_1 = k_1[CH_2\text{=}CHCH_2X][\text{Mg surface}]$$

The rate of the displacement step depends on the concentrations of allyl halide and Grignard reagent.

$$\text{rate}_2 = k_2[\text{CH}_2\text{=}\text{CHCH}_2\text{X}][\text{CH}_2\text{=}\text{CHCH}_2\text{MgX}]$$

When the solution is diluted, the concentrations of the allyl halide and the Grignard reagent decrease, but the surface area of the magnesium remains unchanged. Dilution retards both reactions, but it slows the second reaction more than the first.

Isomeric allylic halides give Grignard reagents with indistinguishable properties. For example, the Grignard reagents derived from 3-bromo-1-butene and 1-bromo-2-butene give an identical mixture of alkenes upon hydrolysis.

$$\text{CH}_3\text{CHBrCH}\text{=}\text{CH}_2 \xrightarrow{\text{Mg}} \text{C}_4\text{H}_7\text{MgBr} \xleftarrow{\text{Mg}} \text{CH}_3\text{CH}\text{=}\text{CHCH}_2\text{Br}$$

$$\downarrow \text{aq H}^+$$

$$\text{CH}_3\text{CH}_2\text{CH}\text{=}\text{CH}_2 + \text{CH}_3\text{CH}\text{=}\text{CHCH}_3$$

$$(57\%) \qquad\qquad (27\% \text{ cis})$$
$$(16\% \text{ trans})$$

This result is understood in terms of rapid isomerization of the allylic Grignard reagent.

$$\text{CH}_3\text{CH}\text{=}\text{CHCH}_2\text{MgBr} \underset{\text{fast}}{\rightleftharpoons} \text{CH}_3\underset{|}{\text{C}}\text{HCH}\text{=}\text{CH}_2$$
$$\text{MgBr}$$

Although Grignard reagents apparently have substantial carbon-magnesium covalent bonding, we have seen that in many reactions they behave as carbanion salts,

$$[\text{R}\text{—}\text{MgX} \longleftrightarrow \bar{\text{R}} \quad \overset{+}{\text{M}}\text{gX}]$$

Similarly, allylic Grignard reagents have a high degree of ionic character involving the magnesium cation salt of an allylic anion.

$$[\text{CH}_2\text{=}\text{CH}\text{—}\text{CH}_2\text{—}\text{MgX} \longleftrightarrow \text{CH}_2\text{=}\text{CH}\text{—}\bar{\text{C}}\text{H}_2 \overset{+}{\text{M}}\text{gX} \longleftrightarrow {}^-\text{CH}_2\text{—}\text{CH}\text{=}\text{CH}_2 \overset{+}{\text{M}}\text{gX}]$$

The negative charge is spread between two **conjugated carbons**. *A conjugated system is one having alternating single and double bonds.* This spreading of ionic character facilitates rearrangement of the magnesium. To summarize, there are two isomeric allylic Grignard reagents derived from 1-bromo-2-butene and 3-bromo-1-butene. The two isomers are in *rapid equilibrium* by allylic rearrangement of the magnesium. In the reaction of either isomer with an acid, protonation may occur at either of the carbons where there is negative charge. The net result on hydrolysis is that a mixture of product alkenes, in the present case 1-butene and 2-butene, is produced.

EXERCISE 19.3 What products are expected from treatment of 3-chloro-1-pentene with magnesium in ether followed by carbon dioxide, and then dilute sulfuric acid?

The spreading of charge in an allylic anion is a stabilizing mechanism; such anions are more stable than simple unconjugated anions. The allylic hydrogen of propene, for example, is substantially more acidic than any hydrogen in ethane or propane.

$$\text{CH}_2\text{=}\text{CHCH}_3 + \text{B}:^- \longrightarrow \text{BH} + [\text{CH}_2\text{=}\text{CH}\text{—}\overset{..}{\text{C}}\text{H}_2 \longleftrightarrow \overset{..}{\text{C}}\text{H}_2\text{—}\text{CH}\text{=}\text{CH}_2]$$
$$\text{more acidic} \qquad\qquad\qquad\qquad \text{delocalized allyl anion}$$

$$\text{CH}_3\text{CH}_3 + \text{B}:^- \longrightarrow \text{BH} + \text{CH}_3\overset{..}{\text{C}}\text{H}_2$$
$$\text{less} \qquad\qquad\qquad \text{localized}$$
$$\text{acidic} \qquad\qquad\qquad \text{ethyl anion}$$

We have encountered similar kinds of conjugated or resonance-stabilized anions be-fore: carboxylate ion (Section 17.4.A), enolate ion (Section 14.6.B), amidate ion (Section 18.10), even nitrite ion (Section 9.4.D).

$$\left[\overset{..}{O}=\overset{|}{C}-\overset{..}{\overset{..}{O}} \longleftrightarrow \overset{..}{\overset{..}{O}}-\overset{|}{C}=O \right] \qquad \left[R_2\overset{..}{C}-\overset{|}{C}=O \longleftrightarrow R_2C=\overset{|}{C}-O^- \right]$$
$$\qquad\qquad R \qquad\qquad R \qquad\qquad\qquad R \qquad\qquad\qquad R$$

carboxylate ion   enolate ion

$$\left[\begin{array}{cc} O & O^- \\ \| & | \\ R-C-NH^- \longleftrightarrow & R-C=NH \end{array} \right] \qquad [O=N-O^- \longleftrightarrow {}^-O-N=O]$$

amidate ion   nitrite ion

All such ions are described in the same way. The resonance structures provide a way of representing a rather complex electronic distribution by means of the formal symbol-ism of Lewis structures. The actual structure is a composite of the resonance structures.

The mathematics of linear combinations is especially useful for describing this situation. In this approach, the wave function of a molecule Ψ is represented as a linear combination of simpler wave functions ψ.

$$\Psi = a\psi_a + b\psi_b + c\psi_c + \cdots$$

For many molecules a single structure provides a satisfactory representation. For exam-ple, methane is well represented by a single Lewis structure ψ_a, and

$$\Psi = \psi_a$$

Other possible Lewis structures, such as

$$\psi_b = \overset{\displaystyle H}{\underset{\displaystyle H}{H-\overset{|}{\underset{|}{C}}:{}^-H^+}}$$

are so unlikely that their contribution to the linear combination is negligible; that is, b for methane is a very small number.

In allyl cation and anion, carboxylate ion, and nitrite ion, the two resonance structures are equivalent and must have equal coefficients in the linear combination

$$\Psi(CH_2\text{---}CH\text{---}CH_2)^+ = a\psi_a(CH_2=CH-\overset{+}{C}H_2) + b\psi_b(\overset{+}{C}H_2-CH=CH_2)$$

where $a = b$.

In enolate ions the two structures are not equivalent. The structure with negative charge on the electronegative oxygen is more stable than that with the charge on carbon. Hence, these two structures enter into the linear combination with unequal coefficients.

$$\Psi(CH_2\text{---}CH\text{---}O)^- = a\psi_a(CH_2=CH-O^-) + b\psi_b(\overset{-}{C}H_2-CH=O)$$

where $a > b$. We say that ψ_a contributes more than ψ_b; hence, the amount of negative charge on oxygen in Ψ, the resonance hybrid, is greater than that on carbon.

Resonance structures whose coefficients are very small contribute so little to the actual structure of the resonance hybrid that their contribution is generally neglected. It is this important property that allows us to represent even complex organic molecules by what is really a rather simple symbolism.

We have already encountered a number of neutral functions that have electronic structures closely related to that of allyl anion. In all such systems a lone pair of electrons is conjugated with a multiple bond.

$$\left[R-\overset{\overset{\displaystyle :O:}{\|}}{C}-\overset{\cdot\cdot}{\underset{\cdot\cdot}{O}}H \longleftrightarrow R-\overset{\overset{\displaystyle :\overset{\cdot\cdot}{O}:^-}{\|}}{C}=\overset{+}{\underset{\cdot\cdot}{O}}H \right] \quad \left[R-\overset{\overset{\displaystyle :O:}{\|}}{C}-\overset{\cdot\cdot}{N}H_2 \longleftrightarrow R-\overset{\overset{\displaystyle :\overset{\cdot\cdot}{O}:^-}{\|}}{C}=\overset{+}{N}H_2 \right]$$

carboxylic acid   amide

These cases involve nonequivalent resonance structures. The dipolar structures involve charge separation and are generally less stable than the normal Lewis structures. Hence the dipolar structures generally contribute less to the overall resonance hybrids. But they do contribute, and we have seen (Section 18.1) how consideration of such structures is essential to the understanding of the chemistry of such functional groups; the normal Lewis structures alone provide an inadequate description of the actual electronic structures of such groups.

EXERCISE 19.4 Amidines are to amides as imines are to ketones:

$$R-C\overset{\displaystyle \nearrow NH}{\underset{\displaystyle \searrow NH_2}{}}$$

an amidine

Write the equation for reaction of an amidine with a proton. Compare the basicity of amidines and amides.

D. Allylic Radicals

Allylic radicals are also stabilized by resonance.

$$[CH_2=CH-\overset{\displaystyle \cdot}{C}H_2 \longleftrightarrow \overset{\displaystyle \cdot}{C}H_2-CH=CH_2]$$

The odd-electron character is shared by two carbons, and this radical is more stable than a simple alkyl radical. This increased stability is reflected in the relatively low bond-dissociation energy of bonds conjugated to a double bond.

$DH°$, *kcal mole*$^{-1}$

CH_3CH_2-H	98
$CH_2=CHCH_2-H$	87

Advantage can be taken of the low bond-dissociation energy of allylic carbon-hydrogen bonds in free radical halogenation—but only under special circumstances because of the alternative reaction path of addition to the double bond. One method for accomplishing **allylic bromination** is with the reagent N-bromosuccinimide. This material is available commercially and is prepared by bromination of the cyclic imide of succinic acid (Section 27.6.C).

N-bromosuccinimide   succinimide

The reaction is normally carried out in carbon tetrachloride, in which both the reactant

N-bromosuccinimide and the product succinimide are insoluble. Reaction occurs in part on the surface of the N-bromosuccinimide, although the active reagent appears to be bromine formed in dilute solution from the reaction of traces of acid and moisture with the bromo imide.

The bromine is then involved in free radical chain bromination of the allylic hydrogen. Under these conditions of high dilution no significant addition of bromine to the double bond occurs.

One of the reasons for using a nonpolar solvent such as CCl_4 in this reaction is that the normal addition of Br_2 to a double bond is an ionic reaction.

In the absence of a suitable solvent to solvate these ions, one or more excess bromine molecules are required for this role.

Thus the reaction kinetics has a relatively high order in bromine and the ionic addition has a low reaction rate when bromine is kept in low concentration.

A free radical initiator or light is often used to promote the reaction. Because the reaction intermediate is a resonance-stabilized radical, two products can be obtained in unsymmetrical cases.

$$[R\dot{C}H\text{—}CH\text{=}CHR' \longleftrightarrow RCH\text{=}CH\text{—}\dot{C}HR'] \xrightarrow{Br_2} R\overset{\overset{\displaystyle Br}{|}}{C}H\text{—}CH\text{=}CHR' + RCH\text{=}CH\text{—}\overset{\overset{\displaystyle Br}{|}}{C}HR'$$

Allyl chloride is prepared commercially in large quantity by the direct free radical chlorination of propylene at high temperature. At higher temperatures the normal addition of chlorine atom to the double bond becomes unfavorable for entropic reasons, and hydrogen abstraction is the principal reaction. In the addition reaction two species become one and freedom of motion is lost, whereas the entropy change in hydrogen abstraction is small. Entropy considerations are especially important at high temperatures.

$$CH_3CH\text{=}CH_2 + Cl_2 \xrightarrow{500°C} ClCH_2CH\text{=}CH_2 + HCl$$

$$Cl_2 \rightleftharpoons 2\,Cl\cdot$$

$$CH_2\text{=}CHCH_3 + Cl\cdot \longrightarrow HCl + CH_2\text{=}CH\dot{C}H_2$$

$$CH_2\text{=}CH\dot{C}H_2 + Cl_2 \longrightarrow Cl\cdot + CH_2\text{=}CHCH_2Cl$$

Allyl alcohol is prepared from the chloride by hydrolysis.

EXERCISE 19.5 Consider two reactions A and B having $\Delta\Delta H^{\ddagger} = 10$ kcal mole^{-1} and $\Delta\Delta S^{\ddagger} = 20$ e.u. Calculate the relative rate constants, k_A/k_B, at 300 K and at 700 K. What is the relevance of this exercise to the reactions discussed in this section?

19.2 Dienes

A. Structure and Stability

Double bonds separated by one or more carbon atoms react more or less independently. The heats of hydrogenation of such double bonds are essentially those of independent units. For example, $\Delta H°$ for the reaction of 1,5-hexadiene with hydrogen is exothermic by 60 kcal mole^{-1}, exactly twice that for the reaction of 1-hexene with hydrogen. (Recall that the heat of hydrogenation of an alkene is $\Delta H°$ for the reaction alkene + H$_2$ → alkane.)

$$CH_2\!\!=\!\!CHCH_2CH_2CH\!\!=\!\!CH_2 + 2\,H_2 \longrightarrow$$
$$CH_3CH_2CH_2CH_2CH_2CH_3 \qquad \Delta H°_{hydrog} = -60\,\text{kcal mole}^{-1}$$
$$CH_3CH_2CH_2CH_2CH\!\!=\!\!CH_2 + H_2 \longrightarrow$$
$$CH_3CH_2CH_2CH_2CH_2CH_3 \qquad \Delta H°_{hydrog} = -30\,\text{kcal mole}^{-1}$$

Heats of hydrogenation for other alkenes and dienes are included in Table 19.1.

Note that 1,3-butadiene is a significant exception to the preceding generalization. Its hydrogenation is about 4 kcal mole^{-1} less exothermic than for the other two dienes. This compound is an example of a **conjugated diene**, a diene in which the two double bonds are separated by a single bond. Dienes in which two or more single bonds separate the double bonds are called **unconjugated dienes**. The double bonds in unconjugated dienes are called **isolated double bonds**.

Conjugated dienes are significantly more stable than would be expected for a compound with completely independent double bonds. This relatively small but significant difference is attributed to two factors, which are shown in Figure 19.3. First, the two double-bond distances are essentially normal, but the C-2—C-3 single bond is shorter than the 1.54 Å distance normally associated with carbon-carbon single bonds.

$$CH_2 \overset{1.34\,\text{Å}}{=\!\!=\!\!=} CH \overset{1.48\,\text{Å}}{\rule{1cm}{0.4pt}} CH =\!\!=\!\!= CH_2$$

This decreased bond length results in part from the increased s-character of the carbon orbitals comprising this bond; the single bond between the double bonds may be described approximately as C_{sp^2}—C_{sp^2}. This shorter bond is somewhat stronger than

TABLE 19.1 Heats of Hydrogenation

	$\Delta H°_{hydrog}$, kcal mole^{-1}
$CH_3CH_2CH\!\!=\!\!CH_2$	-30.2
$CH_3CH_2CH_2CH\!\!=\!\!CH_2$	-29.8
$CH_3CH_2CH_2CH_2CH\!\!=\!\!CH_2$	-30.0
$CH_2\!\!=\!\!CH\!\!-\!\!CH\!\!=\!\!CH_2$	-56.5
$CH_2\!\!=\!\!CHCH_2CH\!\!=\!\!CH_2$	-60.4
$CH_2\!\!=\!\!CHCH_2CH_2CH\!\!=\!\!CH_2$	-60.0

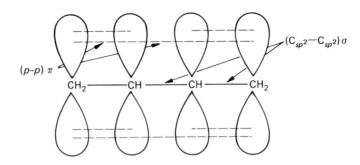

FIGURE 19.3 Structure of 1,3-butadiene.

carbon-carbon bonds having less *s*-character. Second, the p_z-orbitals on C-2 and C-3 can also overlap to give some double-bond character to the C-2,C-3 single bond. This factor also contributes some additional stability to the conjugated double-bond system. However, this overlap is much less than those between C-1 and C-2 and between C-3 and C-4 carbons because of the greater distance between the C-2 and C-3 *p*-orbitals.

B. Addition Reactions

The conjugated character of 1,3-dienes is shown in two-step addition reactions. Such additions are almost invariably initiated at the end of a chain of conjugation to produce a resonance-stabilized allylic intermediate rather than a nonconjugated intermediate.

$$CH_2=CH-CH=CH_2 + HBr \nrightarrow \overset{+}{C}H_2-\underset{\underset{H}{|}}{C}H-CH=CH_2$$

$$\left[\underset{\underset{H}{|}}{C}H_2-\overset{+}{C}H-CH=CH_2 \longleftrightarrow \underset{\underset{H}{|}}{C}H_2-CH=CH-\overset{+}{C}H_2 \right] + Br^-$$

This intermediate reacts in a second step to give a mixture of products characteristic of the intermediate allylic system.

$$[CH_3\overset{+}{C}H-CH=CH_2 \longleftrightarrow CH_3CH=CH-\overset{+}{C}H_2] + Br^- \longrightarrow$$

$$\underset{\underset{Br}{|}}{C}H_3CHCH=CH_2 + CH_3CH=CHCH_2Br$$

(80%)   (20%)

α-methylallyl   crotyl bromide

bromide

A further example is seen in the addition of bromine to 1,3-butadiene.

$$CH_2=CH-CH=CH_2 + Br_2 \xrightarrow[-15°C]{\text{hexane}} \left[\begin{array}{c} CH_2=CH-\overset{+}{C}HCH_2Br \\ \updownarrow \\ \overset{+}{C}H_2-CH=CHCH_2Br \end{array} \right] Br^- \longrightarrow$$

$$BrCH_2CH=CHCH_2Br + CH_2=CHCHBrCH_2Br$$

54%   46%

In this case, the allylic carbocation is sufficiently stabilized that the effect of a cyclic bromonium ion is minimized (see Section 11.6.B).

When the mixture of dibromides in the foregoing example is warmed to 60°C, the composition changes to 90% (E)-1,4-dibromo-2-butene and 10% 3,4-dibromo-1-butene. The major isomer of this mixture is easy to isolate in a pure state because it is a solid, m.p. 54°C, and crystallizes readily.

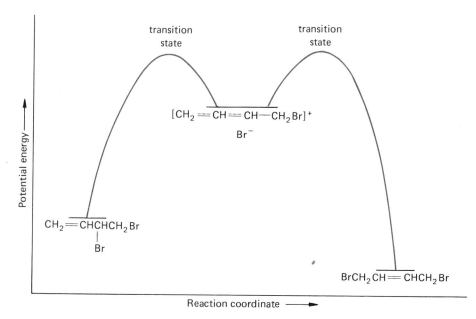

Thus, (E)-1,4-dibromo-2-butene is the most stable product, but it is formed at a rate comparable to the rate of formation of the other isomer.

This example illustrates an important concept in organic chemistry, **kinetic versus thermodynamic control**. In the addition reaction, the product composition is determined by the relative rates of reaction of the nucleophilic reagent at the two positions of positive charge. These relative reactivities need not, and generally do not, reflect the relative thermodynamic stabilities of the products. In the present case, the reaction of the intermediate carbocation with bromide ion occurs approximately equally at both cationic centers; the reaction shows little selectivity. However, 1,4-dibromo-2-butene has a disubstituted double bond and is somewhat more stable than 3,4-dibromo-1-butene, which has a monosubstituted double bond (Section 11.4). Under conditions where the dibromides can react further to reform the carbocation, the more stable isomer predominates. Such a process provides a mechanism for establishing equilibrium.

The situation is illustrated in Figure 19.4. The two alternative transition states derived from the intermediate carbocation have comparable energies and give the alternative products at approximately equal rates. Actually, the rate of formation of 3,4-dibromo-1-butene, which involves reaction at the more positive secondary carbocation, is a little faster than the formation of the 1,4-dibromo isomer. However, the

FIGURE 19.4 Kinetic and thermodynamic effects in the formation of dibromobutenes.

1,4-isomer is the more stable; it reforms the carbocation less readily than the 3,4-isomer. Hence, at equilibrium, some of the 3,4-isomer is converted to 1,4-isomer, and the latter predominates.

The contrast between kinetic and thermodynamic control is important and will be encountered from time to time in our further study of organic chemistry. Another example is found in the reaction products of butadiene with hydrogen bromide. 3-Bromo-1-butene (α-methylallyl bromide) is the dominant product of the addition reaction. However, the equilibrium mixture consists of only 15% of α-methylallyl bromide and 85% of 1-bromo-2-butene (crotyl bromide). Once again, equilibrium favors the more highly substituted double bond. On prolonged reaction or treatment with strong Lewis acids such as ferric bromide, the equilibrium mixture is produced (Figure 19.5).

> **EXERCISE 19.6** The reaction of 1,3-butadiene with aqueous bromine is expected to afford three isomeric bromobutenols (see page 258). Give the structures of these three products and predict the principal product of the reaction of each isomer with sodium hydroxide (page 268).

C. 1,2-Dienes: Allenes

1,2-Propadiene, $CH_2\!=\!C\!=\!CH_2$, has the trivial name "allene". Both double bonds in this hydrocarbon are especially short; the bond distance of 1.31 Å is between those for the double bond in ethylene, 1.34 Å, and the triple bond in acetylene, 1.20 Å. The electronic structure can be represented in terms of two double-bond systems at right angles as in Figure 19.6. Note that the central carbon is sp-hybridized. The additional s-character in these carbon-carbon double bonds accounts for the rather short length.

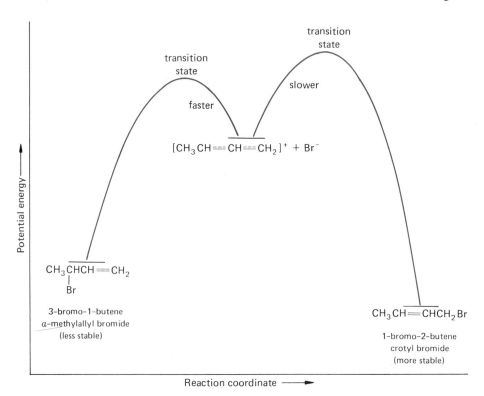

FIGURE 19.5 Kinetic and thermodynamic effects in the formation of bromobutenes.

FIGURE 19.6 Orbital structure of allene.

One especially interesting feature of allenes, which results from the nonplanar character of the molecule, is that suitably substituted allenes are chiral and can be obtained as optically active enantiomers. For example, 2,3-pentadiene has no plane of symmetry. Its mirror images are not superimposable, and this hydrocarbon is capable of existence as a pair of enantiomers.

mirror images of penta-2,3-diene

A stereo representation of such an allene is given in Figure 19.7.

Chiral allenes are examples of compounds that are chiral not because they have a stereocenter, but because they have a **stereoaxis**. The two enantiomers of such a chiral allene may be named using a straightforward extension of the R,S convention (Section 7.3). To make such an assignment, the molecule is viewed along the stereoaxis. The two substituents on the nearer carbon are given priorities of 1 and 2, according to the sequence rule. The two substituents on the farther carbon are given priorities of 3 and 4, on the same basis. The four ranked substituents, 1, 2, 3, and 4, describe the four corners of a distorted tetrahedron. The 1,2,3 face of this tetrahedron is viewed, with apex 4 to the rear. If the arc 1,2,3 is clockwise, the molecule has the R configuration; if it is counterclockwise, the configuration is S.

(S)-2,3-pentadiene

EXERCISE 19.7 In applying the foregoing procedure, it does not matter from which direction the stereoaxis is viewed. Make a model of (S)-2,3-pentadiene and convince yourself that this is true. Make a model of one of the stereoisomers of 1-chloro-1,2-butadiene. Which enantiomer have you prepared?

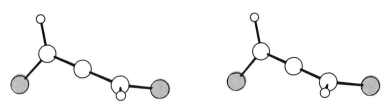

FIGURE 19.7   Stereo representation of a 1,3-disubstituted allene.

Molecules with **cumulated** double bonds, double bonds on successive carbon atoms as in allene, do not constitute an important class of compounds. They are generally difficult to prepare and can frequently be isomerized to more stable dienes. Allene, for example, with $\Delta H_f^\circ = 45.9$ kcal mole^{-1} is 1.6 kcal mole^{-1} less stable than propyne with $\Delta H_f^\circ = 44.3$ kcal mole^{-1}; 1,2-butadiene (methylallene, $CH_3CH{=}C{=}CH_2$, $\Delta H_f^\circ = 38.3$ kcal mole^{-1}), is slightly more stable than 1-butyne ($\Delta H_f^\circ = 39.5$ kcal mole^{-1}), but is almost 4 kcal mole^{-1} less stable than 2-butyne ($\Delta H_f^\circ = 34.7$ kcal mole^{-1}) and almost 13 kcal mole^{-1} less stable than 1,3-butadiene ($\Delta H_f^\circ = 26.1$ kcal mole^{-1}).

> **EXERCISE 19.8**   Use molecular models to show that 1,3-dichloro-1,2-propadiene is chiral and that 1,4-dichloro-1,2,3-butatriene is not. Which enantiomer of 1,3-dichloro-1,2-propadiene have you constructed?

D. Preparation of Dienes

Many dienes can be prepared in much the same way as monoenes except that two functional groups are involved. Some examples are shown below.

$$(CH_3)_2\overset{\overset{\displaystyle OH}{|}}{C}{-}\overset{\overset{\displaystyle OH}{|}}{C}(CH_3)_2 \xrightarrow[420-470°C]{Al_2O_3} CH_2{=}\overset{\overset{\displaystyle }{|}}{\underset{\underset{\displaystyle CH_3}{|}}{C}}{-}\overset{\overset{\displaystyle }{}}{\underset{\underset{\displaystyle CH_3}{|}}{C}}{=}CH_2$$

(79–85%)

2,3-dimethyl-1,3-butadiene

$$CH_3COOCH_2CH_2CH_2CH_2CH_2OOCCH_3 \xrightarrow{575°C} 2\ CH_3COOH + CH_2{=}CHCH_2CH{=}CH_2$$

(63–71%)

1,4-pentadiene

Many other synthetic methods are known, but most require difunctional compounds (to be studied later) as starting materials.

Allylic halides are useful for preparing both conjugated and unconjugated dienes. Displacement by a vinylmagnesium halide on an allyl halide is another route to 1,4-dienes (see Section 19.1.B).

$$CH_2{=}CHCH_2Cl + CH_2{=}CHMgBr \xrightarrow{ether} CH_2{=}CHCH_2CH{=}CH_2 + MgBrCl$$

The Wittig reaction (Section 14.8.E) with allylphosphoranes gives 1,3-dienes.

$$CH_2=CHCH_2Cl + P(C_6H_5)_3 \longrightarrow CH_2=CHCH_2\overset{+}{P}(C_6H_5)_3 \ Cl^-$$

allyltriphenylphosphonium chloride

$$CH_2=CHCH_2\overset{+}{P}(C_6H_5)_3 \xrightarrow{LiOC_2H_5} [CH_2=CH\overset{-}{C}H\overset{+}{P}(C_6H_5)_3] \xrightarrow{C_6H_5CHO}$$

$$CH_2=CHCH=CHC_6H_5 + (C_6H_5)_3PO$$

1-phenyl-1,3-butadiene

Another use of allylic intermediates is exemplified in one preparation of 2-methyl-1,3-butadiene (isoprene).

$$CH_3COCH_3 + HC\equiv CH \xrightarrow{KOH} \underset{\text{2-methyl-3-butyn-2-ol}}{(CH_3)_2\overset{OH}{\underset{|}{C}}C\equiv CH} \xrightarrow{Pd,\ H_2}$$

$$\underset{\text{2-methyl-3-buten-2-ol}}{(CH_3)_2\underset{|}{\overset{}{C}}CH=CH_2} \xrightarrow[\Delta]{Al_2O_3} \underset{\text{isoprene}}{CH_2=\overset{CH_3}{\underset{|}{C}}-CH=CH_2}$$

(CH$_3$)$_2$CCH=CH$_2$ with OH

EXERCISE 19.9 Show how 3-chlorocyclohexene can be converted into (a) 3-vinylcyclohexene and (b) 3-isopropylidenecyclohexene. Note the nomenclature used to name a compound with an *exocyclic* double bond, a double bond attached to a ring.

3-isopropylidenecyclohexene

19.3 Unsaturated Carbonyl Compounds

A. Unsaturated Aldehydes and Ketones

Compounds having both a carbonyl group and a double bond are known as unsaturated aldehydes or ketones. As with dienes, the two centers of unsaturation can be conjugated or unconjugated and the conjugated isomers are generally more stable.

$$CH_2=CHCH_2CHO \longrightarrow CH_3CH=CHCHO \qquad \Delta H° = -6 \text{ kcal mole}^{-1}$$

unconjugated isomer	conjugated isomer

$$CH_2=CHCH_2CH=CH_2 \longrightarrow CH_3CH=CHCH=CH_2 \qquad \Delta H° = -7 \text{ kcal mole}^{-1}$$

unconjugated isomer	conjugated isomer

The stabilizing effect of conjugation in unsaturated carbonyl compounds is of the same order of magnitude as that in the corresponding dienes. It is explained in the same

FIGURE 19.8 Orbital structure of propenal (acrolein).

manner in terms of the stabilizing effect of the central C_{sp^2}—C_{sp^2} bond and by the overlap of p-orbitals to give π-bonding (Figure 19.8).

Because of the greater stability of the conjugated unsaturated aldehydes and ketones, an isolated double bond will tend to **move into conjugation** if a suitable pathway is available. This migration of double bonds is especially facile for double bonds that are β,γ to the carbonyl group because both acid- and base-catalyzed reactions produce an intermediate conjugated enol.

β,γ-unsaturated isomer (less stable) $\rightleftharpoons$ enol form $\rightleftharpoons$ α,β-unsaturated isomer (more stable)

For example, the methylene hydrogens in 3-butenal (vinylacetaldehyde) are appreciably acidic because they are α to the carbonyl group and give rise to a resonance-stabilized enolate ion. However, in this enolate ion a further resonance structure can be written that shows that negative charge is also spread to the γ-carbon.

$$CH_2=CHCH_2CHO + OH^- \rightleftharpoons H_2O + \begin{bmatrix} CH_2=CH-\overset{..}{C}H-CH=\overset{..}{O} \\ \updownarrow \\ CH_2=CH-CH=CH-\overset{..}{\underset{..}{O}}: \\ \updownarrow \\ \overset{..}{C}H_2-CH=CH-CH=\overset{..}{O} \end{bmatrix}$$

vinylacetaldehyde
3-butenal

This delocalized enolate anion now has three positions that can be protonated by water. Protonation on oxygen gives the enol form, protonation of the α-carbon regenerates vinylacetaldehyde, and protonation at the γ-carbon generates crotonaldehyde.

$$\begin{bmatrix} CH_2=CH-CH=CH-\overset{..}{\underset{..}{O}}:^- \\ \updownarrow \\ CH_2=CH-\overset{..}{C}H-CH=O \\ \updownarrow \\ \overset{..}{C}H_2-CH=CH-CH=O \end{bmatrix} + H_2O \rightleftharpoons \begin{matrix} CH_2=CH-CH=CH-OH \\ \text{enol form} \\ CH_2=CH-CH_2-CH=O \\ \text{vinylacetaldehyde} \\ CH_3-CH=CH-CH=O \\ \text{crotonaldehyde} \end{matrix}$$

All of these compounds are interconverted by base, but at equilibrium the most stable isomer, the conjugated crotonaldehyde, predominates to the extent of greater than 99.9% (Figure 19.9).

One way in which these interconversions can be demonstrated is by deuterium exchange. The enolate ion derived from crotonaldehyde or vinylacetaldehyde can react with D_2O at either of the carbons that bear the negative charge.

$$\begin{bmatrix} {}^-CH_2-CH=CHCHO \\ \updownarrow \\ CH_2=CH-\bar{C}HCHO \end{bmatrix} \xrightarrow{D_2O} \begin{array}{l} CH_2D-CH=CHCHO \\ \\ CH_2=CH-CHDCHO \end{array}$$

Repeated reaction with base to reform the enolate ion and reaction with D_2O eventually produces the tetradeuterio compound $CD_3CH=CDCHO$.

EXERCISE 19.10 What is the structure of the deuterated product formed by base-catalyzed exchange of each of the following unsaturated ketones with excess D_2O?

The acid-catalyzed interconversions involve intermediate enols in exact analogy to the similar reactions of simple aldehydes and ketones (Section 14.6). Rapid and reversible protonation occurs at the carbonyl oxygen to form a hydroxycarbocation, which can lose a proton from carbon to form an enol. This enol is also a diene and can reprotonate at either the α- or the γ-carbon to produce the β,γ- or α,β-unsaturated carbonyl, respectively.

$(CH_2\!\!=\!\!=\!\!=\!\!CH\!\!=\!\!=\!\!=\!\!CH\!\!=\!\!=\!\!=\!\!CH\!\!=\!\!=\!\!=\!\!O)^-$
enolate ion

$CH_2\!\!=\!\!CHCH\!\!=\!\!CHOH$
(enol)

E

$CH_2\!\!=\!\!CHCH_2CHO$
vinylacetaldehyde

$\Delta H° = 6$ kcal mole^{-1}

$CH_3CH\!\!=\!\!CHCHO$
crotonaldehyde

FIGURE 19.9 Some energy relationships of an unsaturated aldehyde.

$$CH_2{=}CH{-}CH_2{-}\overset{\displaystyle O}{\overset{\|}{C}}H \;\overset{H^+}{\rightleftharpoons}\; \left[\begin{array}{c} CH_2{=}CH{-}CH_2{-}\overset{\displaystyle \overset{+}{O}H}{\overset{\|}{C}}H \\ \updownarrow \\ CH_2{=}CH{-}CH_2{-}\overset{\displaystyle OH}{\underset{+}{C}}H \end{array} \right] \;\overset{-H^+}{\rightleftharpoons}\; CH_2{=}CH{-}CH{=}\overset{\displaystyle OH}{C}H \;\overset{H^+}{\rightleftharpoons}$$

a dienol

$$\left[CH_3\overset{+}{C}H{-}CH{=}\overset{\displaystyle OH}{C}H \;\longleftrightarrow\; CH_3CH{=}CH{-}\overset{\displaystyle OH}{\underset{+}{C}}H \;\longleftrightarrow\; CH_3CH{=}CH{-}\overset{\displaystyle \overset{+}{O}H}{\overset{\|}{C}}H \right] \;\overset{-H^+}{\underset{H^+}{\rightleftharpoons}}$$

$$CH_3CH{=}CHCHO$$

α,β-Unsaturated aldehydes and ketones are often obtained by dehydration of the β-hydroxy aldehydes and -ketones that are produced in the aldol addition reaction (Section 14.8.C). Under certain circumstances, the treatment of an aldehyde under basic conditions leads directly to the α,β-unsaturated aldehyde. Such products may also be obtained under acidic conditions. For example, the acid-catalyzed self-reaction of acetone produces 4-methylpent-3-en-2-one, commonly called "mesityl oxide."

$$2\ CH_3COCH_3 \;\overset{H_2SO_4}{\longrightarrow}\; CH_3\overset{\displaystyle CH_3}{\underset{}{C}}{=}CHCOCH_3$$

mesityl oxide
4-methylpent-3-en-2-one

The mechanism of this reaction involves a number of straightforward steps. To start, the enol form of acetone adds to another protonated acetone molecule.

$$(1)\ CH_3\overset{\displaystyle O}{\overset{\|}{C}}CH_3 + H^+ \;\rightleftharpoons\; CH_3\overset{\displaystyle \overset{+}{O}H}{\overset{\|}{C}}CH_3$$

$$(2)\ CH_3{-}\overset{\displaystyle \overset{+}{O}H}{\overset{\|}{C}}CH_3 \;\rightleftharpoons\; H^+ + CH_2{=}\overset{\displaystyle OH}{C}CH_3$$

$$(3)\ CH_3{-}\overset{\displaystyle \overset{+}{O}H}{\underset{\displaystyle CH_3}{C}} + CH_2{=}\overset{\displaystyle \ddot{O}H}{C}CH_3 \;\rightleftharpoons\; CH_3\overset{\displaystyle OH}{\underset{\displaystyle CH_3}{C}}{-}CH_2{-}\overset{\displaystyle \overset{+}{O}H}{\overset{\|}{C}}CH_3$$

The resulting oxonium ion can lose a proton from oxygen to give 4-hydroxy-4-methyl-2-pentanone (page 392) or from carbon to give the enol form, 4-methylpent-2-en-2,4-diol.

$$(4)\ CH_3\overset{\displaystyle OH}{\underset{\displaystyle CH_3}{C}}{-}CH_2{-}\overset{\displaystyle \overset{+}{O}H}{\overset{\|}{C}}CH_3 \;\rightleftharpoons\; CH_3\overset{\displaystyle OH}{\underset{\displaystyle CH_3}{C}}{-}CH_2{-}\overset{\displaystyle O}{\overset{\|}{C}}CH_3 + H^+$$

$$(4')\ CH_3\overset{\displaystyle OH}{\underset{\displaystyle CH_3}{C}}{-}CH_2{-}\overset{\displaystyle \overset{+}{O}H}{\overset{\|}{C}}CH_3 \;\rightleftharpoons\; CH_3\overset{\displaystyle OH}{\underset{\displaystyle CH_3}{C}}{-}CH{=}\overset{\displaystyle OH}{C}CH_3 + H^+$$

The latter species is an enol form of a ketone and is unstable relative to the ketone; it is present in only low concentration. Protonation on the tertiary hydroxy gives an oxonium ion that readily eliminates water to form a new cation. The cation is resonance stabilized with the positive charge spread over oxygen and two carbons. The oxonium ion structure is the more important structure because all atoms have octet configurations.

$$
\text{(5)} \quad \underset{\underset{CH_3}{|}}{\overset{\overset{OH}{|}}{CH_3C}}-CH=\overset{\overset{OH}{|}}{C}CH_3 + H^+ \rightleftharpoons \underset{\underset{CH_3}{|}}{\overset{\overset{+OH_2}{|}}{CH_3C}}-CH=\overset{\overset{OH}{|}}{C}CH_3
$$

$$
\text{(6)} \quad \underset{\underset{CH_3}{|}}{\overset{\overset{+OH_2}{|}}{CH_3C}}-CH=\overset{\overset{OH}{|}}{C}CH_3 \rightleftharpoons
$$

$$
H_2O + \left[\underset{\underset{CH_3}{|}}{\overset{+}{CH_3C}}-CH=\overset{\overset{OH}{|}}{C}CH_3 \longleftrightarrow \underset{\underset{CH_3}{|}}{CH_3C}=CH-\underset{+}{\overset{\overset{OH}{|}}{C}}CH_3 \longleftrightarrow \underset{\underset{CH_3}{|}}{CH_3C}=CH-\overset{\overset{+OH}{|}}{C}CH_3 \right]
$$

Loss of the proton from oxygen gives the product mesityl oxide.

$$
\text{(7)} \quad \underset{\underset{CH_3}{|}}{CH_3C}=CH-\overset{\overset{+OH}{||}}{C}CH_3 \rightleftharpoons \underset{\underset{CH_3}{|}}{CH_3C}=CH-\overset{\overset{O}{||}}{C}CH_3 + H^+
$$

It should be emphasized that in this reaction sequence, simple alkyl cations are not involved. *Every organic cationic intermediate either is an oxonium ion or has an oxonium ion resonance form.*

EXERCISE 19.11 Write a mechanism for the acid-catalyzed reaction of cyclohexanone with itself to give 2-cyclohexylidenecyclohexanone.

2-cyclohexylidenecyclohexanone

Recall from Section 14.8.C that mixed aldol reactions are successful ways of preparing α,β-unsaturated ketones in cases where one carbonyl compound cannot form an enol or enolate (because it has no α-protons) and/or has an especially reactive carbonyl group. These conditions are met by aromatic aldehydes, since the aldehyde function is generally more reactive than a ketone carbonyl and aromatic aldehydes have no α-protons. Reactions of aromatic ketones with aromatic aldehydes generally give good yields of enones, which are usually nicely crystalline substances. Such enones are sometimes referred to as "chalcones."

acetophenone + benzaldehyde → chalcone (benzalacetophenone)

Benzaldehyde (460 g) is added all at once to an ice-cold solution of 520 g of acetophenone and 218 g of NaOH in a mixture of 1960 mL of water and 1225 mL of ethanol. The mixture is stirred for several hours, during which time the product separates as light yellow crystals. Filtration affords 770 g of chalcone, m.p. 55-57°C.

Propenal, CH_2=CHCHO, commonly known as acrolein, is the simplest conjugated unsaturated carbonyl compound. This compound is a liquid, b.p. 53°C, having a powerful, pungent odor. It may be prepared by a special reaction in which the readily available triol, glycerol, is heated with sulfuric acid or potassium acid sulfate.

$$HOCH_2CHOHCH_2OH \xrightarrow[200-230°C]{KHSO_4} CH_2=CHCHO$$

glycerol   acrolein
1,2,3-propanetriol   propenal

Most of us are familiar with the odor of acrolein because a similar dehydration occurs thermally when fats burn or decompose on a hot surface. Recall that fats are esters of glycerol (Section 18.12).

α,β-Unsaturated aldehydes and ketones are also available by oxidation of the corresponding unsaturated alcohols, which in turn are frequently available by Grignard syntheses. The oxidation requires mild conditions in order not to oxidize the double bond. One reagent that is specific for allylic alcohols is a specially active form of manganese dioxide, obtained by treatment of manganese sulfate with base and potassium permanganate.

retinol (vitamin A_1)   (80%) retinal

α,β-Unsaturated aldehydes and ketones undergo many of the reactions expected separately for the double bond and carbonyl functions. The C=O group forms normal derivatives such as oximes, phenylhydrazones, and so on (Section 14.7.C).

$$CH_3CH=CHCCH_3 + H_2NOH \longrightarrow CH_3CH=CHCCH_3$$

an oxime

The aldehyde group is oxidized under mild conditions to a carboxylic acid (Section 14.9.A).

$$CH_2=CHCHO + Ag_2O \longrightarrow CH_2=CHCOOH + 2 Ag$$

Bromine can be added to the double bond (Section 11.6.B)

$$C_6H_5CH{=}CHCOCH_3 + Br_2 \xrightarrow[10\text{--}20°C]{CCl_4} C_6H_5CHBrCHBrCOCH_3$$

$$(52\text{--}57\%)$$

However, some reactions are unique to the conjugated system. Additions may occur to the ends of the conjugated system or to either one of the double bonds, just as in the case of conjugated dienes (Section 19.2.B). Additions that occur to a single double bond are called **1,2-additions** or **normal additions**. Additions that occur to the ends of the conjugated system are called **1,4-additions** or **conjugate additions**.

1,2-additions

$$C{=}C{-}C{=}O + X{-}Y \longrightarrow \overset{\underset{|}{X}\ \overset{\underset{|}{Y}}{}}{C{-}C{-}C{=}O} \quad or \quad \overset{\underset{|}{X}\ \overset{\underset{|}{Y}}{}}{C{=}C{-}C{-}O}$$

1,4-additions

$$C{=}C{-}C{=}O + X{-}Y \longrightarrow \overset{X\qquad Y}{C{-}C{=}C{-}O}$$

Do not be confused by the terms *1,2-addition* and *1,4-addition*. The numbers do not refer to the carbon numbers in any given compound. The terms mean that the addition is to the 1 and 2 positions or the 1 and 4 positions of a conjugated system. For example, the addition of Br_2 to the double bond in pent-3-en-2-one is an example of a 1,2-addition.

$$\underset{5\quad 4\quad\ 3\quad\ \ 2\ 1}{CH_3CH{=}CH{-}\overset{O}{\overset{\|}{C}}CH_3} + Br_2 \longrightarrow CH_3\overset{\overset{Br}{|}}{C}H{-}\overset{\overset{Br}{|}}{C}H{-}\overset{O}{\overset{\|}{C}}CH_3$$

Cyanide ion, which normally adds to the carbonyl bond in aldehydes and ketones (Section 14.8.B), frequently adds instead to a carbon-carbon double bond that is conjugated with a carbonyl group.

$$C_6H_5CH{=}CH{-}\overset{O}{\overset{\|}{C}}C_6H_5 + KCN \xrightarrow{CH_3CO_2H} C_6H_5\overset{\overset{CN}{|}}{C}HCH_2\overset{O}{\overset{\|}{C}}C_6H_5$$

$$(93\text{--}96\%)$$

The reaction appears to be 1,2-addition to the double bond. However, the mechanism actually involves 1,4-addition of HCN to the conjugated system. The initial product of the 1,4-addition is an enol, which isomerizes to the more stable keto form (Section 14.6.A).

$$(1)\ C_6H_5CH{=}CH{-}\overset{O}{\overset{\|}{C}}C_6H_5 + H^+ \rightleftharpoons C_6H_5CH{=}CH{-}\overset{^+OH}{\overset{\|}{C}}C_6H_5$$

$$(2)\ C_6H_5CH{=}CH{-}\overset{^+OH}{\overset{\|}{C}}C_6H_5 + CN^- \rightleftharpoons C_6H_5\overset{\overset{CN}{|}}{C}H{-}CH{=}\overset{\overset{OH}{|}}{C}C_6H_5$$

$$(3)\ C_6H_5\overset{\overset{CN}{|}}{C}H{-}CH{=}\overset{\overset{OH}{|}}{C}C_6H_5 + H^+ \rightleftharpoons C_6H_5\overset{\overset{CN}{|}}{C}H{-}CH_2{-}\overset{^+OH}{\overset{\|}{C}}C_6H_5$$

(4) $\underset{\substack{| \\ \text{CN}}}{C_6H_5CH}-CH_2-\underset{\substack{| \\ {}^+OH}}{\overset{||}{C}C_6H_5} \rightleftharpoons \underset{\substack{| \\ \text{CN}}}{C_6H_5CHCH_2}\underset{\substack{|| \\ O}}{\overset{O}{C}C_6H_5} + H^+$

A particularly effective method for accomplishing the 1,4-addition of HCN to α,β-unsaturated ketones employs triethylaluminum as a catalyst. The procedure gives high yields of the conjugate adduct even when the enone is highly substituted at the β-position.

(85%)

EXERCISE 19.12 Suggest a method for the synthesis of 2,2-dimethyl-4-oxopentanoic acid, starting with acetone.

2,2-dimethyl-4-oxopentanoic acid

Organometallic compounds may add either 1,2 or 1,4. Grignard reagents show variable behavior depending on the structure of the conjugated system. The most important factor in determining whether the addition is 1,2 or 1,4 seems to be steric hindrance. All α,β-unsaturated aldehydes and many α,β-unsaturated ketones undergo normal 1,2-addition to the carbonyl group.

(70%)
trans-4-hexen-3-ol

(80%)
2-methyl-*trans*-3-penten-2-ol

However, other α,β-unsaturated ketones give substantial amounts of the 1,4-adduct as well.

$$C_6H_5CH{=}CH{-}\overset{\overset{\textstyle O}{\|}}{C}CH_3 + C_2H_5MgBr \longrightarrow$$

$$\left\{ C_6H_5CH{=}CH{-}\overset{\overset{\textstyle O^- \, {}^+MgBr}{|}}{\underset{\underset{\textstyle C_2H_5}{|}}{C}}CH_3 \quad + \quad C_6H_5\overset{\overset{\textstyle C_2H_5}{|}}{C}H{-}CH{=}\overset{\overset{\textstyle O^- \, {}^+MgBr}{|}}{C}CH_3 \right\} \xrightarrow{\ H_3O^+\ }$$

$$C_6H_5CH{=}CH{-}\overset{\overset{\textstyle OH}{|}}{\underset{\underset{\textstyle C_2H_5}{|}}{C}}CH_3 \quad + \quad C_6H_5\overset{\overset{\textstyle C_2H_5}{|}}{C}H{-}CH_2{-}\overset{\overset{\textstyle O}{\|}}{C}CH_3$$

(37%)   (57%)

1,2-adduct   1,4-adduct

In some cases the 1,4-adduct is the preponderant product. Conjugate addition is particularly likely in reactions of α,β-unsaturated ketones that have large substituents attached to the C=O group.

$$C_6H_5CH{=}CH\overset{\overset{\textstyle O}{\|}}{C}C_6H_5 \xrightarrow{C_6H_5MgBr} \xrightarrow{H_3O^+} \underset{C_6H_5}{\overset{C_6H_5}{>}}CHCH_2\overset{\overset{\textstyle O}{\|}}{C}C_6H_5$$

(96%)

1,3,3-triphenyl-1-propanone

Organolithium compounds show a much greater tendency to engage in 1,2-addition.

$$C_6H_5CH{=}CH\overset{\overset{\textstyle O}{\|}}{C}C_6H_5 \xrightarrow{C_6H_5Li} \xrightarrow{H_3O^+} C_6H_5CH{=}CH\overset{\overset{\textstyle OH}{|}}{C}(C_6H_5)_2$$

(75%)

When one wants to maximize 1,2-addition, it is customary to utilize the organolithium reagent.

On the other hand, 1,4-addition may be achieved by using lithium dialkylcuprates, which are readily prepared from the corresponding alkyllithium reagent and cuprous iodide (Section 8.8).

$$2\ CH_3Li + CuI \longrightarrow (CH_3)_2CuLi$$

These reagents add to α,β-unsaturated ketones exclusively in a 1,4-fashion.

$$CH_3\overset{\overset{\textstyle CH_3}{|}}{C}{=}CH\overset{\overset{\textstyle O}{\|}}{C}CH_3 + (CH_2{=}CH)_2CuLi \longrightarrow \xrightarrow{H_3O^+} CH_2{=}CH\overset{\overset{\textstyle CH_3}{|}}{\underset{\underset{\textstyle CH_3}{|}}{C}}CH_2\overset{\overset{\textstyle O}{\|}}{C}CH_3$$

(72%)

The same result may often be achieved by forming the dialkylcuprate *in situ* from the corresponding Grignard reagent. In practice, it is only necessary to use a catalytic amount of cuprous bromide or iodide.

(68%)

The mechanism for the 1,4-additions of organometallic reagents to α,β-unsaturated carbonyl compounds is not completely understood, but it may involve initial transfer of an electron from an organometallic species to the conjugated system with the formation of an intermediate radical anion, which undergoes further reactions. Compounds such as the cuprates are effective because Cu^+ is readily oxidized to Cu^{2+}. Organolithium and organomagnesium compounds do not react by this mechanism, since neither metal is easily oxidized to a higher valence state. The 1,4-addition reactions that are observed with Grignard reagents arise from traces of transition metal impurities, such as Cu^+ and Fe^{2+}, which are present in commercially available magnesium. If highly purified magnesium is used to prepare the Grignard reagent, 1,4-addition reactions are not observed.

EXERCISE 19.13 Write equations showing how hept-4-en-3-one can be converted into (a) 3-ethylhept-4-en-3-ol and (b) 5-ethylheptan-3-one.

Reduction of α,β-unsaturated carbonyl compounds can also involve either the carbon-carbon or the carbon-oxygen double bond. Lithium aluminum hydride reduction of most such compounds usually gives high yields of the products of simple carbonyl reduction.

$$CH_3CH{=}CHCHO + LiAlH_4 \xrightarrow{\text{ether}} \xrightarrow{H_2O} CH_3CH{=}CHCH_2OH$$

(82%)

(97%)

In contrast, sodium borohydride in ethanol often gives substantial amounts of the 1,4-addition product.

(59%)   (41%)

The fully reduced product in the preceding example arises from the following pathway, which begins with the conjugate addition of hydride to the enone system.

(1) + BH_4^- $\longrightarrow$ + BH_3

(2) $\xrightarrow{C_2H_5OH}$ + $C_2H_5O^-$

(3) + BH_4^- $\longrightarrow$ + BH_3

(4) + C_2H_5OH $\rightleftharpoons$ + $C_2H_5O^-$

The double bond of such a conjugated system may generally be reduced cleanly by either of two procedures, catalytic hydrogenation or lithium-ammonia reduction.

(100%)

(95%)

The mechanism of the latter reduction is similar to that seen earlier in the reduction of alkynes to alkenes (Section 12.6.A). The first step involves addition of an electron to the conjugated system, giving a resonance-stabilized radical anion. This radical anion protonates on carbon giving a radical, which is reduced by another electron with the formation of an enolate ion.

(1) $\diagup\!\!\!\diagdown C{=}C{-}C{=}O$ + Li $\longrightarrow$ $\left[\begin{array}{c} -\overset{..}{\underset{|}{C}}{-}C{=}C{-}\overset{..}{\underset{..}{O}}\cdot \\ \updownarrow \\ -\underset{|}{C}{-}C{=}C{-}\overset{..}{\underset{..}{O}}{:}^{-} \\ \updownarrow \\ -\underset{|}{C}{=}C{-}\overset{..}{\underset{|}{C}}{-}\overset{..}{\underset{..}{O}}{:} \\ \updownarrow \\ -\underset{|}{C}{=}C{-}\overset{..}{\underset{|}{C}}{-}\overset{..}{\underset{..}{O}}{:}^{-} \end{array}\right]$ + Li^{+}

(2) $\left[\diagup\!\!\!\diagdown C{\cdots}C{\cdots}C{\cdots}O\right]^{\bar{\cdot}}$ + NH$_3$ $\longrightarrow$ $-\overset{H}{\underset{|}{C}}{-}C{=}C{-}\overset{..}{\underset{..}{O}}{:}$ + NH$_2^{-}$

(3) $-\overset{H}{\underset{|}{C}}{-}C{=}C{-}\overset{.}{\underset{..}{O}}{:}$ + Li $\longrightarrow$ $\left[-\overset{H}{\underset{|}{C}}{-}C{=}C{-}\overset{..}{\underset{..}{O}}{:}^{-} \longleftrightarrow -\overset{H}{\underset{|}{C}}{-}\overset{..}{\underset{|}{C}}{-}C{=}O\right]$ + Li^{+}

Under the conditions of the reaction, the enolate ion is stable. Its reduction potential is too high for it to accept another electron and be reduced further, and it is not basic enough to be protonated by such a weak acid as ammonia. Upon aqueous workup, the enolate ion is protonated to give the ketone.

$\left[\diagup\!\!\!\diagdown CH{\cdots}C{\cdots}C{\cdots}O\right]^{-}$ + H$_3$O^{+} $\longrightarrow$ $\diagup\!\!\!\diagdown CH{-}CH{-}C{=}O$ + H$_2$O

The partial reduction of a conjugated enone in this reaction is a particularly impressive example of the special properties of conjugated systems, since isolated carbon-carbon double bonds are not reduced by lithium in ammonia and isolated carbon-oxygen double bonds are reduced by the reagent.

EXERCISE 19.14 Write the equations showing the reaction of 4-methylpent-3-en-2-one with each of the following reagents.
(a) n-C$_4$H$_9$Li   (b) n-C$_4$H$_9$MgBr, CuBr   (c) H$_2$/Pd
(d) Li-NH$_3$ (e) HCN, (C$_2$H$_5$)$_3$Al   (f) Br$_2$-CCl$_4$

B. Unsaturated Carboxylic Acids and Derivatives

Both conjugated and unconjugated unsaturated carboxylic acids and acid derivatives are known. As with other multiply unsaturated systems, conjugation provides added stabilization, but the magnitude of this stabilization is rather small, substantially smaller than for dienes or unsaturated aldehydes and ketones. The heats of formation of isomeric ethyl pentenoates summarized in Table 19.2 demonstrate this point. In other words, the carboxylic function is less effective in conjugation than is a simple carbonyl group.

TABLE 19.2 Heats of Formation of Ethyl Pentenoates

Isomer	ΔH_f°, kcal mole^{-1}
$CH_2=CHCH_2CH_2COOC_2H_5$	-92.1 ± 0.6
$\begin{array}{c} CH_3 \diagdown \qquad \diagup CH_2COOC_2H_5 \\ C=C \\ H \diagup \qquad \diagdown H \end{array}$	-92.6 ± 0.9
$\begin{array}{c} CH_3 \diagdown \qquad \diagup H \\ C=C \\ H \diagup \qquad \diagdown CH_2COOC_2H_5 \end{array}$	-93.2 ± 0.7
$\begin{array}{c} CH_3CH_2 \diagdown \qquad \diagup COOC_2H_5 \\ C=C \\ H \diagup \qquad \diagdown H \end{array}$	-94.3 ± 0.7
$\begin{array}{c} CH_3CH_2 \diagdown \qquad \diagup H \\ C=C \\ H \diagup \qquad \diagdown COOC_2H_5 \end{array}$	-94.2 ± 0.9

One way of rationalizing this behavior is to consider that the carbonyl group in a carboxylic function is already involved in conjugation to an atom with a pair of electrons to donate—such as the oxygen of OH or OR or the nitrogen of NH$_2$. Such a carbonyl group is less able to conjugate with another group. This situation is representative of a **cross-conjugated** system as illustrated by the π-overlap of p-orbitals in Figure 19.10. Much qualitative evidence, as well as theoretical considerations, shows that cross conjugation is less effective than linear conjugation in stabilizing a molecule.

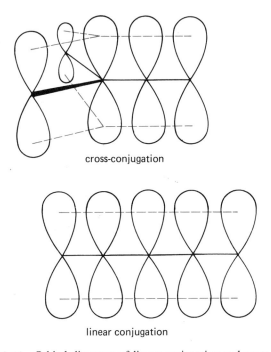

cross-conjugation

linear conjugation

FIGURE 19.10 Orbital diagrams of linear conjugation and cross-conjugation.

As a result of the reduced effectiveness of conjugation in unsaturated acid functions, in some compounds the unconjugated isomer may be the more stable. For example, 4-methylpent-3-enoic acid, with a trisubstituted double bond, is more stable than 4-methylpent-2-enoic acid, which has a conjugated π-system but has only a disubstituted double bond.

$$\underset{\text{4-methylpent-3-enoic acid}}{\overset{\overset{\displaystyle CH_3}{|}}{CH_3C}\!\!=\!\!CHCH_2COOH} \quad\rightleftharpoons\quad \underset{\text{4-methylpent-2-enoic acid}}{\overset{\overset{\displaystyle CH_3}{|}}{CH_3CH}CH\!\!=\!\!CHCOOH}$$

Unsaturated carboxylic acids and their derivatives may be prepared by many of the same routes appropriate for the saturated analogs. One example is the sequence $RX \rightarrow RCOOH$, in which R contains a double bond.

$$CH_2\!\!=\!\!CHCH_2Cl \xrightarrow{\text{CuCN}} CH_2\!\!=\!\!CHCH_2CN \xrightarrow[\Delta]{\text{aq. HCl}} CH_2\!\!=\!\!CHCH_2COOH$$
$$(52\text{–}62\%)$$

allyl chloride

vinylacetic acid
but-3-enoic acid

α,β-Unsaturated acids and derivatives are also available by elimination of HX from α-halo acids and esters.

$$\underset{\text{2-methyldodecanoic acid}}{\overset{\overset{\displaystyle CH_3}{|}}{CH_3(CH_2)_9CH}COOH} \xrightarrow[\text{Br}_2]{\text{PBr}_3} \overset{\overset{\displaystyle CH_3}{|}}{CH_3(CH_2)_9CBrCOBr} \xrightarrow{CH_3OH} \underset{\overset{|}{Br}}{\overset{\overset{\displaystyle CH_3}{|}}{CH_3(CH_2)_9CCOOCH_3}}$$

left branch: $\Big\downarrow \begin{array}{l}(CH_3)_3COK\\(CH_3)_3COH\end{array}$

right branch: $\Big\downarrow \begin{array}{l}\text{quinoline}\\160\text{–}170°C\end{array}$

$$\underset{}{\overset{\overset{\displaystyle CH_2}{\|}}{CH_3(CH_2)_9CCOOC(CH_3)_3}} \qquad \underset{(70\text{–}85\%)}{\overset{\overset{\displaystyle CH_3}{|}}{CH_3(CH_2)_8CH}\!\!=\!\!CCOOCH_3}$$

$\Big\downarrow$ alc KOH $\qquad\qquad\qquad\qquad\qquad\qquad \Big\downarrow$ alc KOH

$\Big\downarrow$ H$^+$ $\qquad\qquad\qquad\qquad\qquad\qquad\qquad \Big\downarrow$ H$^+$

$$\underset{\text{2-decylpropenoic acid}}{\overset{\overset{\displaystyle CH_2}{\|}}{CH_3(CH_2)_9CCOOH}} \qquad \underset{\substack{(68\text{–}83\%)\\ \text{2-methyldodec-2-enoic acid}}}{\overset{\overset{\displaystyle CH_3}{|}}{CH_3(CH_2)_8CH}\!\!=\!\!CCOOH}$$

Note in the foregoing examples that the direction of elimination can sometimes be controlled by the choice of basic reagent used. Although both of these eliminations occur by the E2 mechanism, recall that the bulky reagent potassium *t*-butoxide tends to abstract primary hydrogens (Section 11.5.A).

Aromatic aldehydes may be converted into α,β-unsaturated acids by the **Perkin reaction**, in which the aldehyde is heated with an acid anhydride and the corresponding carboxylate salt. Acetic anhydride and sodium acetate are most commonly used.

$$\xrightarrow[\substack{CH_3COONa\\180°C}]{(CH_3CO)_2O}$$

(72%)
o-chlorocinnamic acid

The reaction is a typical base-catalyzed condensation in which the enolate ion of an acid anhydride is an intermediate.

The Perkin reaction appears to proceed by way of the following interesting mechanism.

(1) $CH_3COCCH_3 + AcO^- \rightleftharpoons {:}CH_2COCCH_3 + AcOH$

(2) $ArCH + {:}CH_2COAc \rightleftharpoons ArCH-CH_2COAc$ (with O^-)

(3) $Ar-CH \rightleftharpoons Ar-CH$

(4) $Ar-CH \rightleftharpoons ArCHCH_2CO_2^-$

(5) $ArCHCH_2CO_2^- + Ac_2O \rightleftharpoons ArCHCH_2COAc + AcO^-$

(6) $ArCHCH_2COAc + AcO^- \rightleftharpoons ArCHCHCOAc + AcOH$

(7) $ArCH-CHCOAc \rightleftharpoons ArCH=CHCOAc + AcO^-$

(8) $ArCH=CHCOAc + AcOH \rightleftharpoons ArCH=CHCOOH + Ac_2O$

The simplest unsaturated carboxylic acid is propenoic acid, $CH_2{=}CHCOOH$, commonly known as acrylic acid, a liquid having b.p. 141.6°C. The corresponding nitrile, $CH_2{=}CHCN$, acrylonitrile, is an important industrial material that is made in large quantity for use in synthetic fibers and polymers; its 1983 production in the United States was 1,073,000 tons. Acrylonitrile is also a liquid, b.p. 78.5°C. It was once prepared industrially by addition of HCN to acetylene.

$$HC{\equiv}CH + HCN \xrightarrow[NH_4Cl]{CuCl} CH_2{=}CHCN$$

It is now prepared by a cheaper process that involves the catalytic oxidation of propene in the presence of ammonia.

$$2\,CH_3CH{=}CH_2 + 3\,O_2 + 2\,NH_3 \xrightarrow[catalyst]{450°C} 2\,CH_2{=}CHCN + 6\,H_2O$$

The methyl ester of α-methylacrylic acid is also an important industrial product. It is prepared from acetone by the following sequence.

$$CH_3COCH_3 + HCN \longrightarrow (CH_3)_2CCN \xrightarrow{H_2SO_4} CH_2{=}CCONH_2 \xrightarrow[H_2SO_4]{CH_3OH} CH_2{=}CCOOCH_3$$

Unsaturated acids and esters are widespread in nature. Ricinoleic acid is a derivative of stearic acid, $CH_3(CH_2)_{16}COOH$, and is obtained from castor oil. Other important unsaturated octadecanoic acids widespread as glyceryl esters in fats are oleic acid, linoleic acid, and linolenic acid (Section 18.12). Linseed oil is an example of a drying oil and contains a high percentage of linolenic acid. On exposure to air, the highly unsaturated chain reacts with oxygen and crosslinks to give a tough transparent polymer. Oil-based paint is a combination of drying oil with suspended pigment. Varnish also contains such drying oils and also involves the formation of a tough waterproof film by oxygen-promoted free radical crosslinking.

B. Ketenes

The compound $CH_2=C=O$ is known as ketene and is the carbonyl analog of allene. It is a toxic gas, b.p. $-48°C$, and is prepared by the pyrolysis of acetone at high temperatures.

$$CH_3COCH_3 \xrightarrow{700°C} CH_4 + CH_2=C=O$$

The reaction mechanism appears to involve free radical chain decomposition.

Substituted ketenes are prepared by treatment of acyl halides with triethylamine or by treatment of α-halo acyl halides with zinc.

(32%)
pentamethyleneketene

(46–54%)
dimethylketene

Ketenes react as "super anhydrides." With water they give carboxylic acids, and with alcohols they give esters. One commercial synthesis of acetic anhydride involves the combination of acetic acid with ketene.

$$CH_3COOH + CH_2=C=O \longrightarrow (CH_3CO)_2O$$

The United States production of acetic anhydride in 1983, mostly by this reaction, was more than 500,000 tons.

The ketene group is extremely reactive and is a relatively unimportant functional group. Like allenes, ketenes have two π-systems at right angles. The two double bonds are cummulated and *not* conjugated (Figure 19.11).

EXERCISE 19.15 In its addition to ketene ethanol probably acts as a base, whereas acetic acid probably adds by an acid-catalyzed mechanism. Write reasonable mechanisms for both processes.

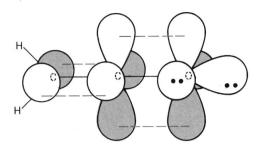

FIGURE 19.11 Orbital structure of ketene.

19.4 Higher Conjugated Systems

Many compounds having more than two conjugated double bonds are known. In such systems each double bond alternates with a single bond to allow extensive π-overlap of *p*-orbitals. One example is *trans*-1,3,5-hexatriene, a liquid, b.p. 79°C.

trans-1,3,5-hexatriene

Another is retinol (vitamin A_1), an alcohol with five conjugated double bonds that we encountered in Section 19.3.A.

Despite the stabilization that such highly conjugated compounds derive from their extensive π-electronic systems, they are generally more reactive, not less reactive, than their nonconjugated isomers. The reason for this apparent paradox is simply that the intermediate radicals or ions are even more stabilized by conjugation. For example, 1,3,5-hexatriene reacts rapidly with acids, bromine, free radicals, and other reagents. The addition of a proton to the terminal carbon atom gives a pentadienyl cation that is highly stabilized by resonance. That is, in this carbocation the positive charge is distributed among three carbons.

$$CH_2{=}CH{-}CH{=}CH{-}CH{=}CH_2 + H^+ \longrightarrow$$

$$
\left[
\begin{array}{c}
CH_2{=}CH{-}CH{=}CH{-}\overset{+}{C}H{-}CH_3 \\
\updownarrow \\
CH_2{=}CH{-}\overset{+}{C}H{-}CH{=}CH{-}CH_3 \\
\updownarrow \\
\overset{+}{C}H_2{-}CH{=}CH{-}CH{=}CH{-}CH_3
\end{array}
\right]
\equiv
\overset{\delta+}{C}H_2{\cdots}CH{\cdots}\overset{\delta+}{C}H{\cdots}CH{\cdots}\overset{\delta+}{C}H{-}CH_3
$$

The resonance stabilization of such carbocation, carbanion, and free radical intermediates and of the transition states leading to them is much greater than the stabilization afforded by π-overlap in the starting polyenes. As a result, such polyenes are highly reactive. Exposure to air or light is often sufficient to initiate free radical chain polymerization.

EXERCISE 19.16 Write the structures of all of the products expected from the addition of 1 mole of bromine to 1,3,5-hexatriene at low temperature. What principal product is expected if this reaction mixture is allowed to stand?

19.5 The Diels-Alder Reaction

Conjugated dienes undergo a **cycloaddition reaction** with certain multiple bonds to form cyclohexenes and related compounds. This reaction, which is an important synthetic method, is called the **Diels-Alder** reaction, after Otto Diels and Kurt Alder, two German chemists who received the 1950 Nobel Prize for its discovery. The simplest Diels-Alder reaction is the reaction of 1,3-butadiene and ethylene to yield cyclohexene.

Although this simple example is known, it is very slow and only occurs under conditions of heat and pressure. However, the Diels-Alder reaction is facilitated by the presence of electron-donating groups on the diene component and by the presence of electron-attracting groups on the monoene component, often referred to as the "dienophile."

diene   dienophile   methyl 4-cyclohexenecarboxylate

The reaction is a particularly versatile method for the preparation of six-membered ring derivatives of varied sorts.

isoprene   methyl vinyl   (70%)   (30%)
          ketone   methyl 4-methyl-   methyl 3-methyl-
                 3-cyclohexenyl   3-cyclohexenyl
                 ketone   ketone

As shown by the foregoing example, many Diels-Alder reactions can give two isomers, depending on the orientation of the diene and the dienophile. The two different orientations are sometimes called head-to-head and head-to-tail.

Head-to-head orientation

(30%)

Head-to-tail orientation

(70%)

In general, the two isomeric products are formed in unequal amounts, as in the present example. A useful way to predict which isomer will predominate is to treat the reaction as though one of the new bonds is stronger at the transition state than the other new bond. We consider the four possible transition states and decide which is the most stable. In the present case, for example

The stars at the ends of the weak bond may be considered to be radicals, but since some electron transfer probably occurs in these reactions they may also be cations and anions— cation at the former diene end and anion at the former dienophile end. Of the four possible transition states, C is the most stable. In a diradical model the most substituted radicals are involved in C; in the charge-transfer model, C involves the most stable allyl cation and conjugated anion.

This method is only an approximate technique for predicting which product will predominate. Actual reaction preferences are often rather weak and steric hindrance effects sometimes offset the electronic effects predicted above.

EXERCISE 19.17 Predict the major product in each of the following Diels-Alder reactions.

$$COOCH_3$$

(a) [diene] + [alkene with COOCH_3 groups]
$$COOCH_3$$

$$OCH_3$$

(b) [diene with OCH_3] + [alkene] CHO

The reaction has wide scope because multiple bonds other than C=C may be used

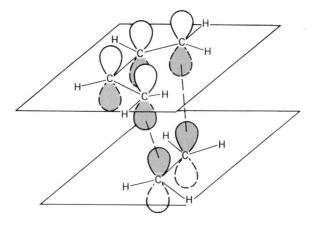

acrolein

diethyl acetylenedicarboxylate → diethyl cyclohexa-1,4-diene-1,2-dicarboxylate

The Diels-Alder reaction is also known as a thermal cycloaddition reaction. The mechanism of the reaction involves σ-overlap of the π-orbitals of the two unsaturated systems, as illustrated in Figure 19.12. The Diels-Alder reaction involves specifically four π-electrons on one system and two on another and is therefore referred to as a [4 + 2] cycloaddition reaction. A remarkable fact is that although such [4 + 2] reactions are common and general, analogous [2 + 2] and [4 + 4] thermal cycloadditions are less common and involve different reaction mechanisms.

FIGURE 19.12 Transition state of a Diels-Alder reaction.

$$\begin{array}{c} CH_2 \\ \| \\ CH_2 \end{array} + \begin{array}{c} CH_2 \\ \| \\ CH_2 \end{array} \xrightarrow[\Delta]{\hspace{0.3cm}//\hspace{0.3cm}} \square$$

2 + 2

4 + 4

The requirement of *six* electrons in the cyclic transition state in Figure 19.12 is now well understood and is closely related to the stability of the benzene ring. Accordingly, this topic is discussed further in the next chapter (Section 20.7).

The transition state of the Diels-Alder reaction depicted in Figure 19.12 has stereochemical consequences. The following examples illustrate that the reaction is a syn addition with respect to both the diene and the dienophile.

When both the diene and dienophile are suitably substituted, a further stereochemical feature arises because the reactants may approach each other in two distinct orientations. The substituent on the dienophile may be directed away from the diene (*exo* approach) or toward the diene (*endo* approach), resulting in two stereoisomeric products.

Exo approach

Endo approach

Diels-Alder reactions often show a preference for *endo* approach, but *endo/exo* ratios depend strongly on reaction conditions (such as temperature and solvent polarity) and on the exact structures of diene and dienophile.

When cyclic dienes are used in the Diels-Alder reaction, bicyclic adducts result. An especially important cyclic diene is cyclopentadiene.

cyclopentadiene   methyl acrylate   methyl bicyclo[2.2.1]-
hept-5-ene-*endo*-2-carboxylate
(79–91%)

Polycyclic compounds are an important group of organic structures. The number of rings (cycles) in such a compound is determined by the minimum number of ring bonds that must be broken to obtain an acyclic compound. For example, in a bicyclic compound, if one of the ring bonds is broken, a monocyclic compound results. If one of the ring bonds of this monocyclic compound is broken, an acyclic product is produced. Bicyclic structures have the following structural features in common.

1. Two bridgehead atoms.
2. Three arms connecting the two bridgehead atoms.

Bicyclic compounds are named as derivatives of the alkane corresponding to the total number of carbons in both ring skeletons. The prefix **bicyclo-**, indicates that the compound has a bicyclic structure. The numbers of carbons in each of the three connecting arms are given in brackets.

bicyclo[2.2.1]heptane   bicyclo[4.4.0]decane   bicyclo[4.1.0]heptane

The resulting compound names are written as all one word, with no spaces or hyphens.

The numbering system used to assign substituents starts at a bridgehead position, proceeds along the *longest* arm to the other bridgehead position, and continues along the next longest arm. The bridgehead position chosen to start the numbering is that which gives the lower substituent number.

7,7-dimethylbicyclo[2.2.1]heptan-2-ol   *trans*-1,6-dichlorobicyclo[4.3.0]nonane

7,7-dicyanobicyclo[4.1.0]hepta-2,4-diene

EXERCISE 19.18 Name the following bicyclic compounds.

(a)   (b)

In many bicyclic structures the stereochemistry at the bridgehead position is established by steric constraints. There is only a single bicyclo[2.2.1]heptane, for example, that in which the methylene bridge is joined cis at the 1,4-positions of a boat cyclohexane. The corresponding compound with a trans attachment is too strained to exist (Figure 19.13). In other systems both cis and trans ring fusions can occur and are specified appropriately in the nomenclature. Some bicyclic systems have a further aspect of stereochemistry that must be noted. For example, the Diels-Alder reaction between cyclopentadiene and methyl acrylate, discussed on page 554, could have given two stereoisomeric products, one in which the methoxycarbonyl group is cis to the two-carbon bridge (called the **endo** isomer) or one in which this group is cis to the one-carbon bridge (called the **exo** isomer). Diels-Alder reactions of cyclopentadiene generally produce the endo isomer as the major product.

methyl bicyclo[2.2.1]-
hept-5-ene-*exo*-2-carboxylate

methyl bicyclo[2.2.1]-
hept-5-ene-*endo*-2-carboxylate

Cyclopentadiene is a low-boiling hydrocarbon, b.p. 46°C, available commercially as a dimer that can be readily cracked thermally. The dimer boils at 170°C. When the free monomer has been prepared by slow distillation of the dimer, it must be used immediately as it re-dimerizes on standing. The dimerization reaction is a Diels-Alder reaction in which one molecule acts as the diene and another takes the role of the dienophile. The endo dimer is produced.

endo addition

dicyclopentadiene

EXERCISE 19.19 Write the equations for the Diels-Alder reactions of cyclopentadiene with (a) vinyl acetate, (b) acrylic acid, and (c) dimethyl acetylenedicarboxylate, $CH_3OOCC{\equiv}CCOOCH_3$. What is the name of each product?

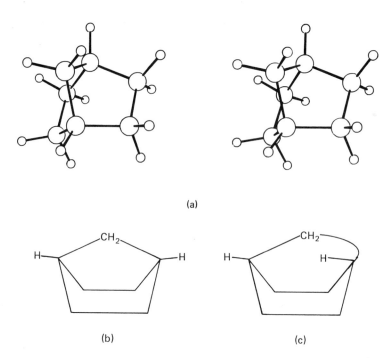

(a)

(b)   (c)

FIGURE 19.13 Bicyclo[2.2.1]heptane (norbornane): *(a)* stereo view; *(b)* conventional perspective drawing; *(c)* hypothetical trans isomer—too strained to exist.

PROBLEMS

1. Draw all of the important resonance structures for each of the following allylic type carbocations.

    (a) CH_2=CH—CH=CH—CH_2^+ ≡

    (b) CH_2=CH—C=CH_2 ≡   with CH_2^+ group

    (c)

2. For each of the following pairs of allylic resonance structures, indicate which contributes more to the resonance hybrid.

    (a) [$^+CH_2$—CH=$CHCH_3$ ⟷ CH_2=CH—$\overset{+}{C}HCH_3$]

    (b) [$CF_3\overset{-}{C}H$—CH=$CHCH_3$ ⟷ CF_3CH=CH—$\overset{-}{C}HCH_3$]

    (c) [$CF_3\overset{+}{C}H$—CH=$CHCH_3$ ⟷ CF_3CH=CH—$\overset{+}{C}HCH_3$]

    (d) [CH_2=CH—O^- ⟷ $^-CH_2$—CH=O]

    (e) $\left[CH_3\overset{\overset{\displaystyle O}{||}}{C}—NH_2 \longleftrightarrow CH_3\overset{\overset{\displaystyle O^-}{|}}{C}=\overset{+}{N}H_2 \right]$

(f) $[CH_2\!=\!CH\!-\!OCH_3 \longleftrightarrow {}^-CH_2\!-\!CH\!=\!\overset{+}{O}CH_3]$

(g)

3. Illustrate the use of allylic halides and Grignard reagents in preparation of the following alkenes.
   (a) $CH_3CH_2CH_2CH\!=\!CH_2$ (b) $C_6H_5CH_2CH\!=\!CH_2$
   (c) $CH_2\!=\!CHCH_2CH\!=\!CH_2$ (d) $(CH_3)_3CCH_2CH\!=\!CH_2$

4. What is the principal product of reaction of each of the following alcohols with activated MnO_2?
   (a) $CH_3CH\!=\!CHCH_2OH$ (b) $CH_3CH_2CH_2CH_2OH$

   (c) $HOCH_2CH_2CH\!=\!CHCH_2OH$ (d)

   (e)

   (f) $CH_3C\!\equiv\!CCHOHCH_3$

5. The reaction of 1-octene with N-bromosuccinimide in carbon tetrachloride with a small amount of benzoyl peroxide, $(C_6H_5COO)_2$, gives a mixture of 17% 3-bromo-1-octene, 44% *trans*-1-bromo-2-octene, and 39% *cis*-1-bromo-2-octene. Account for these products with a reaction mechanism showing all significant intermediates.

6. In the reaction of 1,3-cyclopentadiene with hydrogen chloride at 0°C, no significant amount of 4-chlorocyclopentene is produced. Explain.

7. When 1,3-butadiene is allowed to react with hydrogen chloride in acetic acid at room temperature, there is produced a mixture of 22% 1-chloro-2-butene and 78% 3-chloro-1-butene. On treatment with ferric chloride or on prolonged treatment with hydrogen chloride, this mixture is converted to 75% 1-chloro-2-butene and 25% 3-chloro-1-butene. Explain.

8. Show how each of the following conversions may be accomplished.

(a)

(b)

(c)

(d)

(e)

9. (a) A common procedure for measuring ^{14}C is to obtain it in the form of carbon dioxide, which is passed into aqueous barium hydroxide and precipitated as barium carbonate. The white product is dried and pressed into a pellet, which is counted with a Geiger counter. Given $Ba^{14}CO_3$ as the starting material, present a practical synthesis of $CH_2=CH^{14}CH_2OH$. How would you show that allylic rearrangement occurs when this labeled allyl alcohol reacts with thionyl chloride (page 521)?

(b) Allylic rearrangement can also be demonstrated with deuterium labeling. Present a practical synthesis of $CH_2=CHCD_2OH$. What would the NMR spectrum look like? What product would you expect on treatment with thionyl chloride? What is the expected NMR spectrum of this product?

10. On heating 2-buten-1-ol with dilute sulfuric acid, a mixture of three structurally different isomeric ethers of the type $(C_4H_7)_2O$ is produced. Give the structures of these ethers [do not count cis-trans or R-S isomers] and write a plausible reaction mechanism for their formation.

11. (a) When 1-pentyne is treated with 4 N alcoholic potassium hydroxide at 175°C, it is converted slowly into an equilibrium mixture of 1.3% 1-pentyne, 95.2% 2-pentyne, and 3.5% 1,2-pentadiene. Calculate $\Delta G°$ differences between these isomers for the equilibrium composition. Write a reasonable reaction mechanism showing all intermediates in the equilibrium reaction.

(b) Sodium amide in liquid ammonia is a stronger base system than alcoholic KOH, yet prolonged treatment of 1-pentyne by $NaNH_2$ in liquid ammonia leads to recovery of the 1-pentyne essentially unchanged. Explain.

12. 5-Methylcyclopent-2-en-1-one reacts with refluxing aqueous sodium hydroxide to give 2-methylcyclopent-2-en-1-one. Explain with a mechanism.

13. The gas phase enthalpy of ionization ($\Delta H°$ for $RCl \longrightarrow R^+ + Cl^-$) for *trans*-1-chloro-2-butene is about 161 kcal mole^{-1} and is significantly lower than that for 3-chloro-2-methyl-1-propene, 169 kcal mole^{-1}. Explain, using resonance structures where appropriate.

14. What diene and dienophile produce the following Diels-Alder adducts?

(a)

(b)

(c)

(d)

(e)   (f)

(g)   (h)

15. For each of the following Diels-Alder reactions, predict the orientation and stereochemistry.

(a)

(b)

(c)

16. Allylic chlorination can be accomplished by the use of *t*-butyl hypochlorite, a reagent prepared by passing chlorine into an alkaline solution of *t*-butyl alcohol.
    (a) Write a plausible mechanism for this reaction.
    (b) An example of the use of $(CH_3)_3COCl$ in allylic chlorination is

Write a reasonable reaction mechanism.
    (c) In the example in (b), note that none of the cis isomer is obtained. If we start with the cis olefin, the reaction takes the following course.

What does this experiment reveal concerning the configurational stability around the carbon-carbon bond in an allyl radical, at least at $-78°C$?
    (d) Why was it necessary to do the experiment with both the cis and trans olefins? Could the conclusion in (c) have been derived from the results of part (b) alone?
    (e) The rotation barrier in allyl radical is estimated to be about 10 kcal mole^{-1}. Explain why such a barrier exists.

17. Reaction of 2,3-dimethyl-1,3-butadiene with Cl_2 in carbon tetrachloride in the dark at $-20°C$ gives 45% of the expected product, 1,4-dichloro-2,3-dimethyl-2-butene, in addition to 54% of A and 1% of B, both of which are determined to have the formula C_6H_9Cl.
    The NMR spectrum of compound A shows singlets at $\delta = 1.90$ ppm (3H) and $\delta = 4.20$ ppm (2H) and four peaks at $\delta = 6.06, 6.19, 6.22, 6.30$ ppm (4H). The NMR spectrum of compound B shows singlets at $\delta = 1.78$ ppm (3H), 1.85 ppm (3H), and 6.20 ppm (1H), and two peaks at $\delta = 5.08, 5.00$ ppm (2H). Deduce the structures of A and B and write a plausible mechanism for their formation.

18. The NMR spectrum at $-90°C$ of the Grignard reagent prepared from 4-bromo-2-methyl-2-butene shows the following signals: $\delta = 0.6$ ppm, doublet (2H); $\delta = 1.6$ ppm, doublet (6H); $\delta = 5.6$ ppm, triplet (1H). Which structure best fits this NMR spectrum? On warming the solution to room temperature, the doublet at $\delta = 1.6$ ppm first broadens and then becomes a sharp singlet. How do you interpret this behavior?

19. Reaction of 3-methyl-1,2-butadiene with Cl_2 under free radical conditions gives 3-chloro-2-methyl-1,3-butadiene. Write a reasonable reaction mechanism.

20. One preparation of acrolein involves treating glycerol, $CH_2OHCHOHCH_2OH$, with sulfuric acid. Write a plausible reaction mechanism.

21. Consider the following equilibria between α,β- and β,γ-isomers. For R $= CH_3$ the equilibrium constant is about unity. For R $= (CH_3)_3C$, however, the equilibrium is displaced substantially in the α,β-direction. Explain this result. The use of molecular models may be helpful.

$$\begin{array}{c} R \\ | \\ CH_3CH_2CHCH{=}CCOOC_2H_5 \\ | \\ CH_3 \end{array} \rightleftharpoons CH_3CH_2C{=}CHCHCOOC_2H_5$$
$$\qquad\qquad\qquad\qquad\qquad\qquad\qquad R \quad CH_3$$

R $= CH_3$:   (45%)   (55%)
R $= C(CH_3)_3$:   (86%)   (14%)

Chapter 20

Benzene and the Aromatic Ring

20.1 Benzene

A. The Benzene Enigma

The hydrocarbon now known as benzene was first isolated by Michael Faraday in 1825 from an oily condensate that deposited from illuminating gas. Faraday determined that it has equal numbers of carbons and hydrogens and named the new compound "carbureted hydrogen." In 1834 Mitscherlich found that the same hydrocarbon may be produced by pyrolysis with lime of benzoic acid, which had been isolated from gum benzoin. By vapor density measurements, Mitscherlich established the molecular formula to be C_6H_6. He named the compound benzin, but other influential chemists protested that this name implied a relationship to alkaloids such as quinine. Finally, the German name benzol, based on the German *öl*, oil, was adopted. In France and England, the name **benzene** was adopted, to avoid confusion with the typical alcohol ending.

> During the early history of benzene, Laurent proposed the name pheno (Gk., *phainein*, to shine) in keeping with the discovery of the material in illuminating gas. Although the name never gained acceptance, it persists in **phenyl**, the name of the C_6H_5 group.

Other preparations of benzene followed these early discoveries, and it was soon recognized that benzene is the parent hydrocarbon of a whole family of organic compounds. The physical properties of benzene (b.p. 80.1°C, m.p. 5.5°C) are consistent with its molecular formula of C_6H_6. For example, cyclohexane, C_6H_{12}, has b.p. 80.7°C and m.p. 6.5°C. A six-carbon saturated alkane would have the formula C_6H_{14}. Therefore, benzene must have four double bonds and/or rings. Yet, it does not exhibit the high reactivity of typical polyenes. In fact, it is remarkably inert to many reagents. For example, it does not react with aqueous potassium permanganate or with bromine water. It does not even react with concentrated sulfuric acid in the cold. It is stable to air and tolerates free-radical initiators. It may be used as a solvent for Grignard reagents and alkyllithium compounds. All of these properties are totally inconsistent with such C_6H_6 structures as the following.

$$CH_2=C=\overset{\overset{\displaystyle H}{|}}{C}-\overset{\overset{\displaystyle H}{|}}{C}=C=CH_2 \quad \text{or} \quad CH_3C\equiv C-C\equiv CCH_3$$

The fact that benzene has a formula that suggests a polyene structure but does not behave at all like other polyenes was a dilemma for nineteenth century chemists. Furthermore, new compounds were continually being discovered that were structurally related to benzene. It was clear that there is something fundamentally different about benzene and its derivatives. As a group, the benzene-like compounds were called **aromatic** compounds because many of them have characteristic aromas.

The Kekulé-Couper theory of valence, first proposed in 1858, allowed acceptable structures to be written for aliphatic compounds such as ethane and ethylene, but at first it did not appear to be applicable to aromatic compounds. In 1865, Kekulé suggested a regular hexagon structure for benzene with a hydrogen attached at each corner of a hexagonal array of carbons.

However, this structure violates the tetravalence of carbon inherent in his theory. He later modified his structure to treat benzene as an equilibrating mixture of cyclohexatrienes. However, this structure does not account for the nonolefinic character of benzene.

cyclohexatriene

Other attempts by nineteenth century chemists to explain the benzene problem only emphasize the frustrations inherent in the limited theory of the day. One such example was Armstrong's centroid formula in which the fourth valence of each carbon is directed toward the center of the ring.

Ladenburg, in 1879, proposed an interesting structure that would solve the problem of why benzene displays no polyene properties. In the Ladenburg proposal, benzene was treated as a tetracyclic compound with no double bonds.

EXERCISE 20.1 The nature of a polycyclic compound as bicyclic, tricyclic, etc., is determined by the number of cuts or bond cleavages required to convert the polycyclic framework to an acyclic chain of atoms. Using this definition, show that the Ladenburg structure is tetracyclic.

Ladenburg's representation of benzene, although not the structure of benzene, is a perfectly valid structure for an organic compound. It has come to be known as "Ladenburg benzene" or "prismane." After considerable effort, prismane was finally synthesized in 1973 by organic chemists at Columbia University. Upon heating to 90°C, it isomerizes to benzene.

EXERCISE 20.2 Compare a model of prismane with that of benzene. Consider the various isomers of prismane having two different substituents, A and B. Are any of these isomers chiral? Are any of the corresponding disubstituted benzene isomers chiral? How do your answers provide a method by which nineteenth century chemists could have distinguished between the Kekulé and Ladenburg representations of benzene?

Only with the advent of modern wave mechanics did the structure of benzene take its place within a unified electronic theory. The x-ray crystal structure of benzene shows that the compound does indeed have a regular hexagonal structure as Kekulé had originally suggested. The carbon-carbon bond distance of 1.40 Å is intermediate between those for a single bond (1.54 Å) and a double bond (1.33 Å). In a regular hexagon the bond angles are all 120°, and this suggests the involvement of sp^2-hybrid orbitals. We can now recognize the "fourth valence," which was so difficult for nineteenth century chemists to explain, as being π-bonds from p-orbitals *extending equally around the ring*, as in Figure 20.1.

In resonance language, we may depict benzene by two equivalent resonance structures.

Note the important difference in meaning between this formulation and that of equilibrating cyclohexatrienes. Cyclohexatriene would have alternating single and double bonds, and the chemical equilibrium between the two alternative structures requires the movement of nuclei.

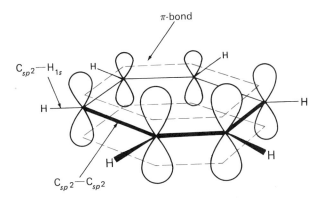

FIGURE 20.1 Orbital structure of benzene.

In the resonance structures the carbon-carbon distances remain the same. The resulting resonance hybrid may be written with dotted lines to indicate the partial double-bond character of the benzene bonds.

B. Resonance Energy of Benzene

From an examination of the heat of hydrogenation of benzene it is possible to estimate how much more stable benzene is compared to a hypothetical "cyclohexatriene." This imaginary quantity is called the **resonance energy** of benzene. The heat of hydrogenation of the double bond in cyclohexene is -28.4 kcal mole^{-1}. That for one double bond in 1,3-cyclohexadiene is -26.5 kcal mole^{-1}.

$$\bigcirc + H_2 \longrightarrow \bigcirc \qquad \Delta H° = -28.4 \text{ kcal mole}^{-1}$$

$$\bigcirc + H_2 \longrightarrow \bigcirc \qquad \Delta H° = -26.5 \text{ kcal mole}^{-1}$$

By a simple extrapolation, we might expect the heat of hydrogenation of one of the double bonds in a 1,3,5-cyclohexatriene with alternating single and double bonds to be about -24.5 kcal mole^{-1}.

$$\bigcirc + H_2 \longrightarrow \bigcirc \qquad \Delta H° \cong -24.5 \text{ kcal mole}^{-1}(?)$$

Benzene can in fact be hydrogenated, but only with difficulty. It hydrogenates slowly under conditions where simple alkenes react rapidly. When hydrogenation does occur, it generally goes all the way and cyclohexane results. The heat of hydrogenation for the complete reduction of benzene to cyclohexane is -49.3 kcal mole^{-1}.

$$\bigcirc + 3 H_2 \longrightarrow \bigcirc \qquad \Delta H° = -49.3 \text{ kcal mole}^{-1}$$

Since the heat of hydrogenation of 1,3-cyclohexadiene to cyclohexane is -54.9 kcal mole^{-1}, the heat of hydrogenation of benzene to 1,3-cyclohexadiene is $-49.3 - (-54.9) = +5.6$ kcal mole^{-1}; the process is actually endothermic!

$$\bigcirc + H_2 \longrightarrow \bigcirc \qquad \Delta H° = +5.6 \text{ kcal mole}^{-1}$$

These energy relationships are shown graphically in Figure 20.2.

resonance energy $\approx$ 30 kcal mole^{-1}

$(\Delta H° \approx -24.5$ kcal mole$^{-1})$

$\Delta H° = -26.5$ kcal mole^{-1}

$\Delta H° = -49.3$ kcal mole^{-1}

$\Delta H° = -28.4$ kcal mole^{-1}

FIGURE 20.2 Estimation of the resonance energy of benzene.

By comparison with the actual heat of hydrogenation of one bond in benzene, we find that benzene is about 30 kcal mole^{-1} more stable than it would be if it had the cyclohexatriene structure. This stabilization energy defines the resonance energy of benzene; that is, the resonance energy is the difference in energy between the real benzene and that of a single principal Lewis resonance structure. Other derivations of this quantity give somewhat different values; one commonly used number is 36 kcal mole^{-1}.

Actually, the true resonance energy of benzene should not be referred to a cyclohexatriene with alternating bonds of different lengths. Rather, it should be referred to a hypothetical model having the geometry of benzene but with π-overlap allowed only between alternating bonds. Such a structure requires the deformation of cyclohexatriene—stretching the double bonds and compressing the single bonds

Various estimates have been made of this distortion energy, but one estimated value of about 30 kcal mole^{-1} appears to be reasonable. This would make the actual resonance energy of benzene about 60 kcal mole^{-1}. To distinguish between these different energy quantities, this number of about 60 kcal mole^{-1} is referred to as a **delocalization energy** because it is the energy liberated when electrons are allowed to *delocalize* or *relax* from a hypothetical compound, with the benzene geometry but with the electrons constrained to alternating single and double bonds, to the electronic structure of benzene itself. The value of about 30 kcal mole^{-1}, derived above from heats of hydrogenation, is referred to as the **empirical resonance energy**.

Furthermore, this use of the term *resonance* should not be confused with the resonance that occurs in, for example, NMR (nuclear magnetic resonance), in which resonance refers to a matching of the frequency of an irradiating electromagnetic beam with the energy difference between two nuclear spin states in a magnetic field. However, both kinds of resonance are in fact related to the resonance phenomena of vibrations that allowed Joshua's horn to bring down the walls of Jericho.

The benzene ring can also conjugate with other π-electron groups and provide additional stabilization. Comparison of some heats of hydrogenation shows that the benzene ring is less effective in this regard than a double bond.

$$CH_3CH_2CH=CH_2 + H_2 \longrightarrow CH_3CH_2CH_2CH_3 \qquad \Delta H° = -30.2 \text{ kcal mole}^{-1}$$
$$CH_2=CH-CH=CH_2 + H_2 \longrightarrow CH_2=CHCH_2CH_3 \qquad \Delta H° = -26.3 \text{ kcal mole}^{-1}$$

$$\Delta H° = -28.2 \text{ kcal mole}^{-1}$$

The resonance energy of benzene associated with its cyclic π-electronic system of six electrons gives benzene a special character known as *aromatic stability*. Examples of other aromatic systems, which are not based on the benzene ring, are discussed later in this chapter. As has already been stated, this use of the term *aromatic* has nothing whatsoever to do with smell. Although the term was first used to describe a class of compounds that had strong odors, it is now recognized that the special property setting benzene and related compounds apart from aliphatic compounds is its resonance energy and cyclic conjugation. Thus, the term aromatic has come to be associated in organic chemistry with the general class of compounds possessing cyclic π-electron systems that have this special stabilizing electronic character.

Many such "aromatic" compounds are known. They include derivatives of benzene in which one or more groups are attached to the ring. Examples are toluene and benzoic acid.

toluene   benzoic acid

There are polycyclic benzenoid compounds in which two or more benzene rings are fused together; examples are naphthalene and coronene.

naphthalene   coronene

There are also aromatic heterocyclic compounds, compounds in which one or more atoms other than carbon participate in the cyclic conjugated ring. Examples are pyridine, furan, thiophene, and pyrrole.

pyridine   furan   thiophene   pyrrole

Polycyclic examples made up of one benzene ring and one heterocyclic ring, or of two or more heterocyclic rings are also known. Examples are indole and purine.

indole   purine

All of these cases involve cyclic systems of six π-electrons.

EXERCISE 20.3 Draw Lewis structures for one of the resonance structures each of toluene, pyridine, and pyrrole. Compare these structures with an orbital diagram showing the cyclic conjugated system of overlapping π-orbitals. Pay special attention to the difference between the ring systems of pyridine and pyrrole: compare the number of p-orbitals in the cyclic π-system with the number of π-electrons for each compound.

C. Symbols for the Benzene Ring

The symbolism used for the benzene ring deserves further comment. We have discussed the electronic structure of benzene in terms of its cyclic system of orbitals and of resonance structures with reference to hypothetical formulations of cyclohexatriene. We have used symbolic representations of cyclic orbitals and various symbols based on hexagons. These symbols are all in common use in various contexts and may be summarized as follows.

The orbital diagram in Figure 20.1 is especially useful for understanding the high stability of the benzene ring, but it is too complex and cumbersome a symbolism for normal use. The hexagon with an inscribed circle is a simple and commonly used representation of the aromatic π-system and is especially useful for the representation of aromatic structures.

benzene   benzoic acid   toluene

1,2,4-trimethylbenzene   phenylacetylene   1-methylnaphthalene

However, this symbol has an important disadvantage in not allowing an accurate accounting of electrons; that is, it does not correspond to a Lewis structure. In all of our other structural representations, a bond symbolized by a straight line corresponds to two electrons. No such simple correspondence applies to the inscribed circle; for example, the circle in benzene corresponds to six π-electrons, whereas the two circles in naphthalene correspond to a total of ten π-electrons.

EXERCISE 20.4 Three resonance structures of the Kekulé type can be drawn for naphthalene. For each structure determine the number of π-electrons involved in each six-membered ring. Draw an orbital structure of naphthalene and compare the total number of p-orbitals in the π-system with the total number of π-electrons.

The alternating-double-bonds symbol does allow a simple and accurate accounting of electrons and does correspond to a Lewis structure.

This symbol is used frequently to represent the benzene ring, and the student must be wary not to read this symbol as that of cyclohexatriene—that is, as a cyclic polyene. Generally, this symbol is used as a shorthand for a resonance hybrid of Kekulé structures.

This is the symbol for benzene rings that we will generally use throughout this textbook when it is desirable to call attention to the aromatic ring itself. We shall see later in this chapter and in Chapter 22 how this symbol lends itself readily to following the mechanisms of reactions at the benzene ring.

In many reactions, the bonding electrons of the benzene ring do not take active part. In such cases, it is often convenient to use the symbol **Ph** for the phenyl group, just as we use Me, Et, *i*-Pr, and *t*-Bu to stand for simple alkyl groups. The following examples illustrate this convention.

$$PhCH_3 \qquad PhCOOH \qquad PhCl$$

toluene   benzoic acid   chlorobenzene

D. Formation of Benzene

The high stability of the benzene ring is further demonstrated by reactions that produce this ring system. Cyclohexane rings can be **dehydrogenated** with suitable reagents or catalysts.

$$\text{cyclohexane} \xrightarrow[\Delta]{\text{Pd or Pt}} \text{benzene} + 3\ H_2$$

$$\text{cyclohexane} + 3\ S \xrightarrow{\Delta} \text{benzene} + 3\ H_2S$$

Dehydrogenation with cyclization can be accomplished from aliphatic hydrocarbons.

$$CH_3(CH_2)_4CH_3 \xrightarrow[450\text{--}550°C]{Cr_2O_3} \text{benzene}$$

(20%)

$$CH_3(CH_2)_5CH_3 \xrightarrow[450\text{--}550°C]{Cr_2O_3} \text{toluene (}CH_3\text{)}$$

(36%)

Such reactions form the basis of the **hydroforming** process of petroleum refining. Gasoline fractions are heated with platinum catalysts (**platforming**) to produce mixtures of aromatic hydrocarbons by cyclization and dehydrogenation of aliphatic hydrocarbons. Most of the benzene used commercially comes from petroleum. United States production in 1983 was almost five million tons. Benzene itself is an important starting material for the preparation of many other compounds. Many of these compounds result from electrophilic aromatic substitution, an important reaction that will be discussed in Chapter 22.

20.2 Substituted Benzenes

A. Nomenclature

Benzene derivatives are named in a systematic manner by combining the substituent prefix with the word benzene. The names are written as one word with no spaces. Since benzene has sixfold symmetry, there is only one monosubstituted benzene for each substituent, and no position number is necessary.

$$NO_2 \qquad C(CH_3)_3 \qquad Br$$

nitro benzene   *t*-butyl benzene   bromo benzene

A number of monosubstituted benzene derivatives have special names that are in such common use that they have IUPAC sanction. We shall refer to the following 12 compounds by their IUPAC—approved common names; thus the student should commit them to memory at this time. Before 1978 *Chemical Abstracts* also used these names for indexing. Beginning with the 1978 indices, however, a new system of nomenclature was introduced. The *Chemical Abstracts* names currently in use are shown in brackets. Although a scientist must be aware of these indexing names, they are not in widespread use for other purposes.

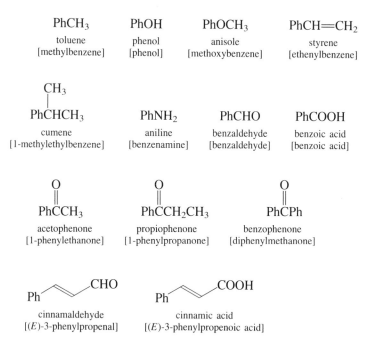

When there are two or more substituents, some specification of position is required. The numbering system is straightforward.

For disubstituted benzene derivatives, the three possible isomers are named using the Greek prefixes ***ortho-***, ***meta-***, and ***para-*** (often shortened to ***o-***, ***m-***, and ***p-***).

The following examples illustrate the use of these prefixes.

ortho-dichlorobenzene   *meta*-bromochlorobenzene   *para*-iodonitrobenzene
o-dichlorobenzene   *m*-bromochlorobenzene   *p*-iodonitrobenzene

Note that the substituent prefixes are ordered alphabetically. When one of the substituents corresponds to a monosubstituted benzene that has a special name, the disubstituted compound is named as a derivative of that parent.

p-nitrotoluene   *m*-chlorophenol   *o*-bromoanisole

However, if a compound has two or more identical substituents that would normally generate one of the foregoing special names, then the compound is named as a derivative of benzene. That is, it is a general rule that identical substituents in a molecule are treated equally for nomenclature purposes.

p-divinylbenzene   1,2,3-trimethylbenzene
(not *p*-vinylstyrene)   (not 3-methyl-*o*-xylene)

For polysubstituted benzenes, the numbering system should be used.

1,3,5-tribromobenzene   2,4-dinitroanisole   2,4,6-trichlorophenol

1,2,4-trinitrobenzene   2-bromo-6-nitrotoluene
(not 1,3,4-trinitrobenzene;   (prefixes are alphabetic)
the lower numbers are used)

Some di- and polysubstituted benzenes have common or trivial names that are widely used and should be learned by the student. Some of these special names follow; others will be brought up in subsequent chapters dealing with the chemistry of such compounds.

p-xylene

mesitylene
1,3,5-trimethylbenzene

p-cymene
1-isopropyl-4-methylbenzene

o-toluic acid
o-methylbenzoic
acid

m-toluic acid
m-methylbenzoic
acid

p-toluic acid
p-methylbenzoic
acid

Aromatic hydrocarbons have the generic name of **arene**. Accordingly, for many purposes the general abbreviation Ar, for aryl, is used just as R is used for alkyl; thus, the symbol ArR refers to arylalkanes. We have already learned that for benzene itself the term **phenyl-** is used. Examples of names employing this prefix are

trans-2-phenylcyclohexanol

3-phenylpropanal

phenylacetylene

Similarly, derivatives of toluene, the xylenes, and mesitylene, where the additional substituent is attached to the ring, may be named by using the prefixes **tolyl-**, **xylyl-**, or **mesityl-**.

2-methyl-3-*o*-tolylbutane

3,4-xylylacetic acid

3-mesitylpropanoic acid

Certain other group names are used for derivatives of these hydrocarbons when the substituent is attached to a side chain. Note in some of these cases how Greek letters are used to define the side-chain position relative to the benzene ring. The prefix **benzyl-** for the phenylmethyl group is especially important.

PhCH$_2$Cl   PhCH=CHCl   PhC=CH$_2$
                              |
                              Br

benzyl chloride   β-styryl chloride   α-styryl bromide
α-chlorotoluene   β-chlorostyrene   α-bromostyrene

OH
|
PhCHCH$_3$ PhCH$_2$CH$_2$Br   Ph⟍⟋⟍Br

α-phenylethyl alcohol   β-phenylethyl bromide   cinnamyl bromide

            O
            ‖
Ph$_2$CHOCCH$_3$ Ph$_3$CCl

benzhydryl acetate   trityl chloride
diphenylmethyl acetate   triphenylmethyl chloride

EXERCISE 20.5 Write the structures and names of the twelve methyl and polymethyl-benzenes and the six (monochlorophenyl)propanoic acids.

B. Körner's Absolute Method

One of the classical methods for distinguishing *ortho-*, *meta-*, and *para*-disubstituted benzenes is based on a simple logical corollary of a hexagonally symmetrical benzene and is known as Körner's absolute method. The method depends on the following simple principles applied to disubstituted benzenes where both substituents are the same.

1. In a *para*-disubstituted benzene, all four hydrogens are equivalent. Further substitution can only lead to a single trisubstituted benzene.

para   1,2,4-trisubstituted

2. In an *ortho*-disubstituted benzene, there are two types of hydrogen, and further substitution can, in principle, lead to two isomeric trisubstituted benzenes.

ortho   1,2,3-trisubstituted   1,2,4-trisubstituted

3. In a *meta*-disubstituted benzene, there are three nonequivalent hydrogens, and further substitution can lead to three different trisubstituted benzenes.

meta   1,2,3-trisubstituted   1,2,4-trisubstituted   1,3,5-trisubstituted

Furthermore, only one trisubstituted isomer, the 1,2,4-, is given by all three disubstituted compounds. In practice, the application of this method requires careful work because the possible products are generally not formed in comparable amounts. The existing groups on a benzene ring provide orientation specificity, to be discussed in detail later, that directs an incoming group to given positions. In practice, some isomers may be formed in such small quantity as to defy detection. This was especially true in earlier years when actual isolation was required. Nevertheless, by careful work the structures of many disubstituted benzenes were established early in the history of modern organic chemistry. By interconversion of functional groups, the structures of many other substituted benzenes could also be assigned.

Körner's absolute method is now only of historical interest as a valuable example of chemical logic. It is now generally feasible to use spectroscopic methods, primarily NMR and CMR, for this purpose.

EXERCISE 20.6 Show how Körner's absolute method could be used to distinguish among the three possible trisubstituted benzenes (for example, 1,2,3-, 1,2,4-, and 1,3,5-trimethylbenzene).

20.3 NMR and CMR Spectra

The NMR spectrum of benzene is shown in Figure 20.3. Since the six hydrogens are equivalent, the spectrum consists of a single line. The unusual feature of the spectrum is the position of the singlet, $\delta = 7.27$ ppm. Recall that δ for olefinic protons is generally about 5 ppm (Section 13.9).

FIGURE 20.3 NMR spectrum of benzene.

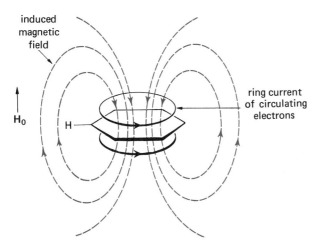

FIGURE 20.4 Effect of ring current in benzene π-system increases effective magnetic field at the proton.

The downfield shift of the benzene hydrogens results from the cyclic nature of the π-electrons of the aromatic ring. This cyclic electronic system can be likened to a circular wire, which in a magnetic field produces a current around the ring. This current is exactly analogous to the current induced in the π-electrons of a double bond (Figure 20.4), except that in benzene this electron current extends around the ring rather than being localized in one double bond. The resulting **ring current** has an induced magnetic field that *adds* to the externally applied field at the protons, just as in the related case of olefinic hydrogens (Figure 13.31). Since a smaller applied field is required to achieve resonance at the nucleus of the proton, the net result is a downfield shift.

> Recall that the ring current shown in Figure 20.4 refers to *circulating electrons* rather than the *positive current* to which the "right hand rule" applies as usually taught in physics courses.

The effect is greater for a benzene ring than for a simple alkene, in part because the benzene ring has six π-electrons in the cycle. The proton resonance of substituted benzene rings occurs generally in the region of $\delta = 7$–8, a region in which few other kinds of proton resonances occur. NMR peaks in this region are diagnostic for aromatic protons. Substituents have a normal type of effect: electronegative substituents generally cause a downfield shift, and electron-donating groups usually produce an upfield shift.

CH$_3$		Br	CCl$_3$
⬡	⬡	⬡	⬡
CH$_3$		Br	CCl$_3$

δ for aromatic H, ppm:　　6.95　　　7.27　　　7.34　　　7.98

In some monosubstituted benzenes all five benzenoid hydrogens have approximately the same chemical shift, and the aromatic protons appear as a singlet. This is usually the case when the substituent is an alkyl group or some other group having approximately the same electronegativity as carbon. An example is toluene, the NMR spectrum of which is shown in Figure 20.5.

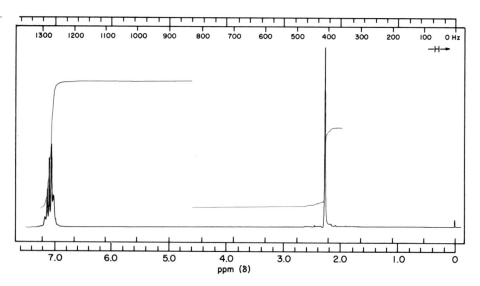

FIGURE 20.5   NMR spectrum of toluene, PhCH₃.

Also note in Figure 20.5 that the methyl group attached to the benzene ring resonates at δ = 2.32 ppm, about 1.4 ppm downfield from the resonance position of a methyl group in an alkane. The main cause of this downfield shift is the diamagnetic anisotropy or ring current of the aromatic ring. The effect is not as great with the methyl group as it is for hydrogens directly attached to the ring because the methyl hydrogens are farther from the circulating electrons than the benzenoid hydrogens. The effect is comparable to that found for allylic protons in alkenes (Section 13.9).

When the substituent in a monosubstituted benzene is sufficiently electronegative or electropositive relative to carbon, the *ortho*, *meta*, and *para* hydrogens have significantly different chemical shifts and the NMR spectrum becomes more complex. Such a spectrum is shown by nitrobenzene (Figure 20.6).

The spectra of disubstituted benzenes can sometimes be rather complex. In *p*-dichlorobenzene the four benzenoid hydrogens are equivalent, and the NMR spectrum is a

FIGURE 20.6   NMR spectrum of nitrobenzene, PhNO₂.

sharp singlet at $\delta = 7.22$ ppm. On the other hand, there are 24 lines in the NMR spectrum of *o*-dichlorobenzene (Figure 20.7). Some of these signals are of low intensity, and others are so close together that they appear merged if instrument resolution is inadequate. The analysis of such complex splitting patterns is beyond the scope of this text, but the student should know that such spectra can be analyzed and interpreted by experts to give structural information.

When the two substituents are of different electronegativity, the NMR spectra are sometimes sufficiently simple to be interpretable by a "first-order" approximation. An example is the spectrum of *p*-nitrotoluene, shown in Figure 20.8. To a first approximation, the benzenoid region in *p*-nitrotoluene may be regarded as a pair of doublets arising from coupling between the hydrogens on C-2 and C-3 with $J = 8$ Hz. Each doublet has an intensity of 2, relative to 3 for the methyl group because the hydrogens at C-2 and C-6 are equivalent and the hydrogens at C-3 and C-5 are equivalent.

The CMR chemical shifts for benzene and several simple alkyl benzenes are collected in Table 20.1. The data point out an important difference between NMR and CMR spectra. *Diamagnetic anisotropy effects are of only minor importance in determining carbon chemical shifts.* For comparison, the chemical shifts of two alkenes analogous to two of the aromatic compounds listed in Table 20.1 are shown below.

FIGURE 20.7 NMR spectrum of *o*-dichlorobenzene, *o*-Cl$_2$C$_6$H$_4$.

FIGURE 20.8 NMR spectrum of *p*-nitrotoluene, p-$NO_2C_6H_4CH_3$.

TABLE 20.1 CMR Spectra of Some Aromatic Compounds

Compound	Aromatic Resonances					Side-Chain Resonances		
	C-1	C-2	C-3	C-4	C-5	C-1′	C-2′	C-3′
benzene	128.7							
toluene	137.8	129.3	128.5	125.6		21.3		
o-xylene	136.4		129.9	126.1		19.6		
m-xylene	137.5	130.1		126.4	128.3	21.3		
p-xylene	134.5	129.1				20.9		
mesitylene	137.6	127.4				21.2		
ethylbenzene	144.1	128.1	128.5	125.9		29.3	16.8	
n-propylbenzene	142.5	128.7	128.4	125.9		38.5	25.2	14.0

Thus, the carbon chemical shifts of aromatic compounds for both the sp^2-carbons of the ring itself and the sp^3-carbons bonded to the ring are similar to those of a comparable alkene.

However, CMR spectroscopy can be useful in determining the substitution pattern on a benzene ring. Note, for example, that *o*-, *m*-, and *p*-xylene have CMR spectra consisting of four, five, and three signals, respectively.

EXERCISE 20.7 Sketch the expected NMR and CMR spectra of (a) 1-chloro-3-nitrobenzene and (b) 1-chloro-4-nitrobenzene.

20.4 Dipole Moments in Benzene Derivatives

Methyl chloride has a dipole moment of 1.94 D in the gas phase. The experimental measurement of the dipole moment gives only its magnitude and not its direction. Nevertheless, there is no doubt that the dipole moment in methyl chloride is oriented from carbon to chlorine.

$$CH_3—Cl$$
$$\mapsto$$

1.94 D

This orientation agrees with quantum-mechanical calculations and with spectroscopic interpretations of related compounds. Chlorobenzene has a dipole moment of 1.75 D in the gas phase. The direction of the dipole is undoubtedly also from carbon to chlorine.

1.75 D

The magnitude of the dipole moment of chlorobenzene is smaller than that of methyl chloride for two reasons. The carbon-chlorine bond in methyl chloride may be represented approximately as $C_{sp^3}—Cl_p$. The bond in chlorobenzene is approximately $C_{sp^2}—Cl_p$. The higher s-character of the benzene orbital makes it more electronegative than an sp^3-orbital; hence, the electronegativity difference with the more electronegative chlorine orbital is reduced. The second contribution to the reduced dipole moment in chlorobenzene results from conjugation of one of the chlorine lone pairs with the benzene π-system, illustrated in Figure 20.9. The lone pair is actually part of the π-system and may be represented in terms of resonance structures by

The effect of conjugation is small; the ionic structures contribute only a slight amount to the overall electronic structure. This slight conjugation, however, is equivalent to a dipole moment for the π-system, μ_π, oriented in the opposite direction from that associated with the carbon-chlorine σ-bond, μ_σ. The net dipole moment is the vector sum and is less than that of μ_σ alone.

$$\longrightarrow \quad \mu_\sigma$$
$$\longleftarrow \quad \mu_\pi$$
$$\longrightarrow \quad \mu_{tot}$$

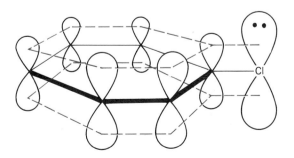

FIGURE 20.9 Conjugation of a chlorine lone pair with the benzene π-system. Actually, a chlorine 3p-orbital is involved, and the additional node is omitted for clarity.

TABLE 20.2 Dipole Moments of Substituted Benzenes

Compound	μ, D (gas phase)	Compound	μ, D (gas phase)
C_6H_6	0	$p\text{-}C_6H_4Cl_2$	0
C_6H_5F	1.63	$o\text{-}CH_3C_6H_4Cl$	1.57
C_6H_5Cl	1.75	$p\text{-}CH_3C_6H_4Cl$	2.21
C_6H_5Br	1.72	$o\text{-}CH_3C_6H_4F$	1.35
C_6H_5I	1.71	$m\text{-}CH_3C_6H_4F$	1.85
$C_6H_5CH_3$	0.37	$p\text{-}CH_3C_6H_4F$	2.01
$C_6H_5NO_2$	4.28	$m\text{-}ClC_6H_4NO_2$	3.72
$o\text{-}C_6H_4Cl_2$	2.52	$p\text{-}ClC_6H_4NO_2$	2.81
$m\text{-}C_6H_4Cl_2$	1.68		

Dipole moments of some other benzene derivatives in the gas phase are summarized in Table 20.2. The dipole moments of multiply substituted benzenes are generally close to the vector sum of the constituent dipoles. *p*-Dichlorobenzene has a net dipole moment of zero because the two component carbon-chlorine dipoles oppose and cancel each other.

net $\mu = 1.75 + (-1.75) = 0$

Because of the geometry of the hexagonal benzene ring, *ortho* and *meta* vector sums are given simply as

$$\mu = (\mu_1{}^2 + \mu_2{}^2 \pm \mu_1\mu_2)^{1/2} \qquad \begin{array}{l} + \, ortho \\ - \, meta \end{array}$$

This equation generally is quite satisfactory for *meta* groups but frequently inadequate for *ortho* groups. *Ortho* groups are so close to each other that electronic effects are mutually perturbed. For example, this equation applied to *o*- and *m*-dichlorobenzene gives

$$\mu_o = [1.75^2 + 1.75^2 + (1.75)(1.75)]^{1/2} = 3.03 \text{ D}$$
$$\mu_m = [1.75^2 + 1.75^2 - (1.75)(1.75)]^{1/2} = 1.75 \text{ D}$$

The *meta* result is close to the experimental value of 1.68 D, but the calculated *ortho* value is substantially higher than the experimental value of 2.52 D.

Toluene has a small but distinct dipole moment of 0.37 D. We note from the data in Table 20.2 that the dipole moment of *p*-chlorotoluene is approximately that of the sum of the dipole moments of toluene and chlorobenzene; hence, both component dipoles are operating in the same direction.

0.37 D   1.75 D

0.37 + 1.75 = 2.12 D   (experimental $\mu = 2.21$ D)

The dipole moment of toluene results in part from the character of the C_{methyl}—C_{ring} bond. This bond can be described approximately as C_{sp^3}—C_{sp^2}. The sp^2-orbital is more electronegative than the sp^3-orbital and produces an electronic displacement corresponding to the direction of the dipole moment indicated for toluene.

The same approach applied to nitrobenzene derivatives shows that the direction of the dipole in nitrobenzene is away from the benzene ring.

1.75 D   4.28 D

$\mu_{net} = 4.28 - 1.75 = 2.53$ D   (experimental $\mu = 2.81$ D)

The direction thus derived for the dipole moment in nitrobenzene is what we would have expected from the electronic structure of the nitro group.

The relatively high magnitude of μ for nitrobenzene also follows from the formal charges required in the Lewis structures for the nitro group.

EXERCISE 20.8 Calculate the dipole moment expected for *p*-fluorotoluene by vector addition and compare with the experimental result in Table 20.2.

20.5 Side-Chain Reactions

A. Free Radical Halogenation

At ordinary temperatures benzene itself does not undergo the type of free radical chlorination typical of alkanes. The bond-dissociation energy of the phenyl-hydrogen bond is rather high ($DH° = 111$ kcal mole^{-1}), undoubtedly because the bond involved is C_{sp^2}—H_s and has extra *s*-character. Consequently, the hydrogen transfer reaction is endothermic and has been observed only at high temperature.

$$C_6H_5—H + Cl· \rightleftharpoons C_6H_5· + HCl \qquad \Delta H° = +8 \text{ kcal mole}^{-1}$$

Instead, chlorine atoms tend to add to the ring with the ultimate formation of a hexachlorocyclohexane.

$$\text{benzene} + Cl_2 \xrightarrow{h\nu} C_6H_6Cl_6$$

benzene hexachloride
1,2,3,4,5,6-hexachlorocyclohexane

Eight geometric isomers are possible. The so-called γ-isomer (gammexane, lindane) has insecticidal properties and constitutes 18% of the mixture.

γ-benzene hexachloride

Reaction of the benzene hexachlorides with hot alcoholic potassium hydroxide gives 1,2,4-trichlorobenzene.

$$C_6H_6Cl_6 + 3\ C_2H_5O^- \xrightarrow{\Delta} \text{[1,2,4-trichlorobenzene]} + 3\ C_2H_5OH + 3\ Cl^-$$

In contrast, toluene undergoes smooth free radical chlorination on the methyl group to give benzyl chloride. Benzyl chloride undergoes further halogenation to give benzal chloride and benzotrichloride.

benzyl chloride   benzal chloride   benzotrichloride

The extent of chlorination may be controlled by monitoring the amount of chlorine used.

The reaction of toluene with chlorine atoms occurs exclusively at the methyl group because of the low bond-dissociation energy of the benzyl-hydrogen bond ($DH° = 88$ kcal mole^{-1}).

benzyl radical

$$\Delta H° = -16 \text{ kcal mole}^{-1}$$

The benzyl radical is especially stable for the same reason the allyl radical is stabilized (Section 19.1.D). Delocalization of the odd electron into the ring spreads out and diffuses the free radical character of the molecule. This conjugation can be represented by orbital overlap between the carbon 2p-orbital containing the odd electron and the ring π-system, as in Figure 20.10.

Alternatively, the conjugated system can be represented by resonance structures.

In the next step of the chain halogenation reaction, benzyl radical reacts with chlorine to regenerate a chlorine atom, which then continues the chain.

Note that benzyl radical reacts exclusively at the exocyclic position. The *ortho* and *para* positions do have odd-electron character, but reaction at these positions produces a chloride that does not have the aromatic stability of a benzene ring. The resulting effect on the thermodynamics of reaction is substantial.

$\Delta H° = -15$ kcal mole^{-1}

$\Delta H° \cong +23$ kcal mole^{-1}

The free radical chain bromination of toluene is exactly analogous and is a suitable route to benzyl bromide. With xylene the two methyl groups undergo successive halogenation.

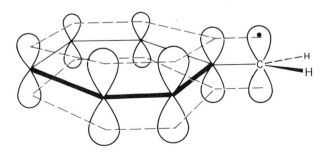

FIGURE 20.10 Delocalization of the benzyl radical.

$$\text{o-xylene} + 2\,Br_2 \xrightarrow[125\,°C]{h\nu} $$

(48–53%)
α,α′-dibromo-*o*-xylene

$$\text{o-xylene} + 4\,Br_2 \xrightarrow[175\,°C]{h\nu}$$

(74–80%)
α,α,α′,α′-tetrabromo-*o*-xylene

With the higher alkylbenzenes chlorination is limited in its synthetic utility because reaction along the alkyl chain occurs in addition to reaction at the benzylic position.

$$CH_2CH_3 + Cl_2 \xrightarrow{h\nu} CHClCH_3 \quad + \quad CH_2CH_2Cl$$

(56%)
α-chloroethylbenzene
1-chloro-1-phenylethane

(44%)
β-chloroethylbenzene
1-chloro-2-phenylethane

However, bromination occurs exclusively at the benzylic position.

$$CH_2CH_3 + Br_2 \xrightarrow{h\nu} CHBrCH_3$$

α-bromoethylbenzene
1-bromo-1-phenylethane

This difference in behavior again reflects the greater reactivity of chlorine atoms compared to bromine; recall that bromine generally is a more selective reagent than chlorine (Section 6.3).

EXERCISE 20.9 Show how cumene can be converted to 2-phenylpropene.

B. Benzylic Displacement and Carbocation Reactions

The reactions of phenylalkyl systems are more or less comparable to those of analogous alkyl systems—halides undergo displacements, eliminations, formation of Grignard reagents, and so on. However, when the halogen is α to a benzene ring, the compounds are especially reactive. Benzyl halides are generally at least 100 times as reactive as ethyl halides in S_N2 displacement reactions. This high reactivity is attributed to conjugation of the ring π-electrons in the transition state (Figure 20.11). Accordingly, such displacement reactions are straightforward and facile.

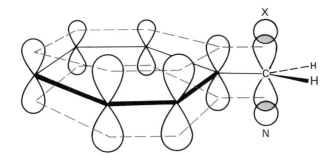

FIGURE 20.11 Transition state for S_N2 reaction with a benzyl halide showing the conjugation of the reacting center with the benzene π-system.

(74–81%)
p-anisylacetonitrile

p-nitrobenzyl chloride

(64–71%)
p-nitrobenzyl alcohol

Benzylic compounds also react rapidly by the S_N1 mechanism because of the relative stability of the benzyl cation.

In fact, the gas-phase enthalpy of ionization of benzyl chloride is more comparable to that of secondary alkyl chlorides than to that of primary alkyl chlorides.

$$\begin{array}{ll} & \Delta H°, \; kcal \; mole^{-1} \\ C_6H_5CH_2Cl \rightleftharpoons C_6H_5CH_2{}^+ + Cl^- & 154 \\ C_2H_5Cl \rightleftharpoons C_2H_5{}^+ + Cl^- & 191 \\ (CH_3)_2CHCl \rightleftharpoons (CH_3)_2CH^+ + Cl^- & 166 \\ (CH_3)_3CCl \rightleftharpoons (CH_3)_3C^+ + Cl^- & 152 \end{array}$$

When the carbocation center is conjugated with two or three benzene rings, the positive charge is distributed to a still greater extent. For example, triphenylmethyl cation has ten resonance structures in which the charge is spread to six *ortho* and three *para* positions. Consequently, triphenylmethyl chloride ionizes readily and shows exceptional reactivity. A liquid sulfur dioxide solution is colored yellow and conducts electricity because of the triphenylmethyl cations and chloride ions present.

$$(C_6H_5)_3CCl \xrightleftharpoons{\;SO_2\;} (C_6H_5)_3C^+ + Cl^-$$
$$\text{(yellow color)}$$

$$K = \frac{[(C_6H_5)_3C^+][Cl^-]}{[(C_6H_5)_3CCl]} = 4 \times 10^{-5}\, M$$

Similarly, triphenylmethanol is converted into substantial amounts of triphenylmethyl cation in strong aqueous sulfuric acid.

$$(C_6H_5)_3COH + H^+ \rightleftharpoons (C_6H_5)_3C^+ + H_2O$$

$$K = \frac{[(C_6H_5)_3C^+]}{[(C_6H_5)_3COH][H^+]} = 2 \times 10^{-7}\, M^{-1}$$

To give some idea of relative magnitudes of reactivity, benzyl chloride undergoes S_N1-type reactions much more slowly than *t*-butyl chloride, diphenylmethyl chloride is 10^1 to 10^3 times faster than *t*-butyl chloride, and triphenylmethyl chloride is 10^6 to 10^7 times more reactive than *t*-butyl chloride.

Order of S_N1 reactivity

$$(C_6H_5)_3CCl > (C_6H_5)_2CHCl > (CH_3)_3CCl > C_6H_5CH_2Cl$$

In fact, the rate of S_N1 reaction of triphenylmethyl chloride with ethanol is comparable to the rate at which the solid triphenylmethyl chloride dissolves.

The most effective conjugation between the carbocation center and the benzene π-electrons in triphenylmethyl cation requires that the whole molecule be coplanar. In such a planar structure, however, the *ortho* hydrogens of the phenyl groups are only about 0.5 Å apart; the resulting steric repulsion forces the rings to tilt apart. The actual structure of triphenylmethyl cation is that of a three-bladed propeller. This twisting of the phenyl groups does somewhat diminish the magnitude of conjugation between the central carbon and each ring, but the effect is not large.

The high reactivity of benzylic compounds in displacement and carbocation reactions is also seen in reactions of benzyl alcohols.

o-methylbenzyl alcohol → (75–89%) α-chloro-*o*-xylene (SOCl₂, benzene, one drop pyridine)

1-(*m*-chlorophenyl)ethanol → (80–82%) *m*-chlorostyrene (KHSO₄, Δ)

> **EXERCISE 20.10** Write the resonance structures for *m*- and *p*-methylbenzyl cations and predict which of these isomeric cations is the more stable.

C. Oxidation

Like allylic alcohols (Section 19.3.A), benzylic alcohols may be oxidized to corresponding aldehydes or ketones using manganese dioxide, a reagent that does not bring about the oxidation of normal alcohols.

(77%)
isobutyrophenone

The benzene ring is rather stable to oxidizing agents, and under appropriate conditions side-chain alkyl groups are oxidized instead. Sodium dichromate in aqueous sulfuric acid or acetic acid is a common laboratory reagent for this purpose, but aqueous nitric acid and potassium permanganate have also been used.

(82–86%)
p-nitrobenzoic acid

(53–55%)
o-toluic acid

The detailed reaction mechanisms by which these oxidations occur are rather complex. They involve numerous intermediates including chromate and permanganate esters, but they also appear to involve an intermediate benzyl cation.

As we have seen, this carbocation is relatively stable because of conjugation of the positive charge with the benzene ring. Reaction with water yields benzyl alcohol, which can oxidize further. Larger side chains can also be oxidized completely so long as there is one benzylic hydrogen for the initial oxidation. Cleavage reactions of larger side chains probably involve the formation of an intermediate alkene.

$$PhCH_2CH_2CH_3 \xrightarrow{[O]} [Ph\overset{+}{C}HCH_2CH_3] \xrightarrow{-H^+} [PhCH{=}CHCH_3] \xrightarrow{[O]} PhCOOH$$

benzoic acid

The more extensive oxidation required in these reactions often results in lower yields so that they are not as useful for laboratory preparations as they are for structural identification. When there is no benzylic hydrogen, the side chain resists oxidation. For example, vigorous conditions are required for the oxidation of *t*-butylbenzene, and the product is trimethylacetic acid, the product of oxidation of the benzene ring.

C(CH$_3$)$_3$

$$\xrightarrow{KMnO_4} (CH_3)_3CCOOH$$

pivalic acid
trimethylacetic acid

Oxidation of side-chain methyl groups is an important industrial route to aromatic carboxylic acids. The most important oxidizing agent for such reactions is air.

CH$_3$ COOH

$$\xrightarrow[\Delta]{\underset{Mn(OAc)_2}{\overset{O_2}{Co(OAc)_3}}} \quad + H_2O$$

An important industrial reaction of this general type is the oxidation of *p*-xylene to the dicarboxylic acid (Section 27.6).

EXERCISE 20.11 Suggest two different two-step ways by which toluene can be converted into benzyl alcohol.

D. Acidity of Alkylbenzenes

Benzyl anion is stabilized by delocalization of the negative charge into the benzene ring.

CH$_2$$^-$ CH$_2$ CH$_2$ CH$_2$

As a result, toluene is more acidic than the alkanes. Its pK_a is about 41 compared to a value of about 50 for ethane. Toluene is still a very weak acid and is not significantly converted to the anion even with NaNH$_2$ in liquid ammonia. As additional benzene

TABLE 20.3 Acidity of Some Hydrocarbons

Hydrocarbon	Conjugate Base	pK_a
ethane	$CH_3CH_2^-$	~50
benzene	$C_6H_5^-$	43
toluene	$C_6H_5CH_2^-$	41
diphenylmethane	$(C_6H_5)_2CH^-$	34
triphenylmethane	$(C_6H_5)_3C^-$	31.5

rings are added, however, the acidity increases markedly. Some relevant pK_a data are summarized in Table 20.3.

Di- and triphenylmethane are sufficiently acidic to be converted significantly to the corresponding carbanions with sodium amide. The resulting anions react as typical nucleophiles in alkylation reactions.

$$(C_6H_5)_2CH_2 \xrightarrow[\text{liq. NH}_3]{\text{NaNH}_2} \xrightarrow[\text{(C}_2\text{H}_5\text{)}_2\text{O}]{\text{CH}_3\text{(CH}_2\text{)}_2\text{CH}_2\text{Br}} (C_6H_5)_2CH(CH_2)_3CH_3$$

(92%)

1,1-diphenylpentane

20.6 Reduction

A. Catalytic Hydrogenation

Benzene rings are substantially more resistant to catalytic hydrogenation than alkenes or alkynes. In molecules that contain both a double bond and a benzene ring, the double bond may be preferentially hydrogenated without difficulty.

trans-stilbene   1,2-diphenylethane

Hydrogenation of the benzene ring occurs under more vigorous conditions and yields the corresponding cyclohexane. It is generally impractical to stop the reaction at an intermediate stage, since cyclohexadienes and cyclohexenes hydrogenate more readily than benzenes. Dialkylbenzenes tend to give predominantly the *cis*-dialkylcyclohexane, although the exact stereochemistry of the reduction depends on the reaction conditions and catalysts used. Platinum or palladium catalysts may be used at temperatures near 100°C; acetic acid is a common solvent. Nevertheless, reactions under these conditions are often inconveniently slow, and ruthenium or rhodium on carbon is often more successful for hydrogenation of aromatic rings.

about 9 : 1

With aromatic aldehydes and ketones the functional group undergoes reduction faster than the ring.

2-bromo-5-methoxybenzaldehyde   (83%)
2-bromo-5-methoxybenzyl alcohol

B. Hydrogenolysis of Benzylic Groups

Benzylic halides can be converted to hydrocarbons in the same ways that suffice for converting alkyl halides to alkanes—formation and hydrolysis of a Grignard reagent or by reduction with lithium aluminum hydride. Benzylic alcohols may be converted into the corresponding halide or sulfonate ester and thence into the hydrocarbon.

p-cyclopropyltoluene

benzyl bromide   toluene (78%)

These reactions differ from comparable reactions of normal alkyl halides only in that they occur a little more rapidly since the reactants are benzylic (Section 20.5.B).

A benzylic alcohol may be reduced directly to the corresponding hydrocarbon by treatment with hydrogen in the presence of palladium and a small amount of perchloric acid.

Since the carbonyl group in aromatic aldehydes and ketones is usually hydrogenated more rapidly than the benzene ring, the carbonyl group in such compounds can be completely removed by the use of two equivalents of hydrogen.

(84%)

This type of process, in which hydrogen breaks a single bond, is known as **hydrogenolysis**. Another example is

di-(*p*-tolyl)methanol

di-(*p*-tolyl)methane

EXERCISE 20.12 Outline a synthesis of phenylcyclohexane, starting with benzene and cyclohexanone.

C. Birch Reduction

Aromatic rings can be reduced by alkali metals in a mixture of liquid ammonia and alcohol. The product of this reduction is an unconjugated cyclohexadiene.

1,4-cyclohexadiene

Recall that a similar reduction is used to prepare trans alkenes from alkynes (Section 12.6.A). A solution of sodium in liquid ammonia contains solvated electrons, which add to a benzene ring to give a radical anion. Benzene and alkylbenzenes are not readily reduced, and the equilibrium lies far to the left.

benzene radical anion

Note that the radical anion has seven electrons in the benzene π-system. Many resonance structures can be written for this species; some are shown below.

Nevertheless, benzene radical anion is less stable than benzene, and the ion reacts readily with proton donors. Ammonia itself is too weakly acidic to react, but ethanol is a sufficiently strong acid to protonate the radical anion. The resulting cyclohexadienyl radical immediately reacts with another solvated electron to form the corresponding cyclohexadienyl anion.

This anion is a strong base and reacts immediately with ethanol to give 1,4-cyclohexadiene and ethoxide ion.

Cyclohexadienyl anion is a conjugated carbanion of the allylic type, and the negative charge is correspondingly distributed over several carbons, as indicated by the resonance structures

Protonation at the central carbon is much faster than at the end carbons of the conjugated chain. This result is quite general, even though the product of protonation at the terminal carbon of the conjugated chain produces a conjugated diene. The reason is not readily apparent, although various more or less sophisticated explanations have been given for this unusual effect.

Since the product contains isolated double bonds, no further reduction takes place, and the cyclohexadiene may be isolated in good yield. On prolonged contact with base, the carbanion is re-formed, allowing eventual isomerization of the unconjugated diene to the conjugated isomer, which is rapidly reduced to the monoene.

Thus, by a proper choice of solvent and temperature one may reduce the benzene ring to either the 1,4-cyclohexadiene or the cyclohexene.

With substituted benzenes a single product is often formed in good yield.

(77–92%)
1,2-dimethyl-1,4-
cyclohexadiene

> Sodium is added in pieces to a mixture of liquid ammonia, ether, ethanol, and *o*-xylene cooled in a dry ice bath. The ammonia is allowed to evaporate, water is added, and the washed and dried organic layer is distilled.

Birch reduction is particularly useful with anisole and alkylanisoles. Addition of hydrogen always occurs in such a way that an enol ether is produced. Hydrolysis occurs readily (Section 14.7.B) to give a β,γ-unsaturated ketone. Under the acidic conditions of the hydrolysis, the double bond moves into conjugation with the carbonyl group (Section 19.3.A).

anisole   (84%)   3-cyclohexenone   2-cyclohexenone
1-methoxycyclohexa-1,4-diene

In contrast to the Birch reductions of toluene and anisole, which provide 1-substituted 1,4-cyclohexadienes, reduction of benzoic acid gives the completely unconjugated product.

(89–95%)
2,5-cyclohexadiene-1-carboxylic acid

Double bonds conjugated to the aromatic ring can also be reduced by alkali metals in liquid ammonia.

(80%)

Although the benzene ring can also be reduced by lithium in ammonia, it is not as reactive as the conjugated double bond. Thus, selective reduction is possible, as in the foregoing example. Of course, the Birch reduction cannot generally be applied to systems that contain other easily reducible functions such as halogens, nitro groups, or carbonyl functions.

> **EXERCISE 20.13** What reaction products, if any, would you expect in the reactions of *cis*-2-butene, 2-phenylpropene, and 4-phenyl-1-butene with H_2–Pd/C and with Na/NH$_3$–C_2H_5OH and from treatment of α- and β-phenylethanols with H_2–Pd/C in C_2H_5OH containing a small amount of perchloric acid?

20.7 Aromatic Transition States

Several types of reaction have transition states in which bonds being made or broken create a cyclic system of interacting orbitals with six electrons that have enhanced stability suggestive of aromatic character. These reactions are part of a group known collectively as **pericyclic reactions**. An example is the Diels-Alder reaction, in which a diene reacts with an alkene to give a cyclohexene derivative (Section 19.5). The transition state involves a cycle of six orbitals and six electrons that resembles the cyclic π-system of benzene.

There is an apparent difference between the two cyclic systems. In benzene, the cyclic conjugation consists of π-overlap of six p-orbitals. In the Diels-Alder transition state, two of the interactions involve σ-overlap of two pairs of p-orbitals (Figure 19.12). Nevertheless, at the transition state this σ-overlap produces relatively weak bonds—more like π-bonds than normal σ-bonds—and the cyclic conjugation is effectively like that in benzene. In Figure 19.12 note that the p-orbitals that are involved in σ-overlap can still engage in π-overlap with their p-orbital neighbors.

The four-electron component of a [4 + 2] cycloaddition reaction need not be only a diene. An example of an alternative four-electron component is ozone. Its reaction with an alkene to form a molozonide (page 267) is also a [4 + 2] cycloaddition reaction that involves an aromatic six-electron transition state.

Another type of pericyclic reaction is the **Cope rearrangement**, a thermal rearrangement reaction of 1,5-dienes.

As shown by the foregoing example, the product is also a 1,5-diene. In some cases, such as with 1,5-hexatriene itself, the product is the same as the reactant, and it is not apparent that reaction has occured upon heating. With suitably substituted or labeled dienes, however, the rearrangement is easily detected.

In this example the product contains more highly substituted double bonds and is predominant at equilibrium.

The central bond in 1,5-hexadiene or biallyl is rather weak; $DH°$ is 58 kcal mole^{-1} compared to a normal carbon-carbon $DH°$ of 82 kcal mole^{-1} for the central bond in hexane. As this bond begins to break, however, a new carbon-carbon bond forms at the opposite ends of the two allyl π-systems that are starting to be produced. An orbital diagram of the transition state is given in Figure 20.12. A cyclic system of six interacting p-orbitals is involved much as in the conjugating system of benzene. Two of the

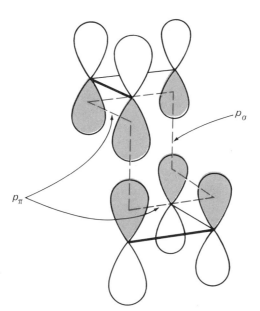

FIGURE 20.12 Electronic structure of the transition state for a Cope rearrangement.

p-orbital interactions are of the σ- rather than π-type in a manner comparable to the transition state of the Diels-Alder reaction. As in that case, the combination of relatively weak σ-overlap combines with the other π-overlaps to produce a cyclic conjugation entirely analogous to benzene.

EXERCISE 20.14 Although *trans*-1,2-divinylcyclopropane is a relatively stable compound, the *cis*-isomer rearranges rapidly even at 0°C. Suggest a reason for the high reactivity of this isomer and give the structure of the rearrangement product.

Reactions similar to the Cope rearrangement occur for compounds with atoms other that carbon in the cyclic conjugating chain. An important example is the **Claisen rearrangement**, a rearrangement reaction of allyl vinyl ethers.

The reaction goes to completion because of the strength of the carbonyl bond produced. Recall (Section 14.7.B) that vinyl ethers may be prepared by an exchange reaction of commercially available ethyl vinyl ether with an alcohol and catalyzed by mercuric ion.

Hence, the reaction provides an efficient method for adding a two-carbon aldehyde group to an allylic unit.

EXERCISE 20.15 (*R*)-2-Cyclohexenol is treated with ethyl vinyl ether and the product is heated to produce an aldehyde. Give the structure and stereochemistry of the product.

The Cope and Claisen rearrangements are two versions of the same general reaction. In both cases a bond between one end of two three-atom fragments is being broken while a new bond at the opposite end is being formed. These reactions are part of a class of such reactions called **sigmatropic rearrangements**. In the Cope and Claisen rearrangements the two rearranging fragments involved are both three atoms in length; hence, both reactions are sigmatropic rearrangements *of order [3.3]*.

Another sigmatropic rearrangement that involves a benzene-like transition state is a 1,5-hydrogen shift, a [1.5] sigmatropic rearrangement. An example of this reaction is given by the thermal rearrangement of 5-methyl-1,3-hexadiene to 2-methyl-2,4-hexadiene.

An orbital model of the transition state shows its relationship to the cyclic congugation in benzene (Figure 20.13).

EXERCISE 20.16 (a) The rearrangement of 5-methyl-1,3-hexadiene to 2-methyl-2,4-hexadiene actually results in an equilibrium mixture of the two compounds. Which compound predominates at equilibrium? What is the transition state for the reverse reaction? (b) 5-Methylcyclopentadiene rearranges on mild warming to a mixture that contains 1-methylcyclopentadiene and 2-methylcyclopentadiene. Show how the rearrangements involved are of the [1.5] sigmatropic type.

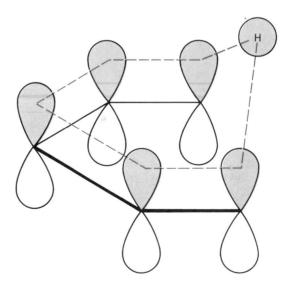

FIGURE 20.13 Orbital interactions for a [1.5] sigmatropic rearrangement.

PROBLEMS

1. Write structures corresponding to each of the following names.
   (a) *m*-fluoroanisole
   (b) 2,4,6-tribromobenzoic acid
   (c) 2,4-dinitrotoluene
   (d) α-bromomesitylene
   (e) *m*-divinylbenzene
   (f) *p*-cyanophenylacetylene
   (g) *o*-diisopropylbenzene
   (h) 2-bromo-6-chloroaniline

2. Give an acceptable name for each of the following structures.

(a) (DDT)

(b)

(c)

(d)

(e)

(f)

(g)

(h)

(i)

(j)

(k)

(l)

3. In Kekulé's day, one puzzling aspect of his dynamic theory for benzene was provided by 1,2-dimethylbenzene. According to his theory, there should be two distinct such compounds, one with a double bond between the two methyl-substituted carbons and one with a single bond in this position.

Only a single 1,2-dimethylbenzene is known, however.
(a) Does Ladenburg's formula solve this problem?
(b) Explain with modern resonance theory.

4. When passed through a hot tube, acetylene gives fair amounts of benzene. What is $\Delta H°$ for the reaction?

$$3 \text{ HC}\equiv\text{CH} \longrightarrow \text{⬡}$$

The entropy change for this reaction is $\Delta S° = -79.7$ eu. How do you explain the negative sign of this entropy change? Calculate $\Delta G°$ for the reaction at 25°C. Where does the equilibrium lie at room temperature? This reaction does not occur spontaneously at room temperature. Can you give a reason?

5. (a) A common method for estimating the empirical resonance energy of benzene is to take the heat of hydrogenation of one Kekulé resonance structure as three times that of cyclohexene. What value of the empirical resonance energy does this procedure yield? Note how the exact value of the empirical resonance energy depends so markedly on the model used for a hypothetical system.

(b) The heat of hydrogenation of cyclooctene to cyclooctane is -23.3 kcal mole^{-1}. That for 1,3,5,7-cyclooctatetraene is -100.9 kcal mole^{-1}. Use the procedure in (a) to calculate an empirical resonance energy for cyclooctatetraene. How do you interpret this result?

(c) Another method for estimating empirical resonance energies makes use of Appendix III, Average Bond Energies. In this table $E(\text{C--H}) = 99$, $E(\text{C--C}) = 83$, $E(\text{C=C}) = 146$ kcal mole^{-1}. Calculate the total bond energy of a hypothetical cyclohexatriene. This energy is the so-called heat of atomization, the heat required to dissociate a molecule into all of its constituent separated atoms. For benzene, this heat is actually $\Delta H°_{\text{atom}} = +1318$ kcal mole^{-1}. What value for the empirical resonance energy results?

6. Consider the possible free radical chain chlorination of benzene.

$$\text{C}_6\text{H}_6 + \text{Cl}\cdot \longrightarrow \text{C}_6\text{H}_5\cdot + \text{HCl}$$

$$\text{C}_6\text{H}_5\cdot + \text{Cl}_2 \longrightarrow \text{C}_6\text{H}_5\text{Cl} + \text{Cl}\cdot$$

From the data in Appendix I calculate $\Delta H°$ for each reaction. What conditions would you recommend for accomplishing this reaction?

7. The CMR spectra of the three isomeric diethylbenzenes are shown below. Which is which?

(a)

(b)

(c)

8. One general reaction of halobenzenes is the formation of Grignard reagents (Section 8.8). Thus, bromobenzene gives a Grignard reagent, which is hydrolyzed by water to give benzene.

All six isomers of bromodimethylbenzene, $BrC_6H_3(CH_3)_2$, are known. Show how the above reaction together with Körner's absolute method may be used to establish the structures of the three isomeric dimethylbenzenes.

9. Give the principal product of the following reactions or reaction sequences.

(a)

(b)
$$\xrightarrow[\text{C}_2\text{H}_5\text{OH}]{\text{Na, NH}_3}$$

(c)
$$\xrightarrow[hv]{\text{Br}_2 \text{ (1 mole)}} \xrightarrow[\Delta]{\text{CH}_3\text{OH}}$$

(d)
$$\xrightarrow[\text{H}_2\text{SO}_4 \ \Delta]{\text{Na}_2\text{Cr}_2\text{O}_7} \xrightarrow[\text{H}^+ \ \Delta]{\text{CH}_3\text{OH}} \xrightarrow[\text{ether}]{\text{CH}_3\text{MgI}}$$

(e)
$$\xrightarrow[\text{HClO}_4]{\text{H}_2\text{-Pd/C}}$$

(f)
$$\xrightarrow{\text{MnO}_2}$$

(g)
$$\xrightarrow[\text{C}_2\text{H}_5\text{OH}]{\text{Li-NH}_3} \xrightarrow{\text{H}_3\text{O}^+}$$

10. Show how one may synthesize each of the following compounds, starting with benzene, toluene, xylene, or ethylbenzene.

(a)

(b)

(c)

(d)

(e)

(f)

11. (a) Write out the steps of the free radical chain bromination of toluene to give benzyl bromide.
    (b) From ΔH_f° and DH° values listed in Appendices I and II, calculate ΔH° for the reactions in part (a).
    (c) Compare these values with those for ethane and the tertiary position of 2-methylpropane. How feasible are these brominations?

12. Write structures for the eight possible benzene hexachlorides. Which one is capable of optical isomerism? Which one is slowest to eliminate HCl by the E2 mechanism?

13. *o*-Phthalyl alcohol, 1,2-bis(hydroxymethyl)benzene, on treatment with acid, gives the corresponding cyclic ether.

Give a reasonable mechanism for this reaction.

14. Allyl acetate is treated with the strong base lithium diisopropylamide. The resulting enolate solution is kept at room temperature for 2 hr and then quenched with dilute acid. The product is found to be 4-pentenoic acid. Propose a reaction mechanism.

15. Heating the deuterated hydrocarbon shown produces via a Cope rearrangement an equilibrium mixture in which the deuterium is also on the bridge position. Of the two methylene proton positions, however, only a single deuterated isomer is produced. Which is it?

(H,D)

16. The **ene reaction** is a reaction of alkenes that is closely analogous to a Diels-Alder reaction. An example of an ene reaction is

457°C

Give the reaction mechanism and show how it involves an aromatic transition state.

17. Show the products of thermal [1.5] sigmatropic rearrangements of the following compounds.

(a) H Δ

(b) H OCH₃ Δ

(c) 220°C

18. On page 594 we showed that the reaction of ozone with an alkene to give a molozonide is an example of a [4 + 2] cycloaddition reaction that proceeds through an aromatic six-electron transition state. In an ozonolysis reaction, the initially formed molozonide undergoes a rapid rearrangement to the normal ozonide.

molozonide   ozonide

Propose a two-step reaction mechanism, in which both steps involve aromatic six-electron transition states analogous to that involved in formation of the molozonide.

Chapter 21

Molecular Orbital Theory

Most of our discussions of electronic structure have made use of resonance structures, although we have used molecular orbital concepts from time to time. In Section 2.7 we considered how bonds arise from the overlap of atomic orbitals. We have learned that the overlap of two atomic orbitals gives rise to two molecular orbitals (MOs), one bonding and one antibonding. When the orbital overlap occurs in a σ-fashion—along the bond axis—the bonding and antibonding MOs are symbolized as σ and σ^*, respectively. When the orbitals are p-orbitals overlapping in a π-fashion, as in double bonds (Section 11.1), the resulting bonding and antibonding MOs are π and π^*, respectively. When more than two orbitals overlap mutually, a more complex pattern of bonding and antibonding MOs result in which the MOs may extend over more than two atoms. Such multicenter or *delocalized* molecular orbitals are particularly important in π-electron systems because they are involved in the unique properties of conjugated molecules. The nature of these MOs will be discussed in this chapter.

21.1 Molecular Orbital Description of Allyl and Butadiene

The resonance description of allylic conjugation involves alternative descriptions of bonding by pairs of electrons in normal Lewis structures.

In the foregoing structures, the asterisk represents a positive or negative charge or an odd electron. Most of the electrons bond the skeleton of the compound and are not involved in the resonance stabilization or conjugation. In the molecular orbital picture these electrons form the σ-bonding framework of the molecule. The π-system consists of p-orbitals overlapping to form π-bonds above and below the plane of the atoms that define the allylic system (Figure 21.1).

The involvement of three p-orbitals in this manner clearly gives greater bonding, and it is not difficult to understand the stabilization that such orbital overlap bestows on allyl cation. However, according to the Pauli principle, only two electrons of opposite spin can be associated with any single orbital. What are we to do with the third and fourth π-electrons of allyl radical and anion?

Three p_z-orbitals overlapping, as in allyl, generate *three* different molecular orbitals, each having its own energy. One is most bonding and is occupied by two electrons of opposite spin in allyl cation. The third electron of allyl radical must be put into the

603

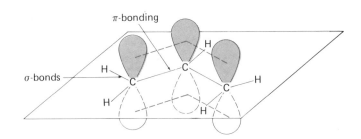

FIGURE 21.1 σ- and π-bonds in allyl systems.

second molecular orbital. The fourth electron of allyl anion can also be put into this second molecular orbital. The third molecular orbital has high energy and is not involved in bonding in any of these compounds. It is a high-lying π^* MO. These relationships are shown in Figure 21.2.

The π-molecular orbitals can be regarded as having molecular orbital quantum numbers or their equivalent in nodes. When p-orbitals overlap as in allyl, they do so in such a way as to generate one molecular orbital having no nodes, a second having one node, and a third having two nodes.

> Since these molecular orbitals are made up of p-orbitals overlapping in a π-fashion, all of the molecular orbitals have one other node, the nodal plane of the component p-orbitals. This plane is illustrated in Figure 21.1. The nodes referred to in the preceeding paragraph are nodes in addition to this nodal plane.

These molecular orbitals for allyl are shown in Figure 21.3. Recall that when functions of the same sign overlap, electron density is put in the overlap region between the nuclei, and bonding results. Electron density does not exist at a node. The overlap of two wave functions of opposite sign creates a node in the overlap region and signifies a region devoid of electron density. The absence of such electron density to counter nuclear repulsion produces **antibonding**. Hence, the first allyl π-molecular orbital, π_1, has no nodes and is completely bonding. In π_2 there is a node going through the middle carbon. The two remaining p-orbital wave functions are so far apart that overlap is small and this molecular orbital is approximately **nonbonding**. The highest molecular orbital, π_3, has two nodes and is antibonding. In general, the greater the number of nodes, the higher the energy of an orbital and the lower the stability. The greatest stability (lowest energy) results when electrons are associated as far as possible with the most bonding molecular orbitals.

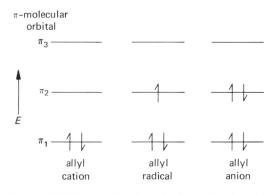

FIGURE 21.2 π-molecular orbital energies in allyl.

605

Sec. 21.1

*Molecular
Orbital
Description of
Allyl and
Butadiene*

These molecular orbitals can be described analytically by the mathematical functions

$$\pi_1 = \frac{1}{2}p_1 + \frac{\sqrt{2}}{2}p_2 + \frac{1}{2}p_3$$

$$\pi_2 = \frac{\sqrt{2}}{2}p_1 - \frac{\sqrt{2}}{2}p_3$$

$$\pi_3 = \frac{1}{2}p_1 - \frac{\sqrt{2}}{2}p_2 + \frac{1}{2}p_3$$

in which, p_1, p_2, and p_3 are the mathematical functions for the three p-atomic orbitals. Note that the node at the middle carbon of π_2 means simply that the coefficient of p_2 in this molecular orbital is zero. It is instructive to compare these molecular orbitals with the standing waves of other linear systems, such as a vibrating violin string or the sound waves in a pipe organ, as in Figure 21.4. The lowest-energy wave has no nodes and is either positive throughout or negative throughout. The next lowest wave has one node, and the third has two nodes. Note the close resemblence to the π-molecular orbitals of allyl. The correspondence reaffirms the common properties of all waves. Moreover, the smooth continuous nature of wave functions allows us to understand why the end coefficients in π_1 and π_3 of allyl are smaller than the middle coefficient and why the middle coefficient is zero in π_2.

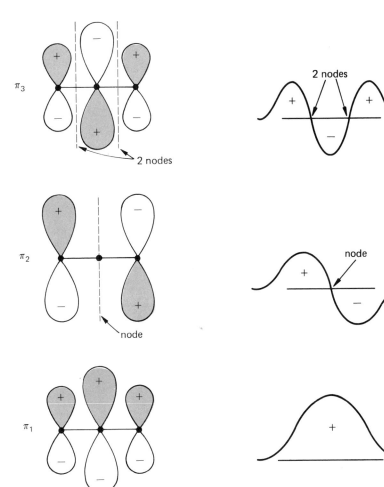

FIGURE 21.3 π-molecular orbitals of allyl.

FIGURE 21.4 Standing waves of a linear system.

The π-system of 1,3-butadiene consists of four overlapping p-orbitals that generate four molecular orbitals. These four MOs are shown schematically in Figure 21.5. The lowest-energy orbital, π_1, has no nodes and is bonding between C-1 and C-2, between C-2 and C-3, and between C-3 and C-4. The second MO, π_2, has one node. Therefore, this orbital is bonding between C-1 and C-2 and between C-3 and C-4 but is antibonding between the center carbons. The four electrons associated with the π-system are in molecular orbitals π_1 and π_2 (Figure 21.6). Therefore, the π-bonding between C-2 and C-3 produced by π_1 is partially offset by the antibonding nature of π_2 in this region of the molecule. The antibonding character of π_2 does not quite cancel the bonding character of π_1, because the bonding and antibonding overlaps differ in

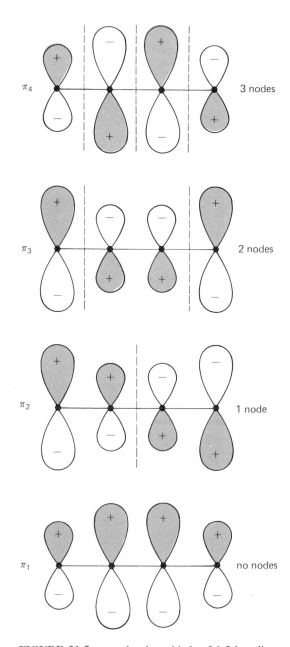

FIGURE 21.5 π-molecular orbitals of 1,3-butadiene.

FIGURE 21.6 Relative energies of π-molecular orbitals of 1,3-butadiene.

magnitude. However, there is little net π-bonding between the center carbons, and the net electronic structure is given to a reasonable approximation by the normal Lewis structure

$$H_2C::CH:CH::CH_2$$

In this kind of analysis note that the nature of unoccupied MOs is not relevant; because they have no electrons in them they do not contribute to the energy of the molecule or to its properties.

Note that the π-MOs of butadiene are analogous to those of allyl. The total number of MOs is equal to the number of p-orbitals involved in π-bonding. The number of nodes form a regular progression and they are placed so as to retain the symmetry of the molecule.

EXERCISE 21.1 Pentadienyl anion, $CH_2{=}CH{-}CH{=}CH{-}CH_2^-$, has five π-molecular orbitals with 0 to 4 nodes. Sketch the five MOs in order of their expected energy. How many π-electrons are involved and which of the π-MOs are occupied?

EXERCISE 21.2 How many π-MOs does 1,3,5-hexatriene have? Sketch these MOs and occupy appropriately with electrons analogous to Figure 21.6. Consider the bonding and antibonding characteristics of the occupied MOs and compare with a Lewis structure for hexatriene.

21.2 Molecular Orbital Theory of Benzene

The π-system of benzene is made up of six overlapping p-orbitals on carbon, which will therefore give rise to six π-molecular orbitals. The lowest, most stable molecular orbital, π_1, has no nodes and consists of all six p-orbitals overlapping around the ring. The next two molecular orbitals, π_2 and π_3, are not as bonding as π_1 and have higher energy. Each has one node. Note the important difference from allyl and butadiene in which only one π-MO has one node. The difference is that the π-overlap in these systems occurs linearly and can be represented as a single dimension. The cyclic overlap in benzene requires a two-dimensional representation in which nodes occur as pairs. The nodes in π_2 and π_3 are at right angles to each other. These two molecular orbitals have identical energies and are therefore said to be **degenerate**. The three molecular orbitals designated as π_1, π_2, and π_3 are the occupied π-molecular orbitals in benzene; one pair of electrons can be put in each to accommodate all six π-electrons of benzene. The three remaining π-MOs have less bonding and higher energy; they are not occupied by electrons. The relative energies of all six π-molecular orbitals and the molecular orbitals themselves are represented in Figure 21.7.

π-quantum
Number

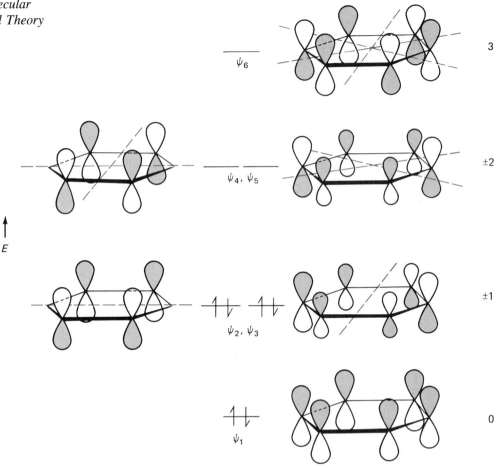

FIGURE 21.7 The π-molecular orbitals and energy levels for benzene. Positive lobes are shown in a different color.

A characteristic feature of this molecular orbital pattern is that the lowest-lying molecular orbital is a single molecular orbital; thereafter the molecular orbitals occur in pairs of equal energy until only one highest-lying level is left. These molecular orbital levels can be identified by quantum numbers, 0, ± 1, ± 2, and so on. Each quantum number represents a **shell** of orbitals, much as we have $2s$- and $2p$-shells in atomic structure. In benzene the ± 1 shell is filled, and we can attribute the stability of benzene to this filled-shell structure in much the same way as the noble gases (helium, neon, argon, and so on) have stability associated with filled atomic orbital shells.

It is important to distinguish between the π-electronic system of benzene as symbolized commonly by a set of six p-orbitals overlapping as in Figure 20.1 and the molecular orbitals as symbolized in Figure 21.7. Allowing the six p-orbitals to overlap in a cyclic fashion generates the MOs of Figure 21.7. According to the Pauli principle (Section 2.5), no two electrons can have the same quantum numbers. The six π-electrons of benzene can be divided into two groups of three based on electronic spin (a quantum number, $\pm \frac{1}{2}$), but each electron in the set of three must then belong to a different orbital. For benzene we have seen that such orbitals are the π-molecular orbitals characterized by quantum numbers of 0, $+1$, and -1.

21.3 Aromaticity

A. Cyclooctatetraene: The Hückel $4n + 2$ Rule

Cyclooctatetraene is a well-known hydrocarbon; it is a liquid, b.p. 152°C, that shows all of the chemistry typical of conjugated polyenes. It polymerizes on exposure to light and air and reacts readily with acids, halogens, and other reagents. In other words, it shows none of the "aromatic" stabilization associated with benzene. If cyclooctatetraene had the structure of a planar regular octagon analogous to the hexagon of benzene, we could write two resonance structures of the benzene Kekulé type.

We would therefore anticipate a significant amount of resonance energy for such a structure. Why, then, is cyclooctatetraene not an "aromatic" compound? The π-molecular orbital energy-level pattern is shown in Figure 21.8. Six of the eight π-electrons are put into the three lowest molecular orbital levels, but the one pair left is not enough to fill the next shell. Thus, planar, octagonal cyclooctatetraene has an incomplete orbital shell and would therefore not be expected to have the special stability characteristic of benzene.

Note that the last two electrons in Figure 21.8 are placed with the same spin, one in each of the degenerate orbitals. This arrangement is a consequence of Hund's rule, just as in atomic structure. Two electrons of the same spin are prevented from close approach by the Pauli principle—two electrons with the same quantum numbers cannot occupy the same region of space. Two electrons of opposite spin stay apart only because of electrostatic repulsion; hence, such a system has higher net energy and is less stable than one in which the electrons have the same spin.

In fact, the structure of cyclooctatetraene is in keeping with this analysis. The molecule is tub-shaped and has bond lengths characteristic of alternating single and double bonds (Figure 21.9).

As a result of the tub shape, the π-orbitals of adjacent double bonds are twisted with respect to one another and overlap is greatly reduced. That is, looking down any single

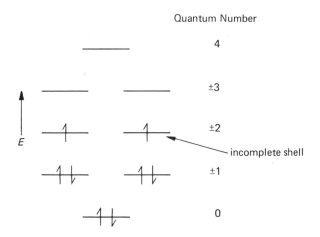

FIGURE 21.8 The π-molecular orbital energy level pattern for a planar octagonal cyclooctatetraene.

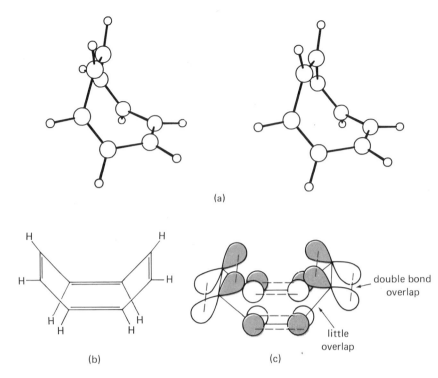

FIGURE 21.9 Cyclooctatetraene *(a)* stereo representation; *(b)* Kekulé structure; *(c)* π-orbital structure.

bond, the π-orbitals are almost at right angles to each other. In short, because of the instability associated with an incomplete orbital shell in the planar octagonal geometry, cyclooctatetraene prefers a nonplanar structure in which the alternating double bonds are effectively not conjugated with each other!

Incomplete atomic orbital shells are associated with a relative ease of gaining or losing electrons to form ions having filled-shell electronic configurations; for example, lithium atom easily loses an electron and fluorine atom easily gains one.

$$\text{Li} \cdot \longrightarrow \text{Li}^+ + e^-$$

$$: \overset{..}{\underset{..}{\text{F}}} \cdot \, + e^- \longrightarrow \, : \overset{..}{\underset{..}{\text{F}}} : ^-$$

The same behavior is seen with incomplete molecular orbital shells. Cyclooctatetraene reacts readily with alkali metals in ether solvents to form alkali metal salts of cyclooctatetraene dianion.

$$\text{(octagon)} + 2\,\text{K} \xrightarrow{\text{THF}} \text{(octagon}^{2-}\text{)} + 2\,\text{K}^+$$

cyclooctatetraene
dianion

The dianion has the planar structure of a regular octagon with carbon-carbon bond distances of 1.4 Å, quite similar to the carbon-carbon bond distances in benzene! Cyclooctatetraene dianion has ten π-electrons, just enough to fill the molecular orbital shell with π-quantum numbers of ±2. This reaction of cyclooctatetraene provides a remarkable demonstration of the usefulness of simple molecular orbital concepts.

Cyclooctatetraene is not an aromatic system; in fact, a planar octagonal cyclooctatetraene could even be described as **antiaromatic**. However, the dianion, with two more π-electrons, is definitely an aromatic system.

The foregoing discussion illustrates a general principle. For all cyclic π-electronic systems, successive molecular orbitals above the lowest level can be characterized by quantum numbers of $\pm n$, where n is an integer.

> The absolute value of the quantum number n indicates the number of nodal planes that bisect the ring. Alternatively, and equivalently, we can consider the quantum number to represent the angular momentum of an electron circling round the ring. The lowest level then corresponds to an electron having zero angular momentum. Thereafter, the momentum can be represented clockwise or counterclockwise about the ring; hence, above zero the quantum numbers come as $\pm$integer pairs.

To summarize, a filled orbital shell corresponds to a relatively stable electronic configuration. Examples in atomic orbitals are the filled $1s$-shell of helium and the filled $2p$-shell of neon. Similarly, filled π-molecular orbital shells give the stability associated with "aromatic" systems and bestow that stabilization commonly known as aromatic character or aromaticity. It takes two electrons of opposite spin to fill the lowest π-molecular orbital level for which $n = 0$. Thereafter, four electrons are required to give a filled π-molecular orbital shell. That is, filled shells are associated with a total of $4n + 2$ electrons, or two ($n = 0$), six ($n = 1$), ten ($n = 2$), fourteen ($n = 3$), and so on, electrons. This rule is known as the **Hückel $4n + 2$ rule** after the late Erich Hückel, the German theoretical chemist who first developed the rule in the mid-1930s.

Many examples of compounds are now known to which the Hückel rule can be applied. The results are truly remarkable for such a simple rule; a vast amount of experimental chemistry can be summarized by the generalization that *those monocyclic π systems with $4n + 2$ electrons show relative stability compared to acyclic analogs.* Furthermore, those monocyclic systems with other than $4n + 2$ electrons appear to be destabilized relative to acyclic analogs and can be said to have "antiaromatic" character. In succeeding sections we will summarize some of the experimental evidence for several values of n.

> **EXERCISE 21.3** Construct a molecular model of cyclooctatetraene. Place the model in the "tub" conformation described on page 610 and note the lack of overlap between adjacent double-bond π-orbitals.

B. Two-Electron Systems

One two-electron cyclic π-system is obviously ethylene, a well known and relatively stable compound. However, another cyclic π-system with two electrons is cyclopropenyl cation, a rather stable carbocation.

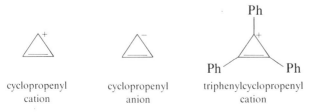

cyclopropenyl   cyclopropenyl   triphenylcyclopropenyl
cation   anion   cation

Triphenylcyclopropenyl cation is such a stable carbocation that many of its salts can be isolated and stored in bottles. On the other hand, the cyclopropenyl anion is unknown. The acidity of the methylene group in the known hydrocarbon cyclopropene has been deduced from several experiments to be less than that of alkanes.

The generalization that cyclic two-electron systems show relative stability makes its appearance in some subtle ways. For example, compounds containing the cyclopropenone ring system have unusually high dipole moments; this result is explained on the basis that the dipolar resonance structure contributes more to the resonance hybrid of cyclopropenone because it embodies the "aromatic" cyclopropenyl cation.

$\mu = 5.08$ D
diphenylcyclopropenone

$\mu = 2.97$ D
benzophenone

As with the structure of cyclooctatetraene dianion on page 610, this example illustrates the use of an inscribed circle to represent an aromatic cycle of $4n + 2$ electrons.

C. Six-Electron Systems

Cyclobutadiene has a cyclic π-system with four electrons and does not fit the $4n + 2$ rule; accordingly, we would expect it to have antiaromatic character. Cyclobutadiene is a known but very reactive hydrocarbon. It can be captured only at very low temperatures. Under most conditions it has but a fleeting existence and yields only dimeric products. This same reactivity is characteristic of various substituted derivatives.

tetramethylcyclobutadiene

Cyclic π-systems with six electrons fit the $4n + 2$ rule, and the most important such cycle is, of course, benzene. Some other six-electron cycles are ions. Cyclopentadienyl anion is a rather stable carbanion whose conjugate acid, cyclopentadiene, is an unusually acidic hydrocarbon with a pK_a of 16. Recall that such a value is far lower than that of triphenylmethane ($pK_a = 31.5$). In fact, cyclopentadiene is comparable in acidity to water and the alcohols.

cyclopentadiene

$pK_a = 16$

cyclopentadienyl anion $+ H^+$

By contrast, cycloheptatriene is a nonacidic hydrocarbon; it appears to be less acidic than the open-chain heptatriene.

CH₃CH=CHCH=CHCH=CH₂

cycloheptatriene   heptatriene

The cycloheptatrienyl anion has seven equivalent resonance structures of the type shown and would be expected to have a well-distributed negative charge. But it also has an incomplete molecular orbital shell with its eight π-electrons, and this property conveys antiaromatic character (Figure 21.10).

cycloheptatrienyl anion

Figure 21.10 also shows that the situation is reversed for the corresponding cations. Cyclopentadienyl cation is highly reactive and difficult to prepare. It has only four π-electrons. On the other hand, cycloheptatrienyl cation has six π-electrons and is a remarkably stable carbocation. It is readily prepared by oxidation of cycloheptatriene and many of its salts are stable crystalline compounds.

cyclopentadienyl
cation

cycloheptatrienyl
cation

EXERCISE 21.4 Of the two ketones shown below, one is highly reactive and one is unusually stable. Which is which?

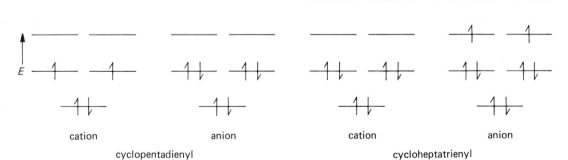

FIGURE 21.10 Molecular orbital energy levels for cyclopentadienyl and cycloheptatrienyl ions showing filled molecular orbital shells for six π-electrons.

D. Ten-Electron Systems

The Hückel $4n + 2$ rule says that monocyclic π-electron systems with ten electrons will have filled π-molecular orbital shells with the highest occupied molecular orbital having quantum numbers of ± 2. We have encountered one such system in cyclooctatetraene dianion. A related system is cyclononatetraenyl anion. This anion is a known system and gives evidence of having a planar nonagon structure, despite the high angle strain in such a ring system.

cyclononatetraenyl anion

A neutral ten-π-electron hydrocarbon homologous to benzene would be cyclodecapentaene. The planar all-cis structure has highly strained bond angles. The alternative structure with two trans double bonds cannot achieve planarity because of interaction between the two interior hydrogens. As a result, cyclodecapentaene does not have the expected aromatic stability, but is instead a highly reactive hydrocarbon.

all-*cis* or all-(*Z*)-cyclodecapentaene

(*Z,Z,E,Z,E*)-cyclodecapentaene

An unusual hydrocarbon has been prepared in which the two interior hydrogens of cyclodecapentaene have been replaced by a bridging methylene group. This hydrocarbon cannot have a completely coplanar π-system, but enough cyclic overlap occurs to give the compound significant aromatic character.

bicyclo[4.4.1]undeca-1,3,5,7,9-pentaene

E. Larger Cyclic π-Systems

Cyclobutadiene, benzene, and cyclooctatetraene are the first three members of a family of monocyclic $(CH)_n$ compounds known as **annulenes**. Cyclobutadiene is [4]annulene, benzene is [6]annulene, and cyclooctatetraene is [8]annulene. Other fully conjugated cyclic polyenes are named in an analogous fashion.

cyclobutadiene
[4]annulene

benzene
[6]annulene

cyclooctatetraene
[8]annulene

cyclodecapentaene
[10]annulene

A number of larger annulenes are known that further confirm the generality of the $4n + 2$ rule. Cyclododecahexaene, [12]annulene, is a polyolefinic compound that reacts with alkali metals to give a dianion that, with 14 electrons, follows the $4n + 2$ rule. The interesting hydrocarbon depicted in Figure 21.11 has a 14-electron π-system and is a stable molecule that has the properties of an aromatic system. The periphery indicated on the right of Figure 21.11 is a [14]annulene that follows the $4n + 2$ rule.

Cyclohexadecaoctaene, [16]annulene, with 16 π-electrons, does not fit the $4n + 2$ rule. It has polyolefinic behavior, but reacts with alkali metals to form the aromatic cyclic dianion with 18 π-electrons.

cyclohexadecaoctaene
[16] annulene

The corresponding neutral 18-π-electron hydrocarbon, cyclooctadecanonaene, [18]annulene, has been synthesized as a relatively stable brown-red compound. X-ray structure analysis suggests that the bonds have equal length.

[18]annulene

EXERCISE 21.5 Which of the following systems are expected to show aromaticity in the Hückel sense?
(a) cycloeicosadecaene
(b) cyclodoeicosaundecaene
(c) cyclooctatetraene radical cation (which is seen in the mass spectrum of cyclooctatetraene)
(d) cyclobutadiene dianion
(e) [26]annulene
(f) cycloundecapentaenyl cation.

FIGURE 21.11 *trans*-10b,10c-Dimethyl-10b,10c-dihydropyrene.

21.4 Hückel Transition States

In the last chapter (Section 20.7) we discussed a number of reactions that have cyclic six-electron transition states with aromatic character. Examples are the Diels-Alder reaction and the Claisen rearrangement. We know that such transition states have Hückel aromaticity because they involve $4n + 2$ electrons in a cycle. We recognize that all of the orbital interactions around the ring may not be equal as they are in benzene. Especially the p_σ-types of overlap in the transition states may not be energetically equivalent to the p_π-overlaps. Such inequality of interactions around the ring has the effect of breaking the degeneracy of the levels having nodes. Nevertheless, although these levels are no longer degenerate, they are still relatively close in energy and still form MO pairs or *shells* as shown in Figure 21.12. These shells are still filled with $4n + 2$ electrons and the Hückel concept still applies.

Many pericyclic reactions involve six electrons, but the Hückel rule is also fulfilled with two, ten, etc., electrons. An important pericyclic reaction with two electrons is the rearrangement of carbocations (Section 10.6.C). Figure 21.13 shows the pericyclic nature of such a transition state. As in the related case of cyclopropenyl (Section 21.3.B) the cation with a total of two electrons has a filled shell and relative stability. The corresponding transition state for a carbanion involves four electrons and an unfilled shell (Figure 21.13c). Accordingly, carbocation rearrangements are common while carbanion rearrangements are not.

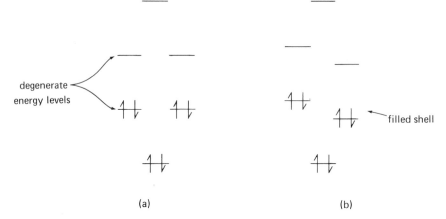

(a)   (b)

FIGURE 21.12   Comparison of MO energy levels for *(a)* benzene and *(b)* a six-electron cyclic transition state.

(a)   (b)   (c)

FIGURE 21.13   *(a)* A 1,2-rearrangement involves a three-center pericyclic transition state. *(b)* The carbocation case has two electrons and a stable filled shell MO pattern. *(c)* The carbanion case with four electrons and an unfilled shell is unstable.

In the same manner it now becomes clear why concerted [2 + 2] and [4 + 4] cycloaddition reactions (page 552) do not generally occur. The corresponding transition states involve four and eight electrons, respectively, and the electronic structures have unfilled shells. On the other hand, a number of cycloaddition reactions are known that involve 10 electrons. An example is the [8 + 2] cycloaddition reaction of heptafulvene with dimethyl acetylenedicarboxylate.

heptafulvene   dimethyl acetylenedicarboxylate

EXERCISE 21.6 (a) Sketch the MO energy level pattern expected for the pericyclic MO systems of the transitions states for [2 + 2] and [4 + 4] cycloadditions and show the unfilled shells. (b) Sketch the transition state for the cycloaddition reaction of heptafulvene with dimethyl acetylenedicarboxylate and show that 10 electrons are involved pericyclically.

21.5 Möbius Transition States

A. Electrocyclic Reactions

cis-1,3,5-Hexatriene undergoes a facile transformation on heating to give 1,3-cyclohexadiene. This type of isomerization is known as an **electrocyclic** reaction. The reaction can be perceived as proceeding through a cyclic six-membered transition state.

cis-1,3,5-hexatriene   1,3-cyclohexadiene

Moreover, if we follow the electrons involved by the conventional symbolism of a curved arrow for each pair of electrons involved, we find that three arrows are required. That is, six electrons participate in the transformation and hint at the involvement of $4n + 2$ in some manner.

There is a complication, however, with regard to stereochemistry. In the open chain hexatriene, best π-overlap of the double bonds is achieved when all six carbons and eight hydrogens lie in the same plane—including both terminal CH_2 groups. In the cyclohexadiene, however, the H—C—H planes of the two methylene groups must be approximately perpendicular to the six-membered ring. That is, in the transformation from hexatriene to cyclohexadiene, the terminal methylene groups must rotate out of coplanarity.

In principle, these rotations can take two possible modes. The two methylene groups can both rotate in the same sense when viewed from the same direction (**conrotatory motion**) or in the opposite sense (**disrotatory motion**)

$$H \overset{\frown}{\underset{}{-C}} H \qquad H \overset{\frown}{\underset{}{-C}} H \qquad H \overset{\frown}{\underset{}{-C}} H \qquad H \overset{\frown}{\underset{}{-C}} H$$

conrotatory motion   disrotatory motion

In the simple case of hexatriene itself, these alternative modes of rotation cannot be distinguished, but substituted compounds would lead to different isomers. Consider the *E,Z,E*-1,6-dimethyl compound as an example. If the end groups rotate in opposite directions (disrotation), the product is the *cis*-dimethylcyclohexadiene. If they rotate together (conrotation), the product is the *trans*-dimethylcyclohexadiene.

conrotatory

cis-5,6-dimethylcyclohexa-1,3-diene

disrotatory

trans-5,6-dimethylcyclohexa-1,3-diene

The reaction involves the conversion of the two terminal *p*-orbitals from π-bonding to σ-bonding. At this point it is important to examine the signs of the orbital wave functions to determine whether the orbital overlaps involved are bonding (positive) or antibonding (negative) (Figure 21.14). In the starting hexatriene the *p*-orbitals have signs assigned to the wave functions to provide the most positive overlaps and lead to a set of π-molecular orbitals that describe the electronic structure. Note that for clarity only the overlap (dotted line) at the top is shown. In disrotatory motion both terminal CH_2 groups rotate so that the positive lobes interact to give positive overlap throughout, exactly as in the related benzene system included for comparison in Figure 21.14. Even though the orbitals in the transition state for electrocyclic reaction are not aligned exactly as in benzene, the all-important overlap characteristics are the same in both; that is, the orbital overlaps are all positive around the ring.

This result is to be contrasted with the pattern for conrotatory motion. In this case the positive lobe of one terminal *p*-orbital starts to overlap with the negative lobe of the other terminal *p*-orbital. The disrotatory transition state clearly more closely resembles orbital interactions in benzene and, indeed, the electrocyclic reactions of hexatrienes are always disrotatory. The product of the dimethyl case shown is exclusively the *cis*-dimethylcyclohexadiene, even though this product is thermodynamically less stable than the alternative trans structure.

The substantial difference in activation energies for the two cases is directly related

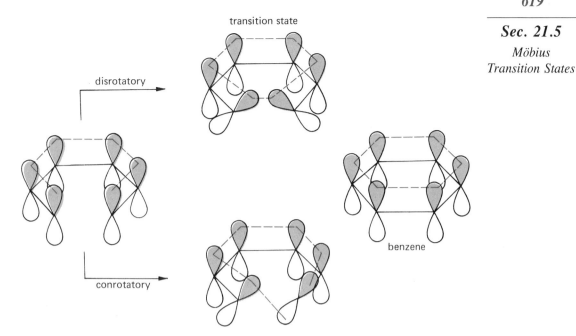

FIGURE 21.14 Orbital interactions involved in disrotatory and conrotatory ring closure of 1,3,5-hexatriene, compared to benzene. Colored lobes represent positive wave functions, uncolored lobes represent negative wave functions.

to the stabilization energies of aromatic systems having cyclic π-systems with $4n + 2$ electrons. The transition state for disrotatory ring closure has a molecular orbital energy pattern as shown in Figure 21.15a and has a filled-shell electronic structure for six electrons.

The negative overlap required for the conrotatory ring closure gives rise to an entirely different pattern of molecular orbital energies. The negative overlap is equivalent to a node; hence, *there cannot be any molecular orbital with zero nodes*. Instead, we find a pair of molecular orbitals of similar energy with one node each, a higher pair

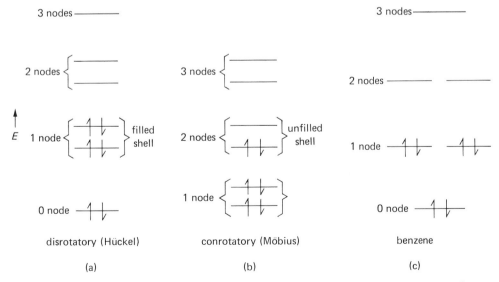

FIGURE 21.15 Energy level diagrams for alternative transition states for ring closure of hexatriene compared to that for benzene.

with two nodes, and so on. This pattern is illustrated in Figure 21.15b. Six electrons leave the second shell unfilled, a condition that represents relative instability.

It is convenient to have names for these two possible patterns of molecular orbital levels. The pattern for disrotatory closure is a **Hückel molecular orbital system** and gives filled molecular orbital shells with $4n + 2$ electrons. The conrotatory pattern in Figure 21.15b is frequently referred to as a **Möbius molecular orbital system**, and has the important characteristic of giving filled molecular orbital shells with $4n$ electrons.

This name derives from the topology of a *Möbius strip*. A Möbius strip is formed by taking a circular band, cutting in one place, giving one twist and rejoining the cut. The resulting strip has no inside or outside! Both are joined in one continuous manner (Figure 21.16). In a Hückel molecular orbital system, the p-orbitals are set up with a positive "top" and a negative "bottom." In the Möbius system, the negative overlap joins the "top" and the "bottom" in a manner that resembles the joining of the inside and outside of a Möbius strip.

strip having
inside and outside

Möbius strip
inside is the outside

FIGURE 21.16 Illustrating the surfaces of a Möbius strip.

Note that this point also emphasizes the difference between setting up atomic orbitals, such as p-orbitals, to overlap in a given fashion (basis functions) and the set of molecular orbitals that results from such overlaps. If we start with *n* interacting atomic orbitals, we must end up with *n* molecular orbitals. The energies of the molecular orbitals depend on how the starting atomic orbitals overlap. We may summarize this discussion as follows: A set of p-orbitals overlapping in a cyclic manner with zero (or an even number of) negative overlap(s) gives rise to a Hückel pattern of molecular orbital energy levels to which quantum numbers can be assigned as 0, ± 1, ± 2, and so on. Cyclic interaction of a set of p-orbitals with one (or an odd number of) negative overlap(s) gives rise to a set of molecular orbitals having the Möbius pattern of energy levels to which quantum numbers can be assigned as ± 1, ± 2, and so on.

Let us now apply these principles to the corresponding electrocyclic ring closure of 1,3,5,7-octatetraenes to 1,3,5-cyclooctatrienes. In contrast to the (*E,Z,E*)-dimethylhexatriene case discussed previously, the (*E,Z,Z,E*)-dimethyloctatetraene compound shown gives, as the first product of thermal electrocyclic reaction, exclusively the *trans*-dimethylcyclooctatriene, the product of *conrotatory* motion!

cis-7,8-dimethylcyclo-
octa-1,3,5-triene

(*E,Z,Z,E*)-deca-2,4,6,8-
tetraene

trans-7,8-dimethylcycloocta-
1,3,5-triene
exclusive product

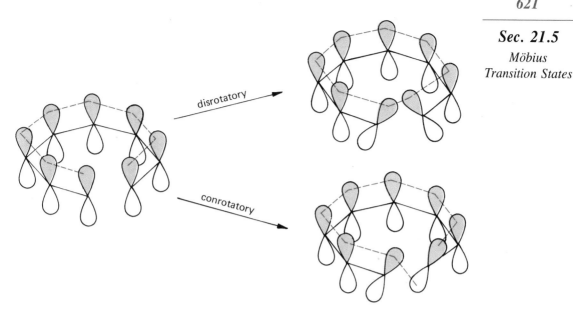

FIGURE 21.17   Orbital overlaps involved in cyclization of octatetraene.

To see why this system changes so dramatically from the hexatriene case, we again look at the orbital overlaps involved (Figure 21.17). In disrotatory motion the overlaps involved are again all positive and give rise to a Hückel pattern of molecular orbital energy levels. But the eight electrons involved in this case do not fit the $4n + 2$ rule. The result is the instability associated with an unfilled orbital shell. On the other hand, the conrotatory transition state gives rise to a Möbius pattern of molecular orbital levels. The eight electrons fill the first two shells and have the stability associated with filled orbital shells (Figure 21.18); that is, conrotatory ring closure of octatetraene

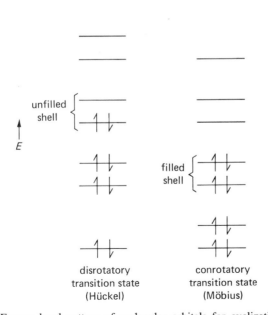

FIGURE 21.18   Energy level pattern of molecular orbitals for cyclization of octatetraene.

involves a transition state that has Möbius aromatic character of the transition state for disrotatory ring closure.

This result may be generalized. *Those thermal electrocyclic reactions that involve 4n + 2 electrons react with disrotatory motion* so that the orbitals involved can overlap in the Hückel sense. *Those thermal electrocyclic reactions that involve 4n electrons react with conrotatory motion* so that the orbitals involved can overlap in the Möbius sense. These generalizations hold whether the reaction involved is that of ring closure or ring opening (principle of microscopic reversibility).

The thermal ring opening of cyclobutenes provides a further example. On heating, *cis*-3,4-dimethylcyclobutene is smoothly converted to (*E,Z*)-hexa-2,4-diene.

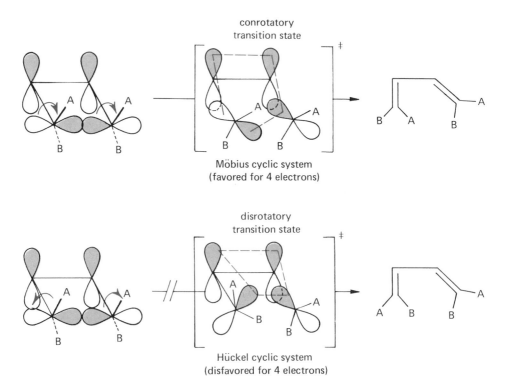

cis-3,4-dimethyl-
cyclobutene

(*E,Z*)-hexa-2,4-diene

The reaction involves a four-electron cycle. The filled-shell molecular orbital system of the transition state thus requires Möbius overlap and conrotatory motion (Figure 21.19). Disrotatory ring opening would give a Hückel cyclic system, which, with four electrons, would be antiaromatic (Figure 21.19).

conrotatory
transition state

Möbius cyclic system
(favored for 4 electrons)

disrotatory
transition state

Hückel cyclic system
(disfavored for 4 electrons)

FIGURE 21.19 Orbital interactions for electrocyclic ring openings of cyclobutene.

EXERCISE 21.7 Consider the conrotatory and disrotatory ring closures of butadiene to cyclobutene. Are the orbital interactions at the transition state the same as for ring opening?

The foregoing considerations lead to the following generalizations for thermal electrocyclic reactions.

$4n$ electrons (4, 8, 12, etc.) conrotatory motion
$4n + 2$ electrons (2, 6, 10, 14, etc.) disrotatory motion

The same generalizations were derived originally on the basis of symmetry properties of molecular orbitals and form part of the **Woodward-Hoffmann rules** for the stereochemistry of pericyclic reactions.

EXERCISE 21.8 The theoretically aromatic hydrocarbon [10]annulene has been the goal of numerous synthetic efforts. One attempted synthesis should have produced the *Z,E,Z,Z,E* stereoisomer. However, an isomer of 9,10-dihydronaphthalene was obtained instead. What is the stereochemistry of this product, cis or trans?

9,10-dihydronaphthalene

EXERCISE 21.9 Of the two stereoisomers of each of the following compounds, which is expected to be the more thermally stable?
(a) bicyclo[4.2.0]octa-2,4-diene
(b) bicyclo[4.2.0]oct-7-ene

EXERCISE 21.10 In each of the following thermal electrocyclic reactions, predict whether the product is cis or trans.
(a) (*E,E*)-hepta-2,5-dien-4-yl cation to 4,5-dimethylcyclopent-2-en-1-yl cation
(b) *cis*-bicyclo[5.2.0]nona-2,8-diene to bicyclo[4.3.0]nona-2,4-diene
(c) (*E,E,E*)-5-phenylnona-2,5,7-trien-4-yl anion to 1-phenyl-4,5-dimethylcyclohepta-2,6-dien-1-yl anion

B. Cycloaddition Reactions

Many examples are known of [*p* + *q*] cycloaddition reactions in which the number of pericyclic electrons equals 6, 10, 14, etc. These reactions are readily understood in terms of Hückel aromatic transition states. In this context, a remarkable exception would appear to be the reaction of heptafulvalene with tetracyanoethylene, a [14 + 2] cycloaddition that does not fit the Hückel rule.

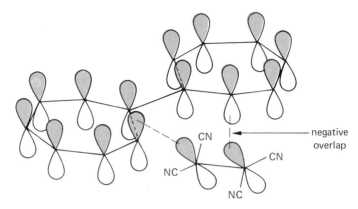

FIGURE 21.20 Orbital interactions for anti addition of tetracyanoethylene to heptafulvalene.

heptafulvalene   tetracyanoethylene

However, note that the product is the result of anti addition. The corresponding transition state (Figure 21.20) involves a negative overlap that would correspond to a Möbius cyclic electronic system, a favorable transition state for a 16-electron cyclic system!

Addition to the same side of a π-system is called **suprafacial** and is symbolized with a subscript s; addition to opposite sides of a π-system is called **antarafacial** and is symbolized with a subscript a. Hence, the normal Diels-Alder reaction is an example of a $(_4\pi_s + _2\pi_s)$ cycloaddition. The reaction of heptafulvalene with tetracyanoethylene is an example of a $(_{14}\pi_a + _2\pi_s)$ cycloaddition. In general, $(_p\pi_s + _q\pi_s)$ cycloadditions are thermally "allowed" when $p + q = 4n + 2$, whereas $(_p\pi_a + _q\pi_s)$ thermal cycloadditions, a somewhat rarer breed, are thermally allowed when $p + q = 4n$. These generalizations also constitute part of the Woodward-Hoffmann rules for pericyclic reactions (page 623).

EXERCISE 21.11 For each of the following cycloaddition reactions determine whether the reaction is thermally allowed for the stereochemistry shown.

(i)

(ii)

+ MeOOCC≡CCOOMe ⟶

(iii)

(iv)

21.6 Ultraviolet Spectroscopy

A. Electronic Transitions

A molecule can absorb a quantum of microwave radiation (about 1 cal mole^{-1}) and change from one rotational state to another. Vibrational energy changes are associated with light quanta in the infrared region of the spectrum (about 3-10 kcal mole^{-1}). A change in the electronic energy of a molecule requires light in the visible (40-70 kcal mole^{-1}) or ultraviolet (70-300 kcal mole^{-1}) regions. The energies required for such **electronic transitions** are of the magnitude of bond strengths because the electrons involved are valence electrons. That is, the energy of light quanta in this region of the electromagnetic spectrum is sufficient to **excite** an electron from a bonding to an antibonding state.

The resulting **excited electronic states**, in contrast to the **ground electronic state**, are often difficult to describe by resonance symbolism. In simple diatomic molecules an excited state can sometimes be described rather simply. For example, one excited state of LiF can be described by the process

$$Li^+F^- \xrightarrow{h\nu} Li \cdot F \cdot$$

ground   excited
state   state

Absorption of a photon is accompanied by a shift in electron density from fluorine to lithium, and the resulting excited state resembles two atoms held in close proximity.

The excited states of polyatomic molecules are not usually described so simply. Fortunately, molecular orbital concepts can often be applied in a relatively simple and straightforward way. For example, the electronic transition of methane involves the excitation of an electron from a bonding molecular orbital, σ, to the corresponding antibonding molecular orbital, σ^*, as illustrated in Figure 21.21.

Recall that the bonding molecular orbital between two atoms is formed by the positive overlap of two hybrid orbitals and is symbolized as in Figure 21.22. The corresponding antibonding molecular orbital, σ^*, is produced by the negative overlap of the hybrid orbitals. This negative overlap produces an additional node between the nuclei and reduces the electron density that is so essential for covalent bonding. In the excited state, the electron in σ^* partially cancels the bonding provided by the remaining electron in σ; hence, the energy required for excitation is of the order of magnitude of bond strengths.

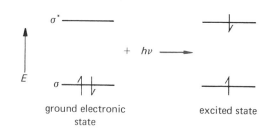

FIGURE 21.21 Ground and excited states.

The bonding molecular orbitals of methane, and of alkanes generally, are relatively low in energy. Excitation of an electron requires light of high energy with a wavelength about 150 nm (1500 Å) or less. Light in this region is strongly absorbed by the oxygen in air, and spectroscopic measurements of such compounds require special instruments in which air is completely excluded. This region of the light spectrum is called the vacuum ultraviolet and is unimportant in routine organic laboratory studies.

Wavelengths of light above about 200 nm are not absorbed by air, and it is this region that is most important for organic chemists. The range of about 200-400 nm is called the ultraviolet; the visible region of the spectrum ranges from wavelengths of about 400 nm (violet light) to about 750 nm (red light). The energy of such light is insufficient to affect most σ-bonds, but it is in the range of π-electron energies, especially for conjugated systems. That is, ultraviolet-visible spectroscopy is an important spectroscopic tool for the study of conjugated multiple bonds. The π-molecular orbitals of such conjugated systems extend over several atoms. The highest occupied or least bonding of such molecular orbitals already have at least one node. Electronic excitation generally involves the transition of an electron to a molecular orbital having an additional node, and, as a general rule, the more nodes an electron has in a wave function, the less energy it takes to add another node.

B. $\pi \rightarrow \pi^*$ Transitions

Absorption of light that produces excitation of an electron from a bonding π- to an antibonding π^*-molecular orbital is referred to as a $\pi \rightarrow \pi^*$ transition. For example, 1,3-butadiene has an intense absorption band at 217 nm (usually written as λ_{max} 217 nm; that is, lambda max = 217 nanometers) that results from the excitation of an electron from π_2 to π_3 (Figure 21.23). Recall that π_2 has one node and π_3 has two

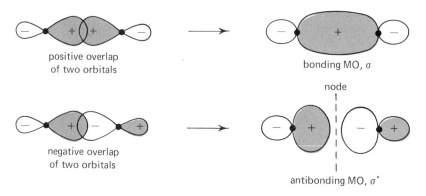

FIGURE 21.22 Bonding and antibonding molecular orbitals.

(Figure 21.6). 1,3,5-Hexatriene absorbs at longer wavelength, $\lambda_{max} = 258$ nm. It takes less energy to excite an electron from π_3, the highest occupied π-molecular orbital of hexatriene, which has two nodes, to π_4, which has three nodes. *The longer the chain of conjugation, the longer the wavelength of the absorption band.* For example, the lowest energy $\pi \rightarrow \pi^*$ transition of 1,3,5,7-octatetraene occurs at the still longer wavelength of 304 nm, whereas ethylene itself absorbs in the vacuum ultraviolet at 175 nm.

Compounds generally have many excited electronic states, but organic chemists are mostly concerned with the lowest or more stable states, since these are the states that are accessible with the energies of ultraviolet and visible light. Many of these states can be described in terms of electron transitions that involve other than just the highest occupied and lowest vacant molecular orbitals. For example, other electronic states of butadiene arise from the electronic transition $\pi_1 \rightarrow \pi_3$ or $\pi_1 \rightarrow \pi_4$, but such transitions occur in the vacuum ultraviolet. However, in other compounds several absorption bands can occur close together. An example is benzene, discussed in Section 21.6.E.

The highly conjugated hydrocarbon *trans-β*-carotene, with eleven double bonds in conjugation, has two intense long-wavelength absorptions in alkane solution at 483 nm and 453 nm. These absorptions are in the visible region of the spectrum and correspond to blue to blue-green light. Since light of this color is absorbed by the compound, β-carotene appears yellow to orange in solution. For further aspects of color, see Section 34.3.

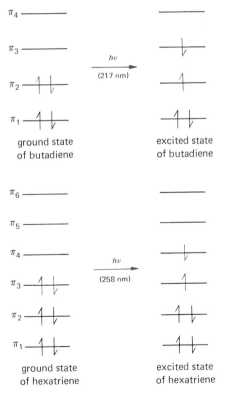

FIGURE 21.23 Electronic excitation of butadiene, $CH_2{=}CH{-}CH{=}CH_2$, and 1,3,5-hexatriene, $CH_2{=}CH{-}CH{=}CH{-}CH{=}CH_2$.

cis-β-Carotene has two absorption peaks at essentially the same wavelengths but with weaker intensities. This result is quite general; π-systems that are prevented from achieving coplanarity show significant changes from coplanar analogs, particularly in absorption intensities. In *cis*-β-carotene the two groups on the same side of the double bond sterically interfere with each other.

trans-β-carotene

cis-β-carotene

α,β-Unsaturated aldehydes and ketones also have high-intensity absorptions resulting from the transition of an electron from π_2 to π_3. These $\pi \rightarrow \pi^*$ transitions occur at almost exactly the same wavelength as those for the corresponding dienes.

$$CH_2=CHCH=CH_2 \qquad\qquad CH_2=CHCHO$$
$$\lambda_{max}\ 217\ nm \qquad\qquad\qquad \lambda_{max}\ 218\ nm$$

As in the case of polyenes, the wavelength of the light absorbed by unsaturated carbonyl compounds increases as the chain of conjugation increases. The effect is illustrated in Table 21.1.

EXERCISE 21.12 Using MO energy level diagrams like those of Figure 21.2, indicate the electronic transitions for the longest wavelength bands of allyl and pentadienyl anions. Which ion is more apt to absorb in the visible region of the spectrum?

**TABLE 21.1 Spectra of Some Polyene
Aldehydes**

Aldehyde	λ_{max}, nm
$CH_3CH=CHCHO$	220
$CH_3CH=CHCH=CHCHO$	270
$CH_3(CH=CH)_3CHO$	312
$CH_3(CH=CH)_4CHO$	343
$CH_3(CH=CH)_5CHO$	370
$CH_3(CH=CH)_6CHO$	393
$CH_3(CH=CH)_7CHO$	415

C. $n \rightarrow \pi^*$ Transitions

Carbonyl groups have another characteristic absorption that is associated with the lone-pair electrons on oxygen. Since these electrons are bound to only a single atom, they are not held as tightly as σ-electrons, and they can also be excited to π^*-molecular orbitals. The process results in a so-called $n \rightarrow \pi^*$ transition and usually occurs at relatively long wavelength.

$$
\begin{array}{cc}
\underset{\substack{\| \\ CH_3-C-CH_3}}{O} & \underset{\substack{\| \\ CH_3CCH=CH_2}}{O} \\
\end{array}
$$

$n \rightarrow \pi^*$:	λ_{max} 270 nm	λ_{max} 324 nm
$\pi \rightarrow \pi^*$:	187 nm	219 nm

The π-system of methyl vinyl ketone is more extended than that of acetone and less energy is required for the excitation in the former case. This difference is illustrated in Figure 21.24. Because of the more extensive π-system of conjugated double bonds of methyl vinyl ketone compared to acetone, both the $n \rightarrow \pi^*$ and $\pi \rightarrow \pi^*$ transitions of methyl vinyl ketone occur at longer wavelength (lower energy).

One important distinguishing characteristic of $n \rightarrow \pi^*$ transitions results from the critical feature that the lone-pair electrons tend to be concentrated in a different region of space from the π-electrons (Figure 21.25). Although $n \rightarrow \pi^*$ transitions often occur at lower energy (longer wavelength) than $\pi \rightarrow \pi^*$ transitions, they are less probable. A given quantum of $n \rightarrow \pi^*$ light must encounter many more molecules before it is absorbed than is the case for $\pi \rightarrow \pi^*$ light quanta. This difference shows up experimentally in an absorption spectrum as an intensity difference; $\pi \rightarrow \pi^*$ absorptions are generally much more intense ("strong absorption") than $n \rightarrow \pi^*$ absorptions ("weak absorption"). The difference in intensity is two to three orders of magnitude.

The intensity is expressed as an **extinction coefficient** ϵ. The amount of light absorbed depends on the extinction coefficient and the number of molecules in the light

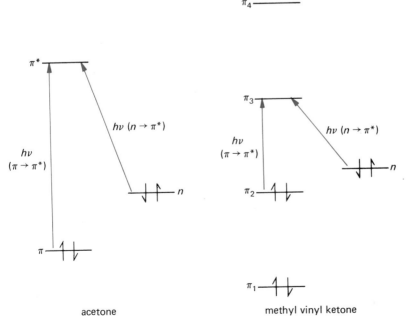

FIGURE 21.24 Illustrating $\pi \rightarrow \pi^*$ and $n \rightarrow \pi^*$ transitions in two ketones.

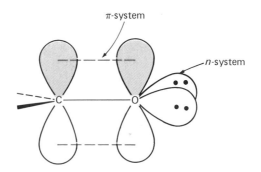

FIGURE 21.25   Lone pairs (*n*-system) and π-system of a carbonyl group.

path. The number of molecules depends on the concentration of the solution and the path length of the absorption cell. The amount of light that passes through a solution (transmittance) is given by Beer's law

$$\log \frac{I_0}{I} = \epsilon c d$$

where I_0 is the intensity of the light before it encounters the cell, I is the intensity of the light emerging from the cell, c is the concentration in moles per liter, and d is the path length in centimeters.

As an example, the ultraviolet spectrum of two concentrations of mesityl oxide, $(CH_3)_2C{=}CHCOCH_3$, in the same 1-cm cell (a common path length) is shown in Figure 21.26. A highly dilute solution is used for the $\pi \rightarrow \pi^*$ absorption at 235 nm. The extinction coefficient for this transition is calculated as

$$\epsilon = \frac{\log I_0/I}{cd} = \frac{1.18}{(9.37 \times 10^{-5})(1)} = 12,600 \text{ L mole}^{-1} \text{ cm}^{-1}$$

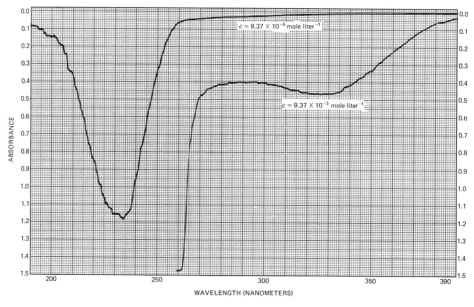

FIGURE 21.26   Ultraviolet absorption spectra of mesityl oxide, $(CH_3)_2C{=}CHCOCH_3$.

In this dilute solution the absorption due to the $n \rightarrow \pi^*$ transition is so weak it is barely discernible. A more concentrated solution gives greater absorption and, from the second curve in Figure 21.26, we may calculate ϵ for this transition at 326 nm to be

$$\epsilon = \frac{\log I_0/I}{cd} = \frac{0.47}{(9.37 \times 10^{-3})(1)} = 50$$

(Note that the units of ϵ are usually omitted.)

This concentration is so high, however, that the $\pi \rightarrow \pi^*$ transition absorbs light essentially completely at its wavelength. The ratio of the two extinction coefficients, 12,600/50 = 252, is typical for unsaturated carbonyl compounds. In general, the $\pi \rightarrow \pi^*$ transitions have ϵ of about 10^4, whereas ϵ for $n \rightarrow \pi^*$ transitions are about 10-100.

EXERCISE 21.14 The ultraviolet spectrum of a solution of 0.00731 g of crotonic acid, $CH_3CH=CHCOOH$, in 10 mL of methanol was measured in a 1-cm cell. Although the $\pi \rightarrow \pi^*$ transition was off scale, the $n \rightarrow \pi^*$ transition at 250 nm showed an absorbance of 0.77. A 1-mL portion of this solution was diluted to 100 mL and the spectrum was recorded again. The $\pi \rightarrow \pi^*$ transition was seen clearly at 200 nm with an absorbance of 0.86. Calculate the extinction coefficients for the two transitions.

D. Alkyl Substituents

We saw in Section 21.6.B that 1,3-butadiene has a $\pi \rightarrow \pi^*$ transition at 217 nm. Alkyl-substituted butadienes have the same π-system, but their absorption spectra vary significantly.

	λ_{max}, nm
$CH_2=CHCH=CH_2$	217
$CH_2=\overset{\overset{\textstyle CH_3}{\mid}}{C}CH=CH_2$	220
$CH_3CH=CHCH=CH_2$	223.5
$CH_2=\overset{\overset{\textstyle H_3C}{\mid}}{C}-\overset{\overset{\textstyle CH_3}{\mid}}{C}=CH_2$	226
$CH_3CH=CHCH=CHCH_3$	227

Each methyl group increases the wavelength of the absorption peak by 3-7 nm. A similar effect shows up with unsaturated carbonyl compounds.

	λ_{max}, nm ($\pi \rightarrow \pi^*$)
$CH_2=CHCOCH_3$	219
$CH_3CH=CHCOCH_3$	224
$(CH_3)_2C=CHCOCH_3$	235

This effect arises from the overlap of σ-orbitals in the alkyl substituent with the

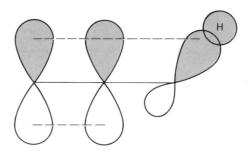

FIGURE 21.27 Hyperconjugation between a carbon-hydrogen σ-bond and the π-system of a double bond.

π-system. The resulting **hyperconjugation** is symbolized in Figure 21.27. The term was previously introduced (page 180) in connection with the stabilization of carbocations by alkyl groups.

Hyperconjugation has a smaller effect on electronic spectra than conjugation. Adding a methyl group to butadiene has little more than 10% of the effect of adding another vinyl group.

E. Benzene

The π-system of benzene has two highest occupied molecular orbitals, π_2 and π_3, and two lowest vacant molecular orbitals, π_4 and π_5 (Figure 21.7). We might expect to see four kinds of $\pi \rightarrow \pi^*$ transitions: $\pi_2 \rightarrow \pi_4$, $\pi_2 \rightarrow \pi_5$, $\pi_3 \rightarrow \pi_4$ and $\pi_3 \rightarrow \pi_5$. These four transitions all correspond to the same energy, and for this type of situation there is a breakdown in our simple picture of an electronic excitation as involving the transition from one molecular orbital to another. Several low-lying excited states of benzene exist that we would have to describe as various composites of the four simple transitions described above. An adequate treatment of the ultraviolet spectrum of benzene requires a rather complex quantum-mechanical discussion, which we will not develop. The longest-wavelength absorption of benzene gives a series of sharp bands centered at 255 nm with $\epsilon = 230$, a relatively low intensity for a $\pi \rightarrow \pi^*$ transition. This low value results from the high symmetry of benzene, which gives this absorption a relatively low probability. Such an absorption is called **symmetry forbidden**.

A vinyl group attached to a benzene ring constitutes a conjugated system. Styrene has two principal absorption bands: λ_{max} 244 nm with $\epsilon = 12,000$ and λ_{max} 282 nm with $\epsilon = 450$. The more intense band is a polyene type of $\pi \rightarrow \pi^*$ transition, whereas the less intense band corresponds to a substituted benzene. 1,2-Diphenylethylene (stilbene) allows another comparison of cis and trans isomers similar to the carotene case discussed in Section 21.6.B.

$$\begin{array}{cc} \underset{H}{\overset{Ph}{\diagdown}}C{=}C\underset{Ph}{\overset{H}{\diagup}} & \underset{H}{\overset{Ph}{\diagdown}}C{=}C\underset{H}{\overset{Ph}{\diagup}} \\ \textit{trans}\text{-stilbene} & \textit{cis}\text{-stilbene} \\ \lambda_{max} = 295 \text{ nm} & \lambda_{max} = 280 \text{ nm} \\ \epsilon = 27,000 & \epsilon = 13,500 \end{array}$$

trans-Stilbene has no significant steric interactions. The compound has an extended coplanar π-system. In *cis*-stilbene, however, the two phenyl groups are on the same side of the double bond and sterically interfere with each other. The rings cannot both be coplanar with the double bond, and π-conjugation is not as effective as it is in the trans isomer. The result is a small change in λ_{max} but a large decrease in the extinction coefficient.

F. Other Functional Groups

Alcohols and ethers do not have conjugated π-systems and are transparent in the normal ultraviolet and visible regions. Ethanol and ether are common solvents for recording ultraviolet spectra. Sulfides, however, have relatively intense absorption at about 210 nm with a weaker band at about 230 nm. These absorptions are probably associated with transition of a lone-pair electron in sulfur to a sulfur $3d$-orbital.

The carbonyl group in carboxylic acid derivatives is significantly different from that in ketones. Alkanoic acids have a low-intensity band about 200-210 nm, anhydrides absorb at somewhat longer wavelength, and the acid chlorides are still longer at about 235 nm.

Simple acetylenes absorb in the vacuum ultraviolet. Conjugated triple bonds show the type of absorption in the accessible ultraviolet expected for extended π-systems. The C≡N group of nitriles also absorbs at short wavelength, below 160 nm.

The simple alkyl fluorides and chlorides have no absorption maxima in the normal ultraviolet region. Alkyl bromides and iodides, however, do have λ_{max} in the region about 250-260 nm. These absorptions are attributed to transition of a lone-pair electron to an antibonding σ^*-orbital. Carbon-bromine and carbon-iodine bonds are sufficiently weak that the corresponding σ^*-orbitals have low enough energy to give transition energies in this ultraviolet region.

G. Photochemical Reactions

An excited state has more electronic energy than the ground state, and such states are generally rather short lived. This excess energy is generally dissipated within less than 10^{-7} sec. One important way in which this energy is removed is by conversion of the electronic energy to vibrational and rotational energy. That is, the energy of moving electrons is converted in part to that of moving nuclei. Such energy, in turn, may simply be distributed as translational energy to other colliding molecules, in which case the net result has been the conversion of light to heat.

Alternatively, the vibrational energy may suffice to cause rearrangements or to break bonds. We saw one example of bond breaking in the light-initiated chlorination of alkanes (Section 6.3).

$$Cl_2 \xrightarrow{h\nu} 2\,Cl\cdot$$

This reaction could have been expressed as follows.

$$Cl_2 \xrightarrow{h\nu} Cl_2^* \longrightarrow 2\,Cl\cdot$$

In this representation, Cl_2^* refers to an electronically excited state of Cl_2. The light promotes an electron to a chlorine-chlorine σ^*-orbital. An electron in an antibonding orbital produces a weaker bond than when such an orbital is vacant and generally gives rise to a lower bond-dissociation energy.

Many examples of different types of photochemical reactions are known for organic compounds, but we will discuss only one at this point (for further examples see Section 34.4). In the electronically excited state of an alkene the double bond is generally weaker than in the ground state, and cis-trans isomerization is more facile.

trans-stilbene   *cis*-stilbene

This type of photochemical reaction is involved in the chemistry of vision. Vitamin A_1 (retinol) is an alcohol that is oxidized enzymatically to vitamin A aldehyde (retinal), a cis form of which combines with a protein, opsin, to produce the light-sensitive compound rhodopsin. This compound is contained in the rods of the retina and absorbs at 500 nm. Absorption of light quanta of this wavelength results in conversion to the trans isomer. This isomerization is accompanied by a conformational change that excites the nerve cell and produces a separation into opsin and *trans*-retinal. The trans aldehyde is converted to the cis form by an enzyme, retinal isomerase, and the cycle starts anew. A wavelength of 500 nm corresponds to the blue-green region of the light spectrum and suggests why the rods are so sensitive to light of this color. Only a few light quanta are required to give a visual response to the dark-adapted eye. Bright light causes temporary impairment of vision because it depletes the rhodopsin and time is required for the protein to be reconstructed via the retinal isomerase cycle.

cis-retinal   *trans*-retinal

EXERCISE 21.14 A 500 nm light quantum accomplishes cis-trans isomerism of retinal. To what energy does light of wavelength 500 nm correspond?

21.7 Perturbational MO Approach to Reactivity

Consider what happens to the molecular orbitals of two reactants at the start of a reaction as the wavefunctions just begin to interact and overlap. Many of the MOs of one reactant will interact with MOs of the second reactant to produce a complex array of MOs of the combined system but these interactions can be dissected into two fundamental types. One is the interaction of a filled MO of reactant A with a filled MO of reactant B. As illustrated in Figure 21.28(a), bonding and antibonding interactions cause a splitting of the two energy levels involved, but because both levels are doubly occupied there is little *net* change in energy. The upper level actually increases somewhat more than the lower level decreases so that there is some net increase in energy.

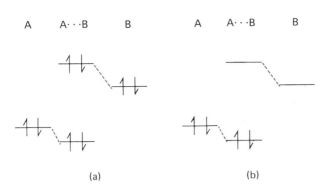

FIGURE 21.28 Two types of orbital interactions between reactants A and B.

This slight energy increase amounts to a net repulsion that contributes to the total energy of activation required for reaction. The second case involves the interaction of a filled MO of reactant A with a vacant MO of reactant B. The levels again split as before but since only occupied MOs contribute to the energy of a molecule, the result is now a net *stabilization*.

The magnitude of the energy splitting between orbitals depends primarily on their energy difference and on the amplitude of the wavefunctions at the point of interaction (their overlap). Two wavefunctions of greatly different energy interact only little. Moreover, only if both wavefunctions have significant amplitude in the region of interaction will such interaction be important. For these reasons, the most important interactions that affect the net energy at the beginning of a reaction are those involving the **highest occupied molecular orbital (HOMO)** of one reactant with the **lowest vacant molecular orbital (LUMO)** of the other reactant. These two types of MOs are also referred to as the **frontier orbitals**.

The most common case is that in which one reactant has the higher HOMO and the other reactant has the lower LUMO. A high HOMO implies weakly held electrons that can be easily lost or donated; hence, the reactant with the higher HOMO is called the **donor**. Similarly, a low-lying LUMO is one that can readily accept additional electrons. Accordingly, the reagent with the lower LUMO is called the **acceptor**. The corresponding HOMO-LUMO interaction between a donor and acceptor (Figure 21.29) can be dominating and determine the course of reaction.

In an S_N2 reaction the donor is the entering nucleophile whose HOMO is a lone-pair orbital. The acceptor is the organic substrate whose LUMO for the reaction is a σ^*-orbital involving the leaving group. The LUMO of methyl fluoride, for example, is illustrated in Figure 21.30. Attack by the nucleophile at the carbon-fluorine bond involves interaction at a node with consequent little net overlap (Figure 21.31). Reaction at the rear of the carbon-fluorine bond, however, involves interaction with the large lobe at that point. Overlap with the HOMO of the nucleophile is substantial and attack at this point is favored. Moreover, the new lower energy level that results from bonding interaction of the HOMO and LUMO in Figure 21.29 belongs to a combined MO that includes LUMO character of the acceptor. Since this new combined MO is occupied by two electrons that formerly resided in an MO (the HOMO) exclusively on the donor, the net result is transfer of electron density from the HOMO of the donor to the LUMO of the acceptor. Putting electron density into an MO that has carbon-fluorine antibonding character weakens the bond to fluorine whereas the positive overlap provides bonding character to the incoming nucleophile. In short, this HOMO-LUMO interaction shows us a displacement reaction with inversion of configuration in the making.

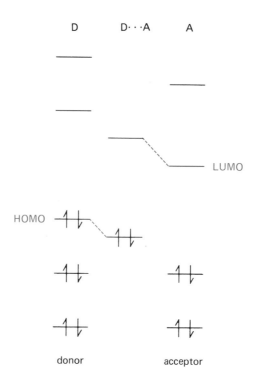

FIGURE 21.29   HOMO-LUMO interaction between donor (D) and acceptor (A) reactants.

EXERCISE 21.15   Figure 21.32 shows the LUMO of ethyl fluoride in a staggered configuration. Locate two regions of maximum overlap with an attacking nucleophile and compare with the expected mechanisms for S_N2 and E2 reactions. For the E2 reaction show how putting electron density into the LUMO starts to form the double bond as well as weakening the bonds to the leaving fluoride and proton.

The frontier orbital approach applies in an especially straightforward way to compounds with conjugated multiple bonds because the HOMOs and LUMOs of such compounds are frequently π-MOs. Butadiene is a simple example. In reaction with an electrophile butadiene is the donor and the electrophile is the acceptor. To determine

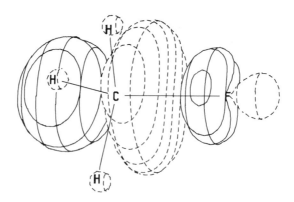

FIGURE 21.30   The LUMO of methyl fluoride is essentially a carbon-fluorine σ^* orbital. [Reproduced with permission from W. L. Jorgensen and L. Salem, *The Organic Chemist's Book of Orbitals*, Academic Press, New York, 1973.]

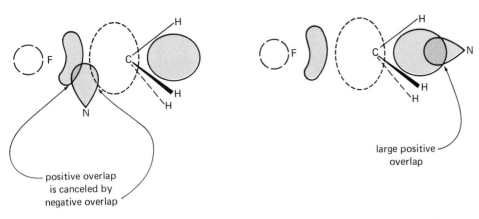

positive overlap
is canceled by
negative overlap

large positive
overlap

FIGURE 21.31 HOMO-LUMO interaction is weak for S_N2 attack at the carbon-fluorine bond *(left)* but strong at the rear of the bond *(right)*.

whether reaction at the 1- or 2-position of butadiene is preferred we examine π_2, the HOMO, of butadiene (Figure 21.5). The amplitude of the end carbon is clearly greater than an interior carbon in this MO and points to preferred reaction at the 1-position (Figure 21.33).

The π-MOs of an α,β-unsaturated carbonyl compound such as acrolein resemble those of the diene but the nodes are shifted because of the electronegative effect of the oxygen. The LUMO (π_3) of acrolein has two nodes as does that for butadiene but acrolein lacks the symmetry of butadiene and the two MOs differ as shown in Figure 21.34. The LUMO of acrolein has large amplitude at both the carbonyl carbon and at the terminal (β) carbon. Reaction with a nucleophile at the former position corresponds to normal carbonyl addition whereas reaction at the terminal carbon is the conjugate addition found for many such reactions of unsaturated carbonyl compounds (Section 19.3).

EXERCISE 21.16 Examine the π-MOs of allyl cation (Figure 21.3) and deduce whether reaction with a nucleophile occurs at an end or central carbon.

The HOMO-LUMO approach is especially useful with cycloaddition reactions of the Diels-Alder type. In such reactions the diene is normally the donor whose HOMO is

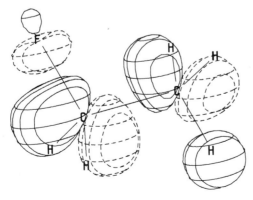

FIGURE 21.32. The LUMO of ethyl fluoride encompasses the entire molecule, including the methyl group. [Reproduced with permission from W. L. Jorgensen and L. Salem, *The Organic Chemist's Book of Orbitals*, Academic Press, New York, 1973.]

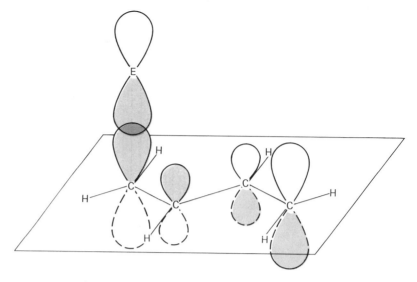

FIGURE 21.33 Reaction of the HOMO of butadiene with the LUMO of a nucleophile occurs preferentially at the 1-position.

considered and the dienophile is the acceptor whose LUMO is significant in reaction. The HOMO of butadiene and the LUMO of ethylene both have a single node and positive overlap is involved between these MOs (Figure 21.35). At the transition state electron transfer occurs from the diene to the dienophile. Note in Figure 21.35 how the electron density lost from bonding and antibonding regions of butadiene and gained by

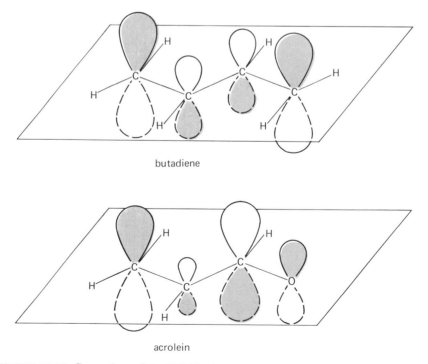

butadiene

acrolein

FIGURE 21.34 Comparison of the LUMO of acrolein and butadiene. Reaction of butadiene with a nucleophile is expected only at the terminal carbon, whereas acrolein can react at both the carbonyl carbon and the terminal carbon.

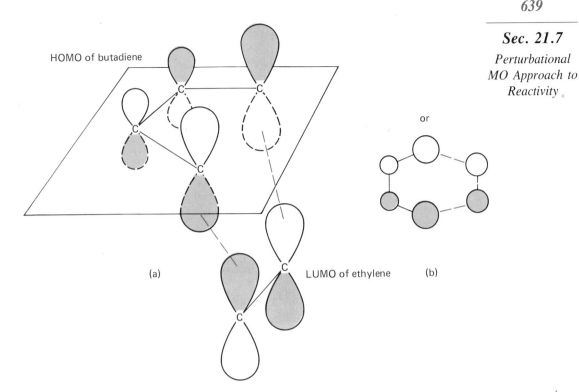

FIGURE 21.35 *(a)* The HOMO of butadiene and LUMO of ethylene can lead to a cycloaddition reaction. The alternative and simpler representation *(b)* shows a cross-section of one side of the orbital lobes.

the antibonding in ethylene corresponds to the bond changes during cycloaddition. However, the LUMO of ethylene has relatively high energy; hence, it is not a good dienophile and Diels-Alder reactions with ethylene generally require high temperature and pressure. Dienophiles with electron-attracting groups have lower LUMOs that can interact more effectively with the HOMOs of dienes and thereby give more facile reactions.

The HOMO-LUMO approach can provide an understanding of directional specificity in cycloaddition reactions with unsymmetrically substituted compounds. To do this we need to examine the effect of substituents on MOs. In ethylene the effects are straightforward. Electron-attracting groups tend to "attract" wave function and nodes. The result is shown schematically in Figure 21.36. Electron-donating groups have the opposite effect. Alkyl groups behave as electron-donating groups on the HOMO but,

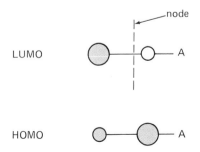

FIGURE 21.36 HOMO and LUMO of ethylene with an electron-attracting substituent A.

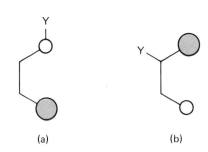

FIGURE 21.37 The HOMOs of 1- and 2-substituted butadienes. In *(a)* the substituent Y represents most common substituents, both electron-donating and electron-attracting, but in *(b)* Y is an electron-donating or an alkyl group.

because of hyperconjugation (Figure 21.27), have the same effect as electron-attracting groups on the LUMO.

The effects with butadiene are more complex. Most substituents at the 1-position of butadiene increase the magnitude of the wavefunction at the 4-position in the HOMO. Similarly, most substituents at the 2-position of butadiene increase the magnitude of the wave function at the 1-position in the HOMO. The results are shown in Figure 21.37. The effects on the LUMOs are less simple and vary with different types of substituents. Fortunately, for most Diels-Alder reactions, the important interaction is that between the HOMO and the diene and the LUMO of the dienophile.

In applying these results the important rule is that *positions of highest wave-function amplitude react preferentially*. In the present case the lower-energy transition state is obtained by reacting the largest lobe of the diene HOMO with the larger lobe of the dienophile LUMO; that is, large-large, small-small gives better net overlap and total bonding than two large-small interactions. In the interaction of virtually all 1-substituted butadienes with an ethylene containing an electron-attracting group or an alkyl group, the interaction symbolized as (a) in Figure 21.38 is preferred to that in (b).

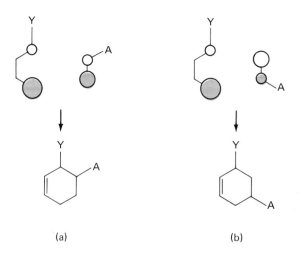

FIGURE 21.38 Interaction *(a)* of a 1-substituted butadiene with an electron-attracting dienophile is favored over interaction *(b)*.

(a)   (b)

FIGURE 21.39 Interaction *(a)* of an electron-attracting dienophile with a butadiene having an electron-donating 2-substituent is favored over interaction *(b)*.

Similarly, interaction of such dienophiles with butadienes substituted with electron-donating groups in the 2-position favors reaction path (a) in Figure 21.39. Experimental reaction preferences are generally in agreement with these theoretical considerations.

In the rare case of dienes containing strong electron-attracting groups and dienophiles with strong electron-donating substituents the predominant interaction may now involve the *LUMO* of the diene and the *HOMO* of the dienophile. The theory in such a case is more complex and depends on the specific substituents.

EXERCISE 21.17 Predict the major product from the Diels-Alder reaction of 2-methyl-1,3-butadiene and acrolein.

PROBLEMS

1. (a) The heat of hydrogenation of cyclooctene to cyclooctane is -23.3 kcal mole^{-1}. The heat of hydrogenation of cyclooctatetraene to cyclooctane is -100.9 kcal mole^{-1}. Use these data to calculate an empirical resonance energy for cyclooctatetraene. How do you interpret this result compared to the resonance energy of benzene?

    (b) Use the table of average bond energies in Appendix III to estimate the atomization energy of cyclooctatetraene. The experimental value is $\Delta H^\circ_{atom} = +1713$ kcal mole^{-1}. What value does this method give for the empirical resonance energy of cyclooctatetraene? Compare this result with that in part (a).

    (c) Thermochemical measurements on [18]annulene give a derived heat of atomization, $\Delta H^\circ_{atom} = +3890$ kcal mole^{-1}. From the method in part (b), calculate the corresponding empirical resonance energy. How does this result compare with expectations from the $4n + 2$ rule?

2. Which one of the following hydrocarbons is expected to be the most acidic? Why?

3. Determine the number of π-electrons involved in each of the following cyclic systems and determine whether each is aromatic according to the Hückel rule.

(a)   (b)   (c)

(d) cyclo-$C_7H_7^{3-}$ (e) cyclo-$C_8H_8^{2+}$

(f)

4. Figure 21.8 gives the MO energy level pattern for planar [8]annulene. Sketch the MOs corresponding to each energy.

5. Each of the following cycloaddition reactions can be written with a pericyclic transition state. Which ones follow the Hückel $4n + 2$ rule?

(a)

(b) CH_2 = CH_2 +

(c)

(d)

6. The following known reaction does not occur with the corresponding seven-membered ring analog. Explain.

7. Consider the cycloaddition reaction of allyl cation with ethylene to give cyclopentyl cation and with butadiene to give a cycloheptenyl cation.
   (a) Which reaction is preferred from considerations of HOMO-LUMO interactions?
   (b) Which transition state has Hückel aromaticity?

8. Predict the favored product of each of the following Diels-Alder reactions.
   (a) 2-methoxybutadiene and ethyl acrylate
   (b) 1-methylbutadiene and propyne
   (c) 1,3-dimethylbutadiene and propargylic acid ($HC\equiv CCOOH$)

9. Alkyl bromides and iodides are normally stored in the dark or in dark bottles. On exposure to light they slowly turn brown or violet, respectively. Give an explanation for this phenomenon based on a reasonable photochemical mechanism.

10. Indicate which of the following compounds would be suitable as solvents for recording normal ultraviolet spectra of substrates and briefly explain your choices: methanol; perfluoropropane; 1-chlorobutane; ethyl ether; ethyl iodide; methylene bromide; methyl butyl sulfide; benzene; cyclohexane; acetonitrile

11. A number of simple conjugated polyenes, $H(CH=CH)_nH$, are now known up to $n = 10$; λ_{max} in nanometers corresponding to values of n are as follows: 2, 217; 3, 268; 4, 304; 5, 334; 6, 364; 7, 390; 8, 410; 10, 447. A crude model of such a conjugated π-system is that of an electron in a box having the dimensions of the π-system. A quantum-mechanical treatment of such a model suggests that $1/\lambda_{max}$ should be approximately a linear function of $1/n$. Test this prediction with the data given and interpolate to find λ_{max} for the missing polyene with $n = 9$.

12. The ultraviolet spectrum of 3,6,6-trimethylcyclohex-2-en-1-one is shown below. The concentration is 1.486×10^{-5} g mL^{-1} in ethanol. Calculate ϵ and determine λ_{max}.

13. The effect of a methyl group on a molecular orbital depends on the magnitude of the wave function at the point of attachment. Explain why the the effect of a methyl group on the UV spectrum of butadiene is greater at the 1-position than the 2-position.

Chapter 22

Electrophilic Aromatic Substitution

In Chapter 20 we encountered aromatic compounds for the first time and learned something of the special properties of the aromatic ring. In this chapter we will look at the most important reaction of the aromatic ring—substitution of one electrophile (usually a proton) by another electron-deficient species. The reaction applies to a number of different electrophilic reagents and provides an important route to many substituted aromatic compounds. Moreover, when applied to benzene systems already containing one or more substituents, the reaction shows specificity and reactivity effects that are readily rationalized by theory. Thus, this chapter provides an especially integrated combination of theory and synthesis.

22.1 Halogenation

Alkenes react rapidly with bromine even at low temperatures to give the product of *addition* of bromine.

$$CH_2{=}CH_2 + Br_2 \longrightarrow BrCH_2CH_2Br \qquad \Delta H^\circ = -29.2 \text{ kcal mole}^{-1}$$

The reaction is highly exothermic because two carbon-bromine bonds are substantially more stable than a bromine-bromine bond and the second bond of a double bond. The corresponding addition reaction of benzene is slightly endothermic.

$$\Delta H^\circ \cong 2 \text{ kcal mole}^{-1}$$

Such an addition reaction destroys the cyclic π-electronic system of benzene. Note that the difference in ΔH° for the two cases is approximately the resonance energy of benzene.

Benzene does react with bromine, but the reaction requires the use of appropriate Lewis acids such as ferric bromide. The product of the reaction is the result of *substitution* rather than addition.

$$\Delta H^\circ = -10.8 \text{ kcal mole}^{-1}$$

> Sixty grams of bromine is added slowly to a mixture of 33 g of benzene and 2 g of iron filings. The mixture is warmed until the red vapors of bromine are no longer visible, about one half hour. Water is added, and the washed and dried organic layer is distilled to give 40 g of bromobenzene, b.p. 156°C.

In this procedure, the iron reacts rapidly with bromine to give ferric bromide. Anhydrous ferric halides are Lewis acids and react avidly with bases such as water.

$$FeX_3 + H_2O \rightleftharpoons H_2O : FeX_3 \longrightarrow \text{higher hydrates}$$

Anhydrous ferric halides are difficult to keep pure and are frequently made from the elements as needed, as in the foregoing procedure.

It is the Lewis-acid character of ferric salts that allows them to function as catalysts in this reaction. Aluminum halides are used frequently for the same purpose. Recall that the first step in the bromination of an alkene is a displacement by the alkene as a nucleophile on bromine with bromide ion as a leaving group (Section 11.6.B).

In nonpolar solvents, the leaving bromide ion requires additional solvation by bromine (page 526).

In this case a bromine molecule serves as a mild Lewis acid to help pull bromide ion from bromine. This type of "pull" is provided more powerfully by a stronger Lewis acid such as ferric bromide.

Benzene is a much weaker nucleophilic reagent than a simple alkene and requires a more electrophilic reagent for reaction.

The intermediate in the bromination of benzene is a conjugated carbocation. Its structure may be expressed by three Lewis structures

The resulting structure is that of an approximately tetrahedral carbon attached to a planar pentadienyl cation, as shown by the stereo representation in Figure 22.1.

This resonance-stabilized pentadienyl cation is often symbolized by using a dotted

FIGURE 22.1 Stereo representation of the intermediate in the bromination of benzene.

line to indicate that the positive charge is delocalized over the three positions indicated in the foregoing resonance structures.

Again, however, this symbol conveys no accounting of electrons. The student is urged to use Lewis structures exclusively at this stage in order to understand more fully the electron displacements that occur in reactions.

Carbocations can generally react with a nucleophilic reagent, rearrange, or lose a proton. Reaction of the pentadienyl cation intermediate with a nucleophile would give a product without the benzene ring resonance. Consequently, this type of reaction is rarely observed in electrophilic aromatic reactions. Rearrangements are significant only in some special cases to be discussed later. The only important reaction of our bromination intermediate is loss of a proton to restore the cyclic π-system and yield the substitution product.

The overall reaction sequence is as follows.

The first step is rate determining as indicated by the energy profile shown in Figure 22.2. The experimental evidence for this reaction mechanism comes from many studies of chemical kinetics, isotope effects, and structural effects.

The reaction mechanism for bromination of benzene is general for other electrophilic aromatic substitutions as well. Reaction occurs with an electron-deficient (electrophilic) species to give a pentadienyl cation intermediate, which loses a proton to give the substituted benzene product.

FIGURE 22.2 Reaction profile for bromination of benzene.

Chlorination is directly analogous to bromination.

The last example allows an important comparison of these electrophilic halogenations and the free radical halogenations of methylbenzenes that we encountered in Section

20.5.A. Recall that under free radical conditions substitution occurs in the side chain, principally at the benzylic position.

Iodobenzene can be prepared by using iodine and an oxidizing agent under acidic conditions. Suitable oxidizing agents include nitric acid or arsenic acid (H_3AsO_4).

$$C_6H_6 + I_2 + HNO_3 \xrightarrow{50°C} NO + NO_2 + C_6H_5I$$
$$(86-87\%)$$

The reaction involves a normal aromatic electrophilic substitution by iodonium ion obtained by oxidation.

$$I_2 \xrightarrow{-2e^-} 2\,I^+$$

EXERCISE 22.1 Write the three important resonance structures for the intermediate obtained by reaction of *p*-xylene with iodonium ion.

22.2 Protonation

Benzene is an extremely weak base, much weaker than an alkene. Benzene is only slightly protonated in concentrated sulfuric acid, whereas isobutylene is significantly protonated even in sulfuric acid containing water. Some protonation does occur, however, and the amount can be significant if substituents are present. For example, hexamethylbenzene is 50% protonated in 90% aqueous sulfuric acid.

Protonation of benzene can be detected by hydrogen isotope exchange reactions in acid. If benzene is stirred for several days at room temperature with 80% aqueous sulfuric acid containing deuterium or tritium, the isotope distributes between the benzene and the aqueous acid.

benzene-*t*

Tritium is normally used as a **radioactive tracer isotope**. It is typically used in a ratio of less than 1 ppm of ordinary hydrogen. Therefore, in an exchange process such as this, it is unlikely that a given molecule will have more than one tritium bound to it. The radioactivity of tritium can be measured by a sensitive instrument called a **liquid scintillation counter**; hence, tritium incorporation can be precisely measured by using only a small amount of the isotope. On the other hand, deuterium is used as a **macroscopic isotope**. Incorporation is monitored by less sensitive analytical techniques, such as NMR or mass spectrometry. The exchange reaction will give mixtures of deuterated benzenes containing varying numbers of deuterium atoms attached to the ring. The amount of deuterium incorporation will depend on the relative amounts of ^{1}H and ^{2}H isotopes in the hydrogen "pool." If a large excess of D_2SO_4 and D_2O is used, benzene-d_6, C_6D_6, can be obtained.

benzene-d_6

The exchange reaction is a simple type of electrophilic aromatic substitution reaction in which the electrophilic reagent is D^+.

The intermediate pentadienyl cation undergoes only one significant reaction—loss of a proton (or a deuteron). This reaction, which regenerates the aromatic π-system, is much faster than its reaction with water. With alkyl cations, reaction with a nucleophilic species is a much more important reaction, because elimination of a proton from such carbocations does not have the formation of an aromatic ring as an additional driving force.

EXERCISE 22.2 What product would you expect from treatment of benzene with excess D_2O–D_2SO_4 containing some tritiated water?

22.3 Nitration

The reaction of alkenes with nitric acid is not a generally useful reaction. Addition of nitric acid to the double bond is accompanied by more or less oxidation. However, benzene is quite stable to most oxidizing agents, and its reaction with nitric acid is an important organic reaction. Actually, the nitrating reagent generally used is a mixture of concentrated nitric acid and sulfuric acid.

nitrobenzene

To a flask containing 65 g of benzene is added a mixture of 110 mL of conc. H_2SO_4 and 85 mL of conc. HNO_3. The acid mixture is added in portions so that the temperature does not exceed 50°C. After all of the acid has been added, the reaction mixture is cooled and the oily nitrobenzene layer is separated, washed, and distilled. The yield of pure product is 85–88 g (83–86%).

The nitro group is an important functional group in aromatic chemistry because it may be converted into many other functional groups. The nitration reaction thus provides a route to many substituted aromatic compounds. The chemistry of the nitro group will be detailed in Section 24.1. Many properties of the nitro group can be interpreted on the basis of a resonance hybrid of two Lewis structures.

$$\left[R-\overset{+}{N}\overset{\displaystyle O}{\underset{\displaystyle O^-}{}} \longleftrightarrow R-\overset{+}{N}\overset{\displaystyle O^-}{\underset{\displaystyle O}{}} \right] \equiv R-\overset{+}{N}\overset{\displaystyle O^{\frac{1}{2}-}}{\underset{\displaystyle O^{\frac{1}{2}-}}{}}$$

In these structures the O—N—O system is seen to have an allylic anion type of π-system.

In a mixture of nitric and sulfuric acids, an equilibrium is established in which many species are present. One of these species is the nitronium ion, NO_2^+, which has been detected by spectroscopic methods. In the mixture of acids, it is produced by a process in which sulfuric acid functions as an acid and nitric acid functions as a base.

$$H_2SO_4 + HONO_2 \rightleftharpoons H_2\overset{+}{O}NO_2 + HSO_4^-$$

$$H_2\overset{+}{O}NO_2 + H_2SO_4 \rightleftharpoons H_3O^+ + NO_2^+ + HSO_4^-$$

$$2\,H_2SO_4 + HONO_2 \rightleftharpoons H_3O^+ + NO_2^+ + 2\,HSO_4^-$$

The structure of nitronium ion is known from spectroscopic measurements. It is related to the isoelectronic compound carbon dioxide. The molecule is linear and is a powerful electrophilic reagent.

$$O\!=\!\overset{+}{N}\!=\!O$$

nitronium ion

Nitronium ion reacts directly with benzene to give a pentadienyl cation intermediate.

Note that reaction occurs on nitrogen rather than oxygen.

Reaction at oxygen gives a nitrite compound, R—O—NO. Nitrites are unstable under such strongly acidic conditions and decompose to products containing carbon-oxygen bonds. These oxidation products react further to give highly colored polymeric compounds. The formation of more or less tarry byproducts is a usual side reaction in most aromatic nitration reactions.

Aromatic nitro compounds are important intermediates for the synthesis of other aromatic derivatives. The most important reaction of the nitro group is reduction. We shall return to this subject in Section 23.6.C.

EXERCISE 22.3 Write equations showing all of the steps involved in the nitration of *p*-xylene. Show all contributing resonance structures for the intermediate carbocation. From a consideration of these resonance structures, can you suggest why *p*-xylene undergoes nitration more rapidly than benzene?

22.4 Friedel-Crafts Reactions

A. Acylations

The electrophile in electrophilic aromatic substitution·can also be a carbocation. Such reactions are called **Friedel-Crafts reactions**. The most useful version of the reaction is Friedel-Crafts **acylation** in which the entering electrophile is an acyl group, RCO—, derived from a carboxylic acid derivative, usually an acyl halide or anhydride. The carbonyl group in such acid derivatives is sufficiently basic that formation of a complex occurs with strong Lewis acids such as aluminum chloride.

$$RCOX + AlCl_3 \rightleftharpoons \left[\begin{array}{ccc} \overset{+}{O}-\overset{-}{AlCl_3} & & O-\overset{-}{AlCl_3} \\ \| & & | \\ R-C-X & \longleftrightarrow & R-\underset{+}{C}-X \end{array} \right]$$

Aluminum chloride, $AlCl_3$, can be prepared by the direct reaction of aluminum with chlorine or hydrogen chloride. The anhydrous compound is available as a white powder that fumes in air and has the strong odor of HCl from reaction with atmospheric moisture. It can be sublimed and is soluble in many organic solvents such as benzene, nitrobenzene, and carbon tetrachloride. In benzene solution aluminum chloride exists as a dimer, Al_2Cl_6. Anhydrous aluminum chloride reacts vigorously with water with evolution of HCl. It is a strong Lewis acid that forms complexes with most oxygen-containing compounds. For laboratory use it is kept in tightly sealed bottles, and the fine powder is handled in air as little as possible, preferably in a hood.

The carbocation character of a carbonyl carbon is greatly enhanced by coordination to aluminum chloride, and in many cases the complex itself is sufficiently electrophilic to react with aromatic rings. In other cases, the complex exists in equilibrium with a small amount of the corresponding **acylium** ion, which is an even more powerful electrophile.

$$\overset{+\overset{-}{O}AlCl_3}{\underset{\|}{R-C-X}} \rightleftharpoons \left[R-\overset{+}{C}\equiv\overset{..}{O} \longleftrightarrow R-\overset{+}{C}=\overset{..}{O} \right] + AlXCl_3^-$$

acylium ion

As shown in the foregoing equations, the mechanism for reaction of the acylium ion with benzene is completely analogous to that of other electrophilic reagents. The final product is an aromatic ketone whose carbonyl group is sufficiently basic to be complexed completely by aluminum chloride.

It is this complex that is the actual reaction product. The work-up procedure involves treatment with water or dilute hydrochloric acid to decompose the complex and dissolve the aluminum salts. The liberated ketone remains in the organic layer and is isolated by crystallization or distillation. Because it complexes with the product, aluminum chloride must be used in equimolar amounts. Furthermore, the complexed ketone is resistant to further reaction so that high yields of pure product are readily available by this reaction. Friedel-Crafts acylation is an important and useful reaction in aromatic chemistry. An example is the acylation of benzene with acetyl chloride.

acetophenone

To a cooled mixture of 40 g of anhydrous aluminum chloride in 88 g of dry benzene, 29 g of acetyl chloride is added slowly with stirring or shaking. The HCl evolved is absorbed in a suitable trap. When the addition is complete, the mixture is warmed to 50°C for 1 hr. After cooling, ice and water are added, and the benzene layer is washed, dried, and distilled. The product acetophenone is distilled, b.p. 201°C, in a yield of 27 g.

EXERCISE 22.4 Outline multistep syntheses for the synthesis from benzene and other necessary organic reagents of each of the following compounds.
(a) 1-phenylpropane   (b) 2-phenyl-2-propanol   (c) styrene

B. Alkylations

Benzene undergoes Friedel-Crafts **alkylation** when treated with an alkyl halide and a Lewis-acid catalyst such as $FeBr_3$ or $AlCl_3$. An example is the reaction of benzene with *t*-butyl chloride to give *t*-butylbenzene.

In this Friedel-Crafts alkylation the attacking electrophile is the *t*-butyl cation, which is produced in the reaction of *t*-butyl chloride with $FeCl_3$. In the absence of other nucleophiles, this electrophilic species reacts with the aromatic ring.

$$(CH_3)_3CCl + FeCl_3 \rightleftharpoons (CH_3)_3C^+ \ FeCl_4{}^-$$

Friedel-Crafts alkylation has two important limitations that severely restrict its usefulness and render the reaction generally less valuable than acylation. As we shall see in Section 22.6, alkylbenzenes are generally *more* reactive in electrophilic substitution reactions than is benzene itself. Hence, Friedel-Crafts alkylation tends to give overalkylation, so that dialkyl and higher alkylated by-products are formed.

$$C_6H_6 \xrightarrow[\text{(CH}_3)_3\text{CCl}]{FeCl_3} C_6H_5C(CH_3)_3 \xrightarrow[\underset{\text{(faster)}}{\text{(CH}_3)_3\text{CCl}}]{FeCl_3} C_6H_4[C(CH_3)_3]_2$$

The only practical way of controlling such additional reactions is to keep benzene in large excess. This approach is practical with benzene itself, since it is an inexpensive compound, but it is impractical with most substituted benzenes, which are more expensive.

Another important limitation of Friedel-Crafts alkylations relates to an alternative reaction of many carbocations, particularly in the absence of reactive nucleophiles, namely, rearrangement to isomeric carbocations. Isopropyl chloride or bromide react normally with aluminum chloride and benzene to give isopropylbenzene.

However, 1-chloropropane also gives isopropylbenzene under these conditions. Rearrangement to the secondary carbocation is essentially complete.

Primary alkyl halides are less reactive than secondary or tertiary halides, and higher temperatures are normally required. Under some conditions, the rearrangement of primary systems is only partial. Under these conditions, a displacement reaction by benzene on the alkyl halide coordinated with the Lewis acid competes with carbocation rearrangement. It should be emphasized, however, that at least some rearrangement always occurs with suitable primary systems and such rearrangement greatly limits the utility of this reaction.

Friedel-Crafts alkylations may also be accomplished with alcohols and a catalyst such as aluminum chloride or boron trifluoride. The reaction has the same limitations as the alkyl halide reactions in requiring a large excess of benzene and in giving rearrangement products in suitable cases. In addition, one reaction product is water, which coordinates with Lewis acids. Thus, with alcohols a stoichiometric amount of Lewis acid is required.

| (67%) | (33%) |
| 2-phenylpentane | 3-phenylpentane |

In this example, the 2:1 ratio of 2-phenylpentane and 3-phenylpentane is exactly equal to the statistical mixture of isomeric secondary carbocations. Thus, equilibration of the isomeric pentyl cations is rapid compared to their rate of reaction with benzene.

EXERCISE 22.5 Explain why reaction of 3-methyl-2-butanol with boron fluoride and benzene gives mostly 2-methyl-2-phenylbutane and no appreciable amount of 2-methyl-3-phenylbutane. Suggest a synthesis of the latter hydrocarbon making use of a Friedel-Crafts acylation in the synthetic sequence.

Alkylation reactions can also be accomplished with alkenes. Typical catalysts used, HF/BF_3 and $HCl/AlCl_3$, generate carbocations in the usual way.

$$(CH_3)_2C{=}CH_2 + HF + BF_3 \rightleftharpoons (CH_3)_3C^+ \, BF_4^-$$

This reaction is used industrially to prepare alkylbenzenes, but it is not an important laboratory reaction.

A reaction that is closely related to Friedel-Crafts alkylation is **chloromethylation**, the reaction of aromatic rings with formaldehyde, hydrogen chloride, and a Lewis acid such as zinc chloride.

The reaction is an electrophilic aromatic substitution, probably by the oxonium ion formed by coordination of the formaldehyde with the Lewis acid.

$$[H_2C{=}\overset{+}{O}{-}\overset{-}{Z}nCl_2 \longleftrightarrow H_2\overset{+}{C}{-}O{-}\overset{-}{Z}nCl_2]$$

The resulting reagent will react with aromatic rings that are at least as reactive as benzene. The product of electrophilic aromatic substitution by the coordinated aldehyde is the corresponding alcohol, but this alcohol is benzylic, and in the presence of $ZnCl_2$-HCl it is converted rapidly to the corresponding chloride.

> The chloromethylation reaction must be conducted in an efficient hood and with extreme care. Under these reaction conditions bis-chloromethyl ether, $ClCH_2OCH_2Cl$ is produced. This compound is a potent carcinogen and should be avoided whenever possible.

An important side reaction in chloromethylation reactions is reaction of the product, which is a reactive alkyl halide, with the starting aromatic compound. For example, chloromethylation of benzene gives some diphenylmethane, which arises from reaction of the initial product, benzyl chloride, with benzene.

diphenylmethane

Of course, by simply using excess benzene and adjusting the reaction conditions appropriately, this side reaction can be made a practical method for the synthesis of diphenylmethane. A related reaction is the Friedel-Crafts alkylation of benzene with carbon tetrachloride.

(84–86%)
triphenylmethyl chloride

> Triphenylmethyl chloride or "trityl" chloride, is a colorless crystalline solid, m.p. 111–112°C, that forms the starting point of a fascinating chapter of organic chemistry. In experiments reported in 1900, Moses Gomberg treated triphenylmethyl chloride with finely divided silver in an inert atmosphere to obtain a white solid hydrocarbon formulated as hexaphenylethane. In organic solvents this hydrocarbon gives yellow solutions that rapidly absorb oxygen from the atmosphere. These solutions contain a relatively stable free radical, triphenylmethyl.
>
> $$(C_6H_5)_3C{-}C(C_6H_5)_3 \rightleftharpoons 2\ (C_6H_5)_3C{\cdot} \xrightarrow{O_2} (C_6H_5)_3COOC(C_6H_5)_3$$
> bis-triphenylmethyl
> peroxide
>
> The stability of triphenylmethyl radical stems from π-conjugation in the radical and steric hindrance in the dimer. Equilibrium studies showed the central bond in the dimer to have a strength of only 11 kcal mole^{-1}. A remarkable epilogue to this story was provided by recent structural studies based primarily on NMR evidence that show that the hydrocarbon

657

Sec. 22.5
Orientation in
Electrophilic
Aromatic
Substitution

considered to be hexaphenylethane for the better part of a century does not have this structure at all, but is instead the product of dimerization at one *para* position.

$$2 \ (C_6H_5)_3C\cdot \rightleftharpoons (C_6H_5)_3C-\underset{H}{\overset{}{\diagdown}}\hspace{-2pt}\text{\large⬡}\hspace{-2pt}=C\overset{C_6H_5}{\underset{C_6H_5}{\diagup}}$$

In other words, hexaphenylethane is so congested that it is less stable than the isomer shown despite the loss of the resonance energy of one benzene ring in this structure!

EXERCISE 22.6 Write the equations illustrating the reaction of benzene with the following reagents.
(a) butanoyl chloride, AlCl$_3$ (b) 2-methylpropene, HF, BF$_3$
(c) 2-butanol, H$_2$SO$_4$ (d) formaldehyde, HCl, ZnCl$_2$

22.5 Orientation in Electrophilic Aromatic Substitution

Benzene can give only a single monosubstituted product in electrophilic aromatic substitution. However, substitution on a compound that already has a group attached to the ring can give three products. The two substituents in a disubstituted benzene can be arranged *ortho*, *meta*, or *para* with respect to each other. These three isomers are generally not formed in equal amounts. The product distribution in such cases is affected by the substituent already present on the ring. With some groups further substitution gives mainly the *ortho-* and *para*-disubstituted products. Examples are seen in the products formed from bromination of bromobenzene or anisole or in the nitration of toluene.

(87%)   (13%)   (0.1%)
para   *ortho*   *meta*

(96%)   (4%)
para   *ortho*

(62%)   (33%)   (5%)
ortho   *para*   *meta*

On the other hand, further substitution on some substituted benzenes gives essentially all *meta*-disubstituted product, with little or none of the *ortho* and *para* products. Examples are the bromination and nitration of nitrobenzene and the nitration of methyl benzoate.

(76% yield)
(essentially no
ortho or *para*)

(93%)   (6%)   (1%)
meta   *ortho*   *para*

(81–85% yield)

As the foregoing examples suggest, substituent groups can be divided into two categories, those that are **ortho,para directors** and those that are **meta directors**. Bromo, methyl, and methoxy groups are *ortho,para* directors and nitro and ester groups are *meta* directors. Note that *ortho* and *para* are produced together, although the *ortho/para* ratio may vary with different groups and under different reaction conditions with the same group.

Substituent groups may also be characterized with respect to their effect on the rate of further substitution reactions. Some substituents cause the aromatic ring to be less reactive than benzene itself; these groups are said to be **deactivating**. An example is the nitro group, which is a powerful deactivating group. Nitrobenzene is much less reactive than benzene, as shown by the conditions required for nitration of benzene (page 650) and nitrobenzene (above). When two deactivating groups are attached to the ring, even more drastic conditions are necessary for further substitution. For example, *m*-dinitrobenzene may be converted into 1,3,5-trinitrobenzene in 45% yield by heating 60 g of the dinitrobenzene with 1 kg of fuming sulfuric acid and 0.5 kg of fuming nitric acid at 100°C for 5 days.

Commercial concentrated sulfuric acid is 98% H_2SO_4. Fuming sulfuric acid contains additional dissolved sulfur trioxide (Section 25.5.B). Concentrated nitric acid is a solution approximately 70% by weight of HNO_3 in water. The solution is colorless but becomes yellow by photochemical decomposition to yield NO_2. The red ''fuming'' nitric acid contains additional dissolved NO_2.

659

Sec. 22.5

Orientation in
Electrophilic
Aromatic
Substitution

Carbonyl groups are also deactivating groups. Thus, the products of Friedel-Crafts acylation are less reactive than the starting material. Consequently, it is quite easy to achieve monosubstitution in such reactions. In fact, Friedel-Crafts acylation is generally not applicable at all to aromatic rings that contain a strongly deactivating group. For example, nitrobenzene does not react under Friedel-Crafts acylation conditions and is even used as a solvent for such reactions!

Other groups are **activating**; electrophilic substitution on rings containing these groups is more rapid than with benzene. As we mentioned in our discussion of Friedel-Crafts alkylation, alkyl groups are activating groups, and hence alkylbenzenes are more reactive than benzene itself. This effect has an important consequence, since it means that the product of Friedel-Crafts alkylation is *more reactive* than the starting material. Thus, it is difficult to avoid the formation of overalkylation by-products.

The activating effect of alkyl groups can also be seen in the conditions required for nitration of mesitylene, which may be compared with the conditions used for the nitration of benzene itself (page 650).

mesitylene   nitromesitylene (74–76%)

Mesitylene, with its three activating groups, is so reactive that it undergoes halogenation even without the normal Lewis-acid catalyst (see Section 22.1).

mesitylene   bromomesitylene (79–82%)

In such a case the reaction may be considered to be a displacement reaction on halogen with the ring acting as a nucleophile.

Mesitylene is especially reactive because the intermediate produced is highly stabilized; all three of the usual resonance structures correspond to tertiary carbocations:

We will elaborate on the foregoing rationale for the activating effect of alkyl groups in Sections 22.6 and 22.7. For the present, however, it is useful to note that substituent groups may be grouped into three different classes with regard to whether they are activating or deactivating and whether they are *ortho,para*-directing or *meta*-directing.

1. *Ortho,para-directing and activating.* Functional groups in this category include R (alkyl), NH$_2$, NR$_2$, and NHCOR (amino, alkylamino, and amide), OH, OR, and OCOR (hydroxy, alkoxy, and ester).
2. *Ortho,para-directing and deactivating.* The most important functional groups in this category are the halogens, F, Cl, Br, and I.
3. *Meta-directing and deactivating.* This group includes NO$_2$ (nitro), SO$_3$H (sulfonic acid), and all carbonyl compounds: COOH, COOR, CHO, and COR (carboxylic acids, esters, aldehydes, and ketones).

Note that all activating groups are *ortho,para* directors and all *meta* directors are deactivating. These generalizations derive from many experimental observations and form a set of empirical and useful rules. However, these rules are also subject to a consistent and satisfying interpretation by the modern theory of organic chemistry. This theory has its basis in the electron-donating and electron-attracting character of different functional groups, as discussed in the next section.

EXERCISE 22.7 Make a six-by-four matrix. On one side put the aromatic compounds toluene, acetophenone, bromobenzene, anisole, nitrobenzene, and acetanilide. On the other side put the four reactions bromination, nitration, Friedel-Crafts alkylation and Friedel-Crafts acylation. Each intersection of the matrix represents a reaction. What products (if any) are formed in each reaction? Which reactions occur more rapidly than the analogous reaction on benzene itself?

22.6 Theory of Orientation in Electrophilic Aromatic Substitution

In Section 22.1 we learned that the mechanism of electrophilic aromatic substitution involves combination of a positive or electrophilic species with a pair of π-electrons of the benzene ring to form an intermediate having a pentadienyl cation structure.

The transition state has much of the character of the pentadienyl cation intermediate to which it leads. Those factors that affect the relative energy or stability of the intermediate also affect to a lesser but substantial degree the relative energy or stability of the transition state. The modern electronic theory of orientation in electrophilic aromatic substitution involves an assessment of the effect of a substituent on the relative energies of the pentadienyl cation-like transition state for reaction at different possible positions.

For example, reaction at the *ortho* position of toluene gives rise to a transition state that resembles the intermediate

661

Sec. 22.6

*Theory of
Orientation in
Electrophilic
Aromatic
Substitution*

FIGURE 22.3 Energy profile for electrophilic substitution on benzene.

Two of the structures are those of secondary carbocations, but the third corresponds to a more stable tertiary carbocation. As a result, this intermediate and *hence also the transition state that leads to it* are more stable—have lower energy—than the corresponding intermediate and transition state for benzene in which all three resonance structures are those of secondary carbocations. The *ortho* position of toluene is therefore expected to be more reactive than a single position of benzene.

This argument must be put on a per-hydrogen basis. Without specific orientation preferences, statistics alone would give a reactivity ratio for benzene:*ortho*:*meta*:*para* of 6:2:2:1.

Reaction at the *meta* position gives rise to the following resonance structures.

All three structures are those of secondary carbocations. Each structure is stabilized slightly by the C_{methyl}—C_{ring} dipole.

Correspondingly, the *meta* position of toluene is expected to be somewhat more reactive than a benzene position but not nearly as reactive as the *ortho* position.

Finally, we apply this approach to the *para* position to generate the resonance structures

Here again we find two secondary carbocation structures and one tertiary carbocation. The overall energy of the transition state is comparable to that for *ortho* substitution. Indeed, this approach does not distinguish between preference for *ortho* relative to *para* substitution, but does indicate why substituents divide into the two broad groups of *ortho,para* and *meta* directors.

The resulting energy profile for reaction at toluene is compared with that for benzene in Figure 22.4. The differences between the alternative structures are somewhat less in the transition state than in the intermediate because the amount of positive charge to be distributed is greater in the intermediate in which a fully formed C—Y bond is developed. We have chosen to examine the intermediates but only for the convenience of symbolism. The same arguments apply to the developing positive charge on the benzene ring in the transition states. The net result is that of predominant *ortho,para* orientation; although the *meta* position is more reactive than a single benzene position, the *ortho* and *para* positions are even more so.

We next apply this approach to the corresponding reaction at the *ortho*, *para*, and *meta* positions of nitrobenzene and derive three sets of resonance structures for the intermediates (and transition states) involved.

ortho

para

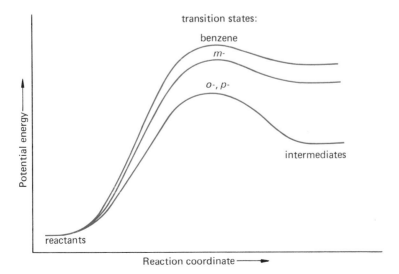

meta

All of these structures involve the electrostatic repulsion of the carbocation charge with the strong dipole of the nitro group.

$$(+) \quad \overset{+\longrightarrow}{C-NO_2}$$

That is, every one of these structures is substantially less stable than the corresponding structure for reaction at benzene; hence, all positions in nitrobenzene are expected to be deactivated relative to benzene. For reaction at the *ortho* and *para* positions, however, one structure is that of a carbocation right next to the positive nitrogen of the nitro group. This structure in each case is of such high energy compared to the other structures, in which the positive charges are separated by one or more atoms, that it contributes very little to the overall resonance hybrid. The *meta* reaction involves only struc-

FIGURE 22.4 Energy profile for reaction at *ortho*, *para*, and *meta* positions of toluene compared to benzene.

tures in which the positive charges are separated; thus, although the transition state for *meta* substitution is of higher energy than for reaction at benzene, it is of lower energy than those for reaction at the *ortho* or *para* positions. We can phrase this result another way: the *meta* reaction is deactivated less than *ortho* or *para* reaction. The corresponding reaction profiles are summarized in Figure 22.5.

These principles apply generally to other types of substituents. For anisole, we may write the same sets of three resonance structures.

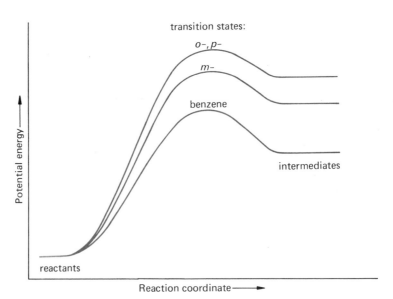

FIGURE 22.5 The intermediate derived from *meta* reaction of nitrobenzene is formed less readily than that from attack at benzene but more readily than that from reaction at the *ortho* or *para* positions.

665

Sec. 22.6
Theory of
Orientation in
Electrophilic
Aromatic
Substitution

All of these structures are expected to be somewhat destabilized by the electrostatic interaction with the C—O dipole, but reaction at the *ortho* and *para* positions also corresponds to oxonium ions.

These additional structures greatly stabilize the intermediates and the transition states leading to them. Similar structures are involved in acid-catalyzed reactions of carbonyl compounds.

The oxonium ion structures so dominate the system that the *ortho* and *para* positions of anisole are highly activated compared to benzene. We shall see in Chapter 26 that electrophilic substitution reactions at these positions in phenols and phenyl ethers and esters are accomplished under rather mild conditions. On the other hand, reaction at the *meta* positions is expected to be somewhat less facile than in benzene. The resulting reaction profile is shown in Figure 22.6.

Reactions at the *ortho* and *para* positions of aromatic amines involve related immonium ion structures, for example,

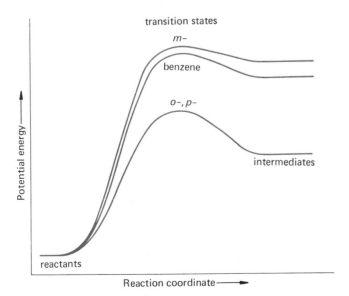

FIGURE 22.6 Reaction profile for reaction at the *ortho*, *para*, and *meta* positions of anisole compared to benzene. The same figure would apply to reaction of phenol and aniline.

Consequently these positions are also highly activated relative to benzene.

Let us now apply the procedure to a halobenzene. Reaction at the *meta* position gives the three structures

meta

All three structures are strongly destabilized by electrostatic interaction of the positive charge with the carbon-halogen dipole.

$$(+) \quad \overset{\longrightarrow}{C-X}$$

Accordingly, the *meta* position in the halobenzene is strongly deactivated relative to benzene. Reactions at the *ortho* and *para* positions involve similar carbocation structures destabilized by interaction with the carbon-halogen dipole.

ortho

para

In both cases, however, one structure is that of an α-halocarbocation in which interaction with a halogen lone pair is possible to give the halonium ion structures.

Such halonium ion structures are not nearly as stable as related oxonium and immonium ions. In practice, the additional contribution of such structures does not compensate for the deactivating effect of the carbon-halogen dipoles on the other structures, but it does make reaction at the *ortho* and *para* positions far more facile than at the *meta* position. The corresponding reaction profile is shown in Figure 22.7.

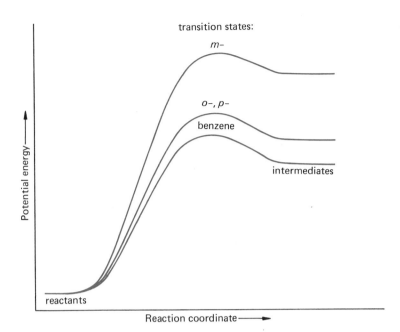

FIGURE 22.7 Energy profile for reaction of a halobenzene compared to benzene.

EXERCISE 22.8 Use the theory developed in this section to predict the orientation specificity and reactivity relative to benzene of vinyl (CH=CH$_2$) and formyl (CHO) groups.

22.7 Quantitative Reactivities: Partial Rate Factors

Nitration reactions have been studied extensively for many aromatic compounds, and relative reactivities at different positions have been determined. Furthermore, by studying the reaction of a mixture of benzene and some other compound, it is often possible to determine the quantitative reactivities of various positions relative to a benzene position. These statistically corrected relative reactivities are known as partial rate factors.

For example, the reaction of equimolar amounts of toluene and benzene with a small amount of nitric acid in acetic anhydride at 30°C gives one part of nitrobenzene to 27 parts of nitrotoluenes. The nitrotoluenes formed are 58.1% *ortho*, 3.7% *meta*, and 38.2% *para*. The partial rate factors, f_i, are calculated as follows.

$$f_o = (\text{fraction } o)\left(\frac{\text{no. benzene positions}}{\text{no. } o \text{ positions}}\right)\left(\frac{\text{toluene reactivity}}{\text{benzene reactivity}}\right)$$
$$= (0.581)(\tfrac{6}{2})(27) = 47$$
$$f_m = (0.037)(\tfrac{6}{2})(27) = 3$$
$$f_p = (0.382)(\tfrac{6}{1})(27) = 62$$

Note that the *meta* position is more reactive than a benzene position, as predicted by the theory developed in Section 22.6.

TABLE 22.1 Partial Rate Factors for Nitration

Partial rate factors for nitration of several substituted benzenes are summarized in Table 22.1. Some effects are clearly apparent in these results. For example, a *t*-butyl group has much the same effect as a methyl group in the *meta* and *para* positions, but at the *ortho* position *t*-butylbenzene is much less reactive than toluene. The difference is clearly to be attributed to steric hindrance caused by the bulky *t*-butyl group. At the distant *meta* and *para* positions the size of the alkyl group has little effect.

The halobenzenes follow the theory outlined in Section 22.6. All positions are less reactive than benzene, but the *meta* positions are more strongly deactivated than *ortho* and *para*. The chloromethyl group is of special interest since the stabilizing effect of an alkyl group is superimposed on the deactivating effect of the carbon-chlorine dipole. The result is a net *ortho,para* orientation with a little net deactivation.

But the quantitative data are sparse. The amounts formed of some isomers are so minute as to defy detection even by modern gas chromatography analytical methods. One approach to obtaining quantitative reactivity data for all positions in a given molecule, even when they differ greatly in reactivity, has been to study the simplest possible electrophilic aromatic substitution reaction, the replacement of one hydrogen isotope by another. Examples of this reaction were given in Section 22.2.

In principle, it is possible to prepare a variety of specifically labeled aromatic compounds and to study quantitatively the rate of loss of the hydrogen isotope under a consistent set of acidic conditions. A comparison of the rates of replacement of deuterium by hydrogen (protodedeuteration) of specifically deuterated anisoles with the corresponding rate for deuteriobenzene in aqueous perchloric acid gives the results displayed in Table 22.2. These results demonstrate the high reactivity of the *ortho* and

TABLE 22.2 Relative Rates of Protodedeuteration in Aqueous Perchloric Acid

para positions compared to benzene and the lower reactivity in the *meta* position. These same relative rates are expected to correspond approximately to nitration as well and imply that nitration of anisole gives only a few parts per million of *m*-nitro product. This minute quantity is extremely difficult to detect directly in the product mixture.

EXERCISE 22.9 Using the data in Table 22.1, calculate the percent composition of the three chloronitrobenzenes formed by nitration of chlorobenzene.

22.8 Effects of Multiple Substituents

The relative rates of replacement of tritium by hydrogen (protodetritiation) in trifluoro-acetic acid for toluene and the dimethylbenzenes compared to benzene are summarized in Table 22.3. The energy effects of two methyl groups are approximately additive compared to the effect of one methyl group in toluene. For example, the 3-position in *o*-dimethylbenzene is *ortho* to one methyl and *meta* to the other. The predicted reactivity is therefore $(219)(6.1) = 1340$, which agrees exactly with the experimental reactivity.

The product of the two partial rate factors is taken because it is the activation energy quantities that are additive

$$\Delta E^{\ddagger} \text{ (3-position in } o\text{-dimethylbenzene)} = \Delta E^{\ddagger}(o\text{-}) + \Delta E^{\ddagger}(m\text{-})$$

The energies are related to the logarithms of the rate constants.

$$RT \ln k(\text{3-position}) = RT \ln (o\text{-}) + RT \ln (m\text{-})$$
$$\log f(\text{3-position}) = \log f_o + \log f_m = \log f_o f_m$$
$$f(\text{3-position}) = f_o f_m$$

The relative reactivities of the toluene positions were used as partial rate factors to derive the predicted reactivities of the dimethylbenzenes given in parentheses in Table 22.3. The approximate agreement can be generalized to electrophilic substitution reactions of polysubstituted benzenes. That is, the net orientation effects of two or more substituents can be predicted approximately by examining the effects of each substituent separately. If all substituents orient preferentially to the same positions, such positions are strongly preferred. For example, nitration of the following disubstituted benzenes gives the percentage of nitration at each position as indicated.

In *m*-chlorotoluene, the 5-position is *meta* both to chlorine and to methyl, and no significant reaction occurs at this position. The other positions are all *ortho* or *para* to both groups, and a disagreeable mixture results. In *p*-nitrotoluene, however, the highly favored 2-position is *ortho* to the *ortho,para*-directing methyl and *meta* to the *meta*-directing nitro.

TABLE 22.3 Relative Rates of Protodetritiation in Trifluoroacetic Acid

If the groups already present have conflicting orientation preferences, it is helpful to divide substituents into three classes:

1. Strongly activating *ortho,para* directors, such as OR and NR_2.
2. Alkyl groups and halogens.
3. All *meta* directors.

If two substituents belong to different classes, the orientation effect of the superior class dominates. The following nitration results are examples.

Note that the effects of all *ortho,para* directors dominate over *meta* directors.

Finally, if both substituents are in the same class, all bets are off and horrible mixtures can be anticipated. The following nitration results are examples.

In our subsequent studies of the reactions of functional groups on benzene rings, we shall see that many syntheses can be accomplished by aromatic substitution reactions combined with functional group transformations. In such sequences, the order in which reactions are accomplished is of great importance because of the orientation preferences of different groups. One example will demonstrate this point.

The first route is clearly to be preferred as a preparation of 2,4-dinitrobenzoic acid.

EXERCISE 22.10   What major product or products are expected in nitration of (a) *p*-nitroanisole, (b) *m*-nitrobenzoic acid, (c) *p*-bromochlorobenzene, and (d) *m*-chlorotoluene?

22.9 Synthetic Utility of Electrophilic Aromatic Substitution

In this chapter we have seen how some important functional groups can be introduced directly into benzene and many of its derivatives by electrophilic substitution reactions. Important examples of such synthetically useful reactions are halogenation, nitration, and Friedel-Crafts acylation. In Chapter 25 we will learn of an additional useful reaction, sulfonation. Each of these functional groups can serve as a substrate for additional electrophilic substitution reactions, or the group can be converted to other functional groups. Halogens can be converted via lithium or Grignard reagents to a variety of functions. These and other reactions of aromatic halides will be discussed in Chapter 26. Nitro compounds can be reduced to amines, which in turn can be transformed to many different groups as detailed in Chapter 24. Aromatic ketones can participate in the usual reactions of carbonyl groups. One important such reaction is reduction of the carbonyl group to a methylene group by either the Wolff-Kishner or the Clemmensen method (Section 14.9.D).

$CO(CH_2)_4CH_3$ $\xrightarrow[\Delta]{H_2NNH_2 \quad KOH}$ $CH_2(CH_2)_4CH_3$

(82%)
hexylbenzene

$CO(CH_2)_{16}CH_3$ $\xrightarrow[\Delta]{Zn/Hg, \ HCl}$ $CH_2(CH_2)_{16}CH_3$

(77%)
octadecylbenzene

Since Friedel-Crafts *acylation* is generally a clean, high-yield reaction, the combination of acylation and reduction is generally to be preferred to Friedel-Crafts *alkylation*.

In our discussion of electrophilic substitution reactions we have considered the effects on orientation and reactivity of other substituents already on the benzene ring. We now need to consider how electrophilic substitution may be used in a practical sense to prepare polysubstituted benzenes. We want especially to consider how the process may be used in some cases to provide practical syntheses of pure compounds.

Remember that the goal of any chemical synthesis is generally to prepare *one pure compound* for some purpose. Therefore, whenever possible, one must use reactions that do not give mixtures of isomers. When there is no known method that provides only one isomer, a synthesis may still be acceptable if the desired isomer is produced in substantial amounts (hopefully as the *major* product) and if it may be separated in some way from the unwanted isomers.

Some electrophilic substitution reactions fit the first criterion; that is, one of the possible isomers is produced almost exclusively. Substitution on *meta*-orienting compounds usually falls into this category. Thus the following substitution reactions are good preparative reactions.

(75–84%)

(60–75%)

Recall that the Friedel-Crafts acylation reaction often *does not work when the ring already contains a* meta-*directing group.* Thus *m*-nitroacetophenone may be prepared by nitration of acetophenone but not by Friedel-Crafts acylation of nitrobenzene.

acetophenone   (55%)

In many of these reactions, a few percent of the *ortho* and *para* isomers are produced. However, if the major isomer is crystalline, as is usually the case, it may easily be purified by recrystallization.

When the substituent already in the ring is an *ortho,para* director, mixtures invariably result, as we have seen in previous sections. In such cases direct electrophilic substitution is less satisfactory as a synthetic method. However, some benzene derivatives may still be obtained in this manner, particularly the *para* isomers. Because of its symmetrical nature, the *para* isomer usually has a significantly higher melting point than the *ortho* or *meta* isomer. Some representative data are summarized in Table 22.4. Recall that a higher melting point represents a more stable crystal lattice and lower solubility. Consequently the higher melting *para* isomer may often be crystallized from the mixture of *ortho* and *para* products of direct substitution. It is generally not possible to isolate the *ortho* isomer in a pure state by this technique.

(80–84%)
m.p. 66°C

673

Sec. 22.9
*Synthetic Utility
of Electrophilic
Aromatic
Substitution*

$$\text{C}_6\text{H}_5\text{Cl} + \text{Br}_2 \xrightarrow{\text{FeBr}_3}$$

(60%)
m.p. 68°C

$$\xrightarrow[\text{H}_2\text{SO}_4]{\text{HNO}_3}$$

(72%)
m.p. 127°C

Another useful generalization is that the acylating agent obtained by coordination of aluminum chloride with an acyl halide behaves as a rather bulky reagent. Consequently, Friedel-Crafts acylation reactions tend to give almost completely *para* products, which are usually easy to separate from the small amounts of other isomers.

$$+ \ \text{C}_6\text{H}_5\text{COCl} \xrightarrow{\text{AlCl}_3}$$

(9%)	(1%)	(90%)
o-methyl-benzophenone	*m*-methyl-benzophenone	*p*-methyl-benzophenone

TABLE 22.4 Melting Points of Disubstituted Benzenes

	Melting Point, °C		
Substituents	*ortho*	*meta*	*para*
Br, Br	7	−7	87
Cl, Cl	−17	−25	53
Br, Cl	−12	−22	68
CH$_3$, Br	−26	−40	29
CH$_3$, NO$_2$	−10	16	55
Br, NO$_2$	43	56	127
Cl, NO$_2$	35	46	84
Br, COOH	150	155	255
Cl, COOH	142	158	243
OH, Br	6	33	66

On the other hand, Friedel-Crafts alkylations tend to be rather nonspecific. Often the orientations appear to be quite unusual. For example, under mild conditions with aluminum chloride in acetonitrile, isopropylation of toluene gives predominantly the expected *ortho* and *para* products, but there is also a substantial amount of *meta* product.

(63%)   (12%)   (25%)

This unusual behavior is due to rearrangements that alkylbenzenes undergo under the conditions of Friedel-Crafts alkylation. For example, if the foregoing mixture of isopropyltoluenes is treated under vigorous conditions with $AlCl_3$ and HCl, the product is exclusively the *meta* isomer. Although we shall not go into these rearrangements in detail, the student should be aware that Friedel-Crafts alkylations are often complicated and difficult to predict. Thus the reaction has less general utility as a synthetic method.

Since *ortho* and *para* isomers usually have closely similar boiling points, fractional distillation is usually not a satisfactory method for separation of such isomer mixtures, but there are exceptions to this generalization. Some representative data collected in Table 22.5 show that *o*- and *p*-nitrotoluenes differ sufficiently in boiling point to be separable by fractional distillation. On the other hand, the melting points of the bromotoluenes are too low for effective crystallization, and their boiling points are too close for simple fractionation; hence, the bromination of toluene is *not* a satisfactory route to any of the bromotoluenes.

In summary, direct electrophilic substitution is a useful synthetic method as such if only one isomer is produced or if the mixture can be conveniently separated by physical means. To predict whether such a reaction will be useful, the chemist must consider both the mechanism of the reaction—that is, what the isomer distribution is expected to be—and the probable physical properties of the expected products. We shall see in

TABLE 22.5 Boiling Points of Disubstituted Benzenes

Substituents	Boiling Point, °C		
	ortho	*meta*	*para*
Br, Br	225	218	219
Cl, Cl	181	173	174
Br, Cl	204	196	196
CH_3, Br	182	184	184
CH_3, Cl	159	162	162
Br, NO_2	258	265	256
Cl, NO_2	246	236	242
CH_3, NO_2	220	233	238
NO_2, NO_2	319	291	299
OCH_3, NO_2	277	258	274

future chapters that the utility of electrophilic substitution may be extended by modification and interrelation of functional groups and by a technique in which one or more positions on the ring are temporarily deactivated or blocked.

EXERCISE 22.11   In this chapter we have learned how Br and $COCH_3$ groups can be introduced into a number of aromatic compounds by bromination and Friedel-Crafts acylation, respectively. Review the transformations you have already learned of ArBr to $ArCH_2CH=CH_2$, $ArCOOH$, $ArCR_2OH$ and of $ArCOCH_3$ to $ArCOOH$, $ArCH_2CH_3$, $ArC(CH_3)_2OH$. How is each of these transformations affected by the presence in the aryl group of each of the following functions: CHO, COOH, Br, NO_2?

22.10 Perturbational MO Approach to Orientation

All of our discussions concerning orientation effects in electrophilic aromatic substitution have been framed in terms of structural effects on transition state energies using the intermediate pentadienyl cation as a model for the transition state. An alternative approach is the perturbational molecular orbital treatment (Section 21.7) in which the relative transition state energy is derived from HOMO-LUMO interactions of the reactants. To apply this approach to aromatic substitution we need to know how substituents affect the benzene MOs.

Recall that benzene has degenerate HOMO and LUMO energy levels (Section 21.2). These MO energies, however, are split by the effect of a substituent. The interaction of a substituent with the two HOMOs of benzene is shown in Figure 22.8. In (b) the substituent is attached at a node and cannot affect the MO energy. In (a), however, the substituent is attached at a position having a large wavefunction amplitude and there-

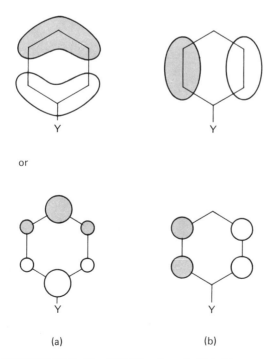

FIGURE 22.8   The HOMOs of a substituted benzene.

fore has a large effect on the MO energy. The effect of an electron-donating substituent is to *raise* this MO energy whereas the effect of an electron-attracting substituent is to stabilize the MO and *lower* the energy. Thus, for benzene with. an electron-donating substituent (a) is the HOMO and reaction with an electrophile is expected to occur preferentially at the *para* position. We have seen that in electrophilic substitution reactions of benzene with *ortho,para*-directing substituents, the *para* reaction dominates (Section 22.5). According to this molecular orbital approach, the preference for *para* reaction is not solely a steric hindrance effect at the *ortho* position. We note also that an electron-donating group tends to ''repel'' a node. As a result, the wave-function amplitude at the *ortho* position is greater than at the *meta* position and the difference between *ortho* and *para* is not as great as suggested in Figure 22.8.

For a benzene ring with an electron-attracting substituent, (b) in Figure 22.8 is the HOMO. Reaction at the *para* position would have to occur at a node in this MO and is clearly not favored. Reaction is expected approximately equally at the *meta* and *ortho* positions. In practice, we know that such substituents are *meta* directors and this difference points up an important limitation. This MO approach applies to the earliest stage of reaction and not necessarily to the transition state structure. That is, treatment of a system as a ''perturbation'' of another system can be satisfactory when the perturbation is relatively small. The treatment is less satisfactory when the perturbation becomes too large. In the present case the transition state is probably closer structurally to the intermediate than to the reactants. Nevertheless, it is interesting to note that many *meta*-orienting groups give substantial amounts of *ortho* product but little *para* (Table 22.1).

EXERCISE 22.12 From the partial rate factors in Table 22.1 calculate the percent *ortho*, *meta*, and *para* nitration products from nitrobenzene and ethyl benzoate.

EXERCISE 22.13 The HOMO of styrene (vinylbenzene) is represented schematically as

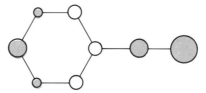

What does this suggest concerning the relative ease of reaction at the vinyl group compared to the ring?

PROBLEMS

1. Benzene can be iodinated with iodine and an oxidizing agent such as nitric acid or hydrogen peroxide. The actual electrophilic reagent in this reaction is probably IOH_2^+, which may be regarded as I^+ bound to a water molecule. Write a balanced equation for the generation of this intermediate from I_2 and H_2O_2. Include this as part of an overall mechanism for the reaction of I_2 and H_2O_2 with benzene to give iodobenzene, C_6H_5I.

2. (a) The chloromethylation reaction of benzene with formaldehyde

$$C_6H_6 + CH_2O + HCl \xrightarrow{ZnCl_2} C_6H_5CH_2Cl + H_2O$$

benzyl chloride

could involve as the principal electrophilic reagent either $CH_2{=}\overset{+}{O}{-}\overset{-}{Z}nCl_2$ or $^+CH_2Cl$. Write complete reaction mechanisms using both intermediates. Note that under these reaction conditions, benzyl alcohol, $C_6H_5CH_2OH$, reacts rapidly with $ZnCl_2$ and HCl (Lucas reagent) to give benzyl chloride.

(b) In such chloromethylation reactions a carcinogenic agent, bis-chloromethyl ether, $ClCH_2OCH_2Cl$, is produced as a by-product. Write a plausible mechanism for formation of this compound from formaldehyde, HCl, and $ZnCl_2$, showing each intermediate involved.

3. Benzene can be mercurated to give phenylmercuric acetate, $C_6H_5HgOOCCH_3$, with mercuric acetate in acetic acid containing some perchloric acid as an acid catalyst. The electrophilic reagent involved is probably $^+HgOOCCH_3$. Write a complete reaction mechanism.

4. Biphenyl, $C_6H_5\text{-}C_6H_5$, may be considered as a benzene with a phenyl substituent. Show why this hydrocarbon is expected to direct to the *ortho,para* positions, using resonance structures.

5. Use resonance structures to show why the COOH group in benzoic acid is a *meta* director.

6. Indicate the principal mononitration product or products expected from each of the following compounds.

7. (a) Toluene is 605 times as reactive as benzene toward bromination in aqueous acetic acid. The bromotoluenes produced are 32.9% *ortho*, 0.3% *meta*, and 66.8% *para*. Calculate the partial rate factors.

(b) The partial rate factors for chlorination of toluene are *ortho*, 620; *meta*, 5.0; *para*, 820. Calculate the isomer distribution in chlorination of *m*-xylene (*m*-dimethylbenzene). The experimental result is 77% 4-, 23% 2-, and 0% 5-.

(c) The partial rate factors for chlorination of chlorobenzene are *ortho*, 0.1; *meta*, 0.002; *para*, 0.41. Calculate the isomer distribution in chlorination of *p*-chlorotoluene (the experimental result is 77% 2,4-dichlorotoluene and 23% 3,4-dichlorotoluene).

8. Which of the following compounds can probably be prepared in a pure state from benzene by using two successive electrophilic substitution reactions? For each compound, write out the reaction sequence and describe how the intermediates and products would be purified.

(a) [structure: benzene with Cl and Br]

(b) [structure: benzene with COCH₃ and COCH₃]

(c) [structure: benzene with NO₂ and COCH₃]

(d) [structure: benzene with Cl and COCH₂CH₃]

(e) [structure: benzene with Cl and NO₂]

(f) [structure: benzene with C(CH₃)₃ and NO₂]

9. Which of the following compounds can probably be prepared in a pure state by electrophilic substitution on a disubstituted benzene? Outline the method in each case.

(a) [structure: benzene with OCH₃, NO₂, NO₂]

(b) [structure: benzene with COOH, NO₂, COOH]

(c) [structure: benzene with NO₂, O₂N, NO₂]

(d) [structure: benzene with NO₂, NO₂, NO₂]

(e) [structure: benzene with Cl, Cl, NO₂]

(f) [structure: benzene with Br, OH, Br]

(g) [structure: benzene with CH₃, Cl, CH₂CH₃]

(h) [structure: benzene with O₂N, OCH₃, CH₃]

(i) [structure: benzene with NO₂, Br, COOH]

(j) [structure: benzene with OCH₃, NO₂, CHO]

10. Toluene is *ortho,para* directing, whereas trifluoromethylbenzene, $C_6H_5CF_3$, is *meta* directing. Explain.

11. An interesting variant of Friedel-Crafts acylation is the Gatterman-Koch aldehyde synthesis, the reaction of an aromatic hydrocarbon with carbon monoxide and hydrogen chloride in the presence of a Lewis acid such as aluminum chloride. The reaction is equivalent to a Friedel-Crafts acylation with formyl chloride, HCOCl. Reaction with toluene gives primarily *p*-tolualdehyde (*p*-methylbenzaldehyde). Write a reasonable reaction mechanism.

12. (a) The reaction of benzene with isobutyl alcohol and BF_3 gives primarily *t*-butylbenzene. Explain.

    (b) The reaction of 2-butanol and BF_3 with benzene at 0°C gives 2-phenylbutane in good yield. When 2-butanol-2-*d*, $CH_3CDOHCH_2CH_3$, is used, a mixture of deuterated compounds is obtained that includes major amounts of

$$CH_3CDCH_2CH_3 \quad \text{and} \quad CH_3CHCHDCH_3$$
$$\underset{C_6H_5}{\vert} \qquad\qquad\qquad \underset{C_6H_5}{\vert}$$

Explain.

(c) By contrast, the reaction of $CD_3CHOHCH_3$ with benzene and BF_3 gives the following compound in good yield and with no deuterium scrambling.

$$CD_3CHCH_3$$
$$\underset{C_6H_5}{\vert}$$

How do you account for this difference?

(d) 2-Propanol-*1*-*d₃*, $CD_3CHOHCH_3$, has a stereocenter and significant optical activity. According to the mechanism of the alkylation reaction, what do you expect for the steric course of the reaction of this optically active alcohol with benzene and BF_3?

13. When a solution of *p*-di-(3-pentyl)benzene in benzene is treated with aluminum chloride at 25°C, a rapid transfer of a pentyl group occurs to give monopentylbenzene. The reaction product is approximately one part of 2-phenylpentane and two parts of 3-phenylpentane. Account for these results with a reasonable reaction mechanism.

14. Show how all three nitrobenzoic acids may be prepared from toluene.

15. On heating with aqueous sulfuric acid, styrene reacts to form a dimer in good yield.

(77–81%)

Write a reasonable mechanism, showing all intermediates involved.

16. Show how each of the following compounds may be prepared from benzene or toluene in a practical manner.

17. The solvolysis reaction of 2-chloro-2-phenylpropane in aqueous acetone is an S_N1 carbocation process that yields 2-phenyl-2-propanol as the principal product.

(a) Write out the mechanism of this reaction, showing any intermediates involved.

(b) The rate of reaction depends markedly on substituents in the phenyl group. The order of reactivity given by *para* substituents is

$$CH_3O > CH_3 > H > NO_2$$

Explain, using resonance structures.

18. The dissociation of triarylmethyl chlorides into ions in liquid sulfur dioxide solution has been studied quantitatively, and a number of dissociation constants have been measured for the equilibrium

$$Ar_3CCl \xrightleftharpoons{K} Ar_3C^+ + Cl^-$$

Rank the following compounds in order of increasing K and explain. $(m\text{-}ClC_6H_4)_3CCl$, $(p\text{-}O_2NC_6H_4)_3CCl$, $(m\text{-}CH_3C_6H_4)_3CCl$, $(p\text{-}CH_3C_6H_4)_3CCl$, $(p\text{-}CH_3OC_6H_4)_3CCl$, $(C_6H_5)_3CCl$

19. (a) Solvolysis of 2-methyl-2-phenylpropyl tosylate in acetic acid gives primarily a mixture of 2-methyl-1-phenyl-2-propyl acetate and 2-methyl-1-phenylpropene. Write a reasonable reaction mechanism.
    (b) Solvolyses of 3-phenyl-2-butyl tosylates in acetic acid also give mixtures of alkenes and esters. The ester product of solvolysis of the optically active 2S,3R diastereomer is racemic [equal amounts of (2S,3R)-3-phenyl-2-butyl acetate and (2R,3S)-3-phenyl-2-butyl acetate], whereas that from the 2R,3R tosylate is the optically active ester (2R,3R)-3-phenyl-2-butyl acetate. Provide a reasonable explanation.

20. Given the following HOMO of naphthalene, does electrophilic substitution occur preferentially at the C-1, C-2, or C-9?

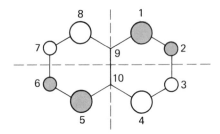

Chapter 23

Amines

23.1 Structure

Amines are compounds in which one or more alkyl or aryl groups are attached to nitrogen. They may be considered to be the organic relatives of ammonia in the same way that alcohols and ethers are related to water.

$$H_2O \qquad ROH \qquad R_2O$$

water alcohols ethers

$$NH_3 \qquad \underbrace{RNH_2 \quad R_2NH \quad R_3N}$$

ammonia amines

Amines are classified as **primary**, **secondary**, or **tertiary**, according to the number of alkyl or aryl groups joined to the nitrogen. Note that these descriptive adjectives are used here to denote the *degree of substitution* on nitrogen, not the nature of the substituent groups. In secondary and tertiary amines the alkyl or aryl groups may be the same or different.

Some Primary Amines

$$CH_3NH_2 \qquad (CH_3)_2CHNH_2 \qquad (CH_3)_3CNH_2$$

Some Secondary Amines

$$(CH_3CH_2)_2NH \qquad CH_3CH_2\overset{\displaystyle CH_3}{\underset{|}{N}}H$$

Some Tertiary Amines

$$(CH_3)_3N$$

Quaternary ammonium compounds are related to simple inorganic ammonium salts. Again the four groups joined to nitrogen in the ammonium ion may be the same or different.

$(CH_3CH_2)_2\overset{+}{N}(CH_3)_2\,Br^-$

$(CH_3)_4\overset{+}{N}\,Cl^-$

$CH_3CH_2CH_2\overset{+}{N}(CH_3)_3\,OH^-$

Recall that ammonia has a pyramidal shape. The nitrogen-hydrogen bond length is 1.008 Å, and the HNH bond angle is 107.3°. The hybridization of nitrogen is approximately sp^3. It forms three approximately sp^3-s σ-bonds to hydrogen and has a **nonbonding electron pair** that occupies the other approximately sp^3-orbital. Amines have similar structures, as shown in Figure 23.1.

ammonia

Consider the following progression of bond lengths (in Å)

$CH_3—CH_3$	1.531	$H—CH_3$	1.085
$CH_3—NH_2$	1.474	$H—NH_2$	1.012
$CH_3—OH$	1.427	$H—OH$	0.957
$CH_3—F$	1.385	$H—F$	0.917

As we proceed along the first row of the periodic table, the increasing nuclear charge causes the electron orbitals to shrink and result in shorter bonds.

The nonbonding electron pair is important in the chemistry of amines, since it is responsible for the typical basic and nucleophilic properties of these compounds. Amines that have an aryl group attached to nitrogen are characterized by somewhat larger HNH and HNC angles; that is, the nitrogen is more nearly planar than in alkylamines. We will discuss the reason for this difference in Section 23.4.

Bond Length, Å		Bond Angle, deg	
NH	1.011	HNH	105.9
CN	1.474	HNC	112.9

Bond Length, Å		Bond Angle, deg	
CN	1.47	CNC	108

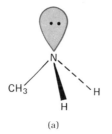

(a)

(b)

FIGURE 23.1 Simple amine structures: *(a)* methylamine; *(b)* trimethylamine.

Because of the pyramidal geometry, an amine with three different groups joined to nitrogen is chiral (alternatively, amines may be regarded as approximately tetrahedral with the nonbonding pair being the fourth "group").

Recall that enantiomeric carbon compounds may be separated and that the individual enantiomers are quite stable because it is necessary to break and reform bonds to interconvert them. In contrast, the two enantiomers of a chiral amine are readily interconvertible by a process known as **nitrogen inversion**. For simple amines the activation energy required for inversion is rather small, on the order of 6 kcal mole^{-1}. In the planar transition state for inversion the nitrogen has sp^2-hybridization with the lone pair in the p_z-orbital.

For quaternary ammonium compounds such inversion is not possible and chiral ions may be separated into enantiomers that are relatively stable.

EXERCISE 23.1 The optically active allylethylmethylphenylammonium halides racemize slowly in solution. The rate of racemization is temperature-dependent and is faster for the iodide than for the bromide. Propose a mechanism for the racemization.

23.2 Nomenclature

Like most other classes of organic compounds, amines have been named in several ways. Simple amines are usually referred to by common names, which are derived by using the suffix **-amine**, preceded by the name or names of the alkyl groups. The names are written as one word.

CH_3NH_2 $(CH_3CH_2)_2NH$ $(CH_3CH_2CH_2)_3N$

methylamine   diethylamine   tri-*n*-propylamine

ethylmethylamine   diethylmethylamine   cyclopropylethyl-methylamine

Under the IUPAC rules amines are named as derivatives of a parent hydrocarbon by using the prefix **amino-** to designate the group NH_2.

CH_3NH_2 $CH_3CH_2\overset{\underset{|}{CH_3}}{C}HNH_2$ $(CH_3)_2CHCH_2\overset{\underset{|}{NH_2}}{C}HCH_2CH_3$

aminomethane   2-aminobutane   4-amino-2-methylhexane

In this system secondary and tertiary amines are named by using a compound prefix that includes the names of all but the largest alkyl group.

$CH_3CH_2N(CH_3)_2$ $(CH_3)_2CHCH_2\overset{\underset{|}{CH_3}}{C}HN(CH_2CH_3)_2$

dimethylaminoethane   2-(diethylamino)-4-methylpentane

2-(ethylmethylamino)butane   1-(methylamino)-3-methylpentane

The simplest arylamine is **aniline**. This well-entrenched common name has the official sanction of the IUPAC. Simple derivatives are named as substituted anilines.

aniline   *m*-bromoaniline   *p*-nitroaniline   N,N-dimethylaniline

When it is necessary to name a compound containing the amino group as a derivative of some other function, the prefix **amino-** is employed.

$CH_3NHCH_2CH_2CH_2COOH$

4-(methylamino)butanoic acid   *p*-aminobenzoic acid   *p*-aminoazobenzene

Several aromatic amines have trivial names that have received IUPAC sanction. Some of the more important examples are shown below.

p-toluidine	*m*-anisidine	*o*-phenetidine
p-aminotoluene	*m*-methoxyaniline	*o*-ethoxyaniline

sulfanilic acid
p-aminobenzenesulfonic acid

anthranilic acid
o-aminobenzoic acid

Chemical Abstracts has recently adopted a new system for naming amines that is more rational than either the common or IUPAC system and will probably gain universal acceptance for the nomenclature of these compounds. In this system amines are named in the same manner as are alcohols (Section 10.2). The name of the alkane is modified by replacing the final -**e** by the suffix -**amine**.

$$CH_3CH_2CH_2NH_2 \qquad (CH_3)_2CHCH_2CH_2CH_2CH_2NH_2 \qquad (CH_3)_2CHNH_2$$

propanamine 5-methylhexanamine 2-propanamine

For secondary and tertiary amines the parent alkane is taken to be the alkyl group with the longest chain. If two alkyl groups are "tied" by this criterion, the parent alkane is the one with the greater number of substituents. The remaining alkyl groups are named as substituents by using the prefix **N**- to indicate that they are attached to nitrogen.

$$(CH_3CH_2)_2NH \qquad CH_3CH_2CH_2NHCH_2CH(CH_3)_2 \qquad (CH_3CH_2CH_2)_2NCH_3$$

N-ethylethanamine 2-methyl-N-propylpropanamine N-methyl-N-propylpropanamine

The *Chemical Abstracts* name for aniline is benzenamine; derivatives are named accordingly.

N,N-dimethylbenzenamine 4-methylbenzenamine 3-methoxybenzenamine

In this book we shall use common names for simple amines such as methylamine, triethylamine, and di-*n*-propylamine. Because it is so widely used in the chemical literature, we shall retain the name aniline for the simplest aromatic amine and name derivatives as substituted anilines. For more complex amines, we shall use the *Chemical Abstracts* system.

EXERCISE 23.2 Write the *Chemical Abstracts* names for all of the amines depicted on pages 684 and 685.

23.3 Physical Properties

A. Colligative Properties

The melting points, boiling points, and densities of some simple amines are collected in Table 23.1. As with other classes of compounds, certain trends are evident in the properties. All three properties increase with molecular weight as a consequence of the greater intermolecular attraction with the larger members in the series.

Like alcohols, the lower amines show the effect of hydrogen bonding (Section 10.3). Since nitrogen is not as electronegative as oxygen, the N—H···N hydrogen bond is not as strong as the analogous O—H···O bond. Thus, primary amines have boiling points that are intermediate between those of alkanes and alcohols of comparable molecular weight (Figure 23.2), just as ammonia, b.p. $-33°C$, is intermediate between methane, b.p. $-161°C$, and water, b.p. $100°C$.

Hydrogen bonding is more important with primary than with secondary amines and is not possible at all with tertiary amines. Thus, a primary amine always boils higher than a secondary or tertiary amine of the same molecular weight (Figure 23.2).

B. Infrared Spectra

The characteristic infrared absorptions of amines are associated with the nitrogen-hydrogen bonds. Typical bands are summarized in Table 23.2. For diagnostic purposes,

TABLE 23.1 Physical Properties of Amines

	Molecular Weight	Melting Point, °C	Boiling Point, °C	Density
Primary Amines				
CH_3NH_2	31	-94	-6.3	0.6628
$CH_3CH_2NH_2$	45	-81	16.6	0.6829
$CH_3CH_2CH_2NH_2$	59	-83	47.8	0.7173
$CH_3CH_2CH_2CH_2NH_2$	73	-49	77.8	0.7414
Secondary Amines				
$(CH_3)_2NH$	45	-93	7.4	0.6804
$(CH_3CH_2)_2NH$	73	-48	56.3	0.7056
$(CH_3CH_2CH_2)_2NH$	101	-40	110	0.7400
$(CH_3CH_2CH_2CH_2)_2NH$	129	-60	159	0.7670
Tertiary Amines				
$(CH_3)_3N$	59	-117	2.9	0.6356
$(CH_3CH_2)_3N$	101	-114	89.3	0.7256
$(CH_3CH_2CH_2)_3N$	143	-94	155	0.7558
$(CH_3CH_2CH_2CH_2)_3N$	185		213	0.7771

FIGURE 23.2 Boiling points: *(a)* alkanes, alcohols, and primary amines; *(b)* primary, secondary, and tertiary amines.

the C—N absorptions are not very useful because these bands occur in a spectral region that normally also contains many bands for other types of compounds (1020-1250 cm^{-1}). Particularly useful absorptions are the weak N—H stretching bands of primary amines, the N—H bending mode of primary amines, and the N—H wagging mode for primary and secondary amines. The N—H stretch of secondary amines is so weak that it is often not observed. Infrared spectroscopy is not useful in diagnosing the presence of a tertiary amino group. The spectrum of *n*-hexylamine is shown in Figure 23.3.

C. Nuclear Magnetic Resonance Spectra

Since nitrogen is more electronegative than carbon, the protons near the amino group are deshielded. The downfield shifts are not as pronounced as in the case of alcohols

TABLE 23.2 Infrared Spectra of Amines

Frequency, cm^{-1}	Intensity	Assignment	Compound Type
3500, 3400 (doublet)	weak	N—H stretching	primary
3310–3350	very weak	N—H stretching	secondary
1580–1650	medium to strong	N—H bending	primary
666–909	medium to strong	N—H wagging	primary, secondary

FIGURE 23.3 Infrared spectrum of *n*-hexylamine.

and ethers (Section 13.11). As with alcohols and ethers, the exact chemical shift is dependent upon whether the protons are part of a CH_3, a CH_2, or a CH group.

$$CH_3NR_2 \quad R'CH_2NR_2 \quad R'_2CHNR_2$$

δ, ppm: 2.2   2.4   2.8

Protons β to nitrogen are affected to a much smaller extent; they are normally seen in the range $\delta = 1.1\text{-}1.7$ ppm.

Protons bound directly to the nitrogen in primary and secondary amines may resonate anywhere in the region from $\delta = 0.6$ ppm to $\delta = 3.0$ ppm. The exact resonance position is dependent on the purity of the sample, the nature of the solvent, the concentration, and the temperature at which the measurement is made. Coupling of the type H—C—N—H is usually not observed because of proton exchange. The spectrum of di-*n*-propylamine is shown in Figure 23.4.

FIGURE 23.4 NMR spectrum of $(CH_3CH_2CH_2)_2NH$.

TABLE 23.3 CMR Chemical Shifts for Some Amines

	C-1	C-2	C-3	C-4	C-5
methylamine	28.3				
ethylamine	36.9	19.0			
propylamine	44.5	27.3	11.2		
butylamine	42.3	36.7	20.4	14.0	
pentylamine	42.5	34.0	29.7	23.0	14.3

The CMR spectra of amines resemble those of corresponding alcohols, except that a carbon directly bonded to nitrogen does not experience as a great a downfield shift as one bonded to oxygen. Representative data are shown in Table 23.3 (see also Table 13.4, page 340).

EXERCISE 23.3 An unknown compound is suspected to be an amine because of its weakly basic properties. The infrared spectrum shows no absorption in the 3300–3500 cm^{-1} or 600–950 cm^{-1} regions. The CMR spectrum has bands at δ 17.0, 20.6, 39.0 and 48.4. The NMR spectrum is shown below. What is the unknown compound?

23.4 Basicity

Because of the presence of a nonbonding electron pair on nitrogen, amines are Lewis bases just like alcohols and ethers (Sections 10.6.B and 18.5). Nitrogen is not as electronegative as oxygen, and amines have a greater tendency to react with a proton than alcohols. Looking at it another way, alkyloxonium ions are more acidic than alkylammonium ions.

$$CH_3OH + H^+ \rightleftharpoons CH_3\overset{+}{O}H_2$$

less   more
basic   acidic

$$CH_3NH_2 + H^+ \rightleftharpoons CH_3\overset{+}{N}H_3$$

more   less
basic   acidic

TABLE 23.4 Acidity of Some Alkylammonium Ions

Conjugate Acid	pK_a, 25°C
NH_4^+	9.24
$CH_3NH_3^+$	10.62
$CH_3CH_2NH_3^+$	10.64
$(CH_3)_3CNH_3^+$	10.68
$(CH_3)_2NH_2^+$	10.73
$(CH_3CH_2)_2NH_2^+$	10.94
$(CH_3)_3NH^+$	9.79
$(CH_3CH_2)_3NH^+$	10.75

Since amines are much more basic than water, aqueous solutions of amines have basic properties.

$$RNH_2 + H_2O \underset{}{\overset{K_b}{\rightleftharpoons}} RNH_3^+ + OH^- \qquad (23\text{-}1)$$

When comparing the base strengths of amines, it is convenient to refer to the dissociation constant of the corresponding ammonium ion. This equilibrium constant, like other dissociation constants, is called K_a (Section 4.5).

$$RNH_3^+ + H_2O \underset{}{\overset{K_a}{\rightleftharpoons}} RNH_2 + H_3O^+$$

$$K_a = \frac{[RNH_2][H_3O^+]}{[RNH_3^+]}$$

As usual, the concentration of water is not included in the equilibrium expression because it is present in large excess and is essentially constant (Section 17.4.A).

The pK_as for some typical ammonium ions are collected in Table 23.4, together with the pK_a for ammonium ion for reference. Notice that the simple alkylammonium ions all have pK_as in the range 10–11 and are therefore slightly less acidic than NH_4^+ itself. In other words, amines are only slightly more basic than NH_3.

It is important to distinguish between K_a for the dissociation of NH_4^+ and K_a for NH_3 itself and not to confuse them. Ammonia itself is an extremely weak acid; the pK_a for NH_3 is about 34. Consequently, the conjugate base of ammonia, NH_2^-, is an exceedingly strong base. Analogous anions derived by deprotonation of amines are known and are useful reagents for some organic reactions. Because amines are such feeble acids, powerful bases are needed for deprotonation; alkyllithium compounds are commonly used.

$$(CH_3CH_2CH_2)_2NH + n\text{-}C_4H_9Li \longrightarrow (CH_3CH_2CH_2)_2N^- Li^+ + C_4H_{10}$$

dipropylamine	butyllithium	lithium	butane
$pK_a \cong 40$		dipropylamide	$pK_a \cong 50$

EXERCISE 23.4 In some older books, one will find the basicity of amines discussed in terms of K_b, the equilibrium constant for reaction (23-1); K_b is given by the expression

$$K_b = \frac{[RNH_3^+][OH^-]}{[RNH_2]}$$

Using the relationship for the dissociation of water, $K_w = [H_3O^+][OH^-] = 10^{-14} M^2$, show that $pK_a + pK_b = 14$. What is pK_b for NH_2^-?

In aqueous solution arylamines are substantially less basic than alkylamines. Correspondingly, the acidity of anilinium ion is substantially greater than that of alkylammonium ions.

$$K_a = 2.5 \times 10^{-5} \ M \qquad pK_a = 4.60$$

$$(CH_3)_2CHNH_3^+ \rightleftharpoons (CH_3)_2CHNH_2 + H_3O^+$$
$$K_a = 2.5 \times 10^{-12} \ M \qquad pK_a = 11.60$$

Aliphatic amines have basicity comparable to dilute solutions of sodium hydroxide; the basicity of aniline is comparable to that of sodium acetate.

The reduced basicity of aniline compared to aliphatic amines may be attributed in part to the electron-attracting inductive effect of a phenyl group; for example phenylacetic acid ($pK_a = 4.31$) is more acidic than acetic acid ($pK_a = 4.6$). However, this effect is small compared to the effect of delocalization of the nitrogen lone pair into the benzene ring.

This delocalization renders the lone pair less accessible for bonding. Alternatively and equivalently, this delocalization effect can be expressed as a resonance stabilization of the amine that is not present in the ammonium ion. This energy effect is illustrated in Figure 23.5. The resonance energy of conjugation results in displacement of the protonation equilibrium toward the amine.

Ammonia itself and amines generally have a pyramidal structure (Section 23.1); the H—N—H bond angle in ammonia is 107.1°. The most effective conjugation of the

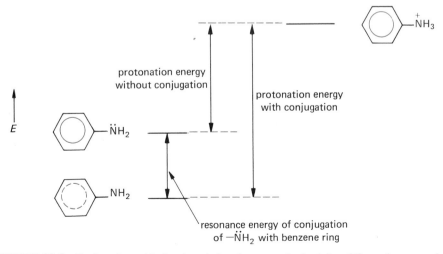

FIGURE 23.5 Conjugation with the phenyl ring decreases the basicity of the amino group in aniline.

nitrogen lone pair with the benzene ring would be obtained for a lone pair in a *p*-orbital parallel to the *p*-orbitals of the aromatic π-system. However, lone pairs are generally more stable in orbitals having some *s*-character. In the case of aniline, an energy compromise is reached in which the lone-pair orbital has more *p*-character than in ammonia but in which the orbital retains some *s*-character. As a result, the NH_2 group in aniline is still pyramidal but with a larger H—N—H angle (113.9°) than in ammonia. The H—N—H plane intersects the plane of the benzene ring at an angle of 39.4°. The orbital structure of aniline is represented in Figure 23.6.

Substituents on the aniline ring affect basicity in ways that are generally interpretable with the principles of substituent effects discussed previously. Table 23.5 summarizes the pK_a values of a number of substituted anilinium ions.

Ortho substituents sometimes give unexpected results because of steric effects; for example, *o*-methylaniline is less basic than aniline, whereas in the *meta* and *para* positions a methyl substituent exerts its typical electron-donating effect to give enhanced basicity. Bromo, chloro, iodo, and CF_3 groups show normal electron-attracting inductive effects that decrease the basicity of aniline. The nitro group has an especially potent effect in the *para* position that is attributed to direct conjugation with the amino group.

Because of their basic properties, amines form salts with acids. Since these salts are ionic compounds they are usually water soluble even in cases where the corresponding amine is insoluble in water.

$$CH_3(CH_2)_9NH_2 + HCl \longrightarrow CH_3(CH_2)_9\overset{+}{N}H_3\ Cl^-$$

n-decylamine   *n*-decylammonium chloride
(insoluble in H_2O)   (soluble in H_2O)

Even though aromatic amines are only one millionth as basic as alkylamines (see Tables 23.4 and 23.5), they are still protonated even in dilute acidic solutions. For

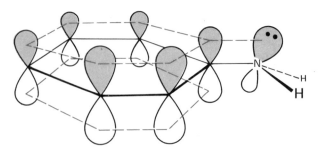

FIGURE 23.6 The partially pyramidal amino group in aniline can still conjugate with the phenyl π-system.

TABLE 23.5 pK_as of Anilinium Ions

	pK_a, 25°C		
Substituent	ortho	meta	para
H	4.60	4.60	4.60
benzoyl			2.17
bromo	2.53	3.58	3.86
chloro	2.65	3.52	3.98
cyano	0.95	2.75	1.74
fluoro	3.20	3.57	4.65
iodo	2.60	3.60	3.78
methoxy	4.52	4.23	5.34
methyl	4.44	4.72	5.10
nitro	−0.26	2.47	1.00
trifluoromethyl		3.20	2.75

example, aniline is essentially completely protonated in 0.1 M HCl solution (pH = 1). Hence, although aniline is only slightly soluble in water, it dissolves completely in dilute hydrohalic and sulfuric acids. The nitroanilines are less basic but also dissolve in strong acids. 2,4-Dinitroanilinium ion has pK = −4.4; this amine is soluble only in rather concentrated acids.

EXERCISE 23.5 Using the data in Tables 23.4 and 23.5, calculate equilibrium constants for the following equilibria.

The basicity of amines provides a convenient method for separating amines from neutral organic compounds. For example, a mixture of n-decylamine (b.p. 221°C) and dodecane (b.p. 216°C) is difficult to separate by fractional distillation. The two compounds may be separated easily by *extracting* the mixture with sufficient 10% aqueous hydrochloric acid to convert all of the amine into the ammonium salt. The alkane, being insoluble in water, is unaffected by this treatment, and the ammonium salt dissolves in the water layer. The layers may be separated by use of a separatory funnel to give the pure alkane. A strong base such as sodium hydroxide is then added to the aqueous solution to neutralize the ammonium salt and liberate the free amine. The water-insoluble amine forms a second layer that may be separated.

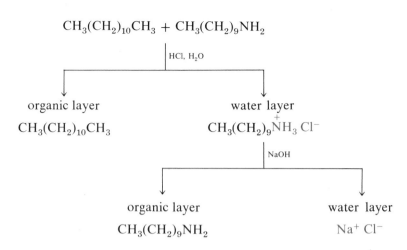

Amines also form salts with carboxylic acids. Again the salts are ionic and are often water soluble.

$$\underset{\substack{\text{acetic}\\\text{acid}}}{CH_3\overset{\displaystyle O}{\overset{\|}{C}}OH} + \underset{\text{methylamine}}{CH_3NH_2} \longrightarrow \underset{\substack{\text{methylammonium}\\\text{acetate}}}{CH_3\overset{\displaystyle O}{\overset{\|}{C}}O^- \ H_3\overset{+}{N}CH_3}$$

This salt-forming reaction is often used as a method for **resolving** racemic mixtures of organic acids.

> The student should review the basic principles of stereochemistry in Chapter 7. **Resolution** is the term used to describe the separation of two enantiomers from each other.

Consider racemic α-hydroxypropionic acid (lactic acid). Recall that the two enantiomers have identical physical properties and cannot be separated by crystallization or distillation techniques. The mixture will react with methylamine to give racemic methylammonium lactate, the enantiomers of which also cannot be separated by physical methods.

$$
\begin{array}{c}
\left.
\begin{array}{c}
\underset{\text{(R)-lactic acid}}{\overset{\displaystyle COOH}{\underset{\displaystyle CH_3}{H\!-\!\overset{|}{\underset{|}{C}}\!\!-\!OH}}}\\[1em]
+\\[1em]
\underset{\text{(S)-lactic acid}}{\overset{\displaystyle COOH}{\underset{\displaystyle CH_3}{HO\!-\!\overset{|}{\underset{|}{C}}\!\!-\!H}}}
\end{array}
\right\}
+ CH_3NH_2 \longrightarrow
\left\{
\begin{array}{c}
\underset{\text{methylammonium (R)-lactate}}{\overset{\displaystyle CO_2^- \ CH_3\overset{+}{N}H_3}{\underset{\displaystyle CH_3}{H\!-\!\overset{|}{\underset{|}{C}}\!\!-\!OH}}}\\[1em]
+\\[1em]
\underset{\text{methylammonium (S)-lactate}}{\overset{\displaystyle CO_2^- \ CH_3\overset{+}{N}H_3}{\underset{\displaystyle CH_3}{HO\!-\!\overset{|}{\underset{|}{C}}\!\!-\!H}}}
\end{array}
\right.
\end{array}
$$

However, consider the situation when one enantiomer of a chiral amine is used to form the salt.

The two salts are now diastereomeric rather than enantiomeric, and they have different physical properties. For example, the S,R salt may be more soluble in some solvents than the S,S salt. Because of this difference in solubility, the two salts can be separated by fractional crystallization. Each of the diastereomeric salts can then be treated with a strong acid such as hydrochloric or sulfuric acid to liberate the free carboxylic acid. Acidification of the S,R salt gives enantiomerically pure (R)-lactic acid, whereas similar treatment of the S,S salt gives pure (S)-lactic acid.

Of course, in order to use this technique for resolution, suitable optically active amines must be available. Fortunately, a number of such compounds are readily available and relatively inexpensive. A particularly useful source of such resolving agents is the class of naturally occurring amines called alkaloids, which occur in nature in only one enantiomeric form. Examples are strychnine and brucine (Section 34.7.C). Another frequently used resolving agent is 1-phenyl-2-propanamine (amphetamine). Although not a natural product, synthetic amphetamine is readily available in both enantiomeric forms.

amphetamine

EXERCISE 23.6 The method outlined for the resolution of racemic lactic acid is sometimes known as the *method of diastereomeric salts*. The same principle may be used, even when actual salts are not employed. For example, show how you could resolve racemic 2-octanol if you had enantiomerically homogeneous (S)-1-methoxy-1-phenylacetic acid.

23.5 Quaternary Ammonium Compounds

A. Tertiary Amines as Nucleophiles

Recall that there is a correlation between Lewis basicity and the nucleophilicity of a species (Section 9.4). Amines are more basic than alcohols or ethers, and they are also more nucleophilic. For example, a mixture of diethyl ether and methyl iodide does not react under ordinary conditions, but triethylamine and methyl iodide react violently at room temperature. If the reaction is carried out in a solvent to moderate its vigor, the product, which is a tetraalkylammonium iodide, may be obtained in good yield.

$$(C_2H_5)_2O + CH_3I \xrightarrow{25°C} \text{no reaction}$$

$$(C_2H_5)_3N + CH_3I \xrightarrow[\text{ether}]{25°C} (C_2H_5)_3\overset{+}{N}CH_3 \ I^-$$

methyltriethylammonium iodide

Such compounds, which have four alkyl groups replacing the four hydrogens of the ammonium ion, are called **quaternary ammonium compounds**. Since they are ionic, they are generally water soluble and have fairly high melting points. They often decompose at the melting point.

$$(CH_3)_4N^+ \ Cl^-$$
tetramethylammonium chloride
m.p. 420°C

$$(CH_3CH_2CH_2)_4N^+ \ Br^-$$
tetrapropylammonium bromide
m.p. 252°C

Quaternary ammonium compounds are important as intermediates in some reactions that we shall encounter and also occur in nature. Acetylcholine, which is important in the neural transport system of mammals, is an example.

$$CH_3\overset{\overset{\displaystyle O}{\|}}{C}OCH_2CH_2\overset{\overset{\displaystyle CH_3}{+|}}{\underset{\underset{\displaystyle CH_3}{|}}{N}}CH_3 \ Br^-$$

acetylcholine bromide

Quaternary ammonium hydroxides are as basic as alkali hydroxides. They decompose on heating (Hofmann degradation; Section 23.7.E) and find use as base catalysts in organic systems.

B. Phase-Transfer Catalysis

In Section 11.6.F we learned that chloroform reacts with strong bases to form dichlorocarbene, which can then add to double bonds to give dichlorocyclopropanes. If a solution of cyclohexene in chloroform is stirred with 50% aqueous sodium hydroxide, only small yields of the cyclopropane are formed. The hydroxide ion stays in the aqueous phase, and the only reaction that occurs is at the interface between the organic and aqueous phases. However, if a small amount of benzyltriethylammonium chloride is added to the heterogeneous mixture, rapid reaction occurs and 7,7-dichloro-bicyclo[4.1.0]heptane is isolated in 72% yield.

$$\text{(cyclohexene)} + CHCl_3 \xrightarrow[\text{50\% aq. NaOH}]{C_6H_5CH_2\overset{+}{N}Et_3\ Cl^-} \text{(bicyclic)} \begin{matrix} Cl \\ Cl \end{matrix}$$

(72%)

To understand what has happened, we need to recognize that although the quaternary ammonium compound is a salt soluble in water, it also has a large organic group and has solubility in organic solvents *as an ion pair*. Although the quaternary ammonium chloride was used because of its availability and greater convenience in handling, chloride ion is swamped by the large excess of hydroxide ion in the aqueous solution. In the heterogeneous mixture some benzyltriethylammonium hydroxide ion pairs are distributed into the chloroform layer. Hydroxide ion is especially reactive in this medium because of the reduced hydrogen bonding. Dichlorocarbene is produced in the chloroform solution, in which there also is a high concentration of cyclohexene.

$$C_6H_5CH_2NEt_3^+(aq.) + OH^-(aq.) \rightleftharpoons C_6H_5CH_2NEt_3^+\ OH^-(CHCl_3)$$

$$C_6H_5CH_2NEt_3^+\ OH^- + CHCl_3 \longrightarrow H_2O + C_6H_5CH_2NEt_3^+\ CCl_3^-$$

$$C_6H_5CH_2NEt_3^+\ CCl_3^- \longrightarrow :CCl_2 + C_6H_5CH_2NEt_3^+\ Cl^-$$

The benzyltriethylammonium chloride ion pairs diffuse into the aqueous phase, where the ammonium ion can again pick up a hydroxide ion and begin the cycle anew. The key to the procedure is the solubility of the quaternary ammonium salt in both water and organic solvents.

$$C_6H_5CH_2N(CH_2CH_3)_3^+\ OH^-$$

soluble in both water and organic solvents

The technique is called **phase-transfer catalysis** and can be applied to a number of different types of reaction. The general procedure is to use concentrated solutions with an aqueous and an organic phase. The quaternary ammonium salt used need only have organic groups that are sufficiently large to provide solubility in organic solvents. Among the ones commonly used are tetrabutylammonium, methyltrioctylammonium, and hexadecyltrimethylammonium salts. Some additional examples of applications of phase-transfer catalysis are given below.

$$CH_3(CH_2)_7CH=CH_2 \text{ (benzene soln.)} \xrightarrow[\substack{\text{aq. KMnO}_4 \\ 40-50^\circ C}]{(CH_3(CH_2)_6CH_2)_3\overset{+}{N}CH_3\ Cl^-} CH_3(CH_2)_7COOH$$

(91%)

$$C_6H_5CH_2COCH_3 + CH_3(CH_2)_3Br \xrightarrow[\text{50\% aq. NaOH}]{C_6H_5CH_2\overset{+}{N}Et_3\ OH^-} CH_3COCHCH_2CH_2CH_2CH_3$$
$$\underset{C_6H_5}{|}$$

(90%)

$$CH_3(CH_2)_9Br \xrightarrow[\substack{\text{aq. NaSCN} \\ 100^\circ C}]{(n\text{-}C_6H_{13})_3\overset{+}{N}CH_3\ Cl^-} CH_3(CH_2)_9SCN$$

(100%)

Note that the examples include alkylation, oxidation, and displacement reactions, that the anions are not restricted to hydroxide ion and that various temperatures may be used.

EXERCISE 23.7 For each of the three foregoing examples of phase-transfer catalysis, what species are in the aqueous phase? In the organic phase? Which species are passing from one phase to another?

23.6 Synthesis

A. Direct Alkylation of Ammonia or Other Amines

In Section 9.2 it was mentioned that ammonia reacts with primary alkyl halides by the S_N2 mechanism to give alkylammonium halides. In principle, this type of displacement reaction might be used as a way of synthesizing primary amines.

$$CH_3CH_2Br + NH_3 \longrightarrow CH_3CH_2NH_3^+ Br^- \xrightarrow{NaOH} CH_3CH_2NH_2$$

In practice, this method is not very useful because of the side reactions that occur. The product alkylammonium ion is fairly acidic and may transfer a proton to a molecule of ammonia that has not yet reacted to give the primary amine and the ammonium ion. Since the primary amine is also nucleophilic, it may undergo further reaction giving a secondary amine. By similar equilibria and further alkylation, the tertiary amine and even the quaternary ammonium compound may be formed. The actual result is a complex mixture even when equivalent molar amounts of ammonia and alkyl halide are used.

$$RBr + NH_3 \longrightarrow RNH_3^+ Br^-$$
$$RNH_3^+ + NH_3 \rightleftharpoons RNH_2 + NH_4^+$$
$$RNH_2 + RBr \longrightarrow R_2NH_2^+ Br^-$$
$$R_2NH_2^+ + NH_3 \rightleftharpoons R_2NH + NH_4^+$$
$$R_2NH + RBr \longrightarrow R_3NH^+ Br^-$$
$$R_3NH^+ + NH_3 \rightleftharpoons R_3N + NH_4^+$$
$$R_3N + RBr \longrightarrow R_4N^+ Br^-$$

The "overalkylation" may be suppressed by using a large excess of ammonia or the amine being alkylated. This ploy is only practical in cases where the amine is relatively inexpensive and sufficiently volatile that the unreacted excess may be easily removed. An example is the preparation of *n*-butylamine by the reaction of *n*-butyl bromide with ammonia.

$$CH_3CH_2CH_2CH_2Br + NH_3 \longrightarrow \xrightarrow{NaOH} CH_3CH_2CH_2CH_2NH_2$$
$$(47\%)$$

A solution of 300 g of NH_3 (20 moles) in 8 L of 90% aqueous ethanol is prepared. *n*-Butyl bromide is added slowly until 1507 g (11 moles) has been added. The reaction mixture is stirred at 25°C for 48 hr and then made basic with aqueous NaOH. Fractional distillation of the organic layer gives 388 g of *n*-butylamine (47%) along with some di-*n*-butylamine and tri-*n*-butylamine, which have higher boiling points.

Secondary and tertiary amines may also be prepared this way, but the yields are again often low due to overalkylation. Also, if the amine is not readily available or is expensive, it is undesirable to use it in excess. In many cases where a pure primary, secondary, or tertiary amine is desired, direct alkylation is not a practical synthetic method. Several indirect methods have been devised to accomplish this purpose, and we shall study some of them in later parts of this section.

We saw in the previous section that aromatic amines are much less basic than alkylamines. They are also less nucleophilic, and their reactions with alkyl halides require somewhat more vigorous conditions. Since these amines are less reactive nucleophiles, it is easier to achieve monoalkylation, as illustrated with the following synthesis of N-benzylaniline.

(85–87%)
N-benzylaniline

The sodium bicarbonate serves to neutralize the HCl that is produced in the reaction.

B. Indirect Alkylation: The Gabriel Synthesis

Pure primary amines can be prepared in good yield by a method called the **Gabriel synthesis**. This method involves the alkylation of a "protected" form of ammonia. The compound phthalimide (Section 27.6.C) is prepared from ammonia and the dicarboxylic acid phthalic acid. Imides have acidic properties because the negative charge of the conjugate base is delocalized over both oxygens and the nitrogen. The pK_a of phthalimide is 8.3. In aqueous basic solution the compound is converted almost completely into the anion.

phthalimide

The phthalimide anion has nucleophilic properties and can enter into displacement reactions with alkyl halides. Reaction could in principle take place on either oxygen or nitrogen, but since nitrogen is more nucleophilic, it occurs mostly on nitrogen. Further alkylation cannot occur because there are no acidic protons. The product is an N-alkylphthalimide, and hydrolysis gives the amine and phthalic acid.

The best solvent for the alkylation appears to be dimethylformamide $HCON(CH_3)_2$. The Gabriel synthesis is frequently used in the preparation of α-amino carboxylic acids, and we shall encounter it again in that context in Chapter 29.

EXERCISE 23.8 Explain why the Gabriel synthesis cannot be used to prepare each of the following amines.
(a) neopentylamine   (b) *t*-butylamine   (c) di-*n*-propylamine

C. Reduction of Nitro Compounds

Nitro compounds undergo ready reduction to yield primary amines. Because aromatic nitro compounds of a wide variety are available from nitration of aromatic compounds (Chapter 22), this method constitutes the most general synthesis of aromatic amines. Reduction may be accomplished by catalytic hydrogenation or by the use of chemical reducing agents in acidic solution.

(87–90%)
2-methyl-5-isopropylaniline

(74%)
2,4-diaminotoluene

Many chemical reducing agents have been used for the conversion of aromatic nitro groups to amines. Among the most common are metals and acid, usually iron or zinc and dilute hydrochloric acid. Stannous chloride, $SnCl_2$, and hydrochloric acid are an especially useful combination when other reducible groups, such as carbonyl groups, are present.

m-nitrobenzaldehyde   *m*-aminobenzaldehyde

The method can be applied to unsymmetrical dinitro compounds as well, and selective reductions are sometimes possible.

m-dinitrobenzene   *m*-nitroaniline
(79–85%)

EXERCISE 23.9   We saw in this section that some aromatic amines are readily synthesized from aromatic compounds by the two-step sequence of (1) nitration and (2) reduction of the NO_2 group to NH_2. Show how this method may be applied to the synthesis of 2,4-dimethylaniline. Explain why the method is not applicable for the synthesis of *m*-methoxyaniline or *o*-aminobenzaldehyde.

D. Reduction of Nitriles

We saw in Section 12.6.A that nitriles are reduced by hydrogen and a catalyst or by lithium aluminum hydride in an ether solvent to give primary amines.

$$RC\equiv N \xrightarrow[\text{or LiAlH}_4]{\text{H}_2/\text{cat.}} RCH_2NH_2$$

In the catalytic hydrogenation procedure, secondary amines are often produced as by-products. The initially produced imine may disproportionate by reaction with some of the primary amine already produced in the reduction to give a new imine. Hydrogenation of this imine gives the secondary amine.

(1) $RCN + H_2 \longrightarrow RCH=NH$
(2) $RCH=NH + H_2 \longrightarrow RCH_2NH_2$
(3) $RCH=NH + RCH_2NH_2 \rightleftharpoons RCH=NCH_2R + NH_3$
(4) $RCH=NCH_2R + H_2 \longrightarrow RCH_2NHCH_2R$

This side reaction may be suppressed by carrying out the hydrogenation in the presence of excess NH_3, which forces equilibrium (3) to the left.

$$RCN \xrightarrow[\text{EtOH,NH}_3]{\text{H}_2\text{-Pd/C}} RCH_2NH_2$$

Secondary amine formation may also be minimized by carrying out the reaction in acetic anhydride as solvent. The primary amine produced is rapidly converted into the amide.

(97%)

The amine may then be obtained by hydrolysis of the amide. Since nitriles are easily available by several methods, many primary amines may be synthesized by this procedure.

Notice that cyanide ion, CN^-, is a synthon for the group CH_2NH_2.

EXERCISE 23.10 Write equations showing how the following conversions may be carried out.

(a) $(CH_3)_2CHCH_2CH_2Br \longrightarrow (CH_3)_2CHCH_2CH_2CH_2NH_2$

(b) $(CH_3)_2CHCHO \longrightarrow (CH_3)_2CH\overset{\overset{\displaystyle OH}{|}}{C}HCH_2NH_2$

E. Reduction of Oximes

Aldoximes and ketoximes, which may be prepared from aldehydes or ketones by reaction with hydroxylamine (Section 14.7.C), can be reduced to primary amines. Since oximes are easily generated in high yield, this is a useful synthetic method.

$$CH_3CH_2CH_2\overset{\overset{\displaystyle O}{||}}{C}CH_3 + H_2NOH \longrightarrow CH_3CH_2CH_2\overset{\overset{\displaystyle NOH}{||}}{C}CH_3 \xrightarrow[C_2H_5OH]{H_2-Ni} CH_3CH_2CH_2\overset{\overset{\displaystyle NH_2}{|}}{C}HCH_3$$
$$(85\%)$$

$$(80\%)$$

F. Reduction of Imines: Reductive Amination

Ammonia and primary amines condense with aldehydes and ketones to give imines (Section 14.7.C). In the case of ammonia, the imines are unstable and cannot be isolated. However, if a mixture of a carbonyl compound and ammonia is treated with hydrogen and a suitable hydrogenation catalyst, the C=N bond of the unstable imine is reduced and an amine results. The process is often called "reductive amination."

benzaldehyde   (89%)
                                              benzylamine

A significant side reaction complicates the reductive amination method. As the primary amine begins to build up, it may condense with the starting aldehyde to give a different imine. Reduction of this imine gives a secondary amine.

dibenzylamine

This side reaction may be minimized by using a large excess of ammonia in the reaction medium. On the other hand, it may actually be exploited and used as a method for the synthesis of secondary amines, as shown by the following reaction. This example also demonstrates that ketones may be used as well as aldehydes.

$$HOCH_2CH_2NH_2 + CH_3\overset{\overset{\textstyle O}{\|}}{C}CH_3 \xrightarrow[C_2H_5OH]{H_2-Pt} HOCH_2CH_2N\overset{\overset{\textstyle CH_3}{|}}{H}CHCH_3$$
(95%)

One version of reductive amination, which is frequently employed for the synthesis of tertiary amines where at least one of the alkyl groups is methyl, is the **Eschweiler-Clarke** reaction. Instead of hydrogen, the reducing agent is formic acid, which is oxidized to carbon dioxide.

(94%)

(95%)
t-butyldimethylamine

As shown by the two foregoing examples, the reaction proceeds in excellent yield. The intermediate that is reduced is an **immonium ion**, and the reduction may be visualized as follows.

$$R_2NH + CH_2{=}O \overset{H^+}{\rightleftharpoons} R_2N{-}CH_2OH$$

$$R_2N{-}CH_2OH + HCOOH \rightleftharpoons R_2\overset{+}{N}{=}CH_2 + HCO_2^- + H_2O$$

An earlier version of this reaction, called the **Leukart** reaction, gives lower yields, but is more general. It can be used to prepare primary, secondary, or tertiary amines. In this method, the ketone is heated with a formate salt or a formamide at 180–200°C.

(60–66%)

(75%)
(dimethylamino)cyclooctane

EXERCISE 23.11 What are the products of each of the following reactions?

(a)

+ NH$_3$ (excess) $\xrightarrow{\text{H}_2/\text{Ni}}$

(b) CH$_3$CH$_2$CH$_2$NH$_2$ +

$\xrightarrow{\text{H}_2/\text{Pt}}$

(c)

CH$_2$CCH$_3$ + HCN(CH$_3$)$_2$ $\xrightarrow{200\,°C}$

(d)

CH$_3$ + CH$_2$=O + HCOOH $\xrightarrow{100\,°C}$

G. Reduction of Amides

Amides are reduced by lithium aluminum hydride in refluxing ether to give amines (Section 18.8). The reduction is unusual in that a C=O group is reduced to CH$_2$. Yields are generally good.

N,N-dimethylcyclohexane-
carboxamide

(88%)
N,N-dimethylcyclohexyl-
methanamine

Diborane, B$_2$H$_6$, may also be used as the reducing agent.

$$(CH_3)_3CCN(CH_3)_2 \xrightarrow[\text{THF}]{\text{B}_2\text{H}_6} (CH_3)_3CCH_2N(CH_3)_2$$

N,N,2-tetramethylpropanamide   (79%)
N,N,2-tetramethylpropanamine

The method also serves as a method to prepare primary or secondary amines, depending on the structure of the amide used.

$$RCNH_2 \xrightarrow{\text{LiAlH}_4} RCH_2NH_2$$

$$RCNHR' \xrightarrow{\text{LiAlH}_4} RCH_2NHR'$$

EXERCISE 23.12 The two-step sequence of (1) acylation of an amine and (2) reduction of the resulting amide to an amine constitutes a method for the indirect addition of an alkyl group to nitrogen. Show how this sequence of reactions can be used to accomplish the following transformations.

(a) $CH_2CH_2CH_2CH_2NH_2 \longrightarrow CH_3CH_2CH_2CH_2NHCH_2CH(CH_3)_2$

(b) $(CH_3)_2CHNH_2 \longrightarrow (CH_3)_2CHNCH_2CH_2CH_2CH_3$
$\qquad\qquad\qquad\qquad\qquad\;\; |$
$\qquad\qquad\qquad\qquad\quad CH_2CH_3$

H. Preparation from Carboxylic Acids: The Hofmann, Curtius, and Schmidt Rearrangements

The Hofmann, Curtius, and Schmidt rearrangements all accomplish the same overall process—conversion of a carboxylic acid to a primary amine with loss of the carboxy carbon of the acid.

$$R\overset{\overset{\displaystyle O}{\|}}{-}COH \longrightarrow R-NH_2 + CO_2$$

Examples of the three reactions are shown below.

Hofmann

$$CH_3(CH_2)_7CH_2CONH_2 + Cl_2 + OH^- \longrightarrow CH_3(CH_2)_7CH_2NH_2$$
$$\text{(66\%)}$$

decanamide · nonanamine

Curtius

cyclopropanecarbonyl chloride · · · · · cyclopropanecarbonyl azide · · · · · cyclopropanamine (60%)

$$+ Na^+N_3^- \longrightarrow \qquad \xrightarrow[H_2O]{\Delta}$$

Schmidt

$$+ NaN_3 \xrightarrow[\text{2. NaOH}]{\text{1. H}_2\text{SO}_4, \text{CHCl}_3}$$

m-chlorobenzoic acid · · · · · · · · · · · m-chloroaniline (75%)

Although the Hofmann rearrangement begins with an amide, the Curtius reaction with an acyl azide, and the Schmidt reaction with an acid, the three reactions are related mechanistically. In each case, the crucial intermediate is probably the same, an **acyl nitrene**.

The probable mechanism for the Hofmann rearrangement is outlined below. The first two steps are simply the base-catalyzed halogenation of the amide, which is mechanistically related to the base-catalyzed halogenation of ketones (Section 14.6.D).

$$(1) \quad R\overset{\overset{\displaystyle O}{\|}}{C}NH_2 + OH^- \rightleftharpoons R\overset{\overset{\displaystyle O}{\|}}{C}NH^- + H_2O$$

$$(2) \quad R\overset{\overset{\displaystyle O}{\|}}{C}NH^- + Cl_2 \rightleftharpoons R\overset{\overset{\displaystyle O}{\|}}{C}NHCl + Cl^-$$

The N-chloroamide is more acidic than the starting amide and also reacts with base to give the corresponding anion. This intermediate loses chloride ion to give a highly reactive intermediate called a **nitrene**. Nitrenes are neutral molecules in which the nitrogen has only six electrons; they are structurally similar to carbenes (Section 11.6.F).

$$(3) \quad R\overset{\overset{\displaystyle O}{\|}}{C}\overset{..}{N}HCl + OH^- \rightleftharpoons R\overset{\overset{\displaystyle O}{\|}}{C}\overset{..}{\overset{\displaystyle -}{N}}Cl + H_2O$$

$$(4) \quad R\overset{\overset{\displaystyle O}{\|}}{C}\overset{..}{\overset{\displaystyle -}{N}}Cl \rightleftharpoons R\overset{\overset{\displaystyle O}{\|}}{C}-\overset{..}{N} + Cl^-$$

an acyl
nitrene

Acyl nitrenes undergo rapid rearrangement to give compounds called **isocyanates**, which are similar to allenes (Section 19.2.C) or ketenes (Section 19.3.A).

$$(5) \quad R-\overset{\overset{\displaystyle O}{\|}}{C}\overset{\frown}{\overset{..}{N}}: \longrightarrow R-\overset{..}{N}=C=O$$

an isocyanate

Like ketenes, isocyanates react rapidly with water; the products in this case are **carbamic acids**, which are thermally unstable. Decarboxylation of the carbamic acid occurs to give the amine and carbon dioxide.

$$(6) \quad R-N=C=O + H_2O \longrightarrow RNH\overset{\overset{\displaystyle O}{\|}}{C}OH$$

an alkyl isocyanate   a carbamic acid

$$(7) \quad RNH\overset{\overset{\displaystyle O}{\|}}{C}OH \longrightarrow RNH_2 + CO_2$$

If the Hofmann rearrangement is carried out in alcohol solution rather than in water, steps (6) and (7) are not possible. Instead, the isocyanate adds the alcohol to give the ester of the carbamic acid, which is stable and may be isolated.

$$(6') \quad R-N=C=O + CH_3OH \longrightarrow RNH\overset{\overset{\displaystyle O}{\|}}{C}OCH_3$$

a methyl carbamate

In the Curtius reaction, the acyl azide loses nitrogen upon heating to give the acyl nitrene directly. The remaining steps (5)-(7) are the same. Acyl azides are potentially explosive, and the decomposition is therefore somewhat hazardous to carry out.

$$R-\overset{\overset{\displaystyle O}{\|}}{C}-\overset{..}{\underset{..}{N}}-\overset{+}{N}\equiv N: \xrightarrow{\Delta} R-\overset{\overset{\displaystyle O}{\|}}{C}-\overset{..}{N}: + N_2$$

The Schmidt reaction also proceeds by way of the acyl azide, which is formed by reaction of the carboxylic acid with hydrazoic acid, HN_3, under the acidic conditions of the reaction.

$$R-\overset{\overset{\displaystyle O}{\|}}{C}-OH + HN_3 \xrightarrow{H_2SO_4} R-\overset{\overset{\displaystyle O}{\|}}{C}-N_3 + H_2O$$

> **EXERCISE 23.13** Write equations showing the preparation of 3-methylpentanamine and *o*-bromoaniline by the Hofmann, Curtius, and Schmidt rearrangements.

23.7 Reactions

Certain important reactions of amines that have already been presented will not be discussed further here. These are the reactions with protons (Section 23.4) and with alkyl halides (Sections 23.5 and 23.6.A).

A. Formation of Amides

Recall that ammonia and primary and secondary amines react with acyl halides and acid anhydrides to give amides (Section 18.7.B). If an acyl halide is used, the hydrohalic acid produced will neutralize an additional equivalent of amine.

$$CH_2=CH\overset{\overset{\displaystyle O}{\|}}{C}Cl + 2\ CH_3NH_2 \longrightarrow CH_2=CH\overset{\overset{\displaystyle O}{\|}}{C}NHCH_3 + CH_3NH_3{}^+\ Cl^-$$

Aromatic amines can also be converted to amides with acyl chlorides or anhydrides. We shall find that this is frequently a useful procedure because the amide group is less strongly activating than the amino group in electrophilic aromatic substitution reactions. Thus the high reactivity of the amine can be moderated by conversion into an amide. For this **moderating** purpose the acetyl group is used most often and is usually introduced with acetic anhydride. Acetanilides can also be prepared by direct heating of aniline or a substituted aniline with acetic acid, but this process is slower.

acetanilide

> Acetanilide is a colorless crystalline solid, m.p. 114°C, that behaves as a neutral compound under normal conditions. The basic character of aniline is reduced by the acetyl group. The conjugate acids of amides have pK_as of about 0 to +1; that is, they are extensively protonated in 10% sulfuric acid.
>
> $$RNH\overset{\overset{\displaystyle +OH}{\|}}{C}CH_3 \underset{K_a}{\rightleftharpoons} H_3O^+ + RNHCOCH_3 \qquad K_a \cong 0.1\text{--}1\ M$$

Acetanilide is a somewhat weaker base than aliphatic amides, just as aniline is a weaker base than aliphatic amines; the pK_a of the conjugate acid of acetanilide is about -1 to -2. It is protonated by strong sulfuric acid solutions. Acetanilide is also a weak acid with a pK_a estimated to be about 15. It is not appreciably soluble in dilute aqueous alkali hydroxides and requires more basic conditions to form the conjugate anion.

p-phenetidine
p-ethoxyaniline

phenacetin
p-ethoxyacetanilide

Phenacetin has been used as an analgesic and in mixture with aspirin and caffeine as formerly popular over-the-counter analgesic pills (the "P" in APC). It has since been removed from such compositions because of suspected side effects.

The mixture of HCl and sodium acetate creates a buffered medium that keeps the amine in solution as the ammonium salt in equilibrium with a small amount of free amine. The free amine reacts rapidly with acetic anhydride to form the amide in high yield and in a pure state. Acetic anhydride hydrolyzes slowly under these conditions. The amide can be hydrolyzed back to the amine by heating with alcoholic HCl.

B. Reactions with Nitrous Acid

Amines undergo interesting reactions with nitrous acid, HNO_2. The reaction products depend on whether the amine is primary, secondary, or tertiary, and whether it is aromatic or aliphatic.

Secondary amines, either aromatic or aliphatic, give N-nitroso compounds, also known as **nitrosamines**. Aliphatic nitrosamines are often colored.

piperidine

N-nitrosopiperidine
(yellow)

N-nitroso-N-methylaniline

The reaction mechanism may be thought of in terms of the following steps.

(1) $HO-N=O + H^+ \rightleftharpoons H_2\overset{+}{O}-N=O$

(2) $H_2\overset{+}{O}-N=O \rightleftharpoons H_2O + {}^+\overset{..}{N}=\overset{..}{\underset{..}{O}}$

(3) $R_2\overset{..}{N}H + NO^+ \rightleftharpoons R_2\overset{+}{N}\overset{\displaystyle N=O}{\underset{\displaystyle H}{\diagdown}}$

(4) $R_2\overset{+}{N}\overset{\displaystyle N=O}{\underset{\displaystyle H}{\diagup}} \rightleftharpoons R_2N-N=O + H^+$

Since tertiary amines have no proton on nitrogen, step (4) is blocked. Thus no overall reaction occurs by this pathway. However, if the tertiary amine is aromatic, an alternative reaction path is available. The mild electrophile NO^+ (the **nitrosonium ion**) attacks the highly reactive aromatic ring, and electrophilic aromatic substitution occurs (Section 23.7.D). Substitution occurs only at the *para* position.

(80-89%)
p-nitrosodimethylaniline

With primary amines, the reaction with nitrous acid proceeds beyond the nitrosamine stage and a **diazonium compound** is produced.

(5) $R-\underset{..}{\overset{\displaystyle H}{N}}-N=O + H^+ \rightleftharpoons \left[R-\underset{..}{\overset{\displaystyle H}{N}}-\overset{+}{N}=\overset{..}{O}H \longleftrightarrow R-\underset{+}{\overset{\displaystyle H}{N}}=N-OH \right]$

(6) $R-\underset{+}{\overset{\displaystyle H}{N}}=N-OH \rightleftharpoons R-N=N-OH + H^+$

(7) $R-\overset{..}{N}=\overset{..}{N}-OH + H^+ \rightleftharpoons R-\overset{..}{N}=\overset{..}{N}-OH_2{}^+$

(8) $R-\overset{..}{N}=\overset{..}{N}-OH_2{}^+ \rightleftharpoons H_2O + R-\overset{+}{N}\equiv\overset{..}{N}$

alkanediazonium cation

Alkanediazonium compounds are exceedingly unstable and decompose, even at low temperatures, to give nitrogen and various products and intermediates including carbocations. An example is the reaction of *n*-butylamine with nitrous acid, generated *in situ* from sodium nitrite and aqueous hydrochloric acid.

$$CH_3(CH_2)_3NH_2 \xrightarrow[\substack{H_2O \\ 25°C}]{\substack{NaNO_2 \\ HCl}} CH_3(CH_2)_3OH + CH_3CH_2\overset{\displaystyle OH}{\overset{|}{C}}HCH_3 + CH_3(CH_2)_3Cl +$$

(25%)   (13%)   (5%)

$$CH_3CH_2CHClCH_3 + CH_3CH_2CH=CH_2 + \underset{H}{\overset{CH_3}{\diagup}}C=C\underset{H}{\overset{CH_3}{\diagdown}} + \underset{H}{\overset{CH_3}{\diagup}}C=C\underset{CH_3}{\overset{H}{\diagdown}}$$

(3%)   (26%)   (3%)   (7%)

Because the reaction with nitrous acid gives complex mixtures of products, it is not a generally useful one with aliphatic amines.

The diazonium ions produced by the reaction of primary aromatic amines are more stable than alkanediazonium ions. Aqueous solutions of these **arenediazonium ions** are stable at ice-bath temperatures.

benzenediazonium
cation

The overall process of converting a primary aromatic amine into an arenediazonium salt is called **diazotization**. As we shall see in Chapter 24, diazotization provides access to a wide variety of substituted aromatic compounds.

The mechanism of diazotization formulated on page 709 is probably oversimplified. In solution nitrous acid is in equilibrium with several other species, such as dinitrogen trioxide, the anhydride of nitrous acid.

$$2 \text{ HONO} \rightleftharpoons \text{H}_2\text{O} + \text{N}_2\text{O}_3$$

With halide ions, the equilibria contain nitrosyl halides, which are the mixed anhydrides of nitrous acid and hydrohalic acids.

$$\text{HONO} + \text{HX} \rightleftharpoons \text{ONX} + \text{H}_2\text{O}$$

The actual nitrosating agent in many cases is probably N_2O_3, although in solutions containing halide ion the corresponding nitrosyl halide may also play a role. Nitrous acid itself is an intermediate oxidation state of nitrogen and disproportionates to nitric oxide and nitric acid.

$$3 \text{ HONO} \longrightarrow 2 \text{ NO} + \text{H}_3\text{O}^+ + \text{NO}_3^-$$

The rate of this reaction is temperature-dependent and is also strongly dependent on the concentration of nitrous acid—the rate is proportional to $[\text{HONO}]^4$. Consequently, nitrous acid solutions are usually kept cold and dilute and are used immediately.

EXERCISE 23.14 Write equations showing the reaction product(s) expected from treatment of each of the following amines with an aqueous solution of NaNO₂ and HCl at 0°C.
(a) *n*-propylamine   (b) di-*n*-propylamine   (c) tri-*n*-propylamine
(d) aniline   (e) N-ethylaniline   (f) N,N-diethylaniline

C. Oxidation

Because of their basic nature, amines are oxidized with ease. With primary amines, oxidation is complicated by the variety of reaction paths that are available. Few useful oxidation reactions are known for this class. Secondary amines are easily oxidized to hydroxylamines. Again yields are generally poor due to over oxidation.

$$\text{R}_2\text{NH} + \text{H}_2\text{O}_2 \longrightarrow \text{R}_2\text{NOH} + \text{H}_2\text{O}$$

Tertiary amines are oxidized cleanly to tertiary amine oxides. Useful oxidants are H_2O_2 or organic peroxyacids, RCO_3H.

(90%)

> A mixture of 49 g of N,N-dimethylcyclohexylmethanamine, 45 mL of methanol, and 120 g of 30% aqueous H_2O_2 is kept at room temperature for 36 hr. The excess H_2O_2 is destroyed by the addition of a small amount of colloidal platinum. The solution is then filtered and evaporated to obtain the crude amine oxide in greater than 90% yield.

Amine oxides fall into the class of organic compounds for which no completely uncharged Lewis structure may be written. The Lewis electron-dot representation of trimethylamine oxide shows that both the oxygen and the nitrogen have octet configurations and that they bear (−) and (+) formal charges, respectively.

trimethylamine oxide

Aromatic amines are readily oxidized by a variety of oxidizing agents as well as by air. As a result, the oxidation of other functional groups cannot usually be carried out as satisfactorily if amino groups are also present.

> The nature of amine oxidations is demonstrated by oxidation of *p*-bis(dimethylamino)benzene, which gives a relatively stable *radical cation* called Wurster's blue.

Wurster's blue

As the name implies, radical cations are species that have a free electron and a positive charge. They are usually produced by removal of one electron from a neutral molecule and are common intermediates in mass spectrometry (Chapter 32). Wurster's blue is an example of a radical cation that is stable in solution. Other examples are now known to be important intermediates in various oxidation reactions. For example, the radical cation formed from aniline reacts further with aniline to produce highly colored polymeric compounds. On treatment with acidic potassium dichromate, aniline gives a black insoluble dye, aniline black, that is difficult to characterize. A proposed structure is

Other oxidation conditions give *p*-benzoquinone, a compound we will consider in detail in Chapter 26.

p-benzoquinone

D. Electrophilic Aromatic Substitution

Aromatic amines are highly activated toward substitution in the ring by electrophilic reagents. Reaction with such amines generally occurs under rather mild conditions. For example, halogenation is so facile that all unsubstituted *ortho* and *para* positions become substituted.

m-aminobenzoic acid → 3-amino-2,4,6-tribromo-benzoic acid

anthranilic acid → 2-amino-3,5-dichloro-benzoic acid (69–78%)

Nitration of aromatic primary amines is not generally a useful reaction because nitric acid is an oxidizing agent and amines are sensitive to oxidation. A mixture of aniline and nitric acid can burst into flame. Nitration of tertiary aromatic amines can be accomplished conveniently and in good yield; a satisfactory method is nitration in acetic acid.

1:2

The *ortho/para* ratio is 1:2, and the amount of 2,4-dinitro-N,N-dimethylaniline depends on the reaction conditions.

In general, electrophilic aromatic substitution reactions can be applied to tertiary aromatic amines. Furthermore, the dialkylamino group is such a strongly activating substituent that rather mild reaction conditions may be used.

In this example, no additional Lewis-acid catalyst is required, even with a deactivating nitro group in the ring.

Friedel-Crafts acylations can also be accomplished under mild conditions.

p,p′-bis-(dimethylamino)benzophenone
Michler's ketone
(a dye intermediate)

Aromatic tertiary amines can undergo a useful variant of Friedel-Crafts acylation, the **Vilsmeier reaction**, the reaction of an aromatic compound with dimethylformamide and phosphorus oxychloride to produce an aldehyde. The reaction requires a rather activated aromatic ring and is unsuccessful with aromatic compounds of only moderate reactivity, such as benzene, toluene and chlorobenzene.

dimethylaniline   dimethylformamide
(DMF)

(80–84%)
p-dimethylaminobenz-
aldehyde

The electrophilic reagent in the Vilsmeier reaction is a chloroimmonium ion, which is formed in the following manner.

This electrophilic species reacts only with aromatic rings that contain highly activating groups such as OH and NR$_2$. The initial product, an α-chloroamine, hydrolyzes rapidly during work-up to afford the aldehyde.

The Vilsmeier reaction has been an important industrial process, particularly for formylation of reactive heterocyclic compounds. However, large quantities of byproduct phosphorus compounds are produced, and the disposal of these waste materials presents an ever-increasing problem. Thus, there is a trend away from using this method.

The reactivity of aromatic amines to electrophilic reagents is reduced when the amino group is converted into an amide. The nitrogen lone pair that is so available to help stabilize the developing positive charge in the electrophilic substitution transition state is partially tied up by delocalization into the carbonyl group of the amide. Amide groups are still *ortho,para* directors, but they are not nearly as activating as amino groups and electrophilic reactions on amide derivatives are readily controlled. Another way of understanding the moderating effect of the acyl group on nitrogen is by consideration of the resonance structures for the intermediate that results from electrophilic attack *para* to the amide group.

The fact that the developing positive charge can be placed on the nitrogen still causes attack at this position (or at the *ortho* position) to be more favorable than attack at the *meta* position. However, this resonance structure is not quite as important as it is in the intermediate resulting from attack at the *para* position of the corresponding amine because the positive nitrogen is now adjacent to the positive carbon of the carbonyl group.

Acetanilides are widely used as substrates for electrophilic aromatic substitution reactions. Several examples are given below.

p-methoxyacetanilide → 2-nitro-4-methoxyacetanilide (75–79%)

Reagents: HNO_3, CH_3COOH, 45°C

Reagents: CH_3COOH, Δ; then Br_2, CH_3COOH, 55°C; then HCl, alcohol, Δ; then NaOH → 2-bromo-4-methylaniline (60–67%)

90% aq. HNO_3, −20°C	(23%)	(77%)
HNO_3, Ac_2O, 20°C	(68%)	(30%)

The last examples show that the *ortho/para* ratio can sometimes be altered by choosing the proper reaction conditions.

EXERCISE 23.15 Write equations showing the reactions of aniline, *m*-nitroaniline, and *p*-methoxyaniline with the following reagents or series of reagents.
(a) Br_2, water
(b) (i) acetic anhydride, pyridine; (ii) nitric acid, acetic acid; (iii) HCl, ethanol, heat; (iv) 1 *N* aqueous NaOH (work-up)

E. Elimination of the Amino Group: The Cope and Hofmann Elimination Reactions

Simple amines undergo neither base-catalyzed nor acid-catalyzed elimination reactions. In the former case, the leaving group would be NH_2^-, which is the conjugate base of a very weak acid, ammonia ($pK_a = 34$). In the latter case, the leaving group NH_3 is still not a very good one, since its conjugate acid, the ammonium ion, NH_4^+, has a relatively low acidity ($pK_a = 9.4$).

$$B:^- + H-\underset{|}{\overset{|}{C}}-\underset{|}{\overset{|}{C}}-NH_2 \xrightarrow{\;/\!\!\!\!\to\;} BH + \underset{/}{\overset{\backslash}{C}}=\overset{/}{\underset{\backslash}{C}} + ^-:NH_2$$

$$B: + H-\underset{|}{\overset{|}{C}}-\underset{|}{\overset{|}{C}}-\overset{+}{N}H_3 \xrightarrow{\;/\!\!\!\!\to\;} BH^+ + \underset{/}{\overset{\backslash}{C}}=\overset{/}{\underset{\backslash}{C}} + :NH_3$$

However, quaternary ammonium hydroxides do undergo elimination upon being heated.

$$\underset{\text{tetraethylammonium hydroxide}}{CH_3CH_2\overset{+}{N}(CH_2CH_3)_3\ OH^-} \xrightarrow{\Delta} CH_2{=}CH_2 + \underset{\text{triethylamine}}{N(CH_2CH_3)_3} + H_2O$$

Elimination proceeds by the E2 mechanism with hydroxide ion as the attacking base.

$$HO^- + H-CH_2-CH_2-\overset{+}{N}R_3 \longrightarrow \left[\overset{\delta-}{HO}\cdots H\cdots CH_2 \colonequals CH_2 \cdots \overset{\delta+}{N}R_3\right]^{\ddagger} \longrightarrow$$

$$HOH + CH_2{=}CH_2 + NR_3$$

The elimination reaction itself is the final step in a process known as **Hofmann degradation**. In this process a primary, secondary, or tertiary amine is first treated with enough methyl iodide to convert it into the quaternary ammonium iodide. The iodide is then replaced by hydroxide by treatment with silver oxide and water. The elimination reaction to give the alkene is effected by heating the dry quaternary ammonium hydroxide at 100°C or higher. In the process, the carbon-nitrogen bond is broken and an amine and an alkene are produced.

If the amine is cyclic, then the product is an amino alkene.

N-methyl-piperidine   N,N-dimethyl-piperidinium iodide   N,N-dimethyl-pent-4-en-1-amine

The process may be repeated with the initial amino alkene to yield a diene, liberating the nitrogen as trimethylamine.

1,4-pentadiene

A side reaction that may occur is S_N2 displacement. This is seldom a significant reaction except in cases where there are no β-hydrogens.

$$(CH_3)_3\overset{+}{N}-CH_3 \quad OH^- \xrightarrow[\Delta]{H_2O} (CH_3)_3N + CH_3OH$$

When the quaternary ammonium hydroxide has two or more different β-hydrogens, more than one alkene may be formed in the elimination. Unlike normal bimolecular eliminations with alkyl halides, the Hofmann elimination gives predominantly the less highly substituted alkene, as comparison of the following examples shows.

$$CH_3CH_2\overset{\underset{\displaystyle Br}{|}}{C}HCH_3 \xrightarrow[\underset{\Delta}{EtOH}]{NaOEt} CH_3CH=CHCH_3 + CH_3CH_2CH=CH_2$$
$$(81\%) \qquad\qquad (19\%)$$

$$CH_3CH_2\overset{\underset{\displaystyle \overset{+}{N}(CH_3)_3}{|}}{C}HCH_3 \quad OH^- \longrightarrow CH_3CH=CHCH_3 + CH_3CH_2CH=CH_2$$
$$(5\%) \qquad\qquad (95\%)$$

This type of behavior is also seen when the ammonium compound contains two different alkyl groups that may be lost as the alkene.

For ammonium hydroxides having only simple alkyl groups, such as the foregoing examples, the mode of elimination may be generalized as follows (Hofmann rule): "In the decomposition of quaternary ammonium hydroxides, the hydrogen is lost most easily from CH_3, next from RCH_2, and least easily from R_2CH." The direction of elimination in the Hofmann reaction is probably governed mostly by steric factors. The generality of the rule is shown by the following additional examples.

One way in which steric effects contribute to this preference for the less substituted olefin is by their effect on the populations of different conformations. For example, in the 2-butyl case, the most stable conformation may be represented by a Newman projection of the C-2—C-3 bond as follows.

However, this conformation has no anti hydrogen at C-3. Anti elimination can only occur in one of the two conformations in which the trimethylammonium group is anti to a hydrogen.

Both of these conformations have a methyl group gauche to the bulky trimethylammonium group, a group comparable in size to *t*-butyl. Hence, the populations of these conformations are small. On the other hand, all conformations with respect to the C-1—C-2 bond have an anti hydrogen.

Although removal of a proton from C-3 would be faster because a more stable disubstituted ethylene results (Section 11.4), the population of conformations with anti hydrogen at C-3 is so small that the inherently slower reaction at C-1 dominates. An interesting example is the elimination reaction of the following cyclohexane derivative.

This compound has a fixed conformation with two anti hydrogens, one secondary and one tertiary. Reaction at the tertiary hydrogen is faster and gives the more highly substituted olefin.

When electron-withdrawing groups are attached to one of the β-carbons, the Hofmann rule is not followed.

Elimination of the amino group may also be brought about by the thermal elimination of amine oxides (Section 23.7.C). These compounds undergo elimination when heated to 150–200°C, provided that there is at least one hydrogen β to the nitrogen. The reaction is called the **Cope elimination** and is a useful alternative to the Hofmann degradation as a method for removing nitrogen from a compound. It is also useful as a preparative method for certain alkenes.

Crude N,N-dimethylcyclohexylmethanamine oxide (about 50 g) is placed in a flask that has been evacuated to a pressure of about 10 mm. The liquefied amine oxide is heated at 160°C for 2 hr. Water is added, and the alkene layer is separated and distilled to obtain 30 g of methylenecyclohexane (98%).

Amine oxide pyrolysis is similar mechanistically to ester pyrolysis (Section 18.11). The mechanism is a sort of internal E2 process in which the oxide oxygen acts as the attacking base, abstracting the β-proton in a concerted reaction.

This mechanism is supported by experiments that clearly show the elimination to be syn (see Section 18.11).

EXERCISE 23.16 Write equations showing the product(s) expected from each of the following reactions.
(a) N,N-dimethyl-2-pentanamine + methyl iodide; silver hydroxide; heat
(b) N,N-diethyloctanamine + methyl iodide; silver hydroxide; heat
(c) triethylamine + hydrogen peroxide; heat
(d) (1R,2S)-1-deuterio-N,N,2-trimethyl-1-butanamine + hydrogen peroxide; heat

23.8 Enamines and Immonium Ions

Enamines are compounds in which an amino group is attached directly to a carbon-carbon double bond. They are the nitrogen analogs of enols.

an enol   an enamine

Like enols, enamines are generally unstable and undergo rapid conversion into the imine isomer.

When the nitrogen of an enamine is tertiary, such isomerization cannot occur, and the enamine may be isolated and handled.

N,N-dimethyl-1-cyclohexenamine

Tertiary enamines are prepared by reaction of a secondary amine with an aldehyde or ketone. Water must be removed as it is formed in order to shift the equilibrium to the enamine product. Cyclic secondary amines are commonly used.

pyrrolidine   N-(1-cyclo-
hexenyl)pyrrolidine

The mechanism for enamine formation is similar to the mechanism for formation of an imine; the reaction is subject to both acid and base catalysis (Section 14.7.C).

(1)

(2)

(3)

(4) + H⁺ ⇌

(5) ⇌ + H_2O

(6) ⇌ + H⁺

The products are sensitive to aqueous acid and revert to the carbonyl compound and the amine in dilute acid.

+ H_3O^+ ⟶ +

Enamines are useful intermediates in some reactions because the β-carbon of the double bond has nucleophilic character, as shown in the following resonance structures.

Reaction occurs rapidly with reactive alkyl halides to give alkylated immonium compounds, which undergo facile hydrolysis to give the alkylated ketone.

+ CH_2=$CHCH_2Br$ ⟶ $\xrightarrow{H_2O}$ +

2-allylcyclohexanone

Enamines may also be prepared by the dehydrogenation of tertiary amines. Dehydrogenation is accomplished by oxidation to an immonium ion with mercuric acetate, followed by deprotonation of the immonium ion with sodium bicarbonate.

Immonium ions are intermediates in an important reaction for formation of carbon-carbon bonds, the **Mannich reaction**. In this reaction, a secondary amine, a ketone, or other carbonyl compound that can undergo easy enolization, and an aldehyde (often formaldehyde) combine to give a β-amino ketone.

acetophenone β-(N,N-dimethylamino)propiophenone

A mixture of 60 g of acetophenone, 52.7 g of dimethylamine hydrochloride, 19.8 g of paraformaldehyde, 1 mL of concentrated hydrochloric acid, and 80 mL of 95% ethanol is heated on a steam bath for 2 hr. The warm yellow solution is diluted with 400 mL of acetone and cooled in an ice bath. The product separates as large crystals, 72–77 g (68–72%), m.p. 138–141°C.

The Mannich reaction involves an intermediate immonium ion, which reacts with the enol form of the ketone.

$$CH_2{=}O + R_2\overset{+}{N}H_2 \longrightarrow CH_2{=}\overset{+}{N}R_2 + H_2O$$

We shall see that chemistry such as this is important in connection with methods for preparation of heterocyclic compounds (Chapter 31).

EXERCISE 23.17 Show how the Mannich reaction can be used to prepare 2-methyl-1-(N,N-dimethylamino)-3-pentanone.

PROBLEMS

1. Name the following compounds. For amines, use the convention enunciated at the end of Section 23.2.

(a) $CH_3CH_2\overset{\overset{\textstyle CH_3}{|}}{C}HCH_2NH_2$

(b) $(CH_3)_3N$

(c) $CH_2{=}CHCH_2N\overset{\diagup CH_3}{\diagdown CH_2CH_3}$

(d)

(e)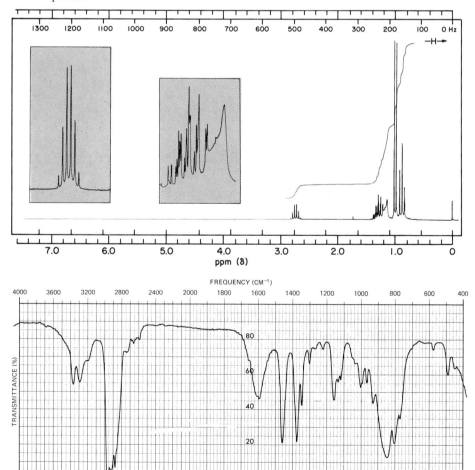

(f)

(g) $CH_3CH_2\overset{+}{N}(CH_3)_3\ I^-$

(h) $CH_3CH_2CH_2\overset{+}{\underset{|}{N}}(CH_3)_2$ with O^-

(i) $(CH_3CH_2)_2CHN(CH_3)_2$

(j)

(k)

(l)

2. The NMR and IR spectra of an unknown compound are shown below. The CMR spectrum shows four resonances, with δ 8.2, 24.3, 35.0, and 49.0 ppm. Propose a structure for the compound.

3. The NMR and IR spectra of an unknown compound are shown below. Propose a structure for the compound.

4. Although the inversion barrier for trimethylamine is only 6 kcal mole^{-1}, that for the heterocyclic tertiary amine N-methylaziridine is about 19 kcal mole^{-1}. Propose an explanation.

$$\underset{\text{N-methylaziridine}}{\overset{\displaystyle \begin{array}{c}CH_2\\ |\\ CH_2\end{array}\!\!\!\diagdown\!\!\!\diagup N-CH_3}{}}$$

5. Consider a solution of methylamine in water.
   (a) At what pH are the CH_3NH_2 and $CH_3NH_3^+$ concentrations exactly equal?
   (b) Calculate the $[CH_3NH_2]/[CH_3NH_3^+]$ ratio at pH 6, 8, 10, and 12.

6. Consider the reaction of methylamine with acetic acid.

$$CH_3NH_2 + CH_3COOH \overset{K}{\rightleftharpoons} CH_3NH_3^+ + CH_3CO_2^-$$

   (a) Using the data in Tables 17.2 and 23.4, calculate K.
   (b) At what pH does $[CH_3CO_2^-] = [CH_3NH_3^+]$?

7. (a) Propose a method for separating a mixture of cyclohexanecarboxylic acid, tributylamine, and decane.

(b) Alcohols react with phthalic anhydride to give monophthalate esters.

Suggest a method for the resolution of racemic 2-octanol.

8. What is (are) the principal organic product(s) of each of the following reactions?

(a) NHCOCH₃ / CH₃ ring, $\xrightarrow[\text{CH}_3\text{COOH}]{\text{HNO}_3}$

(b) CH₃ / NO₂ ring, $\xrightarrow[\Delta]{\text{SnCl}_2,\ \text{HCl}}$

(c) NHCOCH₃ / NH₂ ring, $\xrightarrow[\text{aq. HCl}]{\text{Cl}_2}$

(d) NO₂ / COOH ring, $\xrightarrow{\text{H}_2/\text{Pt}}$

(e) ring with C(=O)CH₂CH₃, $\xrightarrow[\substack{(\text{CH}_3)_2\text{NH}\\ \text{H}^+}]{\text{CH}_2=\text{O}}$

(f) CH₃ / NO₂ / CH₃ / NO₂ ring, $\xrightarrow[\text{CH}_3\text{OH}]{\text{NaSH}}$

9. Suggest a sequence of reactions involving the Mannich condensation and the Hofmann elimination that can be used to convert acetone into methyl vinyl ketone.

10. How will each of the following compounds behave with aqueous nitrous acid?

(a) NH₂

(b) NHCH₃

(c) NHCOCH₃

(d) N(CH₃)₂

(e) CH₂NH₂

(f) NHNH₂

(g) CH₂NHCH₃

(h) CH₂N(CH₃)₂

(i) CH₂NHCOCH₃

11. The dipole moment of p-(N,N-dimethylamino)benzonitrile, 6.60 D, is substantially greater than the sum of the dipole moments of N,N-dimethylaniline, 1.57 D, and benzonitrile, 3.93 D. Explain.

12. Write out the mechanism for bromination of N,N-dimethylaniline in the *para* position with Br$_2$ and show why this compound is so much more reactive than benzene.

13. Although *o*-methylaniline (pK_a = 4.44) is a somewhat weaker base than aniline (pK_a = 4.60), *o*-methyl-N,N-dimethylaniline (pK_a = 6.11) is a much stronger base than N,N-dimethylaniline (pK_a = 5.15). Give a rational explanation.

14. In each of the following pairs of compounds, which is the more basic in aqueous solution? Give a brief explanation.

15. Outline a synthesis of each of the following compounds from alcohols containing five or fewer carbon atoms.

(a) $CH_3(CH_2)_4NH_2$ (b) $CH_3(CH_2)_4N(CH_3)_2$

(c) $CH_3CH_2CH_2\overset{\overset{\displaystyle CH_3}{|}}{N}CH_2CH_2CH_3$ (d) $(CH_3)_2CHCH_2CH_2NHCH_2CH_3$

16. Propose a method for the stereospecific conversion of
(a) (*R*)-2-octanol into (*S*)-2-octylamine
(b) (*R*)-2-octanol into (*R*)-2-octylamine

17. Propose a synthesis for each of the following compounds.

(a) $H_2N\overset{\overset{\displaystyle CH_3}{|}}{C}H CH\underset{\underset{\displaystyle OH}{|}}{}CH_2CH_3$ (mixture of diastereomers)

(b) (indicated diastereomer only)

(c)

HO CH$_2$NH$_2$

[cyclohexane ring structure]

(d) CH$_3$CH$_2$CCHCH$_2$N(CH$_2$CH$_3$)$_2$ with O double bond and CH$_3$ substituent

(e) [cyclohexane ring]—CH$_2$NH$_2$　　　(*Hint:* See Section 19.5)

(f)

NH$_2$
[benzene ring]
NO$_2$

(from [benzene ring])

(g)

NH$_2$
Cl—[benzene ring]—Cl
Cl

(from [benzene ring])

18. Diphenylamine, (C$_6$H$_5$)$_2$NH, is a rather weak base; the pK_a of the conjugate acid, 0.79, shows that diphenylamine is about 10^{-4} as basic as aniline. Give a reasonable explanation.

19. The trimethylanilinium cation, C$_6$H$_5$N(CH$_3$)$_3^+$, is prepared by an S$_N$2 reaction of dimethyl-aniline with a methyl halide or sulfonate. The compound undergoes a number of electro-philic substitution reactions such as nitration. Write the resonance structures involved for the intermediate produced by reaction at the *meta* and *para* positions and determine whether the trimethylammonium group is activating or deactivating, and *ortho,para* or *meta* directing.

20. Show how to accomplish each of the following conversions.

(a) CH$_2$=CHCO$_2$C$_2$H$_5$ $\longrightarrow$ H$_2$NCH$_2$CH$_2$CH$_2$CH$_2$N(CH$_3$)$_2$

(b) [cyclopentanone] $\longrightarrow$ [cyclopentylamine with NH$_2$]

(c) [cyclohexanone with CH$_3$] $\longrightarrow$ [cyclohexane with H$_3$CNH and CH$_3$]

(d) [cyclohexane with NH$_2$] $\longrightarrow$ [cyclohexane with N(CH$_3$)$_2$]

(e) —CH$_2$CCH$_3$ $\longrightarrow$ —CH$_2$CHCH$_3$

21. What is the expected product when piperidine is subjected to each of the following sets of reactions?

(a) $\xrightarrow{\text{CH}_3\text{CCl}}$ $\xrightarrow{\text{LiAlH}_4}$

piperidine

(b) $\xrightarrow[(-\text{H}_2\text{O})]{}$

(c) $\xrightarrow{\text{HNO}_2}$

(d) $\xrightarrow[\substack{\text{CH}_2=\text{O} \\ \text{HCl}}]{}$

(e) $\xrightarrow[\text{Na}_2\text{CO}_3]{2\text{CH}_3\text{I}}$ $\xrightarrow{\text{Ag}_2\text{O}}$ $\xrightarrow{\Delta}$

(f) $\xrightarrow{\text{H}_2\text{O}_2}$

22. *cis*-2-Butene is subjected to the following sequence of reactions.

$\xrightarrow[\text{2. H}_2\text{O}_2, \text{OH}^-]{\text{1. B}_2\text{D}_6}$ CH$_3$CHDCHCH$_3$ (OH) $\xrightarrow{\text{C}_6\text{H}_5\text{SO}_2\text{Cl}}$

CH$_3$CHDCHCH$_3$ (OSO$_2$C$_6$H$_5$) $\xrightarrow[\text{(page 000)}]{\text{Gabriel synthesis}}$ CH$_3$CHDCHCH$_3$ (NH$_2$) $\xrightarrow[\text{HCO}_2\text{H}]{\text{CH}_2\text{O}}$ CH$_3$CHDCHCH$_3$ (N(CH$_3$)$_2$) $\xrightarrow{\text{H}_2\text{O}_2}$

CH$_3$CHDCHCH$_3$ ($^-$O—$\overset{+}{\text{N}}$(CH$_3$)$_2$) $\xrightarrow{150°\text{C}}$ 1-butene + *cis*-2-butene + *trans*-2-butene

Two of the butene isomers produced in the pyrolysis contain one atom of deuterium per molecule and the other isomer contains only hydrogen. Which isomer contains no deuterium? Explain.

23. Predict the major product in each of the following elimination reactions.

(a) CH$_3$CH$_2$$\overset{+}{\text{N}}CH_2$CH(CH$_3$)$_2$ OH$^-$ $\xrightarrow{\Delta}$ with CH$_3$ groups above and below N

(b) (CH$_3$)$_2$CHCHCH$_3$ ($^+$N(CH$_3$)$_3$) OH$^-$ $\xrightarrow{\Delta}$

(c) (CH$_3$CH$_2$)$_3$$\overset{+}{\text{N}}CH_2CH_2CCH_3$ OH$^-$ $\xrightarrow{\Delta}$

(d)

(e)

24. Show how to accomplish each of the following conversions.

25. Reaction of (cyclopentylmethyl)amine with aqueous nitrous acid gives a mixture of two alcohols and three olefins. Deduce their structures using a reasonable reaction mechanism.

26. Show how each of the following reactions can be carried out using phase-transfer catalysis.

(a) $n\text{-}C_{10}H_{21}Br + NaOOCCH_3 \longrightarrow n\text{-}C_{10}H_{21}OOCCH_3$

(b) $3,4\text{-}(CH_3)_2C_6H_3COCH_3 + NaOD + D_2O \longrightarrow 3,4\text{-}(CH_3)_2C_6H_3COCD_3$

(c) $(CH_3)_2CH(CH_2)_4OH + (CH_3)_2SO_4 \longrightarrow (CH_3)_2CH(CH_2)_4OCH_3$

(d) $(CH_3)_2CHCHO + C_6H_5CH_2Cl \longrightarrow C_6H_5CH_2C(CH_3)_2CHO$

(e) $C_6H_5CH{=}CH_2 + CHCl_3 \longrightarrow$

27. Which member of each of the following pairs of substituted ammonium ions is the more acidic? Explain briefly.
(a) $ClCH_2CH_2NH_3^+$; $CH_3CH_2CH_2NH_3^+$
(b) $CH_3ONH_3^+$; $CH_3NH_3^+$
(c) $CH_3CONH_3^+$; $CH_3CH_2NH_3^+$
(d) $CH_2{=}NH_2^+$; $CH_3NH_3^+$
(e) $CH_3OOCCH_2NH_3^+$; $CH_3CH_2CH_2NH_3^+$
(f) $CH_2{=}CHNH_3^+$; $CH_3CH_2NH_3^+$

28. Granatine, $C_9H_{17}N$, is an alkaloid that occurs in pomegranate. Two stages of the Hofmann exhaustive methylation remove the nitrogen and yield a mixture of cyclooctadienes identified by catalytic hydrogenation to cyclooctane. The ultraviolet spectrum of the mixture shows the absence of the conjugated diene, 1,3-cyclooctadiene. Deduce the structure of granatine.

29. N-Chloroacetanilide is converted to a mixture of 32% *o*-chloroacetanilide and 68% *p*-chloroacetanilide in the presence of HCl. The use of ^{36}Cl-enriched HCl finds the isotopic Cl incorporated into the product. The reaction of acetanilide with chlorine under the same reaction conditions gives the same product composition. Write a reaction mechanism for the rearrangement of N-chloroacetanilide (Orton rearrangement) to account for these facts.

30. Treatment of (1-hydroxycyclohexyl)methylamine with aqueous nitrous acid gives a single product in good yield. The product shows a strong infrared absorption at 1705 cm^{-1} and has a four-line CMR spectrum; δ 23.5, 29.7, 42.7 and 211.7. What is the structure of this product? Propose a mechanism for its formation.

Chapter 24

Other Nitrogen Functions

Although the amino group is the most important functional group of nitrogen, others are known and have been mentioned at times in this text. Several are listed in Table 24.1 and discussed in this chapter. The diazonium group is an example of a functional group having particular importance when attached to an aromatic ring and is useful for the preparation of a wide variety of other compounds.

24.1 Nitro Compounds

Nitroalkanes are relatively rare, although a few of the simpler ones are commercially available. Examples are nitromethane (which is used as a high-power fuel in racing engines), nitroethane, and 2-nitropropane.

$$\left[CH_3\overset{+}{N}\overset{O^-}{\underset{O}{\diagup}} \longleftrightarrow CH_3\overset{+}{N}\overset{O}{\underset{O^-}{\diagup}} \right] \equiv CH_3NO_2 \quad CH_3CH_2NO_2 \quad (CH_3)_2CHNO_2$$

nitromethane   nitroethane   2-nitropropane

Aromatic nitro compounds are much more common because they are easily prepared by the electrophilic nitration of aromatic compounds (Section 22.3).

TABLE 24.1 Functional Groups Containing Nitrogen

Structure	Name	Example	
$R{-}NO_2$	nitro	$C_6H_5NO_2$	nitrobenzene
$R{-}NCO$	isocyanate	C_6H_5NCO	phenyl isocyanate
$R{-}NHCOOR'$	urethane, carbamate	$C_6H_5NHCOOCH_3$	methyl N-phenyl-carbamate
$R{-}NHCONH{-}R'$	urea	H_2NCONH_2	urea
$R{-}N_3$	azide	$CH_3CH_2N_3$	ethyl azide
$R{-}N{=}N{-}R'$	azo	$C_6H_5N{=}NC_6H_5$	azobenzene
$R{-}\underset{+}{N}{=}N{-}R$ (with O^- on N)	azoxy	$C_6H_5\underset{+}{N}{=}NC_6H_5$ (with O^-)	azoxybenzene
$R{-}NHNH_2$	hydrazine, diazine	$C_6H_5NHNH_2$	phenylhydrazine
$R_2C{=}N_2$	diazo	$CH_2{=}N_2$	diazomethane
$R{-}N_2^+$	diazonium	$C_6H_5N_2^+\ Cl^-$	benzenediazonium chloride

A. Nitroalkanes

Nitroalkanes are prepared industrially by the free radical nitration of alkanes (see problem 11, page 112).

$$CH_4 + HNO_3 \xrightarrow{400°C} CH_3NO_2 + H_2O$$

Some nitro compounds may be prepared in the laboratory by the displacement of alkyl halides with nitrite ion. Since nitrite is an ambident anion, some alkyl nitrite is usually produced as a by-product (Section 9.4.D).

$$\underset{\text{CH}_3(CH_2)_5\overset{I}{\text{CHCH}_3}}{} + NaNO_2 \longrightarrow \underset{\text{CH}_3(CH_2)_5\overset{NO_2}{\text{CHCH}_3}}{} + \underset{\text{CH}_3(CH_2)_5\overset{ONO}{\text{CHCH}_3}}{}$$
$$(58\%) \qquad\qquad (30\%)$$

Yields of nitroalkane are higher when silver nitrite is used, but this added economy is tempered by the cost of the silver salt.

$$CH_3(CH_2)_6CH_2I + AgNO_2 \longrightarrow CH_3(CH_2)_6CH_2NO_2 + CH_3(CH_2)_6CH_2ONO$$
$$(83\%) \qquad\qquad (11\%)$$

The most striking chemical property of nitroalkanes is their acidity. The pK_a of nitromethane is 10.2, that of nitroethane is 8.5, and that of 2-nitropropane is 7.8. 2-Nitropropane is so acidic that it is extensively ionized in neutral solution (pH = 7). Like carboxylic acids and ketones, nitro compounds owe their acidity to the fact that the conjugate base is resonance-stabilized.

$$CH_3\overset{+}{N}\!\!\begin{smallmatrix}O\\\\O^-\end{smallmatrix} \longrightarrow H^+ + \left[:CH_2-\overset{+}{N}\!\!\begin{smallmatrix}O\\\\O^-\end{smallmatrix} \longleftrightarrow :CH_2-\overset{}{N}\!\!\begin{smallmatrix}O^-\\\\O\end{smallmatrix} \longleftrightarrow CH_2\!\!=\!\!\overset{+}{N}\!\!\begin{smallmatrix}O^-\\\\O^-\end{smallmatrix} \right]$$

methylnitronate ion

The anions derived from nitroalkanes are nucleophilic and enter into typical nucleophilic reactions. One particularly useful reaction is the **Henry reaction**, which is analogous to the aldol addition reaction of aldehyde and ketone enolates (Section 14.8.C).

$$CH_3(CH_2)_7CHO + CH_3NO_2 \xrightarrow[\text{EtOH}]{\text{NaOH}} CH_3(CH_2)_7\overset{OH}{\underset{}{\text{CHCH}_2NO_2}}$$
$$(80\%)$$
1-nitro-2-decanol

Since nitro compounds are so acidic, only weakly basic catalysts are required. In the case of aromatic aldehydes, dehydration of the initial β-hydroxy nitro compound usually results.

$$\text{⟨benzene ring⟩}-CHO + CH_3NO_2 \xrightarrow[25°C]{n\text{-}C_5H_{11}NH_2} \text{⟨benzene ring⟩}-CH\!\!=\!\!CHNO_2$$
$$(75\%)$$
β-nitrostyrene

Another general reaction of nitro compounds is reduction to the corresponding amine (Section 23.6.C). Reduction of β-hydroxy nitroalkanes produced by the Henry reaction provides a convenient method for preparing 1,2-amino alcohols.

$$HO\!\!\diagdown\!\!\diagup\!\!\diagdown\!\!-NO_2 \xrightarrow[\substack{H_2O\\H_2SO_4}]{\text{Fe, FeSO}_4} HO\!\!\diagdown\!\!\diagup\!\!\diagdown\!\!\underset{HSO_4^-}{-NH_3^+} \xrightarrow{\text{NaOH}} HO\!\!\diagdown\!\!\diagup\!\!\diagdown\!\!-NH_2$$
2-amino-2-methyl-1-propanol

> **EXERCISE 24.1** Show how 2-pentanone can be converted into each of the following compounds.
> (a) 2-methylpentanamine (b) 2-hydroxy-2-methylpentanamine

B. Nitroarenes

Nitrobenzene and related nitro compounds are generally high-boiling liquids. Nitrobenzene is a pale yellow oil, b.p. 210-211°C, having a characteristic odor of almonds. It was used at one time in shoe polish, but its use for this purpose has now been discontinued because it is readily absorbed through the skin and is poisonous.

2,4,6-Trinitrotoluene, TNT, is an important explosive. It is relatively insensitive to shock and is used with a detonator. It melts at 81°C, and it can be poured as the melt into containers for the manufacture of high explosive devices. 1,3,5-Trinitrobenzene is less sensitive than TNT to shock and has more explosive power, but is more difficult to prepare. Direct introduction of the third nitro group into toluene is assisted by the methyl group. Small amounts of 1,3,5-trinitrobenzene are prepared by oxidation of TNT to trinitrobenzoic acid.

2,4,6-trinitrotoluene   →(Na₂Cr₂O₇, H₂SO₄, 45-55°C)→   2,4,6-trinitrobenzoic acid (57-69%)

2,4,6-Trinitrobenzoic acid is a strong acid ($pK_a = 0.7$) whose anion decomposes on heating to give carbon dioxide and a phenyl anion that is stabilized by the electron-attracting inductive effect of the three nitro groups.

1,3,5-trinitrobenzene

> **EXERCISE 24.2** The protons attached to the methyl carbon in 2,4,6-trinitrotoluene (TNT) are fairly acidic. For example, a mixture of benzaldehyde and TNT react with the aid of a secondary amine catalyst to give an adduct that is analogous to the product of the Henry reaction.
>
>
> Suggest a reason for the acidity of these protons.

C. Reactions of Nitroarenes

The nitro group is relatively stable to many reagents. It is generally inert to acids and most electrophilic reagents; hence, it may be present in a ring when reactions with such reagents are used. The nitro group is also stable to most oxidizing agents, but it reacts with Grignard reagents and other strongly basic compounds such as lithium aluminum hydride. The most important reaction of the nitro group in aromatic compounds is reduction, but the reduction product depends on the reaction conditions used. Catalytic hydrogenation and reduction in acidic media yield the corresponding amine (Section 23.6.C).

$$ArNO_2 \longrightarrow ArNH_2$$

Reduction of the nitro group actually proceeds in a series of two-electron steps. In acid the intermediate compounds cannot be isolated, but are reduced rapidly in turn.

nitrobenzene   nitrosobenzene   phenylhydroxylamine   aniline

In neutral media a higher reduction potential is required, and reduction is readily stopped at the hydroxylamine stage.

Aromatic hydroxylamines are relatively unimportant compounds. Phenylhydroxylamine is a water-soluble, crystalline solid, m.p. 82°C, that deteriorates in storage. It may be oxidized to nitrosobenzene as shown in the foregoing equation. Hydroxylamines and nitroso compounds are readily reduced to amines by chemical reduction in acidic solution or by catalytic hydrogenation.

Reduction of nitro compounds in basic media gives binuclear compounds.

(85%)
azoxybenzene

(84–86%)
azobenzene

(80%)
hydrazobenzene

All of these compounds are reduced to aniline under acidic conditions. They may also be interconverted by the following reactions.

These binuclear compounds may best be considered to arise by condensation reactions during reduction.

In fact, azoxybenzene can be prepared by the base-catalyzed condensation of phenyl-hydroxylamine with nitrosobenzene. The azoxy function is the least important functional group among these compounds. Azobenzene is a bright orange-red solid. Although azobenzene itself has only limited significance, the azo linkage is an important component of azo dyes (Section 34.3).

Many azo compounds show cis-trans isomerism. The trans isomer is generally the more stable, and the activation energy for the conversion is sufficiently low that the cis isomer is generally not seen. For example, azobenzene can be converted in part to the cis isomer by photolysis, but the activation energy required to convert back to *trans*-azobenzene is only 23–25 kcal mole^{-1} in various solvents. This reaction has a half-life on the order of hours at room temperature.

$t_{1/2}$ = 1–3 hr
at 25°C

cis-azobenzene   trans-azobenzene

Hydrazobenzene or 1,2-diphenylhydrazine is a colorless solid that air-oxidizes on standing to azobenzene. It is significant principally because of a rearrangement that it undergoes in strongly acidic solution, the **benzidine rearrangement**.

hydrazobenzene   4,4′-diaminobiphenyl
                                  (benzidine)

This remarkable reaction involves the mono- or diprotonated salt in which bonding occurs between the *para* positions as the nitrogen-nitrogen bond is broken.

transition state

The benzidine rearrangement is an example of a [5.5] sigmatropic rearrangement and involves a 10-electron Hückel transition state. Benzidine has had important uses as an intermediate in dye manufacture, but the compound has been found to be carcinogenic.

Azoxybenzene, azobenzene, and hydrazobenzene are all conveniently reduced to aniline with sodium hydrosulfite.

$$C_6H_5-N{=}N-C_6H_5 + 2\,Na_2S_2O_4 + 2\,H_2O \longrightarrow 2\,C_6H_5NH_2 + 4\,NaHSO_3$$

> Sodium hydrosulfite, or sodium dithionite, is a useful reagent in neutral or alkaline solution. In acidic medium it decomposes with the liberation of sulfur. It is especially useful in the reductive cleavage of the azo groups in azo dyes. These dyes are generally water-soluble, and reduction is accomplished by adding sodium hydrosulfite to an aqueous solution until the color of the dye has been discharged.

> **EXERCISE 24.3** Review in Section 22.3 the preparation of *o*-nitrotoluene. Write the equations showing the application of each reaction presented in this section with *o*-nitrotoluene.

24.2 Isocyanates, Carbamates, and Ureas

We have encountered alkyl isocyanates previously as intermediates in the Hofmann rearrangement of amides (Section 23.6.H). They may also be prepared by displacement of alkyl halides with cyanate ion. This ion is ambident and reacts preferentially at the nitrogen end.

$$CH_3CH_2CH_2CH_2Br + Na^+\,NCO^- \longrightarrow CH_3CH_2CH_2CH_2NCO$$
n-butyl isocyanate

Isocyanates react with water to give N-alkyl carbamic acids, which are unstable and spontaneously lose carbon dioxide to give the corresponding amine.

$$R-NCO + H_2O \longrightarrow [R-NHCOOH] \longrightarrow RNH_2 + CO_2$$

Isocyanates give carbamate esters with alcohols and ureas with amines.

methyl N-cyclohexylcarbamate

N-methyl-N'-cyclohexylurea

Carbamate esters are also called urethanes. An important class of commercial polymers is the polyurethanes, which are formed from an aromatic diisocyanate and a diol. One type of diol used is actually a low molecular weight copolymer made from ethylene glycol and adipic acid. When this polymer, which has free hydroxy end groups, is mixed with the diisocyanate, a larger polymer is produced.

$$HOCH_2CH_2OH + HOOC(CH_2)_4COOH \longrightarrow$$

a polyurethane

In the manufacturing process, a little water is mixed in with the diol. Some of the diisocyanate reacts with water to give an aromatic diamine and carbon dioxide. The carbon dioxide forms bubbles that are trapped in the bulk of the polymer as it solidifies. The result is a spongy product called polyurethane foam.

24.3 Azides

Organic azides are compounds with the general formula RN_3. They are related to the inorganic acid, hydrazoic acid, HN_3. Azide ion, N_3^-, is a resonance hybrid of the following important dipolar structures.

$$\left[:N{\equiv}\overset{+}{N}-\overset{..}{\underset{..}{N}}:^{2-} \longleftrightarrow :\overset{-}{\underset{..}{N}}{=}\overset{+}{N}{=}\overset{-}{\underset{..}{N}}: \longleftrightarrow {}^{2-}\overset{..}{\underset{..}{N}}-\overset{+}{N}{\equiv}N: \right]$$

This anion is relatively nonbasic for anionic nitrogen (the pK_a of HN_3 is 11) and is a good nucleophile. Alkyl azides are best prepared by nucleophilic displacement on alkyl halides.

$$CH_3CH_2CH_2CH_2Br + N_3^- \xrightarrow[\substack{H_2O \\ (90\%)}]{CH_3OH} CH_3CH_2CH_2CH_2N_3 + Br^-$$

A mixture of 34.5 g of NaN$_3$, 68.5 g of *n*-butyl bromide, 70 mL of water, and 25 mL of methanol is refluxed for 24 hr. The *n*-butyl azide separates as an oily layer. It is dried and distilled behind a safety barricade to obtain 40 g of pure *n*-butyl azide (90%).

Azide ion is also sufficiently nucleophilic to open the epoxide ring. β-Hydroxyalkyl azides may be prepared in this way.

$$CH_3CH{-}CH_2 + N_3^- \xrightarrow[25°C, 24\ hr]{H_2O} CH_3CHCH_2N_3$$

(70%)

Acyl azides may be prepared from acyl halides and azide ion (Section 23.6.H).

$$RCCl + N_3^- \longrightarrow RCN_3 + Cl^-$$

Alkyl azides are reduced by lithium aluminum hydride or by catalytic hydrogenation to give the corresponding amines. The two-step process of (1) displacement of halide ion by azide ion, and (2) reduction of the resulting azide provides a convenient synthesis of pure primary amines. Also, since azide ion is relatively nonbasic yet still highly nucleophilic, its substitution/elimination ratio is high, even with secondary and β-branched alkyl halides.

$$\text{Br} + Na^+ N_3^- \xrightarrow[H_2O]{C_2H_5OH} \underset{\text{2-pentyl azide}}{N_3} \xrightarrow{LiAlH_4} \underset{\text{2-pentanamine}}{NH_2}$$

Both alkyl and acyl azides are thermally unstable and lose nitrogen on heating. In some cases, particularly when the nitrogen content of the molecule is higher than about 25%, the decomposition can occur with explosive violence. Decomposition of alkyl azides gives a complex mixture of products. Acyl azides decompose to the acyl nitrene, which rearranges to an isocyanate (Schmidt and Curtius rearrangements; Section 23.6.H).

$$R{-}\overset{O}{\overset{\|}{C}}{-}N_3 \longrightarrow N_2 + R{-}\overset{O}{\overset{\|}{C}}{-}\ddot{\overset{..}{N}} \longrightarrow R{-}N{=}C{=}O$$

an isocyanate

EXERCISE 24.4 Compare the Lewis structures of an isocyanate and an azide. What is the expected product of the reaction of benzyl chloride with sodium cyanate in methanol solution?

24.4 Diazo Compounds

Diazo compounds have the general formula $R_2C{=}N_2$. The electronic structure of diazomethane, the simplest diazo compound, shows that the carbon has nucleophilic properties.

$$\left[{}^-\ddot{C}H_2{-}\overset{+}{N}{\equiv}N\colon \longleftrightarrow CH_2{=}\overset{+}{N}{=}\ddot{N}\colon^- \right]$$

diazomethane

We have encountered diazomethane previously as a reagent for converting carboxylic acids into methyl esters (Section 17.7.A).

$$\underset{\text{O}}{\text{R}\overset{\|}{\text{C}}\text{OH}} + \text{CH}_2\text{N}_2 \longrightarrow \underset{\text{O}}{\text{R}\overset{\|}{\text{C}}\text{OCH}_3} + \text{N}_2$$

Diazomethane is prepared by treating an N-methyl-N-nitrosoamide with concentrated potassium hydroxide solution.

$$\underset{\substack{\text{O} \\ \text{RCN} \\ \text{N}=\text{O}}}{\overset{\text{CH}_3}{}} + \text{OH}^- \longrightarrow \text{CH}_2\text{N}_2 + \text{RCO}_2^- + \text{H}_2\text{O}$$

The preparation is carried out in a two-phase mixture consisting of ether and aqueous KOH. The diazomethane dissolves in the ether as it is formed and it is generally used as an ether solution.

Other diazo compounds are also known. α-Diazo ketones and α-diazo esters are relatively stable since the carbonyl group can delocalize the carbanionic electron pair.

$$\left[\underset{\text{O}}{\text{R}-\overset{\|}{\text{C}}-\overset{..}{\text{C}}\text{H}-\overset{+}{\text{N}}\equiv\text{N}:} \longleftrightarrow \underset{\text{O}^-}{\text{R}-\overset{|}{\text{C}}=\text{CH}-\overset{+}{\text{N}}\equiv\text{N}:} \longleftrightarrow \underset{\text{O}}{\text{R}-\overset{\|}{\text{C}}-\text{CH}=\overset{+}{\text{N}}=\text{N}:^-} \right]$$

This type of diazo compound is conveniently prepared by the reaction of diazomethane with an acyl halide.

Excess diazomethane must be used to react with the HCl that is produced in the reaction. If only one equivalent of diazomethane is used, a chloromethyl ketone results.

(83–85%)

The reaction of diazomethane with acyl halides is another reaction that shows the nucleophilic nature of the carbon in this compound. The mechanism of the reaction may be visualized as follows.

(1) $\text{R}-\overset{\text{O}}{\overset{\|}{\text{C}}}-\text{Cl} + :\overset{-}{\text{C}}\text{H}_2-\overset{+}{\text{N}}\equiv\text{N}: \rightleftharpoons \text{R}-\overset{\text{O}^-}{\underset{\text{Cl}}{\overset{|}{\text{C}}}}-\text{CH}_2-\overset{+}{\text{N}}\equiv\text{N}:$

(2) $\text{R}-\overset{\text{O}^-}{\underset{\text{Cl}}{\overset{|}{\text{C}}}}-\text{CH}_2-\overset{+}{\text{N}}\equiv\text{N}: \rightleftharpoons \text{R}-\overset{\text{O}}{\overset{\|}{\text{C}}}-\text{CH}_2-\overset{+}{\text{N}}\equiv\text{N}: + \text{Cl}^-$

$$(3) \quad R-\overset{\overset{\displaystyle O}{\|}}{C}-CH_2-\overset{+}{N}\equiv N: \; \rightleftharpoons \; R-\overset{\overset{\displaystyle O}{\|}}{C}-CHN_2 + H^+$$

If there is no excess diazomethane to react with the proton liberated in step (3), the chloride ion displaces nitrogen to give the chloro ketone.

$$(4) \quad Cl^- + R-\overset{\overset{\displaystyle O}{\|}}{C}-CH_2-\overset{+}{N}\equiv N: \; \longrightarrow \; R-\overset{\overset{\displaystyle O}{\|}}{C}-CH_2Cl + :N\equiv N:$$

Like azides, diazo compounds lose nitrogen either thermally or when irradiated with ultraviolet light. The decomposition is catalyzed by transition metals such as copper or rhodium. The initial product is a carbene (Section 11.6.F), which then reacts further. In the case of α-diazo ketones, the resulting acylcarbene rearranges to give a ketene (see the Curtius rearrangement; Section 23.6.H).

$$C_6H_5-\overset{\overset{\displaystyle N_2}{\|}}{C}-\overset{\overset{\displaystyle O}{\|}}{C}-C_6H_5 \xrightarrow[-N_2]{110°C} \left[C_6H_5-\overset{\cdot\cdot}{C}-\overset{\overset{\displaystyle O}{\|}}{C}-C_6H_5 \right] \longrightarrow \begin{array}{c} C_6H_5 \\ \diagdown \\ C_6H_5 \end{array} C=C=O$$

(65%)

diphenylketene

The carbenes derived from some diazo compounds may be trapped by reaction with an alkene; the products are cyclopropane derivatives.

$$\bigcirc\!\!\!\parallel + N_2CHCOOC_2H_5 \xrightarrow[Cu]{\Delta} \text{(bicyclic structure)} \begin{array}{c} H \\ COOC_2H_5 \end{array} + N_2$$

ethyl 7-bicyclo[4.1.0]-
heptanecarboxylate

EXERCISE 24.5 Show how propanoic acid can be converted into the following compounds by routes involving the use of diazomethane.
(a) methyl propanoate   (b) 1-diazo-2-butanone   (c) 1-chloro-2-butanone
(d) ethylketene (a reactive ketene that rapidly dimerizes)

24.5 Diazonium Salts

In Section 23.7.B we found that aromatic amines react with nitrous acid in aqueous solution to give solutions of arenediazonium salts, which are moderately stable if kept cold.

$$\text{(aniline)} \quad \underset{NH_2}{\bigcirc} \xrightarrow[H_2O,\ 0°C]{NaNO_2,\ HCl} \underset{N_2^+\ Cl^-}{\bigcirc}$$

aniline   benzenediazonium
                                 chloride

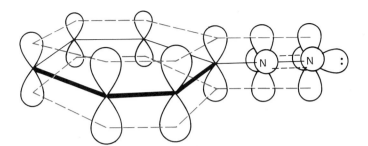

FIGURE 24.1 Orbital structure of benzenediazonium cation.

These unstable compounds comprise an important class of synthetic intermediates. In a sense, they are the "Grignard reagents" of aromatic chemistry, since they can be used in the synthesis of such a wide variety of aromatic compounds. In this section we shall discuss the chemistry of this useful group of compounds.

A. Acid-Base Equilibria of Arenediazonium Ions

In acid solution arenediazonium salts have the diazonium ion structure with a linear C—N—N bond system. The diazonium ion has a π-system that can conjugate with the aromatic π-system (Figure 24.1). This conjugation is responsible in part for the relative stability of these compounds. Recall that aliphatic diazonium ions are not at all stable and generally react immediately upon formation (Section 23.7.B).

Arenediazonium ions behave as dibasic acids. The two steps in the equilibria are represented as

$$Ar{-}\overset{+}{N}{\equiv}N + 2\,H_2O \underset{}{\overset{K_1}{\rightleftharpoons}} Ar{-}N{=}NOH + H_3O^+$$
arenediazohydroxide

$$Ar{-}N{=}NOH + H_2O \underset{}{\overset{K_2}{\rightleftharpoons}} Ar{-}N{=}N{-}O^- + H_3O^+$$
arenediazotate ion

The diazonium ions represent an unusual class of dibasic acids in that $K_2 \gg K_1$. That is, the arenediazohydroxide is present only in small amount. For the phenyl group, equal concentrations of benzenediazonium ion and benzenediazotate are present at a pH of 11.9. Even in neutral solutions with pH = 7, the diazonium ions are generally the most predominant species present.

Benzenediazotate ion exists in syn and anti forms, like other compounds containing carbon-nitrogen and nitrogen-nitrogen double bonds. The anti form is the more stable, but the less stable syn isomer is that formed first by reaction of the diazonium cation with hydroxide ion.

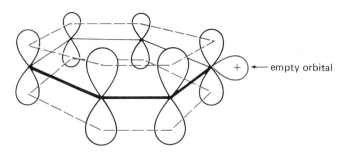

FIGURE 24.2 Orbital diagram of phenyl cation.

Alkanediazonium ions react by direct nucleophilic displacement of nitrogen (S_N2 mechanism), formation of carbocations (S_N1 mechanism, with attendant rearrangements), and elimination by both the E1 and E2 mechanisms (Section 23.7.B). None of these pathways is readily available to arenediazonium ions. The most likely reaction, formation of an aryl cation, is limited by the high energy of these species. In phenyl cation, the empty orbital has approximately sp^2-hybridization and cannot conjugate with the π-electronic system (Figure 24.2). For example, the enthalpy of formation in the gas phase of phenyl cation from chlorobenzene is about the same as that for the ionization of vinyl chloride and is almost as high as the enthalpy of formation of methyl cation from methyl chloride.

$$C_6H_5Cl \longrightarrow C_6H_5^+ + Cl^- \qquad \Delta H° = 224 \text{ kcal mole}^{-1}$$
$$CH_2{=}CHCl \longrightarrow C_2H_3^+ + Cl^- \qquad \Delta H° = 225 \text{ kcal mole}^{-1}$$
$$CH_3Cl \longrightarrow CH_3^+ + Cl^- \qquad \Delta H° = 228 \text{ kcal mole}^{-1}$$

Nevertheless, many reactions of diazonium ions are the reactions expected if aryl cations were intermediates. In many preparative methods, however, the aryl cation is not free; it is combined as a complex with a metal, often copper. Other reactions involve free radical intermediates. All of the following types of compounds can be prepared by appropriate reactions of the arenediazonium ions, ArN_2^+.

ArOH	ArCN	Ar—Ar′
ArI	ArF	ArNHNH$_2$
ArSH	ArNO$_2$	ArN$_3$
ArCl	ArH	ArN=NAr′
ArBr	Ar—Ar	

B. Thermal Decomposition of Diazonium Salts: Formation of ArOH, ArI, and ArSH

Aqueous solutions of arenediazonium ions are not stable. Nitrogen gas is evolved slowly in the cold and rapidly on heating. The net reaction is that of hydrolysis.

NH$_2$ $\xrightarrow[5°C]{\substack{NaNO_2 \\ aq.\ H_2SO_4}}$ [N$_2^+$] $\xrightarrow[H_2O]{\Delta}$ OH

2-bromo-4-methylaniline   (80–92%)
2-bromo-4-methylphenol

NH$_2$ $\xrightarrow[\text{5°C}]{\substack{\text{NaNO}_2 \\ \text{aq. H}_2\text{SO}_4}}$ $\xrightarrow{\Delta}$ OH + CH$_3$OH + N$_2$

with CH(OCH$_3$)$_2$ substituent → with CHO substituent

m-aminobenzaldehyde
dimethyl acetal

m-hydroxybenzaldehyde

Hydrolysis of the diazonium ion appears to be an S$_N$1 type of process involving the aryl cation.

$$\text{ArN}_2^+ \longrightarrow \text{N}_2 + \text{Ar}^+$$

The aryl cation forms despite its high energy because of the great stability of nitrogen. That is, the formation of N$_2$ is a powerful driving force for the decomposition of diazonium ions. The aryl cation intermediate is highly reactive and reacts rapidly with water to form the corresponding phenol.

$$\text{Ar}^+ + \text{H}_2\text{O} \longrightarrow \text{Ar}-\text{OH}_2^+ \rightleftharpoons \text{ArOH} + \text{H}^+$$

However, the aryl cation also reacts with other nucleophiles that may be present—such as halide ion. If HCl is used in the diazotization, some chloroarene is also produced.

$$\text{Ar}^+ + \text{Cl}^- \longrightarrow \text{ArCl}$$

For this reason sulfuric acid is normally used as the acid in diazotizations in which the diazonium salt is to be thermally decomposed. Bisulfate ion is a much poorer nucleophile than chloride ion and does not compete well with water for the aryl cation.

When aqueous solutions of diazonium ions containing chloride ion are allowed to decompose, the rate of reaction is independent of the chloride ion concentration, but the amount of chloroarene formed is proportional to [Cl$^-$]. Thus, the rate-determining step does not depend on chloride ion, but the product-determining steps do. This result is interpretable by the scheme

$$\text{Ar}-\text{N}_2^+ \xrightarrow{\text{slow}} \text{N}_2 + \text{Ar}^+ \begin{array}{c} \xrightarrow{\text{H}_2\text{O}} \text{ArOH} + \text{H}_3\text{O}^+ \\ \xrightarrow{\text{Cl}^-} \text{ArCl} \end{array}$$

The competition of chloride ion with water for the intermediate aryl cation is usually inadequate for this method to be a successful preparation of chloroarenes; the Sandmeyer reaction (Section 24.5.C) is generally better.

Highly nucleophilic anions can compete successfully with water for the intermediate aryl cation and lead to satisfactory syntheses. A useful example is the preparation of aryl iodides by treatment of arenediazonium compounds with aqueous potassium iodide.

NH$_2$ $\xrightarrow[\text{7°C}]{\substack{\text{NaNO}_2 \\ \text{aq. HCl}}}$ N$_2^+$ $\xrightarrow[\text{25°C}]{\text{KI}}$ I

(74–76%)

In this case HCl is used for the diazotization, and the resulting solution contains Cl$^-$.

Nevertheless, the more nucleophilic I⁻ dominates the reaction. The diazotization can also be accomplished with hydriodic acid, but this acid is far more expensive than HCl.

Reaction of aqueous diazonium salts with HS⁻ or with metal polysulfides has been used for preparation of thiophenols, but violent reactions and explosions have been reported and the method is not recommended. An alternative route involves potassium ethyl xanthate, $KSCSOC_2H_5$, which is available commercially from the reaction of potassium ethoxide with carbon disulfide.

m-toluidine   *m*-tolyl ethyl xanthate   (63–75%)
m-methylthiophenol
m-thiocresol

This reaction involves a variation of the hydrolysis reaction discussed on page 743. Reaction of the diazonium ion with the ethyl xanthate ion gives first the diazoxanthate.

$$Ar-N=N-\overset{\overset{\displaystyle S}{\|}}{S}COC_2H_5$$

This intermediate decomposes with liberation of nitrogen by an ion-pair or radical mechanism. Even this method is hazardous because the intermediate diazoxanthate can detonate and should be allowed to decompose as formed. The use of traces of nickel—even a nichrome stirrer—has been recommended to facilitate the controlled decomposition.

EXERCISE 24.6 Write equations showing how *p*-xylene may be converted into 2,5-dimethylphenol and into 2,5-dimethyl-1-iodobenzene.

C. The Sandmeyer Reaction: Preparation of ArCl, ArBr, and ArCN

Decomposition of diazonium salts is catalyzed by cuprous salts. In laboratory practice, the cold diazonium solution is added dropwise to a hot suspension of cuprous bromide, chloride, or cyanide to give the corresponding aromatic product in a method known as the **Sandmeyer reaction**. The process is the only practical way to obtain certain aryl halides uncontaminated by isomers.

o-chloroaniline   (89–95%)
o-bromochlorobenzene

p-toluidine   p-chlorotoluene
(70–79%)

Note in these cases that the hydrohalic acid is used to correspond to the halogen introduced; the use of HCl with CuBr would give a mixture of chloro and bromo product.

The Sandmeyer reaction is also a preferred method for the preparation of most aryl cyanides.

(64–70%)
p-tolunitrile

Note that the decomposition with CuCN occurs even in the cold.

Cupric chloride is normally obtained as a blue-green hydrate, $CuCl_2 \cdot 2H_2O$. This color is characteristic of many cupric salts. Cupric chloride and bromide are readily soluble in water. Cuprous bromide and chloride are white, insoluble powders prepared by reducing an aqueous solution of cupric sulfate and sodium bromide or chloride with sodium bisulfite. The cuprous halide precipitates as a white powder, which is filtered and used directly. On standing in air the white cuprous salts darken by oxidation. Cuprous cyanide is prepared by treating an aqueous suspension of cuprous chloride with sodium cyanide. Cuprous cyanide is also insoluble in water, but dissolves in excess sodium cyanide with formation of a complex, $Cu(CN)_2^-$. This solution is used directly in the Sandmeyer reaction.

The aromatic nitriles prepared by the Sandmeyer reaction can, of course, be hydrolyzed to carboxylic acids, reduced to benzylamines, treated with Grignard reagents to produce ketones, and so on. Consequently, the diazonium salts provide an entry to a host of aromatic compounds.

EXERCISE 24.7 Write equations showing the conversion of benzene into each of the following compounds by multistep procedures involving the Sandmeyer reaction as one step.
(a) chlorobenzene   (b) bromobenzene   (c) benzoic acid
(d) benzylamine   (e) benzamide

D. Preparation of Fluoro- and Nitroarenes

Some diazonium salts are fairly stable and can be isolated and handled. One such salt is the fluoborate. This salt is prepared by diazotization with sodium nitrite and fluoboric acid. The diazonium fluoborate usually precipitates and is filtered.

The names fluoboric and fluoborate are a frequent source of confusion, even to practicing chemists. It is one of the idiosyncrasies of inorganic nomenclature that HBF_4 may be called either *fluo*boric acid or *tetrafluoro*boric acid, but not *fluoro*boric acid.

The isolated diazonium fluoborate salts are useful in two significant reactions. In one reaction a suspension of the salt in aqueous sodium nitrite is treated with copper powder. Nitrogen is evolved, and the corresponding nitro compound is produced.

p-nitroaniline   *p*-nitrobenzenediazonium fluoborate   (67–82%) *p*-dinitrobenzene

This example is similar to the Sandmeyer reaction, which was discussed in the previous section. Note that in this case copper powder, rather than a cuprous salt, is used to bring about decomposition of the diazonium ion. This variant is sometimes called the **Gatterman reaction**. The Gatterman method can also be used to prepare aryl halides, but it is not as useful for this purpose as is the Sandmeyer reaction.

The isolated diazonium fluoborate can be decomposed thermally either as the dry salt or in an inert solvent such as THF to provide a satisfactory preparation of aryl fluorides (**Schiemann reaction**).

m-toluidine   (76–84%) *m*-methylbenzenediazonium fluoborate   *m*-fluorotoluene

An improved procedure makes use of fluophosphoric acid, HPF_6. The corresponding diazonium fluophosphates are less soluble than the fluoborates and are obtained in generally higher yield. The dry salt is thermally decomposed to form the aryl fluoride.

o-bromoaniline   *o*-bromobenzenediazonium hexafluorophosphate   (76–78%) *o*-bromofluorobenzene

EXERCISE 24.8 Outline methods for the synthesis of all three isomeric dinitrobenzenes.

E. Replacement of the Diazonium Group by Hydrogen

The diazonium group may also be replaced by hydrogen. This reaction allows use of the amino group to direct the orientation of an electrophilic aromatic substitution reaction, after which the amino group is removed. The most generally useful reagent for the reaction is hypophosphorous acid, H_3PO_2.

Hypophosphorous acid is a low-melting (m.p. 26.5°C), crystalline compound having a structure with two phosphorus-hydrogen bonds.

Salts of the acid are prepared by treating white phosphorus with alkali or alkaline earth hydroxides. The free acid can be liberated from the water-soluble calcium salt with sulfuric acid. Aqueous solutions are available commercially and can be used directly. The monobasic acid has $pK_a = 1.2$ and is a powerful reducing agent.

In the foregoing example, the amino group is used to direct the facile introduction of three bromines (Section 23.7.D). Since NH_2 is a powerful *ortho,para*-directing group, reaction occurs at the positions indicated. Having served its function of activating the ring and directing the incoming bromines to specific positions, the amino group is diazotized and the diazonium group is replaced by hydrogen. The yield of tribromobenzoic acid is 70–80% from *m*-aminobenzoic acid.

Some diamines can be diazotized at both amino groups and subsequent reaction of both diazonium groups can be accomplished. An example is provided by the following reaction of a substituted benzidine.

4,4'-diamino-3,3'-dimethylbiphenyl   3,3'-dimethylbiphenyl

EXERCISE 24.9 Write equations showing how benzene can be converted into 1,3,5-trichlorobenzene.

F. Arylation Reactions

Arylation provides a convenient preparation of unsymmetrical biaryls in which the diazonium group is replaced by an aromatic ring. Diazotization is carried out in the usual way except that a minimum of water is used. The solution is made basic, and the resulting concentrated aqueous solution is stirred in the cold with a liquid aromatic compound.

(21%)
4-methylbiphenyl

The reaction is called the **Gomberg-Bachmann reaction**. Yields are generally low, but the starting materials are often readily available, and there are few other methods for the synthesis of such biaryls (Section 30.2.A).

The mechanism of the Gomberg-Bachmann reaction involves free radicals. Recall that in basic solution the diazonium salt is in equilibrium with the covalent diazohydroxide (Section 24.5.A). This material is extracted into the organic phase, where homolytic fission of the carbon-nitrogen and nitrogen-oxygen bonds occur. The resulting products of this homolysis are an aryl radical, a nitrogen molecule, and a hydroxy radical. The driving force for simultaneous rupture of two bonds is the formation of the highly stable nitrogen molecule.

$$Ar-N=N-OH \longrightarrow Ar\cdot + N_2 + \cdot OH$$

The aryl radicals produced are, of course, highly reactive intermediates. They react rapidly with the aromatic ring of the solvent.

The resulting radical reacts with some other radical in solution to afford the final product. The overall result is substitution of a hydrogen atom of the solvent by the aryl radical corresponding to the beginning arylamine.

Although the mechanism involves intermediate free radicals, it does not appear to be a radical chain reaction. The reaction is somewhat different than most free radical reactions in that the concentration of radicals becomes rather high. The typical low yields result from the many alternative reactions that are available to the intermediate radicals.

Because the aromatic substitution involves radicals, the normal orientation rules do not hold; almost all substituents tend to give *ortho* and *para* orientation, and mixtures of products are common. In using this method to prepare an unsymmetrical biaryl, it is best to start with the substituents on the diazonium ring and to keep the ring to be added as simple as possible.

(66% *o*-, 19% *m*-, 14% *p*-)

The same reaction can usually be carried out in better yield by using an N-nitrosoamide. This intermediate is prepared in straightforward fashion from the amine and is heated in an aromatic solvent. The N-nitrosoamide rearranges to a diazo ester, which forms the same aryl radical intermediate involved in the Gomberg-Bachmann reaction.

N-nitroso-*m*-nitro-acetanilide

(56–60%)
3-nitrobiphenyl

The rearrangement of the intermediate nitrosoamide can be regarded as an intramolecular transesterification.

$$Ar-N=N-O-\overset{\overset{\displaystyle O}{\|}}{C}CH_3 \longrightarrow Ar\cdot + N_2 + \cdot O\overset{\overset{\displaystyle O}{\|}}{C}CH_3$$

EXERCISE 24.10 4-Ethylbiphenyl can be prepared by the Gomberg-Bachmann reaction of 4-ethylaniline with benzene or of aniline with ethylbenzene. Write the equations for these two syntheses and explain why one combination is superior to the other.

G. Diazonium Ions as Electrophiles: Azo Compounds

The diazonium cation bears a resemblance to some other species that are known as intermediates in electrophilic aromatic substitution reactions.

$$Ar-\overset{+}{N}\equiv N: \qquad R-\overset{+}{C}\equiv O: \qquad \overset{+}{O}\equiv N:$$

Arenediazonium ions *can* react as electrophilic reagents in aromatic substitutions, but they are such mild reagents that only highly activated rings can be used. In practice, such reactions are limited primarily to aromatic amines and phenols.

Benzenediazonium ion reacts with excess aniline in acidic medium to give the aromatic substitution product *p*-aminoazobenzene.

p-aminoazobenzene

The mechanism of the foregoing reaction actually involves initial attack of the benzenediazonium ion on the nitrogen of aniline, to give diazoaminobenzene, a derivative of the unstable inorganic compound triazine, $HN=N-NH_2$.

(82–85%)
diazoaminobenzene
1,3-diphenyltriazene

Diazoaminobenzene reacts with aniline to give the aromatic substitution product *p*-aminoazobenzene.

p-aminoazobenzene

This reaction is usually assumed to involve a reversal of diazoaminobenzene formation followed by the slower reaction of benzenediazonium cation with the *para* position of aniline.

This mechanism incorporates the frequently encountered distinction between kinetically and thermodynamically controlled reactions and explains many features of the reaction. However, the reaction also produces a variety of minor by-products that suggest a more complex reaction mechanism.

Electrophilic substitution of aniline derivatives with diazonium ions is an important method of synthesis of colored substances that are used as dyes.

p-dimethylaminoazobenzene
butter yellow

Butter yellow was used at one time as a yellow food coloring, but as a suspected carcinogen it is no longer used for this purpose. Substituted azoarenes form an important class of dyes (Section 34.3). Several are also useful as indicators in the laboratory. Methyl orange, *p*-dimethylaminoazobenzene-*p'*-sulfonic acid, is prepared from diazotized sulfanilic acid and N,N-dimethylaniline.

sulfanilic
acid

methyl orange

The product is isolated as the sodium salt by salting out with sodium chloride. Note that these so-called "coupling reactions" of diazonium salts occur almost exclusively at the *para* position. Reaction occurs generally at the *ortho* position only when the *para* position is blocked.

The azo group has nitrogen lone pairs and is expected to show basic properties. However, each of these lone pairs is in an approximately sp^2-orbital and is less basic than an amino lone pair in which the orbital has less *s*-character. Furthermore, the adjacent nitrogen further reduces the basicity. As a result the azo group in azobenzene itself is a rather weak base; the pK_a of the protonated compound is -2.5.

$K_a = 300\ M$

Azobenzene itself is protonated only in rather strong acid. Methyl orange has a pK_a of 3.5; this value refers to the protonated azo group, not to the dimethylamino or sulfonic acid groups. At pH above 3.5, methyl orange is in the yellow azo form. At pH lower than 3.5 it is present in the red protonated form.

$$K_a = 3 \times 10^{-4} \, M$$

Note that the azo-protonated form of methyl orange is stabilized by the p-N(CH$_3$)$_2$ group. This stabilization renders the protonated form less acidic than protonated azobenzene.

H. Synthetic Utility of Arenediazonium Salts

We saw in Chapter 22 that the nitro group may be introduced with ease into a wide variety of aromatic compounds. We have also seen that the nitro group may be reduced to the amino group by several reliable methods (Section 23.6.C) and that the resulting aromatic amines may be converted into arenediazonium salts (Section 23.7.B). In this section we have learned how the diazonium group may be replaced by OH, I, SH, Cl, Br, F, CN, NO$_2$, H, and Ar. Thus, *any of these functions can be introduced into an aromatic ring at any position that can be nitrated.*

But diazonium chemistry can be used in another advantageous manner for the synthesis of aromatic compounds. Suppose, for example, that it is desired to convert radiolabelled benzoic acid into radiolabelled *p*-nitrobenzoic acid.

We are unable to accomplish this conversion by direct nitration because the COOH group is a strong *meta* director (Section 22.5). However, in *m*-acetamidobenzoic acid, which we can prepare in a straightforward synthesis from benzoic acid, the *ortho,para*-directing $NHCOCH_3$ group overcomes the *meta*-directing COOH group, and nitration occurs primarily *para* to COOH. The amide protecting group is then removed by hydrolysis, the resulting amine is diazotized, and the diazonium salt is treated with H_3PO_2.

With these examples, we see the central position that the versatile diazonium function holds in aromatic synthesis.

EXERCISE 24.11 Write equations showing how the strategy just introduced may be used in the conversion of *p*-toluic acid into 2-chloro-4-methylbenzoic acid.

PROBLEMS

1. What is the principal product obtained from *p*-toluenediazonium cation with each of the following reagents?

 (a) I^- (b) CuCN
 (c) OH^- (cold)   (d) H_2O (hot)
 (e) CuBr   (f) $NaNO_2$, copper powder
 (g) aq. NaOH, benzene, 5°C   (h) (i) $NaBF_4$; (ii) heat
 (i) H_3PO_2 (j) CuCl
 (k) N,N-diethylaniline   (l) (i) HPF_6; (ii) heat

2. Each of the following compounds is a significant dye intermediate. Give a practical laboratory preparation for each starting with benzene or toluene.

(a) (b) (c)

(d) (e) (f)

(g) (h) (i)

3. Show how each of the following conversions can be accomplished in a practical manner.

(a) (b)

(c) (d)

(e)

(f)

(g) (h)

4. A small amount of methyl orange is added to a solution containing equimolar amounts of acetic acid and sodium acetate. Is this solution yellow or red?

5. A diazonium salt prepared from *p*-nitroaniline, when decomposed in nitrobenzene, gives a 69% yield of 4,4'-dinitrobiphenyl. That is, reaction of the aryl radical formed from the diazonium salt occurs primarily at the *para* position of the nitrobenzene. Give a reasonable explanation of this orientation behavior.

6. Give the principal reduction product from *m*-nitrotoluene under each of the following conditions.
   (a) Zn, alcoholic NaOH
   (b) Pt/H$_2$
   (c) Zn, aq. NH$_4$Cl
   (d) SnCl$_2$, HCl
   (e) H$_2$NNH$_2$, Ru/C, alcoholic KOH
   (f) As$_2$O$_3$, aq. NaOH

7. When an α-diazo ketone is irradiated or heated in aqueous solution, the product obtained is a carboxylic acid.

$$\underset{\text{RCCHN}_2}{\overset{O}{\parallel}} \xrightarrow[\text{H}_2\text{O}]{\textit{hv} \text{ or } \Delta} \text{RCH}_2\text{COOH}$$

   (a) Propose a mechanism for the transformation (**Wolff rearrangement**).
   (b) Predict the product when diazoacetone is irradiated in methanol solution.

8. When cyclohexanone is treated with diazomethane, a mixture of cycloheptanone and methylenecyclohexane oxide is produced. Propose a mechanism.

9. When cyclohexanecarboxamide is treated with bromine and sodium methoxide in methanol, the product obtained is methyl N-cyclohexylcarbamate.

   Rationalize with a plausible mechanism.

10. When ethyl N-cyclohexylcarbamate is refluxed with 1 *M* KOH in methanol for 100 hr, the only product obtained is the methyl ester in 95% yield.

   Explain why no cyclohexylamine is produced.

11. A laboratory technician attempted to prepare *p*-bromocumene by diazotizing *p*-amino-cumene with a mixture of aqueous sodium nitrite and hydrochloric acid at 0°C followed by reaction with hot cuprous bromide, but a mixture of products was obtained. What was the nature of the mixture?

12. When *p*-bromoaniline was diazotized with sodium nitrite and hydrochloric acid, and the mixture was allowed to decompose at room temperature, the *p*-bromophenol formed as principal product was found to be contaminated by some *p*-chlorophenol. Explain.

Chapter 25

Sulfur, Phosphorus, and Silicon Compounds

Several interesting functional groups contain sulfur or phosphorus as a central element. Although these classes of compounds are not as common as those containing oxygen and nitrogen, some of them have particular significance in biochemistry. In addition, sulfur-, phosphorus-, and silicon-containing compounds have important uses as synthetic intermediates. Sulfur, phosphorus, and silicon are in the same columns of the periodic table as oxygen, nitrogen, and carbon, respectively. Thus, we expect to find similarities in the chemistry of analogous sulfur and oxygen functions. Similarly, we expect comparable chemistry of analogous nitrogen and phosphorus compounds. Finally, we expect that organosilicon compounds will show some of the typical chemistry of their carbon analogs. To some extent this correspondence is observed. However, the third-period elements are both less electronegative and more polarizable than their second-period relatives, and these differences result in significant quantitative differences in chemistry. Furthermore, all three elements have higher oxidation states available and can form some compounds that have no counterparts in oxygen and nitrogen chemistry. We have already encountered some of these functional groups (for example, sulfonate esters, phosphorus ylides). In this chapter we shall take an abbreviated look at the characteristic organic chemistry of sulfur, phosphorus, and silicon.

25.1 Thiols and Sulfides

Thiols, RSH, and sulfides, R_2S, bear an obvious relationship to alcohols and ethers. In the IUPAC system the alkane name is combined with the suffix -**thiol** in the same way that alcohols are named as alkanols. One difference is that the final -e of the alkane name is retained in naming thiols.

$$CH_3CH_2SH \qquad CH_3CH_2\overset{\overset{\displaystyle CH_3}{|}}{C}HSH$$

ethanethiol   2-butanethiol

A common name is that of alkyl mercaptan, analogous to alkyl alcohol, but the mercaptan nomenclature is falling into disuse in favor of IUPAC systematic names.

Sulfides are commonly named in a manner analogous to the common nomenclature of ethers. The two alkyl group names are followed by the word **sulfide**.

$$CH_3SCH_3 \qquad CH_3CH_2SCH_2CH_2CH_3$$

dimethyl sulfide   ethyl propyl sulfide

In the IUPAC system sulfides are named as alkylthioalkanes. The prefix **alkylthio-** is analogous to **alkoxy-** and refers to a group RS—. As with ethers, the larger of the two alkyl groups is taken as the stem.

$$CH_3SCH_2\overset{\overset{\displaystyle CH_3}{|}}{C}HCH_2CH_3$$

2-methyl-1-(methylthio)butane

$$CH_3\overset{\overset{\displaystyle CH_3}{|}}{C}HSCH_2CH_2CH_2CH_3$$

1-isopropylthiobutane

The IUPAC system for naming sulfides is only used in practice for complex structures that are not conveniently named as dialkyl sulfides.

The principal structural differences between methanethiol and methanol are that the carbon-sulfur bond is about 0.4 Å longer than the carbon-oxygen bond and the C—S—H angle is relatively more acute than the C—O—H angle. In thiols, as in H_2S itself, sulfur uses orbitals that are rich in *p*-character for bonding. The barrier to rotation about the carbon-sulfur bond is identical to that about the carbon-oxygen bond in methanol, 1.1 kcal mole^{-1}.

Bond Distances, Å		Bond Angles, deg	
C—H	1.10	H—C—H	110.2
C—S	1.82	H—C—S	108
S—H	1.33	C—S—H	100.3

A similar structure is found for dimethyl sulfide. Again, the C—S—C angle is relatively small (98.9°), corresponding to carbon-sulfur bonds in which sulfur uses a high percentage of its 3*p*-orbitals.

Thiols have boiling points that are almost normal for their molecular weight; they generally boil somewhat higher than the corresponding chlorides. For example, ethanethiol has b.p. 37°C compared to ethyl chloride, b.p. 13°C. Thiols are stronger acids than alcohols, just as H_2S is a stronger acid than water. The pK_a of ethanethiol, 10.60, indicates that the compound is completely converted to its anion by hydroxide ion.

$$C_2H_5SH + OH^- \rightleftharpoons C_2H_5S^- + H_2O$$
$$\text{p}K_a\ 10.6 \qquad\qquad\qquad \text{p}K_a\ 15.7$$

Although thiols are more acidic than alcohols, sulfur is less electronegative than oxygen. Hence, thiols have lower dipole moments (CH_3SH, $\mu = 1.26$ D; CH_3OH, $\mu = 1.71$ D) and hydrogen bonding between thiol molecules is much weaker than for alcohols. However, hydrogen bonding from the acidic SH protons to water oxygen is significant, and the thiols have some water solubility.

The most impressive property of thiols is their odor. Their intensely disagreeable odors discourage use as laboratory reagents. Thiols contribute to the characteristic odors of skunk and onion. Two methanethiol esters are known to give the urine of many persons a distinctive odor after eating asparagus. The nose is more sensitive than any laboratory instrument in detecting ethanethiol; one part in 50 billion parts of air can be detected. Small amounts are included in heating gas, which is otherwise almost odorless, as an effective warning device against leaks. The lower molecular weight sulfides have similarly repugnant odors.

Thioaldehydes and thioketones are known, but are relatively rare. The lower molecular weight compounds are red liquids with intensely obnoxious odors. Although they may be prepared in a monomeric form, they rapidly polymerize to give cyclic trimers.

$$CH_3\overset{\overset{\displaystyle S}{||}}{C}CH_3 \longrightarrow$$

thioacetone

758

Chap. 25

*Sulfur,
Phosphorus, and
Silicon
Compounds*

Thioacids, RCOSH, and thioesters, RCOSR′, are more common.

$$CH_3\overset{\overset{\displaystyle O}{\|}}{C}SH \qquad CH_3CH_2\overset{\overset{\displaystyle O}{\|}}{C}SC(CH_3)_3$$

t-butyl thiopropanoate

Note that the stable form of thioacids is the one with C=O and S—H groups and not the alternative structure with C=S and O—H groups. A particularly important example of a thioester is acetyl coenzyme A, "acetyl CoA," an important intermediate used by nature in the biosynthesis of numerous organic compounds (for examples, see Sections 18.9 and 34.8).

EXERCISE 25.1 Write the structure corresponding to each of the following names.
(a) ethyl isopropyl sulfide   (b) butyl mercaptan   (c) 3-methylthiooctane
(d) diphenyl sulfide   (e) 3-pentanethiol   (f) thioacetaldehyde
(g) ethyl thioacetate

25.2 Preparation of Thiols and Sulfides

Thiols can be prepared from alkyl halides by displacement with hydrosulfide ion, HS⁻, in ethanol solution.

$$CH_3(CH_2)_{16}CH_2I + Na^+SH^- \xrightarrow{\text{C}_2\text{H}_5\text{OH}} CH_3(CH_2)_{16}CH_2SH + Na^+I^-$$

1-octadecanethiol

In preparing thiols by this method it is necessary to employ a large excess of hydrosulfide because of the equilibrium

$$HS^- + RSH \rightleftharpoons H_2S + RS^-$$

The thiol anion produced by this equilibrium is itself a good nucleophile and can react with the alkyl halide to give the corresponding sulfide.

$$RS^- + RBr \longrightarrow RSR + Br^-$$

The use of a large excess of hydrosulfide makes its reaction with the alkyl halide more probable and maximizes the yield of thiol.

For this reason HS⁻ been almost exclusively replaced by thiourea for such displacement reactions.

$$H_2N-\overset{\overset{\displaystyle S}{\|}}{C}-NH_2$$

thiourea

Thiourea, a commercially available solid, m.p. 178°C, is soluble in water and alcohols. The sulfur is nucleophilic and readily takes part in S_N2 displacement reactions on alkyl halides. The product salt is readily hydrolyzed to the alkanethiol.

$$CH_3(CH_2)_{11}Br + H_2N-\overset{\overset{\displaystyle S}{\|}}{C}-NH_2 \xrightarrow[\Delta]{\text{95\% ethanol}} CH_3(CH_2)_{11}S-\overset{\overset{\displaystyle \overset{+}{N}H_2}{\|}}{C}NH_2\ Br^-$$

n-dodecyl bromide

$$CH_3(CH_2)_{11}S-\overset{\overset{+}{N}H_2}{\underset{}{C}}NH_2 \ Br^- \xrightarrow[\Delta]{aq. \ NaOH} CH_3(CH_2)_{11}SH + H_2N\overset{O}{\overset{\|}{C}}NH_2$$

(79–83%)
1-dodecanethiol

This route avoids formation of sulfides. The other product of the hydrolysis is urea, H_2NCONH_2 (Section 24.2).

Thiols can also be prepared by reaction of Grignard reagents with sulfur.

$$(CH_3)_3CMgBr + S_8 \longrightarrow (CH_3)_3CSMgBr \xrightarrow{HCl} (CH_3)_3CSH + MgBrCl$$

t-butyl mercaptan
2-methyl-2-propanethiol

Both symmetrical and unsymmetrical sulfides can be prepared by S_N2 displacement of alkylthio anions on alkyl halides or sulfonates.

$$CH_3CH_2SH + OH^- \xrightarrow{H_2O} CH_3CH_2S^-$$

$$CH_3CH_2S^- + (CH_3)_2CHCH_2Br \longrightarrow (CH_3)_2CHCH_2 \ SCH_2CH_3$$

(95%)
ethyl isobutyl sulfide

This general method for preparing dialkyl sulfides is directly analogous to the Williamson ether synthesis (Section 10.9).

EXERCISE 25.2 Show how the following conversions can be accomplished.
(a) $(CH_3)_3CCH_2Br \rightarrow (CH_3)_3CCH_2SH$ (b) $CH_3CH_2CH_2OH \rightarrow (CH_3CH_2CH_2)_2S$

25.3 Reactions of Thiols and Sulfides

One of the characteristic similarities between thiol chemistry and alcohol chemistry is that both classes of compounds are weak acids. However, just as HCl is a stronger acid in aqueous solution than HF, RSH compounds are substantially more acidic than their ROH counterparts. The pK_a of ethanethiol, 10.6, tells us that the compound is half ionized at pH 10.6, which corresponds roughly to the pH of a 5% sodium carbonate solution. Thus, unlike alcohols, thiols may be converted essentially quantitatively into the corresponding anions in aqueous solution.

$$CH_3CH_2SH \qquad CH_3CH_2OH$$

ethanethiol ethanol
$pK_a = 10.6$ $pK_a = 15.7$

Thiols are readily oxidized to **disulfides**. The disulfide bond is weak and is easily reduced to give the thiol.

$$2 \ RSH \ \underset{reduction}{\overset{oxidation}{\rightleftharpoons}} \ RS-SR$$

a disulfide

Mild oxidizing agents such as iodine suffice for the oxidation.

760

Chap. 25

Sulfur,
Phosphorus, and
Silicon
Compounds

$$2 \ CH_3CH_2SH + I_2 \longrightarrow CH_3CH_2SSCH_2CH_3 + 2 \ HI$$
diethyl disulfide

A commonly used reducing agent for regeneration of the thiol is lithium in liquid ammonia.

$$CH_3CH_2SSCH_2CH_3 \xrightarrow[NH_3]{Li} \xrightarrow[\text{(work-up)}]{H_3O^+} 2 \ CH_3CH_2SH$$

The facile thiol-disulfide redox system is especially important in biological systems. The disulfide link occurs in proteins and hormones, and the redox reaction itself plays an important role in molecular biology. It has been suggested that this reaction may be involved in the mechanism of memory in the brain. An interesting natural product is thioctic acid, which contains a cyclic disulfide link. Thioctic acid is an essential substance for the growth of various organisms and has been used for the treatment of liver disease and as an antidote for the toxin of poisonous *Amanita* mushrooms.

thioctic acid

The sulfur-sulfur bond of disulfides is susceptible to cleavage by nucleophiles.

$$N:^- \ + \ RS{-}SR \longrightarrow N{-}SR + RS:^-$$

A synthetically useful version of this reaction is found in the thiolation of ketone and ester enolates.

Strong oxidants such as potassium permanganate or hot nitric acid oxidize thiols or disulfides to the corresponding sulfonic acids. If a mixture of chlorine and nitric acid is used as the oxidant, the corresponding sulfonyl chloride is obtained. Sulfonyl chlorides have the same relationship to sulfonic acids as acyl halides have to carboxylic acids. Thus they are hydrolyzed to sulfonic acids by water.

di-o-nitrophenyl disulfide   o-nitrobenzenesulfonyl chloride   84%
o-nitrobenzenesulfonic acid

Sulfides are also easily oxidized. The initial oxidation product is a **sulfoxide**. Further oxidation of the sulfoxide yields a **sulfone**.

$$CH_3SCH_3 + H_2O_2 \longrightarrow CH_3-\overset{O^-}{\underset{}{S^+}}-CH_3 \xrightarrow{RCO_3H} CH_3-\overset{O^-}{\underset{O^-}{S^{2+}}}-CH_3$$

or

$$CH_3-\overset{O}{\underset{}{\overset{\parallel}{S}}}-CH_3$$

dimethyl sulfoxide
(DMSO)

or

$$CH_3-\overset{O}{\underset{O}{\overset{\parallel}{\underset{\parallel}{S}}}}-CH_3$$

dimethyl sulfone

An especially convenient oxidant, which converts sulfides to sulfoxides without the danger of over-oxidation to the sulfone, is sodium periodate, $NaIO_4$.

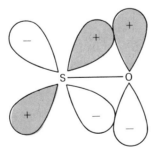

methyl phenyl sulfide   methyl phenyl sulfoxide

(99%)

To 210 mL of a 0.5 *M* solution of $NaIO_4$ at 0°C is added 12.4 g of methyl phenyl sulfide. The mixture is stirred at ice-bath temperature overnight, the precipitated $NaIO_3$ is removed by filtration, and the filtrate is extracted with chloroform. Evaporation of solvent gives a crude product, which is distilled to obtain 13.9 g (99%) of methyl phenyl sulfoxide, m.p 29–30°C.

Sulfur compounds such as sulfoxides and sulfones are frequently represented for convenience as having sulfur-oxygen double bonds and an expanded octet around sulfur However, the sulfur-oxygen bond is not a double bond in the same sense as carbon-carbon or carbon-oxygen double bonds in which the "second bond" is viewed as arising from π-overlap of atomic *p*-orbitals. Because sulfur has *d*-orbitals of rather low energy, it has long been speculated that sulfur-oxygen "double" bonds result from overlap of an oxygen *p*-orbital with a sulfur *d*-orbital.

Some such bonding may be involved, but classical coulombic attraction of the partially positive sulfur for the partially negative oxygen provides much of the bonding. It also appears that the high polarizability of the sulfur valence electrons is involved.

We have previously encountered dimethyl sulfoxide as an important solvent in the class of dipolar aprotic solvents (Section 9.4.B). It is a relatively inexpensive colorless

762

Chap. 25

*Sulfur,
Phosphorus, and
Silicon
Compounds*

liquid that is miscible with water in all proportions. It is prepared industrially by the NO_2-catalyzed air-oxidation of dimethyl sulfide, a by-product produced in tonnage quantities in the sulfite pulping process for paper manufacture.

$$CH_3SCH_3 \;+\; \tfrac{1}{2}\,O_2 \xrightarrow{\;NO_2\;} \overset{\displaystyle O}{\overset{\displaystyle \|}{CH_3SCH_3}}$$

dimethyl sulfide   dimethyl sulfoxide
(DMSO)

Dimethyl sulfoxide owes its utility to the fact that it readily dissolves many inorganic salts as well as most organic compounds. It is an excellent solvent for reactions such as displacements on alkyl halides. However, the potent solvent properties of DMSO result in a particular hazard that is associated with its use. The compound diffuses through the skin almost instantaneously and carries any solutes along with it. For this reason, one should always wear impermeable gloves when working with DMSO solutions.

Note that sulfoxides are similar in electronic structure to amine oxides (Section 23.7.C). Like amine oxides, sulfoxides undergo thermal elimination to give alkenes (Section 23.7.E). The process is a syn elimination (Section 18.11).

(96%)

The sulfur-containing by-product in this reaction is a **sulfenic acid**. Sulfenic acids are unstable and undergo disproportionation to the corresponding **sulfinic acid** and disulfide, which are the actual by-products of a sulfoxide elimination.

$$3\,CH_3SOH \longrightarrow CH_3SSCH_3 + CH_3SO_2H + H_2O$$

methanesulfenic   dimethyl   methanesulfinic
acid   disulfide   acid

EXERCISE 25.3 Using reactions learned in this section, show how the following transformation can be accomplished.

The sulfur in an dialkyl sulfide is nucleophilic. Consequently, sulfides react readily with alkyl halides by the normal S_N2 mechanism to produce **trialkylsulfonium salts**, which are usually hygroscopic solids.

$$(CH_3)_2\ddot{S}\colon + CH_3\!-\!I \longrightarrow (CH_3)_2\overset{..}{S}{}^+\!-\!CH_3\;I^-$$

trimethylsulfonium iodide

Like other S_N2 displacements, the reaction works best with primary halides.

$$(CH_3)_2CHCH_2Br + (CH_3)_2S \longrightarrow (CH_3)_2CHCH_2\overset{+}{S}(CH_3)_2Br^-$$

isobutyldimethylsulfonium bromide

When trialkylsulfonium salts are heated the reaction reverses. Halide ion acts as the nucleophile, and the dialkyl sulfide is the leaving group. The driving force for reaction is vaporization of the volatile products.

$$Br:^- + CH_3 \overset{+}{-}S(CH_3)_2 \overset{\Delta}{\longrightarrow} CH_3Br\uparrow + (CH_3)_2S\uparrow$$

Nature makes extensive use of this S_N2 reaction. The compound S-adenosylmethionine is a methylating agent in biochemical S_N2 reactions, which are catalyzed by appropriate enzymes. It can be regarded as the body's equivalent of methyl iodide.

S-adenosylmethionine

Like 1,2- and 1,3-diols, the analogous 1,2- and 1,3-dithiols react with aldehydes and ketones under conditions of acid catalysis to give cyclic thioacetals and thioketals.

$$CH_3CHO + HS(CH_2)_3SH \overset{BF_3}{\longrightarrow}$$

1,3-propanedithiol   2-methyl-1,3-dithiane

> **EXERCISE 25.4** Write a mechanism for the reaction of acetaldehyde and 1,3-propanedithiol to give 2-methyl-1,3-dithiane.

The thioacetals that are prepared in this way using 1,3-propanedithiol are useful as synthetic reagents (Section 25.8). The carbon-sulfur bond can be reductively cleaved by certain reagents, the most common of which is Raney nickel. The products of the reaction are the hydrocarbons formed by hydrogenolysis of each carbon-sulfur bond.

$$R-S-R' + H_2 \overset{Raney\ Ni}{\longrightarrow} RH + R'H$$

Desulfurization of thioacetals and thioketals provides a method for net deoxygenation of aldehydes and ketones, and is complementary to the Wolff-Kishner and Clemmensen deoxygenations (Section 14.9.D).

$$+ CH_3SH \overset{BF_3}{\longrightarrow} \overset{Raney\ Ni}{\longrightarrow}$$

(75%)

764

Chap. 25

Sulfur,
Phosphorus, and
Silicon
Compounds

EXERCISE 25.5 Write equations illustrating the following reaction sequences beginning with 1-butanethiol.

(a) (i) NaOH, CH_3Br; (ii) $NaIO_4$, H_2O; (iii) 150°C
(b) (i) I_2, KI; (ii) Li, NH_3
(c) (i) NaOH, CH_3CH_2I; (ii) CH_3I
(d) (i) NaOH, CH_3CH_2Br; (ii) excess H_2O_2

25.4 Sulfate Esters

Sulfuric acid, H_2SO_4, is a strong dibasic inorganic acid with $pK_1 \cong -5$ and $pK_2 = 1.99$.

$$H_2SO_4 \rightleftharpoons H^+ + HSO_4^- \qquad K_a \cong 1.4 \times 10^5 \ M$$
$$HSO_4^- \rightleftharpoons H^+ + SO_4^{2-} \qquad K_a = 1.0 \times 10^{-2} \ M$$

Although the acidity of sulfuric acid in dilute aqueous solution corresponds to $K_1 \cong 1.4 \times 10^5 \ M$, its effective acidity or "protonating power" increases markedly in highly concentrated solutions. In order to quantify the protonating power of concentrated solutions, a property known as an "acidity function" has been defined. The acidity function is a property of a given medium that provides a quantitative measure of the proton donating ability of the medium. The best-known acidity function is the Hammett acidity function, which was developed by using a series of weak bases that are protonated only in exceedingly "acidic" media. For a given medium the ratio of protonated and unprotonated forms of the indicator base is measured, usually spectrophotometrically. The Hammett acidity function, H_0, is defined in terms of the pK of the indicator and the negative logarithm of the ratio of protonated and unprotonated species.

$$H_0 = pK(BH^+) - \log \frac{[BH^+]}{[B]}$$

In dilute solutions H_0 is equal to the pH of the solution. Hammett acidity functions for some sulfuric acid solutions are listed in Table 25.1. Note that the effective acidity of sulfuric acid increases by $10^{1.59}$ or 39-fold in going from 30% to 50% sulfuric acid and by a factor of $10^{3.11}$ or 1288-fold in going from 70% to 90% sulfuric acid.

TABLE 25.1 H_0 for Sulfuric Acid–Water Mixtures

% H_2SO_4	H_0
5	−0.02
10	−0.43
30	−1.82
50	−3.41
70	−5.92
90	−9.03
95	−9.73
98	−10.27
99	−10.57
100	−11.94

Both mono- and diesters of sulfuric acid are known. Like sulfuric acid itself, the sulfuric acid esters are often considered as resonance hybrids involving an expanded sulfur octet.

$$\left[RO-\overset{O^-}{\underset{O_-}{\overset{|}{\underset{|}{S^{2+}}}}}-OH \longleftrightarrow RO-\overset{O^-}{\underset{O}{\overset{|}{\underset{||}{S^{+}}}}}-OH \longleftrightarrow RO-\overset{O}{\underset{O_-}{\overset{||}{\underset{|}{S^{+}}}}}-OH \longleftrightarrow RO-\overset{O}{\underset{O}{\overset{||}{\underset{||}{S}}}}-OH \right]$$

For convenience, we shall only use the Kekulé structure represented as having two S=O bonds.

Diesters of sulfuric acid are named by combining the alkyl group name(s) with the word "sulfate" just as though they were salts of sulfuric acid.

$$\underset{\text{dimethyl sulfate}}{CH_3O\overset{O}{\underset{O}{\overset{||}{\underset{||}{S}}}}OCH_3} \qquad \underset{\text{methyl isopropyl sulfate}}{CH_3O\overset{O}{\underset{O}{\overset{||}{\underset{||}{S}}}}OCH(CH_3)_2}$$

Monoesters are named as alkylsulfuric acids.

$$\underset{\text{methylsulfuric acid}}{CH_3O\overset{O}{\underset{O}{\overset{||}{\underset{||}{S}}}}OH} \qquad \underset{\text{ethylsulfuric acid}}{CH_3CH_2O\overset{O}{\underset{O}{\overset{||}{\underset{||}{S}}}}OH}$$

Dialkyl sulfates are highly polar compounds and generally have rather high boiling points. Their water solubility is surprisingly low (Table 25.2). Alkylsulfuric acids are approximately as acidic as sulfuric acid itself.

$$CH_3O\overset{O}{\underset{O}{\overset{||}{\underset{||}{S}}}}OH \rightleftharpoons H^+ + CH_3O\overset{O}{\underset{O}{\overset{||}{\underset{||}{S}}}}O^-$$

They readily form inorganic salts, which are named as metal alkyl sulfates.

$$\underset{\text{sodium methyl sulfate}}{CH_3OSO_3^- \; Na^+} \qquad \underset{\text{barium ethyl sulfate}}{(CH_3CH_2OSO_3^-)_2 \; Ba^{2+}}$$

The monoesters are rarely encountered as reagents in organic chemistry. Ethylsulfuric acid is an intermediate in the industrial hydration of ethylene to give ethanol.

$$CH_2{=}CH_2 + H_2SO_4 \xrightarrow{0°C} CH_3CH_2OSO_3H \xrightarrow{H_2O} CH_3CH_2OH + H_2SO_4$$

TABLE 25.2 Physical Properties of Dialkyl Sulfates

	Melting Point, °C	Boiling Point, °C	Solubility in H_2O, g/100 ml
$CH_3OSO_2OCH_3$	−27	188	2.8
$CH_3CH_2OSO_2OCH_2CH_3$	−25	210	very low

766

Chap. 25

Sulfur,
Phosphorus, and
Silicon
Compounds

Dimethyl sulfate and diethyl sulfate are encountered rather more frequently as organic reagents. Both diesters are readily available, inexpensive materials. They are prepared commercially from the corresponding alcohol and sulfuric acid.

$$2 \ ROH + H_2SO_4 \longrightarrow ROSO_2OR + H_2O$$

Since alkylsulfuric acids are such strong acids, the alkyl sulfate ion is a good leaving group, roughly comparable to iodide ion. Hence, dimethyl sulfate and diethyl sulfate readily enter into S_N2 displacement processes (Section 9.5).

$$(CH_3)_2CHCH_2O^- + CH_3OSO_2OCH_3 \longrightarrow (CH_3)_2CHCH_2OCH_3 + CH_3OSO_3^-$$

They are used in organic chemistry mainly for this purpose—as alkylating agents.

EXERCISE 25.6 Fluorosulfonic acid, FSO_3H, is sometimes used as a reagent in organic synthesis. Write Kekulé structures for this substance and explain why it is a much stronger acid than sulfuric acid.

25.5 Sulfonic Acids

Sulfonic acids contain the functional group SO_3H joined to carbon. They are named as alkane**sulfonic acids** or arene**sulfonic acids**.

methanesulfonic acid   2-propanesulfonic acid   trifluoromethanesulfonic acid

benzenesulfonic   *p*-toluenesulfonic
acid   acid

Sulfonic acids are strong acids, as strong as typical mineral acids.

Because of the inductive effect of the fluorines, trifluoromethanesulfonic acid is much more acidic and, indeed, is one of the strongest acids known.

A. Alkanesulfonic Acids

Alkanesulfonic acids can be prepared by nucleophilic displacement of alkyl halides with bisulfite ion, an ambident anion. Because of the greater nucleophilicity of sulfur, alkylation occurs primarily on sulfur rather than on oxygen. The initial product is the salt of the sulfonic acid, which is converted into the sulfonic acid by treatment with strong acid.

$$(CH_3)_2CHCH_2CH_2Br + HO\overset{O}{\underset{O}{\overset{\|}{\underset{\|}{S}}}}O^- \, Na^+ \xrightarrow{\ H_2O\ } (CH_3)_2CHCH_2CH_2\overset{O}{\underset{O}{\overset{\|}{\underset{\|}{S}}}}O^- \, Na^+$$

(96%)
sodium 3-methylbutanesulfonate

Sodium salts of α-hydroxysulfonic acids are obtained by the addition of sodium bisulfite to aldehydes and some ketones.

$$CH_3\overset{O}{\overset{\|}{C}}H + NaHSO_3 \longrightarrow CH_3\overset{OH}{\underset{}{\overset{}{C}}}H\overset{O}{\underset{O}{\overset{\|}{\underset{\|}{S}}}}O^- \, Na^+$$

(89%)
sodium 1-hydroxyethanesulfonate

$$CH_3\overset{O}{\overset{\|}{C}}CH_3 + NaHSO_3 \longrightarrow (CH_3)_2\overset{OH}{\underset{}{\overset{}{C}}}SO_3^- \, Na^+$$

(59%)
sodium 2-hydroxy-2-propanesulfonate

Sulfonic acid esters are best prepared from sulfonyl chlorides, which are obtained from the sodium sulfonates by treatment with phosphorus pentachloride (PCl_5) or thionyl chloride ($SOCl_2$).

$$CH_3CH_2\overset{O}{\underset{O}{\overset{\|}{\underset{\|}{S}}}}O^- \, Na^+ + PCl_5 \longrightarrow CH_3CH_2\overset{O}{\underset{O}{\overset{\|}{\underset{\|}{S}}}}Cl + POCl_3 + NaCl$$

ethanesulfonyl chloride

$$CH_3CH_2\overset{O}{\underset{O}{\overset{\|}{\underset{\|}{S}}}}Cl + CH_3O^- \, Na^+ \longrightarrow CH_3CH_2\overset{O}{\underset{O}{\overset{\|}{\underset{\|}{S}}}}OCH_3 + NaCl$$

methyl ethanesulfonate

EXERCISE 25.7 Outline a synthesis of methyl 3-methylbutanesulfonate starting with 1-chloro-3-methylbutane.

As with the alkyl sulfates, the alkanesulfonates are potent alkylating agents because the sulfonate ion is a reactive leaving group. One class of alkanesulfonates in common use is the esters of methanesulfonic acid, which are prepared from methanesulfonyl chloride ("mesyl chloride"), an inexpensive commercial material. Methanesulfonates, frequently called "mesylates," are used in substitution and elimination processes in the same way as alkyl halides.

768

Chap. 25

Sulfur,
Phosphorus, and
Silicon
Compounds

methanesulfonyl chloride
"mesyl chloride"

cyclohexyl
methanesulfonate

B. Arenesulfonic Acids

Aromatic sulfonic acids are more common than the aliphatic acids because of their availability through electrophilic sulfonation reactions.

In the reactions of alkenes with sulfuric acid, the acid acts primarily as a protonating reagent to produce a carbocation that reacts with any nucleophile present (Section 11.6.C). We have seen that benzene itself undergoes protonation in sulfuric acid (Section 22.2). However, unless such a reaction is followed by means of a hydrogen isotope, it remains an invisible reaction.

In concentrated sulfuric acid, a substantial amount of sulfur trioxide, SO_3, is present as a result of the following equilibrium.

$$2 \ H_2SO_4 \rightleftharpoons SO_3 + H_3O^+ + HSO_4^-$$

Sulfur trioxide is electrophilic, and its reaction with benzene to give benzenesulfonic acid is a useful and important one. In practice, the reaction is usually carried out with fuming sulfuric acid, a solution of sulfur trioxide in sulfuric acid (Section 22.5).

benzenesulfonic
acid

Sulfur trioxide, SO_3, exists in several allotropic forms. The so-called α- and β-forms are polymers that form long fibrous needles. The monomer is a liquid, called the γ-form; it is available commercially with an inhibitor, which is added to prevent polymerization. Sulfur trioxide is prepared by the catalytic oxidation of sulfur dioxide with oxygen. Sulfur trioxide is the anhydride of sulfuric acid and reacts vigorously with water with evolution of much heat. The reaction with heavy water, D_2O, is used to prepare D_2SO_4. Sulfuric acid is prepared commercially by dissolving sulfur trioxide in sulfuric acid to produce "fuming sulfuric acid." Commercial fuming sulfuric acid contains 7–8% of SO_3. Dilution with water gives ordinary concentrated sulfuric acid.

Sulfonation is a general reaction, and occurs with substituted benzenes as well as with benzene itself.

Note that milder reaction conditions suffice to bring about sulfonation of toluene, which is more reactive than either chlorobenzene or benzene because of the electron-donating effect of the methyl group. The isomer distribution often depends on the exact experimental conditions. For example, at 100°C a typical product composition from toluene is 13% *ortho*, 8% *meta*, and 79% *para*. The sulfonation reaction is reversible, and the product depends on whether the reaction conditions favor kinetic or thermodynamic control. In the sulfonation of toluene at low temperature, the reaction product is the product of kinetic control; that is, the product composition reflects relative energies of transition states. At higher temperatures the reverse reaction has a significant rate, and the reaction takes on the aspects of an equilibrium.

$$Ar-H + SO_3 \rightleftharpoons Ar-SO_3H$$

important at high
temperatures

The sulfonic group is a rather bulky group, and steric interaction with *ortho* substituents is significant. At equilibrium the relatively unhindered *p*-toluenesulfonic acid dominates over *o*-toluenesulfonic acid. Such steric effects are much less evident in the transition state for sulfonation, because the carbon-sulfur bond is not yet completely formed. Hence, *o*- and *p*-toluenesulfonic acids are formed at comparable rates.

According to the principle of microscopic reversibility (page 98), the back reaction must be the exact reverse of the forward reaction. The forward reaction is a reaction with sulfur trioxide to form a dipolar neutral intermediate that loses a proton to form the arenesulfonate ion.

770

Chap. 25

*Sulfur,
Phosphorus, and
Silicon
Compounds*

Consequently, the reverse reaction involves reaction by a proton at a ring carbon of the sulfonate ion. This reverse reaction is faster for a more hindered *ortho*-substituted sulfonic acid because steric congestion effects are relieved in the dipolar intermediate.

EXERCISE 25.8 Is it likely that the product composition given above for sulfonation of toluene at 100°C corresponds to the equilibrium composition? Explain.

Reversal of sulfonation can be accomplished by heating the sulfonic acid in dilute aqueous sulfuric acid. In this way the sulfonic acid group can serve as a protecting group to direct aromatic substitution into other positions. An example of this strategy is provided by the following preparation of pure *o*-bromophenol.

In this example, the highly reactive aromatic ring is sulfonated at the *ortho* and *para* positions, relative to the activating hydroxy group. Bromine is then introduced at the remaining *ortho* position (which is also *meta* to the sulfonic acid groups). Finally, sulfonation is reversed to obtain the pure *o*-bromophenol.

The sulfonic acid function is deactivating and strongly *meta* directing in electrophilic aromatic substitution reactions. This is easy to understand in light of the Lewis structure of benzenesulfonic acid, which has a doubly positive sulfur adjacent to the ring. Because of this deactivation, introduction of a second sulfonic acid group into an aromatic ring is much more difficult than introduction of the first one. Benzene can be disulfonated by the use of hot 20% fuming sulfuric acid (sulfuric acid containing 20% sulfur trioxide).

(90%)
m-benzenedisulfonic acid

As was shown by the foregoing example of sulfonation of phenol, aromatic amines and phenols undergo sulfonation readily. Aniline undergoes sulfonation first on the nitrogen; the initial product must be heated to obtain the ring-sulfonated product.

sulfanilic acid

Sulfanilic acid contains an acidic and a basic group in the same molecule and exists in the **zwitterionic** or **internal salt** form.

Arenesulfonyl chlorides may be prepared by sulfonation of aromatic compounds with chlorosulfonic acid, $ClSO_3H$. An example is chlorosulfonation of acetanilide.

acetanilide   *p*-acetamidobenzenesulfonyl chloride

Arenesulfonic acids are strong acids, about as strong as hydrochloric acid. They are completely dissociated in aqueous solution, and are normally rather water soluble. Indeed, their water solubility presents problems in isolations. Consequently, the products of sulfonation reactions are usually isolated as salts. The sodium salts, like most sodium salts, are also water soluble, but they are generally not as soluble as sodium sulfate or sodium chloride. The less soluble sodium arenesulfonates can usually be "salted out" by saturation of the aqueous solution with sodium sulfate or sodium chloride.

$$ArSO_3^- + Na^+ \rightleftharpoons ArSO_3^- \, Na^+\downarrow$$

The sodium salts of benzenesulfonic acid that have a long alkyl side chain behave as detergents. The sulfonate end is hydrophilic and dissolves in water. The alkane end is hydrophobic and fat soluble, and the combination serves to emulsify fatty materials (Section 17.4.D). At one time the alkane side chain was made by the carbocation polymerization of propylene to give a tetrameric olefin that was used to alkylate benzene; this alkylate was then sulfonated to give the product, which was widely used in many common household detergents.

The widespread use of large quantities of this material caused problems in the purification of sewage effluent because the branched chains were only slowly biodegradable. The detergent industry has now completely replaced this product with one prepared from a mixture of straight-chain C_{12}-C_{15} alkanes. The hydrocarbon mixture is chlorinated and used for Friedel-Crafts alkylation of benzene. The resulting mixture of phenylalkanes is sulfonated to give a product that has the linear character necessary for rapid biodegradability by bacteria.

modern household detergent

p-Toluenesulfonic acid is readily available as the crystalline monohydrate, $C_7H_7SO_3^- \, H_3O^+$, m.p. 105°C. It is prepared by salting out the product from sulfona-

772

Chap. 25

*Sulfur,
Phosphorus, and
Silicon
Compounds*

tion of toluene with concentrated hydrochloric acid. Alternatively, the barium salt is treated with the stoichiometric amount of sulfuric acid, and the insoluble barium sulfate is filtered. The filtrate is a strong acid, and concentrated solutions will dehydrate cellulose (filter paper!) just like sulfuric acid. *p*-Toluenesulfonic acid is used as an acid catalyst in many organic reactions.

EXERCISE 25.9 *p*-Chlorobenzenesulfonic acid is a relatively inexpensive, commercially available material. Suggest a way in which it may be used to prepare 2,6-dinitrochlorobenzene.

The sulfonate group in aromatic sulfonic acid can be replaced by **nucleophilic aromatic substitution** reactions. The conditions are drastic: fusion with alkali hydroxide or other salts at temperatures of 200–350°C.

$SO_3^- Na^+$ $\xrightarrow[230-330°C]{\text{NaOH–KOH}}$ $\xrightarrow{H^+}$ OH

CH_3 CH_3

sodium *p*-toluenesulfonate   (63–72%)
p-cresol

$SO_3^- Na^+$ $\xrightarrow[285-300°C]{\text{NaCN}}$ CN

sodium 1-naphthalenesulfonate   (60–70%)
1-naphthonitrile

The method is used primarily for preparing phenols and nitriles. The necessary reaction conditions are tolerated by few other functional groups; hence, the scope of the reaction is limited. Other nucleophilic aromatic substitution reactions will be considered in Section 26.2.

An unusual feature of this reaction is the fact that it takes place in a fused-salt medium. Such media are highly polar liquids composed almost wholly of ions. In general, neutral organic compounds are not soluble in such ionic media; hence, we have encountered them only rarely in organic reactions. Fused-salt media are useful in organic chemistry only when the organic compound is itself a salt.

EXERCISE 25.10 Show how toluene can be converted into 2,4-dihydroxytoluene.

As with the aliphatic sulfonic acids, one of the most important reactions of aromatic sulfonic acids is conversion to the corresponding sulfonyl chloride. This reaction is most conveniently carried out on the sodium salt by treatment with PCl_5 or $POCl_3$. The product can be distilled or crystallized from benzene. Benzenesulfonyl chloride is a high boiling liquid, b.p. 251.5°C, and *p*-toluenesulfonyl chloride is a solid, m.p. 68°C. Alternatively, the acid chloride may be prepared by direct sulfonation with chlorosulfonic acid as discussed on page 771.

p-Toluenesulfonyl chloride (often called "tosyl" chloride) is used to prepare *p*-toluenesulfonate esters ("tosylates") from alcohols. The procedure involves combining the reagents with excess pyridine at room temperature. Pyridinium chloride separates from solution; the mixture is then added to dilute hydrochloric acid, and the product tosylate is filtered or extracted into ether.

an alkyl tosylate

Sulfonyl chlorides are effective in Friedel-Crafts acylations. The products of such acylations are aromatic sulfones (see page 761).

$$C_6H_5SO_2Cl \xrightarrow[C_6H_6]{AlCl_3} C_6H_5SO_2C_6H_5$$

phenyl sulfone

Reaction of sulfonyl chlorides with ammonia or amines gives the corresponding sulfonamides. Many such compounds have important medicinal use as antibacterial agents. Examples are sulfanilamide (*p*-aminobenzenesulfonamide), sulfadiazine [*p*-amino-N-(2-pyrimidyl)benzenesulfonamide], and sulfathiazole [*p*-amino-N-(2-thiazolyl)benzenesulfonamide].

sulfanilamide   sulfadiazine   sulfathiazole

Reduction of a sulfonyl chloride with zinc and water gives a sulfinic acid (page 762).

(64%)

sodium *p*-toluenesulfinate

The salts of sulfinic acids have the interesting property of being ambident nucleophiles (Section 9.4.D). In their reactions with alkyl halides, reaction occurs mainly on sulfur rather than oxygen to produce sulfones.

774

Chap. 25

*Sulfur,
Phosphorus, and
Silicon
Compounds*

methyl *p*-tolyl
sulfone

Under more strongly reducing conditions sulfonyl chlorides give the corresponding thiols.

EXERCISE 25.11 Sulfonation of bromobenzene gives *p*-bromobenzenesulfonic acid, which is isolated as the sodium salt. This salt is frequently called sodium brosylate, and the brosylate group is sometimes used instead of the analogous tosylate group. How can sodium brosylate be converted into brosyl chloride? Give the reaction product resulting from treatment of *p*-bromobenzenesulfonyl chloride with each of the following sets of reagents.
(a) *n*-CH₃CH₂CH₂CH₂OH, pyridine   (b) toluene, AlCl₃
(c) (i) Zn, water; (ii) Na₂CO₃; (iii) C₆H₅CH₂Cl   (d) Zn, H₂SO₄

EXERCISE 25.12 Sulfonium salts with three different groups, RR′R″S⁺, are chiral and have inversion barriers that are sufficiently high (25-30 kcal mole⁻¹) that enantiomerically homogeneous samples may be obtained at room temperature. Which two of the following compounds are also chiral?
(a) methyl phenyl sulfide   (b) methyl phenyl sulfoxide
(c) methyl phenyl sulfone   (d) methyl benzenesulfonate
(e) methyl benzenesulfinate
Of the three achiral compounds, propose chiral analogs that incorporate isotopes.

25.6 Phosphines and Phosphonium Salts

Phosphines are the phosphorus analogs of amines. They are named by appending the suffix **-phosphine** to the stem names of the alkyl groups attached to phosphorus.

$$CH_3CH_2PH_2 \qquad (CH_3CH_2CH_2CH_2)_2PH \qquad (C_6H_5)_3P$$

ethylphosphine   di-*n*-butylphosphine   triphenylphosphine

Tertiary phosphines are the most important. They are conveniently prepared by reaction of Grignard reagents with phosphorus trichloride.

tricyclohexylphosphine

Phosphines are more highly pyramidal than amines, but there is considerable variation in the bond angles about phosphorus. Trimethylphosphine has a C—P—C angle of 99°, somewhat expanded from the H—P—H angle of 93° in phosphine itself. Triphenylphosphine has a C—P—C angle of 103°.

Since phosphines are analogs of amines, we expect the phosphorus lone pair to show characteristic basic properties. Phosphines do act as Lewis bases, but the base strength is strongly dependent on structure, particularly on the degree of substitution at phosphorus. The changes may depend in part on bond-angle variations between the pyramidal phosphine and tetrahedral phosphonium salt. Representative pK_a values for the protonated forms of some phosphines are collected in Table 25.3. Comparison of the pK_as in Table 25.3 with the pK_as of amines given in Table 23.4 (page 690) shows that tertiary phosphines are about 100-fold less basic than the corresponding amines. For secondary and primary phosphines the difference is much greater. Phosphine itself, PH_3, shows no basic properties whatsoever; the pK_a of PH_4^+ has been estimated to be -14! Like the analogous amines, phenylphosphines are less basic than the alkyl compounds.

Even though phosphines are considerably less basic than amines, the phosphorus is highly polarizable, and phosphines are highly nucleophilic and readily participate in S_N2 reactions.

$$(C_6H_5)_3P + C_6H_5CH_2Cl \longrightarrow (C_6H_5)_3\overset{+}{P}CH_2C_6H_5 \ Cl^-$$

benzyltriphenylphosphonium chloride

Phosphonium salts are most important for their use as reagents in the Wittig synthesis of alkenes (Section 14.8.E).

Tertiary phosphines also act as good donor ligands toward metals and are commonly used in the preparation of organometallic complexes such as tris-triphenylphosphine-rhodium(I) chloride (Section 34.2).

$$
\begin{array}{c}
(C_6H_5)_3P \searrow \quad \swarrow P(C_6H_5)_3 \\
\qquad\qquad Rh \\
(C_6H_5)_3P \nearrow \quad \searrow Cl
\end{array}
$$

Trialkylphosphines are readily oxidized, even by air, to the corresponding phosphine oxides.

$$(n\text{-}C_4H_9)_3P \xrightarrow{[O]} (n\text{-}C_4H_9)_3\overset{+}{P}\!\!-\!\!O^-$$

tri-*n*-butylphosphine   tri-*n*-butylphosphine oxide

TABLE 25.3 Acidity of Phosphonium Ions

R_3PH^+	pK_a
$(C_2H_5)_3PH^+$	8.69
$(n\text{-}C_4H_9)_3PH^+$	8.43
$(C_4H_9)_2PH_2^+$	4.51
$(CH_3)_2PH_2^+$	3.91
$i\text{-}C_4H_9PH_3^+$	-0.02
$n\text{-}C_8H_{17}PH_3^+$	0.43
$(C_6H_5)_3PH^+$	2.73
$(C_6H_5)_2PH_2^+$	0.03

776

Chap. 25

*Sulfur,
Phosphorus, and
Silicon
Compounds*

EXERCISE 25.13 Review the discussion of the Wittig reaction in Section 14.8.E. Write the equations illustrating the use of benzyltriphenylphosphonium chloride to prepare several alkenes. How could the triphenylphosphine that is used in this sequence be prepared?

25.7 Phosphate and Phosphonate Esters

There are several oxyacids of phosphorus. The most common one is orthophosphoric acid, more commonly called simply phosphoric acid, H_3PO_4. When orthophosphoric acid is heated above 210°C, it loses water with the formation of pyrophosphoric acid, which may be regarded as an anhydride of phosphoric acid.

$$\text{HO}-\overset{\overset{\displaystyle O}{\|}}{\underset{\underset{\displaystyle OH}{|}}{P}}-\text{OH} \xrightarrow{210°C} \text{HO}-\overset{\overset{\displaystyle O}{\|}}{\underset{\underset{\displaystyle OH}{|}}{P}}-\text{O}-\overset{\overset{\displaystyle O}{\|}}{\underset{\underset{\displaystyle OH}{|}}{P}}-\text{OH}$$

orthophosphoric acid pyrophosphoric acid

"Polyphosphoric acid" (PPA) is a mixture of phosphoric anhydrides that is prepared by heating H_3PO_4 with phosphorus pentoxide, P_2O_5. It consists of about 55% tripolyphosphoric acid, the remainder being H_3PO_4 and higher polyphosphoric acids.

$$\text{HO}-\overset{\overset{\displaystyle O}{\|}}{\underset{\underset{\displaystyle OH}{|}}{P}}-\text{O}-\overset{\overset{\displaystyle O}{\|}}{\underset{\underset{\displaystyle OH}{|}}{P}}-\text{O}-\overset{\overset{\displaystyle O}{\|}}{\underset{\underset{\displaystyle OH}{|}}{P}}-\text{OH}$$

tripolyphosphoric acid

Polyphosphoric acid is sometimes used as an acid catalyst in organic reactions.

Orthophosphoric acid is a tribasic acid having $pK_1 = 2.15$, $pK_2 = 7.20$, and $pK_3 = 12.38$.

$$H_3PO_4 \rightleftharpoons H^+ + H_2PO_4^- \qquad K_a = 7.1 \times 10^{-3}\ M$$
$$H_2PO_4^- \rightleftharpoons H^+ + HPO_4^{2-} \qquad K_a = 6.3 \times 10^{-8}\ M$$
$$HPO_4^{2-} \rightleftharpoons H^+ + PO_4^{3-} \qquad K_a = 4.2 \times 10^{-13}\ M$$

It may form mono-, di-, and triesters.

isopropyl phosphate   diethyl phosphate   trimethyl phosphate

The mono- and diesters still contain OH groups and have acidic properties. They are actually stronger acids than phosphoric acid itself.

$$CH_3OP(OH)_2 \rightleftharpoons H^+ + CH_3O\overset{\overset{\displaystyle O}{\|}}{\underset{\underset{\displaystyle OH}{|}}{P}}O^- \qquad pK_a = 1.54$$

methyl phosphate

$$CH_3O\overset{\displaystyle O}{\underset{\displaystyle OCH_3}{\overset{\|}{P}}}OH \rightleftharpoons H^+ + CH_3O\overset{\displaystyle O}{\underset{\displaystyle OCH_3}{\overset{\|}{P}}}O^- \qquad pK_a = 1.29$$

dimethyl phosphate

Analogous esters are possible for pyrophosphoric acid, but the most common are the monoesters.

cyclohexyl pyrophosphate

Phosphate triesters are commonly prepared from the alcohol and phosphorus oxychloride, which is the acid halide corresponding to phosphoric acid.

$$3\ n\text{-}C_4H_9OH + Cl\overset{\displaystyle O}{\underset{\displaystyle Cl}{\overset{\|}{-P-}}}Cl \longrightarrow (n\text{-}C_4H_9O)_3P{=}O + 3\ HCl$$

tributyl phosphate

Compounds prepared by the replacement of two of the chlorines of POCl$_3$ (phosphorochloridates) may be used in a similar way to prepare mixed phosphates.

di-*t*-butyl phosphorochloridate   cyclohexyl di-*t*-butyl phosphate

The only reaction of phosphate esters that we shall consider here is hydrolysis. Hydrolysis may be either acid- or base-catalyzed and may involve either carbon-oxygen or phosphorus-oxygen bond rupture. Under basic conditions hydrolysis occurs mainly by an addition-elimination mechanism, similar to that involved in the hydrolysis of carboxylic acid esters.

The first alkyl group of a trialkyl phosphate is hydrolyzed most easily; the second and third groups are hydrolyzed rather more sluggishly.

Under acidic conditions carbon-oxygen bond cleavage is the predominant mode of hydrolysis, although P—O rupture may also be observed. Cleavage of the carbon-

778

Chap. 25

Sulfur,
Phosphorus, and
Silicon
Compounds

oxygen bonds may occur by either the S_N2 or the S_N1 mechanism, the former being preferred with primary alkyl phosphates and the latter with tertiary systems.

$$S_N2: \quad CH_3O-\overset{\overset{\displaystyle O}{\|}}{\underset{\underset{\displaystyle OCH_3}{|}}{P}}-OCH_3 + H^+ \rightleftharpoons CH_3O-\overset{\overset{\displaystyle OH}{|}}{\underset{\underset{\displaystyle O-CH_3}{|}}{P^+}}-OCH_3$$

$$CH_3O-\overset{\overset{\displaystyle OH}{|}}{\underset{\underset{\displaystyle O\frown CH_3}{|}}{P^+}}-OCH_3 \rightleftharpoons CH_3O-\overset{\overset{\displaystyle OH}{|}}{\underset{\underset{\displaystyle O}{\|}}{P}}-OCH_3 + CH_3OH + H^+$$

$$\overset{\cdot\cdot}{:}\ddot{O}H_2$$

$$S_N1: \quad t\text{-}C_4H_9O-\overset{\overset{\displaystyle O}{\|}}{\underset{\underset{\displaystyle OH}{|}}{P}}-OH + H^+ \rightleftharpoons t\text{-}C_4H_9O-\overset{\overset{\displaystyle OH}{|}}{\underset{\underset{\displaystyle OH}{|}}{P^+}}-OH$$

$$t\text{-}C_4H_9O-\overset{\overset{\displaystyle OH}{|}}{\underset{\underset{\displaystyle OH}{|}}{P^+}}-OH \rightleftharpoons O=\overset{\overset{\displaystyle OH}{|}}{\underset{\underset{\displaystyle OH}{|}}{P}}-OH + t\text{-}C_4H_9^+ \xrightarrow{H_2O} t\text{-}C_4H_9OH + H^+$$

As a leaving group in such substitution reactions, phosphate is comparable to bromide ion. The pyrophosphate group is a somewhat better leaving group, being about 100-fold more effective than iodide ion. The pyrophosphate group is an important leaving group in nucleophilic substitution reactions that occur in nature. A number of compounds are built up by plants (**biosynthesized**) from acetic acid units. By a series of enzyme-catalyzed steps, acetic acid is transformed into the compound isopentenyl pyrophosphate, which undergoes enzyme-catalyzed isomerization to γ,γ-dimethylallyl pyrophosphate.

isopentenyl pyrophosphate γ,γ-dimethylallyl pyrophosphate

Since the pyrophosphate ion is such a good leaving group, γ,γ-dimethylallyl pyrophosphate readily ionizes to give the allylic cation.

The dimethylallyl cation so produced reacts with isopentenyl pyrophosphate to give a new carbocation, which loses a proton to give geranyl pyrophosphate.

geranyl pyrophosphate

Although the foregoing reactions are illustrated as simple carbocation reactions, they are undoubtedly under enzyme control. Repetition of these types of reactions leads to more complex structures. A more detailed discussion of biosynthesis is given in Section 34.8. Phosphate esters of carbohydrates are also important natural products (Section 28.9) and constitute one of the basic building units of nucleic acids (Section 34.6).

Phosphorous acid, H_3PO_3, is a less important oxyphosphorus acid. Trialkyl phosphites are generally prepared by treatment of phosphorus trichloride with the alcohol and pyridine.

$$PCl_3 + 3\ C_2H_5OH + 3\ C_5H_5N \longrightarrow (C_2H_5O)_3P + 3\ C_5H_5NH^+\ Cl^-$$

triethyl phosphite

Phosphonic acids contain the functional group PO_3H_2 attached to carbon. They are named as alkylphosphonic acids.

methylphosphonic acid   *n*-propylphosphonic acid

The most common derivatives are the diesters.

dimethyl ethylphosphonate   diethyl ethylphosphonate

Dialkyl phosphonates are best prepared from trialkylphosphites by a reaction known as the **Arbuzov-Michaelis reaction**. For example, when trimethyl phosphite is heated at 200°C with a catalytic amount of methyl iodide, dimethyl methylphosphonate is produced in virtually quantitative yield.

trimethyl phosphite   dimethyl methylphosphonate

The reaction mechanism involves two successive S_N2 processes. In the first step the nucleophilic phosphorus of the trialkyl phosphite displaces iodide from methyl iodide, giving an alkyltrialkoxyphosphonium salt.

(1) $(CH_3O)_3P: + CH_3{-}I \longrightarrow (CH_3O)_3P^+{-}CH_3\ I^-$

methyltrimethoxyphosphonium iodide

The liberated iodide ion attacks one of the methoxy groups in a second S_N2 process, displacing the neutral dialkyl phosphonate.

780

Chap. 25
Sulfur,
Phosphorus, and
Silicon
Compounds

$$(2) \quad I:^- + CH_3 - O - \overset{\overset{\displaystyle OCH_3}{|}}{\underset{\underset{\displaystyle OCH_3}{|}}{P^+}} - CH_3 \longrightarrow CH_3I + \quad CH_3 - \overset{\overset{\displaystyle O}{\|}}{\underset{\underset{\displaystyle OCH_3}{|}}{P}} - OCH_3$$

dimethyl methylphosphonate

Since the alkyl halide is regenerated in the second step, only a catalytic amount is required in order to initiate reaction.

EXERCISE 25.14 A mixture of 1.0 mole of triethyl phosphite and 0.01 mole of methyl iodide is heated at 200°C. What is the reaction product?

The Arbuzov-Michaelis reaction has been applied to the synthesis of numerous dialkyl phosphonates. If a full equivalent of alkyl halide is used, dialkyl phosphonates having different groups attached to oxygen and phosphorus may be prepared.

$$(CH_3CH_2O)_3P: + BrCH_2COOC_2H_5 \xrightarrow{200\,°C} C_2H_5O\overset{\overset{\displaystyle O}{\|}}{C}CH_2\overset{\overset{\displaystyle O}{\|}}{P}(OC_2H_5)_2 + CH_3CH_2Br$$

triethyl phosphite   ethyl bromoacetate   triethyl phosphonoacetate

Monoalkyl phosphonates are readily obtained from the diesters by alkaline hydrolysis. Hydrolysis of the second group is more difficult.

$$CH_3CH_2CH_2CH_2\overset{\overset{\displaystyle O}{\|}}{P}(OCH_3)_2 + NaOH \xrightarrow[\Delta]{C_2H_5OH}$$

dimethyl butylphosphonate

$$CH_3CH_2CH_2CH_2 \overset{\overset{\displaystyle O}{\|}}{\underset{\underset{\displaystyle OCH_3}{|}}{P}}O^-Na^+ \xrightarrow{dil.\ H_2SO_4} CH_3CH_2CH_2CH_2\overset{\overset{\displaystyle O}{\|}}{\underset{\underset{\displaystyle OCH_3}{|}}{P}}OH$$

sodium methyl butylphosphonate   methyl butylphosphonate

EXERCISE 25.15 Write equations illustrating the preparation of the following phosphate and phosphonate esters using $POCl_3$ and PCl_3 as the source of phosphorus.

(a) $CH_3O\overset{\overset{\displaystyle O}{\|}}{P}(OC_2H_5)_2$ (b) $(i\text{-}C_4H_9O_3)_3PO$

(c) $CH_3CH_2CH_2\overset{\overset{\displaystyle O}{\|}}{P}(OC_2H_5)_2$ (d) $CH_3CH_2\overset{\overset{\overset{\displaystyle O}{\|}}{P}}{\underset{\underset{\displaystyle OH}{|}}{}}OCH_2CH_3$

25.8 Sulfur- and Phosphorus-Stabilized Carbanions

Sulfur- and phosphorus-containing functional groups stabilize adjacent carbanions to varying degrees, depending on the exact nature of the function. This property gives rise to carbanionic reagents that have important uses in organic synthesis.

781

Sec. 25.8

Sulfur- and
Phosphorus-
Stabilized
Carbanions

The most well-known and useful compounds in this class are the phosphorus ylides, or Wittig reagents (Section 14.8.E). These compounds are formed by reaction of alkyl phosphonium salts with a strong base such as n-butyllithium.

$$(C_6H_5)_3\overset{+}{P}-CH_3 + n\text{-}C_4H_9Li \longrightarrow (C_6H_5)_3\overset{+}{P}-CH_2^- + n\text{-}C_4H_{10}$$

The bonding in such ylides is still a subject of controversy. At one time, it was thought that the ylide phosphorus-carbon bond could be described as a double bond resulting from overlap of the carbon p-orbital with a phosphorus d-orbital. However, quantum-mechanical calculations suggest that such p-d double bonds are relatively unimportant. As in the case of the sulfur-oxygen bond (page 761), a large part of the bonding in ylides is electrostatic—attraction of the positive phosphorus for the negative carbon. However, this cannot be the complete answer, since alkylammonium salts are not converted into ylides under conditions that suffice to form phosphorus ylides. Electrostatic bonding in the nitrogen ylide should be as important as in a phosphorus ylide.

$$R_3\overset{+}{N}-CH_2^-$$

an ammonium ylide

The higher polarizability of the phosphorus valence electrons is probably involved in stabilizing the dipolar ylide structure. Such polarization can be viewed as an induced dipole on phosphorus.

$$R_3\overset{+}{P}-CH_2^-$$
$$\overset{\longleftrightarrow}{}$$

Whatever the exact explanation for the bonding in phosphorus ylides, it is quantitatively significant. Although pK_as for simple phosphonium salts have not been measured, salts that also contain a keto or ester function attached to the acidic position are substantially more acidic than 1,3-diketones and 1,3-keto esters (Section 27.7).

$$(C_6H_5)_3\overset{+}{P}-CH_2\overset{\overset{O}{\|}}{C}C_6H_5 \qquad (C_6H_5)_3\overset{+}{P}-CH_2COOC_2H_5$$
$$\text{p}K_a = 6.0 \qquad\qquad\qquad \text{p}K_a = 9.1$$

From these pK_as it may be concluded that alkyltriphenylphosphonium salts are somewhat more acidic than ketones! Since the pK_a of acetone is 19, it may be estimated that the pK_a of methyltriphenylphosphonium ion is on the order of 15-18.

Simple phosphonates may be deprotonated by strong bases such as n-butyllithium, and the resulting carbanions add to aldehydes and ketones. Aqueous work-up of the initial adducts affords β-hydroxyphosphonates.

$$CH_3\overset{\overset{O}{\|}}{P}(OC_2H_5)_2 + n\text{-}C_4H_9Li \longrightarrow {}^-CH_2\overset{\overset{O}{\|}}{P}(OC_2H_5)_2 \xrightarrow{CH_3CHO}$$

diethyl methylphosphonate

$$CH_3\overset{\overset{O^-}{|}}{C}HCH_2\overset{\overset{O}{\|}}{P}(OC_2H_5)_2 \xrightarrow{H_2O} CH_3\overset{\overset{OH}{|}}{C}HCH_2\overset{\overset{O}{\|}}{P}(OC_2H_5)_2$$

diethyl 2-hydroxypropylphosphonate

Phosphonates that have a carbonyl group attached to the α-carbon are more acidic, having pK_as of about 15.

782

Chap. 25

Sulfur,
Phosphorus, and
Silicon
Compounds

triethyl phosphonoacetate
estimated $pK_a \cong 15$

Comparison of this value with the pK_as of malonic ester and acetoacetic ester (Table 27.6, page 872) shows that the dialkylphosphono group, $(RO)_2PO—$, is not quite as effective as a carbonyl group at stabilizing an adjacent carbanion. Anions of such activated phosphonates add to aldehydes and ketones, and the resulting products eliminate dialkylphosphonate ion to give α,β-unsaturated esters or ketones (**Horner-Emmons** reaction, Section 19.3.B).

$$(C_2H_5O)_2\overset{O}{\underset{\|}{P}}CH_2CN \xrightarrow{\text{NaH}} \xrightarrow[]{\text{CH}_3O-\langle\rangle-\text{CHO}} CH_3O-\langle\rangle-CH=CHCN$$

(88%)

EXERCISE 25.16 Write equations showing how trimethyl phosphite may be employed in each of the following multistep transformations.

(a) $CH_3\overset{O}{\underset{\|}{C}}CH_3 \longrightarrow (CH_3)_2\overset{OH}{\underset{|}{C}}CH_2\overset{O}{\underset{\|}{P}}(OCH_3)_2$

(b) $CH_3CHO \longrightarrow CH_3CH=CHCOOCH_3$

Sulfur also stabilizes adjacent carbanions. An example is thioanisole, which may be deprotonated by *n*-butyllithium. The resulting lithium compound may be alkylated by primary alkyl halides and also reacts with aldehydes and ketones.

$$C_6H_5SCH_3 \xrightarrow[\text{THF}]{n\text{-}C_4H_9Li} C_6H_5SCH_2Li$$

$$\xrightarrow[\substack{\text{THF} \\ 25°C}]{\text{CH}_3(\text{CH}_2)_9\text{I}} C_6H_5SCH_2(CH_2)_9CH_3$$
(93%)

$$\xrightarrow{\text{CH}_3\text{CHO}} C_6H_5SCH_2\overset{OH}{\underset{|}{C}}HCH_3$$
(85%)

The acetal protons in dithioacetals are activated by two sulfur atoms and are correspondingly more acidic than simple sulfides. An extensively studied member of this class is 1,3-dithiane, the product of reaction of 1,3-propanedithiol and formaldehyde. The pK_a of 1,3-dithiane is less than 40, and it is readily converted into the 1,3-dithianyl anion by treatment with *n*-butyllithium.

$$CH_2=O + \underset{\text{SH}}{\overset{\frown}{}} SH \xrightarrow{\text{HCl}} \underset{\underset{H \quad H}{\overset{\frown}{S}}}{S} \underset{}{S} \xrightarrow{n\text{-BuLi}} \underset{\underset{H}{\overset{\frown}{S}}}{S} \underset{}{S} Li^+ + C_4H_{10}$$

1,3-dithiane

Analogous anions may be produced from other 1,3-dithianes.

The 1,3-dithianyl anions are nucleophilic and undergo addition to aldehyde and ketone carbonyl groups. The resulting thioacetals are stable to normal hydrolytic conditions, but hydrolyze easily when treated with mercuric chloride in aqueous acetonitrile.

(91%)   (90%)

The overall process constitutes one method for the synthesis of α-hydroxy ketones (Section 27.4.A).

The dithiane method may also be used as a method of preparing certain β-hydroxy ketones. If the dithianyl anion is used as a nucleophile to open an epoxide ring (Section 10.11.A), hydrolysis of the resulting hydroxy dithiane affords the β-hydroxy ketone.

(81%)

(83%)
2-hydroxy-4-nonanone

EXERCISE 25.17 Outline a synthesis of each of the following compounds by routes employing dithianyl anions.
(a) 4-hydroxyheptan-3-one   (b) 4-hydroxyheptan-2-one

Like phosphonium salts, the analogous sulfonium salts are acidic. Because the sulfur bears a positive charge, which aids in stabilizing the conjugate base, sulfonium salts are much more acidic than simple sulfides or even dithioacetals. One way in which the enhanced acidity of sulfonium salts is shown is by base-catalyzed exchange of the acidic protons in deuterated media such as D_2O.

$$(CH_3)_3S^+ \ I^- \longrightarrow (CD_3)_3S^+ \ I^-$$

Although exact pK_as of such sulfonium ions have not been measured, they are probably on the order of 20. If a strong base such as n-butyllithium is used, the sulfonium salt can be converted completely into ylides, which are analogous to the phosphonium ylides.

$$(CH_3)_3S^+ \ I^- + n\text{-}C_4H_9Li \xrightarrow[-70°C]{THF} (CH_3)_2\overset{+}{S}\!-\!\overset{-}{C}H_2 + C_4H_{10} + LiI$$

Sulfonium ylides are unstable at temperatures higher than 0°C. However, at lower temperatures they add to aldehydes and ketones. The initial product is a zwitterion that behaves differently from the zwitterion produced by addition of a phosphonium ylide to a carbonyl compound (Section 14.8.E). In this case, the alkoxide ion acts as the nucleophile in an intramolecular S_N2 process and dimethyl sulfide is the leaving group. The product is an epoxide.

784

Chap. 25

*Sulfur,
Phosphorus, and
Silicon
Compounds*

(93%)

Sulfoxides and sulfones (page 761) are also relatively acidic; the pK_as of dimethyl sulfoxide and dimethyl sulfone are 35 and 31, respectively, in DMSO solution.

dimethyl sulfone
$pK_a = 31$ (in DMSO)

dimethyl sulfoxide
$pK_a = 35$ (in DMSO)

The anions derived from sulfones react with electrophiles in the same manner as the other sulfur-stabilized anions we have considered. An example is the reaction of the dimethyl sulfone anion with carboxylic acid esters to give β-keto sulfones.

$$CH_3SO_2CH_3 \xrightarrow[\text{DMSO}]{\text{NaH}} CH_3SO_2CH_2^- \xrightarrow{CH_3(CH_2)_{14}COOCH_3} CH_3(CH_2)_{14}\overset{O}{\overset{||}{C}}CH_2\overset{O}{\underset{||}{\underset{O}{S}}}CH_3$$

(83%)

This reaction is analogous to the mixed Claisen condensation (Section 18.9). Note that dimethyl sulfoxide is used as a solvent even though it is also acidic. The difference of 4 pK_a units between dimethyl sulfone and DMSO suffices for synthetic usefulness.

EXERCISE 25.18 What is the structure of the product of each of the following reactions?
(a) dimethyl sulfoxide + *n*-butyllithium, followed by benzaldehyde
(b) trimethylsulfonium iodide + *n*-butyllithium, followed by benzaldehyde
(c) 2-phenyl-1,3-dithiane + *n*-butyllithium, followed by benzaldehyde

---

25.9 Organosilicon Compounds: Structure and Properties

Because silicon is just below carbon in the periodic table, it is expected that there would be structural similarities in the two classes of compounds, and that analogous physical and chemical properties would be found. To some extent, such similarities exist. For example, tetramethylsilane (b.p. 26.5°C) and neopentane (b.p. 9.4°C) are both volatile substances in which the central atom is at the center of a perfect tetrahedron of methyl groups.

tetramethylsilane
b.p. 26.5°C

neopentane
b.p. 9.4°C

785

Sec. 25.9

*Organosilicon
Compounds:
Structure and
Properties*

The similarity in structure stems from a similarity in bonding; for silicon the orbitals used are Si_{sp^3}, while for carbon they are C_{sp^3}. However, silicon is a third-period element, and utilizes 3s- and 3p-orbitals, so its bonds are longer but are roughly comparable in strength to corresponding carbon bonds. For example, in tetramethylsilane the carbon-silicon bond length is 1.89 Å and the bond-dissociation energy is 89 kcal mole^{-1}. Comparable values for the carbon-carbon bonds in neopentane are 1.54 Å and 84 kcal mole^{-1}.

However, the analogy between hydrocarbons and analogous silicon compounds fails in the case of multiple bonds. While compounds containing a carbon-silicon double bond can be prepared in the vapor phase, they are highly reactive materials that polymerize or react with other materials present. The Si=C bond is weak for several reasons. An important factor is the "mismatch" that results from the π-overlap of Si_{3p} and C_{2p} orbitals. As shown by the following diagram, the Si_{3p} orbital has one more node than a C_{2p} orbital. Although there *is* a bonding interaction between the parallel p-orbitals, there is also an antibonding one. In addition, the greater length of a silicon-carbon bond, relative to a carbon-carbon bond, results in less effective π-overlap.

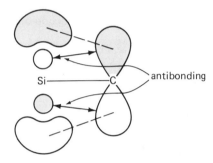

Compounds with silicon-silicon double bonds are also unstable and have only been detected under special conditions. In this case also the great length of the silicon-silicon bond does not allow effective π-overlap.

On the other hand, silicon-halogen and silicon-oxygen bonds are especially strong, relative to the analogous carbon-heteroatom bonds. Representative values are given in Table 25.4. The enhanced strength of silicon-heteroatom bonds is largely due to the fact that silicon is more electropositive than carbon (Table 8.6, page 148). As a consequence, there is a substantial coulombic component to the bond energy. In addition, the polarizability of silicon provides an effective method of stabilization of oxygen and halogen lone pairs.

$$[Si—X \longleftrightarrow Si^+ \; :X^-]$$

TABLE 25.4 Bond Lengths and Bond-Dissociation Energies for Silicon Compounds

Compound	Bond Length, Å	$DH°$, kcal mole^{-1}
$(CH_3)_3Si—H$		90
$(CH_3)_3Si—CH_3$	1.89	89
$(CH_3)_3Si—OCH_3$	1.48	127
$(CH_3)_3Si—F$	1.60	193
$(CH_3)_3Si—Cl$	2.05	113
$(CH_3)_3Si—Br$	2.21	96
$(CH_3)_3Si—I$	2.44	77

786

Chap. 25

*Sulfur,
Phosphorus, and
Silicon
Compounds*

We shall see that the great strength of silicon-heteroatom bonds plays an important role in the chemistry of organosilicon compounds.

25.10 Organosilicon Compounds: Preparation

The ultimate raw materials for the preparation of silicon compounds are metallic silicon and the silicon halides. The reaction of silicon with alkyl and aryl halides, usually under the influence of copper catalysis, is an important industrial process.

$$2\,CH_3Cl + Si \xrightarrow[250°C]{Cu} (CH_3)_2SiCl_2 + \text{by-products}$$

$$(70\text{–}90\%)$$

Although the foregoing reaction gives a number of by-products, the yield of dichlorodialkylsilane is good, and the reactants are inexpensive. Dichlorodimethylsilane is prepared in tonnage quantity for the production of silicone polymers, which are formed by hydrolysis.

$$(CH_3)_2SiCl_2 + H_2O \longrightarrow \left[\begin{array}{cc} CH_3 & CH_3 \\ | & | \\ -O-Si-O-Si- \\ | & | \\ CH_3 & CH_3 \end{array} \right]_n$$

Organosilicon compounds are readily available by the reaction of Grignard reagents and organolithium compounds with silicon halides. Reaction of silicon tetrachloride with excess methylmagnesium chloride gives tetramethylsilane.

$$4\,CH_3MgCl + SiCl_4 \longrightarrow (CH_3)_4Si + 4\,MgCl_2$$

However, each substitution of chlorine by alkyl makes the next substitution more difficult, and it is easy to achieve stepwise replacement of the four halogens.

$$CH_3MgCl + SiCl_4 \longrightarrow CH_3SiCl_3 + MgCl_2$$

$$CH_3MgCl + CH_3SiCl_3 \longrightarrow (CH_3)_2SiCl_2 + MgCl_2$$

$$(CH_3)_3CLi + (CH_3)_2SiCl_2 \longrightarrow (CH_3)_3C\overset{\overset{\displaystyle CH_3}{|}}{\underset{\underset{\displaystyle CH_3}{|}}{Si}}Cl + LiCl$$

The last example shows that organosilicon compounds having two or more different alkyl or aryl groups bonded to silicon may be easily prepared.

EXERCISE 25.19 Outline syntheses of the following compounds.
(a) phenyltrimethylsilane   (b) diphenylsilyl dichloride
(c) allyltrimethylsilane   (d) vinyltrimethylsilane

787

Sec. 25.11

*Organosilicon
Compounds:
Reactions*

25.11 Organosilicon Compounds: Reactions

A. Nucleophilic Substitution at Silicon

Nucleophilic substitution at silicon is much easier than in corresponding carbon compounds. For example, trimethylsilyl chloride reacts with alcohols at room temperature to give the corresponding ethers; an amine such as triethylamine or pyridine is usually added to neutralize the HCl produced in the reaction.

$$CH_3CH_2OH + (CH_3)_3SiCl \xrightarrow{Et_3N} CH_3CH_2OSi(CH_3)_3 + Et_3\overset{+}{N}H\ Cl^-$$

The high reactivity of the silicon-halogen bond toward nucleophilic substitution is also seen in the fact that trimethylsilyl chloride reacts with enolate ions at −78°C to give enolsilanes.

$$
\begin{array}{cc}
\overset{\displaystyle O^-\ Li^+}{\underset{|}{}} & \overset{\displaystyle OSi(CH_3)_3}{\underset{|}{}} \\
CH_3C{=}CH_2 + (CH_3)_3SiCl & \xrightarrow[-78°C]{THF} \quad CH_3C{=}CH_2 \\
& \qquad\qquad (85\%)
\end{array}
$$

In principle, nucleophilic substitution at silicon could occur by either the S_N1 or S_N2 mechanism. In practice, substitution by the S_N1 mechanism is virtually unknown, not because the R_3Si^+ ion is especially unstable, but because the S_N2-Si mechanism is especially good. The two foregoing examples show that even a tertiary silyl halide is easily replaced under typical S_N2 conditions. In part, this is because the silicon-carbon bonds are much longer than carbon-carbon bonds; thus, steric hindrance effects at silicon are much smaller than at carbon. In addition, the great strength of silicon-heteroatom bonds stabilizes the transition state for nucleophilic substitution.

$$
\begin{array}{c}
CH_3 \\
| \\
RO{\overset{\delta-}{\cdots\cdots}}Si{\cdots\cdots}Cl^{\delta-} \\
\diagup\ \diagdown \\
H_3C\ \ CH_3
\end{array}
$$

This pentacoordinate structure may actually be an intermediate; for example, the carbon-fluorine bond is so strong that the product of addition of fluoride ion to trimethylsilyl fluoride is an isolable, stable species.

$$
\begin{array}{c}
CH_3 \\
| \\
F{-}\overset{|}{Si}{-}F \\
\diagup\ \diagdown \\
H_3C\ \ CH_3
\end{array}
$$

difluorotrimethylsiliconate
ion

The difluorotrimethylsiliconate ion has a trigonal bipyramid geometry, as shown. Its structure is analogous to that of PCl_5 (page 15).

Pentacoordinated species such as the difluorotrimethylsiliconate ion have two kinds of groups attached to silicon—the three that form the base of the bipyramid (the equatorial positions) and the two that form the apices of the bipyramid (the apical positions). The three equatorial ligands are bonded to silicon by orbitals that are essentially Si_{sp^2}. The two apical ligands are bonded by weaker bonds to the two lobes of the remaining Si_{3p} orbital. Consequently, the silicon-equatorial bond lengths are shorter than the silicon-apical bonds (see the bond lengths in PCl_5, page 15).

788

Chap. 25

Sulfur,
Phosphorus, and
Silicon
Compounds

a = apical positions; e = equatorial position

Species such as this are capable of a molecular rearrangement called **pseudorotation**, in which the two apical ligands switch positions with two of the three equatorial ligands. The process is illustrated by the following example, in which ligand 2 may be considered to be the "pivot" for the pseudorotation, which results in the isomerization of the apical ligands 1 and 5 to equatorial positions while the equatorial ligands 3 and 4 adopt apical positions.

The foregoing pseudorotation is actually a form of molecular vibration in which the 2—Si—1 and 2—Si—5 angles enlarge from 90° to 120° while the 2—Si—3 and 2—Si—4 angles shrink from 120° to 90°.

EXERCISE 25.20 How many pseudorotations are required in order to change the difluorotrimethylsiliconate ion from a structure having both fluorines in apical positions into one having one apical and one equatorial fluorine?

Silicon may be a stereocenter, and the stereochemistry of nucleophilic substitution at silicon has been investigated. Most substitutions proceed with *inversion of configuration*, just as in carbon compounds. The system that has been most investigated is the methylnaphthylphenylsilyl series of compounds (Me = methyl; Ph = phenyl; Np = 1-naphthyl, see Chapter 30).

Ph Np
   Si   + KOH $\xrightarrow{\text{MeOH}}$
Me   OCCH$_3$
          ‖
          O

(*R*)-methylnaphthylphenyl
acetate

Ph Np
   Si
HO   Me

(*S*)-methylnaphthylphenylsilanol

However, nucleophilic substitution with *retention of configuration* is also known in organosilicon compounds. An example is seen in the following reaction of a cyclic silane.

CH$_3$ Cl
       Si $\xrightarrow{\text{LiAlH}_4}$
      CH$_3$

CH$_3$ H
       Si   (25-1)
      CH$_3$

The mechanism for the latter kind of substitution is one in which the incoming nucleophile adds to silicon, to give a stable trigonal bipyramid intermediate. On the basis of a large number of experiments, the following preference rules have been

worked out for substitution reactions that involve the intermediacy of such intermediates.

1. Nucleophiles enter, and leaving groups depart, from apical positions.
2. Electronegative substituents prefer apical positions.
3. Four- and five-membered rings must span one apical and one equatorial position.

In the substitution reaction shown in equation 25-1, the first rule tells us that the
incoming nucleophile (hydride) must initially occupy an apical position and rule 3 tells
us that one of the ring carbons must occupy the other apical position.

However, rule 1 also requires that the leaving chloride ion depart from an apical
position. Thus, the initial adduct exists until pseudorotation places Cl in an apical
position. The pivot for the pseudorotation is the methyl group; C-1 of silacyclobutane
ring becomes equatorial and C—3 becomes apical. Simultaneously, the apical hydrogen and equatorial chlorine switch roles. When the apical chloride ion leaves, the net
stereochemical result is retention of configuration—the two methyl groups on the
silacyclobutane ring are still trans.

EXERCISE 25.21   Consider a chiral silane $R^1R^2R^3SiCl$ that undergoes nucleophilic substitution by a mechanism involving *two* pseudorotation steps of an intermediate trigonal bipyramid intermediate. What is the expected stereochemistry of the process?

B. Electrophilic Cleavage of the Carbon-Silicon Bond

Organosilicon compounds owe a great deal of their special utility to the fact that the
carbon-silicon bond may be heterolytically cleaved with relative ease. For example,
arylsilanes react with a variety of electrophiles with net **electrophilic substitution** of
the silyl group.

790

Chap. 25

*Sulfur,
Phosphorus, and
Silicon
Compounds*

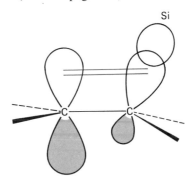

In both of the foregoing reactions the electrophile appears to defy the normal direct-ing effect of the groups attached to the benzene ring; reaction occurs *meta* to the methyl group and *para* to the carboxy group. In fact, these examples illustrate a strong propen-sity of the silyl group to direct the incoming electrophile to the position it occupies ("ipso attack"). The same property is shown by the silicon substituent in triethylsilyl-benzene, which undergoes protodesilylation 10^4 times faster than proton exchange in benzene.

The directing effect of the silicon stems from the fact that *silicon strongly stabilizes a cationic center β to it.* This stabilization results partly from the fact that silicon is relatively electropositive. However, part of the stabilization appears to result from a type of hyperconjugation of the empty *p*-orbital of the carbocation with the relatively diffuse carbon-silicon bond (see also page 180).

The ability of silicon to stabilize a β-carbocation is manifest also in the reactions of vinylsilanes. Although normal addition reactions do occur in some cases, electrophilic substitution is not uncommon.

Allylsilanes undergo ready electrophilic substitution with specific rearrangement of the double bond.

The mechanism of this reaction involves protonation of the double bond, with concommitant loss of the silicon. The cation-stabilizing effect of silicon is graphically illustrated in this example, since protonation produces a secondary, rather than a tertiary, carbocation.

Other electrophiles may also enter into the reaction. Again, specific rearrangement of the double bond occurs.

C. Silyl Ethers as Protecting Groups

Because the silicon-oxygen bond is easily formed by nucleophilic substitution on a silyl halide, and because it is easily hydrolyzed, silicon finds much use as a protecting group (Section 16.4). Several reagents are in general use for this purpose. The most

792

Chap. 25

*Sulfur,
Phosphorus, and
Silicon
Compounds*

common is trimethylsilyl chloride, which reacts with alcohols in the presence of a weak base such as triethylamine.

(90%)

After desired reaction or sequence of reactions has been carried out elsewhere in the molecule, the protecting group is easily removed by the use of dilute aqueous acid.

Another useful protecting group, which is more stable to some reaction conditions than the trimethylsilyl group, is *t*-butyldimethylsilyl. This group is normally introduced by treating the alcohol with a mixture of *t*-butyldimethylsilyl chloride and the heterocyclic base imidazole (Section 31.5).

(85%)

This example also demonstrates that primary hydroxy groups react more rapidly than secondary or tertiary ones. In most cases, selective protection of the less substituted hydroxy may be achieved.

Like trimethylsilyl ethers, the *t*-butyldimethylsilyl ethers may sometimes be hydrolyzed by dilute aqueous acid. However, a convenient alternative is cleavage by fluoride ion. Benzyltrimethylammonium fluoride, which is soluble in organic solvents, is frequently used for this purpose. The reaction is carried out in a solvent such as THF in the presence of a small amount of water.

EXERCISE 25.24 Illustrate the use of silyl protecting groups in the following transformations.

Explain why the protecting group is needed in each case.

PROBLEMS

1. Give the structure corresponding to each of the following names.
   (a) ethyl neopentyl sulfide
   (b) isobutyl mercaptan
   (c) 2-methylthiocyclopentanone
   (d) dibutyl disulfide
   (e) cyclohexanethiol
   (f) isobutylsulfuric acid
   (g) diethyl sulfate
   (h) methyl *p*-nitrobenzenesulfonate
   (i) tributyl phosphate
   (j) diethyl ethylphosphonate
   (k) cyclohexyl methanesulfonate
   (l) triphenyl phosphite
   (m) allyl pyrophosphate
   (n) trimethylpropylsilane
   (o) diphenylmethylsilyl chloride

2. Give the IUPAC name corresponding to each of the following structures.

(a)
$$
\overset{\displaystyle SH}{\underset{}{(CH_3)_2CHCH_2CHCH_3}}
$$

(b)
$$
(CH_3)_2CHCHCH_2CH_3 \\ \underset{SCH_3}{|}
$$

(c)
$\left(\ \right)_4$ P$^+$ Br$^-$

(d)
CH(CH$_3$)$_2$ ... SO$_2$NHCH$_3$

(e)
Br, COOCH$_2$C(CH$_3$)$_3$, SO$_2$OH

(f)
SO$_2$Cl ... NO$_2$

(g)
SO$_2$—CH$_3$ ... Br

(h)
—S—S—

(i) CH$_3$CH$_2$P̈(OEt)$_2$ with O double bond

(j)
SiMe$_3$

3. What is the expected product of each of the following reactions?

(a) *t*-BuO$^-$ K$^+$ + CH$_3$OSO$_2$OCH$_3$ $\xrightarrow[\Delta]{t\text{-BuOH}}$

(b) CH$_3$CH$_2$S$^+$(CH$_3$)$_2$ I$^-$ $\xrightarrow{\Delta}$

(c) (CH$_3$)$_3$CCH$_2$S$^+$(CH$_2$CH$_3$)$_2$ Br$^-$ $\xrightarrow{\Delta}$

(d)
$^+$S(CH$_2$CH$_3$)$_2$, CH$_3$, Cl$^-$ $\xrightarrow{\Delta}$

794

Chap. 25

Sulfur,
Phosphorus, and
Silicon
Compounds

(e) [structure: naphthalene with SO$_3$H group] $\xrightarrow[\text{fuse}]{\text{NaOH–KOH}}$

(f) $C_6H_5SO_2^- + C_6H_5CH_2Cl \longrightarrow$

(g) $HS(CH_2)_4SH \xrightarrow{I_2,\ KI}$

(h) $HS(CH_2)_3SH + $ [benzene ring]$-CHO \xrightarrow{HCl}$

(i) [structure: 1,3-dithiane with H,H] $\xrightarrow{n\text{-}C_4H_9Li} \xrightarrow{CH_3\overset{O}{\overset{\|}{C}}CH_3}$

(j) $(CH_3)_3S^+\ Br^- \xrightarrow{n\text{-}C_4H_9Li}$ [benzaldehyde structure with CHO] $\longrightarrow$

4. What is the expected product of each of the following reactions?

(a) $(CH_3CH_2CH_2CH_2O)_3P + CH_3CH_2CH_2CH_2Br \xrightarrow{200°C}$
$\qquad$ (trace)

(b) $CH_3CH_2CH_2\overset{O}{\overset{\|}{P}}(OCH_3)_2 + NaOH \xrightarrow[\Delta]{C_2H_5OH} \xrightarrow[\text{(workup)}]{H^+}$

(c) $(C_2H_5O)_2\overset{O}{\overset{\|}{P}}Cl + (CH_3)_2CHCH_2CH_2OH \longrightarrow$

(d) $POCl_3 + CH_3OH \text{ (excess)} \longrightarrow$

(e) $(C_6H_5)_3P + CH_2{=}CHCH_2Br \xrightarrow{\Delta}$

(f) $CH_3\overset{O}{\overset{\|}{P}}(OCH_3)_2 \xrightarrow{n\text{-}C_4H_9Li}$ [cyclohexanone structure] $\longrightarrow$

(g) $CH_3CH_2\overset{O}{\overset{\|}{P}}(OCH_3)_2 \xrightarrow{n\text{-}BuLi} \xrightarrow{CH_3CO_2CH_3}$

5. What is the expected product of each of the following reactions?

(a) [cyclohexene with CH$_2$SiMe$_3$ substituent] $+ Br_2 \xrightarrow[25°C]{CCl_4}$

(b) [structure] $\diagup\diagdown\diagup$SiMe$_3$ $+ DCl \xrightarrow[0°C]{CH_2Cl_2}$

(c) [benzene ring with two CH$_3$ groups and SiMe$_3$] $+ Cl_2 \xrightarrow{FeCl_3}$

(d)

(e)

6. To minimize the odor released by traces of mercaptans it is recommended that reaction vessels be rinsed with aqueous potassium permanganate as soon as possible. Nitric acid may also be used for this purpose. The thiols are oxidized to alkanesulfonic acids, and the sulfides are oxidized to sulfones. Write balanced equations for each of the following reactions.

(a) $CH_3SH + KMnO_4 \xrightarrow{H_2O} CH_3SO_3K + MnO_2 + KOH$

(b) $(CH_3)_2S + KMnO_4 \xrightarrow{H_2O} CH_3SO_2CH_3 + MnO_2 + KOH$

(c) $(CH_3)_2S + HNO_3 \longrightarrow CH_3SO_2CH_3 + H_2O + NO_2$

7. The following reaction sequences are impractical. Determine what is wrong in each case.

(a) $(CH_3)_3CO^- K^+ \xrightarrow{PCl_3} [(CH_3)_3CO]_3P \xrightarrow[200°C]{(CH_3)_3CBr} (CH_3)_3CP(OC(CH_3)_3)_2$

(b)

(c)

(d)

8. Show how to accomplish each of the following conversions in a practical manner.

(a) $(CH_3)_3CBr \longrightarrow (CH_3)_3CSCH_3$

(b) $CH_3CH_2CH_2CH_2OH \longrightarrow (CH_3CH_2CH_2CH_2)_2S_2$

(c)

796

Chap. 25
Sulfur,
Phosphorus, and
Silicon
Compounds

(d)

(e)

(f)

(g)

(h)

9. How may each of the following transformations be accomplished?

(a)

(b)

(c)

(d)

10. Mustard gas or bis(β-chloroethyl) sulfide, $(ClCH_2CH_2)_2S$, is an oily liquid that was used extensively as a poison gas in World War I. It is a deadly vesicant that causes blindness and numerous other effects. The active agent is actually the cyclic sulfonium salt.

This intermediate reacts with nucleophilic materials in the body. The formation of the cyclic sulfonium salt can be regarded as an intramolecular S_N2 reaction. Write out the reaction mechanism. What mechanism does this process suggest for the subsequent reaction of the cyclic sulfonium salt with nucleophilic reagents?

11. Thiols are used as inhibitors in free radical reactions. In such use they end up as disulfides. The bond-dissociation energy of CH_3S—H is 91 kcal mole^{-1}. Calculate $\Delta H°$ for the reaction of methane with the methylthio radical.

$$CH_4 + CH_3S \cdot \rightleftharpoons CH_3 \cdot + CH_3SH$$

In which direction does the equilibrium lie? Explain how CH_3SH works as an inhibitor.

12. Compare the relative acidities of benzenesulfonic acid with benzoic acid and of benzenesulfonamide with benzamide. Predict the relative acidities of acetophenone and phenyl methyl sulfone.

13. The normal phosphorus-oxygen single bond distance is about 1.60 Å. The dative phosphorus-oxygen bond as in phosphorus oxychloride and in phosphates is almost 0.2 Å shorter. What does this comparison imply about the relative bond strengths of the two types of phosphorus-oxygen bonds? The rearrangement of trimethyl phosphite to dimethyl methylphosphonate is exothermic by 47 kcal mole^{-1}. What do you think might be the principal driving force for this reaction?

14. The intermediate in base-catalyzed hydrolysis of phosphate and phosphonate esters is a pentacoordinated species similar to that involved in nucleophilic substitution of some silicon compounds. The three generalizations enumerated on page 789 also apply to these intermediates. In hydrolysis of the following cyclic phosphate esters, the six-membered compound undergoes hydrolysis of both methoxy and ring alkoxy bonds, but in the five-membered compound, only ring cleavage is observed. Explain.

15. One of the products of the reaction of sodium 3,5-dibromo-4-aminobenzenesulfonate with aqueous bromine is 2,4,6-tribromoaniline, the product of an ipso-substitution reaction. Write a reasonable reaction mechanism.

16. β-Keto sulfoxides react with aqueous acids or other acidic reagents to give α-hydroxy sulfides (**Pummerer rearrangement**).

Propose a mechanism for the Pummerer rearrangement. What product will result if such a β-keto sulfoxide is treated with acetic anhydride in pyridine?

798

Chap. 25

Sulfur,
Phosphorus, and
Silicon
Compounds

17. Suggest a general synthetic method whereby organosulfur chemistry could be used to convert saturated ketones and esters into their α,β-unsaturated counterparts.

18. Oxidation of diphenyl disulfide with hydrogen peroxide gives a dioxide that could be formulated as either a disulfoxide or as a thiosulfonic ester.

$$\underset{\text{a disulfoxide}}{C_6H_5\overset{\overset{O}{\|}}{S}-\overset{\overset{O}{\|}}{S}C_6H_5} \qquad \underset{\text{a thiosulfonic ester}}{C_6H_5S-\overset{\overset{O}{\|}}{\underset{\underset{O}{\|}}{S}}C_6H_5}$$

Based on thermodynamic analogies available in Appendix I, which formulation do you think is correct?

19. Oxidation of trithioformaldehyde gives a mixture of two bis-sulfoxides, A and B. Further oxidation of A with H_2O_2 gives a single tris-sulfoxide, C, whereas further oxidation of B gives a mixture of tris-sulfoxides, C and D. What are the structures of the bis-sulfoxides, A and B, and the tris-sulfoxides, C and D?

trithioformaldehyde

20. Show how 1-trimethylsilyl-1,3-butadiene can be used to synthesize the following compounds.

(a)   (b)

21. Treatment of α-trimethylsilylbenzyl alcohol with alcoholic potassium hydroxide gives benzyltrimethylsilane (**Brook rearrangement**). Propose a mechanism for the rearrangement.

Rationalize the fact that, when the Brook rearrangement is carried out with a chiral substrate in which silicon is a stereocenter, retention of configuration at silicon is observed.

Chapter 26

Aromatic Halides, Phenols, Phenyl Ethers, and Quinones

26.1 Introduction

When halogen is in the side chain of an alkyl-substituted benzene, the chemistry is essentially the same as for any alkyl halide. As we saw in Section 20.5, enhanced reactivity is seen in the displacement and carbocation reactions of benzylic halides, since the phenyl group stabilizes either an S_N2 transition state or a cationic center to which it is directly attached. Side-chain halides are prepared by methods analogous to those used for the preparation of normal alkyl halides, mainly from corresponding alcohols (Section 10.6.B). Recall that free radical halogenation is especially useful for preparation of benzylic halides (Section 20.5.A).

When halogen is attached directly to the benzene ring, there is some special chemistry, in regard to both preparations and reactions, that is different from the normal chemistry of alkyl halides. We shall take up these unique reactions pertaining to aryl halides in Sections 26.2 and 26.3. Since several of the important reactions of aryl halides give rise to phenols, it is convenient to study that important family of organic compounds next, and we shall do so in Sections 26.4-26.7. Finally, we shall take up the quinones in Section 26.8, since the chemistry of this class of compounds is intimately associated with the chemistry of phenols.

26.2 Preparation of Halobenzenes

One important preparation of ring halides is by electrophilic aromatic substitution (Section 22.1). The active reagent in these reactions is an actual or incipient halonium ion. For suitably activated rings the halogen alone may be used as the reagent.

mesitylene   bromomesitylene
(79–82%)

For less reactive rings a Lewis acid such as a ferric salt is used to catalyze the reaction.

800

Chap. 26

*Aromatic
Halides,
Phenols, Phenyl
Ethers, and
Quinones*

In general, direct electrophilic aromatic substitution is only used as a method for synthesis of halobenzenes in cases where the reaction gives essentially a single product. This is usually the case when the benzene ring contains a *meta*-directing group or when the structure of the starting material is such that only a single product can be produced. Thus bromination of *p*-nitrotoluene gives only one product.

When the ring contains a single *ortho,para*-directing group, a mixture of products generally results. If the group is very large, as in the case of *t*-butyl, the amount of *ortho* product is small, and the *para*-disubstituted product may be obtained in good yield.

(94%)

However, in most such cases direct halogenation gives a mixture of isomeric products that is difficult to separate. For example, bromination of toluene gives a mixture consisting of 65% *p*-bromotoluene and 35% *o*-bromotoluene.

(65%)   (35%)

It is in situations like this that arenediazonium salts are useful (Section 24.5). For example, although the *ortho* and *para* isomers of bromotoluene cannot easily be separated by distillation, the nitrotoluenes are readily separated by this method (see Table 22.5, page 674). Since toluene is an inexpensive starting material, direct nitration followed by fractional distillation represents an economical method for the preparation of both the *ortho* and *para* isomers.

(55%)   (45%)
b.p. 238°C   b.p. 220°C

Both isomers may be converted into the corresponding bromotoluenes by reduction of nitro to amino (Section 23.6.C), followed by Sandmeyer reaction (Section 24.5.C). For example, p-aminotoluene

The foregoing example illustrates the indirect replacement of a nitro group by halogen via the diazonium group. However, arenediazonium chemistry may also be utilized in another way. For example, bromination of *p*-acetamidotoluene followed by hydrolysis of the protecting group affords 4-amino-3-bromotoluene in good purity, since the acetamido function is a more powerful *ortho,para*-directing group than is methyl (Section 22.8). Diazotization of this product, followed by reduction of the arenediazonium salt with hypophosphorous acid, affords *m*-bromotoluene.

EXERCISE 26.1   Write equations illustrating the preparation of the three chlorobromobenzenes starting with benzene.

26.3 Reactions of Halobenzenes

A. Nucleophilic Aromatic Substitution: The Addition-Elimination Mechanism

The halogen of an aryl halide can be replaced by other nucleophiles. However, such substitution reactions do *not* occur by the S_N2 mechanism. Like vinyl halides (Section 12.7), aryl halides cannot achieve the geometry necessary for a backside displacement; the ring shields the rear of the carbon-halogen bond.

Instead, nucleophilic substitution occurs by two other mechanisms, **addition-elimination** and **elimination-addition**.

Aryl halides that have electron-attracting groups in positions *ortho* and *para* to the halogen undergo substitution under rather mild conditions. The most effective groups are nitro and carbonyl.

o-nitrochlorobenzene   *o*-nitrophenol

802

Chap. 26

*Aromatic
Halides,
Phenols, Phenyl
Ethers, and
Quinones*

p-nitrochlorobenzene   p-nitroanisole

With two nitro groups in conjugating positions, this type of displacement reaction is quite facile:

2,4-dinitrophenylhydrazine

2,4-Dinitrophenylhydrazine is a common reagent used for preparing the corresponding 2,4-dinitrophenylhydrazone derivatives of aldehydes and ketones (Section 14.7.C). These derivatives are usually crystalline compounds with well-defined melting points and are useful for characterizing aldehydes and ketones; the 2,4-dinitrophenylhydrazones are commonly abbreviated as DNPs.

The mechanism of these substitution reactions involves two steps, an addition followed by an elimination. It is analogous to the nucleophilic addition-elimination mechanism so prevalent in the chemistry of carboxylic acids and derivatives of carboxylic acids (Chapter 18).

In the first step the attacking nucleophile adds to the benzene ring to give a resonance-stabilized pentadienyl anion.

The pentadienyl anion can eject the nucleophile, regenerating the reactants, or it can eject halide ion, giving the substitution product.

However, even a conjugated pentadienyl anion is not sufficiently stable for this mechanism to operate with such simple aryl halides as chlorobenzene or *o*-bromotoluene. Electron-attracting groups provide further resonance stabilization of the anion, thus lowering its energy enough for it to be formed as a reaction intermediate. As the foregoing resonance structures show, the nitro or carbonyl groups are most effective when they are *ortho* or *para* to the leaving group.

EXERCISE 26.2   Write equations illustrating the conversion of chlorobenzene to *p*-methoxyaniline.

B. Nucleophilic Aromatic Substitution: The Elimination-Addition Mechanism

After the foregoing discussion it may seem surprising that one commercial preparation of phenol involves heating chlorobenzene itself with aqueous sodium hydroxide.

However, this reaction is not a simple displacement of chloride by hydroxide. For example, *o*-chlorotoluene gives not only *o*-methylphenol in this reaction but also *m*-methylphenol.

An analogous reaction occurs under milder conditions with amide ion in liquid ammonia.

804

Chap. 26

*Aromatic
Halides,
Phenols, Phenyl
Ethers, and
Quinones*

The remarkable feature of these reactions is that the entering group substitutes not only at the position of the displaced halide but also at the ring position adjacent to the original halide. Even iodobenzene shows this behavior, as has been demonstrated using ^{14}C-labeled materials.

These results are rationalized by the involvement as a reactive intermediate or the product of an elimination reaction—dehydrobenzene or "benzyne."

"benzyne"

The detailed mechanism involves a series of steps. Benzene itself is a weak acid, but its pK_a of 43 corresponds to a much higher acidity than the alkanes (pK_as $\cong$ 50). The close proximity of an electronegative halogen renders an adjacent hydrogen sufficiently acidic that it is removed by a strong base such as NH_2^-.

The intermediate iodophenyl anion can itself pick up a proton to regenerate the original iodobenzene, or it can lose iodide ion.

The driving force for this reaction is the formation of a stable halide ion. The "benzyne" generated is a very reactive intermediate. The "triple bond" in benzyne is highly strained. Recall that the two carbons in acetylene are *sp*-hybridized and that the H—C—C angles are 180°. That is, the two carbons of an alkyne as well as the two atoms directly attached to the triple bond comprise a linear array. For geometric reasons this is impossible when the triple bond is in a small ring. In fact, the smallest stable cycloalkyne is cyclooctyne, and even it is less stable than acyclic alkynes. Nevertheless, benzyne does form as a transient reaction intermediate. It has even been detected spectroscopically by using special techniques. The electronic structure of benzyne may be visualized readily as a distorted acetylene. A triple bond has two π-bonds, as shown in Figure 26.1. One π-bond is constructed from *p*-orbitals perpendicular to the plane of the paper (dotted line in Figure 26.1); the other π-bond derives from overlap of *p*-orbitals in the plane of the page, as illustrated. When the triple bond is distorted from linearity, one π-bond is essentially unchanged, but the other π-bond now involves hybrid orbitals directed away from each other with consequent reduced overlap. Reduced overlap means a weaker and more reactive bond. Benzyne is related in this sense to the distorted acetylenes. The two orbitals shown in Figure 26.1 provide inefficient overlap and a weak, reactive bond. The resulting strained triple bond reacts readily with any available nucleophilic reagent at either end of the triple bond.

Benzyne may also be generated by decomposition of the diazonium salt produced by diazotization of anthranilic acid. The diazonium compound is an inner salt and is insoluble. The dry salt will detonate and must be kept moist and handled with care. The controlled decomposition in ethylene chloride provides the unusual strained hydrocarbon, biphenylene.

In this preparation, no nucleophilic reagent is present to react with the benzyne, and therefore dimerization occurs to a significant extent.

FIGURE 26.1 Electronic structure of benzyne.

806

Chap. 26

*Aromatic
Halides,
Phenols, Phenyl
Ethers, and
Quinones*

EXERCISE 26.3 What products are produced by treatment of *o*-, *m*-, and *p*-bromotoluene with KNH_2 in liquid NH_3?

C. Metallation

Aryl bromides form Grignard reagents in a normal fashion, and these derivatives undergo all the usual reactions of Grignard reagents; they react with aldehydes and ketones, CO_2, D_2O, and so on.

However, aryl chlorides do not react with magnesium in ether. Consequently a bromochlorobenzene may be converted into a chloro-Grignard reagent.

m-chlorophenylmagnesium
bromide

(82–88%)
1-(*m*-chlorophenyl)ethanol

Grignard reagents *can* be produced from aryl chlorides by using tetrahydrofuran (THF) as the solvent.

Of course, the formation of the Grignard reagent is successful only if no functional group is present that will react with such reagents: examples of such reactive groups are NO_2, NO, COR, SO_3R, CN, OH, and NH_2.

Aryllithium reagents may be prepared from lithium metal and the aryl chloride or bromide.

The lithium reagents generally undergo the same reactions as the Grignard reagents. Furthermore, aryllithiums can be prepared by **transmetallation** of an aryl bromide or iodide with an alkyllithium.

(85%)

With aryl bromides or iodides the reaction is rapid, even at low temperature. The reaction may be regarded as a displacement reaction on halogen to form the lithium salt of a more stable anion.

$$ArX + R^- Li^+ \longrightarrow Ar^- Li^+ + RX$$

Transmetallation is most successful with aromatic bromides and iodides; aryl chlorides do not react as cleanly or rapidly.

When a mixture of an alkyl halide and an aryl halide is treated with sodium in ether, coupling occurs to give the arylalkane. The reaction, known as the **Wurtz-Fittig** reaction, is sometimes an excellent preparative method.

$$C_6H_5Br + CH_3(CH_2)_3CH_2Br + 2\,Na \xrightarrow[20°C]{ether} C_6H_5(CH_2)_4CH_3 + 2\,NaBr$$
$$(65-70\%)$$

In this reaction the sodium reacts first with the aryl bromide to form the arylsodium which then reacts with the alkyl bromide by the S_N2 mechanism.

$$ArBr + 2\,Na \longrightarrow ArNa + NaBr$$
$$ArNa + RX \longrightarrow ArR + NaX$$

Under the proper conditions, the yields are quite good. Like all organometallic reactions, the Wurtz-Fittig reaction is only applicable to compounds not having highly reactive functional groups (hydroxy, carbonyl, nitro, and so on).

A reaction that is superficially related to the Wurtz-Fittig reaction is the **Ullmann** reaction, in which two molecules of an aryl halide are coupled by heating with copper powder. The product is a **biaryl**, a compound in which two benzene rings are joined together.

2,2'-dinitrobiphenyl

The chemistry of biaryls will be detailed in a subsequent chapter (Chapter 30). The Ullmann reaction works well with chlorides, bromides, and iodides and is facilitated by electron-attracting groups such as NO_2 and CN functions. The reaction involves the formation of an arylcopper intermediate that undergoes a free-radical-like coupling, probably while still coordinated to copper.

A method of coupling aryl halides that is complementary to the Ullmann reaction involves formation of the diarylcuprate (Section 8.8), which is oxidized by oxygen at low temperature.

lithium diphenylcuprate   biphenyl (75%)

The cuprate method avoids the high temperatures of the Ullmann reaction, but it is only applicable with arenes not having functional groups that react with the aryllithium intermediate.

808

Chap. 26

*Aromatic
Halides,
Phenols, Phenyl
Ethers, and
Quinones*

EXERCISE 26.4 Show how *p*-bromotoluene may be converted into *p*-toluic acid (page 572), 4,4′-dimethylbiphenyl, and 4-*n*-propyltoluene.

26.4 Nomenclature of Phenols and Phenyl Ethers

Compounds having a hydroxy group directly attached to a benzene ring are called **phenols**. The term phenol is also used for the parent compound, hydroxybenzene. Hydroxybenzene may be regarded as an enol (Section 14.6), as implied by the name phenol, from **ph**enyl + **enol**. However, unlike simple ketones, which are far more stable than their corresponding enols, the analogous equilibrium for phenol lies far on the side of the enol form. The reason for this difference is the resonance energy of the aromatic ring, which provides an important stabilization of the enol form.

$$CH_3-\overset{\overset{\displaystyle O}{\|}}{C}-CH_3 \; \rightleftharpoons \; CH_3-\overset{\overset{\displaystyle OH}{|}}{C}=CH_2 \qquad \Delta H° \cong +14 \text{ kcal mol}^{-1}$$

$$\Delta H° \cong -16 \text{ kcal mol}^{-1}$$

cyclohexa-2,4-dien-1-one   phenol

Since the functional group occurs as a suffix in phen**ol**, many compounds containing an aromatic hydroxy group are named as derivatives of the parent compound phenol, as illustrated by the following IUPAC names. Although *Chemical Abstracts* utilizes the IUPAC-approved name phenol for the parent compound, substituted phenols are indexed as derivatives of **benzenol**. The *Chemical Abstracts* names are given in brackets for the following compounds. We shall not use the name benzenol in this text.

m-bromophenol   *p-t*-butylphenol   2,4-dinitrophenol
[3-bromobenzenol]   [4-(1,1-dimethylethyl)benzenol]   [2,4-dinitrobenzenol]

Suffix groups such as sulfonic acid and carboxylic acid take priority, and when these groups are present, the hydroxy group is used as a modifying prefix.

p-hydroxybenzoic acid   *m*-hydroxybenzaldehyde   2,4-dihydroxybenzene-
                                                          sulfonic acid

Phenyl ethers are named in the IUPAC system as alkoxyarenes, although the "ether" nomenclature is used for some compounds.

t-butoxybenzene   *p*-benzyloxytoluene   phenyl ether

Phenols and their ethers are widespread in nature, and, as is usual for such compounds, trivial names abound. Many of these names are in such common use that they should be learned.

anisole
methoxybenzene

phenetole
ethoxybenzene

o-cresol
o-methylphenol

catechol
o-dihydroxybenzene

resorcinol
m-dihydroxybenzene

hydroquinone
p-dihydroxybenzene

picric acid
2,4,6-trinitrophenol

salicylic acid
o-hydroxybenzoic acid

guaiacol
o-methoxyphenol

Note that compounds with more than one hydroxy group are named with the hydroxy prefix. Terms such as "phen-diol" or "benzene-triol" are not used.

More complex examples of naturally occuring phenols are urushiols and lignins.

a urushiol

Urushiols are the active constituents of the allergenic oils of poison ivy, sumac, and oak. They are C-3 alkylated catechols in which the side chain can be saturated or can contain up to three double bonds. In poison ivy and poison sumac the side chain contains 15 carbons; in poison oak it contains 17 carbons.

Lignins are complex natural products that occur together with cellulose in the "woody" part of plants such as shrubs and trees. Because lignins are high molecular weight polymers, their exact structures are not known. They are composed of three basic building blocks: coniferyl alcohol, sinapyl alcohol, and p-coumaryl alcohol.

coniferyl alcohol   sinapyl alcohol   p-coumaryl alcohol

Different plants apparently have lignins of different composition. Guaiacyl lignins are derived mainly from coniferyl alcohol. Guaiacyl-syringyl lignins are also derived principally from coniferyl alcohol, but contain significant amounts of sinapyl alcohol. p-Coumaryl alcohol is a minor constituent (1-5%) of all lignins. The actual polymeric structures of the lignins contain a variety of types of linkages between the phenolic monomers and to cellulose units in the wood.

26.5 Preparation and Properties of Phenols and Ethers

Phenols are generally crystalline compounds with distinctive odors. Phenol itself melts at 40.9°C, but is often found to be semiliquid because of the presence of water, which lowers the melting point; it is completely liquefied by the addition of 8% of water. It is soluble to the extent of 6.7 g per 100 mL of cold water and is totally miscible with hot water. The lower alkylphenols are sparingly soluble in water; for example, o-cresol dissolves to the extent of 2.5 g per 100 mL of water at 25°C. Phenol and the cresols are widely used in commercial disinfectants. Phenol turns pink on exposure to air because of oxidation. The sensitivity of phenols to air oxidation is enhanced by the presence of more than one hydroxy group and by alkali. The oxidation of phenols to quinones will be discussed in Section 26.8.B. Phenols are sufficiently acidic that they are caustic toward flesh and are poisonous.

The lower phenyl ethers are liquids; for example, anisole boils at 154°C. Unlike phenols, the ethers are essentially insoluble in water. They lack the hydroxy group of phenol, which can hydrogen bond to water oxygens. The ether oxygens have relatively low basicity and form only weak hydrogen bonds to water hydrogens. The low basicity of the oxygens of phenyl ethers compared to aliphatic ethers stems from conjugation of a lone pair with the aromatic ring. The same phenomenon is responsible for the reduced basicity of aromatic amines compared to aliphatic amines.

Aryl ethers are also more stable to oxidation than phenols.

811

Sec. 26.5
Preparation and
Properties of
Phenols and
Ethers

A. Preparation of Phenols

All of the important preparations of phenols involve reactions that have already been discussed. Fusion of arenesulfonic acids with alkali hydroxide is an excellent method in cases where sulfonation gives a good yield of sulfonic acid and no base-sensitive functional group is present (Section 25.5).

$$Ar SO_3^- \xrightarrow[\Delta]{NaOH} ArO^- \xrightarrow{H^+} ArOH$$

The hydrolysis of haloarenes with alkali at high temperature is a commercial preparation, but is not suitable for general laboratory use because of the involvement of benzyne intermediates and the formation of mixtures of isomeric phenols (Section 26.3.A).

$$ArCl \xrightarrow[\Delta]{NaOH} ArO^- \xrightarrow{H^+} ArOH$$

On the other hand, compounds in which the halogen is *ortho* or *para* to strongly electron-attracting groups, such as nitro groups, undergo hydrolysis by the addition-elimination mechanism to give phenols in good yield (Section 26.3.A). The hydrolysis of arenediazonium salts is a good route to many phenols and has been discussed in Section 24.5.B.

$$ArN_2^+ \xrightarrow[\Delta]{H_2O} ArOH + H_3O^+ + N_2$$

An important industrial preparation of phenol involves the oxidation of cumene, an inexpensive hydrocarbon that may be prepared by alkylation of benzene (Section 22.4.B).

cumene

Cumene is air-oxidized to obtain cumene hydroperoxide.

cumene hydroperoxide

The oxidation is a typical free radical chain process. It is especially facile because the intermediate cumyl radical is tertiary and benzylic.

812

Chap. 26

*Aromatic
Halides,
Phenols, Phenyl
Ethers, and
Quinones*

propagation
steps

The cumene hydroperoxide is treated with sulfuric acid to obtain phenol and acetone.

This interesting fragmentation is related to the Baeyer-Villiger oxidation (page 399).

EXERCISE 26.5   Write a mechanism for the reaction of cumene hydroperoxide with sulfuric acid.

The cumene process is a good example of the economics of industrial organic synthesis. It owes its economic feasibility in part to the fact that *two* important commercial products are formed. Note that in the overall process from benzene and propene to phenol and acetone the only reagent that is consumed is oxygen. In fact, the overall process amounts to a circuitous oxidation of both starting hydrocarbons. The sulfuric acid that is used both in the alkylation and in decomposition of the hydroperoxide is recycled.

EXERCISE 26.6   Write equations illustrating four ways by which benzene may be converted into phenol.

B. Acidity of Phenols

Phenol has $pK_a = 10.00$. The pK_as of some substituted phenols are summarized in Table 26.1; most values are in the range from 8 to 10.

$$K_a = 1.0 \times 10^{-10} \; M \qquad pK_a = 10.00$$

Phenols are generally several orders of magnitude less acidic than carboxylic acids, but are far more acidic than alcohols. If we recall that the value of the pK_a corresponds to that pH at which the conjugate acid and base are in equal concentrations, pK_as of 8-10 imply that phenols will dissolve in dilute alkali hydroxide solutions (pH 12-14); how-

813

Sec. 26.5

*Preparation and
Properties of
Phenols and
Ethers*

TABLE 26.1 Acidities of Phenols

Substituent	pK_a (25°C)		
	ortho	*meta*	*para*
H	10.00	10.00	10.00
methyl	10.29	10.09	10.26
fluoro	8.81	9.28	9.81
chloro	8.48	9.02	9.38
bromo	8.42	8.87	9.26
iodo	8.46	8.88	9.20
methoxy	9.98	9.65	10.21
methylthio		9.53	9.53
cyano			7.95
nitro	7.22	8.39	7.15

ever, water-insoluble phenols will not dissolve in aqueous sodium bicarbonate (pH ≅ 6-7). Carboxylic acids dissolve in aqueous bicarbonate.

Table 26.1 shows the expected effect of substitution on acidity. Electron-donating groups on the ring are acid weakening. Halogens increase acidity, and strongly electron-attracting groups such as cyano and nitro have pronounced acid-strengthening effects. With these substituents, the negative charge in the anion can be delocalized onto the oxygen or nitrogen of the substituent.

Note that a nitro group is more acid strengthening when it is *ortho* or *para* to the hydroxy group. Dinitrophenols are comparable to carboxylic acids in acidity; for example, the pK_a of 2,4-dinitrophenol is 4.09. Picric acid, 2,4,6-trinitrophenol, has pK_a = 0.25 and is a rather strong acid, comparable to trifluoroacetic acid.

EXERCISE 26.7 Using graph paper, plot the pK_as of phenols from Table 26.1 versus the pK_as of the corresponding anilinium ions from Table 23.5. Explain the result.

EXERCISE 26.8 Calculate the pH of a 0.1 *M* solution of phenol in water. What is the pH of a solution containing 0.1 *M* phenol and 0.1 *M* sodium phenolate?

C. Preparation of Ethers

Alkyl phenyl ethers can be prepared by the Williamson synthesis—the S$_N$2 reaction of phenoxide ions with alkyl halides. As is usually the case with S$_N$2 reactions, this preparation works best for primary halides and is least successful with tertiary halides. The reaction can be carried out in water, acetone, dimethylformamide, or even alco-

814

Chap. 26

Aromatic
Halides,
Phenols, Phenyl
Ethers, and
Quinones

hol. Because of the great difference in acidities of alcohols and phenols, the following equilibrium lies far to the left.

$$ArO^- + ROH \rightleftharpoons ArOH + RO^-$$

Thus, reaction of the alkyl halide with alkoxide ion is not an important side reaction. An example of the preparation of an aryl ethers is the formation of 1-bromo-3-phenoxypropane from phenol and 1,3-dibromopropane.

(84–85%)
1-bromo-3-phenoxypropane

For the preparation of aryl methyl ethers, dimethyl sulfate is especially convenient.

(72–75%)

Ethers can also be prepared by nucleophilic aromatic substitution in suitable cases (see Section 26.3.A).

2,4-dinitroanisole

EXERCISE 26.9 Write an equation illustrating the synthesis of allyl phenyl ether, $C_6H_5OCH_2CH{=}CH_2$.

26.6 Reactions of Phenolate Ions

Phenolate ions may be considered as enolate ions, and many of the reactions of phenolate ions point up this relationship. It is convenient to distinguish such reactions from those of the conjugate acids, the phenols. Many of the reactions of phenols resemble those of the corresponding ethers and may be considered together.

A. Halogenation

The reaction of an aqueous solution of phenol with bromine gives a precipitate of 2,4,4,6-tetrabromocyclohexa-2,5-dienone. This precipitate is normally washed with aqueous sodium bisulfite to generate 2,4,6-tribromophenol. The reactive form of phenol in this process is the phenolate ion. As successive bromines are introduced into the ring, the products are progressively more acidic, and a greater fraction of the phenol is present in the phenolate form. Thus each bromine is attacked more rapidly than the previous one, until the product is no longer a phenol. The overall process is similar to the bromination of a ketone under basic conditions (Section 14.6.D).

precipitates

Corresponding reactions occur with chlorine and iodine and with other phenols. The net reaction is halogenation of all available *ortho* and *para* positions. Halogenation of phenol is possible under acid conditions, and the incorporation of successive halogens can be controlled (Section 26.7.B). Here also we see an analogy to the acid-catalyzed, as well as the base-catalyzed, halogenation of carbonyl compounds (Section 14.6.D).

B. Addition to Aldehydes

A characteristic reaction of enolate ions from aldehydes and ketones is the condensation with other carbonyl groups as in the aldol addition reaction (Section 14.8.C). A similar reaction occurs with phenolate ions. Phenol reacts with formaldehyde in the presence of dilute alkali to give a mixture of *o*- and *p*-hydroxybenzyl alcohols.

The reaction is difficult to control because of further condensations that lead to a polymeric product.

816

Chap. 26

*Aromatic
Halides,
Phenols, Phenyl
Ethers, and
Quinones*

Under proper conditions the final product is a dark, brittle, crosslinked polymer known as Bakelite, one of the oldest commercial plastics. The general class of such polymers is called phenol-formaldehyde resins.

EXERCISE 26.10 Draw the structure of a portion of the resin derived from phenol and formaldehyde.

C. Kolbe Synthesis

The reaction of carbanions with carbon dioxide to give carboxylate salts (Section 17.6.B) has its counterpart in the reaction of phenolate ions with CO_2.

The reaction of phenols with carbon dioxide under basic conditions is called the **Kolbe synthesis**. The product depends on the manner in which the reaction is carried out. Carbonation of sodium phenolate at relatively low temperature gives sodium salicylate. However, the reaction is reversible, and best yields are obtained only if carried out under pressure.

Under more severe conditions isomerization to the more stable *para* isomer occurs. Thus potassium salicylate smoothly isomerizes to the *para* isomer at 240°C.

potassium salicylate   potassium *p*-hydroxy-
benzoate

Although the Kolbe synthesis may be written simply as the enolate condensation of phenolate ion with carbon dioxide it is clear that coordination phenomena are involved. However, these mechanistic details are not yet fully understood.

D. Reimer-Tiemann Reaction

The **Reimer-Tiemann** reaction is the reaction of a phenol with chloroform in basic solution to give a hydroxybenzaldehyde. Reaction occurs primarily in an *ortho* position unless both are blocked. The reaction mechanism involves the prior formation of dichlorocarbene by the reaction of chloroform with alkali (page 269).

$$CHCl_3 + OH^- \rightleftharpoons \; ^-:CCl_3 \longrightarrow \quad :CCl_2$$
dichlorocarbene

The dichlorocarbene then reacts with the phenolate ion to give a dichloromethyl compound, which rapidly hydrolyzes.

The final hydrolysis reaction is facilitated by the phenoxide ion in the following way.

The essential correctness of the overall mechanism is revealed by an interesting by-product of the Reimer-Tiemann reaction on *p*-cresol.

2-hydroxy-5-methyl-
benzaldehyde   4-methyl-4-dichloromethyl-
cyclohex-2,5-dienone
(5%)

818

Chap. 26

*Aromatic
Halides,
Phenols, Phenyl
Ethers, and
Quinones*

EXERCISE 26.11   In the foregoing reaction explain why the dichloromethyl group is hydrolyzed to form an aldehyde group in the principal product but remains as a dichloromethyl group in the minor product.

E. Diazonium Coupling

Phenols react in basic solution with diazonium salts to give the corresponding arylazophenols. The reaction is an electrophilic aromatic substitution reaction by a weak electrophile, the diazonium ion, on an aromatic ring that is highly activated by the oxide anion.

p-phenylazophenol

The product is almost exclusively the *para* isomer; the *ortho* isomer is formed to the extent of only 1%. Arylazophenols constitute an important class of azo dyes. Further examples will be discussed in Section 34.3.

Resorcin Yellow
(silk and leather dye)

EXERCISE 26.12   Write equations showing the reactions (if any) of *o*-cresol with the following reagents.
(a) aqueous NaHCO$_3$ (b) (i) Br$_2$-H$_2$O; (ii) NaHSO$_3$ (c) KOH, CHCl$_3$
(d) NaOH, CO$_2$, 150°C   (e) aqueous NaOH; C$_6$H$_5$N$_2$$^+$ Cl$^-$

26.7 Reactions of Phenols and Ethers

A. Esterification

Phenols can be converted to esters but *not* generally by direct reaction with carboxylic acids. Although the esterification equilibrium is exothermic for alcohols, it is slightly endothermic for phenols, as shown by the following gas phase enthalpies of reaction.

$$C_6H_5OH + CH_3COOH \rightleftharpoons C_6H_5OOCCH_3 + H_2O \qquad \Delta H^\circ = +1.5 \text{ kcal mole}^{-1}$$

$$C_2H_5OH + CH_3COOH \rightleftharpoons C_2H_5OOCCH_3 + H_2O \qquad \Delta H^\circ = -4.6 \text{ kcal mole}^{-1}$$

Aryl esters *can* be prepared by allowing the phenol to react with an acid chloride or anhydride under basic or acid catalysis.

phenyl benzoate

One of the best-known aromatic acetates is acetylsalicylic acid, or aspirin, which is prepared by the acetylation of salicylic acid.

salicylic acid
o-hydroxybenzoic acid

aspirin
acetylsalicylic acid
o-acetoxybenzoic acid

Aspirin is widely used, primarily for its analgesic effect but also as an antipyretic and antirheumatic. It is not so innocuous a drug as one might imagine from its widespread use and ready availability. Excessive use may cause gastrointestinal bleeding, and large doses can provoke a host of reactions including vomiting, diarrhea, vertigo, and hallucinations. The average dose is 0.3–1 g; single doses of 10–30 g can be fatal.

B. Electrophilic Substitutions on Phenols and Phenyl Ethers

In acidic solutions electrophilic substitutions occur on the nonionized phenol. Such substitutions are still rather facile because of the activating nature of the hydroxy group, which is a strong *ortho,para* director. Reaction at one of these positions gives an intermediate cation that is essentially a protonated ketone.

The last structure shows the role of an oxygen lone pair in stabilizing the intermediate and the transition state leading to it. Exactly the same phenomenon applies to the aromatic ethers; that is, alkoxy groups are also powerful *ortho,para* directors. Consequently, for many electrophilic aromatic substitution reactions, phenols and ethers can be considered together. The principal difference between the two groups of compounds lies in the greater water solubility of the phenols. Many electrophilic reactions of phenols can be carried out in aqueous solutions.

819

820

Chap. 26

*Aromatic
Halides,
Phenols, Phenyl
Ethers, and
Quinones*

The phenol ring is sufficiently reactive that reaction occurs readily even with such feeble electrophiles as nitrous acid. Nitrosation is usually carried out in aqueous solution or in acetic acid; the principal product is the *p*-nitrosophenol.

15 : 1

p-nitrosophenol   *o*-nitrosophenol

Phenol is nitrated by dilute aqueous nitric acid, even at room temperature. Nitration of phenol also yields large amounts of tarry by-products produced by oxidation of the ring. Nevertheless, nitration is a satisfactory method for preparing both *o*- and *p*-nitrophenol because the isomers can be readily separated and purified.

(30–40%)   (15%)
o-nitrophenol   *p*-nitrophenol

o-Nitrophenol has lower solubility and higher volatility because of the **chelation** or intramolecular hydrogen bonding between the hydroxy group and the nitro group. Chelation (Gk., *chele*, claw) refers to formation of a ring by coordination with a pair of electrons.

Because the acceptor hydrogen of *o*-nitrophenol is involved in chelation, it is not available for hydrogen bonding to solvent water molecules. The resulting lower solubility and higher volatility are such that *o*-nitrophenol can be steam-distilled from the reaction mixture. The *o*- and *p*-nitrophenols are also available by hydrolysis of *o*- and *p*-chloronitrobenzenes (Section 26.3.A).

2,4-Dinitrophenol can be prepared by dinitration of phenol, using somewhat stronger nitric acid than is used for mononitration. However, a more convenient preparation of this phenol involves dinitration of chlorobenzene and hydrolysis of the resulting 2,4-dinitrochlorobenzene (page 802).

Picric acid, 2,4,6-trinitrophenol, is prepared by treating phenol with concentrated sulfuric acid at 100°C, followed by nitric acid, first in an ice bath, then at higher temperature. The first reaction that occurs in this sequence is disulfonation of the ring to give 4-hydroxybenzene-1,3-disulfonic acid. This substance is nitrated at the remaining *ortho* position by cold nitric acid. At higher temperature, sulfonic acid groups are replaced by nitro groups.

4-hydroxybenzene-
1,3-disulfonic acid

(90%)
picric acid

The reaction in which a sulfonic acid group is replaced by a nitro group is not uncommon in electrophilic aromatic substitutions but occurs more often as a side reaction rather than the main reaction. The mechanism is exactly the same as for substitution of a proton, except that a different cation is lost.

The reaction is best when strong *ortho,para*-directing groups such as OR and NR_2 are present and with functions that form relatively stable electrophilic molecules. The sulfonic acid group is prone to such replacement because it is lost as a neutral molecule, SO_3.

We have previously seen examples of such *ipso*-substitutions in some reactions of aryl silicon compounds (pages 789–90).

Picric acid forms yellow crystals, m.p. 123°C. It explodes at temperatures above 300°C and was once used as a synthetic dye. It is now important principally because of the molecular complexes it forms with many compounds, especially with polycyclic aromatic hydrocarbons and their derivatives. These complexes are of the "charge-transfer" type to be discussed in Section 26.8.D. Such picric acid complexes are called picrates. They can be crystallized and are useful for purification purposes. On treatment with base, the picric acid component is converted to the picrate ion, which does not form complexes; thus the other component of the complex is readily recovered.

Anisole is readily nitrated to give a mixture of *o-* and *p*-nitroanisole. These compounds are also available from the corresponding chloronitrobenzenes by substitution with methoxide ion (Section 26.3.A).

Monosulfonation of phenol gives an equimolar mixture of *ortho* and *para* substitution products if the reaction is carried out at room temperature, but predominantly *p*-hydroxybenzenesulfonic acid if steam-bath temperature is used. The behavior is typical for sulfonation reactions and is due to the easy reversibility of sulfonation (Section 25.5).

822

Chap. 26

*Aromatic
Halides,
Phenols, Phenyl
Ethers, and
Quinones*

20°C	(49%)	(51%)
100°C	(10%)	(90%)

With concentrated sulfuric acid the disulfonic acid is formed. This product can be isolated as the sodium salt or can be used directly for further reactions as in the preparation of picric acid (pages 820–21).

We saw in Section 26.6.A that halogenation of phenol in neutral solution involves reaction of the phenolate ion rather than the phenol itself. In acidic solution phenolate ion is suppressed, and the free phenol is involved in electrophilic halogenation. By a proper choice of reaction conditions one, two, or three halogens can be introduced into the available *ortho* and *para* positions.

Anisole behaves in an analogous manner.

Anisole functions as an excellent substrate for Friedel-Crafts acylation. Mild reaction conditions suffice because the alkoxy group is highly activating.

Other alkoxybenzenes also give good results in Friedel-Crafts acylation, provided the alkyl group is primary.

Direct Friedel-Crafts acylation of phenol is generally unsatisfactory. However, there are some exceptions. For example, treatment of phenol with acetic acid and boron trifluoride affords *p*-hydroxyacetophenone in excellent yield. Almost none of the *ortho* isomer is produced.

Many other phenol acylations are known, but most proceed in low yield, partly because of competing esterification of the hydroxy group.

Phenols undergo a special Friedel-Crafts acylation with phthalic anhydride and sulfuric acid or zinc chloride. In this case two molecules of phenol condense with one molecule of phthalic anhydride to give triarylmethane derivatives known as **phthaleins**.

phenolphthalein
(colorless lactone form)

The phthaleins are an important class of indicators and dyes. For example, phenolphthalein has the colorless lactone structure shown in solutions below pH 8.5. Above pH 9 two protons are lost to form an intensely colored red dianion.

colorless   red

The red color comes from an electronic transition in the visible region associated with the extended π-system of the ion.

Highly conjugated anions or cations of this type are invariably highly colored.

Phenolphthalein is used medicinally as a laxative and is the principal active ingredient in some proprietary preparations sold as laxative agents.

The condensation of resorcinol and phthalic anhydride gives an intensely fluorescent dye, fluorescein.

resorcinol   fluorescein

824

Chap. 26

*Aromatic
Halides,
Phenols, Phenyl
Ethers, and
Quinones*

The yellowish green fluorescence of fluorescein is detectable even in extremely dilute solutions and has been used for tracing the course of underground rivers. Fluorescein also finds use in ophthalmology; a minute amount added to the eye assists the visual fitting of contact lenses under ultraviolet illumination.

Phenyl esters (Section 26.7.A) undergo a Lewis-acid-catalyzed rearrangement that amounts to intramolecular Friedel-Crafts acylation. The reaction is known as the **Fries rearrangement** and is carried out by heating the ester with aluminum chloride, often with no solvent.

	(32–35%)	(45–50%)
phenyl propionate	o-hydroxypropiophenone	p-hydroxypropiophenone

The two products can be conveniently separated by fractional distillation.

EXERCISE 26.13 Why do the two foregoing hydroxypropiophenones have different volatilities? Which is expected to be the more volatile?

EXERCISE 26.14 Write equations showing the reactions, if any, of o-cresol with the following reagents.
(a) acetic acid, H_2SO_4 (b) acetic anhydride, H_2SO_4
(c) $NaNO_2$, HCl, 0°C   (d) HNO_3, H_2O, 25°C
(e) conc. H_2SO_4, 100°C   (f) Br_2, CCl_4, 25°C
(g) acetic acid, BF_3 (h) (i) acetic anhydride, H_2SO_4; (ii) $AlCl_3$, 150°C
(i) phthalic anhydride, H_2SO_4, heat

C. Reactions of Ethers

Alkyl aryl ethers are cleaved by acids just as are dialkyl ethers. Hydrobromic or hydriodic acid is commonly used.

The reaction mechanism is the same as for aliphatic ethers; the protonated ether undergoes S_N1 or S_N2 cleavage. Because the phenyl group is not susceptible to either S_N1 or S_N2 reaction, cleavage of the aliphatic carbon-oxygen bond always occurs.

When R is a tertiary alkyl group, the ether cleavage is especially facile; cleavage occurs by the S_N1 mechanism.

t-butyl
phenyl ether

Allyl aryl ethers, like allyl vinyl ethers, undergo the Claisen rearrangement reaction (Section 20.7). The reaction requires heating to about 200°C and results in apparent migration of the allyl group to the *ortho* position on the benzene ring.

allyl phenyl ether

(73%)
o-allylphenol

If both *ortho* positions are occupied by substituents, rearrangement occurs to the *para* position.

The reaction mechanism involves the concerted formation of a carbon-carbon bond between the *ortho* carbon and the terminal position of the allyl group as the carbon-oxygen bond is broken.

The reaction is of the pericyclic type with an aromatic six-electron Hückel transition state.

Note that the γ-carbon of the allyl group becomes attached to the benzene ring. When the ether contains an unsymmetrical allyl group, the allylic rearrangement is apparent.

o-(α-methylallyl)phenol

If no *ortho* hydrogen is available, enolization to the phenol cannot occur, and a second rearrangement occurs to the *para* position.

826

Chap. 26

*Aromatic
Halides,
Phenols, Phenyl
Ethers, and
Quinones*

2,6-dimethyl-4-(but-2-enyl)phenol

Note that two successive allylic rearrangements restore the original orientation of the allylic group. The second rearrangement is an example of a Cope rearrangement (Section 20.7).

EXERCISE 26.15 Write the equations showing the following reaction sequences starting with *p*-cresol.
(a) (i) NaOH, $CH_3CH{=}CHCH_2Br$; (ii) 200°C
(b) (i) NaOH, $CH_3OSO_3CH_3$; (ii) HNO_3, Ac_2O, 10°C; (iii) HBr, 100°C.

26.8 Quinones

A. Nomenclature

Quinones are cyclohexadiendiones, but they are named as derivatives of aromatic systems: benzoquinones are derived from benzene, toluquinones from toluene, naphthoquinones from naphthalene, and so on. "Quinone" is used both as a generic term and as a common name for *p*-benzoquinone.

p-benzoquinone   *o*-benzoquinone   toluquinone
or quinone

| 1,4-naphthoquinone | 9,10-anthraquinone | 9,10-phenanthraquinone |

Many quinones, especially hydroxyquinones, occur in nature. Some examples are the antibiotics fumigatin and phthiocol.

fumigatin
3-hydroxy-2-methoxy-
5-methyl-1,4-benzoquinone

phthiocol
2-hydroxy-3-methyl-
1,4-naphthoquinone

Hydroxynaphthoquinones and hydroxyanthraquinones are also common, either free or bound to glucose. Many natural pigments have quinone structures.

alizarin
(madder root)

juglone
(walnut shells)

rhein
(rhubarb)

Quinone structures are frequently associated with color and the following structural units are referred to as "quinoid" structures.

and

B. Preparation

The only important method for the preparation of quinones is oxidation of phenols and aromatic amino compounds. Substituted phenols or aniline derivatives can be used with some oxidizing agents. For example, *p*-benzoquinone can be prepared by oxidation of benzene or aniline with a variety of oxidizing agents, but the usual laboratory preparation involves the oxidation of hydroquinone.

828

Chap. 26

Aromatic
Halides,
Phenols, Phenyl
Ethers, and
Quinones

(86–92%)

hydroquinone   quinone

p-Benzoquinone forms yellow crystals, m.p. 115.7°C, that are slightly soluble in water and can be sublimed or steam-distilled.

Aminophenols are easily oxidized to quinones, and this route constitutes one of the best methods for the preparation of substituted quinones.

2-chloro-1,4-benzoquinone

Other oxidizing agents that are used for the preparation of quinones are ferric ion, dinitrogen tetroxide (N_2O_4), and sodium chlorate-vanadium pentoxide. Many other oxidizing agents have also been used, and the best one for any given compound must be determined by experiment. For example, the preparation of chloranil makes advantageous use of nitric acid.

(60%)
2,3,5,6-tetrachloro-1,4-benzoquinone
chloranil

Chloranil is commercially available and has several uses in organic chemistry that we will encounter later (Sections 26.8.D and 30.3.B).

The oxidation of *o*-dihydroxybenzenes to *o*-quinones can be carried out with silver oxide in ether.

catechol   *o*-benzoquinone

o-Benzoquinone forms red crystals that are water-sensitive; anhydrous sodium sulfate is used in its preparation to remove the water formed in the oxidation.

In many cases phenyl ethers and esters undergo oxidation to the corresponding quinone with loss of the alkyl or acyl group. An example is the oxidation of 2,6-di-*t*-butyl-4-methoxyphenyl propionate by ceric ammonium nitrate.

$$(CH_3)_3C \quad \text{...} \quad C(CH_3)_3 \xrightarrow{(NH_4)_2Ce(NO_3)_6} (CH_3)_3C \quad \text{...} \quad C(CH_3)_3 + CH_3CH_2COOH$$

C. Reduction-Oxidation Equilibria

Quinones, which are readily produced by oxidation of 1,2- and 1,4-dihydroxyben-zenes, are easily reduced to regenerate the starting compounds. This reduction can be carried out chemically.

2-methyl-1,4-naphthoquinone   2-methyl-1,4-dihydroxy-
                                                    naphthalene
                                               (95%)

However, the most important aspect of this redox system is that it is electrochemically reversible.

The electrical potential of this cell is given by the Nernst equation (26-1)

$$E = E° + \frac{2.303\,RT}{n\mathscr{F}} \log \frac{[\text{quinone}][\text{H}^+]^2}{[\text{hydroquinone}]} \qquad (26\text{-}1)$$

in which $\mathscr{F}$ is the Faraday. At 25°C equation (26-1) may be written as (26-2), in which the electrical potential is given in volts.

$$E^{25°C} = E° - 0.059\,\text{pH} + 0.0296 \log \frac{[\text{quinone}]}{[\text{hydroquinone}]} \qquad (26\text{-}2)$$

The standard potential $E°$ is that given at unit hydrogen ion concentration and equal concentrations of quinone and hydroquinone. Some values of $E°$ are listed in Table 26.2. The more positive the value of the potential, the more readily the quinone is reduced. Note that electron-donating groups such as methyl and hydroxy stabilize the quinone form relative to the hydroquinone and result in lowering the reduction poten-tial; electron-attracting groups such as halogen have the opposite effect.

830

Chap. 26

*Aromatic
Halides,
Phenols, Phenyl
Ethers, and
Quinones*

TABLE 26.2 Reduction Potentials of Quinones

Quinone	Reduction Potential $E°$, volts (25°C)
1,4-benzoquinone	0.699
2-methyl-1,4-benzoquinone	0.645
2-hydroxy-1,4-benzoquinone	0.59
2-bromo-1,4-benzoquinone	0.715
2-chloro-1,4-benzoquinone	0.713
1,2-benzoquinone	0.78
1,4-naphthoquinone	0.47
1,2-naphthoquinone	0.56
9,10-anthraquinone	0.13
9,10-phenanthraquinone	0.44

The reduction potentials in Table 26.2 allow one to see a clear parallel between redox phenomena in organic compounds and those observed with inorganic species. Recall that oxidation corresponds to the loss of electrons, and reduction to the gain of electrons.

$$Fe^{2+} \xrightleftharpoons[\text{reduction}]{\text{oxidation}} Fe^{3+} + e^-$$

The more electron-rich a species is, the easier is its oxidation and the more difficult is its reduction. In Table 26.2 we see that the electron-attracting substituents chloro and bromo do indeed cause the quinone to be reduced more easily (more positive reduction potential). Similarly, the electron-donating substituents hydroxy and methyl cause the quinone to be reduced less easily.

The reduction of quinone occurs in two one-electron steps. The product of the first step is a radical anion that can be detected in dilute solution by the technique of electron spin resonance spectroscopy.

Electron spin resonance, ESR, is closely related to nuclear magnetic resonance. Electrons, like protons, have spin, and in molecules with an odd number of electrons (radicals) the resulting net electronic spin is aligned with or against an applied magnetic field. With commercial magnets the energy difference between the two states is in the microwave region of electromagnetic radiation. The resulting ESR spectra have been extremely useful for detecting small concentrations of radicals, and the details of the spectra provide important information about the electronic structures of radicals. These details, however, are beyond the scope of an introductory textbook.

The same radical anions are produced by one-electron oxidations of hydroquinone dianions.

Phenoxide ions are also subject to one-electron oxidation to give the corresponding neutral radicals.

phenoxy radical

Such radicals are involved in many of the reactions of phenols, including reactions of naturally occurring phenols.

Vitamin E, α-tocopherol, is a phenol that is widespread in plant materials. It appears to have several functions in animals, but one important function seems to be as a radical scavanger. The corresponding phenoxy radical is less reactive and less damaging to body constituents. Free radicals have been implicated in the aging process.

α-tocophenol
vitamin E

Quinone-hydroquinone redox systems have a number of important uses. Hydroquinone itself, for example, is an important photographic developer.

Silver bromide crystals that have become photoactivated by exposure to light are reduced by hydroquinone. The photoactivated silver bromide is reduced to black silver metal and the hydroquinone is oxidized to p-benzoquinone. The residual silver bromide is then removed by "hypo," sodium hyposulfite, which forms a soluble complex with silver cation. The result is a black image where the silver bromide emulsion was exposed to light. Some developer formulas include p-methylaminophenol, usually as the sulfate (Elon, Metol), which also oxidizes to p-benzoquinone.

p-methylaminophenol

832

Chap. 26

Aromatic
Halides,
Phenols, Phenyl
Ethers, and
Quinones

The oxidation-reduction reactions of hydroquinone and quinone derivatives play an important role in physiological redox processes.

Vitamin K is actually many vitamins; for example, K_1, K_2, K_3, and so on. They are all related to 1,4-naphthoquinone or compounds that are oxidized to it. For example, vitamin $K_{2(30)}$ is

Others vary in the length of the side chain. The K vitamins are present in blood as coagulation factors.

A related series of compounds is coenzyme Q, which occurs in many kinds of cells with $n = 6$, 8, or 10 ($n = 10$ in mammalian cells); indeed, when first discovered, it was called **ubiquinone** because it was so ubiquitous in cells. Coenzyme Q is involved in electron-transport systems, and the long isoprenoid chain is undoubtedly designed to promote fat solubility.

coenzyme Q

EXERCISE 26.16 Using the reduction potentials in Table 26.2 predict the direction of equilibrium for the following reaction.

$$\left.\begin{array}{c} \text{1,4-benzoquinone} \\ + \\ \text{2-chlorohydroquinone} \end{array}\right\} \Longleftrightarrow \left\{\begin{array}{c} \text{hydroquinone} \\ + \\ \text{2-chloro-1,4-benzoquinone} \end{array}\right.$$

What voltage would a cell generate that has equal concentrations of the four compounds?

D. Charge-Transfer Complexes

An equimolar mixture of *p*-benzoquinone and hydroquinone forms a dark green crystalline molecular complex, "quinhydrone," having a definite melting point of 171°C. This material dissolves in hot water, and the solution is largely dissociated into its components.

quinhydrone

The buffered solution has been used as a standard reference electrode.

The structure of the crystals consists of alternating molecules of quinone and hydro-quinone with the rings parallel to each other (Figure 26.2). This complex is only one example of many complexes now known as **charge-transfer** complexes. Such complexes are characterized by one component that is electron-rich (the donor) and another component that is strongly electron attracting (the acceptor); hence, they are also known as donor-acceptor complexes. In resonance language the complexes are characterized as a hybrid of two resonance structures.

$$[D : A \longleftrightarrow \overset{+}{D} \cdot \overset{-}{A} \cdot]$$

The second structure, the "charge-transfer structure," makes only a small contribution to the total electronic structure. That is, this second structure provides the bonding that holds the two components together, but the bond strength involved is only a few kcal mole^{-1}.

In molecular orbital theory, the donors have a high-lying HOMO in which electrons are held rather loosely; that is, this highest occupied molecular orbital has a low ionization potential. The acceptors have a relatively low-lying LUMO or lowest unoccupied molecular orbital; in fact, common acceptors frequently form radical anions readily on one-electron reduction in which the electron enters the LUMO. In the complex there is some overlap of the HOMO of the donor with the LUMO of the acceptor that results in transfer of some electron density from donor to acceptor. The amount of charge transferred is small and corresponds typically to a small fraction ($\cong 0.05$) of an electron. This molecular orbital approach is entirely equivalent to the resonance interpretation.

Typical donors that form charge-transfer complexes are benzene rings with electron-donating groups such as OH, OCH_3, $N(CH_3)_2$, CH_3, and so on. Common acceptors are compounds with several nitro groups, such as 1,3,5-trinitrobenzene and picric acid, or quinones. Especially potent are quinones with additional electron-attracting groups; chloranil (tetrachloro-*p*-benzoquinone) is an important example. The structure of the complex formed from hexamethylbenzene and chloranil is shown in Figure 26.3; this complex has a bond strength of about 5 kcal mole^{-1}. Compounds with several CN groups are also used as acceptors. Some examples are tetracyanoethylene and 2,3-dicyano-1,4-benzoquinone.

Charge-transfer complexes are often intensely colored. The color is associated with an electronic transition in which a substantial fraction of an electron is transferred from donor to acceptor. Charge-transfer interactions are now recognized as being important in other solid-state structures in which the interactions are weaker. Furthermore, many reactions and reaction mechanisms are now recognized to involve charge-transfer phenomena; however, a detailed treatment of such phenomena must be deferred to advanced organic chemistry texts.

FIGURE 26.2. Stereo diagram of quinhydrone. [Adapted with permission from *Molecular Structure and Dimensions*, International Union of Crystallography, 1972.]

834

Chap. 26

*Aromatic
Halides,
Phenols, Phenyl
Ethers, and
Quinones*

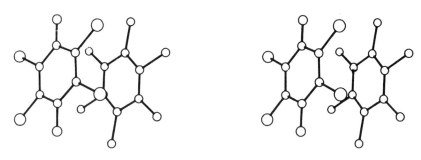

FIGURE 26.3. Stereo diagram of hexamethylbenzene-chloranil complex. [Adapted with permission from *Molecular Structure and Dimensions*, International Union of Crystallography, 1972.]

E. Reactions of Quinones

Quinones are α,β-unsaturated carbonyl compounds and show double bond reactions typical of such structures. One significant reaction is addition of hydrogen chloride.

chlorohydroquinone

This reaction is simply an acid-catalyzed conjugate addition (see Section 19.3.A).

Amines add readily. 1,4-Benzoquinone reacts with aniline to give 2,5-dianilino-1,4-benzoquinone and hydroquinone.

This reaction provides an interesting contrast to the addition of HCl, where the product is the chlorohydroquinone. In this case the group entering the hydroquinone ring is electron donating. Thus the initial product of conjugate addition of aniline to 1,4-benzoquinone, 2-anilinohydroquinone, is rapidly oxidized by an equivalent of 1,4-benzoquinone, which is reduced to hydroquinone.

This equilibrium lies far to the right because of the reduction potentials of the two quinones. The 2-anilino-1,4-benzoquinone then undergoes a second conjugate addition resulting in the formation of 2,5-dianilinohydroquinone, which is similarly oxidized to produce the isolated product.

Quinones also function as potent dienophiles in the Diels-Alder reaction (Section 19.5). An example is the reaction of 1,4-benzoquinone with butadiene, which occurs in acetic acid solution at room temperature. The product may be isolated or it may be treated with HCl, whereupon rearrangement to the more stable hydroquinone form occurs.

(87%)

EXERCISE 26.17 Write equations illustrating the reaction of 2,3-dimethyl-1,4-benzoquinone with each of the following reagents.
(a) HCl   (b) CH$_3$NH$_2$ (c) 2-methyl-1,3-butadiene (25°C).

PROBLEMS

1. Write structures for each of the following names.
   (a) *m*-cresol   (b) benzyne
   (c) 3-chloro-1,2-benzoquinone   (d) *o*-methoxyphenol
   (e) picric acid   (f) benzyl phenyl ether
   (g) 3-(*o*-hydroxyphenyl)pentanoic acid (h) *p*-isobutylphenol
   (i) 2-methoxy-1,4-naphthoquinone   (j) 2,5-dichloro-1,4-benzoquinone

2. When 2,4,6-trinitroanisole is treated with methoxide ion in methanol, a red anion having the composition $(C_8H_8O_8N_3)^-$ is produced. Such anions are called Meisenheimer complexes after the chemist who first suggested the correct structure. What structure do you think he suggested? One of Meisenheimer's experiments compared the product of reaction of 2,4,6-trinitroanisole and ethoxide ion with the product of 2,4,6-trinitrophenyl ethyl ether and methoxide ion. What do you think he found?

3. The reaction of chlorobenzene with hot aqueous sodium hydroxide actually goes in part by way of a benzyne intermediate and in part by the addition-elimination mechanism. Reaction of chlorobenzene labeled with ^{14}C at the 1-position with 4 *M* NaOH at 340°C gives phenol in which 58% of the ^{14}C remains at the 1-position and 42% is at the 2-position. Calculate the fraction of reaction proceeding by each of the two mechanisms.

836

Chap. 26

*Aromatic
Halides,
Phenols, Phenyl
Ethers, and
Quinones*

4. Give the principal product of the following reactions or reaction sequences:

(a) [structure: 3,5-disubstituted toluene with CH_3 at top, Cl and Br on ring] $\xrightarrow[\text{ether}]{\text{excess Mg}}$ $\xrightarrow{\text{DCl}}$

(b) [structure: chlorobenzene with Cl] $\xrightarrow[\text{fuming } H_2SO_4]{\text{fuming } HNO_3 \text{ (2 moles)}}$ $\xrightarrow{NH_3}$

(c) [structure: benzene ring with NO_2 at top, Cl and Cl substituents] $+ \text{ NaOCH}_3$ $\xrightarrow[\Delta]{CH_3OH}$

(d) [structure: ethylbenzene with CH_2CH_3] $\xrightarrow[hv]{Br_2}$ $\xrightarrow[\text{ether}]{Mg}$ $\xrightarrow{CH_2-CH_2 \text{ (epoxide)}}$ $\xrightarrow{H^+}$

5. Write the principal reaction product or products, if any, of *o*-cresol with the following reagents.

(a) $(CH_3O)_2SO_2$, NaOH
(b) $Na_2S_2O_4$
(c) $SnCl_2$, HCl
(d) $Na_2Cr_2O_7$, H_2SO_4
(e) $C_6H_5N_2{}^+$, aqueous NaOH
(f) CH_3COOH, H_2SO_4, heat
(g) aqueous NH_3
(h) 98% H_2SO_4, 25°C
(i) $KMnO_4$, heat
(j) cold, dilute HNO_3
(k) bromine water
(l) $(CH_3CO)_2O$
(m) $CHCl_3$, aqueous NaOH
(n) HONO
(o) $LiAlH_4$
(p) HNO_3 (2 moles) in CH_3COOH
(q) HBr, heat
(r) CO_2, K_2CO_3, 240°C
(s) bromine (1 mole) in CCl_4

6. Write the principal reaction product or products, if any, when 2-methylanisole is subjected to the following conditions.

(a) $Na_2S_2O_4$
(b) conc. H_2SO_4
(c) HBr, heat
(d) bromine in CH_3COOH
(e) HNO_3 (2 moles) in CH_3COOH
(f) $LiAlH_4$
(g) $(CH_3CO)_2O$
(h) CH_3COCl, $ZnCl_2$
(i) phthalic anhydride, $C_6H_5NO_2$, $AlCl_3$, 0°C
(j) Na, liquid NH_3

7. Each of the following phenol or quinone derivatives has the common or trivial name shown and is a compound of some significance. Provide the IUPAC name and show how each may be synthesized from the indicated starting material.

(a) [structure: benzene ring with $CH_2CH_2NH_2$ at top, CH_3O and OCH_3 at meta positions, OCH_3 at para position]

Mescaline is the active ingredient in peyote (mescal buttons) and is used as a psychoto-mimetic (that is, mimics psychosis) drug. Show how it may be prepared from gallic acid, 3,4,5-trihydroxybenzoic acid.

(b)

$$O_2N \quad \overset{OH}{\underset{NO_2}{\bigcirc}} \quad \overset{CH_3}{\underset{}{CHCH_2CH_3}}$$

The ester of this phenol with 3-methylbut-2-enoic acid is **binapacryl**, which is used as a fungicide and mitocide. Show how the phenolic portion may be prepared from phenol.

(c) $O_2N-\bigcirc-N{=}N-\overset{COOH}{\underset{OH}{\bigcirc}}$

Alizarine yellow R is used as an indicator in alkaline solutions. The color changes from yellow to red over the pH range from 10 to 12. Starting from aniline, outline a synthesis of this dye.

(d)

$$\overset{CON(C_2H_5)_2}{\underset{\underset{OH}{OC_2H_5}}{\bigcirc}}$$

Anacardiol is a drug that acts as a stimulant on the central nervous system. Propose a synthesis, beginning with catechol.

(e)

$$\overset{CHO}{\underset{\underset{OH}{OCH_3}}{\bigcirc}}$$

Vanillin occurs naturally in vanilla and other plant materials and is used as a flavoring agent. Indicate how it may be prepared from guaiacol.

(f)

$$\overset{\overset{NH_2}{\underset{}{CH_2CHCOOH}}}{\underset{\underset{OH}{OH}}{\bigcirc}}$$

This material (**L-dopa**) is found in some beans and is also used in a treatment of Parkinson's disease. Show how the racemate may be prepared from catechol.

(g)

$$\overset{COOCH_3}{\underset{\underset{OH}{NH_2}}{\bigcirc}}$$

Orthocaine is used as a surface anesthetic. Suggest a synthesis from phenol.

8. Show how each of the following conversions may be accomplished.

(a)

(b)

(c)

(d)

(e)

9. What is the principal organic product of each of the following sequences?

(a) $C_6H_5CH=CHCH_2Cl \xrightarrow{C_6H_5O^-} \xrightarrow{200°C}$

(b)

(c) $(CH_3)_2C=CHCH_2OCH=CH_2 \xrightarrow{\Delta} \xrightarrow{CH_2=P(C_6H_5)_3} \xrightarrow{\Delta}$

(d) $C_6H_5NH_2 \xrightarrow[HCl]{NaNO_2}$ $\xrightarrow{aq.\ NaOH}$

(e)

10. 2,6-Dichlorophenol is present in some ticks and is thought to be a sex pheromone. Devise a practical synthesis from phenol.

11. In Table 22.2 (page 668) the relative rates of protodedeuteration of *o*-, *m*-, and *p*-anisole-*d* are summarized. Show how each of these deuterated anisoles can be prepared uncontaminated by the other isomers.

12. Another component of urushiol, the active constituent of the irritating oil of poison ivy, is 3-pentadecyl-1,2-dihydroxybenzene. Synthesize this compound from catechol (be careful in handling the product!).

13. When *n*-butyl benzenesulfonate is heated with an ethanolic solution of potassium benzyloxide, the product is a mixture of *n*-butyl ethyl ether and *n*-butyl benzyl ether. However, if the isomeric salt, potassium *p*-methylphenolate, is used, the product is almost exclusively *n*-butyl *p*-methylphenyl ether. Explain.

14. Acetanilide is oxidized in the body by oxygen and a hydroxylase enzyme to *p*-hydroxyacetanilide. Show how this compound can be synthesized from phenol.

15. 2,2-Bis-(*p*-hydroxyphenyl)propane or "Bisphenol A," used commercially in the manufacture of epoxy resins and as a fungicide, is prepared by the reaction of phenol with acetone in acid.

Bisphenol A

Write out the mechanism of this reaction, showing all intermediates involved.

16. The sulfonation of *p*-cymene (1-methyl-4-isopropylbenzene) gives the 2-sulfonic acid. Is this the expected orientation? Explain. Use this fact to synthesize carvacrol, 2-methyl-5-isopropylphenol, from *p*-cymene. Carvacrol is found in the essential oils from thyme, marjoram, and summer savory. It has a pleasant thymol-like odor.

17. Tri-*o*-cresyl phosphate, $(o\text{-}CH_3C_6H_4O)_3PO$, is used as a gasoline additive. Suggest a preparation.

18. Rank each group in order of increasing acidity.
    (a) phenol, 3-acetylphenol, 4-acetylphenol
    (b) *p*-dimethylaminomethylphenol, *p*-dimethylaminophenol, trimethyl-(*p*-hydroxyphenyl) ammonium ion
    (c) 2-hydroxy-1,4-benzoquinone, 2,5-dimethoxyphenol, 4-hydroxy-1,2-benzoquinone

19. A student attempted the following synthesis of *o*-methoxybenzyl alcohol from *o*-cresol, but got almost none of the desired product. What went wrong?

20. Hydrolysis of 2,4,6-triaminobenzoic acid by refluxing with dilute NaOH gives 1,3,5-trihydroxybenzene (phloroglucinol).

840

Chap. 26

*Aromatic
Halides,
Phenols, Phenyl
Ethers, and
Quinones*

Write a reasonable mechanism for this reaction. (*Hint*: The reaction involves the nonaromatic keto forms.)

21. *o*-Phenylazophenol is readily separable from the *para* isomer by steam distillation. Give a reasonable explanation for the greater volatility of the *ortho* isomer.

22. (a) Write a reasonable mechanism for the sulfuric acid-catalyzed condensation of phenol with phthalic acid. Be sure to show all intermediates.

    (b) Phenol does not form diphenyl ether with sulfuric acid, yet the condensation of resorcinol with phthalic anhydride to give fluorescein includes the formation of an ether link from two phenolic hydroxy groups. Give a reasonable explanation.

23. Equimolar mixtures of *p*-benzoquinone with hydroquinone and of 2-chloro-1,4-benzoquinone with chlorohydroquinone in the same buffer solution are contained in separate beakers. The beakers are connected by a salt bridge, and the potential difference between them is measured. What is this potential difference? Which beaker constitutes the negative end (cathode) of this battery?

24. Allyl chloride labeled with ^{14}C is allowed to react with the anion from 2-methyl-6-allylphenol to form the corresponding ether. When this ether is heated, the Claisen rearrangement product 2-methyl-4,6-diallylphenol is formed. More than half, but not all, of the ^{14}C is found in the allyl group in the 4-position. Explain.

25. Diazotization of 2,4-dinitroaniline in aqueous solution is accompanied by some conversion to phenols in which a nitro group is replaced by a hydroxy group.

Suggest a mechanism for this reaction.

26. In the chlorination of aniline in aqueous solution some chlorophenol is produced. Suggest a mechanism for this substitution.

Chapter 27

Difunctional Compounds

27.1 Introduction

To a first approximation the chemical properties of difunctional compounds are a summation of those of the individual functions. For example, cyclohex-2-en-1-one is a difunctional compound that undergoes typical alkene reactions (catalytic hydrogenation) and normal ketone reactions (reduction by lithium aluminum hydride).

However, in many cases the two functional groups interact in such a way as to give the compound chemical properties that are not observed with the simple monofunctional compounds. In cyclohex-2-en-1-one the two functional groups form a conjugated system (Chapter 19), so this molecule undergoes some special reactions, such as 1,4-addition of lithium dimethylcuprate (Section 19.3.A).

This is a special reaction of the difunctional compound because neither simple alkenes nor simple ketones react with the reagent.

In other cases the chemical properties of a difunctional compound are similar to those of a corresponding monofunctional compound in a qualitative sense but not in a quantitative sense. An example is the reaction of allyl bromide with azide ion. The reaction is a normal S_N2 replacement of a primary halide, but since the organic group is allylic, the reaction is over 50 times faster than it is with propyl bromide (Section 19.1.B).

$$CH_2\!\!=\!\!CHCH_2Br + N_3^- \xrightarrow{\text{faster}} CH_2\!\!=\!\!CHCH_2N_3 + Br^-$$

$$CH_3CH_2CH_2Br + N_3^- \xrightarrow{\text{slower}} CH_3CH_2CH_2N_3 + Br^-$$

In still other cases two functional groups in a molecule may enter into a chemical reaction with each other. An example is the intramolecular S_N2 reaction leading to cyclic amines (problem 13, Chapter 9).

As may be seen in the foregoing examples, we have already encountered the reactions of a number of difunctional compounds, mainly in the study of conjugated systems (Chapter 19). In this chapter, we shall take up a few specific types of difunctional compounds, pointing out some of the unique chemistry that results from the cooperation or interaction of the two functional groups. Specific difunctional compounds we shall consider at this time are those containing the functional groups OH and C=O: diols, diketones, dicarboxylic acids, hydroxy aldehydes, hydroxy ketones, hydroxy acids, and keto acids. The chemistry of these difunctional compounds forms a necessary foundation for our study of the chemistry of carbohydrates (Chapter 28). In Chapter 29 we shall consider another large and important class of difunctional compounds, amino acids.

27.2 Nomenclature of Difunctional Compounds

Recall that most simple monofunctional compounds are named in such a way that the ending of the name denotes the functional group: acetic **acid**, 3-pentan**ol**, cyclohexan**one**, 1-but**ene**. Alkyl halides are exceptions to this generalization, in that they are considered as derivatives of the parent alkane, for example, 2-chloroheptane. When a compound contains two like functional groups, it is generally named in the same way except that the typical group suffix is combined with **di-** to indicate the presence of two groups. Numbers are used to locate the positions of the groups on the carbon skeleton.

(2*E*,5*Z*)-7-methyl-2,5-octadiene or
trans,cis-7-methyl-2,5-octadiene

1,3-pentadiyne

2,4-pentanedione

cis-1,3-cyclohexanediol

1,5-dibromo-3-methylhexane

trans-1,2-cyclopentanedicarboxylic acid

Diols are sometimes called **glycols**. This is a trivial nomenclature widely used in the chemical industry, particularly for some of the simpler diols, which are important commercial items. For example, ethylene glycol (1,2-ethanediol) is the most widely used antifreeze additive for automobile radiators.

The aliphatic dicarboxylic acids having up to ten carbons in their chains have common names that are used extensively in the chemical literature (Table 27.1). Although these names are no longer used for indexing purposes, the student should be aware of

TABLE 27.1 Names of Some Dicarboxylic Acids

n	Formula	Common	IUPAC
C_2	$HOCCOH$ (O O)	oxalic acid	ethanedioic acid
C_3	$HOCCH_2COH$ (O O)	malonic acid	propanedioic acid
C_4	$HOC(CH_2)_2COH$ (O O)	succinic acid	butanedioic acid
C_5	$HOC(CH_2)_3COH$ (O O)	glutaric acid	pentanedioic acid
C_6	$HOC(CH_2)_4COH$ (O O)	adipic acid	hexanedioic acid
C_7	$HOC(CH_2)_5COH$ (O O)	pimelic acid	heptanedioic acid
C_8	$HOC(CH_2)_6COH$ (O O)	suberic acid	octanedioic acid
C_9	$HOC(CH_2)_7COH$ (O O)	azelaic acid	nonanedioic acid
C_{10}	$HOC(CH_2)_8COH$ (O O)	sebacic acid	decanedioic acid

them since they were uniformly used before about 1975. The benzenedicarboxylic acids are known as phthalic, isophthalic, and terephthalic acids. The last-named acid is a highly important industrial material; it forms one of the building blocks of the synthetic fiber known as polyester, Dacron, or Terylene.

phthalic acid
1,2-benzenedicarboxylic acid

isophthalic acid
1,3-benzenedicarboxylic acid

terephthalic acid
1,4-benzenedicarboxylic acid

Two unsaturated aliphatic diacids that have widely used common names are maleic and fumaric acids.

maleic acid
cis-butenedioic acid

fumaric acid
trans-butenedioic acid

Aldehydes and functional derivatives corresponding to common diacids are frequently named as derivatives of the acids, in the same manner as is used to name simple aldehydes and functional derivatives.

$$\underset{\text{succinaldehyde}}{\overset{\displaystyle\overset{O}{\|}\qquad\overset{O}{\|}}{HCCH_2CH_2CH}}\qquad\qquad\underset{\beta,\beta\text{-dimethylglutaraldehyde}}{\overset{\displaystyle\overset{O}{\|}\quad\overset{CH_3}{|}\;\overset{O}{\|}}{HCCH_2CCH_2CH}}$$

$$\underset{\text{oxalyl chloride}}{\overset{\displaystyle\overset{O}{\|}\;\overset{O}{\|}}{ClC-CCl}}\qquad\underset{\text{dimethyl adipate}}{\overset{\displaystyle\overset{O}{\|}\qquad\qquad\quad\overset{O}{\|}}{CH_3OCCH_2CH_2CH_2CH_2COCH_3}}\qquad\underset{\text{fumaronitrile}}{\overset{\displaystyle H\quad CN}{\underset{NC\quad H}{C=C}}}$$

When a compound contains two different functional groups, one of the groups (the principal function) is usually expressed in the ending of the name and the other as a prefix.

$$HOCH_2CH_2COOH$$

3-hydroxypropanoic acid
β-hydroxypropionic acid

4-hydroxycyclohexanone

Alkenes and alkynes are exceptions in that the double or triple bond cannot be expressed as a prefix. For compounds containing a multiple bond and another functional group, two suffixes are used.

$$\underset{\text{3-buten-1-ol}}{CH_2=CHCH_2CH_2OH}\qquad\underset{\text{3-butyn-2-one}}{HC\equiv CCCH_3}\qquad\underset{\text{2-butenoic acid}}{CH_3CH=CHCOH}$$

In the naming of a difunctional compound, a choice must be made as to which group is the principal function. The generally accepted order is carboxylic acid, sulfonic acid, ester, acyl halide, amide, nitrile, aldehyde, ketone, alcohol, thiol, amine, alkyne, alkene. Since alkenes and alkynes cannot be designated by prefixes, they are always indicated by a second suffix, which is placed before the final suffix of any function higher in the order. Table 27.2 contains a listing of the common functions with the appropriate prefix and suffix used to designate each one.

EXERCISE 27.1 Write a structure for a six-carbon compound containing each pairwise combination of the following functional groups: OH, C=C, C=O (both aldehyde and ketone), COOH. Assign a name to each of your 15 structures.

TABLE 27.2 Functional Groups as Prefixes and Suffixes

Group	Prefix	Suffix
—COOH	carboxy-	-oic acid
		-carboxylic acid
—SO₃H	sulfo-	-sulfonic acid
—COOR	alkoxycarbonyl-	-carboxylate
—COCl	chloroformyl-	-oyl chloride
		-carbonyl chloride
—CONH₂	carbamoyl-	-amide
		-carboxamide
—CN	cyano-	-nitrile
		-carbonitrile
—CHO	formyl-	-al
	oxo-	-carboxaldehyde
		-carbaldehyde
$\overset{\displaystyle O}{\underset{\displaystyle -C-}{\|}}$	{ oxo- (IUPAC) keto- (common) }	-one
—OH	hydroxy-	-ol
—SH	mercapto-	-thiol
—NH₂	amino-	-amine
—C≡C—	—	-yne
—C=C—	—	-ene
—Cl	chloro-	—

27.3 Diols

A. Preparation

1,2-Diols are usually prepared from the corresponding alkene by the net addition of two hydroxy groups to the double bond (**hydroxylation**). Direct hydroxylation may be accomplished by oxidation of the alkene with $KMnO_4$ or OsO_4 (Section 11.6.E). Overall hydroxylation may be achieved by conversion of the alkene to an epoxide (Section 11.6.E), which is then hydrolyzed to the 1,2-diol (Section 10.11.A).

Direct hydroxylation with $KMnO_4$ or OsO_4 is a stereospecific process; the overall result is syn addition of the two hydroxy groups to the double bond.

cis-cyclooctene   *cis*-1,2-cyclooctanediol

The two-step procedure for hydroxylation of an alkene is also stereospecific, but this process produces net anti addition of the two hydroxy groups to the double bond. For example, cyclohexene reacts with peroxyacetic acid to give cyclohexene oxide. This compound undergoes acid-catalyzed ring opening by the S_N2 mechanism, resulting in inversion of configuration at one of the two carbon-oxygen bonds. Thus, the overall result is formation of the trans 1,2-diol.

cyclohexene oxide   *trans*-1,2-cyclohexanediol

Different diols result from addition to the cis or trans isomer of the alkene. For a symmetrical alkene, such as 2-butene, syn hydroxylation of the cis isomer gives a meso diol.

meso-2,3-butanediol

Syn hydroxylation of the trans isomer gives a 50:50 mixture of two enantiomeric diols. These two products arise from addition of the reagent to the two faces of the planar alkene molecule. Since the reagent is achiral, the transition states leading to the two products are enantiomeric and equal in energy. The product is therefore a racemate (Section 7.4). To distinguish this mixture of enantiomers from the meso diol, it is frequently designated as ($\pm$) or *dl* (meaning an equimolar or racemic mixture of the dextrorotatory and levorotatory enantiomers).

(2R,3R)-butanediol

(2S,3S)-butanediol
[mixture = ($\pm$)-2,3-butanediol]

For anti hydroxylation, the situation is just exactly reversed—the cis alkene gives the ($\pm$)-diol and the trans alkene affords the meso diol. When the acyclic alkene is not symmetrical, both syn and anti additions of each isomer produce racemic mixtures. The following equations illustrate the syn hydroxylation of the two isomers of 2-pentene.

(2S,3R)-pentanediol

(2R,3S)-pentanediol

(2S,2S)-pentanediol

(2R,3R)-pentanediol

The 2R,3S and 2S,3R isomers of 2,3-pentanediol are called **erythro** isomers, and the 2R,3R and 2S,3S isomers are called **threo** isomers. These names derive from carbohydrate chemistry (Chapter 28) and are frequently used for other simple difunctional compounds. When a compound contains two stereocenters that have two identical attached groups and a third that differs, the isomer that would be meso if the third groups were identical is the erythro isomer. The other isomer is the threo isomer.

(2R,3S)-3-bromo-2-butanol
(erythro)

(2R,3R)-2,3-dibromopentane
(threo)

EXERCISE 27.2 In Section 11.4 we learned that both cis and trans isomers are capable of existence in rings containing eight or more members. What is the structure of the diol produced by hydroxylation of *trans*-cyclooctene with KMnO$_4$? Use your molecular model kit in formulating the answer to this question. Compare your answer with the reaction given for *cis*-cyclooctene on page 845.

A reaction that serves as a preparation for some symmetrical 1,2-diols involves the **reductive dimerization** of ketones. The reducing agent is generally an electropositive metal, such as sodium or magnesium. The reaction occurs by electron transfer from the metal to the ketone to produce a **ketyl**, or **radical anion**. Dimerization of two radical anions affords the dianion of a 1,2-diol, which is hydrolyzed in a separate step to the diol itself.

$$2\ CH_3\overset{O}{\overset{\|}{C}}CH_3 + Mg \longrightarrow \left[Mg^{2+} + 2\ CH_3\overset{\overset{\displaystyle :\overset{..}{O}:^-}{|}}{C}CH_3 \right] \longrightarrow \left[\overset{Mg^{2+}}{\underset{CH_3\ \ CH_3}{CH_3\overset{-O\ \ \ \ O^-}{\underset{|}{C}\!-\!\underset{|}{C}CH_3}}} \right] \overset{H_2O}{\longrightarrow} (CH_3)_2\overset{HO\ \ OH}{\underset{|}{C}\!-\!\underset{|}{C}(CH_3)_2}$$

ketyl
radical anion

(43–50%)
pinacol

Because the diol produced from acetone has the trivial name "pinacol," this reaction is called the **pinacol reaction**.

Other types of diols are generally prepared by reduction of the appropriate dicarbonyl compounds, as indicated by the following examples.

$$C_2H_5O\overset{O}{\overset{\|}{C}}(CH_2)_8\overset{O}{\overset{\|}{C}}OC_2H_5 \overset{LiAlH_4}{\longrightarrow} HOCH_2(CH_2)_8CH_2OH$$

(75%)
1,10-decanediol

$$CH_3\overset{O}{\overset{\|}{C}}(CH_2)_3\overset{O}{\overset{\|}{C}}CH_3 + NaBH_4 \overset{C_2H_5OH}{\longrightarrow} CH_3\overset{OH}{\overset{|}{C}}H(CH_2)_3\overset{OH}{\overset{|}{C}}HCH_3$$

(80%)
2,6-heptanediol

EXERCISE 27.3 Write equations for the overall anti hydroxylation of each of the following alkenes using the sequence of reagents (1) peroxyacetic acid and (2) aqueous sulfuric acid. Clearly illustrate the stereochemistry at each step of the process.
(a) *cis*-2-butene   (b) *trans*-2-butene   (c) *cis*-2-pentene
(d) *trans*-2-pentene   (e) *trans*-cyclooctene

B. Reactions of Diols

One unique reaction of 1,2- and 1,3-diols is their reaction with aldehydes and ketones to form cyclic acetals and ketals (Section 14.7.B).

Diols with more than three carbons intervening between the two hydroxy functions do not generally give the reaction, because the resulting ring would be seven-membered or greater.

Dehydration of 1,2-diols under acid catalysis is frequently accompanied by skeletal rearrangement. For example, pinacol (2,3-dimethylbutane-2,3-diol, shown above) reacts with sulfuric acid to give *t*-butyl methyl ketone, which has the trivial name "pinacolone."

CH₃ OH   CH₃ O

CH₃C——CCH₃ $\xrightarrow{H_2SO_4}$ CH₃C——CCH₃

OH CH₃   CH₃

pinacol   pinacolone

The mechanism of this pinacol rearrangement involves 1,2-migration of a methyl group and its bonding electron pair from one carbinyl position to an adjacent electron-deficient center (Section 10.6.C). The driving force for the rearrangement is formation of a stable oxonium ion, the conjugate acid of a ketone.

OH OH   OH $\overset{+}{O}H_2$

$(CH_3)_2C$——$C(CH_3)_2$ + H⁺ ⇌ $(CH_3)_2C$——$C(CH_3)_2$ ⇌

:OH CH₃ $\overset{+}{O}H$ O

CH₃C—C⁺   ⇌ CH₃C—C(CH₃)₃ ⇌ CH₃CC(CH₃)₃ + H⁺

CH₃ CH₃

tertiary carbocation   oxonium ion   pinacolone

By combining the pinacol reaction with this acid-catalyzed rearrangement process, interesting and unusual compounds may be prepared.

spiro[4.5]decan-6-one

Bicyclic compounds having one carbon common to both rings are **spiro** compounds. The nomenclature is based on the following scheme.

$(CH_2)_n C (CH_2)_m$ ≡ spiro[*n.m*]alkane

Numbering starts next to the common carbon and proceeds around the smaller ring first.

spiro[4.5]decane

Dehydration of 1,4- and 1,5-diols often leads to the formation of cyclic ethers, particularly when one of the hydroxy groups is tertiary.

HOCH₂CH₂CH₂CH₂OH $\xrightarrow{H^+}$ [cyclic ether] + H₂O

In the first of the two foregoing examples, the reaction undoubtedly occurs by intramolecular nucleophilic displacement on the initially formed oxonium ion.

The second example probably involves the formation of a tertiary carbocation which is trapped by the secondary hydroxy group.

In this case the cyclization is possible because the two groups are cis; the trans analog cannot give a cyclic product.

EXERCISE 27.4 What are the principal products of the pinacol rearrangements of the following diol when (a) Y = CH$_3$ and (b) Y = NO$_2$?

1,2-Diols undergo easy cleavage of the carbon-carbon bond joining the two hydroxy carbons when treated with periodic acid ("per-iodic" acid, HIO$_4$) or lead tetraacetate. Combined with the hydroxylation process, this oxidation constitutes a method for the cleavage of alkenes that is complementary to ozonolysis (Section 11.6.E).

(85%)
bicyclo[2.2.1]heptan-2-one
norbornanone

The periodic oxidation involves the formation of a cyclic diester of periodic acid. Decomposition of this cyclic diester yields the two carbonyl fragments and iodic acid.

Various procedures have been developed in which alkene hydroxylation and the diol cleavage reactions are combined into one operation. One such reaction (the **Lemieux-Johnson reaction**) involves treating an alkene with sodium periodate and a catalytic amount of osmium tetroxide.

A mixture of 15 mL of ether, 15 mL of water, 0.41 g of cyclohexene, and 0.065 g of OsO_4 is stirred at 25°C while 2.32 g of $NaIO_4$ is added over a period of 40 min. After an additional 80 min at 25°C, the product adipaldehyde is isolated in 77% yield.

EXERCISE 27.5 What is the product of the reaction of cyclohexanone with magnesium, followed by hot aqueous sulfuric acid?

27.4 Hydroxy Aldehydes and Ketones

A. Synthesis

α-Hydroxy ketones result from the treatment of esters with sodium in an inert solvent such as ether or benzene. Such compounds are called **acyloins**, and the reaction is called the **acyloin condensation**. The initial product of the reaction is the disodium salt of an enediol, which is hydrolyzed to give the acyloin.

an acyloin

The acyloin condensation is a useful method for the synthesis of ring compounds, particularly for medium-sized rings (8-13 members). In such cases, the reaction must be carried out under conditions of high dilution to suppress intermolecular reactions.

(66%)
2-hydroxycyclodecanone

The acyloin condensation is related mechanistically to the pinacol reaction (page 848) in that electron transfer from sodium to the ester carbonyl produces an intermediate ketyl. The chief side reaction is the Claisen condensation (Section 18.9), which stems from the alkoxide ion produced as a by-product in the reaction.

Aromatic aldehydes are converted into acyloins by sodium cyanide in aqueous ethanol. The reaction is called the **benzoin condensation**, and cyanide ion is a specific catalyst.

benzaldehyde

(92%)
benzoin

The catalyst functions by first adding to the carbonyl group to form the cyanohydrin (see Section 14.8.B). The former aldehyde hydrogen is now α to a cyano group and is sufficiently acidic to be removed by a base. The resulting carbanion then adds to another molecule of aldehyde to give an intermediate cyano diol. Elimination of cyanide ion yields the acyloin and regenerates the catalyst.

Although the acyloin and benzoin condensations produce the same type of product, it is important to remember that they involve *entirely different mechanisms*.

The most general synthesis of β-hydroxy aldehydes and ketones is the aldol addition reaction (Section 14.8.C). Recall that simple aldehydes condense to form β-hydroxy aldehydes when treated with cold aqueous base.

$$2 \ CH_3CHO \xrightarrow[\substack{H_2O \\ 0°C}]{NaOH} CH_3\overset{\overset{\displaystyle OH}{|}}{C}HCH_2CHO$$

Under more forcing conditions, such as are necessary to accomplish the initial condensation with aldehydes of more than six carbons, the β-hydroxy aldehyde undergoes dehydration to give the α,β-unsaturated aldehyde.

heptanal

(70%)
2-pentyl-2-nonenal

Mixed aldol reactions can be performed by converting a ketone completely into the lithium enolate, which is then allowed to react with an aldehyde. Hydrolysis of the initially formed alkoxide with water affords the β-hydroxy ketone, usually in good yield.

(88%)
4-hydroxy-4-phenyl-2-butanone

EXERCISE 27.6 The acyloin, benzoin, and aldol addition reactions may be used as routes to diols. Show how the following diols can be prepared using one of these reactions as a key step.
(a) 1,2-diphenylethane-1,2-diol   (b) hexane-3,4-diol
(c) butane-1,3-diol   (d) hexane-2,4-diol
Discuss the stereochemical problem that arises in three of these syntheses.

B. Reactions

β-Hydroxy aldehydes and ketones undergo acid-catalyzed dehydration more easily than normal alcohols. The following examples illustrate the magnitude of the differences.

Relative Rate

1

$> 10^5$

Recall that the dehydration of a secondary or tertiary alcohol involves the formation of an intermediate carbocation; the rate of formation of this intermediate determines the rate of dehydration (Section 10.6.D).

β-Hydroxy ketones undergo dehydration by a different mechanism, involving the enol form of the ketone. The rate-determining step is formation of the enol. Elimination of water from the protonated enol gives a resonance-stabilized oxonium ion, which is simply the protonated form of the α,β-unsaturated ketone.

(1) $-\overset{\underset{|}{\overset{|}{O}H}}{C}-CH-\overset{\overset{O}{\|}}{C}- \underset{slow}{\rightleftharpoons} -\overset{\underset{|}{\overset{|}{O}H}}{C}-\overset{\overset{|}{O}H}{C}=\overset{|}{C}-$

(2) $-\overset{\underset{|}{\overset{|}{O}H}}{C}-\overset{\overset{|}{O}H}{C}=\overset{|}{C}- + H^+ \underset{fast}{\rightleftharpoons} -\overset{\underset{|}{\overset{+}{O}H_2}}{C}-\overset{\overset{|}{O}H}{C}=\overset{|}{C}-$

(3) $-\overset{\underset{|}{\overset{+}{O}H_2}}{C}-\overset{\overset{|}{O}H}{C}=\overset{|}{C}- \underset{fast}{\rightleftharpoons} \left[\overset{+}{\underset{/}{\searrow}}C-\overset{\overset{|}{O}H}{C}=\overset{|}{C}- \longleftrightarrow \overset{\searrow}{/}C=\overset{\overset{|}{O}H}{C}-\overset{|}{C^+}- \longrightarrow \overset{\searrow}{/}C=\overset{|}{C}-\overset{\overset{+}{O}H}{C}- \right]$

(4) $\overset{\searrow}{/}C=\overset{\overset{\overset{+}{O}H}{\|}}{C}-\overset{|}{C}- \underset{fast}{\rightleftharpoons} \overset{\searrow}{/}C=\overset{\overset{O}{\|}}{C}-\overset{|}{C}- + H^+$

Normal alcohols do not undergo dehydration under basic conditions, as shown by the fact that *t*-butyl alcohol solutions of potassium *t*-butoxide are quite stable. However, β-hydroxy aldehydes and ketones undergo dehydration fairly easily under basic conditions. In this case the dehydration actually proceeds via the enolate ion (Section 14.6.B).

$$-\overset{\underset{|}{\overset{|}{O}H}}{C}-CH-\overset{\overset{O}{\|}}{C}- + OH^- \rightleftharpoons -\overset{\underset{|}{\overset{|}{O}H}}{C}-\overset{\overset{O^-}{\|}}{C}=\overset{|}{C}-$$

$$-\overset{\overset{|}{O}H}{C}-\overset{\overset{O^-}{\|}}{C}=\overset{|}{C}- \rightleftharpoons \overset{\searrow}{/}C=\overset{|}{C}-\overset{\overset{O}{\|}}{C}- + OH^-$$

In contrast to the easy dehydration of β-hydroxy carbonyl compounds, α-hydroxy ketones undergo acid-catalyzed dehydration with even more difficulty than normal alcohols. In this case, the intermediate carbocation would be destabilized by the inductive effect of the adjacent carbonyl group.

$$-\overset{\underset{|}{\overset{+}{O}H_2}}{C}-\overset{\overset{O}{\|}}{C}- \underset{slow}{\overset{very}{\longrightarrow}} \left[\overset{\searrow}{/}\overset{+}{C}-\overset{\overset{O}{\|}}{C}- \longleftrightarrow \overset{\searrow}{/}\overset{+}{C}-\overset{\overset{O^-}{\|}}{C}- \right]$$

An example is the preparation of 3-methylbut-3-en-2-one by heating a mixture of the α-hydroxy ketone and *p*-toluenesulfonic acid in an oil bath at 150°C. These conditions are far more vigorous than required for dehydration of normal tertiary alcohols.

$$CH_3\overset{\underset{|}{\overset{\overset{H}{|}\overset{O}{|}}{C}}}{\underset{\overset{|}{CH_3}}{C}}-\overset{\overset{O}{\|}}{C}CH_3 + CH_3-\!\!\left\langle\!\!\bigcirc\!\!\right\rangle\!\!-SO_3H \xrightarrow{150°C} CH_2=\overset{\underset{|}{CH_3}}{\overset{\overset{O}{\|}}{C}}CCH_3$$

(74%)
3-methylbut-3-en-2-one

Many hydroxy aldehydes and ketones exist to some extent in a cyclic hemiacetal or hemiketal form (Section 14.7.B). This tendency is particularly pronounced when the ring is five- or six-membered.

The data in Table 27.3 show that the cyclic form predominates with 4- and 5-hydroxy aldehydes. The formation of a cyclic hemiacetal from a hydroxy aldehyde or ketone is subject to acid or base catalysis, as in the formation of acetals by intermolecular reaction (Section 14.7.B). However, when five- or six-membered rings are involved, the cyclization is so facile that it occurs even under neutral conditions. Thus, any reaction that would nominally give a 4- or 5-hydroxy aldehyde or ketone will yield an equilibrium of the open-chain and ring-closed isomers.

TABLE 27.3
$HOCH_2(CH_2)_nCH_2CHO \rightleftharpoons$

n	Ring Size	Percent Free Aldehyde
1	5	11
2	6	6
3	7	85

Like noncyclic hemiacetals, these compounds react with alcohols under acid catalysis to give acetals or ketals.

$$CH_3 \underset{O}{\overset{H}{\diagdown}} OH + CH_3OH \overset{HCl}{\rightleftharpoons} CH_3 \underset{O}{\overset{H}{\diagdown}} OCH_3 + H_2O$$

Since there is usually a small amount of the open-chain hydroxy carbonyl compound in equilibrium with the cyclic hemiacetal form, solutions of such compounds can show reactions of either form, as the following examples show.

	(Section 14.9.B)
	(Section 14.7.C)
	(Section 14.8.A)
	(Section 18.7.A)
	(Section 11.6.E)

α-Hydroxy aldehydes and ketones, like 1,2-diols, are oxidized with C—C bond cleavage by periodic acid.

$$\underset{\underset{O}{\parallel}}{CH_3C}\text{—}\underset{\underset{OH}{|}}{CHCH_3} + HIO_4 \longrightarrow CH_3COOH + CH_3CHO + HIO_3$$

$$\underset{\underset{OH}{|}}{CH_3CH_2CHCHO} + HIO_4 \longrightarrow CH_3CH_2CHO + \underset{\underset{O}{\parallel}}{HCOH} + HIO_3$$

The reaction constitutes a useful method for structure determination in the carbohydrate field (Chapter 28).

EXERCISE 27.8 Write mechanisms for the five reactions of the cyclic hemiacetal of 5-hydroxypentanal shown above. Clearly indicate each step.

27.5 Hydroxy Acids

A. Natural Occurrence

Many hydroxy acids are important in nature and have trivial names that are in common use. Glycolic acid is a constituent of cane-sugar juice. Lactic acid is responsible for the characteristic odor and taste of sour milk. Malic acid occurs in fruit juices. Tartaric acid has been known since antiquity as the monopotassium salt (cream of tartar), which deposits in the lees of wine. Citric acid is a hydroxytricarboxylic acid that is widespread in nature. It is especially prevalent, as its trivial name implies, in the juice of citrus fruits. Chiral hydroxy acids are normally found in nature in the enantiomerically homogeneous, optically active form.

$$HOCH_2COOH \qquad CH_3CHOHCOOH$$

glycolic acid   lactic acid

OH   OH   OH

$$HOOCCH_2CHCOOH \qquad HOOCCH—CHCOOH$$

malic acid   tartaric acid

$$CH_2COOH$$

$$HO—C—COOH$$

$$CH_2COOH$$

citric acid

OH

CHCOOH

mandelic acid

Both the (+) and (−) forms of tartaric acid are found in nature, although the (+) acid is by far the more common. Two optically inactive forms are known. "Racemic acid," m.p. 206°C, is simply a mixture of (+)- and (−)-tartaric acids. *meso*-Tartaric acid, m.p. 140°C, is the *R,S* diastereomer.

HOOC   COOH   HOOC   COOH

C—C   C—C

H   OH   H   H

OH   H   OH   OH

(+)-(*R,R*)-tartaric acid   *meso*-tartaric acid

Tartaric acid played an important role in the development of stereochemistry. In 1848, Louis Pasteur noticed that crystals of sodium ammonium tartrate are chiral and that all of the crystals show chirality in the same sense. He proceeded to investigate 19 different tartrate salts and found that they all gave chiral crystals. On the basis of these observations, he postulated that there is a relationship between the chirality of the crystals and the fact that, in solution, the salts rotate the plane of polarized light.

However, there was a problem. The optically inactive racemic acid, obtained as a by-product in the crystallization of tartaric acid, was also known at this time. Racemic acid and tartaric acid were recognized to be isomers, and Mitscherlich had reported that crystals of sodium ammonium tartrate and sodium ammonium racemate are identical in all respects except that the tartrate gives a dextrorotatory solution whereas the racemate gives an optically inactive solution. This report could only be rationalized to Pasteur's hypothesis if the crystals of sodium ammonium racemate turned out to be achiral.

Pasteur repeated Mitscherlich's work on sodium ammonium racemate and was disappointed to discover that Mitscherlich had been correct and that crystals of the racemate salt are indeed chiral. Upon closer examination, however, he noticed that the crystals are not all chiral in the same sense. In his words, "the hemihedral faces which in the tartrate are all turned one way are in the racemate inclined sometimes to the right and sometimes to the left." In short, the racemate salt gives a mixture of nonsuperimposable mirror image crystals. Using a pair of tweezers, Pasteur carefully separated the left-handed from the right-handed crystals, dissolved each in water, and measured their optical rotations. To his great excitement, he discovered that one solution was dextrorotatory and the other was levorotatory. When he converted the separated salts back to the free acids, he found that one was identical with natural (+)-tartaric acid and that the other was a new tartaric acid isomer, identical in all respects save the sign of its optical rotation. Pasteur had accomplished the first resolution—separation of a racemate into its component enantiomers.

Pasteur's work paved the way for an understanding of stereoisomerism. He made the important suggestion that since the crystals of the enantiomeric salts show handedness, the molecules themselves might also show handedness—and this before the idea of chemical bonds had even been conceived.

A. Synthesis

α-Hydroxy acids are most commonly prepared by hydrolysis of α-halo acids. Recall that α-halo acids are readily available by bromination of carboxylic acids (Section 17.7.B). Thus the two-step sequence provides a way to introduce the hydroxy group at the α-position of a carboxylic acid.

$$CH_3CH_2COOH \xrightarrow[P]{Br_2} CH_3CHBrCOOH \xrightarrow{OH^-} CH_3CHOHCO_2^-$$

β-Hydroxy acids cannot be prepared by hydrolysis of the corresponding β-halo acid, since these compounds undergo elimination in base to give the unsaturated acids.

$$CH_3CHBrCH_2COOH \xrightarrow{OH^-} CH_3CH{=}CHCO_2^-$$

α-Hydroxy acids are also generally available by hydrolysis of cyanohydrins, which result from the reaction of HCN with aldehydes or ketones (Section 14.8.B). Since the addition of HCN to a carbonyl group is reversed by the strongly basic conditions necessary to hydrolyze a nitrile to an acid, the hydrolysis is done under acidic conditions.

$$CH_3CH_2\overset{\overset{O}{\|}}{C}CH_3 \xrightarrow{HCN} CH_3CH_2\underset{\underset{OH}{|}}{\overset{\overset{CH_3}{|}}{C}}CN \xrightarrow[25°C]{conc.\ HCl} CH_3CH_2\underset{\underset{OH}{|}}{\overset{\overset{CH_3}{|}}{C}}COOH$$

(55%)
2-methyl-2-hydroxybutanoic acid

β-Hydroxy acids and their derivatives are available by methods analogous to the aldol addition reaction (Section 18.9).

(95%)
methyl 3-hydroxy-2-methyl-3-phenylpropanoate

A variety of hydroxy acids are available by hydrolysis of lactones, which may be obtained by the Baeyer-Villiger oxidation of cyclic ketones (Section 14.9.A).

CF$_3$CO$_3$H

1. NaOH-C$_2$H$_5$OH
2. H$_3$O$^+$

OH

COOH

> **EXERCISE 27.9** Show how 2-hydroxypentanoic acid may be prepared from (a) pentanoic acid and (b) butanal. Outline a synthesis of 3-hydroxypentanoic acid.

C. Reactions

Recall that carboxylic acids react with alcohols under acid catalysis to yield esters (Section 17.7.C).

$$RCOH + R'OH \xrightarrow{H^+} RCOR' + H_2O$$

A hydroxy acid contains both of these functional groups, and thus it can undergo intramolecular esterification to yield a cyclic ester, which is called a **lactone**.

$$HOCH_2CH_2CH_2COOH \xrightarrow{H^+} \quad + H_2O$$

γ-hydroxybutyric acid   γ-butyrolactone

Lactonization, like normal esterification, is an equilibrium process. Only when the lactone has a five- or six-membered ring is there a substantial amount of lactone present under equilibrium conditions, as shown by the data in Table 27.4. These data also reveal that alkyl substitution on the ring increases the amount of lactone present at equilibrium.

Although the larger lactones do not exist to any appreciable extent in equilibrium with the free hydroxy acids, such lactones may be prepared under the proper conditions. It is necessary to treat the hydroxy acid with acid under conditions where the water formed in the reaction is removed so as to shift the unfavorable equilibrium toward the lactone. It is also necessary to operate in very dilute solution so as to minimize the intermolecular esterification reaction, which leads to a polymer.

OH
COOH

$\xrightarrow[\text{benzene}]{H^+}$

$+ H_2O$

(100%)

15-hydroxypentadecanoic acid   15-hydroxypentadecanoic
(0.007 *M*)   acid lactone

γ-Lactones and δ-lactones form from the hydroxy acids so readily that it is often not necessary even to add acid to catalyze the intramolecular esterification; mere traces of acid in the solvent or on the glassware suffice to bring about lactonization. Thus, in any reaction that would yield a 4- or 5-hydroxy acid, the corresponding lactone is often the isolated product.

TABLE 27.4 Hydrolytic Equilibria of Lactones

Lactone Formula	Equilibrium Composition	
	Hydroxy Acid, %	Lactone, %
	100	0
	27	73
	5	95
	2	98
	91	9
	79	21
	75	25
	~100	~0

Lactones may also result from reactions of other substituted carboxylic acids, as shown by the following examples.

(50%)

(56%)

The latter reaction must be carried out under high dilution to suppress intermolecular displacement reactions.

EXERCISE 27.10 Suggest a multistep synthesis of the following lactone, starting with ethyl acetate and 4-bromo-2-methyl-2-butene.

Hydroxy acids that cannot form five- or six-membered rings undergo polymerization unless the reaction is carried out under high dilution conditions.

$$n \; HO(CH_2)_8\overset{O}{\overset{\|}{C}}OH \longrightarrow HO(CH_2)_8\overset{O}{\overset{\|}{C}}O(CH_2)_8\overset{O}{\overset{\|}{C}}O(CH_2)_8\overset{O}{\overset{\|}{C}}O \ldots$$

α-Hydroxy acids cannot form a stable lactone ring (three-membered), so they undergo intermolecular self-esterification under acid catalysis. However, the initial dimeric product is now a form of 5-hydroxy acid, so lactonization occurs. The product, which is a dilactone containing two molecules of the original α-hydroxy acid, is called a **lactide**.

lactic acid   lactide

Like β-hydroxy aldehydes and ketones, β-hydroxy acids and their derivatives undergo dehydration easily under acidic conditions. The mechanism is similar to that for dehydration of the other β-hydroxy carbonyl compounds discussed previously (Sections 19.3.A and 27.4.B). Since conjugation of a double bond with an acid or ester carbonyl group is less stabilizing than with an aldehyde or ketone carbonyl (Section 19.3), mixtures of the α,β-unsaturated and β,γ-unsaturated acids often result from dehydration of a β-hydroxy acid.

(57%)   (43%)

EXERCISE 27.11 What are the principal products when each of the following hydroxy acids is treated with acid?
(a) 2-hydroxybutanoic acid   (b) 3-hydroxybutanoic acid   (c) 4-hydroxybutanoic acid

27.6 Dicarboxylic Acids

The simple aliphatic dicarboxylic acids are fairly widespread in nature and crystallize readily from aqueous solutions. Consequently, they are easy to isolate and were among the earliest known organic compounds. Oxalic acid occurs in many plants, such as rhubarb, usually as the potassium salt. The insoluble calcium salt is found in plant cells and in some calculi, which are stony deposits found in the human body. The acid is poisonous. Succinic acid occurs in fossils, fungi, lichens, and amber. It was first isolated in 1546 from the distillate of amber. Glutaric acid occurs in sugar beets and is also found in the aqueous extract of crude wool. Adipic acid may also be isolated from sugar beets, but it is normally synthesized from cyclohexane and its derivatives, as discussed in the next section.

A. Synthesis

Several dicarboxylic acids may be prepared by methods involving the hydrolysis of nitriles. For example, malonic acid is prepared from chloroacetic acid via cyanoacetic acid. The displacement reaction and the alkaline hydrolysis are carried out in one operation, and the product is isolated in about 80% yield.

$$ClCH_2COOH + NaOH + NaCN \xrightarrow{H_2O} [NCCH_2CO_2^- \ Na^+] \xrightarrow[H_2O]{NaOH}$$

$$Na^+ \ ^-O_2CCH_2CO_2^- \ Na^+ \xrightarrow{HCl} HOOCCH_2COOH$$
$$(77-82\%)$$

A similar example is the synthesis of glutaric acid by the acid-catalyzed hydrolysis of 1,3-dicyanopropane.

$$BrCH_2CH_2CH_2Br \xrightarrow[H_2O]{NaCN} NCCH_2CH_2CH_2CN \xrightarrow[H_2O]{HCl} HOOCCH_2CH_2CH_2COOH$$
$$(82\%) \qquad\qquad (84\%)$$
$$\text{glutaric acid}$$

Succinic acid derivatives are often available by conjugate addition of cyanide to α,β-unsaturated esters (Section 19.3.B). Hydrolysis of the β-cyano acid yields the corresponding succinic acid.

$$CH_3CH{=}CHCOOC_2H_5 + NaCN \xrightarrow{H_2O} CH_3\overset{\displaystyle CN}{\underset{\displaystyle |}{C}}HCH_2COOH \xrightarrow[H_2O]{Ba(OH)_2}$$

$$\xrightarrow{H_3O^+} CH_3\overset{\displaystyle COOH}{\underset{\displaystyle |}{C}}HCH_2COOH$$
$$(66-70\%)$$
$$\alpha\text{-methylsuccinic acid}$$
$$\text{2-methylbutanedioic acid}$$

Certain diacids are conveniently prepared by the oxidation of cyclic alkenes or ketones. This is particularly true for adipic acid derivatives because cyclohexane derivatives are generally readily available. Examples are

cyclohex-3-ene-
carbonitrile

3-cyanohexanedioic
acid

3,5-dimethylcyclohexanone

2,4-dimethylhexanedioic acid
(60%)

Adipic acid is manufactured on a large scale for use in making nylon and derived polymers (Section 34.5). One of several methods that are used for its synthesis is the oxidation of cyclohexane or cyclohexene.

adipic acid

One acid that is usually considered to be an inorganic acid of carbon is carbonic acid. However, important organic derivatives are known. The diacyl chloride, phosgene, $COCl_2$, is prepared commercially by allowing CO and Cl_2 to react in the presence of a catalyst. Phosgene reacts with alcohols to give dialkyl carbonates.

$$CO Cl_2 + 2\ ROH \longrightarrow RO\overset{\overset{\displaystyle O}{\|}}{C}OR + 2\ HCl$$

dialkyl
carbonate

The diamide of carbonic acid, urea, H_2NCONH_2, is a metabolic product that has important commercial and historical significance in organic chemistry (Chapter 1).

On a tonnage basis, the most important dicarboxylic acid by far is terephthalic acid, which is prepared on an industrial scale by the air oxidation of *p*-xylene (Section 20.5.C). The oxidation of the two side chains occurs in stages, first to *p*-toluic acid, which in turn is oxidized to terephthalic acid.

p-toluic acid

terephthalic
acid

The first step proceeds much more easily than the second. Indeed, the oxidation of
p-toluic acid requires such high temperatures that oxidation of the acetic acid solvent
becomes a significant cost concern and corrosion of reaction vessels is a problem.

Phthalic acid is another important industrial product. Various high-boiling esters,
particularly the bis-2-ethylhexyl ester, are widely used as plasticizers. Phthalic acid is
prepared commercially by the oxidation of naphthalene (Section 30.3.D) or *o*-xylene.
On heating it readily loses water to produce phthalic anhydride, a compound with a
characteristic odor that forms long colorless needles on sublimation.

Phthalic anhydride is used in the manufacture of glyptal resins, highly crosslinked,
infusible polyesters prepared by heating the anhydride with glycerol. Potassium hydrogen phthalate is a well-characterized compound available in pure anhydrous form. It is
used as a primary standard in titrations with bases.

B. Acidity

The dicarboxylic acids are dihydric acids and are characterized by two dissociation
constants, K_1 and K_2.

$$\text{HOOC(CH}_2)_n\text{COOH} \underset{}{\overset{K_1}{\rightleftharpoons}} \text{HOOC(CH}_2)_n\text{CO}_2^- + \text{H}^+$$

$$\text{HOOC(CH}_2)_n\text{CO}_2^- \underset{}{\overset{K_2}{\rightleftharpoons}} {}^-\text{O}_2\text{C(CH}_2)_n\text{CO}_2^- + \text{H}^+$$

The dissociation constants for several diacids are summarized in Table 27.5. If we
treat the COOH group as a substituent in acetic acid, YCH_2COOH, the higher acidity
of malonic acid compared to acetic acid ($\text{p}K_a = 4.76$) indicates that the COOH group
acts as an electron-attracting inductive group.

> Be careful of statistical effects in this comparison. Malonic acid has two COOH groups
> that can lose a proton and would be expected to have a dissociation constant twice that of
> acetic acid because of this statistical effect alone.

TABLE 27.5 Acidity of Alkanedioic Acids

Acid	$K_1 \times 10^{-5}\ M$	$K_2 \times 10^{-5}\ M$	$\text{p}K_1$	$\text{p}K_2$
oxalic	5400	5.4	1.27	4.27
malonic	140	0.20	2.85	5.70
succinic	6.2	0.23	4.21	5.64
glutaric	4.6	0.39	4.34	5.41
adipic	3.7	0.39	4.43	5.41

The acid-strengthening effect of a carboxylic acid substituent is not unexpected. All carbonyl groups have this effect because of the associated dipole which provides electrostatic stabilization of the negative charge of a carboxylate anion.

electrostatic attraction

$$\overset{\longleftarrow \quad +}{\overbrace{}}$$
$$HOOC\sim\sim\sim CO_2^-$$

On the other hand, K_2 for a dicarboxylic acid is generally less than the dissociation constant of acetic acid. The presence of a carboxylate ion substituent reduces the acidity of an acid. This effect is clearly associated with the electrostatic repulsion of two negative charges in the dicarboxylate ion.

electrostatic repulsion

$$^-O_2C\sim\sim\sim CO_2^-$$

As expected for such a phenomenon, both the acid-strengthening effect of a carboxylic acid substituent and the acid-weakening effect of a carboxylate anion diminish with distance down a chain.

The second dissociation constant of oxalic acid seems anomalous by this comparison. Oxalate monoanion is more acidic than a neutral alkanoic acid despite the high electrostatic repulsion inherent in the oxalate dianion. This exception to the above-mentioned generalization is probably a solvation phenomenon and is associated with the high charge density on the oxalate dianion.

C. Reactions of Dicarboxylic Acids and Their Derivatives

Dicarboxylic acids undergo a variety of thermal reactions. Anhydrous oxalic acid can be sublimed by careful heating, but at higher temperatures it decomposes to carbon dioxide and formic acid. Formic acid also decomposes under these conditions to carbon monoxide and water.

Malonic acid decarboxylates smoothly at 150°C to give acetic acid.

$$HOOCCH_2COOH \xrightarrow{\ 150°C\ } CO_2 + CH_3COOH$$

This reaction is general for all substituted malonic acids and for β-keto acids as well. The mechanism may involve a cyclic six-center transition state similar to that discussed previously for the Diels-Alder reaction (Sections 19.5, 20.7). The initial product is an enol, which rapidly isomerizes to acetic acid.

Decarboxylation

Diels–Alder Reaction

Decarboxylation of substituted malonic acids is a frequently used process for the synthesis of carboxylic acids (Section 27.7.C). Decarboxylation is usually accomplished by heating the pure diacid at 120-180°C for several hours.

Succinic and glutaric acids lose water on heating to give cyclic anhydrides.

succinic anhydride

However, the preparation of these anhydrides is best accomplished by heating with acetyl chloride or acetic anhydride. These reagents react with the water produced by the dehydration.

(76%)

The easy dehydration of phthalic acid to phthalic anhydride was mentioned in Section 27.6.A. Other dehydrating agents that have been used for the formation of cyclic anhydrides are PCl_5, P_2O_5, $POCl_3$, and $SOCl_2$.

Succinic and glutaric acid and their derivatives also form cyclic **imides** with ammonia and primary amines. Five-membered ring imides form the most readily; pyrolysis of the diammonium salt often gives excellent yields.

ammonium phthalate

(97%)
phthalimide

Six-membered ring imides form less readily; a convenient method of preparation involves pyrolysis of the monoamide of the corresponding dicarboxylic acid, as illustrated by the following example.

(65% overall)
glutarimide

EXERCISE 27.13 There are four isomeric diacids having the formula $C_5H_8O_4$. Write their structures and predict the product of heating each isomer at 200°C for 2 hr.

Adipic and pimelic acid esters undergo a cyclic Claisen condensation (Section 18.9) known as a **Dieckmann condensation**; the products of such reactions are five- and six-membered cyclic β-keto esters.

(80%)

(54%)

The Dieckmann condensation is not satisfactory for the preparation of other sized rings.

EXERCISE 27.14 Write the stepwise mechanism for the reaction of diethyl adipate with sodium ethoxide in refluxing benzene.

27.7 Diketones, Keto Aldehydes, Keto Acids, and Keto Esters

This diverse group of difunctional compounds is best considered together because their chemistry is dominated by the interaction of two carbonyl groups in each case. As we shall see, the 1,2-compounds, though fairly rare, do have some interesting aspects in their chemistry. The most important group of dicarbonyl compounds are the 1,3-isomers because of their importance in synthesis. Other dicarbonyl compounds show chemical behavior that is simply that of the monofunctional counterparts except that the presence of two functional groups in the same molecule allows intramolecular reactions, leading to the formation of ring compounds.

A. Synthesis

α-Diketones may be obtained by the mild oxidation of α-hydroxy ketones, which are available by the acyloin condensation (Section 27.4.A). Since the product α-diketones are also susceptible to oxidation (with cleavage of the carbonyl-carbonyl bond), especially mild oxidants must be used. Cupric acetate is especially effective.

(88%)

α-Diketones and α-keto aldehydes are also available by the direct oxidation of simple ketones with selenium dioxide.

(60%)

Selenium dioxide, SeO_2, is a white, crystalline material that melts at 340°C. It is prepared by oxidizing selenium metal with nitric acid. Although it is rather high melting, it has a substantial vapor pressure at moderate temperatures (12.5 mm at 70°C). The yellowish green vapor has a pungent odor. In the body it is reduced to selenium metal, which may produce liver damage. Prolonged occupational exposure to selenium or SeO_2 leads to a garlic odor of breath and sweat.

1,3-Dicarbonyl compounds are almost uniformly prepared by some version of the Claisen condensation. In Section 18.9 we saw that esters react with base to give β-keto esters.

$$2\ CH_3COOC_2H_5 \xrightarrow{C_2H_5O^-Na^+} \xrightarrow{H_3O^+} CH_3\overset{O}{\overset{\|}{C}}CH_2COOC_2H_5$$

β-Diketones and β-keto aldehydes may be prepared by a mixed Claisen condensation using a ketone and an ester.

$$CH_3\overset{O}{\overset{\|}{C}}CH_3 + CH_3\overset{O}{\overset{\|}{C}}OEt \xrightarrow[\text{ether}]{NaH} \xrightarrow{H_3O^+} CH_3\overset{O}{\overset{\|}{C}}CH_2\overset{O}{\overset{\|}{C}}CH_3$$

(85%)

$$C_6H_5\overset{O}{\overset{\|}{C}}OEt + C_6H_5\overset{O}{\overset{\|}{C}}CH_3 \xrightarrow[\text{benzene}]{NaNH_2} \xrightarrow{H_3O^+} C_6H_5\overset{O}{\overset{\|}{C}}CH_2\overset{O}{\overset{\|}{C}}C_6H_5$$

(73%)

When ethyl formate is used in a mixed Claisen condensation, the product is a β-keto aldehyde, which exists almost entirely in the enolic form (Section 27.7.B).

(75%)

The mixed Claisen condensation of ketones and esters works well because ketones are considerably more acidic than are esters (Section 18.9). Thus, in the basic medium, the ketone is deprotonated to a larger extent than the ester.

869

Sec. 27.7

*Diketones,
Keto Aldehydes,
Keto Acids, and
Keto Esters*

$$CH_3\overset{O}{\overset{\|}{C}}CH_3 + EtO^- \rightleftharpoons CH_3\overset{O^-}{\overset{|}{C}}=CH_2 + EtOH \qquad K \cong 10^{-3}$$

$$CH_3\overset{O}{\overset{\|}{C}}OEt + EtO^- \rightleftharpoons CH_2=\overset{O^-}{\overset{|}{C}}OEt + EtOH \qquad K \cong 10^{-9}$$

Of course, once the ketone enolate is formed, it may react with another nonionized ketone molecule (aldol addition) or with the ester. However, the aldol reaction is usually thermodynamically unfavorable with ketones (page 392), and this reaction is only a minor side reaction.

$$CH_3\overset{O^-}{\overset{|}{C}}=CH_2 + CH_3\overset{O}{\overset{\|}{C}}CH_3 \rightleftharpoons CH_3\overset{O}{\overset{\|}{C}}CH_2\overset{O^-}{\overset{|}{C}}(CH_3)_2$$

On the other hand, the Claisen condensation is driven by the all-important final deprotonation of the acidic product. Thus the β-diketone is formed in high yield.

Cyclic β-diketones are formed by *intramolecular* Claisen condensation of 1,4- and 1,5-keto esters. The reaction is a useful method for the formation of five- and six-membered rings. This reaction is clearly analogous to the Dieckmann condensation (Section 27.6.C).

(90%)

EXERCISE 27.15 Outline syntheses of the following dicarbonyl compounds.
(a) 3,4-hexanedione   (b) 2,4-pentanedione   (c) 3-oxobutanal

B. Keto-Enol Equilibria in Dicarbonyl Compounds

Simple ketones exist largely in the keto form with but a trace of the enol (vinyl alcohol) form present at equilibrium (Section 14.6.A).

$$CH_3\overset{O}{\overset{\|}{C}}CH_3 \rightleftharpoons CH_3\overset{OH}{\overset{|}{C}}=CH_2$$

$$6 \times 10^{-6}\%$$

In contrast, 1,2- and 1,3-dicarbonyl compounds often contain a large amount of enol form in equilibrium with the dicarbonyl form. For example, 2,4-pentanedione is a mixture of 84% dione and 16% enolic form in aqueous solution. In hexane solution the compound exists almost entirely in the enolic form.

water solution:	84%	16%
hexane solution:	8%	92%

One important reason for this phenomenon is the ability of the enol to form an intramolecular hydrogen bond. Such intramolecular hydrogen bonds are especially favorable when six-membered rings are formed. The enolic form also benefits from resonance stabilization in a way not available to the dicarbonyl compound itself.

$$\left[\begin{array}{cc} \text{CH}_3\text{C} & \text{CCH}_3 \\ \text{CH} \end{array} \longleftrightarrow \begin{array}{cc} \text{CH}_3\text{C} & \text{CCH}_3 \\ \text{CH} \end{array} \right]$$

Note that the type of delocalization shown in the foregoing example is precisely the kind that is involved in carboxylic acids.

$$\text{RC}-\text{OH} \longleftrightarrow \text{RC}=\overset{+}{\text{O}}\text{H}$$

In the enolic form of a 1,3-diketone, a hydroxy lone pair is delocalized *through the double bond* into the carbonyl oxygen.

Whenever two functional groups are joined to a double bond in this way, the molecule has properties similar to the corresponding compound without the double bond. This empirical concept is called the principle of **vinylogy**, and such compounds are called **vinylogs**.

$$\text{CH}_3\text{CCH}=\text{CCH}_3 \quad \text{is a vinylog of} \quad \text{CH}_3\text{C}-\text{OH}$$

$$\text{CH}_3\text{CCH}=\text{CCH}_3 \quad \text{is a vinylog of} \quad \text{CH}_3\text{C}-\text{NH}_2$$

Note that the percentage of enol form at equilibrium is higher in nonpolar aprotic solvents because in such solvents the intramolecular hydrogen bond is most beneficial. In protic solvents the dicarbonyl compound itself as well as the enol can hydrogen-bond to solvent molecules, and the ability of the enol to form an intramolecular hydrogen bond provides no extra stabilization.

Other 1,3-dicarbonyl compounds also contain substantial amounts of enolic forms in solution. β-Keto esters are in equilibrium with significant amounts of the form in which the ketone carbonyl is enolized.

$$\text{CH}_3\text{C}\overset{\text{O}}{}\text{CH}_2\overset{\text{O}}{}\text{COCH}_3 \rightleftharpoons \text{CH}_3\text{C}\overset{\text{O}}{}\text{CH}\overset{\text{O}}{}\text{COCH}_3$$

water solution: 90% 10%
hexane solution: 51% 49%

β-Keto aldehydes exist almost entirely in the enolic form; both carbonyl groups are enolized to an appreciable extent. The two enolic forms are easily interconvertible, since only small shifts in bond distances are required.

871

Sec. 27.7

*Diketones,
Keto Aldehydes,
Keto Acids, and
Keto Esters*

0%　　　　　76%　　　　　24%
(CCl$_4$ solution)

Cyclic 1,3-diketones also exist predominantly in the enolic form, even though they cannot participate in intramolecular hydrogen bonding for reasons of geometry.

5%　　　　　95%
(water solution)

1,2-Diketones also show enhanced amounts of enol form. The main driving force for enolization in this case is relief of the electrostatic repulsion that occurs when the two electrophilic carbonyl groups are adjacent to each other.

minor　　　　　major

EXERCISE 27.16 Sketch the expected NMR spectrum of a CCl$_4$ solution of 2,4-pentanedione.

C. Decarboxylation of β-Keto Acids

β-Keto acids undergo thermal decarboxylation in the same manner as do 1,3-diacids (Section 27.6.C). In this case milder conditions suffice to bring about decarboxylation; 2-ethyl-3-oxohexanoic acid has a half-life of only 15 min at 50°C.

The mechanism may involve a concerted, six-center transition state as depicted on page 865 for the decarboxylation of malonic acid. The initial product in the case of a β-keto acid is the enol form of the ketone. This mechanism is consistent with the resistance of bridgehead bicyclic β-keto acids to decarboxylation; the product would be a highly strained bridgehead olefin.

EXERCISE 27.17 Use your molecular models to confirm that bridgehead olefins such as the one just discussed are highly strained.

D. 1,3-Dicarbonyl Compounds as Carbon Acids

1,3-Dicarbonyl compounds that have a hydrogen bound to the carbon between the two carbonyl groups are much stronger acids than normal aldehydes, ketones, or esters because the charge in the resulting enolate ion can be delocalized into both carbonyl groups.

Some typical pK_as for such systems are contained in Table 27.6. The acidities of 1,3-dicarbonyl compounds are sufficiently high that they are converted to their conjugate bases essentially quantitatively by hydroxide ion in water or by alkoxide ion in alcoholic solvent.

TABLE 27.6 Acidity of
β-Dicarbonyl Compounds

Compound	pK_a
$NCCH_2COCH_3$	9
$CH_3CCH_2CCH_3$	9
$CH_3CCH_2COCH_3$	11
$CH_3CCHCCH_3$ $\quad\ CH_3$	11
$NCCH_2CN$	11
$CH_3OCCH_2COCH_3$	13

873

Sec. 27.7

Diketones,
Keto Aldehydes,
Keto Acids, and
Keto Esters

As we shall see, these easily accessible carbanions are valuable synthetic intermediates.

EXERCISE 27.18 Using the pK_a values given in Table 27.6, estimate the equilibrium constant for the reaction of 2,4-pentanedione with sodium methoxide in methanol.

E. The Malonic Ester and Acetoacetic Ester Syntheses

The anions of 1,3-dicarbonyl compounds are nucleophiles and may take part in S_N2 displacement reactions with alkyl halides. Diethyl malonate and ethyl acetoacetate are inexpensive commercial compounds that are often alkylated in this manner. Hydrolysis of the alkylated product followed by decarboxylation of the resulting β-diacid or β-keto acid (Sections 27.6.C, 27.7.C) provides an important general synthesis of acids and methyl ketones. The overall processes are called the **malonic ester synthesis** or the **acetoacetic ester synthesis**.

$$CH_2(COOEt)_2 \xrightarrow[EtOH]{NaOEt} \xrightarrow{n\text{-}C_4H_9Br} n\text{-}C_4H_9CH(COOEt)_2 \xrightarrow[115°C]{conc.\ HCL} n\text{-}C_4H_9CH_2COOH$$

(80–90%)
diethyl *n*-butylmalonate   hexanoic acid

$$CH_2(COOEt)_2 \xrightarrow[EtOH]{NaOEt} \xrightarrow{(CH_3)_2CHI} (CH_3)_2CHCH(COOEt)_2 \xrightarrow[115°C]{conc.\ HCl} (CH_3)_2CHCH_2COOH$$

(70–75%)
diethyl isopropylmalonate   3-methylbutanoic acid

The initially formed alkylmalonic ester may be alkylated again with the same alkyl halide or with a different one to widen the scope of the procedure.

$$CH_2(COOEt)_2 \xrightarrow[EtOH]{NaOEt} \xrightarrow{n\text{-}C_4H_9Br} n\text{-}C_4H_9CH(COOEt)_2 \xrightarrow[EtOH]{NaOEt} \xrightarrow{CH_3Br}$$

$$\overset{\overset{\displaystyle CH_3}{|}}{CH_3CH_2CH_2CH_2C(COOEt)_2} \xrightarrow[115°C]{conc.\ HCl} \overset{\overset{\displaystyle CH_3}{|}}{CH_3CH_2CH_2CH_2CHCOOH}$$

2-methylhexanoic acid

The overall synthetic result of alkylation and decarboxylation of malonic ester is formation of an alkyl or dialkylacetic acid.

$$CH_2(COOEt)_2 \xrightarrow{NaOEt} \xrightarrow{R'X} R'CH(COOEt)_2 \xrightarrow{NaOEt} \xrightarrow{R''X}$$

$$R'R''C(COOEt)_2 \xrightarrow[\Delta]{H^+} \overset{R'}{\underset{R''}{>}}CHCOOH$$

A principal limitation in the synthetic sequence is that the alkylation process is an S_N2 reaction; bimolecular elimination is an expected side reaction whose importance depends on the structure of RX. If a suitable dihalide is used in the reaction, 2 moles of malonic ester can be added to both ends of a chain; alternatively, intramolecular alkylation in the second step leads to a cyclic diester.

$$CH_2(COOEt)_2 \xrightarrow[\text{EtOH}]{2\ NaOEt} \xrightarrow{Br(CH_2)_3Cl} \square\!\!<^{COOEt}_{COOEt} \xrightarrow[\text{EtOH}]{KOH} \xrightarrow[\Delta]{H_3O^+} \square\!\!<^{H}_{COOH}$$

(42–44%)
cyclobutanecarboxylic acid

If ethyl acetoacetate is used as the starting material, the combination of alkylation, hydrolysis, and decarboxylation provides a synthesis of various methyl alkyl ketones.

(69–72%)

(61% overall)
2-heptanone

As in the malonic ester synthesis, the starting β-keto ester may be alkylated successively with two different alkyl halides. After hydrolysis and decarboxylation, the product is a ketone that is branched at the α-carbon.

3-methylhex-5-en-2-one

The net result is summarized below and is again subject to the usual limitations of S_N2 reactions.

$$CH_3COCH_2COOEt \xrightarrow{R'X} \xrightarrow{R''X} \xrightarrow[\Delta]{H^+} CH_3CCH\!\!<^{R'}_{R''}$$

Other β-diketones and β-keto esters may be alkylated in the same manner. The following examples show the tremendous utility of these reactions in building up complicated organic structures.

1 equiv NaOH
CH₃I, H₂O

(70%)
2-methyl-1,3-cyclohexanedione

2 equiv NaOMe
CH₃I, MeOH

(80%)
2,2-dimethyl-1,3-cyclohexanedione

875

Sec. 27.7

*Diketones,
Keto Aldehydes,
Keto Acids, and
Keto Esters*

(60%)
2-(3-bromopropyl)cyclopentanone

EXERCISE 27.19 Write equations showing all of the steps involved in the preparation of the following compounds by the malonic ester and acetoacetic ester syntheses.
(a) hex-5-en-2-one   (b) 5-methylhexanoic acid
(c) 2-ethylpent-4-enoic acid   (d) 4-oxopentanoic acid

F. The Knoevenagel Condensation

Esters of malonic acid readily react with aldehydes and ketones under basic conditions to give α,β-unsaturated diesters.

$$(CH_3)_2CHCH_2CHO + CH_2(COOEt)_2 \xrightarrow[\substack{benzene \\ \Delta}]{piperidine} (CH_3)_2CHCH_2CH{=}C(COOEt)_2$$
$$(78\%)$$

(80%)

The transformation is similar to the aldol reaction (Section 14.8.C) and the related reactions of ester enolates with aldehydes and ketones (Section 18.9). In the present case, however, only weakly basic catalysts are required, because of the high acidity of malonic esters. The reaction works best for aldehydes, although ketones sometimes may be used.

A variation of this reaction makes use of malonic acid with an amine catalyst. In this case some of the carboxylate anion is present, but since amines are weak bases, the fraction of carboxylate anion is small. The carbanion derived from the α-hydrogen is also present because the carbonyl groups of the carboxylic acid stabilize the carbanion just as they stabilize the ester carbonyls. The resulting condensation products decarboxylate on heating to give α,β-unsaturated acids. The catalyst usually employed in this reaction is the tertiary amine pyridine.

(75– 85%)
non-2-enoic acid

This version of the Knoevenagel condensation works well with all aldehydes. It can be employed with ketones, but yields are generally low.

EXERCISE 27.20 The Knoevenagel condensation provides a synthesis of unsaturated malonic esters or of α,β-unsaturated acids. Outline syntheses of the following compounds.
(a) $CH_3CH_2CH{=}CHCOOH$ (b) $CH_3CH_2CH{=}C(COOEt)_2$

G. The Michael Addition Reaction

In Section 19.3.A., we saw that α,β-unsaturated carbonyl compounds can react with such nucleophiles as cyanide ion and Grignard reagents either by 1,2- or 1,4-addition. The 1,4-addition of a carbanion to an α,β-unsaturated carbonyl system is called a **Michael addition**. It is a common and useful reaction. For example, when a mixture of 2-cyclohexen-1-one and diethyl malonate is treated with a catalytic amount of sodium ethoxide in ethanol, the following addition reaction occurs.

(90%)

The mechanism of the Michael addition is illustrated as follows with diethyl malonate and acrolein; the product is obtained in 50% yield.

(1) $CH_2(COOEt)_2 + EtO^- \rightleftharpoons {}^-{:}CH(COOEt)_2 + EtOH$

(2) $HC{-}CH{=}CH_2 + {}^-{:}CH(COOEt)_2 \rightleftharpoons HC{=}CH{-}CH_2{-}CH(COOEt)_2$

(3) $HC{=}CHCH_2CH(COOEt)_2 + EtOH \rightleftharpoons HCCH_2CH_2CH(COOEt)_2 + EtO^-$

A Michael addition such as this is similar to the alkylation of a carbanion by an alkyl halide—with one important exception. In the alkylation with an alkyl halide, a stoichiometric amount of base is consumed; in the Michael addition, the base functions as a catalyst. Thus, only a small amount of base need be used in Michael additions, and the process is reversible. The driving force for the reaction is the formation of a new carbon-carbon single bond at the expense of the π-bond of the unsaturated carbonyl compound; this driving force is essentially the same as that of all additions to a double bond.

Michael additions are observed between carbon acids containing an acidic proton and a variety of α,β-unsaturated carbonyl systems.

$$CH_2(COOEt)_2 + CH_2{=}CHCCH_3 \xrightarrow[\substack{EtOH \\ 0°C}]{NaOEt} CH_3CCH_2CH_2CH(COOEt)_2$$

(71%)

877

Sec. 27.7

*Diketones,
Keto Aldehydes,
Keto Acids, and
Keto Esters*

$$CH_3CCH_2CCH_3 + CH_2=CHCN \xrightarrow[\text{t-BuOH}]{\text{Et}_3\text{N}} CH_3CCHCCH_3$$

(with ketone oxygens; product bears CH_2CH_2CN substituent)

(77%)

$$+ CH_2=CHCOOEt \xrightarrow[\text{EtOH}]{\text{NaOEt}} (\text{cyclohexane-1,3-dione with } CH_2CH_2COOEt)$$
$$0°C$$

If an excess of the α,β-unsaturated carbonyl component is used, it is possible to achieve dialkylation.

$$CH_2(COOEt)_2 + CH_2=CHCCH_3 \xrightarrow{\text{OH}^-} $$

(excess)

(product: central C bearing two COOEt and two $CH_3CCH_2CH_2$ groups)

(85%)

The Michael addition constitutes a useful method for the synthesis of 1,5-dicarbonyl systems. When diethyl malonate or acetoacetic ester is used as the adding group, the product may be hydrolyzed and decarboxylated to obtain the alkylated acid or ketone.

$$CH_3CCH_2COOEt + CH_2=CHCOOEt \xrightarrow{\text{NaOEt}}_{\text{EtOH}} CH_3CCHCH_2CH_2COOEt \xrightarrow[\Delta]{\text{H}_3\text{O}^+}$$
$$\overset{|}{COOEt}$$

$$\left[CH_3CCHCH_2CH_2COOH \atop \overset{|}{COOH} \right] \longrightarrow CH_3CCH_2CH_2CH_2COOH + CO_2$$

EXERCISE 27.21 Make a 3 × 3 matrix with methyl acrylate, acrolein, and methyl vinyl ketone on one side and diethyl malonate, acetoacetic ester, and 2-ethoxycarbonylcyclopentanone on the other. Each of the nine intersections of the matrix represents a Michael addition reaction. Assuming that the reactants are used in a ratio of 1:1 in each case, write the structures of the nine reaction products. Now write the products expected from the hydrolysis and decarboxylation of each of the nine initial adducts.

Although the Michael addition is most successful when the carbon acid is relatively acidic, such as a 1,3-dicarbonyl compound, the reaction also occurs with simple ketones.

$$(\text{2-methylcyclohexanone}) + CH_2=CHCC_6H_5 \xrightarrow[\text{ether}]{\text{KOEt} \atop \text{EtOH}} (\text{product with } CH_3 \text{ and } CH_2CH_2CC_6H_5)$$

(64%)

$$CH_3\overset{O}{\overset{\|}{C}}CH_2CH_3 + CH_2{=}CHCN \xrightarrow[\text{t-BuOH}]{\text{KOH}} CH_3\overset{O}{\overset{\|}{C}}\underset{\underset{CH_3}{|}}{C}(CH_2CH_2CN)_2$$

(excess)

A useful variant of the Michael addition occurs with methyl vinyl ketone and its derivatives. The initially formed 1,5-diketone undergoes a subsequent intramolecular aldol reaction to yield a cyclohexenone ring. The process is essentially a combination of the Michael reaction and aldol reaction and is called **Robinson annelation**.

(50%)

The Robinson annelation sequence has been useful in building up the carbon framework of complex natural products such as steroids (Section 34.7). An example of the use of the reaction as the first step in the laboratory synthesis of a steroid is given below.

EXERCISE 27.22 Propose a synthesis of the following spirocyclic compound.

PROBLEMS

1. Name the following compounds.

(a) $(CH_3)_2CH\overset{O}{\overset{\|}{C}}CH_2COOCH_3$

(b) $HOCH_2\underset{\underset{CH_3}{|}}{\overset{\overset{CH_3}{|}}{C}}CH_2OH$

(c) $HOCH_2CH_2CH_2COOH$

(d) $CH_3\overset{O}{\overset{\|}{C}}CH_2CH_2CN$

(e) HOOCCH₂CHCH₂COOH $\overset{CH_3}{|}$

(f) HOOCCH₂CH₂CH₂CHCOOH $\overset{CH_3}{|}$

(g) CH₃CH₂CH₂   COOCH₃ with central C bearing CH₃ and COOCH₃

(h) HOOCCH₂CHCH₂CHO $\overset{CH_3}{|}$

(i) HOCH₂CH₂CH₂CNH₂ with C=O

(j) CH₂=CHCH₂CH₂CCH₃ with C=O

(k) cyclohexane dione with CH₃, CH₃

(l) CH₃CCH₂CHCOOH with C=O and CH₃

(m) NCCH₂CH₂CH₂CN

(n) CH₃CHCH₂CCH₂CH₂CHO with CH₃ and O

2. Compare the stereostructure of the 1,2-cyclodecanediol produced from *cis-* and *trans-*cyclodecene by each of the following reactions.
   (a) (i) HCO₃H; (ii) aqueous NaOH
   (b) OsO₄, H₂O₂
   (c) (i) aqueous Br₂; (ii) aqueous NaOH

3. Pinacol rearrangement of 1,1-diphenyl-1,2-ethanediol gives diphenylacetaldehyde and not phenylacetophenone. Explain.

$(C_6H_5)_2CCH_2OH$ with OH, $\xrightarrow{H^+}$ → (C₆H₅)₂CHCHO

→/→ C₆H₅CCH₂C₆H₅ with O

4. Give the principal product(s) of each of the following reactions or reaction sequences.

(a) cyclopentane with OH and CH₂OH $\xrightarrow{H^+}$

(b) HOCH₂CCHOHCH₂OH + HIO₄ ⟶ with CH₃ and CH₃

(c) HO(CH₂)₆COOH $\xrightarrow{\Delta}$

(d) CH₃CH₂CHOHCOOH $\xrightarrow{\Delta}$

(e) HOCH₂CH₂CH₂COOH $\xrightarrow{\Delta}$

(f) benzene with COOEt, COOEt + EtOOC(CH₂)₃COOEt $\xrightarrow[EtOH]{EtONa}$ $\xrightarrow[\Delta]{dil\ H^+}$ C₁₁H₁₀O₂

(g) $\xrightarrow[\text{pyridine}]{C_6H_5SO_2Cl}$ $\xrightarrow[\text{EtONa/EtOH}]{CH_2(COOEt)_2}$ $\xrightarrow[\Delta]{\text{dil } H^+}$ $C_4H_7DO_2$
optically
active

(h) $2 \text{ CH}_2(\text{COOEt})_2 + \text{C}_6\text{H}_5\text{CHO} \xrightarrow[\text{EtOH}]{\text{EtONa}} \xrightarrow[\Delta]{\text{dil } H^+} \text{C}_{11}\text{H}_{12}\text{O}_4$

(i) $\text{C}_6\text{H}_5\text{COCH}_2\text{COOEt} \xrightarrow[\text{EtOH}]{\text{EtONa}} \xrightarrow{\text{CH}_3\text{CH}_2\text{I}} \xrightarrow[\text{EtOH}]{\text{EtONa}} \xrightarrow{\text{CH}_3\text{I}} \xrightarrow[\Delta]{H^+} \text{C}_{11}\text{H}_{14}\text{O}$

(j) $\text{EtOOCCOOEt} + \text{CH}_3\text{COOEt} \xrightarrow[\text{EtOH}]{\text{EtONa}}$

5. (a) Write alternative Lewis structures for periodic acid, $HOIO_3$, and iodic acid, $HOIO_2$, making use of $^-O\!\!-\!\!I^+$ or $O\!=\!I$ bonds. Be careful to count electrons and assign formal charges properly; note that iodic acid has a lone pair of electrons on iodine. Follow the changes in electron pairs symbolized in the cyclic mechanism on page 851.
   (b) *cis*-1,2-Cyclopentanediol is oxidized to glutaraldehyde (1,5-pentanedial) by periodic acid much more rapidly than the trans isomer. Explain.
   (c) Suggest a method whereby periodic acid could be used to distinguish between 1,2,3-pentanetriol and 1,2,4-pentanetriol.

6. (a) 4,5-Dihydroxypentanal exists in solution largely as a cyclic hemiacetal. From the data in Table 27.3 predict which form will predominate at equilibrium.

   (b) When 4,5-dihydroxypentanal is treated with silver oxide and the resulting dihydroxyhexanoic acid is treated with acid, a lactone results. What is the structure of the lactone (see Table 27.4)?

7. Propose mechanisms for the following reactions.

(a) $+ (\text{CH}_3)_2\text{CHCH}_2\text{OH} \xrightarrow[\text{benzene}]{H_2SO_4}$ $+ H_2O$

(b) $\text{CH}_2(\text{COOCH}_3)_2 \xrightarrow[\text{CH}_3\text{OH}]{\text{NaOCH}_3} \xrightarrow{\overset{O}{CH_2-CH_2}}$

(c) $\xrightarrow{C_6H_5CO_3H} \xrightarrow[\text{CH}_3\text{OH}]{\text{CH}_3\text{O}^-}$

(d) $p\text{-CH}_3\text{OC}_6\text{H}_4\text{C}(\text{C}_6\text{H}_5)_2\text{CH}_2\text{OH} + \text{SOCl}_2 \longrightarrow (\text{C}_6\text{H}_5)_2\text{C}\!=\!\text{CHC}_6\text{H}_4\text{OCH}_3\text{-}p$

8. When ethyl acetoacetate is treated with 1,3-dibromopropane and 2 moles of sodium ethoxide in ethanol, a product (A) is produced that has the formula $\text{C}_9\text{H}_{14}\text{O}_3$. Compound A has an infrared spectrum that shows only one carbonyl absorption and no OH bond. Suggest a structure for A and rationalize its formation.

9. Give the expected product for each reaction sequence.

(a) $\xrightarrow[H_2O_2]{OsO_4}$ $(C_7H_{14}O_2)$ $\xrightarrow{HIO_4}$ $(C_7H_{12}O_2)$

(b) $CH_3CH_2\overset{\overset{\displaystyle O}{\|}}{C}CH_2CH_3$ $\xrightarrow[benzene]{Mg}$ $\xrightarrow{H_2O}$ $(C_{10}H_{22}O_2)$ $\xrightarrow[\Delta]{H_3O^+}$ $(C_{10}H_{20}O)$

(c) —CHO $\xrightarrow[C_2H_5OH]{KCN}$ $(C_{10}H_8O_4)$ $\xrightarrow{Cu(OAc)_2}$ $(C_{10}H_6O_4)$ $\xrightarrow[\Delta]{conc.\ KOH}$ $\xrightarrow{H_3O^+}$ $(C_{10}H_8O_5)$

(d) *trans*-2-butene $\xrightarrow{HCO_3H}$ $\xrightarrow[H_2O]{NaOH}$ $(C_4H_{10}O_2)$ $\xrightarrow[H^+]{}$ $(C_9H_{16}O_2)$

10. Show how one may accomplish each of the following conversions.

(a) $CH_3CH_2COOH \longrightarrow CH_3CH_2CHOH\overset{\overset{\displaystyle CH_3}{|}}{C}HCOOH$

(b) CH_3——CHO $\longrightarrow$ CH_3——$\overset{\overset{\displaystyle OH}{|}}{C}H$—$\overset{\overset{\displaystyle OH}{|}}{C}H$——$CH_3$

(c) $\longrightarrow$

(d) $CH_3CH_2COOH \longrightarrow CH_3CH_2CHOHCHOHCH_2CH_3$

(e) $\longrightarrow$

(f) $C_6H_5CH_2COOEt \longrightarrow C_6H_5CH(COOEt)_2$

(g) $C_6H_5CH(COOEt)_2 \longrightarrow HOOC\overset{\overset{\displaystyle C_6H_5}{|}}{C}HCH_2COOH$

11. Show how each of the following compounds may be prepared starting with diethyl malonate.

(a) $(CH_3)_2CHCH_2CH_2COOH$

(b) $CH_2{=}CHCH_2\overset{\overset{\displaystyle CH_3}{|}}{C}HCOOH$

(c) $CH_2{=}\overset{\overset{\displaystyle CH_3}{|}}{C}CH_2CH_2COOH$

(d)

(e) $HOOCCH_2CH_2COOH$

(f)

12. Show how each of the following compounds may be prepared starting with ethyl acetoacetate.

(a) $CH_3CCH_2CH_2CH_2CH(CH_3)_2$

(b) $CH_3CCH_2CH_2CH_2COOH$

(c) $CH_3CCHCH_2CH_2CH_3$
   CH_2CH_3

(d) $CH_3CCHCH_2CH_2CHCCH_3$
   CH_3 CH_3

13. Show how each of the following compounds may be synthesized from compounds containing five or fewer carbons.

(a)

(b)

(c) Me_2N

(d)

(e) $HOOC$

(f)

(g)

(h)

(i)

(j)

(k)

(l) $HOOC$

(m)

(n)

14. Suggest a procedure for the dialkylation of diethyl malonate with benzyl chloride using phase-transfer catalysis. What is the final product of hydrolysis of this product and heating in acid?

15. Show how the Robinson annelation may be used to prepare each compound.

(a)

(b)

(c)

(d)

16. 1-Phenylethane-*1-d*, $C_6H_5CHDCH_3$ (B), has been prepared in optically active form. This compound is particularly interesting because its chirality is due entirely to the isotopic difference between H and D. Nevertheless, the magnitude of its rotation has the relatively high value of $[\alpha]_D = 0.6°C$. The absolute configuration of B is related to the known configuration of mandelic acid by the following reaction sequences.

$$H-\overset{\text{COOH}}{\underset{\text{C}_6\text{H}_5}{\text{C}}}-OH \xrightarrow[\text{C}_2\text{H}_5\text{I}]{\text{Ag}_2\text{O}} C_{12}H_{16}O_3 \xrightarrow[\text{ether}]{\text{LiAlH}_4} C_{10}H_{14}O_2 \xrightarrow[\text{pyridine}]{\text{C}_6\text{H}_5\text{SO}_2\text{Cl}} \xrightarrow[\text{ether}]{\text{LiAlH}_4} C_{10}H_{14}O$$

(−)-mandelic acid   (−)-C   (−)-D   (−)-E

$$C_8H_{10}O \xrightarrow{\text{K}} \xrightarrow{\text{C}_2\text{H}_5\text{I}} (−)\text{-D}$$
(−)-F

$$\xrightarrow[\text{pyridine}]{\text{C}_6\text{H}_5\text{SO}_2\text{Cl}} C_{14}H_{14}SO_3 \xrightarrow[\text{ether}]{\text{LiAlD}_4} (−)\text{-C}_6\text{H}_5\text{CHDCH}_3$$
                                                                      B

Deduce the absolute configuration of (−)-B and the structure and configuration of each intermediate, C through F, in the sequence. Assign the proper *R*,*S* notation to each structure B through F.

17. α-Diketones undergo an interesting rearrangement reaction upon being treated with strong base.

$$\underset{\text{benzil}}{\text{Ph}-\overset{\text{O}}{\underset{}{\text{C}}}-\overset{\text{O}}{\underset{}{\text{C}}}-\text{Ph}} \xrightarrow[\underset{100°C}{\text{H}_2\text{O, EtOH}}]{\text{KOH}} \xrightarrow{\text{H}_3\text{O}^+} \underset{\underset{\text{benzilic acid}}{(95\%)}}{\overset{\text{OH}}{\underset{}{\text{Ph}_2\text{CCOOH}}}}$$

The reaction is called the **benzilic acid rearrangement** after the trivial name of (diphenyl)-hydroxyacetic acid.

(a) Suggest a mechanism for the reaction.

(b) Propose a mechanism for the following related transformation.

$$\xrightarrow[\text{2. H}_3\text{O}^+]{\text{1. KOH}}$$

(c) Outline a multistep conversion of cyclohexanone into 1-hydroxycyclopentanone.

18. The following reaction is similar to the acyloin condensation. Propose a mechanism for the reaction.

19. Treatment of ethyl 2,2-dimethyl-3-oxobutanoate with aqueous sodium hydroxide gives 2-methylpropanoic and acetic acids, after acidification of the basic reaction mixture.

   (a) Propose a mechanism for the transformation.
   (b) Outline a multistep conversion of 2-ethoxycarbonylcyclopentanone into 2-methyladipic acid.

Chapter 28

Carbohydrates

28.1 Introduction

The carbohydrates are an important group of naturally occurring organic compounds. They are extremely widespread in plants, comprising up to 80% of the dry weight. Especially important in the vegetable kingdom are cellulose (the chief structural material of plants), starches, pectins, and the sugars sucrose and glucose. These sugars are obtained on an industrial scale from various plant sources. In higher animals, the simple sugar glucose is an essential constituent of blood and occurs in a polymeric form as glycogen in the liver and in muscle. Carbohydrates also occur in a bound form in adenosine triphosphate, which is a key material in biological energy storage and transport systems, and in the nucleic acids, which control the production of enzymes and the transfer of genetic information.

The term **carbohydrate** is used loosely to characterize the whole group of natural products related to the simple sugars. The name first arose because the simple sugars, such as glucose ($C_6H_{12}O_6$), have molecular formulas that appear to be "hydrates of carbon," that is, $C_6H_{12}O_6 = (C \cdot H_2O)_6$. Although subsequent structural investigations revealed that this simple-minded view was erroneous, the term carbohydrate has persisted.

Sugars, also called **saccharides**, are the simplest type of carbohydrate. An example is glucose, which is the cyclic hemiacetal form of one of the diastereomers of 2,3,4,5,6-pentahydroxyhexanal. As we shall see in a later section, although glucose exists almost entirely in the cyclic form, in solution it is in equilibrium with a minute amount of the noncyclic pentahydroxyaldehyde form.

glucose

As is generally true for natural products, *the carbohydrates occur in enantiomerically homogeneous form*, and only one enantiomer is found in nature. Glucose is an example of a **monosaccharide**, a term that means that glucose is not hydrolyzable into smaller units.

Maltose is an example of a disaccharide; upon hydrolysis under mildly acidic conditions, maltose yields two equivalents of the monosaccharide glucose.

A **trisaccharide** yields three monosaccharides on hydrolysis, a **tetrasaccharide** four, and so forth. **Oligosaccharide** is a general term applied to sugar polymers containing up to eight units. **Polysaccharide** refers to polymers in which the number of subunits is greater than eight; the natural polysaccharides generally consist of 100-3000 subunits.

The monosaccharides are also characterized in terms of the number of carbons in the chain and the nature of the carbonyl group, aldehyde or ketone. Glucose, which is a six-carbon aldehyde, is a **hexose**, which specifies the number of carbons, and an **aldose**, which shows that it is an aldehyde. It is completely characterized by the general term **aldohexose**. Other aldoses are glyceraldehyde, an **aldotriose**, erythrose, an **aldotetrose**, and arabinose, an **aldopentose**. The structures of these examples are shown below as their open-chain forms.

Most of the naturally occurring sugars are derived from the aldoses, and the most widespread are the aldohexoses and the aldopentoses.

A few important saccharides are **ketoses**, meaning that they contain a ketone, rather than an aldehyde, carbonyl group. Fructose is an example of a **ketohexose**, a six-carbon pentahydroxy ketone. An example of a **ketopentose** is ribulose. Both compounds are shown below in open-chain form.

EXERCISE 28.1 Reduction of the C=O group of fructose by sodium borohydride gives a mixture of two isomeric hexanehexols. The CMR spectrum of one isomer has six absorptions, but the CMR spectrum of the other has only three. Explain.

28.2 Stereochemistry and Configurational Notation of Sugars

The simplest polyhydroxy aldehyde is the compound 2,3-dihydroxypropanal or glyceraldehyde. The molecule has one stereocenter, so there are two enantiomers (Chapter

887

Sec. 28.2

*Stereochemistry
and
Configurational
Notation of
Sugars*

7). The absolute configurations of the glyceraldehyde enantiomers are known, and the isomer with $[\alpha]_D = +8.7°$ has the structure shown below on the left.

D-(+)-glyceraldehyde   L-(−)-glyceraldehyde
(R)-glyceraldehyde   (S)-glyceraldehyde

This enantiomer may be distinguished from the other by calling it (+)-glyceraldehyde, meaning "the dextrorotatory enantiomer of glyceraldehyde." Alternatively, it may be described in a manner that specifies the absolute configuration, as (R)-glyceraldehyde (Section 7.3). In the carbohydrate field, it is customary to use another and older system of configurational notation, wherein this enantiomer is called D-(+)-glyceraldehyde. Under this convention, all D-sugars have the same stereochemistry as D-(+)-glyceraldehyde at the stereocenter most distant from the carbonyl group. Sugars with the opposite stereochemistry at this center are members of the L-family. Thus, natural glucose is D-(+)-glucose and fructose is D-(−)-fructose.

D-(+)-glucose   D-(−)-fructose

The projection representations used so far in this chapter are useful and unambiguous in meaning. An alternative projection system, which is widely used in the carbohydrate field, is called the Fischer system. In a **Fischer projection** a stereocenter is represented with two of its four bonds extending horizontally, to the left and right, and with the other two extending vertically, to the top and bottom. The horizontal lines represent bonds extending forward from the stereocenter. The two vertical lines represent bonds extending back away from the plane of the page. The atom that is the stereocenter is often omitted, in which case it is symbolized by the intersection point of the two lines of a cross. A Fischer projection for (R)-glyceraldehyde is compared to the wedge-and-dashed-line structure (Section 7.3) and the "zig-zag" structure as follows.

(R)-glyceraldehyde

It is important to remember that Fischer projections are two-dimensional projections of three-dimensional objects. For purposes of visualizing whether or not two structures are identical, these projections can be manipulated only in certain ways. In order to change one Fischer projection to another correct projection for the same enantiomer, one may interchange any *two* pairs of substituents. If only one pair of groups is interchanged, a projection for the enantiomer is generated.

Fischer projections are especially useful for compounds that have two or more stereocenters. In such cases, two conventions are observed. First, the structure must be written with the chain of atoms that includes the stereocenters drawn vertically. Second, all of the appendage bonds must extend to the right and left of this vertical representation. Fischer projections of (2R,3R)-2,3,4-trihydroxybutanal (D-erythrose) illustrate this convention.

$$
\begin{array}{ccc}
& CHO & & CH_2OH \\
H-\!\!&\!\!\underset{|}{\overset{|}{C}}\!\!&\!\!-OH & HO-\!\!&\!\!\underset{|}{\overset{|}{C}}\!\!&\!\!-H \\
H-\!\!&\!\!\underset{|}{\overset{|}{C}}\!\!&\!\!-OH & HO-\!\!&\!\!\underset{|}{\overset{|}{C}}\!\!&\!\!-H \\
& CH_2OH & & CHO
\end{array}
$$

$$\equiv$$

D-erythrose

It is important to note that the Fischer projection is simply a device for depicting the absolute configuration at the various stereocenters of a compound. It *does not* tell us anything about the preferred *conformation* of the molecule. Indeed, the Fischer projections that were just depicted for D-erythrose both correspond to the eclipsed conformation.

EXERCISE 28.2 Construct a molecular model of (2R,3R)-2,3,4-trihydroxybutanal and use it to confirm the points that were made in the foregoing paragraph.

If a compound has more than two stereocenters, the same convention is followed. The chain containing the stereocenters is placed in a vertical position with the other two bonds from each stereocenter projecting to the right and left of this chain. The following structures are Fischer projections of D-glucose and D-fructose.

$$
\begin{array}{cc}
CHO & CH_2OH \\
H-C-OH & C=O \\
HO-C-H & HO-C-H \\
H-C-OH & H-C-OH \\
H-C-OH & H-C-OH \\
CH_2OH & CH_2OH \\
\text{D-glucose} & \text{D-fructose}
\end{array}
$$

One must remember to observe the conventions upon which the Fischer projections are based. Thus, the following structures, in which the chain containing the stereocenters is written in a horizontal, rather than a vertical manner, are *not valid Fischer projections*.

$$
HO-\underset{H}{\overset{H}{C}}-\underset{OH}{\overset{H}{C}}-\underset{OH}{\overset{H}{C}}-\underset{H}{\overset{OH}{C}}-\underset{OH}{\overset{H}{C}}-CHO
\qquad
HOCH_2-\overset{H\ \ H\ \ OH\ H}{\underset{OH\ OH\ H\ \ OH}{|\ \ |\ \ \ |\ \ \ |}}-CHO
$$

incorrect Fischer projections

Recall that for a compound with *n* stereocenters, there are 2^n possible optical isomers. Thus, there are 2 aldotrioses, 4 aldotetroses, 8 aldopentoses, and 16 aldohexoses. Half of these compounds belong to the D-family (are related to D-glyceraldehyde) and half belong to the L-family. To avoid cumbersome names, each isomer has been given a trivial name; that is, D-(+)-glucose is (2R,3S,4R,5R)-2,3,4,5,6-pentahydroxyhexanal. Fischer projections depicting the complete D-family of the aldoses in their open-chain forms are shown in Table 28.1.

Although the naturally occurring sugars generally belong to the D-family shown in Table 28.1, an equal number of compounds have the L-configuration. Each D-sugar has an enantiomeric L-counterpart.

Recall that a molecule with two or more stereocenters may be achiral if it has a plane of symmetry. Such compounds are called meso compounds (page 125). It often happens in carbohydrate chemistry that a chiral compound undergoes a chemical reaction to yield a meso product. For example, consider the reduction of the aldotetrose D-(−)-erythrose by sodium borohydride. The product is meso-1,2,3,4-butanetetraol (erythritol). The same compound would be produced by the reduction of L-(+)-erythrose.

On the other hand, the aldotetroses D-(−)-threose and L-(+)-threose each yield an optically active butanetetraol on reduction.

The formation of a meso compound can be a powerful piece of information for use in determining the relative stereochemistry of a compound. For example the fact that erythrose undergoes reduction to give a meso tetraol proves that its two stereocenters are either R,R or S,S. Conversely, since threose gives a tetraol that is optically active, it must have either the R,S or S,R configuration.

EXERCISE 28.3 Write Fischer projections for the products of NaBH$_4$ reduction of D-(+)-galactose, L-(−)-xylose, and D-(+)-mannose. Are any of these products achiral?

TABLE 28.1 The D-Family Aldoses

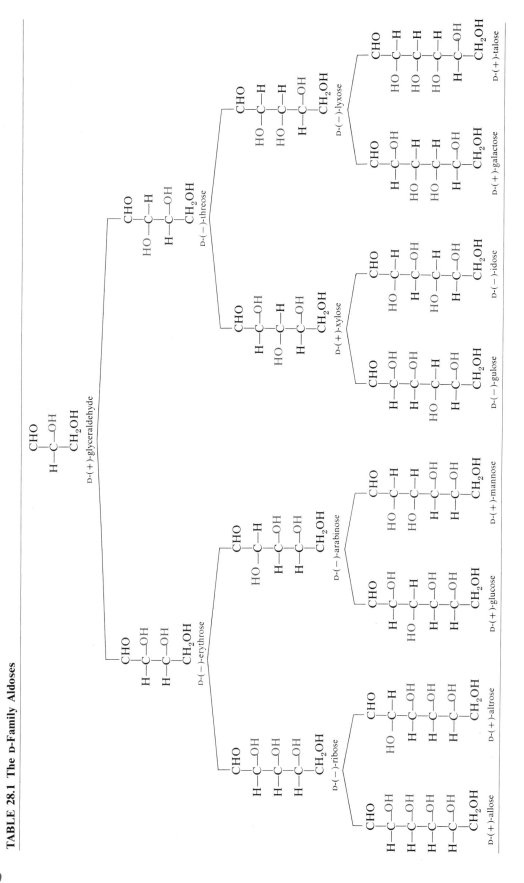

891

Sec. 28.3

*Cyclic
Hemiacetals:
Anomerism;
Glycosides*

28.3 Cyclic Hemiacetals: Anomerism; Glycosides

In the last chapter (Section 27.4), we learned that 4- and 5-hydroxy aldehydes and ketones exist mainly in the cyclic hemiacetal or hemiketal form.

It is not surprising then that the sugars also exist in such a cyclic form. Although either the five- or six-membered hemiacetal structure is possible, almost all of the simple sugars exist in the six-membered ring form (see Table 27.3, page 855). Note that when the hemiacetal is formed, *the former aldehyde carbon becomes a stereocenter*. Thus, there are two cyclic forms of glucose.

β-D-glucose   α-D-glucose

The two cyclic isomers of glucose differ only in the stereochemistry at C-1, the hemi-acetal carbon (former aldehyde carbon). Such isomers are called **anomers**, and the hemiacetal carbon (or the hemiketal carbon in the case of a cyclic ketose) is called the **anomeric** carbon. The two anomers are commonly differentiated by the Greek letters α and β; for example, α-D-glucose, β-D-glucose. For the aldohexoses, the β anomer is the one that has the OH at C-1 and the CH$_2$OH at C-5 cis with respect to each other on the ring.

The Fischer projection formulas shown in Table 28.1 are a convenient way in which to represent the open-chain form of sugars. Modified Fischer projections have frequently been used to depict the cyclic hemiacetal form. For example, the two D-glucose anomers may be represented as follows.

β-D-glucose   α-D-glucose

Note the convention used to represent stereochemistry at anomeric carbon. The OH at C-1 in the β-anomer is written to the left and that in the α-anomer is written to the right.

Because these modified projections lead to awkward drawings of bond lengths, which offend the sensibilities of many chemists, Haworth introduced an alternate projection formula, which is used extensively by sugar chemists. In a **Haworth projection**, the sugar ring is written as a planar hexagon with the oxygen in the upper right vertex. Substituents are indicated by straight lines through each vertex, either above or below the plane. The OH at the anomeric carbon is up in the β-anomer and down in the α-anomer. Hydrogens attached to the ring are omitted.

β-D-glucose α-D-glucose

There is a simple way to convert a Fischer projection to a Haworth projection, or vice versa. The OH groups that project to the left in a Fischer projection project up in a Haworth projection. In this book, we shall use Fischer projections to depict open-chain sugars and the more accurate chair representations to depict cyclic forms.

The six-membered ring form of a sugar is called a **pyranose** from the name of the simplest heterocyclic compound containing such a ring, pyran. Thus, β-D-glucose is a pyranose form, and it may be completely described by the name β-D-glucopyranose. Although the free sugars normally do not exist as the five-membered ring form, numerous derivatives are known that have such a structure. They are called **furanoses** from the name of the parent heterocyclic compound, furan.

pyran   furan

Pure β-D-glucose has an optical rotation $[\alpha]_D = +18.7°$; the α-anomer has $[\alpha]_D = +112°$. Both anomers have been isolated in pure crystalline states. If either pure anomer is dissolved in water, the optical rotation of the solution gradually changes until it reaches an equilibrium value of $+52.7°$. This phenomenon, which was first observed in 1846, results from the interconversion of the two anomers in solution and is called **mutarotation**. At equilibrium, the solution contains 63.6% of the more stable β-anomer and 36.4% of the α-anomer.

The phenomenon of anomerism caused considerable confusion for the early workers in carbohydrate chemistry, who believed the sugars to be acyclic compounds. After their cyclic structures were recognized, there arose the problem of how to name the two anomers for each sugar. In 1909, a system of nomenclature based purely on optical rotation was adopted. In the D series, the more dextrorotatory member of a pair of anomers is defined as the α-D-anomer and the less dextrorotatory anomer is the β-D-anomer. When reliable methods for determining the stereochemistry at C-1 became available, it turned out that all α-anomers have the same absolute configuration at C-1.

Interconversion of the two anomers is subject to both acid and base catalysis and occurs by the normal mechanism for acetal formation and hydrolysis (Sections 14.7.B

893

Sec. 28.3

Cyclic
Hemiacetals:
Anomerism;
Glycosides

27.4.B). The open-chain form is probably an intermediate in the process. The ....chanism of acid-catalyzed interchange of the α- and β-anomers of glucose is outlined as follows (all ring hydrogens except the one on the anomeric carbon are omitted for clarity).

(1)

α-D-glucopyranose

(2)

(3)

(4)

(5)

β-D-glucopyranose

When an aldose is dissolved in an alcohol and the solution is treated with a mineral acid catalyst, a cyclic acetal is produced (Section 27.4.B). In carbohydrate chemistry such cyclic acetals are called **glycosides**. A glycoside derived from glucose is a **glucoside**, one derived from mannose is a **mannoside**, and so on. Like the hemiacetals, these cyclic acetals may exist in both α- and β-anomeric forms as shown below for the methyl mannosides.

HOCH$_2$

HO—

HO—

HO—O

OH

H

β-D-mannose

$+ \, CH_3OH \xrightarrow{\text{HCl}}$

HOCH$_2$

HO—

HO—

HO—O

OCH$_3$

H

methyl β-D-mannoside
methyl β-D-mannopyranoside

$+$

HOCH$_2$

HO—

HO—

HO—O

OH

OCH$_3$

methyl α-D-mannoside
methyl α-D-mannopyranoside

$+ \, H_2O$

Glycosides form only under acid catalysis; the mechanism for the formation of the methyl galactosides is outlined as follows.

(1)

OH

CH$_2$OH

O

HO—

OH

OH

H

β-D-galactose

$\underset{-H^+}{\overset{+H^+}{\rightleftharpoons}}$

OH

CH$_2$OH

O

HO—

$\overset{+}{O}H_2$

OH

H

(2)

OH

CH$_2$OH

O

HO—

$\overset{+}{O}H_2$

OH

H

$\rightleftharpoons$

OH

CH$_2$OH

$\overset{+}{O}$

HO—

OH

H

$+ \, H_2O$

(3)

OH

CH$_2$OH

$\overset{+}{O}$

HO—

OH

H

$+ \, CH_3OH$

$\rightleftharpoons$

OH

CH$_2$OH

O

HO—

OH

H

CH$_3$

$\overset{+}{O}$

H

OH

CH$_2$OH

O

HO—

OH

H

H

$\overset{+}{O}$

CH$_3$

895

Sec. 28.3
Cyclic
Hemiacetals:
Anomerism;
Glycosides

(4)

$$\xrightarrow[+H^+]{-H^+}$$

methyl β-D-galactoside
methyl β-D-galactopyranoside

The formation of glycosides is a reversible process under acidic conditions. If a glycoside is treated with an acid catalyst in aqueous solution where water is present in excess, the equilibrium shifts and hydrolysis occurs. Of course, under acidic conditions a mixture of the anomeric sugars results.

$+ H_2O \xrightarrow{H^+}$

ethyl β-D-glucoside

OH + ... H + C_2H_5OH

β-D-glucose   α-D-glucose

The hydrolysis of glycosides may also be brought about by certain **enzymes**. Enzymes are complex natural products, mainly protein in nature (Chapter 29), that function as catalysts in biological reactions. They are extremely potent catalysts, often speeding up reactions by factors as large as 10^{10}. They also show remarkable structural specificity, as shown by the present example. Methyl α-D-glucopyranoside is hydrolyzed in the presence of an enzyme, isolated from yeast, called α-glucosidase. This particular enzyme only catalyzes the hydrolysis of α-glucoside linkages; methyl β-D-glucopyranoside is unaffected by it.

$\xrightarrow[H_2O]{\alpha\text{-glucosidase}}$

methyl α-D-glucopyranoside   α-D-glucopyranose

Another enzyme, β-glucosidase, from almonds, has opposite properties; it only catalyzes the hydrolysis of β-glucosides.

$\xrightarrow[H_2O]{\beta\text{-glucosidase}}$

methyl β-D-glucopyranoside   β-D-glucopyranose

Similar enzymes are known that specifically catalyze the hydrolysis of α- and β-galactosides (α- and β-galactosidase) and other glycosidic bonds. These enzymes are useful in determining the stereochemistry of the glycoside links in oligosaccharides and polysaccharides (Sections 28.7 and 28.8).

EXERCISE 28.4 Write Haworth and chair perspective formulas for α-D-altrose. Using the chair perspective formula, write all of the steps for mutarotation to β-D-altrose.

28.4 Conformations of the Pyranoses

As has been tacitly implied in the structures used thus far in this chapter, the pyranose forms of sugars exist in a chair conformation similar to the stable conformation of cyclohexane (Section 5.6). As in cyclohexane, two alternative chair forms are possible, and the one that predominates is that one with the fewer repulsive interactions. For β-D-glucose there is a large difference between the two forms. In one form all five substituents are in equatorial positions, whereas they are all axial in the other conformation; the difference between these two conformations has been estimated to be 6 kcal mole^{-1}.

Of the eight D-aldohexoses, glucose is the only one that can have all five substituents equatorial. It is no accident that glucose is the most abundant natural monosaccharide. A stereo structure of β-D-glucose is shown in Figure 28.1.

If one remembers that β-D-glucose has all substituents equatorial, it is easy to write conformational structures for the other aldohexoses by simply referring to Table 28.1. For example, D-allose differs from D-glucose only in the configuration at C-3. Thus, β-D-allose is

β-D-allose

FIGURE 28.1 Stereo structure of β-D-glucose. [Reproduced with permission from *Molecular Structure and Dimensions*, International Union of Crystallography, 1972.]

For most of the aldohexoses, the more stable conformation is the one with the CH$_2$OH group in an equatorial position. However, in a few cases the two conformations are nearly equal in energy and substantial amounts of both may be present at equilibrium. For α-D-idose, the stable conformation is that in which the CH$_2$OH group is axial.

α-D-idose

EXERCISE 28.5 Write chair perspective formulas for β-D-gulose and α-D-talose.

28.5 Reactions of Monosaccharides

A. Ether Formation

In Section 28.3 we discussed the formation of glycosides, in which the OH group at the anomeric carbon is replaced by an alkoxy group under mildly acidic conditions. The remaining hydroxy groups are unaffected by this process because such a process would involve a primary or secondary carbocation, rather than the far more stable oxonium ion that is involved in glycoside formation.

The other hydroxy groups can be converted into ethers by an application of the Williamson ether synthesis (Section 10.9). The most common ethers are the methyl ethers, which are prepared by treating the sugar with 30% aqueous sodium hydroxide and dimethyl sulfate, or with silver oxide and methyl iodide. Since the free aldehyde form of an aldose is not stable to strongly basic conditions, it is customary to protect the anomeric carbon by converting the sugar into the methyl glycoside. The glycoside linkage can then be cleaved by mild acid hydrolysis because the normal ether linkages are stable under these conditions.

methyl β-D-xyloside → methyl 2,3,4-tri-O-methyl-β-D-xyloside

2,3,4-tri-O-methyl-β-D-xylose + 2,3,4-tri-O-methyl-α-D-xylose

Methylation can be a useful method for determining the size of the acetal ring in a glycoside. For example, oxidation of the foregoing mixture of anomeric tri-O-methyl-xyloses yields a 2,3,4-trimethoxyglutaric acid, thus establishing that the original methyl xyloside had the pyranose structure.

2,3,4-trimethoxy-glutaric acid

EXERCISE 28.6 Using chair perspective formulas, write equations showing the reaction of methyl β-D-glucopyranoside with Ag_2O and CH_3I. What products are produced when this material is treated with HCl?

B. Formation of Cyclic Acetals and Ketals

Recall that 1,2- and 1,3-diols condense with aldehydes and ketones to form cyclic acetals or ketals. If the diol is itself cyclic, the acetal or ketal forms only when the two OH groups are cis, for geometric reasons.

Since sugars are polyhydroxy compounds, they also undergo this reaction. The reaction is often complicated by the fact that the ring size in the product is not the same as it is in the free sugar. This complication usually occurs when the more stable pyranose form does not have cis vicinal hydroxy groups, but the furanose form does. Thus galactose reacts with acetone to give the diketal shown because in the α-form,

898

which is present under the acidic conditions of the reaction, there are two pairs of cis vicinal OH groups.

α-D-galactose

1,2:3,4-di-O-isopropylidine-
α-D-galactopyranoside

Glucose, on the other hand, reacts by way of the furanose form.

1,2:5,6-di-O-isopropylidine-
α-D-glucofuranose

Similar condensations occur with aldehydes. Benzaldehyde shows a tendency to form six-membered ring acetals. Thus, benzaldehyde reacts with methyl α-D-galactoside to give the 4,6-benzylidine derivative.

methyl 4,6-O-benzylidine-
α-D-galactopyranoside

These cyclic acetals and ketals serve the useful function of protecting either two or four of the OH groups normally present in the free sugar. The acetal groups are sensitive to acid, but are relatively stable to neutral and basic conditions. Reactions may be carried out on the remaining OH groups, and the protecting groups may then be removed by mild acid hydrolysis. An example is the synthesis of 3-O-methylglucose, a feat that cannot be accomplished by selective methylation of glucose itself.

β-D-allose   α-D-allose

Another example is the following, which shows how D-glucose can be converted into D-allose by inversion of stereochemistry at C-3.

EXERCISE 28.7   The reaction product of glucose and acetone, 1,2:5,6-di-O-isopropylidine-α-D-glucofuranose, is a valuable synthetic intermediate, as shown by the examples in this section. Suggest a way in which this intermediate might be used in a synthesis of 3-deoxyglucose (glucose lacking the hydroxy group at C-3).

C. Esterification

The hydroxy groups in sugars can be esterified by normal methods (Section 18.7.A). The most common procedure to form acetates uses acetic anhydride and a mild basic catalyst such as sodium acetate or pyridine. At low temperature, acetylation in pyridine occurs more rapidly than interconversion of the anomers; at 0°C either α-D- or β-D-glucose gives the corresponding pentaacetate. At higher temperatures the anomers interconvert rapidly, and the β-pentaacetate is produced preferentially, since the equatorial OH of the β-anomer reacts more rapidly than does the axial OH of the α-anomer.

slow at 0°C

The more stable pentaacetate is actually the α-form, but equilibrium is established only under still more drastic conditions.

$$K = 6.7$$

This example provides a further illustration of the importance of kinetic and thermodynamic factors in organic reactions.

It may seem surprising that the axial α-pentaacetate is more stable than the equatorial β-pentaacetate. This equilibrium is an example of the **anomeric effect**, which frequently causes an electronegative anomeric substituent such as an alkoxy or acyloxy group to prefer the axial position. The anomeric effect has its origins in conformational aspects of an electronegative interaction between the two oxygens.

D. Reduction: Alditols

Monosaccharides may be reduced by various methods to the corresponding polyalcohols, which as a class are called **alditols**. Reduction of D-glucose gives D-glucitol (D-glucitol is referred to as D-sorbitol in the older literature), which also occurs in nature. The same compound is produced by the reduction of L-gulose. D-Glucitol is prepared on an industrial scale by catalytic hydrogenation of D-glucose over a nickel catalyst. The reduction probably occurs on the small amount of open-chain form that is present in equilibrium with the cyclic form. As the open-chain form is removed in this way, the equilibrium continually shifts until all of the sugar is reduced.

D-Mannitol, produced by the sodium borohydride reduction of D-mannose, is widespread in nature, occurring in such varied sources as olives, marine algae, onions, and mushrooms. It is also produced, along with a little D-glucitol, in the reduction of the ketohexose D-fructose.

| D-mannose | D-mannitol | D-fructose |

E. Oxidation: Aldonic and Saccharic Acids

Sugars are oxidizable in several ways. In the aldoses, the most susceptible group is the aldehyde group. For preparative purposes, the most convenient method employs bromine in a buffered solution at pH 5-6. Yields of the polyhydroxy carboxylic acids (**aldonic acids**) are usually in the range 50-70%. With glucose, yields as high as 95% have been achieved.

D-glucose   D-gluconic acid

Since they are 4-hydroxyalkanoic acids, the aldonic acids lactonize readily (Section 27.5). Although either a five- or six-membered lactone might, in principle, be formed, the more stable lactones are those containing a five-membered ring (see Table 27.4).

D-gluconic acid   D-gluconic acid
                                γ-lactone

The easy oxidation of aldoses provides a basis for two qualitative tests that were widely used in the early days of sugar chemistry—Fehling's test, employing cupric ion as the oxidant, and Tollens' test, in which silver ion is the oxidant. In the Fehling reaction the presence of a potential aldehyde group is shown by the formation of cuprous oxide as a brick-red precipitate. In Tollens' test the silver ion is reduced to metallic silver, which deposits in the form of a mirror on the inside of the test tube.

β-D-2-deoxyribose

β-D-glucose

If the sugar is in the form of a glycoside, then the anomeric carbon is protected under basic conditions, and the sugar is stable to these mild oxidizing conditions.

methyl β-D-allopyranoside

Such compounds are called **nonreducing sugars**; sugars that do reduce basic solutions of Cu^{2+} or Ag^+ are called **reducing sugars**.

Under more vigorous oxidizing conditions, one or more hydroxy groups may be oxidized. The primary OH groups are attacked most readily and are generally oxidized all the way to the carboxylic acid stage. The product is a polyhydroxy dicarboxylic acid called a **saccharic acid**. A convenient oxidizing agent for the preparation of saccharic acids is aqueous nitric acid.

β-D-galactose

mucic acid
(galactaric acid)

The saccharic acids have been useful in unraveling the puzzle of the relative configuration of the aldoses. Since the two ends of the chain in such a dicarboxylic acid are the same, meso compounds are possible, depending on the relative stereochemistry of the stereocenters. Note, for example, that mucic acid is a meso compound and hence is optically inactive. The observation that galactose gives a meso saccharic acid automatically limits its structure to only 4 of the 16 possible aldohexoses.

Like the aldonic acids, the saccharic acids lactonize readily and are generally found to be dilactones. The 1,4:3,6-dilactone of glucaric acid, which is derived from D-glucose, is shown below.

EXERCISE 28.8   Write Fischer projection formulas for the aldonic and saccharic acids derived from D-galactose, D-mannose and D-xylose. Are any of these acids achiral? What are the principal lactones expected from the three aldonic acids?

F. Oxidation by Periodic Acid

Like other vicinal diols, sugars are cleaved by periodic acid ("per-iodic" acid, Section 27.3.B). For example, methyl 2-deoxyribopyranoside reacts with one equivalent of periodic acid to give the dialdehyde shown below.

methyl β-D-2-deoxy-
ribopyranoside

When there are more than two adjacent hydroxy groups, the initially formed α-hydroxy aldehyde undergoes further oxidation (Section 27.4.B).

methyl β-D-glucopyranoside

+ HCOOH

As shown in the foregoing example, each time an α-hydroxy aldehyde is cleaved, one equivalent of formic acid is produced. With the free sugars it is the open-chain form that is oxidized, and complete oxidation occurs. Glucose yields five equivalents of formic acid and one equivalent of formaldehyde, which arises from C-6.

Periodate oxidation has been applied as a method for determining whether glycosides have the furanose or the pyranose structure. For example, methyl D-glucopyranoside reacts with two equivalents of the reagent and gives one equivalent of formic acid along with the dialdehyde as shown above. The corresponding furanoside also reacts with two equivalents of reagent, but it yields only one equivalent of formaldehyde because the carbon lost corresponds to C-6.

Periodic acid has also been used to determine the configuration at the anomeric carbon in the pyranosides. Note that oxidation of methyl β-D-glucopyranoside yields a dialdehyde that contains two stereocenters corresponding to C-1 and C-5 in the glucoside itself. Since the methyl β-D-glucosides of all of the aldohexoses have the same absolute configuration at C-1 and C-5, they all give this same dialdehyde on oxidation. One stereocenter in the product is determined by the D-configuration, whereas the other is determined by the β-glycoside linkage.

methyl β-D-galactopyranoside

EXERCISE 28.9 How many equivalents of periodic acid are required for complete oxidation of each of the following sugars? For each case, indicate how many equivalents of formaldehyde and formic acid are produced and write the structure of any dialdehyde that remains.
(a) methyl 4,6-O-benzylidine-α-D-galactopyranoside (page 899)
(b) methyl β-D-xyloside (page 898)
(c) L-(−)-threitol (page 889)

G. Phenylhydrazones and Osazones

Because of their polyhydroxy nature, sugars are rather difficult to isolate and purify. They are extremely water soluble and tend to form viscous syrups that crystallize poorly. Naturally occurring examples of such syrups are honey and molasses. These properties caused severe problems in working with sugars in the nineteenth century, before the advent of today's powerful spectroscopic methods of analysis. At that time the only way to ascertain the identity or nonidentity of two compounds was to compare melting points. In 1884 Emil Fischer introduced the use of phenylhydrazine as a reagent in sugar chemistry and opened up a new vista in the subject. Fischer found that a monosaccharide, such as glucose, will react by way of its open-chain form with phenylhydrazine in acetic acid to give a normal phenylhydrazone (Section 14.7.C). However, the initially formed phenylhydrazone reacts further with two more equivalents of phenylhydrazine to yield a derivative called an **osazone**.

D-glucose

D-glucose phenylhydrazone

D-glucose phenylosazone

The osazones produced from various sugars are bright yellow materials with characteristic crystal forms. Consequently, they were useful as derivatives for characterization. However, the osazones proved to be even more valuable than they appeared at first sight. Notice that C-2 is no longer a stereocenter in the phenylosazones derived from aldoses. Thus, *D-mannose gives the same phenylosazone as does D-glucose*, proving that the two aldohexoses have the same absolute stereochemistry at C-3, C-4, and C-5. Furthermore, the ketohexose, D-fructose, also gives glucose phenylosazone, thereby establishing that it also has this configuration at C-3, C-4, and C-5 (and, incidentally, that its carbonyl group is at C-2). Notice that osazones are bis-phenylhydrazones and that the reaction with phenylhydrazine stops at this stage; that is, further reaction at the C-3 hydroxy group does not normally occur.

$$
\begin{array}{ccc}
\text{CHO} & \text{CH}{=}\text{NNHC}_6\text{H}_5 & \text{CHO} \\
\text{H—C—OH} & \text{C}{=}\text{NNHC}_6\text{H}_5 & \text{HO—C—H} \\
\text{HO—C—H} & \text{HO—C—H} & \text{HO—C—H} \\
\text{H—C—OH} & \text{H—C—OH} & \text{H—C—OH} \\
\text{H—C—OH} & \text{H—C—OH} & \text{H—C—OH} \\
\text{CH}_2\text{OH} & \text{CH}_2\text{OH} & \text{CH}_2\text{OH} \\
\text{D-glucose} & \text{D-glucose phenylosazone} & \text{D-mannose}
\end{array}
$$

$$
\begin{array}{c}
\text{CH}_2\text{OH} \\
\text{C}{=}\text{O} \\
\text{HO—C—H} \\
\text{H—C—OH} \\
\text{H—C—OH} \\
\text{CH}_2\text{OH} \\
\text{D-fructose}
\end{array}
$$

EXERCISE 28.10 D-(+)-Sorbose is a ketohexose that gives the same osazone as does the aldohexose D-(−)-gulose. What is the structure of D-(+) sorbose? What other aldohexose gives this same osazone?

H. Chain Extension: The Kiliani-Fischer Synthesis

When D-glyceraldehyde is treated with HCN, a mixture of two cyanohydrins is produced. Both have the *R* configuration at C-3, corresponding to the same configuration at C-2 in D-glyceraldehyde. They differ only in the configuration at C-2, the new stereocenter. Hydrolysis of the two cyanohydrins yields the same aldonic acids as are produced by the mild oxidation of the aldotetroses D-erythrose and D-threose. Since glyceraldehyde is a chiral molecule, the transition states leading to the two cyanohydrins are diastereomeric rather than enantiomeric, and the two products are not produced in equal amounts (see Sections 7.8 and 14.8.D).

CHO
H—C—OH
CH₂OH
D-glyceraldehyde

HCN

CN
H—C—OH
H—C—OH
CH₂OH

CN
HO—C—H
H—C—OH
CH₂OH

H₃O⁺

H₃O⁺

CHO
H—C—OH
H—C—OH
CH₂OH
D-erythrose

→ Br₂/H₂O →

COOH
H—C—OH
H—C—OH
CH₂OH

COOH
HO—C—H
H—C—OH
CH₂OH

← Br₂/H₂O ←

CHO
HO—C—H
H—C—OH
CH₂OH
D-threose

The cyanohydrin chain-lengthening procedure has been applied extensively in sugar chemistry and has come to be known as the **Kiliani-Fischer synthesis**. Fischer discovered that the aldonic acids produced by hydrolysis of the cyanohydrins lactonize on heating to aldonolactones. He also discovered that these lactones may be reduced with

α-D-arabinopyranoside

HCN

CN
HO—C—H
HO—C—H
H—C—OH
H—C—OH
CH₂OH

1. Ba(OH)₂
2. heat

reduction →

CHO
HO—C—H
H—C—OH
H—C—OH
CH₂OH
D-mannose

CN
H—C—OH
HO—C—H
H—C—OH
H—C—OH
CH₂OH

1. Ba(OH)₂
2. heat

reduction →

CHO
H—C—OH
HO—C—H
H—C—OH
H—C—OH
CH₂OH
D-glucose

sodium amalgam at pH 3.0-3.5 to give new aldoses. A more modern method involves reduction of the lactone with aqueous sodium borohydride at pH 3-4. The complete Kiliani-Fischer synthesis provides a method for converting an aldopentose into an aldohexose or an aldohexose into an aldoheptose. The synthesis always provides two diastereomers, usually in unequal amounts, which differ only in their configuration at the new C-2 (old C-1). An example is D-arabinose, which yields a mixture of D-glucose and D-mannose.

EXERCISE 28.11 What two aldohexoses result from application of the Kiliani-Fischer synthesis to (a) D-(−)-ribose and (b) D-(+)-xylose?

I. Chain Shortening: The Ruff and Wohl Degradations

In 1896 Ruff discovered that the calcium salts of aldonic acids are oxidized by hydrogen peroxide, the reaction being catalyzed by ferric salts. The oxidation occurs with cleavage of the C-1,C-2 bond and the product is the lower aldose.

$$\begin{array}{c} CO_2^- \quad \tfrac{1}{2}Ca^{2+} \\ | \\ CHOH \end{array} \xrightarrow[Fe^{3+}]{H_2O_2} \begin{array}{c} \\ CHO \end{array} + CO_2$$

Since aldohexoses may be readily oxidized to aldonic acids by bromine water (Section 28.5.E), the two-stage process provides a way of converting an aldohexose into an aldopentose; it is called the **Ruff degradation**. Although yields are not high, the Ruff degradation has been a useful technique for the synthesis of certain aldopentoses. Two aldohexoses that differ only in configuration at C-2 yield the same aldopentose.

Unfortunately, the process is not very useful for the conversion of aldopentoses into aldotetroses because of low yields.

Another process, called the **Wohl degradation**, accomplishes the same overall conversion, shortening the aldose chain by the removal of C-1. The Wohl degradation is essentially the reverse of the Kiliani-Fischer synthesis. The aldose is first converted into its oxime by treatment with hydroxylamine (Section 14.7.C). When the resulting polyhydroxy oxime is heated with acetic anhydride and sodium acetate, all of the hydroxy groups are acetylated and the oxime group is dehydrated to a cyano group. The product is the acetate ester of a cyanohydrin. The ester groups are removed by treatment with base. Under the basic conditions of hydrolysis, the cyanohydrin is decomposed to the corresponding aldehyde. Again, the process does not give especially high yields, but it is applicable to pentoses as well as to hexoses.

CHO
H—C—OH
H—C—OH
H—C—OH
CH₂OH
D-ribose

$\xrightarrow{\text{H}_2\text{NOH}}$

CH=NOH
H—C—OH
H—C—OH
H—C—OH
CH₂OH

$\xrightarrow[\text{NaOAc}]{\text{Ac}_2\text{O}}$

C≡N
H—C—OAc
H—C—OAc
H—C—OAc
CH₂OAc

$\xrightarrow[\text{CHCl}_3]{\text{NaOCH}_3}$

$\begin{bmatrix} \text{CN} \\ \text{H—C—OH} \\ \text{H—C—OH} \\ \text{H—C—OH} \\ \text{CH}_2\text{OH} \end{bmatrix}$

$\xrightarrow{\text{NaOCH}_3}$

CHO
H—C—OH
H—C—OH
CH₂OH
D-erythrose

+ NaCN + CH₃OH

EXERCISE 28.12 What tetrose results from application of the Wohl degradation to D-(−)-lyxose? Which other pentose also affords this tetrose?

28.6 Relative Stereochemistry of the Monosaccharides: The Fischer Proof

In the late nineteenth century organic chemists were faced with a puzzle regarding the structures of the monosaccharides. A number of compounds had been isolated that were known to have the same formula and that had the same connectivity. That is, the available evidence showed that glucose, galactose, and mannose were all 2,3,4,5,6-pentahydroxyhexanals. The Le Bel-van't Hoff theory of stereoisomerism provided an explanation for this phenomenon. The challenging question was, which relative arrangement of the four stereocenters corresponds to glucose, which to mannose, and so on?

The challenge was taken up by Emil Fischer, who succeeded in establishing the correct stereostructures for D-glucose, D-mannose, D-fructose, and D-arabinose in 1891. The structure proof consists of an elegant series of logical deductions and has come to be known as "the Fischer proof." We will present a modernized version of the proof here because it typifies the method that has been used to establish the structures of all the sugars.

At the outset Fischer realized that he could establish the *relative configuration* of the various stereocenters in a sugar, but that he had no way to determine the *absolute configuration* of any of the compounds. In order to understand this distinction, consider the four aldotetroses D- and L-threose and D- and L-erythrose. All four compounds

911

Sec. 28.6

*Relative
Stereochemistry
of the
Monosaccharides:
The Fischer
Proof*

are oxidized by nitric acid to saccharic acids. The enantiomeric D- and L-threoses give enantiomeric D- and L-2,3-dihydroxysuccinic acids, which are called D-tartaric acid and L-tartaric acid. However, both D- and L-erythrose are oxidized by nitric acid to a saccharic acid that is an optically inactive diacid, *meso*-tartaric acid. *Meso*-tartaric acid owes its optical inactivity to an internal symmetry plane, and hence the relative configuration of its two stereocenters is fixed. It follows that one of the erythroses has the R,R configuration and the other has the S,S configuration. However, there was no way to tell which is which.

The question of the absolute configuration was not settled until 1954, when Bijvoet determined the absolute configuration of a salt of D-tartaric acid by an x-ray crystallographic technique known as anomalous dispersion.

1. Fischer started by arbitrarily choosing what is now called the R configuration for the stereochemistry at C-5 in D-glucose. He had a 50% chance of being correct in this assignment, but it has no bearing on the rest of the proof because the other centers were to be determined relative to C-5. In 1954 Bijvoet's work showed that Fischer had actually made the correct choice in an absolute sense. The structures of the eight aldohexoses having the R configuration at C-5 are shown in Table 28.2 and are designated **1** through **8**.

2. It was known that glucose and mannose give the same osazone (Section 28.5.G). Therefore the two compounds have the same configuration at C-3, C-4, and C-5; they differ only at C-2. The two compounds must be **1** and **2**, **3** and **4**, **5** and **6**, or **7** and **8**.

TABLE 28.2 The (5*R*)-Aldohexoses

CHO	CHO	CHO	CHO
H—C—OH	HO—C—H	H—C—OH	HO—C—H
H—C—OH	H—C—OH	HO—C—H	HO—C—H
H—C—OH	H—C—OH	H—C—OH	H—C—OH
H—C—OH	H—C—OH	H—C—OH	H—C—OH
CH₂OH	CH₂OH	CH₂OH	CH₂OH
1	**2**	**3**	**4**
CHO	CHO	CHO	CHO
H—C—OH	HO—C—H	H—C—OH	HO—C—H
H—C—OH	H—C—OH	HO—C—H	HO—C—H
HO—C—H	HO—C—H	HO—C—H	HO—C—H
H—C—OH	H—C—OH	H—C—OH	H—C—OH
CH₂OH	CH₂OH	CH₂OH	CH₂OH
5	**6**	**7**	**8**

3. *Both* D-glucose and D-mannose are oxidized by nitric acid to *optically active* saccharic acids (Section 28.5.E). The aldohexoses with structures **1** and **7** would give meso saccharic acids. Therefore D-glucose and D-mannose must be either **3** and **4** or **5** and **6**. (Remember that the two compounds differ only at C-2, so eliminating **1** also eliminates **2**, and eliminating **7** also eliminates **8**.)

4. Kiliani-Fischer chain extension of the aldopentose D-arabinose yields both D-glucose and D-mannose (Section 28.5.H). Therefore, D-arabinose has the same configuration at its C-2, C-3, and C-4 as D-glucose and D-mannose at C-3, C-4, and C-5, respectively. D-Arabinose must be either **9** or **10**.

CHO
HO—C—H
H—C—OH —Kiliani–Fischer→ **3 and 4**
H—C—OH
CH₂OH

9

or

CHO
H—C—OH
HO—C—H —Kiliani–Fischer→ **5 and 6**
H—C—OH
CH₂OH

10

However, oxidation of D-arabinose gives an *optically active* diacid. The saccharic acid derived from aldopentose **10** would be meso, so D-arabinose must be **9**, and D-glucose and D-mannose must be **3** and **4**.

$$
\begin{array}{ccc}
\text{CHO} & & \text{COOH} \\
\text{HO—C—H} & & \text{HO—C—H} \\
\text{H—C—OH} & \xrightarrow{HNO_3} & \text{H—C—OH} \\
\text{H—C—OH} & & \text{H—C—OH} \\
\text{CH}_2\text{OH} & & \text{COOH} \\
\textbf{9}, \text{D-arabinose} & & \text{optically active}
\end{array}
$$

or

$$
\begin{array}{ccc}
\text{CHO} & & \text{COOH} \\
\text{H—C—OH} & & \text{H—C—OH} \\
\text{HO—C—H} & \xrightarrow{HNO_3} & \text{---HO—C—H---} \quad \text{symmetry plane} \\
\text{H—C—OH} & & \text{H—C—OH} \\
\text{CH}_2\text{OH} & & \text{COOH} \\
\textbf{10} & & \text{meso}
\end{array}
$$

5. Fischer developed a method that allowed him to interchange the two ends of an aldose chain. The method is fairly involved, and we need not go into the chemical details here. However, consider the results when the method is applied to the aldohexoses that have structures **3** and **4**.

$$
\begin{array}{ccccc}
\text{CHO} & & \text{CH}_2\text{OH} & & \text{CHO} \\
\text{H—C—OH} & & \text{H—C—OH} & & \text{HO—C—H} \\
\text{HO—C—H} & & \text{HO—C—H} & & \text{HO—C—H} \\
\text{H—C—OH} & \dashrightarrow & \text{H—C—OH} & \equiv & \text{H—C—OH} \\
\text{H—C—OH} & & \text{H—C—OH} & & \text{HO—C—H} \\
\text{CH}_2\text{OH} & & \text{CHO} & & \text{CH}_2\text{OH} \\
\textbf{3} & & \text{rotate structure } 180° & &
\end{array}
$$

$$
\begin{array}{ccccc}
\text{CHO} & & \text{CH}_2\text{OH} & & \text{CHO} \\
\text{HO—C—H} & & \text{HO—C—H} & & \text{HO—C—H} \\
\text{HO—C—H} & & \text{HO—C—H} & & \text{HO—C—H} \\
\text{H—C—OH} & \dashrightarrow & \text{H—C—OH} & \equiv & \text{H—C—OH} \\
\text{H—C—OH} & & \text{H—C—OH} & & \text{H—C—OH} \\
\text{CH}_2\text{OH} & & \text{CHO} & & \text{CH}_2\text{OH} \\
\textbf{4} & & \text{rotate structure } 180° & &
\end{array}
$$

When C-1 and C-6 are interchanged compound **3** gives a *different aldohexose*. However, when the same operation is performed on compound **4**, the final product is the same as the starting material. Fischer applied his method to D-glucose and discovered that a new aldohexose was produced, which he named L-gulose. The proof was complete: D-glucose must have structure **3** and D-mannose must have structure **4**!

EXERCISE 28.13 Referring to Table 28.1, choose any aldohexose except glucose or mannose. Work through the reactions involved in the Fischer proof and write the structures of the compounds that would be involved if glucose has the structure you have chosen. Which experiments show that the chosen aldohexose is not glucose?

28.7 Oligosaccharides

Oligosaccharides (Gr., *oligos*, a few) are polysaccharides that yield from two to eight monosaccharide units upon hydrolysis. The most common are the disaccharides, which are dimers composed of two monosaccharides. The two monosaccharides may be the same or different. Disaccharides are joined by a glycoside linkage from the OH group of one monosaccharide to the anomeric carbon of the other.

A simple example of a disaccharide is maltose, which is produced by the enzymatic hydrolysis of starch. Maltose contains two D-glucose units, both in the pyranose form. The C-4 hydroxy group of one glucose is bound by an α glycoside bond to the anomeric carbon of the other unit. The disaccharide is obtained in crystalline form in which the hydroxy group on the other anomeric carbon is β, but it mutarotates in solution to a mixture of the α- and β-forms.

4-O-(α-D-glucopyranosyl)-β-D-glucopyranose
β-maltose

4-O-(α-D-glucopyranosyl)-α-D-glucopyranose
α-maltose

In maltose, one of the glucose units has its aldehyde carbon firmly bound in the glycosidic linkage to the other unit. However, the carbonyl group of the second ring is in the hemiacetal form, and it may therefore undergo normal carbonyl reactions, just as the monosaccharides do. Thus maltose is oxidized by Tollens' reagent and by Fehling's solution and is a reducing sugar. Disaccharides undergo most of the same reactions as do the monosaccharides. For example, maltose is oxidized by bromine water to maltobionic acid.

maltose

maltobionic acid

Cellobiose is a disaccharide that is obtained by the partial hydrolysis of cellulose. It is isomeric with maltose and contains a β-glycosidic linkage. The structure of β-cellobiose is shown in Figure 28.2.

FIGURE 28.2 β-Cellobiose, 4-O-(β-D-glucopyranosyl)-β-D-glucopyranose: *(a)* conventional structure; *(b)* stereo structure. [Part (b) reproduced with permission from *Molecular Structure and Dimensions*, International Union of Crystallography, 1972.]

Lactose is an example of a disaccharide in which the two monosaccharide units are different. It constitutes about 5% by weight of mammalian milk. It is produced commercially from whey, which is obtained as a by-product in the manufacture of cheese. Evaporation of the whey at temperatures below 95°C causes the less soluble α-anomer to precipitate. Hydrolysis of lactose affords one equivalent of glucose and one equivalent of galactose. The galactose unit is bound in the glycoside form and both rings are pyranoses. The hydrolysis of lactose is catalyzed by an enzyme called β-galactosidase, which is specific for the hydrolysis of β-galactoside links.

Sucrose is one of the most widespread sugars in nature. It is produced commercially from sugar cane and sugar beets. It is a disaccharide composed of one D-glucose and D-fructose unit which are joined by an acetal linkage between the two anomeric carbons. The glucose unit is in the pyranose form and the fructose is in the furanose form. The structure is shown in Figure 28.3. Since both anomeric carbons are bound in the acetal form, sucrose is a nonreducing sugar.

Acidic hydrolysis of sucrose yields an equimolar mixture of D-glucose and D-fructose. Sucrose itself is dextrorotatory, having an optical rotation $[\alpha]_D = +66°$. D-Glucose is also dextrorotatory (the equilibrium mixture of α- and β-anomers has $[\alpha]_D = +52.5°$), but D-fructose is strongly levorotatory (the equilibrium mixture of fructose isomers has $[\alpha]_D = -92.4°$). In the early days of carbohydrate chemistry D-glucose was known as "dextrose" and D-fructose was called "levulose," terms that were derived from the signs of rotation of the two monosaccharides.

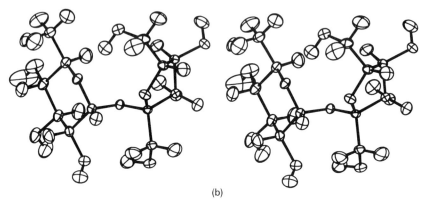

(b)

FIGURE 28.3 Sucrose, α-D-glucopyranosyl-β-D-glucopyranoside: *(a)* conventional structure; *(b)* stereo structure. The stereo structure also illustrates the way in which modern x-ray structure determinations are presented. The noncircular shapes of atoms, called "thermal ellipsoids," represent thermal motions of the atoms in the crystal. [Part (b) reproduced with permission from G. M. Brown and H. A. Levy, *Acta Cryst.*, B29, 790 (1973).]

In the process of hydrolysis the dextrorotatory sucrose solution becomes levorotatory because an equimolar mixture of D-glucose and D-fructose has $[\alpha]_D = -20°$. This commonly encountered mixture is called "invert sugar" from the inversion in the sign of rotation that occurs during its formation. A number of organisms, including honeybees, have enzymes that catalyze the hydrolysis of sucrose. These enzymes are usually called **invertases** and are specific for the β-D-fructofuranoside linkage. Honey is largely a mixture of D-glucose, D-fructose, and sucrose. It has been shown that the equilibrium mixture resulting from hydrolysis of sucrose contains 32% β-D-glucopyranose, 18% α-D-glucopyranose, 34% β-D-fructopyranose, and 16% β-D-fructofuranose. Note that although glucose exists only in pyranose forms, fructose exists as a mixture of pyranose and furanose forms.

Raffinose is an example of a trisaccharide. It is a minor constituent in sugar beets (0.01-0.02%) and is obtained as a by-product in the isolation of sucrose from this source. Raffinose is nonreducing and on hydrolysis yields one equivalent each of D-galactose, D-glucose, and D-fructose. If the hydrolysis is catalyzed by the enzyme α-galactosidase, the products are galactose and sucrose.

EXERCISE 28.14 Write the structures of the species present in the equilibrium mixture that results from hydrolysis of sucrose.

raffinose

D-galactose +
D-glucose + D-fructose

D-galactose +
sucrose

28.8 Polysaccharides

Polysaccharides differ from the oligosaccharides only in the number of monosaccharide units that make up the molecule. The majority of the natural polysaccharides contain from 80 to 100 units, but some materials have much larger molecular weights; cellulose, for example, has an average of about 3000 glucose units per molecule. Polysaccharides may have a linear structure in which the individual monosaccharides are joined one to the other by glycosidic bonds, or they may be branched. A branched polysaccharide has a linear backbone, but additional OH groups on some of the monosaccharide units are involved in glycosidic bonding to another chain of sugars. A few cyclic polysaccharides are also known. The three types are illustrated schematically in Figure 28.4.

Cellulose is probably the single most abundant organic compound on the earth. It is the chief structural component of plant cells. For example, it comprises 10–20% of the dry weight of leaves, about 50% of the weight of tree wood and bark, and about 90% of the weight of cotton fibers, from which pure cellulose is most easily obtained.

Structurally, cellulose is a polymer of D-glucose in which the individual units are linked by β-glucoside bonds from the anomeric carbon of one unit to the C-4 hydroxy of the next unit. It may be hydrolyzed by 40% aqueous hydrochloric acid to give D-glucose in 95% yield. Partial hydrolysis, which may be brought about by enzymatic methods, yields the disaccharide cellobiose (Section 28.7). It is a linear polysaccharide, the isolated form containing an average of 3000 units per chain, corresponding to an average molecular weight of about 500,000. Some degradation occurs during the isolation; the actual "native cellulose" as it exists in plants may contain as many as 10,000–15,000 glucose units per chain, corresponding to a molecular weight of 1.6–2.4 million. The strength of wood derives principally from hydrogen bonds of one chain with hydroxy groups of neighboring chains.

Although the higher animals do not have enzymes that can catalyze the degradation of cellulose to glucose, such enzymes (**cellulases**) are common in microorganisms.

linear polysaccharide

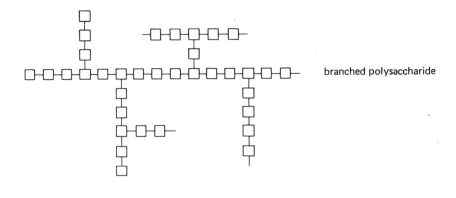

branched polysaccharide

cyclic polysaccharide

FIGURE 28.4 Types of polysaccharides.

cellulose

Cellulases produced by the microflora that reside in the digestive tracts of herbivorous animals permit these animals to utilize cellulose as a food source.

Various chemically modified forms of cellulose have long been used in commercial applications. Cellulose may be nitrated by a mixture of HNO_3 and H_2SO_4. The product is a partially degraded cellulose in which some of the free OH groups have been converted into nitrate esters. The average number of nitrate ester groups per glucose unit is variable and depends on the composition of the nitrating mixture and the reaction time. Highly nitrated cellulose, in which 2.5–2.7 OH groups per glucose unit are nitrated, has explosive properties and has been used in the manufacture of blasting

cellulose $\xrightarrow[\text{H}_2\text{SO}_4]{\text{HNO}_3}$ cellulose trinitrate powder. Nitrated cellulose possessing a lower nitrogen content (2.1–2.5 ONO_2 groups per glucose unit) is used in the preparation of plastics (celluloid) and lacquers.

Starch is the second most abundant polysaccharide and occurs in both the vegetable and animal kingdoms. It is the chief source of carbohydrate for humans and is therefore of considerable economic importance. The polysaccharide is deposited in the plant in the form of small insoluble particles called starch granules. Like cellulose, the term starch is a general one; there is a considerable variety in the nature of the starch molecules produced by a given plant. Natural starch may be separated into two gross fractions, called **amylose** and **amylopectin**.

Like cellulose, starch yields only D-glucose on hydrolysis. Although amylose appears to be essentially unbranched, amylopectin has a highly branched structure. Both types of starch have high molecular weights, corresponding to many thousands of glucose units per molecule. The main chain consists of D-glucose units bound through the C-4 OH group as in cellulose but with the glucoside bond having the α-configuration. In the branched form, the branches appear to be to the C-6 OH group.

amylose

amylopectin

Partial hydrolysis of starch yields the disaccharide maltose (Section 28.7).

Glycogen is a polysaccharide that is structurally similar to starch. It is the form in which animals store glucose for further use. It is found in most tissues, but the best source is liver or muscle. Glycogen has a structure similar to that of amylopectin but is more highly branched.

28.9 Sugar Phosphates

The sugar phosphates are a class of carbohydrates that is particularly important in living systems. The chemistry of phosphate esters was discussed in Section 25.7. Sugar phosphates are intermediates in many metabolic processes, such as the degradation of glycogen to lactic acid in muscle (glycolysis), the fermentation of sugars to alcohol, and the biosynthesis of carbohydrates in plants by the process of photosynthesis. They are also constituents of ribonucleic and deoxyribonucleic acids (RNA and DNA), which are of importance in the transfer of genetic information.

Typical sugar phosphates, which are known to be involved in the biosynthesis and biodegradation of the polysaccharides glycogen and starch, are α-D-glucopyranosyl phosphate and D-glucose 6-phosphate.

α-D-glucopyranosyl phosphate   D-glucose 6-phosphate

These polysaccharides are synthesized in organisms by an enzyme-catalyzed process in which glucose units are added in a stepwise fashion onto the growing polysaccharide chain. The glucose units are in the form of α-D-glucopyranosyl phosphate, in which form the anomeric carbon is "activated" toward nucleophilic substitution processes (phosphate ion is a much better leaving group than hydroxide ion). The process is reversible, and the reverse process is the method whereby the organism degrades, or depolymerizes, the polysaccharide.

Similar enzymes catalyze the formation and cleavage of the $1 \rightarrow 6$ glycosidic bond by way of D-glucose-6-phosphate.

α-D-Glucopyranosyl phosphate is also involved in the formation and degradation of sucrose.

sucrose

α-D-glucopyranosyl phosphate

D-fructose

28.10 Natural Glycosides

Sugars are often found to occur in organisms in the form of glycosides. Hydrolysis of a glycoside yields the sugar (the **glycon**) and the alkyl or aryl group to which it is bound (the **aglycon**). There are many types of glycosides, and we shall only give a few examples here.

Amygdalin was one of the first glycosides to be discovered. It occurs in bitter almonds and is a glycoside formed from the disaccharide gentiobiose and the cyanohydrin of benzaldehyde. Almonds contain an enzyme that catalyzes the conversion of amygdalin to HCN, benzaldehyde, and two molecules of D-glucose.

amygdalin

Amygdalin is the chief constituent of laetrile, which has been reputed to be effective in the treatment of cancer. Considerable controversy has surrounded this substance, which was banned by the United States Food and Drug Administration on the grounds that it is ineffective. In spite of this prohibition, a lively black-market in the drug persisted, and a number of State legislatures legalized its use in 1978. In 1979 the National Cancer Institute announced that it was reopening investigations of the possible efficacy of the substance. The results of the investigation were reported 3 years later in the *New England Journal of Medicine*. It was found that the substance is not effective as a cancer treatment. In addition, it was found that the material has chronic toxicity as a result of hydrolysis of the glycoside linkage, with the release of HCN.

Another natural glycoside is peonin, which is responsible for the color of the dark red peony (Section 34.3).

peonin

A number of naturally occurring antibiotics contain sugars bound as glycosides. The glycosyl groups often have unusual structures. An example is erythromycin A, a widely used antibiotic. The aglycon is a 14-membered lactone containing five hydroxy groups, two of which are bound to the rare monosaccharides cladinose and desosamine.

erythromycin A

PROBLEMS

1. Assign *R* and *S* notations to all of the aldoses in Table 28.1.

2. Construct a "family tree," similar to that in Table 28.1 that contains the structures for all of the D-ketoses having six or fewer carbons. Identify which aldoses and ketoses will give the same osazones.

3. Using Table 28.1, identify all of the aldoses that give meso saccharic acids on oxidation by nitric acid.

4. 5-Hydroxyheptanal exists in two cyclic hemiacetal forms. Write three-dimensional structures for the two compounds. Which is more stable? Write a mechanism for interconversion of the two forms under conditions of acid catalysis and base catalysis.

5. (a) Draw three-dimensional projection structures for the two conformations of β-D-xylopyranose. Predict which conformation predominates in solution.
   (b) Answer part (a) for α-D-arabinopyranose.

6. Suggest a method for the synthesis of 6-deoxygalactose from galactose. (*Hint*: See page 899.)

galactose   6-deoxygalactose

7. (a) Write equations that show the application of the Kiliani-Fischer synthesis to each of the D-aldotetroses. Which aldopentoses are obtained from D-threose and which from D-erythrose?
   (b) Answer part (a) for the aldopentoses.

8. Write equations that show the application of the Ruff degradation to each of the D-aldohexoses. Which aldopentoses are obtained from each aldohexose?

9. Under the proper conditions D-glucose reacts with benzaldehyde to give 2,4-O-benzylidine-D-glucose.

2,4-O-benzylidine-D-glucose

This compound is reduced to 2,4-O-benzylidine-D-glucitol, which reacts with periodic acid to give the benzylidine derivative of an aldopentose. Hydrolysis of the latter compound gives the aldopentose. What are the structure and name of the aldopentose?

10. Complete acid- or base-catalyzed hydrolysis of one class of nucleic acids yields a D-aldopentose, A, phosphoric acid, and several purine and pyrimidine bases. Nitric acid oxidation of A yields a meso diacid, B. Treatment of A with hydroxylamine forms the oxime, C, which upon treatment with acetic anhydride is converted into an acetylated cyanohydrin, D. Hydrolysis of compound D gives an aldotetrose, E, which is oxidized by nitric acid to a meso diacid, F. What are the structures of compounds A through F?

11. A disaccharide, G, $C_{11}H_{20}O_{10}$, is hydrolyzable by α-glucosidase, yielding D-glucose and a D-pentose. The disaccharide does not reduce Fehling's solution. Methylation of G with dimethyl sulfate in NaOH yields a heptamethyl ether, H, which upon acid hydrolysis yields 2,3,4,6-tetra-O-methyl-D-glucose and a pentose tri-O-methyl ether, I. Oxidation of I by bromine water yields 2,3,4-tri-O-methyl-D-ribonic acid. Assign structures to compounds G through I.

12. A naturally occurring compound, J, has the formula $C_7H_{14}O_6$. It is nonreducing and does not mutarotate. Compound J is hydrolyzed by aqueous HCl to compound K, $C_6H_{12}O_6$, a reducing sugar. Oxidation of K with dilute HNO_3 gives an optically inactive diacid, L ($C_6H_{10}O_8$). Ruff degradation of K gives a new reducing sugar, M ($C_5H_{10}O_5$), which is oxidized by dilute HNO_3 to an optically active diacid, N ($C_5H_8O_7$). Compound J is treated successively with NaOH and dimethyl sulfate, aqueous HCl, and hot nitric acid. From the product mixture, one may isolate α,β-dimethoxysuccinic acid and α-methoxymalonic acid.

$$
\begin{array}{cc}
\begin{array}{l}
\text{COOH} \\
| \\
\text{CH—OCH}_3 \\
| \\
\text{CH—OCH}_3 \\
| \\
\text{COOH}
\end{array}
&
\begin{array}{l}
\text{COOH} \\
| \\
\text{CH—OCH}_3 \\
| \\
\text{COOH}
\end{array}
\\[2em]
\alpha,\beta\text{-dimethoxysuccinic acid} & \alpha\text{-methoxymalonic acid}
\end{array}
$$

   (a) Give structures for compounds J through N.
   (b) What structural ambiguity exists, if any?

13. An aldopentose, O, is oxidized to a diacid, P, which is optically active. Compound O is also degraded to an aldotetrose, Q, which undergoes oxidation to an optically inactive diacid, R. Assuming that O has the D-configuration $4R$, what are the structures of O through R?

14. Aldohexose S is reduced by sodium borohydride ($NaBH_4$) to an optically inactive alditol, T. Ruff degradation of S gives an aldopentose, U, which is oxidized by nitric acid to an optically active saccharic acid, V. What are compounds S through V, assuming them to be D-sugars?

15. Oxidation of aldohexose W by nitric acid gives an optically active saccharic acid, X. Ruff degradation of W gives an aldopentose, Y, which yields an optically inactive diacid, Z, on nitric acid oxidation. When compound W is subjected to a series of reactions that exchange C-1 and C-6, the same aldohexose is obtained. Assuming them to be D-sugars, what are compounds W through Z?

16. The optical rotations for the α- and β-anomers of D-mannose are $[\alpha]_D = +29.3°$ and $[\alpha]_D = -17.0°$, respectively. In water solution each form mutarotates to an equilibrium value of $[\alpha]_D = +14.2°$. Calculate the percentage of each anomer present at equilibrium.

17. The disaccharide melibiose is hydrolyzed by dilute acid to a mixture of D-glucose and D-galactose. Melibiose is a reducing sugar and is oxidized by bromine water to melibionic acid, which is methylated by sodium hydroxide and dimethyl sulfate to octa-O-methyl-melibionic acid. Hydrolysis of the latter gives a tetra-O-methylgluconic acid, AA, and a tetra-O-methylgalactose, BB. Compound AA is oxidized by nitric acid to tetra-O-methylglucaric acid. Compound BB is also obtained by the acidic hydrolysis of methyl 2,3,4,6-tetra-O-methylgalactopyranoside. Melibiose is hydrolyzed by an α-galacto-sidase from almonds. What is the structure of melibiose?

18. The trisaccharide gentianose is hydrolyzed by acid to two equivalents of D-glucose and one of D-fructose. Partial acid hydrolysis yields D-fructose and gentibiose (page 921). The enzymes of almond emulsion cleave gentianose into D-glucose and sucrose. What is the structure of gentianose?

19. Write Haworth projections for the following saccharides.
   (a) α-D-galactopyranose
   (b) methyl β-D-mannoside
   (c) α-maltose
   (d) β-cellobiose

20. 1,2:5,6-Di-O-isopropylidine-α-D-glucofuranose reacts with aqueous acetic acid to give 1,2-O-isopropylidine-α-D-glucofuranose. That is, the 5,6-ketal is hydrolyzed selectively. This selective hydrolysis of the 5,6-ketal in compounds of this series is normal. Making use of this general reaction, along with other reactions discussed in this chapter, outline methods for the conversion of D-glucose into the following products.
    (a) D-(+)-xylose
    (b) *meso* − 2,4-dihydroxyglutaric acid
    (c) L-(+)-ribose

21. It is not possible to convert glyceraldehyde into its ketal with acetone by the direct reaction of the two compounds in the presence of acid. However, D-mannitol (page 902) reacts smoothly with acetone in the presence of zinc chloride to form a bis-ketal, 1,2:5,6-di-O-isopropylidine-D-mannitol. How might this observation be used to achieve the indirect synthesis of 2,3-O-isopropylidine-D-glyceraldehyde?

Chapter 29

Amino Acids, Peptides, and Proteins

29.1 Introduction

Amino acids constitute a particularly important class of difunctional compounds because they are the building blocks from which proteins are constructed. Since the two functional groups in an amino acid are, respectively, basic and acidic, the compounds are amphoteric and actually exist as **zwitterions** or **inner salts**. For example, glycine, the simplest amino acid, exists mostly in the form shown, rather than as aminoacetic acid.

$$H_3\overset{+}{N}CH_2CO_2^- \;\rightleftharpoons\; H_2NCH_2COOH$$

glycine
zwitterion form

glycine
amino acid form

Amino acids owe their important place in nature to the fact that they may form amide bonds between two molecules. Such a linkage is also called a **peptide bond**, and the resulting compounds are called **peptides**. For example, the peptide formed from two molecules of glycine is glycylglycine, a **dipeptide**. Like glycine, it is amphoteric and exists as a zwitterion.

peptide bond

$$H_3\overset{+}{N}CH_2\overset{\overset{\displaystyle O}{\|}}{C}-NHCH_2CO_2^-$$

glycylglycine
a dipeptide

Higher peptides are also possible; a **tripeptide** contains three amino acid building blocks, a **tetrapeptide** four, and so on.

$$H_3\overset{+}{N}CH_2\overset{\overset{\displaystyle O}{\|}}{C}NHCH_2\overset{\overset{\displaystyle O}{\|}}{C}NHCH_2CO_2^-$$

glycylglycylglycine
a tripeptide

As more units are added to the chain, a polymer of any length may be achieved. Such polymers are called, as a class, **polypeptides**. **Proteins** are special types of polypeptides composed primarily of about 20 different specific amino acids. They are large molecules, with molecular weights from 6000 to more than 1,000,000 (from about 50 to more than 8000 amino acids per molecule).

927

Sec. 29.2

*Structure,
Nomenclature,
and Physical
Properties of
Amino Acids*

In this chapter we will review the individual amino acids, especially those important in nature, and their chemical and physical properties. In the discussion of the peptides and polypeptides that follows, we shall learn of the importance of the strength of the amide linkage and the dominating role played by its conformational tendencies.

29.2 Structure, Nomenclature, and Physical Properties of Amino Acids

Most of the important natural amino acids are α-amino acids; that is, the amino group occurs at the position adjacent to the carboxy function.

$$\overset{+}{\underset{\underset{CH_3\overset{|}{C}HCO_2^-}{|}}{NH_3}} \qquad H_3\overset{+}{N}CH_2CH_2CO_2^-$$

alanine β-alanine
an α-amino acid   a β-amino acid

The important natural amino acids are listed in Table 29.1, along with the three letter code that is conventionally used as an abbreviation for the name of each. The structures are all written in the amino acid form, rather than as zwitterions since alternative zwitterionic structures are possible for some.

> EXERCISE 29.1 Commit to memory the names, structures, and abbreviations of the 20 common amino acids in Table 29.1 (pages 928–29).

The inner-salt nature of the amino acids results in physical properties that are somewhat different from the properties normally found in organic compounds. Zwitterions are highly polar substances for which intermolecular electrostatic attractions lead to rather strong crystal lattice structures. Consequently, melting points are generally high. Most amino acids decompose instead of melting, and it is customary to record decomposition points (Table 29.2). In general, decomposition points are dependent on the rate of heating of the sample and are not reliable physical properties. Most of the amino acids are only sparingly soluble in water, again as a consequence of the strong intermolecular forces acting in the crystal lattice. Exceptions are glycine, alanine, proline, lysine, and arginine, which are all quite soluble in water.

With the exception of glycine, all of the common amino acids are chiral molecules. The naturally occurring compounds all have the same absolute configuration at the stereocenter. As with carbohydrates, it is traditional to use the D- and L-nomenclature with amino acids. Natural amino acids belong to the L-series (Figure 29.1). The stereo

L-alanine   L-proline   L-glyceraldehyde

FIGURE 29.1   The relationship of L-alanine and L-proline to L-glyceraldehyde.

TABLE 29.1 Common Amino Acids

$R-\overset{\overset{\displaystyle NH_2}{\mid}}{C}HCOOH$	Name	Abbreviation
$H-\overset{\overset{\displaystyle NH_2}{\mid}}{C}HCOOH$	glycine	Gly
$CH_3-\overset{\overset{\displaystyle NH_2}{\mid}}{C}HCOOH$	alanine	Ala
$CH_3\overset{\overset{\displaystyle CH_3}{\mid}}{C}H-\overset{\overset{\displaystyle NH_2}{\mid}}{C}HCOOH$	valine	Val
$CH_3\overset{\overset{\displaystyle CH_3}{\mid}}{C}HCH_2-\overset{\overset{\displaystyle NH_2}{\mid}}{C}HCOOH$	leucine	Leu
$CH_3CH_2\overset{\overset{\displaystyle CH_3}{\mid}}{C}H-\overset{\overset{\displaystyle NH_2}{\mid}}{C}HCOOH$	isoleucine	Ile
$CH_3SCH_2CH_2-\overset{\overset{\displaystyle NH_2}{\mid}}{C}HCOOH$	methionine	Met
proline structure	proline	Pro
phenylalanine structure $-CH_2-\overset{\overset{\displaystyle NH_2}{\mid}}{C}HCOOH$	phenylalanine	Phe
tryptophan structure $-CH_2-\overset{\overset{\displaystyle NH_2}{\mid}}{C}HCOOH$	tryptophan	Trp
$HOCH_2-\overset{\overset{\displaystyle NH_2}{\mid}}{C}HCOOH$	serine	Ser
$CH_3\overset{\overset{\displaystyle OH}{\mid}}{C}H-\overset{\overset{\displaystyle NH_2}{\mid}}{C}HCOOH$	threonine	Thr
$HSCH_2-\overset{\overset{\displaystyle NH_2}{\mid}}{C}HCOOH$	cysteine	Cys
$HO-\text{⟨benzene⟩}-CH_2-\overset{\overset{\displaystyle NH_2}{\mid}}{C}HCOOH$	tyrosine	Tyr
$H_2N\overset{\overset{\displaystyle O}{\|}}{C}CH_2-\overset{\overset{\displaystyle NH_2}{\mid}}{C}HCOOH$	asparagine	Asn
$H_2N\overset{\overset{\displaystyle O}{\|}}{C}CH_2CH_2-\overset{\overset{\displaystyle NH_2}{\mid}}{C}HCOOH$	glutamine	Gln

TABLE 29.1 (continued)

R—CHCOOH (NH₂)	Name	Abbreviation

$$R-\underset{\underset{NH_2}{|}}{C}HCOOH$$

Structure	Name	Abbreviation
$HO\overset{O}{\overset{\|}{C}}CH_2-\underset{\underset{NH_2}{\|}}{C}HCOOH$	aspartic acid	Asp
$HO\overset{O}{\overset{\|}{C}}CH_2CH_2-\underset{\underset{NH_2}{\|}}{C}HCOOH$	glutamic acid	Glu
$H_2NCH_2CH_2CH_2CH_2-\underset{\underset{NH_2}{\|}}{C}HCOOH$	lysine	Lys
$H_2N\overset{NH}{\overset{\|}{C}}NHCH_2CH_2CH_2-\underset{\underset{NH_2}{\|}}{C}HCOOH$	arginine	Arg
(imidazole ring)$-CH_2-\underset{\underset{NH_2}{\|}}{C}HCOOH$	histidine	His

structure of L-proline is shown in Figure 29.2. Optical rotations for the natural L-amino acids are given in Table 29.2.

EXERCISE 29.2 Assign R and S stereochemical descriptors to L-alanine, L-serine, and L-cysteine (see Section 7.3).

TABLE 29.2 Physical Properties of Amino Acids

Amino Acid	Decomposition Point, °C	Water Solubility, g/100 ml H₂O at 25	$[\alpha]_D^{25}$	pK_1	pK_2	pK_3
glycine	233	25		2.35	9.78	
alanine	297	16.7	+8.5	2.35	9.87	
valine	315	8.9	+13.9	2.29	9.72	
leucine	293	2.4	−10.8	2.33	9.74	
isoleucine	284	4.1	+11.3	2.32	9.76	
methionine	280	3.4	−8.2	2.17	9.27	
proline	220	162	−85.0	1.95	10.64	
phenylalanine	283	3.0	−35.1	2.58	9.24	
tryptophan	289	1.1	−31.5	2.43	9.44	
serine	228	5.0	−6.8	2.19	9.44	
threonine	225	very	−28.3	2.09	9.10	
cysteine			+6.5	1.86	8.35	10.34
tyrosine	342	0.04	−10.6	2.20	9.11	10.07
asparagine	234	3.5	−5.4	2.02	8.80	
glutamine	185	3.7	+6.1	2.17	9.13	
aspartic acid	270	0.54	+25.0	1.99	3.90	10.00
glutamic acid	247	0.86	+31.4	2.13	4.32	9.95
lysine	225	very	+14.6	2.16	9.20	10.80
arginine	244	15	+12.5	1.82	8.99	13.20
histidine	287	4.2	−39.7	1.81	6.05	9.15

FIGURE 29.2 Stereo structure of L-proline. [Reproduced with permission from *Molecular Structure and Dimensions*, International Union of Crystallography, 1972.]

29.3 Acid-Base Properties of Amino Acids

Amino acids show both acidic and basic properties (**amphoterism**). In acidic solution, the amino acid is completely protonated and exists as the conjugate acid.

$$\overset{+}{H_3}NCH_2CO_2^- + H^+ \longrightarrow \overset{+}{H_3}NCH_2COOH$$

The titration curve for glycine hydrochloride is shown in Figure 29.3. The salt behaves as a typical dihydric acid.

$$\overset{+}{H_3}NCH_2COOH \overset{K_1}{\rightleftharpoons} H^+ + \overset{+}{H_3}NCH_2CO_2^-$$

$$\overset{+}{H_3}NCH_2CO_2^- \overset{K_2}{\rightleftharpoons} H^+ + H_2NCH_2CO_2^-$$

$$K_1 = \frac{[H^+][\overset{+}{H_3}NCH_2CO_2^-]}{[\overset{+}{H_3}NCH_2COOH]}$$

$$K_2 = \frac{[H^+][H_2NCH_2CO_2^-]}{[\overset{+}{H_3}NCH_2CO_2^-]}$$

FIGURE 29.3 Titration curve for glycine hydrochloride.

When the hydrochloride has been half neutralized, $[H_3\overset{+}{N}CH_2COOH]$ is equal to $[H_3\overset{+}{N}CH_2CO_2{}^-]$. The pH of the solution at this point is equal to pK_1. This first dissociation constant refers to ionization of the COOH, which is the more acidic of the two acidic groups in the dibasic acid. Note that glycine is substantially more acidic than acetic acid, which has $pK_a = 4.76$, because of the large inductive effect of the $\overset{+}{N}H_3$ group (see Sections 10.4 and 17.4).

After one equivalent of base has been added, the chief species in solution is the zwitterionic form of the amino acid itself. The pH of the solution at this point is simply the pH of a solution of the amino acid in pure water. This point represents the pH at which the solubility of the amino acid is at a minimum, and is called the **isoelectric point**.

Addition of a further half-equivalent of base corresponds to half-neutralization of the acid $H_3\overset{+}{N}CH_2CO_2{}^-$. At this point $[H_3\overset{+}{N}CH_2CO_2{}^-] = [H_2NCH_2CO_2{}^-]$, and the pH of the solution is equal to pK_2, the dissociation constant for the protonated amino group. Note that pK_2 for glycine, 9.78, is slightly lower than that for the conjugate acid of methylamine, which has pK_a 10.4.

$$H_3\overset{+}{N}CH_2CO_2{}^- \rightleftharpoons H^+ + H_2NCH_2CO_2{}^- \qquad pK_a = 9.8$$

$$H_3\overset{+}{N}CH_3 \rightleftharpoons H^+ + H_2NCH_3 \qquad pK_a = 10.4$$

Thus, the ammonium group of glycine is slightly more acidic than the methylammonium ion.

It may seem surprising that a carboxylate anion, with its negative charge, should make an ammonium cation more acidic. The explanation probably has to do with solvation effects. A dipolar or zwitterionic compound with its charges sufficiently separated can have both ionic centers solvated in a normal fashion—as if the charges were on separate molecules. When the two charges are close together, however, solvation becomes less efficient. As shown in Figure 29.4, solvent dipoles (a) and (b) provide normal solvation. Solvent dipoles (c) and (d), however, provide a stabilizing Coulombic attraction to one charge but repulsion with the other. As a result, a dipolar system of this type is less stabilized by solvation and is less favored in an equilibrium.

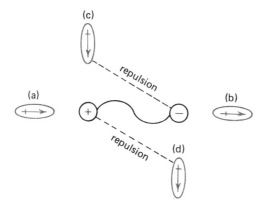

FIGURE 29.4 Solvation effects in a zwitterion.

EXERCISE 29.3 What is the principal organic species present in an aqueous solution of glycine at (a) pH 2, (b) pH 4, (c) pH 8, and (d) pH 11?

As shown in Table 29.2, most of the amino acids show similar values of pK_1 and pK_2. Aspartic and glutamic acids each have an additional carboxy group, with pK_as of 3.90 and 4.32, respectively.

Lysine has two amino groups with pK_as of 9.20 and 10.8. The more basic group is probably the one more remote from the carboxy group. Consequently, the principal form of lysine is probably the zwitterion in which the terminal amino group is protonated.

$$\overset{+}{H_3}NCH_2CH_2CH_2CH_2\overset{\overset{\displaystyle NH_2}{|}}{C}HCO_2^-$$

lysine

Arginine contains the strongly basic guanadino group, corresponding to pK_a 13.2. It exists in the following zwitterionic form.

$$H_2N\overset{\overset{\displaystyle \overset{+}{N}H_2}{||}}{C}NHCH_2CH_2CH_2\overset{\overset{\displaystyle NH_2}{|}}{C}HCO_2^-$$

arginine

Guanidines are compounds of the general formula

$$RNH\overset{\overset{\displaystyle NH}{||}}{C}NH_2$$

Protonation of the guanidino group on the imino nitrogen results in a cation that is highly resonance stabilized. Guanidines are among the strongest organic bases.

$$RNH\overset{\overset{\displaystyle NH}{||}}{C}NH_2 + H^+ \rightleftharpoons \left[RNH-\overset{\overset{\displaystyle \overset{+}{N}H_2}{||}}{C}-NH_2 \longleftrightarrow R\overset{+}{N}H=\overset{\overset{\displaystyle NH_2}{|}}{C}-NH_2 \longleftrightarrow RNH-\overset{\overset{\displaystyle NH_2}{|}}{C}=\overset{+}{N}H_2 \right]$$

The high pK_3 for arginine shows that the guanidino group is half protonated even at pH 13.2.

Tyrosine and histidine also contain other titratable groups, corresponding to pK_as of 10.07 and 6.05, respectively. These ionization constants refer to the phenolic hydroxy in tyrosine and the imidazole ring in histidine. The pK_a of about 10 is a normal value for a phenol (Section 26.5.B). We shall discuss imidazole in Chapter 31. The third titratable group in cysteine is the SH, which has a pK_a of 10.34, a normal value for a mercaptan (Section 25.1).

EXERCISE 29.4 Sketch the expected general appearance of the titration curve for histidine.

29.4 Synthesis of Amino Acids

A. Commercial Availability

All of the common amino acids are available from chemical suppliers in optically active form. Table 29.3 lists the prices per 100 g of the amino acids quoted by various suppliers in 1983. These prices reflect several factors.

All of the racemic amino acids are synthetic and are prepared commercially by methods to be outlined later in this section. The prices of the synthetic amino acids reflect both the ease of synthesis and the demand for the various compounds. Note that one of the more expensive racemic amino acids is the cyclic compound proline, which cannot be easily prepared by the standard methods that serve for the other amino acids.

Some of the available L-amino acids are isolated from natural sources; this is generally true when the price is lower than that for the racemate. The relatively low price of glutamic acid is a consequence of the fact that monosodium glutamate (MSG) is widely used as flavor enhancer in food preparation. The L-amino acid is prepared by a fermentation process in tonnage quantities, and its low price reflects this volume. Some of the commercially available L-amino acids and all of the D-enantiomers are prepared by resolution of the synthetic racemates. Their high costs result from the additional expenses incurred in the resolution process (see Section 29.4.F).

B. Amination of α-Halo Acids

α-Halo acids are available by the halogenation of carboxylic acids (Section 17.7.B). Recall that the direct alkylation of ammonia or an amine is not generally a satisfactory

TABLE 29.3 Prices of Amino Acids

Amino Acid	Price per 100 g, $		
	L-enantiomer	D-enantiomer	Racemate
glycine	—	—	1.10
alanine	14.00	91.00	3.00
valine	13.25	89.00	5.00
leucine	8.25	160.00	5.25
isoleucine	28.00	7500.00	18.00[a]
methionine	7.25	65.00	1.40
proline	17.00	1430.00	168.00
phenylalanine	13.50	76.00	12.75
tryptophan	22.00	62.00	15.00
serine	22.00	100.00	8.75
threonine	29.00	100.00	20.00
cysteine	15.00	1840.00[a]	210.00[a]
tyrosine	7.90	510.00	44.80
asparagine	6.00	33.50	6.00
glutamine	9.50	710.00	—
aspartic acid	2.95	47.00	2.85
glutamic acid	1.25	110.00	7.00
lysine	2.85[b]	460.00[b]	9.90[b]
arginine	6.00	690.00[b]	90.00[b]
histidine	12.00	250.00	30.00

[a] Mixture of diastereomers.
[b] Hydrochloride salt.

method for preparing amines owing to the overalkylation problem (Section 23.6.A). The reaction is somewhat better for preparing α-amino acids because the amino group in the product amino acids is less basic (by about 0.8 pK_a unit) than the amine itself. Thus the second alkylation reaction is now slower than the first. A number of α-amino acids may be prepared in this way.

$$\underset{\overset{|}{\text{CH}_3\text{CHCOOH}}}{\overset{\text{Br}}{|}} + \text{NH}_4{}^+ \text{ OH}^- \xrightarrow[\substack{25^\circ\text{C} \\ 4 \text{ days}}]{\text{H}_2\text{O}} \underset{\overset{|}{\text{CH}_3\text{CHCO}_2{}^-}}{\overset{\overset{+}{\text{N}}\text{H}_3}{|}} + \text{NH}_4{}^+ \text{ Br}^-$$

> α-Bromopropionic acid (153 g) is added to 5.8 L of concentrated aqueous ammonia and the resulting solution is kept at room temperature for 4 days. The solution is evaporated to dryness and extracted with warm absolute ethanol to remove ammonium bromide. The amino acid, 50 g (56%), is obtained as a white crystalline mass.

EXERCISE 29.5 Write equations for the syntheses of phenylalanine, valine, and leucine, starting with the corresponding carboxylic acids. What special problems arise in the application of this method for the synthesis of serine or tyrosine?

C. Alkylation of N-Substituted Aminomalonic Esters

An especially useful general method for the synthesis of α-amino acids involves a variation of the malonic ester synthesis (Section 27.7.D). Diethyl malonate may be monobrominated to yield a bromide that enters into the S_N2 reaction with the potassium salt of phthalimide to give N-phthalimidomalonic ester.

potassium phthalimidate   N-phthalimidomalonic ester

The ester may be alkylated by a variety of alkyl halides or α,β-unsaturated carbonyl compounds. Vigorous acid hydrolysis causes hydrolysis of both ester groups and the phthalimido group and decarboxylation of the resulting malonic acid. The product is a racemic α-amino acid.

Representative examples of this procedure are the synthesis of methionine and glutamic acid.

N-phthalimidomalonic ester scheme:

The phthalimide reagent NCH(COOEt)$_2$ gives:

$$\xrightarrow{\text{NaOEt}} \xrightarrow{\text{CH}_3\text{SCH}_2\text{CH}_2\text{Cl}} \xrightarrow[\Delta]{\text{H}_3\text{O}^+} CH_3SCH_2CH_2\overset{\overset{+}{N}H_3}{\underset{}{C}}HCO_2^-$$

(50% overall)
methionine

$$\xrightarrow[\text{NaOEt}]{\text{CH}_2=\text{CHCOOEt}} \xrightarrow[\Delta]{\text{H}_3\text{O}^+} HOOCCH_2CH_2\overset{\overset{+}{N}H_3}{\underset{}{C}}HCO_2^-$$

(75% overall)
glutamic acid

EXERCISE 29.6 Write the equations illustrating the synthesis of aspartic acid, phenylalanine, and valine by the N-phthalimidomalonic ester method.

Other procedures similar to the foregoing are also useful. The best method utilizes the N-acetamido rather than the N-phthalimido derivative. The starting material is readily prepared from malonic ester. Treatment of the diester with nitrous acid gives a nitroso derivative, which rearranges to the oxime. Hydrogenation of the oxime in acetic anhydride solution gives acetamidomalonic ester (Section 23.6.E).

$$\underset{\underset{\text{COOEt}}{|}}{\overset{\overset{\text{COOEt}}{|}}{CH_2}} + HNO_2 \longrightarrow \left[\underset{\underset{\text{COOEt}}{|}}{\overset{\overset{\text{COOEt}}{|}}{O=N-CH}} \right] \longrightarrow \underset{\underset{\text{COOEt}}{|}}{\overset{\overset{\text{COOEt}}{|}}{HON=C}} \xrightarrow[\text{Ac}_2\text{O}]{\text{H}_2\text{-Pt}} CH_3\overset{\overset{O}{||}}{C}NHCH(COOEt)_2$$

acetamidomalonic ester

The acetamidomalonic ester is alkylated, and the resulting product is hydrolyzed and decarboxylated to obtain the amino acid.

$$CH_3\overset{\overset{O}{||}}{C}NHCH(COOEt)_2$$

With imidazole-CH$_2$Cl reagent:

$$\xrightarrow{\text{NaOEt}} \xrightarrow{} \xrightarrow[\Delta]{\text{H}_3\text{O}^+} \text{imidazole-}CH_2\overset{\overset{+}{N}H_3}{\underset{}{C}}HCO_2^-$$

(35% overall)
histidine

$$\xrightarrow{\text{NaOEt}} \xrightarrow{\text{(CH}_3)_2\text{CHCH}_2\text{Br}} \xrightarrow[\Delta]{\text{H}_3\text{O}^+} (CH_3)_2CHCH_2\overset{\overset{+}{N}H_3}{\underset{}{C}}HCO_2^-$$

(51% overall)
leucine

EXERCISE 29.7 Write the equations illustrating the synthesis of serine, tyrosine, and valine by the N-acetamidomalonic ester method.

D. Strecker Synthesis

Another method of some generality for the preparation of α-amino acids is the hydrolysis of α-amino nitriles, which are available by the treatment of aldehydes with ammonia and HCN (**Strecker synthesis**).

$$RCHO + NH_3 + HCN \longrightarrow \overset{\overset{\displaystyle NH_2}{|}}{R}CHCN \xrightarrow{H_3O^+} \overset{\overset{\displaystyle \overset{+}{N}H_3}{|}}{R}CHCO_2^-$$

The mechanism of formation of the α-amino nitrile probably involves the addition of HCN to the imine, which is formed by condensation of the aldehyde with ammonia.

$$RCHO + NH_3 \rightleftharpoons H_2O + RCH=NH \xrightarrow{HCN} \overset{\overset{\displaystyle NH_2}{|}}{R}CHCN$$

An example of the application of the Strecker synthesis is the following preparation of phenylalanine.

(74%)
phenylalanine

EXERCISE 29.8 Show how you could prepare tyrosine, specifically labelled with ^{14}C in the C-1 (carboxy) position. What problem arises in application of the Strecker synthesis for preparation of lysine?

E. Miscellaneous Methods

The foregoing methods are of general applicability for the synthesis of the simpler amino acids, either natural or unnatural. Some of the more complicated structures must be prepared in other ways. For example, the heterocyclic amino acid proline has been synthesized by the following route.

(70%)

The basic amino acid lysine has been prepared in a variety of ways. One interesting method involves application of the Schmidt reaction (Section 23.6.H) to 2-

oxocyclohexanecarboxylic acid. The product is a cyclic amido acid, which may be hydrolyzed to an amino dicarboxylic acid.

A second application of the Schmidt reaction yields lysine. Fortunately, only the carboxy group that is not α to the amino group reacts; in fact, α-amino acids fail to react at all in the Schmidt reaction.

$$\text{HOOC(CH}_2)_4\overset{\overset{+}{\underset{|}{N}H_3}}{C}HCO_2^- \xrightarrow[\text{H}_2\text{SO}_4]{\text{HN}_3} \overset{+}{H}_3N(CH_2)_4\overset{\overset{NH_2}{\underset{|}{}}}{C}HCO_2^-$$
$$(74\%)$$

The Schmidt reaction, introduced in Section 23.6.H as a reaction of carboxylic acids, also may be applied to ketones. It is a general method for the conversion of ketones to amides.

A probable mechanism for the conversion is shown below.

EXERCISE 29.9 Show how the Schmidt reaction could be used to prepare the unnatural amino acid 2-aminoadipic acid.

F. Resolution

Amino acids that are synthesized by the methods outlined in the preceding sections are obtained as racemates. It is usually desirable to have one of the two enantiomers, usually the L-enantiomer. For this reason a good deal of attention has been paid to the problem of resolving racemic amino acids.

One method that may be used for the resolution of amino acids involves converting them into diastereomeric salts (Section 23.4). The amino group is usually converted into an amide so that the material is not amphoteric. For example, alanine reacts with benzoyl chloride in aqueous base to give N-benzoylalanine, which is a typical acid.

benzoyl chloride   N-benzoylalanine

The racemic N-benzoylalanine is resolved in the normal way (Section 23.4) with brucine or strychnine. If brucine is used, it is the brucine salt of D-alanine that is less soluble. If strychnine is used, the strychnine salt of L-alanine crystallizes. Acidification of the salts yields the D- and L-enantiomers of N-benzoylalanine. Basic hydrolysis then affords the pure enantiomeric amino acids. The process is outlined schematically as follows.

DL-alanine

↓

N-benzoyl-DL-alanine

| brucine

brucine salt of   brucine salt of
N-benzoyl-D-alanine   N-benzoyl-L-alanine
"insoluble"   "soluble"

| H₃O⁺ | H₃O⁺

N-benzoyl-D-alanine   N-benzoyl-L-alanine

| 1. OH⁻, H₂O, Δ | 1. OH⁻, H₂O, Δ
| 2. H₃O⁺ | 2. H₃O⁺

D-alanine (optically pure)   L-alanine (optically impure)

In cases such as that outlined, the enantiomer that forms the less soluble salt is usually obtained in an optically pure state. The other enantiomer is usually obtained in an impure state because some of the less soluble salt invariably remains in solution. In the case diagrammed, the impure N-benzoyl-L-alanine may be treated with strychnine to give the insoluble strychnine salt. In this way both enantiomers may be obtained in an optically pure state.

For all its simplicity, the **method of diastereomeric salts** suffers from several severe drawbacks. The less soluble diastereomeric salt is usually contaminated with the other salt, and several tedious recrystallizations may be required in order to purify it. These repetitive crystallizations are wasteful of both time and material, which may often be quite valuable. There is no way to predict which chiral base will give well-defined crystals with a given amino acid or which enantiomer of the amino acid will form the less soluble salt.

Various biological procedures are much more useful for the routine large-scale resolution of amino acids. The success of biological resolution stems from the fact that organisms are generally capable of utilizing only one enantiomer of a racemic substance. Thus, if a racemic amino acid is fed to an animal or microorganism, one enantiomer is consumed. The unreacted enantiomer may then be isolated from the culture medium in the case of microorganisms or from the urine of the animal. Since L-enantiomers are utilized by almost all organisms, this method is useful for preparing optically pure D-enantiomers.

In practice, the procedure of using the whole animal for resolution is of only limited value. A more useful adaptation of the basic principle employs the use of crude enzyme preparations that catalyze some reaction on only one enantiomer. An example is the resolution of DL-leucine by *hog renal acylase*, an enzyme isolated from hog kidneys. The enzyme functions as a catalyst for the hydrolysis of amide linkages and is specific for amides of L-amino acids. For resolution, the racemic amino acid is first converted into the N-acetyl derivative, which is then incubated with a small amount of the crude enzyme preparation. The enzyme catalyzes hydrolysis of N-acetyl-L-leucine to the amino acid, leaving N-acetyl-D-leucine unchanged. The two enantiomers are easily separable, since one is acidic and the other is amphoteric.

$$\text{DL-leucine} \xrightarrow{\text{Ac}_2\text{O}} \text{N-acetyl-DL-leucine} \xrightarrow[\text{acylase}]{\text{hog renal}} \begin{cases} \text{L-leucine} \\ + \\ \text{N-acetyl-D-leucine} \end{cases}$$

A suspension of 17.3 g of N-acetyl-DL-leucine in 1 L of water is adjusted to pH 7.0 with ammonium hydroxide solution, and 0.012 g of hog renal acylase powder is added. The mixture is agitated at 38°C for 24 hr. The mixture is acidified with 10 mL of acetic acid, filtered, and evaporated under vacuum to a volume of about 50 mL. Upon addition of ethanol, L-leucine crystallizes. The semipure amino acid is recrystallized from ethanol-water to give 5 g (80%) of optically pure L-leucine.

The filtrates from the foregoing process are acidified to pH 2 with HCl and chilled, whereupon N-acetyl-D-leucine crystallizes. One recrystallization from water gives 7 g (80%) of optically pure product. It may be hydrolyzed by refluxing with 2 *N* HCl to obtain pure D-leucine.

29.5 Reactions of Amino Acids

A. Esterification

The carboxy group of an amino acid can be esterified in the normal way. Methyl, ethyl, and benzyl esters are employed extensively as intermediates in the synthesis of peptides (Section 29.6). The methyl and ethyl esters are normally prepared by treating a suspension of the amino acid in the appropriate alcohol with anhydrous hydrogen chloride. The amino acid ester is isolated as the crystalline hydrochloride salt.

(90%)
phenylalanine methyl
ester hydrochloride

Benzyl esters are often prepared using benzenesulfonic acid as the catalyst. The water produced in the reaction is removed by azeotropic distillation, thus avoiding the use of a large excess of benzyl alcohol.

$$\text{H}_3\overset{+}{\text{N}}\text{CH}_2\text{CO}_2^- + \text{C}_6\text{H}_5-\text{CH}_2\text{OH} \xrightarrow{\text{C}_6\text{H}_5\text{SO}_3\text{H}} \text{H}_3\overset{+}{\text{N}}\text{CH}_2\text{COOCH}_2-\text{C}_6\text{H}_5 \quad \text{C}_6\text{H}_5\text{SO}_3^-$$

(90%)
glycine benzyl ester benzenesulfonate

As we shall see later, the benzyl esters are especially useful derivatives because they may be converted back to acids by nonhydrolytic methods. For example, glycine benzyl ester reacts with hydrogen in the presence of palladium to give glycine and toluene (Section 20.6.B).

$$H_3\overset{+}{N}CH_2COOCH_2\text{—}\langle\bigcirc\rangle \quad Cl^- \xrightarrow{H_2\text{-}Pd} H_3\overset{+}{N}CH_2COOH \ Cl^- + \langle\bigcirc\rangle\text{—}CH_3$$

B. Amide Formation

Acylation of the amino group in amino acids is best carried out under basic conditions, so that a substantial concentration of the free amino form is present. A typical procedure calls for treatment of a mixture of the amino acid and benzoyl chloride with concentrated aqueous sodium hydroxide. At the end of the reaction, it is necessary to acidify the aqueous solution to obtain the acidic product.

$$(CH_3)_2CH\overset{\overset{+}{N}H_3}{\underset{|}{C}}HCO_2^- + C_6H_5\overset{O}{\overset{\|}{C}}Cl \xrightarrow[\substack{H_2O \\ 2\ hr,\ 4°C}]{OH^-} \xrightarrow{HCl} (CH_3)_2CH\overset{\overset{O}{\overset{\|}{NHCC_6H_5}}}{\underset{|}{C}}HCOOH$$

$$(80\%)$$
N-benzoylvaline

Amides may also be prepared by reaction with acetic anhydride.

$$\underset{\underset{H}{\overset{N}{\diagup}}\diagdown}{\overset{N}{\diagup}}\text{—}CH_2\overset{\overset{+}{N}H_3}{\underset{|}{C}}HCO_2^- + Ac_2O \xrightarrow[\text{2 hr}]{100°C} \underset{\underset{H}{\overset{N}{\diagup}}\diagdown}{\overset{N}{\diagup}}\text{—}CH_2\overset{\overset{O}{\overset{\|}{NHCCH_3}}}{\underset{|}{C}}HCOOH$$

$$(80\%)$$
N-acetylhistidine

EXERCISE 29.10 Write equations illustrating the conversion of phenylalanine into N-acetylphenylalanine methyl ester.

C. Oxidative Deamination

When an aqueous solution of an α-amino acid is treated with triketohydrindene hydrate (ninhydrin), a violet color is produced.

$$2 \ \underset{\text{ninhydrin}}{\overset{O}{\diagup\diagdown}\overset{OH}{\underset{O}{\diagdown\diagup}}\overset{OH}{\underset{}{}}} + R\overset{NH_2}{\underset{|}{C}}HCOOH \longrightarrow$$

$$\underset{\text{violet}}{\overset{O \quad O}{\diagup\diagdown}=N\text{—}\overset{OH}{\diagdown\diagup}} + RCHO + CO_2 + 3\ H_2O$$

The reaction mechanism is complicated, and we shall not go into it here. Note that the amino acid contributes only a nitrogen to the violet-colored product. The manner in which this nitrogen becomes separated from the amino acid is known and is an example of a reaction of α-amino acids that is biologically important.

In the first stages of the ninhydrin reaction, the amino acid is oxidized to give an α-imino acid. In aqueous solution this imino acid is hydrolyzed to an α-keto acid and ammonia. The ammonia reacts further to give the violet pigment, and the α-keto acid decarboxylates to give an aldehyde.

$$\underset{\substack{|\\ \text{RCHCOOH}}}{\text{NH}_2} \xrightarrow{[O]} \underset{\substack{||\\ \text{RCCOOH}}}{\text{NH}} \xrightarrow{\text{H}_2\text{O}} \text{NH}_3 + \underset{\substack{||\\ \text{RCCOOH}}}{\text{O}} \longrightarrow \text{RCHO} + \text{CO}_2$$

The process of **oxidative deamination**, outlined above, is an important pathway for the biodegradation of α-amino acids.

The ninhydrin reaction has practical importance because it may be used as an analytical method for α-amino acids. The violet solutions show a significant absorption at 570 nm, and the intensity of the absorption is proportional to the amount of α-amino acid present. The reaction is not given by proline, in which the α-amino group is secondary. Another reaction occurs with proline to give a product that can be assayed at another wavelength.

29.6 Peptides

A. Structure and Nomenclature

Peptides, also called polypeptides, are amino acid polymers containing from 2 to about 50 individual units. The individual amino acids are connected by amide linkages from the amino group of one unit to the carboxy group of another. Unless a polypeptide is cyclic, it will contain a free NH_3^+ group (the N-terminal end) and a free CO_2^- group (the C-terminal end).

a polypeptide

By convention, peptide structures are always written with the N-terminal unit on the left and the C-terminal unit on the right. They are named by prefixing the name of the C-terminal unit with the group names of the other amino acids, beginning with the N-terminal unit. Since the names tend to become rather unintelligible, a shorthand notational system is used employing the three-letter codes given in Table 29.1. The stereo structure of Gly-Phe-Gly is shown in Figure 29.5.

Peptides are formed by partial hydrolysis of proteins, which are amino acid polymers of much higher molecular weight (more than 50 amino acid units). Upon hydrolysis of a protein, some amide linkages are broken and a complex mixture of peptides results. Complete hydrolysis gives a mixture of amino acids. Some peptides are also

FIGURE 29.5 Stereo structure of Gly-Phe-Gly. [Reproduced with permission from *Molecular Structure and Dimensions*. International Union of Crystallography, 1972.]

$$\overset{+}{H_3}NCH_2\overset{\overset{O}{\|}}{C}-NHCHCO_2^-$$
$$\qquad\qquad\qquad CH_3$$

glycylalanine
Gly-Ala

$$\overset{+}{H_3}NCH_2\overset{\overset{O}{\|}}{C}-NHCH\overset{\overset{O}{\|}}{C}-NHCH_2CO_2^-$$
$$\qquad\qquad\qquad CH_2C_6H_5$$

glycylphenylalanylglycine
Gly-Phe-Gly

$$\overset{+}{H_3}NCH_2\overset{\overset{O}{\|}}{C}-NHCH\overset{\overset{O}{\|}}{C}-NHCH\overset{\overset{O}{\|}}{C}-NHCH_2CO_2^-$$
$$\qquad\qquad\qquad CH_2OH \quad CH_2C_6H_5$$

glycylserylphenylalanylglycine
Gly-Ser-Phe-Gly

important natural products. An example is the nonapeptide bradykinin, which occurs in blood plasma and is involved in the regulation of blood pressure.

Arg-Pro-Pro-Gly-Phe-Ser-Pro-Phe-Arg
bradykinin

The central feature of the polypeptide chain is the succession of amide linkages. Recall from our previous study (Chapter 18) that the carbon-nitrogen bond in an amide has a high degree of "double bond character" resulting from delocalization of the nitrogen lone pair into the carbonyl group. This delocalization reduces the basicity of the nitrogen and causes restricted rotation about the carbon-nitrogen bond.

The restricted rotation has an important effect on the three-dimensional structure of proteins, as we shall see later.

The only other type of covalent bond between amino acids in proteins and peptides is the disulfide linkage between two cysteine units.

$$
\begin{array}{ccc}
\text{NH} & & \text{HN} \\
| & & | \\
\text{O}=\text{C} & & \text{C}=\text{O} \\
| & & | \\
\text{CHCH}_2\text{S}{-}\text{SCH}_2\text{CH} & & \\
| & & | \\
\text{NH} & & \text{NH}
\end{array}
$$

disulfide
bond

Recall that disulfides, R—S—S—R, are formed by the mild oxidation of thiols (page 759). The disulfide linkage is easily reduced to regenerate the thiols.

$$
2\,\text{RSH} \; \underset{\text{reduction}}{\overset{\text{oxidation}}{\rightleftharpoons}} \; \text{RSSR}
$$

When such a disulfide bond occurs between two cysteine residues in the same chain, a "loop" results, as in the posterior pituitary hormone oxytocin. If the cysteine units are in different chains, the disulfide link may bind the two chains together, as in the A and B chains of insulin (Figure 29.6).

Like the simpler amino acids, peptides are amphoteric compounds, since they usually still contain a free α-amino and a free α-carboxy group; they exist as zwitterions. The pK_as for the two functions in a few simple peptides are listed in Table 29.4. Also included are the isoelectric points, pH_1, the pH at which the peptide is least soluble in aqueous solution.

EXERCISE 29.11 Write the structure of the tetrapeptide Val-Phe-Ser-Leu.

B. Synthesis of Peptides

The simplest method for the synthesis of peptides is the polymerization of an amino acid. The resulting **homopolymer** is a mixture of peptides of variable chain length. Such homopolymers are not found in nature, but the synthetic ones have been useful in understanding some of the physical and spectral properties of proteins.

FIGURE 29.6 Amino acid sequence and disulfide bridges of bovine oxytocin and bovine insulin. The N-terminal units are at the left and the C-terminal units are at the right. All three C-terminal units occur as amides, —CONH_2.

TABLE 29.4 pK_a Values for Some Peptides

Peptide	pK_1 COOH	pK_2 NH_3	Isoelectric Point, pH_1
Gly-Gly	3.14	8.25	5.70
Gly-Ala	3.15	8.23	5.69
Ala-Gly	3.17	8.18	5.68
Gly-Gly-Gly	3.23	8.09	5.66
Ala-Ala-Ala-Ala	3.42	7.94	5.68

$$\overset{+}{H_3}NCH_2CO_2^- \longrightarrow \overset{+}{H_3}NCH_2\overset{O}{\overset{\|}{C}}\left(NHCH_2\overset{O}{\overset{\|}{C}}\right)_n NHCH_2CO_2^-$$

polyglycine

The first product formed when two amino acids condense is a dipeptide. The terminal amino and carboxy groups are now situated so that they can interact to form a six-membered ring diamide. We have seen previously that intramolecular reactions to form five- and six-membered rings are frequently much faster than their intermolecular analogs (Sections 14.8.C, 27.5.C). Thus, when glycine is heated, the cyclic dimer 2,5-diketopiperazine is produced.

$$2\ \overset{+}{H_3}NCH_2CO_2^- \xrightarrow{\text{slow}} \overset{+}{H_3}NCH_2\overset{O}{\overset{\|}{C}}NHCH_2CO_2^- \xrightarrow{\text{fast}}$$

2,5-diketopiperazine
"glycine anhydride"

Piperazine is a heterocyclic diamine, which is numbered as shown. It is the nitrogen analog of 1,4-dioxane (page 198).

piperazine

1,4-dioxane

EXERCISE 29.12 In 1914 Maillard reported a study of the polymerization of glycine. The amino was heated in glycerol solution. The main product of the reaction was found to be 2,5-diketopiperazine. A polypeptide fraction was produced in low yield. The predominant peptides in this fraction were the even peptides tetraglycine and hexaglycine. Explain.

Hydrolysis of one of the amide bonds in a 2,5-diketopiperazine is one method for preparing simple dipeptides.

$$\text{(structure)} \xrightarrow[\substack{100\,°C \\ 90-100\ \text{sec}}]{\text{conc. HCl}} \overset{+}{H_3}NCH_2\overset{O}{\overset{\|}{C}}NHCH_2COOH\ Cl^-$$

(90%)

glycylglycine hydrochloride

The rational synthesis of peptides is a challenging task that has only been solved in the past few decades. In order to illustrate the difficulty, consider the synthesis of the simple dipeptide glycylalanine (Gly-Ala) from glycine and alanine. The problem is to form an amide linkage between the carboxy group of glycine and the amino group of alanine.

$$\overset{+}{H_3}NCH_2CO_2^- + \overset{+}{H_3}N\overset{CH_3}{\overset{|}{C}H}CO_2^- \dashrightarrow \overset{+}{H_3}NCH_2\overset{O}{\overset{\|}{C}}NH\overset{CH_3}{\overset{|}{C}H}CO_2^-$$

The normal method for converting a carboxylic acid into an amide is to activate the carboxy group by converting it to an acyl halide and then to add the amine.

$$RCOOH \xrightarrow{SOCl_2} R\overset{O}{\overset{\|}{C}}Cl \xrightarrow{R'NH_2} R\overset{O}{\overset{\|}{C}}NHR'$$

But an amino acid cannot be converted into an acyl halide; polymerization would result. Another possibility would be the direct formation of the amide link by treatment of a mixture of the two amino acids with some dehydrating agent to remove the water produced. However, such a direct approach will give a mixture of four different dipeptides. Furthermore, each of these dipeptides can react further to give higher peptides.

$$\text{glycine} + \text{alanine} \xrightarrow{-H_2O} \text{Gly-Gly} + \text{Ala-Ala} + \text{Gly-Ala} + \text{Ala-Gly}$$

An additional complication enters in with amino acids that have other reactive functional groups.

The general method that has been developed to avoid these difficulties involves the use of **protecting groups** (Section 16.4). Protecting groups have been developed for both the amino and carboxy groups, as well as for the other groups that occur in the side chains of the various amino acids. A suitable protecting group must fulfill several criteria.

1. The protecting group must be easy to introduce into the molecule.
2. It must protect the functional group under conditions of amide formation.
3. It must be removable under conditions that leave the newly created amide link intact.

Carboxy groups are normally protected by conversion into the methyl, ethyl, or benzyl ester. Since esters are hydrolyzed more easily than amides, the protecting group can be removed by alkaline hydrolysis.

$$\sim\overset{O}{\overset{\|}{C}}NH\overset{}{\overset{|}{C}H}COOCH_3 \xrightarrow[H_2O]{OH^-} \xrightarrow{H_3O^+} \sim\overset{O}{\overset{\|}{C}}NH\overset{}{\overset{|}{C}H}COOH + CH_3OH$$

Benzyl esters may be cleaved by hydrogenolysis (Section 20.6.B).

$$\sim\!\!\underset{\underset{O}{\parallel}}{C}NHCHCOOCH_2\!\!-\!\!\bigcirc \xrightarrow{H_2-Pd/C} \sim\!\!\underset{\underset{O}{\parallel}}{C}NHCHCOOH + CH_3\!\!-\!\!\bigcirc$$
$$\qquad\qquad\underset{R}{|} \qquad\qquad\qquad\qquad\qquad \underset{R}{|}$$

Of the many amino protecting groups that have been developed, we shall discuss only two, the benzyloxycarbonyl ("**carbobenzoxy**," **Cbz**) and the *t*-butoxycarbonyl (**Boc**) groups. The benzyloxycarbonyl group is introduced by treating the amino acid with benzyl chloroformate in alkaline solution.

$$\overset{+}{H_3}NCH_2CO_2^- + \bigcirc\!\!-\!\!CH_2O\overset{\overset{O}{\parallel}}{C}Cl \xrightarrow[\substack{H_2O \\ 5^\circ C \\ 30\ min}]{NaOH \quad H_3O^+} \bigcirc\!\!-\!\!CH_2O\overset{\overset{O}{\parallel}}{C}NHCH_2COOH$$

$$\text{glycine} \qquad\qquad \text{benzyl chloroformate} \qquad\qquad\qquad\qquad \underset{\substack{\text{benzyloxycarbonylglycine} \\ \text{Cbz-Gly}}}{(70\text{--}80\%)}$$

Benzyl chloroformate is the half benzyl ester, half acyl chloride of carbonic acid. It is prepared by treating benzyl alcohol with phosgene.

$$\bigcirc\!\!-\!\!CH_2OH + COCl_2 \longrightarrow \bigcirc\!\!-\!\!CH_2O\overset{\overset{O}{\parallel}}{C}Cl$$
$$\qquad\qquad\qquad\qquad\qquad\qquad (95\text{--}99\%)$$

The new carbon-nitrogen linkage in a benzyloxycarbonyl amino acid is part of a carbamate grouping (Section 23.6.H). Like amides, carbamates hydrolyze with difficulty. However, the benzyl-oxygen bond can be cleaved by catalytic hydrogenolysis, yielding the unstable carbamic acid, which undergoes decarboxylation (Section 23.6.H).

$$\bigcirc\!\!-\!\!CH_2O\overset{\overset{O}{\parallel}}{C}NHCHCOOH \xrightarrow{H_2-Pd}$$
$$\qquad\qquad\qquad\qquad \underset{R}{|}$$

$$\bigcirc\!\!-\!\!CH_3 + \left[HO\overset{\overset{O}{\parallel}}{C}NHCHCOOH \right] \longrightarrow CO_2 + \overset{+}{H_3}NCHCO_2^-$$
$$\qquad\qquad\qquad\qquad\quad \underset{R}{|} \qquad\qquad\qquad\qquad\qquad \underset{R}{|}$$

The *t*-butoxycarbonyl group is introduced by treating the amino acid with *t*-butoxycarbonyloximinophenylacetonitrile ("Boc-On").

t-butoxycarbonyloximino-
phenylacetonitrile
"Boc-On"

(100%)
t-butoxycarbonylproline
Boc-Pro

The t-butoxycarbonyl group is removed by treating the protected amino acid or peptide with anhydrous acid, such as trifluoroacetic acid or hydrogen chloride in acetic acid.

$$\underset{\text{t-BuOCNHCHCOOH}}{\overset{\overset{\displaystyle O \quad\; R}{\|\quad\;\; |}}{}} \xrightarrow{\text{HCl}} \underset{\text{H}_3\text{NCHCOOH Cl}^-}{\overset{\overset{\displaystyle R}{\overset{+}{|}}}{}}$$

The initial reaction is cleavage of the alkyl-oxygen bond to give the relatively stable t-butyl cation and a carbamic acid. The resulting carbamic acid then decarboxylates, giving the amine.

$$(\text{CH}_3)_3\text{COCNHR} \longrightarrow (\text{CH}_3)_3\text{C}^+ + \text{HOCNHR}$$

$$\text{HOCNHR} \longrightarrow \text{CO}_2 + \text{H}_2\text{NR}$$

The most generally useful coupling reagent is **dicyclohexylcarbodiimide (DCC)**, a commercially available reagent that is prepared from cyclohexylamine and carbon disulfide by the route indicated below.

(86%)
dicyclohexylcarbodiimide
DCC

Dicyclohexylcarbodiimide is an effective catalyst for condensation of carboxylic acids with alcohols and amines. It functions by activating the free carboxy group of the N-protected amino acid. An equimolar mixture of a carboxylic acid, an amine, and DCC results in formation of the corresponding amide and the highly insoluble N,N'-dicyclohexylurea.

$$\text{RCOOH} + \text{R}'\text{NH}_2 + \text{C}_6\text{H}_{11}\text{N}=\text{C}=\text{NC}_6\text{H}_{11} \longrightarrow \text{RCNHR}' + \text{C}_6\text{H}_{11}\text{NHCNHC}_6\text{H}_{11}$$

N,N'-dicyclohexylurea

947

The probable mechanism for the DCC coupling reaction is outlined as follows. Addition of the carboxylic acid to the diimide gives the ester of isourea, an O-acylisourea.

$$\underset{O}{\overset{\parallel}{R\overset{}{C}OH}} + R'N{=}C{=}NR' \longrightarrow \underset{O}{\overset{\parallel}{R{-}\overset{}{C}}}{-}O{-}\underset{}{\overset{NHR'}{\overset{|}{C}}}{=}NR'$$

an O-acylisourea

The intermediate O-acylisourea is an *activated carboxylic acid derivative* similar in reactivity to an anhydride or an acyl halide. Nucleophilic substitution by the amine yields the amide and the dialkylurea.

$$\underset{O}{\overset{\parallel}{R\overset{}{C}}}{-}O{-}\underset{}{\overset{NHR'}{\overset{|}{C}}}{=}NR' + R''NH_2 \rightleftharpoons \left[\underset{\overset{|}{NHR''}}{\overset{OH}{\overset{|}{R\overset{}{C}}}{-}O{-}\overset{NHR'}{\overset{|}{C}}{=}NR'} \right] \rightleftharpoons$$

$$\left[\underset{\overset{|}{NHR''}}{\overset{O^-}{\overset{|}{R\overset{}{C}}}{-}O{-}\overset{NHR'}{\overset{|}{C}}{=}\overset{+}{N}HR'} \right] \longrightarrow \underset{O}{\overset{\parallel}{R\overset{}{C}NHR''}} + \underset{O}{\overset{\parallel}{R'NH\overset{}{C}NHR'}}$$

An example of the synthesis of a dipeptide utilizing this method is the synthesis of threonylalanine (Thr-Ala) from benzyloxycarbonylthreonine and alanine benzyl ester.

$$\underset{\underset{CH_3}{\overset{|}{CHOH}}}{\overset{}{CbzNHCHCOOH}} + \underset{\overset{|}{CH_3}}{H_2NCHCOOCH_2C_6H_5} \xrightarrow{DCC} \underset{\underset{CH_3}{\overset{|}{CHOH}}\ \overset{|}{CH_3}}{\overset{O}{\overset{\parallel}{CbzNHCH\overset{}{C}NHCHCOOCH_2C_6H_5}}} \xrightarrow[\text{HOAc}]{H_2{-}Pd/C}$$

N-protected threonine   C-protected alanine   Cbz-Thr-Ala-CH$_2$C$_6$H$_5$

$$\underset{\underset{CH_3}{\overset{|}{CHOH}}\ \overset{|}{CH_3}}{\overset{O}{\overset{\parallel}{\overset{+}{H_3}NCH\overset{}{C}NHCHCO_2^-}}} + 2\ C_6H_5CH_3 + CO_2$$

Thr-Ala

Thus far we have discussed peptide synthesis only with amino acids containing no other reactive groups. When there is another functional group present in the molecule, it too must be protected until after the peptide has been formed. Typical protecting groups are benzyloxycarbonyl for the second amino group in lysine and benzyl for the sulfur in cysteine.

$$\text{\Large⌬}{-}\underset{O}{\overset{\parallel}{CH_2O\overset{}{C}NH(CH_2)_4}}\underset{}{\overset{NH_3^+}{\overset{|}{CHCO_2^-}}} \qquad \text{\Large⌬}{-}CH_2SCH_2\underset{}{\overset{NH_3^+}{\overset{|}{CHCO_2^-}}}$$

ε-benzyloxycarbonyllysine   S-benzylcysteine

Both protecting groups are removable by cleavage with anhydrous acids such as hydrogen bromide in acetic acid. The second carboxy group in aspartic acid or glutamic acid is usually protected as a methyl or benzyl ester.

A recent development that has revolutionized peptide synthesis is the **solid phase technique** introduced by R. B. Merrifield of Rockefeller University, for which he received the 1984 Nobel prize in chemistry. In the Merrifield method the peptide or protein is synthesized throughout a swollen cross-linked polymer network that is insoluble and can be recovered by filtration. The polymer used is polystyrene (Section 34.5) in which some of the benzene rings are substituted by —CH_2Cl groups. The polystyrene used is cross-linked with about 1% of divinylbenzenes. The particle sizes range from 20 to 70 μ in diameter.

chloromethylated polystyrene

Typically, about one out of every 10-100 phenyl groups is chloromethylated.

The C-terminal amino acid of the desired peptide is bound to the polymer by shaking the insoluble polymer with a solution of the N-protected amino acid salt in an organic solvent such as DMF. The product is an amino acid ester in which the alkoxy group of the ester is the polymer itself.

polymer-bound, N-protected amino acid

Excess reagents are removed by filtration, the insoluble polymer-bound amino ester is washed and the Boc group is removed by treatment with acid.

polymer-bound amino acid

A solution of an N-protected amino acid is then added with DCC, and the heterogeneous mixture is shaken until coupling is complete.

N-protected amino acid   polymer-bound amino acid

N-protected, polymer-bound dipeptide

The polymer, now bound to an N-protected dipeptide, is again filtered and washed, and a strong anhydrous acid, usually trifluoroacetic acid, is added to remove the protecting group.

$$t\text{-BuOCNHCHCNHCHCOCH}_2 \boxed{\text{polymer}} \xrightarrow{\text{H}^+} \xrightarrow{\text{Et}_3\text{N}} \text{H}_2\text{NCHCNHCHCOCH}_2 \boxed{\text{polymer}}$$

polymer-bound dipeptide

The process may now be repeated to add the third amino acid, and so on. At the end of the synthesis, the peptide is removed from the resin by treatment with anhydrous hydrogen fluoride. At the same time, all side-chain protecting groups are also removed. This final cleavage step does not affect the amide linkages of the peptide chain. The synthetic peptide is then purified by a suitable chromatographic method.

The great advantages of the solid-phase technique are the ease of operation and the high overall yield. Since the growing peptide chain is bound to the highly insoluble polystyrene resin, no mechanical losses are entailed in the intermediate isolation and purification stages. Furthermore, since the method involves the repetitive use of a small number of similar operations, the synthesis is easily automated. Almost all synthetic peptides are now made by the solid-phase technique.

EXERCISE 29.13 Write out all of the steps in a rational synthesis of the pentapeptide Ala-Val-Phe-Ala-Ala. As N-protecting groups use Cbz and for coupling use DCC. Assuming a yield of 95% in each step in your synthesis, what is the overall yield, based on the starting amino acid?

C. Structure Determination

The first step in determining the structure of a polypeptide or protein is the cleavage of any disulfide bridges that may be present. This reaction is commonly done by oxidizing the substance with peroxyformic acid, which converts the two cysteine units into cysteic acid units. If the compound contains no disulfide bridges, this step is not necessary.

The next analytical step is to determine the total amino acid composition. The material is subjected to total hydrolysis by some suitable method, typically heating with 6 N HCl at 112°C for 24–72 hr. The hydrolyzate is then purified and analyzed by a chromatographic technique. The analytical method currently in use employs a commercial instrument called an **amino acid analyzer**. The mixture of amino acids is chromatographed on an ion exchange column with an aqueous buffer solution as eluent. The effluent from the column is automatically mixed with ninhydrin solution, and the presence of an amino acid is indicated by the typical violet color produced in the reaction (Section 29.5.C). The effluent is monitored at appropriate wavelengths with a spectrophotometer, and the absorbance is plotted by a recorder as a function of time. By comparing the chromatogram of an unknown mixture with that of a mixture of known composition, the analyst may arrive at a quantitative analysis of the mixture. The chromatogram for a standard mixture of amino acids is shown at the right in Figure 29.7. The left curve is a chromatogram of hydrolyzed bradykinin (page 942).

There are two methods available for identifying the amino acid unit that occupies the N-terminal position in the polypeptide chain. The first is called the **Sanger method**. The NH_2 group in amino acids and peptides reacts with 2,4-dinitrofluorobenzene to form yellow 2,4-dinitrophenyl (DNP) derivatives. The reaction, illustrated for glycine, is an example of aromatic nucleophilic substitution (see Section 26.3.A).

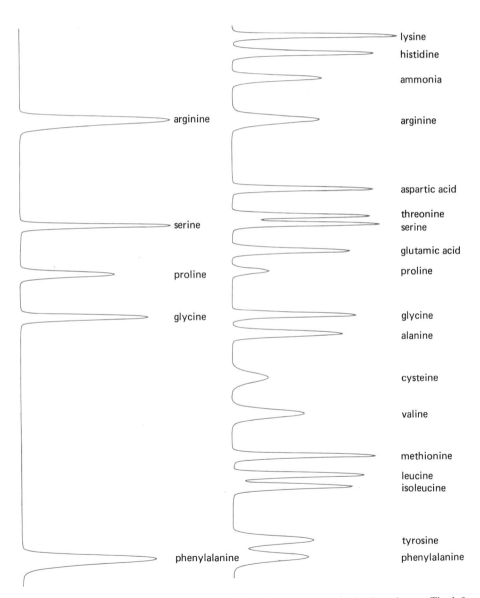

FIGURE 29.7 Amino acid analyzer traces. The right curve is an equimolar mixture. The left curve is the analysis of a sample of hydrolyzed bradykinin.

2,4-dinitrofluorobenzene

N-(2,4-dinitrophenyl)glycine
(yellow)

If the Sanger reaction is carried out on a peptide, the only α-amino group that is available for the reaction is the free group on the N-terminal end. Total hydrolysis of the DNP-labeled peptide then gives a mixture of amino acids, only one of which is labeled with the DNP function on the α-amino group. By knowing which amino acid bears the label, the investigator can deduce which amino acid is at the N-terminal end of the peptide.

The other technique for N-terminal analysis, which is actually more useful, is called the **Edman degradation**. In the Edman degradation, the peptide is allowed to react with phenyl isothiocyanate, $C_6H_5N=C=S$. The terminal NH_2 group reacts to form the phenylthiocarbamoyl derivative of the peptide. The labeled peptide is then treated with anhydrous HCl in an organic solvent. Although these conditions do not hydrolyze the amide linkages, the labeled amino acid undergoes a cyclization reaction, giving a phenylthiohydantoin. In the process the end group also becomes separated from the remainder of the peptide chain.

peptide

phenylthiocarbamoyl-peptide

shorter peptide

The substituted phenylthiohydantoin produced can be identified chromatographically by comparing it with known materials. Furthermore, the degraded peptide can be isolated and subjected to another cycle of the Edman degradation to identify the new N-terminal unit. The process has been automated and has been used to identify the first 60 amino acids in whale myoglobin, a protein that contains 153 amino acids in its chain.

> **EXERCISE 29.14** A tetrapeptide is subjected to total amino acid analysis and found to contain serine, valine, alanine, and glycine. Edman degradation gives a tripeptide and the N-phenylthiohydantoin of valine. A second Edman degradation on the tripeptide gives a dipeptide and the N-phenylthiohydantoin of serine. The dipeptide is analyzed by the Sanger method and N-(2,4-dinitrophenyl)alanine is isolated. What is the structure of the original tetrapeptide? Write the equations illustrating the entire degradation sequence.

The C-terminal amino acid may be identified by hydrolyzing with the enzyme carboxypeptidase, which specifically catalyzes the hydrolysis of the C-terminal amide link in a peptide or protein chain.

Thus, when the material is incubated with carboxypeptidase, the first free amino acid to appear in solution is the one that occupies the C-terminal position. Of course, once that amino acid has been removed from the chain, the enzyme continues to function and goes to work on the next residue, and so on. Eventually, the entire peptide or protein will be hydrolyzed to the constituent amino acids. By measuring the rate of appearance of amino acids in the hydrolyzate, one may identify the C-terminal unit. In favorable cases the first three or four units may be identified in this way.

> **EXERCISE 29.15** A tripeptide having the empirical composition (PheGlySer) is subjected to the action of carboxypeptidase. The first free amino acid to appear in solution is phenylalanine. When the tripeptide is subjected to Edman degradation, the N-phenylthiohydantoin of glycine is obtained. What is the structure of the tripeptide?

Several methods are available to fragment a polypeptide or protein chain into smaller peptides. The most useful method is enzymatic hydrolysis. There are several enzymes available, called **proteases**, that catalyze hydrolysis of the peptide chain, usually at specific positions. For example, the enzyme **trypsin**, which occurs in the intestines of mammals, causes cleavage of peptide bonds only when the carbonyl group is part of a lysine or arginine unit. In a similar way, **chymotrypsin**, another intestinal enzyme, catalyzes hydrolysis of phenylalanine, tryptophan, and tyrosine positions. **Pepsin**, a gastric protease, is much less specific, causing rupture of the chain wherever there is phenylalanine, tryptophan, tyrosine, leucine, aspartic acid, or glutamic acid (Figure 29.8). Abnormal cleavage is sometimes observed.

Another useful method for selective cleavage of polypeptide chains employs **cyanogen bromide**, BrCN. This reagent cleaves the chain only at the carbonyl group of methionine units; the methionine is converted into a C-terminal homoserine lactone unit.

homoserine lactone
unit

Partial degradation of the polypeptide chain, using one of the aforementioned methods, is an important step in determining the proper amino acid sequence of the molecule. Usually the purified polypeptide or protein is first incubated with trypsin, the most selective protease. The resulting mixture of peptide fragments is chromatographed, and the pure fragments are isolated. The peptides produced will usually contain from 2 to about 20 amino acid units. If the polypeptide chain is very long and if it contains relatively few lysine and arginine units, much larger fragments may be produced. The purified fragments are then analyzed for total amino acid content and subjected to repetitive Edman degradation to determine their structures.

The process is then repeated using a different cleavage method, usually cyanogen bromide. This second set of peptide fragments is then analyzed and sequenced. The various peptide blocks from the two degradation methods are then fitted together to produce a structure that unequivocally satisfies both sets of data.

As an example of the reasoning employed, consider a hypothetical eicosapeptide (20 amino acid units) having the amino acid composition ($Gly_2Ala_4Leu_4Phe_3TrpLys_2$-$Met_2SerArg$). End-group analysis shows that the polypeptide has alanine at the N-terminus (Sanger method) and phenylalanine at the C-terminus (carboxypeptidase). The material is hydrolyzed with trypsin to give four fragments: a tripeptide, two pentapeptides, and a heptapeptide. The four peptide fragments are each sequenced by repetitive Edman degradation and found to have the following structures.

I   Trp-Phe-Arg
II Ala-Leu-Gly-Met-Lys
III Leu-Gly-Leu-Leu-Phe
IV Ala-Ala-Ser-Met-Ala-Phe-Lys

At this point the investigator knows that fragment III must correspond to the last five amino acids in the chain because trypsin does not cleave a chain at a phenylalanine

Enzyme	R_1
trypsin	Lys, Arg
chymotrypsin	Phe, Trp, Tyr
pepsin	Phe, Trp, Tyr, Leu, Asp, Glu

954

FIGURE 29.8   Specificity of proteases.

carbonyl. Furthermore, fragment II or IV must correspond to the N-terminal end, but it is not possible with this information alone to write a unique complete sequence.

The intact polypeptide is then cleaved with cyanogen bromide, and the fragments are isolated, purified, and sequenced as before. Three fragments are produced, having the structures

    V   Ala-Leu-Gly-Met
    VI   Ala-Phe-Lys-Leu-Gly-Leu-Leu-Phe
    VII Lys-Trp-Phe-Arg-Ala-Ala-Ser-Met

The four fragments in the first degradation and the three fragments in the second are then ordered in an overlapping way to arrive at an unambiguous structure.

In practice, identification of the complete sequence of a complicated polypeptide or protein is rarely as simple as this example, and the actual process is usually tedious and time consuming. It often happens that almost the entire sequence is elucidated, but the exact positions of a few amino acids remain doubtful. The general process is still being improved, and new methods for routine sequencing are being developed. One technique that offers promise for sequencing relatively small polypeptides on microgram quantities is mass spectrometry (Chapter 32).

The first major structure determination was that of bovine insulin (page 943) by Sanger in 1953. The next significant accomplishment in this area was the sequencing of adrenocorticotrophin (40 amino acid units), the hormone produced in the anterior pituitary gland that stimulates the adrenal cortex.

        5   10

Ser-Tyr-Ser-Ser-Met-Glu-His-Phe-Arg-Trp-Gly-Lys-Pro-Val-

15   20   25

Gly-Lys-Lys-Arg-Arg-Pro-Val-Lys-Val-Tyr-Pro-Asn-Gly-

   30   35   40

Ala-Glu-Asp-Glu-Ser-Ala-Glu-Ala-Phe-Pro-Leu-Glu-Phe

human adrenocorticotrophin

Using techniques such as these, such large proteins as bovine chymotrypsinogen (245 amino acid units) and glyceraldehyde 3-phosphate dehydrogenase (333 amino acid units) have been sequenced. Recently, the new techniques of genetic engineering have provided a powerful new method for sequencing relatively large proteins such as chymotrypsinogen and glyceraldehyde 3-phosphate dehydrogenase. It is frequently possible to clone the gene that codes for the biosynthesis of the protein of interest. If this can be done, it is now usually easier to sequence the gene and deduce the structure of the protein from the known genetic code (Section 34.6) than to go through the foregoing procedure to sequence the protein itself.

EXERCISE 29.16 What is the structure of a pentapeptide that gives Gly-Ala, Leu-Phe, Leu-Leu, and Ala-Leu upon partial hydrolysis and the N-phenylthiohydantoin of glycine upon Edman degradation? What products will be obtained from incubation of this pentapeptide with pepsin?

29.7 Proteins

A. Molecular Shape

Proteins serve several important biological functions. On the one hand, they serve as structural material. The structural proteins tend to be **fibrous** in nature. That is, the long polypeptide chains are lined up more or less parallel to each other and are bonded one to another by hydrogen bonds. Depending on the actual three-dimensional structure of the individual protein molecule and its interaction with other similar molecules, a variety of structural forms may result. Examples are protective tissues such as hair, skin, nails, and claws (α- and β-keratins), connective tissues such as tendon (collagen), and the contractile material of muscle (myosin). Fibrous proteins are usually insoluble in water.

Proteins also have important roles as biological catalysts and regulators. They are responsible for increasing and regulating the speed of biochemical reactions and for the transport of various materials throughout an organism. The catalytic proteins (**enzymes**) and transport proteins tend to be **globular** in nature. In such a compound, the polypeptide chain is folded around itself in such a way as to give the entire molecule a rounded shape. Each globular protein has its own characteristic geometry, which is a result of interactions between different sites on the chain. The intrachain interactions may be of four types: disulfide bridging, hydrogen bonding, dipolar interactions, or van der Waals attraction.

Sometimes each molecule of a globular protein consists of a single long polypeptide chain twisted about and folded back upon itself. In other cases the molecule is composed of several subunits. Each subunit is a single polypeptide chain that has adopted its own unique three dimensional geometry. Several of the subunits are then bonded together by secondary forces (hydrogen bonding and van der Waals attraction) to give the total globular unit. Although they are highly complex molecules of relatively large molecular weight, globular proteins have specific molecular shapes as a result of various intrachain interactions to be discussed later in this section. In some cases, the stable three-dimensional structure of the molecule is such that the surface contains a high percentage of amino acids having polar groups. In such a case, the globular protein is water soluble and exists in the cytoplasm or some other aqueous environment. The surfaces of other globular proteins are covered with amino acids having nonpolar side chains—such structures are found for globular proteins that exist embedded in intercellular membrane structures.

Globular proteins often carry a nonprotein molecule (the **prosthetic group**) as a part of their structure. The prosthetic group may be covalently bonded to the polypeptide chain, or it may be held in place by other forces.

B. Factors That Influence Molecular Shape

As we saw in the previous section, proteins are amino acid polymers containing more than about 50 individual units per chain. The backbone of the protein chain is the repeating unit

$$\underset{\underset{-NHCHCO-}{\overset{R}{|}}}{}$$

The linear amino acid sequence of a peptide or protein is referred to as its **primary structure**.

In addition to the rigidity imparted to the protein chain by the restricted rotation about the amide bond (Sections 18.1 and 29.6), the three-dimensional structure of the macromolecule is determined by two other factors, inter- or intrachain bonding and van der Waals or coulombic interactions.

There are two kinds of secondary bonds that may exist between two different polypeptide chains, or between different regions of the same chain. Disulfide bridges between cysteine units in separate chains result in cross-linking of the two chains. An example is seen in insulin (Figure 29.6), in which the A and B chains are bonded together by two disulfide links. When the two cysteine units are in the same chain, as in oxytocin or the A chain of insulin (Figure 29.6), disulfide bridging results in loops in the chain.

Hydrogen bonding is another type of secondary bonding that may occur between two different chains or between different regions of the same chain. Although hydrogen bonds are inherently weak (about 5 kcal mole^{-1} per hydrogen bond), a polypeptide chain contains many C=O and N—H groups that may engage in such bonding. The total amount of bonding that results from many small interactions is substantial and plays an important role in the actual shape or conformation of the molecule. Reciprocal hydrogen bonding may occur between the C=O and N—H groups of different chains and thus bind them together. Intrachain hydrogen bonding causes the chain to fold back on itself in some specific fashion.

The combined effect of disulfide bridges and hydrogen-bonds is to give the protein a preferred conformation that is referred to as its **secondary structure**.

The other important factor that governs the final molecular shape of a protein is the polar or nonpolar nature of the side-chain groups of the amino acids that constitute the molecule. Some of the side-chain groups that project from the polypeptide backbone are nonpolar or **hydrophobic** (Figure 29.9). In globular proteins, these nonpolar groups are found to be about equally distributed between the interior and the surface of the molecule.

Other side chains are polar and can hydrogen-bond to water molecules. Since the globular proteins exist mainly in aqueous solutions, the polar side chains are found mainly on the outer surface of the molecule. The polar or **hydrophilic** side chains are listed in Figure 29.10. Some are neutral, and others bear either a negative or a positive charge at neutral pH. The combined effect of the small interactions of the various

FIGURE 29.9 Nonpolar (hydrophobic) side chains.

amino acid side chains with each other and with the external environment contributes in a major way to the preferred conformation of the molecule. The molecular structure that is fostered by these attractive and repulsive interactions is referred to as the **tertiary structure** of the compound.

C. Structure of the Fibrous Proteins

The most important type of conformation found in fibrous proteins is the **α-helix**. In this structure the polypeptide chain coils about itself in a spiral manner. The spiral or helix is held together by intrachain hydrogen bonding. The α-helix is right-handed and has a pitch of 5.4 Å or 3.6 amino acid units (Figure 29.11). Although a right-handed α-helix can form from either D- or L-amino acids (but not from DL), the right-handed version is more stable with the natural L-amino acids. A dramatic demonstration of the α-helix is shown by the stereo representation of polyalanine in Figure 29.12.

Not all polypeptide chains can form a stable α-helix. The stability of the coil is governed by the nature of the side-chain groups and their sequence along the chain. Polyalanine, where the side chains are small and uncharged, forms a stable α-helix.

FIGURE 29.10 Polar (hydrophilic) side chains.

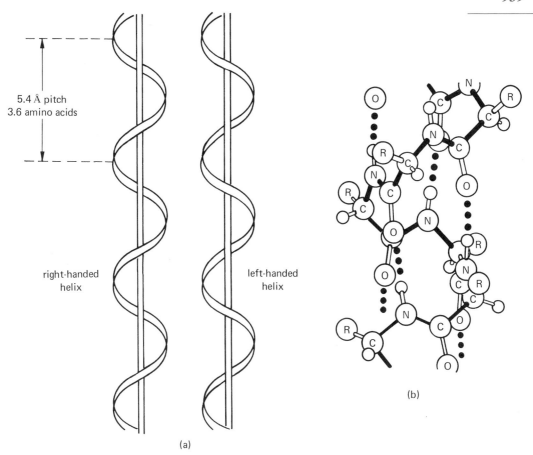

5.4 Å pitch
3.6 amino acids

right-handed
helix

left-handed
helix

(b)

(a)

FIGURE 29.11 (a) Right-handed and left-handed helix. Note that ordinary screws are right-handed helices. (b) Diagram of a peptide [[alpha]]-helix.

However, polylysine does not. At pH 7 the terminal amino groups in the lysine side chains are all protonated. Electrostatic repulsion between the neighboring ammonium groups disrupts the regular coil and forces polylysine to adopt a **random coil** conformation. At pH 12 the lysine amino groups are uncharged, and the material spontaneously adopts the α-helical structure. In a similar way, polyglutamic acid exists as a random coil at pH 7, where the terminal carboxy groups are ionized, and as an α-helix at pH 2, where they are uncharged.

Proline is particularly interesting. Since the α-amino group in proline is part of a five-membered ring, rotation about the carbon-nitrogen bond is impossible. Furthermore, the amide nitrogen in polyproline has no hydrogens, and intrachain hydrogen bonding is not possible. Wherever proline occurs in a polypeptide chain, the α-helix is disrupted and a "kink" or "bend" results (Figure 29.13).

In some cases, such as the keratins of hair and wool, several α-helices coil about one another to produce a **superhelix**. In other cases, the helices are lined up parallel to one another and are held together by intercoil hydrogen bonding.

Another type of conformation found in the fibrous proteins is the β- or **pleated-sheet** structure of β-keratin (silk). In the β-structure, the polypeptide chains are extended in a "linear" or zigzag arrangement. Neighboring chains are bonded together by reciprocal interchain hydrogen bonding. The result is a structure resembling a pleated sheet (Figure 29.14). Side-chain groups extend alternately above and below the general plane of the sheet. The pleated-sheet structure results in the side-chain groups

FIGURE 29.12   Stereo representation of polyalanine. [Courtesy of C. K. Johnson, Oak Ridge National Laboratory.]

being fairly close together. For this reason side chains that are bulky or have like charges disrupt the arrangement. In the β-keratin of silk fibroin 86% of the amino acid residues are glycine, alanine, and serine, all of which have small side chains.

D. Structure of the Globular Proteins

Globular proteins are designed by nature either to be soluble in the aqueous body fluids or in the intercellular membrane structures. They often must have a unique structure that creates an active site where the catalytic or transport function of the protein is carried out. The specific coiling that produces the proper geometry of the protein results from a delicate interplay of all the forces we have discussed up until now. Some

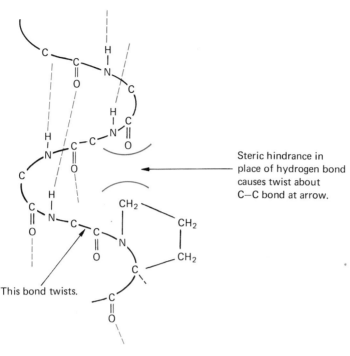

Steric hindrance in place of hydrogen bond causes twist about C—C bond at arrow.

This bond twists.

FIGURE 29.13 Showing the origin of a kink in an [[alpha]]-helix at proline. The proline unit in a peptide chain has no N—H for hydrogen bonding.

folding is stabilized by disulfide bridges. In globular proteins that exist in the aqueous medium of the cytoplasm, the molecule tends to orient itself so that the nonpolar side chains lie inside the bulk of the structure where they attract each other by van der Waals forces. The polar side chains tend to be on the surface of the molecule where they can hydrogen-bond to the solvent molecules and confer the necessary water solubility. Further coiling and compacting of the structure result from intrachain hydrogen bonds between the amide linkages inside the bulk of the molecule. Some segments of the

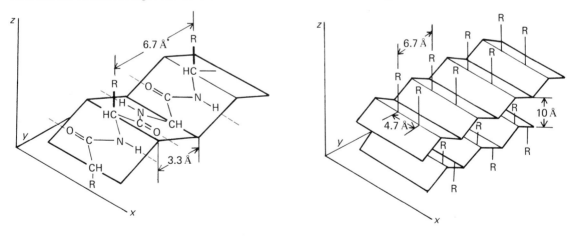

extended polypeptide chain   array of chains to give pleated sheets

FIGURE 29.14 Schematic diagrams of pleated-sheet structure of polypeptides. The peptide bonds lie in the plane of the pleated sheet; the sidechains lie above and below the sheet alternately. The polypeptide chains are held together by interchain hydrogen bonds, shown as dotted lines.

polypeptide chain may have the typical α-helical structure, and others may be random coil. In other cases the chain may fold back on itself in the β- or pleated-sheet fashion. A schematic representation of a globular protein is shown in Figure 29.15.

If the protein contains a prosthetic group, that group will be imbedded at some point within the overall three-dimensional structure of the protein, either covalently bonded to the polypeptide chain or simply held by secondary forces. An example of a prosthetic group is heme, which is found in hemoglobin and myoglobin (Figure 29.16). In these proteins, both of which are oxygen carriers—myoglobin in muscle and hemoglobin in the bloodstream—the function of the prosthetic group is to bind an oxygen molecule. In both cases the polypeptide chain folds in such a way as to leave a hydrophobic "pocket" into which the heme just fits. The heme pocket is equipped with a histidine situated in such a way that its imidazole nitrogen can act as a fifth ligand for the ferrous ion in the center of the heme molecule. The prosthetic group is further held in its pocket by hydrogen bonding between the two propionic acid side chains and other appropriate side chains within the pocket.

The stereo representation of myoglobin in Figure 29.17 shows only the backbone of the polypeptide chain and the heme; substituent groups have been deleted for clarity. Note how the globular protein coils up on ifself. There are several α-helical regions in the chain. An extensive one is seen at the top of the molecule and is viewed almost end-on in this representation. The imidazole "fifth ligand" (not shown) is just above the heme.

Under proper conditions the delicate three-dimensional structure of globular proteins may be disrupted. This process is called **denaturation**. Denaturation commonly occurs when the protein is subjected to extremes in temperature or pH. It is usually attended by a dramatic decrease in the water solubility of the protein. An example is the coagulation that results when skim milk is heated or acidified (denaturation of lactalbumin). A similar process is involved in the hardening of the white and the yolk of an egg upon heating.

Until fairly recently it was believed that denaturation was an irreversible process. It

FIGURE 29.15 Schematic diagram of a globular protein with intrachain bonds (hydrogen bonds, van der Waals forces, and so on), showing reversible denaturation to random coil chain. [Adapted with permission from S. J. Baum, *Introduction to Organic and Biological Chemistry, 2nd ed.* Macmillan Publishing Co., Inc., 1978.]

FIGURE 29.16 Hemin, the prosthetic group of hemoglobin and myoglobin.

now appears, however, that in some cases the process is reversible. The reverse process is called **renaturation**. Many cases are now known in which a soluble denatured protein reverts to its natural folded geometry when the pH and temperature are adjusted back to the point where the native protein is stable. Thus the three-dimensional structure of a protein seems to be a natural consequence of its primary structure; the unique conformation of each protein is simply the most stable structure that molecule can have under biological conditions.

E. Biological Functions of Proteins and Polypeptides

Although a complete discussion of the biological function of proteins is beyond the scope of this book, we shall give an overview of the topic here. In addition, we will take a brief look at the relationship between structure and function of one simple polypeptide.

FIGURE 29.17 Stereo representation of myoglobin (sidechain substituents are not shown). [Courtesy of C. K. Johnson, Oak Ridge National Laboratory.]

As discussed previously, one important function of the proteins is structural. We have already mentioned α-keratin, the important structural component of skin, hair, feathers and nails. Collagen is the material that forms the basis of the connective tissues—tendon, bone, and cartilage. Fibroin is the silk of spider webs and of cocoons. The hard exoskeletons of insects are composed of sclerotin. Muscle tissue contains two important structural proteins—myosin is the stationary component and actin is the contractile component.

The regulatory proteins serve an immense variety of purposes. We have already encountered carboxypeptidase, pepsin, and trypsin, **enzymes** that catalyze the hydrolysis of polypeptide chains (Section 29.6.C). Hemoglobin and myoglobin (Figure 29.17) are **transport** substances; their function is to carry oxygen, the former in the bloodstream and the latter in muscle tissue. Cytochrome c and cytochrome P-450 also have a transport function; these compounds carry electrons in the oxidative phosphorylation cycle. Some proteins are used for **storage**. Ovalbumin is employed by nature as a food reservoir in egg white. Casein plays a similar role in mammalian milk. The body manufactures antibodies as **defensive substances**—these materials form insoluble complexes with foreign substances that invade the bloodstream. Finally, some polypeptides are **hormones**. Examples are insulin (Figure 29.6), which regulates the metabolism of glucose, and β-endorphin (Figure 29.18), a polypeptide with morphine-like activity that appears to be a natural pain reliever.

Before closing this section, we shall have a brief look at a simple polypeptide and see how its structure was evolved for its specific role in nature. Melittin is a 26-amino acid peptide that is responsible for the toxic property of bee venom. It has several biological functions, including the ability to lyse (puncture the cell membrane of) erythrocytes (red blood cells). The primary structure of melittin is shown in Figure 29.19. It is believed that the first 20 amino acids (from the NH$_2$ end) form an α-helix and that the 6 amino acids on the COOH end of the chain are the part of the molecule that is responsible for the lytic activity. Since proline is a "helix-breaker" (Figure 29.13), it is probable that the molecule has a kink or bend at position 14.

The melittin α-helix is diagrammed in the form of an "Edmundson helical wheel" in Figure 29.20. In this depiction, the amino acids of the chain are shown at the places they occupy on the periphery of the helix when the molecule is viewed along the axis of helix from the NH$_2$ end. In an α-helix there are 3.6 amino acid units per turn. Thus, in an Edmundson helical depiction of a polypeptide, each amino acid is displaced exactly 100° from its two immediate neighbors along the chain. In the Edmundson projection of melittin it is seen that one side of the molecule contains amino acids that have hydrophilic side-chain groups, whereas the other side contains amino acids with lipophilic side chains. (Glycine and alanine are considered as hydrophilic because the small protruding groups, H and CH$_3$, do not significantly shield the polar peptide backbone from an aqueous environment.) The result of this structure is that the molecule is **amphiphilic**—one side wants to dissolve in water and the other wants to dissolve in hydrocarbon media. Thus, the polypeptide readily binds to the surfaces of membranes, such as those of erythrocytes.

The COOH-terminal hexapeptide contains a cluster of positive charges at physiological pH. If these six amino acids are removed from melittin, the resulting truncated peptide still binds to erythrocytes, but is not capable of lysing them. The resulting

$$
\text{H}_2\text{N}-\overset{}{\text{Tyr}}-\text{Gly}-\text{Gly}-\text{Phe}-\overset{5}{\text{Met}}-\text{Thr}-\text{Ser}-\text{Gly}-\text{Lys}-\overset{10}{\text{Ser}}-\text{Gln}-\text{Thr}-\text{Pro}-\text{Leu}-\overset{15}{\text{Val}}-\text{Thr}-
$$

$$
\overset{20}{\text{Leu}}-\text{Phe}-\text{Lys}-\text{Asn}-\text{Ala}-\overset{25}{\text{Ile}}-\text{Ile}-\text{Lys}-\text{Asn}-\text{Ala}-\overset{30}{\text{Tyr}}-\text{Lys}-\text{Lys}-\text{Gly}-\text{Glu}-\text{COOH}
$$

FIGURE 29.18 Amino acid sequence of human β-endorphin.

H$_2$N —— Gly– Ile– Gly– Ala– Val– Leu– Lys– Val– Leu– Thr– Thr– Gly– Leu–
                              5   10

Pro– Ala– Leu– Ile– Ser– Trp– Ile– Lys– Arg– Lys– Arg– Gln– Gln —CONH$_2$
         15   20   25

FIGURE 29.19 Amino acid sequence of melittin, the principal toxin of bee venom.

model for activity of this polypeptide is that the substance binds to the erythrocyte membrane because of the amphiphilic nature of the NH$_2$-terminal eicosapeptide. Once bound, the positively charged COOH-terminal hexapeptide punctures the cell membrane and allows release of hemoglobin, eventually depriving the cells of their ability to carry oxygen.

EXERCISE 29.17 A team of scientists headed by E. T. Kaiser, of the Rockefeller University, have recently synthesized a polypeptide having the following primary structure: H$_2$N- Leu- Leu- Gln- Ser- Leu- Leu- Ser- Leu- Leu- Gln- Ser- Leu- Leu- Ser- Leu- Leu- Leu- Gln- Trp- Leu-Lys-Arg-Lys-Arg-Gln-Gln-CONH$_2$. Make an Edmundson helical wheel projection of this synthetic polypeptide and predict whether it should show lytic activity toward erythrocytes.

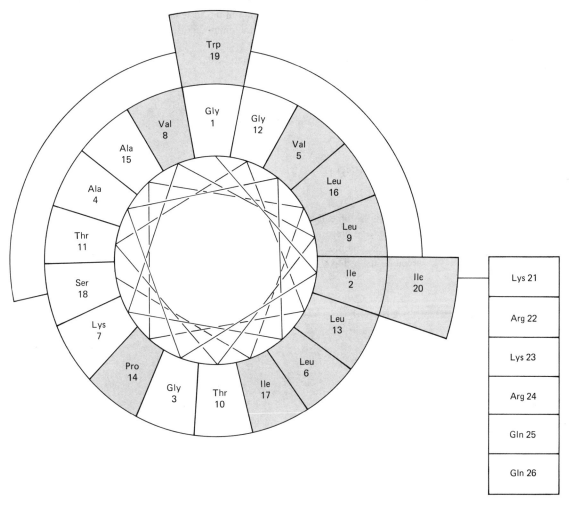

FIGURE 29.20 Edmundson helical wheel representation of melittin. Hydrophobic residues are shown in color.

PROBLEMS

1. For each of the following compounds write the structure of the principal ionic species present in aqueous solution at pH 2, 7, and 12.
   (a) isoleucine
   (b) aspartic acid
   (c) lysine
   (d) glycylglycine (Gly-Gly)
   (e) lyslyglycine (Lys-Gly)
   (f) alanylaspartylvaline (Ala-Asp-Val)

2. Show how the isoelectric point of an amino acid can be computed from pK_1 and pK_2.

3. The pK_as for β-alanine and 4-aminobutanoic acid are shown below. Compare these values with the pK_as for the α-amino acids in Table 29.2 and explain the differences.

$$\overset{+}{H_3}NCH_2CH_2CO_2^- \qquad \overset{+}{H_3}NCH_2CH_2CH_2CO_2^-$$

$$\beta\text{-alanine} \qquad \qquad 4\text{-aminobutanoic acid}$$

$$pK_1 = 3.55 \qquad \qquad pK_1 = 4.03$$
$$pK_2 = 10.24 \qquad \qquad pK_2 = 10.56$$

   What are the isoelectric points for these two amino acids?

4. The dipeptide Gly-Asp has three known pK_a values: 2.81, 4.45, and 8.60. Associate each pK_a with the appropriate functional group in the structure of this peptide. Give a practical synthesis of this peptide starting with the amino acids.

5. Propose syntheses for the following amino acids.

$$\overset{\overset{+}{N}H_3}{\underset{|}{}}$$
   (a) $CH_3CH_2CH_2CH_2CHCO_2^-$

$$\overset{\overset{+}{N}H_3}{\underset{|}{}}$$
   (b) $\langle\text{C}_6\text{H}_5\rangle-CHCO_2^-$

$$\overset{\overset{+}{N}H_3}{\underset{|}{}}$$
   (c) $(CH_3)_3CCHCO_2^-$

$$\overset{\overset{+}{N}H_3}{\underset{|}{}}$$
   (d) $CH_3CH_2CCO_2^-$
   $\qquad\quad \underset{|}{CH_3}$

   (e) $H_3\overset{+}{N}\;\;CO_2^-$ (on cyclohexane)

   (f) (piperidine ring with $\overset{+}{N}H_2$ and CO_2^-)

6. The following isotopically labeled amino acids are desired for biochemical research. Show how each may be prepared. The only acceptable sources of ^{14}C are $Ba^{14}CO_3$ and $Na^{14}CN$. The ^{14}C-labeled atom is marked with an asterisk in each case. Deuterated compounds may be prepared using D_2O, $LiAlD_4$, or D_2.

$$\overset{\overset{+}{N}H_3}{\underset{|}{}}$$
   (a) $CH_3CH—^*CO_2^-$

$$\overset{\overset{+}{N}H_3}{\underset{|}{}}$$
   (b) $CH_3—^*CHCO_2^-$

$$\overset{\overset{+}{N}H_3}{\underset{|}{}}$$
   (c) $CD_3CHCO_2^-$

$$\overset{\overset{+}{N}H_3}{\underset{|}{}}$$
   (d) $\langle\text{C}_6\text{H}_5\rangle-CH_2CDCO_2^-$

$$\overset{\overset{+}{N}H_3}{\underset{|}{}}$$
   (e) $^*CH_3SCH_2CH_2CHCO_2^-$

$$\overset{\overset{+}{N}H_3}{\underset{|}{}}$$
   (f) $(CD_3)_2CHCHCO_2^-$

$$\overset{\overset{+}{N}H_3}{\underset{|}{}}$$
   (g) $HOO\overset{*}{C}CH_2CHCO_2^-$

$$\overset{NH_2}{\underset{|}{}}$$
   (h) $H_3\overset{+}{N}CD_2CH_2CH_2CH_2CHCO_2^-$

7. Glycine undergoes acid-catalyzed esterification more slowly than does propanoic acid. Explain.

8. Explain why the benzoyl group cannot be used as a N-protecting group for peptide synthesis.

9. In 1903 Emil Fischer introduced a rational method for the stepwise construction of peptides. The process, known as the α-haloacyl halide method, is outlined below in a synthesis of glycylglycine.

$$BrCH_2\overset{\overset{\displaystyle O}{\|}}{C}Br + H_2NCH_2CO_2^- \longrightarrow BrCH_2\overset{\overset{\displaystyle O}{\|}}{C}NHCH_2CO_2^- \xrightarrow[\Delta]{NH_3} H_3\overset{+}{N}CH_2\overset{\overset{\displaystyle O}{\|}}{C}NHCH_2CO_2^-$$

(a) Show how the α-haloacyl halide method can be used to synthesize glycyl-L-alanine and glycylglycyl-L-alanine.
(b) Which α-haloacyl halides would be used to add alanyl or valyl units?
(c) If the method is applied to L-alanine using the acyl halides in part (b), what will the products be?
(d) What would be the chief problem in applying the α-haloacyl halide method to a fairly complex polypeptide such as Ala-Val-Phe-Ala-Ala?

10. Write out all the steps in a synthesis of the hexapeptide Gly-Ala-Pro-Ala-Ala-Val. As N-protecting groups use either the benzyloxycarbonyl or *t*-butoxycarbonyl groups. For coupling use DCC.

11. Propose a synthesis of the pentapeptide Ala-Lys-Glu-Gly-Gly. Note that the terminal amino group of lysine and the terminal carboxy group of glutamic acid must be protected.

12. Propose a synthesis of the decapeptide Ala-Val-Phe-Ala-Ala-Ala-Val-Phe-Ala-Ala.

13. Pyroglutamic acid, pyroGlu, is a cyclic lactam obtained by heating glutamic acid.

pyroGlu

This derivative of proline occurs in an important tripeptide, thyrotropin-releasing hormone, pyroglutamylhystidylprolineamide (TRH), which occurs in brain tissue. It also occurs in the anterior lobe of the pituitary gland where it stimulates the secretion of several other hormones. Write out the structure of TRH. A sensitive assay method has been developed that makes use of synthetic hormone. Propose a synthesis of TRH from pyroglutamic acid and other required reagents.

14. The cyanogen bromide method for cleavage of peptide chains involves reaction of the nucleophilic sulfur of a methionine unit with the carbon of BrCN. Write out the complete reaction mechanism.

15. Ribonuclease A is a 124-amino acid enzyme that catalyzes the hydrolysis of the phosphate backbone of ribonucleic acid. The protein has the following primary structure:

H$_2$N-Lys-Glu-Thr-Ala-Ala-Ala-Lys-Phe-Glu-Arg-Glu-His-Met-Asp-Ser-Ser-Thr-Ser-Ala-Ala-Ser-Ser-Ser-Asn-Tyr-Cys-Asn-Glu-Met-Met-Lys-Ser-Arg-Asn-Leu-Thr-Lys-Asp-Arg-Cys-Lys-Pro-Val-Asn-Thr-Phe-Val-His-Glu-Ser-Leu-Ala-Asp-Val-Glu-Ala-Val-Cys-Ser-Glu-Lys-Asn-Val-Ala-Cys-Lys-Asn-Gly-Glu-Thr-Asn-Cys-Tyr-Glu-Ser-Tyr-Ser-Thr-Met-Ser-Ile-Thr-Asp-Cys-Arg-Glu-Thr-Gly-Ser-Ser-Lys-Tyr-Pro-Asn-Cys-Ala-Tyr-Lys-Thr-Thr-Glu-Ala-Asn-Lys-His-Ile-Ile-Val-Ala-Cys-Glu-Gly-Asn-Pro-Tyr-Val-Pro-Val-His-Phe-Asp-Ala-Ser-Val-COOH

There are disulfide bridges between the Cys units 26-84, 40-95, 58-110 and 65-72. What polypeptide fragments will be produced when ribonuclease A is partially hydrolyzed with (a) trypsin, (b) chymotrypsin, or (c) cyanogen bromide? Assume that the disulfide bonds are cleaved prior to hydrolysis.

16. Gastrins are heptadecapeptide (17 amino acid units) hormones that stimulate the secretion of gastric acid in the stomach of mammals. Feline gastrin has the empirical amino acid composition ($Ala_2AspGly_2Glu_5LeuMetPheProTrp_2Tyr$). The peptide was digested with chymotrypsin and four peptide fragments were isolated. The four fragments were sequenced and found to have the following structures.

$$
\begin{array}{ll}
\text{I} & \text{Glu-Gly-Pro-Trp} \\
\text{II} & \text{Gly-Trp} \\
\text{III} & \text{Met-Asp-Phe} \\
\text{IV} & \text{Leu-Glu-Glu-Glu-Glu-Ala-Ala-Tyr}
\end{array}
$$

End-group analysis revealed that the N-terminal unit is Glu and the C-terminal unit is Phe. What two structures for feline gastrin are compatible with the foregoing evidence?

17. Porcine pancreatic secretory trypsin inhibitor I is a protein containing 56 amino acid units. Acidic hydrolysis, followed by amino acid analysis, gave the following empirical composition: ($Asp_4Thr_6Ser_6Glu_7Pro_5Gly_4AlaVal_4Cys_6Ile_3Leu_2Tyr_2Lys_4Arg_2$). (*Note*: Complete hydrolysis does not distinguish Gln from Glu or Asn from Asp.) After cleavage of disulfide bridges, the protein was digested with trypsin. Nine fragments were isolated and purified by chromatography. The nine fragments were each sequenced by repetitive Edman degradation. Eight of the fragments were found to have the following structures.

$$
\begin{array}{ll}
\text{T-1} & \text{Lys} \\
\text{T-2} & \text{Arg} \\
\text{T-3} & \text{Ser-Gly-Pro-Cys} \\
\text{T-4} & \text{Thr-Ser-Pro-Gln-Arg} \\
\text{T-5} & \text{Gln-Thr-Pro-Val-Leu-Ile-Gln-Lys} \\
\text{T-6} & \text{Ser-Asn-Glu-Cys-Val-Leu-Cys-Ser-Glu-Asn-Lys} \\
\text{T-7} & \text{Ile-Tyr-Asn-Pro-Val-Cys-Gly-Thr-Asp-Gly-Ile-Thr-Tyr} \\
\text{T-8} & \text{Glu-Ala-Thr-Cys-Thr-Ser-Glu-Val-Ser-Gly-Cys-Pro-Lys}
\end{array}
$$

The ninth fragment contained 24 amino acid units and had the empirical composition ($Asp_4Thr_2Ser_2Glu_2Pro_2Gly_2Val_2Cys_3Ile_2LeuTyr_2Lys$). Seven cycles of Edman degradation showed that the N-terminal end of fragment T-9 had the composition

T-9 Ile-Tyr-Asn-Pro-Val-Cys-Gly ...

Edman degradation of the intact protein showed the N-terminal unit to be Thr. The C-terminal residue was shown to be Cys.

The protein was then digested with chymotrypsin and three peptide fragments were isolated. The three chymotryptic fragments were each subjected to total hydrolysis and analyzed for amino acid composition. They were also subjected to three cycles of Edman degradation to identify the N-terminal sequence and incubated with carboxypeptidase to identify the C-terminal unit. The partial structures of the three fragments were found to be

$$
\begin{array}{ll}
\text{Ch-1} & \text{Thr-Ser-Pro}(Thr_2Ser_2Glu_3ProGlyAlaValCys_2IleLysArg)\text{Tyr} \\
\text{Ch-2} & \text{Asn-Pro-Val}(AspThr_2Gly_2Cys_2Ile)\text{Tyr} \\
\text{Ch-3} & \text{Ser-Asn-Glu}(AspThrSer_2Glu_3Pro_2GlyVal_2Cys_2IleLeu_2Lys_3Arg)\text{Cys}
\end{array}
$$

The intact protein was then treated with methyl isothiocyanate. This reagent modifies the lysine side chains so that they are not cleaved by trypsin. The modified protein was digested with trypsin and three fragments were isolated. The three fragments were isolated, hydrolyzed, and analyzed and shown to have the following empirical compositions:

$$
\begin{array}{ll}
\text{*T-1} & (ThrSerProArgGlu) \\
\text{*T-2} & (ThrSerGlu_2Pro_2GlyValCysIleLeuLys) \\
\text{*T-3} & (Asp_4Thr_4Ser_4Glu_4Pro_2Gly_3AlaVal_3Cys_5IleLeuTyr_2Lys_3Arg)
\end{array}
$$

From the data, what is the primary structure of the protein?

Chapter 30

Polycyclic Aromatic Hydrocarbons

30.1 Nomenclature

Polycyclic aromatic hydrocarbons may be dissected into two broad classes: the biaryls and the condensed benzenoid hydrocarbons. The latter class is by far the larger and more important group.

The biaryls are benzenoid compounds in which two rings are linked together by a single bond. The parent system of this class is biphenyl. In numbering the ring positions, the rings are considered to be joined at the 1-position, and the two rings are distinguished by the use of primes.

biphenyl

Simple derivatives can be named by use of *ortho*, *meta*, *para* nomenclature.

o,m'-dimethylbiphenyl
2,3'-dimethylbiphenyl

More complex compounds are named using numbers. Again, substituents in one ring are designated by the use of primes.

2',6'-dichloro-6-nitrobiphenyl-3-carboxylic acid

The condensed benzenoid compounds are characterized by two or more benzene rings fused or superimposed together at *ortho* positions in such a way that each pair of rings shares two carbons. The simplest members of this group are naphthalene, with two rings, and anthracene and phenanthrene, with three rings. In the IUPAC system all carbons that may bear a substituent are numbered. Carbons that are part of a ring junction are denoted by a lowercase a or b following the number of the immediately preceding carbon. The numbering systems for naphthalene, anthracene, and phenanthrene are

Derivatives are named using these numbering systems.

1-nitronaphthalene   9,10-dihydroanthracene   9,10-phenanthraquinone

cis-4a,8a-dihydronaphthalene   *trans*-1,2,3,4,4a,10a- hexahydrophenanthrene

EXERCISE 30.1   Name the following compounds.

(a)   (b)   (c)

30.2 Biphenyl

A. Synthesis

Biphenyl is prepared commercially by the pyrolysis of benzene.

$$2 C_6H_6 \xrightarrow{\Delta} C_6H_5-C_6H_5 + H_2$$

It is a colorless crystalline solid with a melting point of 70°C. Substituted biphenyls are prepared by electrophilic aromatic substitution reactions on the parent hydrocarbon

(Section 30.2.C) or from benzene derivatives using reactions we have already studied. One of the most useful methods is the benzidine rearrangement (page 735).

hydrazobenzene

benzidine
4,4'-diaminobiphenyl

The amino groups in benzidine can be converted to many other functional groups by way of the bis-diazonium salt. Thus, benzidine and substituted benzidines are useful intermediates for the preparation of a variety of symmetrical biphenyls.

"tetrazotization"

(80%)
2,2'-dimethyl-5,5'-dimethoxybiphenyl

The Ullmann reaction (Section 26.3.B) is also useful for the preparation of symmetrically substituted biphenyls, as is the oxidation of certain lithium diarylcuprates (Section 26.3.B). The Gomberg-Bachmann reaction (Section 24.5.F) is suitable for the preparation of some unsymmetrical biphenyls.

EXERCISE 30.2 Propose syntheses of (a) *m,m'*-dimethylbiphenyl and (b) *m*-methylbiphenyl beginning with *o*-nitrotoluene.

B. Structure

In the crystal both benzene rings of biphenyl lie in the same plane. However, in solution and in the vapor phase the two rings are twisted with respect to each other by an angle of about 45° (Figure 30.1). This twisting is the result of steric interactions between the 2,2' and 6,6' pairs of hydrogens (Figure 30.2). The magnitude of these repulsions is relatively small, only a few kcal mole^{-1}, and in the crystal is less than the stabilization obtained by stacking biphenyls together in coplanar arrays. Of course, these crystal-packing forces do not exist in the vapor phase, and the twisting of the rings provides greater separation of the hydrogens.

These repulsion effects are enhanced by *ortho* substituents larger than hydrogen. When the groups are sufficiently large, rotation of the phenyl rings with respect to each other is hindered or prevented. For example, 6,6'-dinitrobiphenyl-2,2'-dicarboxylic acid can be resolved into its enantiomers and each enantiomer is stable indefinitely (Figure 30.3). The nitro and carboxylic acid groups are so bulky that they cannot pass by each other, and rotation about the bond joining the two rings is prevented.

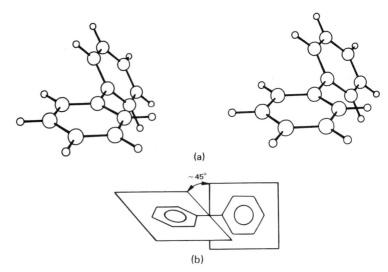

FIGURE 30.1 Structure of biphenyl in the solution or vapor phase: *(a)* stereo representation; *(b)* perspective diagram.

FIGURE 30.2 Steric interactions between *ortho*-hydrogens in biphenyl.

If the bulky nitro groups are replaced by the smaller fluorine atoms, the resulting compound, 6,6′-difluorobiphenyl-2,2′-dicarboxylic acid, can still be obtained in optically active form. However, the compound racemizes readily; that is, the enantiomers are readily interconverted. The racemization process involves squeezing the fluorines past the adjacent COOH groups via a planar transition state.

6,6′-difluorobiphenyl-2,2′-dicarboxylic acid

This transition state is congested and requires the bending of bonds. The process takes energy and is measurably slow. On the other hand, all attempts to resolve biphenyl-2,2′-dicarboxylic acid (diphenic acid) have failed. The process of slipping a small hydrogen past the carboxylic acid group is so facile that racemization of enantiomers occurs rapidly.

diphenic acid

Mirror plane

side view

end view

HOOC——NO$_2$

O$_2$N——COOH

FIGURE 30.3 Enantiomers of 6,6'-dinitrobiphenyl-2,2'-dicarboxylic acid.

EXERCISE 30.3 (a) Construct a molecular model of a biphenyl having different substituents in the 2,2'- and 6,6'-positions. Demonstrate that the molecule is chiral so long as the two rings are not coplanar. (b) Assign *R* and *S* designations to the enantiomers in Figure 30.3. (*Hint*: See page 531.)

C. Reactions

Biphenyl undergoes electrophilic aromatic substitution more readily than benzene; a phenyl substituent is activating and is an *ortho,para* director. Nitration in acetic anhydride solution gives primarily 2-nitrobiphenyl, but most other substitution reactions give primarily *para* orientation. Bromination, for example, gives almost wholly 4-bromobiphenyl, and excess reagent leads readily to 4,4'-dibromobiphenyl. Typical partial rate factors are

for Br$_2$ in 50% aqueous acetic acid

Friedel-Crafts acylation with acetyl chloride and AlCl$_3$ yields 4-acetyl- and 4,4'-diacetylbiphenyl depending on the conditions.

In general, 4-substituted and 4,4'-disubstituted biphenyls can be prepared by electrophilic substitution reactions of biphenyl. Other derivatives are constructed from benzene compounds by way of the syntheses described in Section 30.2.A.

EXERCISE 30.4 Write the resonance structures for the intermediate cation resulting from attack of Br$^+$ at the *para* position and at the *meta* position of biphenyl. Explain why a phenyl substituent is *ortho,para* directing.

D. Related Compounds

The terphenyls have three benzene rings linked together. All three possible isomers, *ortho*, *meta*, and *para*, are known. Note how the greater symmetry of the *para* isomer confers a much higher melting point.

o-terphenyl	*m*-terphenyl	*p*-terphenyl
m.p. 57°C	m.p. 87°C	m.p. 171°C

Many of the higher polyphenyls are known, especially for the *para* isomers. *p*-Quaterphenyl has four phenyl groups linked and melts at 320°C. These compounds are generally such insoluble materials that they are difficult to work with.

Fluorene is a biphenyl in which two *ortho* positions are linked by a methylene group. It is obtained commercially from coal tar.

fluorene

The 2- and 7-positions correspond to the *para* positions of biphenyl and are, accordingly, the most reactive positions in electrophilic aromatic substitution reactions.

(79%)
2-nitrofluorene

The methylene group is an important center for other reactions. Oxidation gives the corresponding yellow ketone, fluorenone.

fluorenone

One of the especially interesting aspects of the chemistry of fluorene is its relatively high acidity. The pK_a value of 23 puts the methylene group of this hydrocarbon in the same range as ketones and esters. Alkali metal salts can be prepared by melting with potassium hydroxide or by treatment with butyllithium.

9-fluorenyllithium   9-fluorenylpotassium

The reason for this remarkably high acidity is related to the central five-membered ring structure. Cyclopentadiene is a highly acidic hydrocarbon with a pK_a of 16—an acidity comparable to that of water and alcohols (Section 21.3.C). The six-electron aromatic character of this electronic system stabilizes the anion relative to the hydrocarbon. If one or both double bonds in cyclopentadiene are replaced by benzene rings, the corresponding anion has reduced stability relative to its conjugate acid because the delocalization of negative charge disrupts the benzene conjugation.

Indene, unlike cyclopentadiene, has a benzene ring. Structures A and C of indenyl anion also have benzene rings, but the other structures, B, D, E, and so on, have no benzene rings and are expected to be much less stable. The same principles apply to fluorene and fluorenyl anion. The corresponding pK_a values are summarized in Table 30.1 and compared with several other hydrocarbons for reference.

TABLE 30.1 Acidities of Some Hydrocarbons

Formula	Name	pK_a
	cyclopentadiene	16
	indene	20
	fluorene	23
$(C_6H_5)_3CH$		31.5
$(C_6H_5)_2CH_2$		34
$C_6H_5CH_3$		41

30.3 Naphthalene

A. Structure and Occurrence

Naphthalene is a colorless crystalline hydrocarbon, m.p. 80°C. It sublimes readily and is isolated in quantity from coal tar.

> Coal tar is obtained from the conversion of bituminous coal to coke. The coal is heated in the absence of oxygen, giving gas and a distillate boiling over a wide range. The low-boiling range contains benzene, toluene, and xylenes. A fraction boiling at 195–230°C, called naphthalene oil, yields crude naphthalene on cooling. The higher-boiling coal tar is a black odoriferous complex mixture containing many polycyclic hydrocarbons and hetero-cyclic compounds.

Naphthalene is the parent hydrocarbon of the series of fused benzene polycyclic structures. X-ray analysis shows it to have the structure shown in Figure 30.4. The bonds are not all of the same length, but are close to the benzene value of 1.397 Å. Naphthalene can be considered to be resonance hybrid of three Kekulé structures.

Accordingly, it has an empirical resonance energy of about 60 kcal mole^{-1}, a value somewhat greater than that of benzene (Section 20.1.B).

Substituted naphthalenes are named using the numbering system given in Section 30.1. Monosubstituted naphthalenes are often named using α- and β-nomenclature for the 1- and 2-positions, respectively; for example,

α-methylnaphthalene β-naphthol
1-methylnaphthalene   2-naphthol

Reduced naphthalenes are widespread in nature, particularly in terpenes and steroids (Section 34.7). The fully reduced form, decahydronaphthalene, has the trivial name

FIGURE 30.4 Structure of naphthalene.

(a)

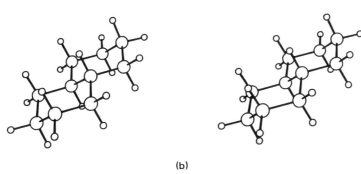

(b)

FIGURE 30.5 *trans*-Decalin: *(a)* conventional representation; *(b)* stereo structure.

decalin. Two diastereomeric forms are possible, in which the hydrogens at the ring juncture carbons are either cis or trans. The decalins may also be named using the systematic nomenclature for bicyclic compounds (page 554).

cis-bicyclo[4.4.0]decane
(*cis*-decalin)

trans-bicyclo[4.4.0]decane
(*trans*-decalin)

In both *cis*- and *trans*-decalin the two cyclohexane rings are each in the chair conformation. In *trans*-decalin the two chair cyclohexanes are fused together in such a way that each ring comprises two equatorial substituents on the other one (Figure 30.5). In *cis*-decalin the cyclohexane chairs are joined together as equatorial and axial substituents (Figure 30.6).

EXERCISE 30.6 From the resonance structures on page 976, determine the fractional double bond character of all of the different carbon-carbon bonds in naphthalene. A pure C_{sp^2}—C_{sp^2} single bond is expected to have a length of about 1.50 Å. Using this value and the bond lengths of ethylene and benzene, draw a smooth curve for bond length as a function of double bond character. Calculate the bond lengths expected for the different bonds in naphthalene using this curve and compare with the experimental values in Figure 30.4.

B. Synthesis

The naphthalene ring system can be prepared from suitable benzene derivatives by making use of a general method for building up a second ring that starts with a Friedel-Crafts acylation using a cyclic anhydride. A typical sequence is illustrated by the following example.

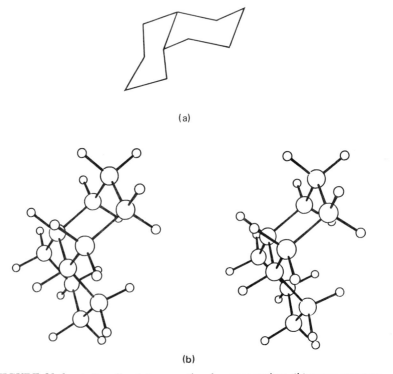

toluene   succinic
anhydride

4-*p*-tolyl-4-oxo-
butanoic acid

4-*p*-tolylbutanoic
acid

1-oxo-7-methyl-1,2,3,4-
tetrahydronaphthalene

1,7-dimethyl-1,2,3,4-
tetrahydro-1-naphthol

4,6-dimethyl-1,2-
dihydronaphthalene

1,7-dimethylnaphthalene

Note that cyclic anhydrides function normally as acylating reagents in Friedel-Crafts reactions and that the resulting keto acids can be reduced to the corresponding alkanoic acids by Wolff-Kishner or Clemmensen conditions (Section 14.9.D). β- and γ-Arylalkanoic acids readily undergo intramolecular Friedel-Crafts acylation reactions

(a)

(b)

FIGURE 30.6 *cis*-Decalin: *(a)* conventional representation; *(b)* stereo structure.

to generate the corresponding five- or six-membered ring ketone. Commonly used reagents are $AlCl_3$ with the acid chloride and sulfuric acid, polyphosphoric acid, or liquid hydrogen fluoride with the free acid.

> The example shown makes use of liquid HF, a convenient reagent for this purpose if special precautions are taken. Anhydrous HF is a low-boiling liquid, b.p. 19°C, available in cylinders. It is highly corrosive to glass and tissue and must be handled with due caution. The liquid is an excellent solvent for oxygen-containing organic compounds (hydrogen bonding). It does not attack polyethylene or Teflon, and these polymers make suitable reaction vessels. Because of the etching of glass windows, it is generally best to use one specific hood in a laboratory for HF reactions. The vapors should not be inhaled, and the material causes severe burns on contact with skin. For the intramolecular Friedel-Crafts reaction the carboxylic acid is weighed into a polyethylene beaker and—in an efficient hood—liquid HF is added from an inverted tank previously cooled to 5°C (use polyethylene or rubber gloves). The mixture is stirred and the HF is allowed to evaporate over the course of several hours. The residue is mixed with aqueous Na_2CO_3 and extracted with benzene. The product is obtained by distillation or crystallization. Yields are typically 70–90%.

The last step in the foregoing synthesis of 1,7-dimethylnaphthalene illustrates the **aromatization** of a hydroaromatic compound. The driving force is formation of the stable aromatic ring. When sulfur or selenium is used for aromatization, it is concomitantly reduced to H_2S or H_2Se, respectively. Palladium metal can also be used to catalyze the aromatization. In this case, which amounts to the reverse of catalytic hydrogenation, hydrogen is eliminated.

naphthalene

Tetrachloro-*p*-benzoquinone, chloranil, may also be used as a reagent for such dehydrogenation reactions. Although aromatization of partially hydrogenated benzenes is also possible, the reaction is primarily used for the synthesis of polycyclic aromatic compounds. Note that the preceding reaction sequence is subject to wide variation for the synthesis of many naphthalene hydrocarbons. It is less useful for the introduction of functional groups because of the sensitivity of most groups to several of the reactions involved.

Another important way of building up the second ring makes use of the Diels-Alder reaction of quinones and dienes (page 835).

> **EXERCISE 30.7** Outline syntheses of (a) 1-propyl-7-methoxynaphthalene and (b) 2,3-dimethyl-1,4-naphthoquinone.

C. Electrophilic Substitution

Naphthalene undergoes a number of the usual electrophilic aromatic substitution reactions such as nitration, halogenation, sulfonation, and Friedel-Crafts acylation. The 1-position is the more reactive.

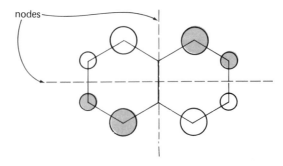

1-nitronaphthalene   2-nitronaphthalene

The reason for the generally greater reactivity of the 1-position can be seen by examination of the resonance structures for the two transition states or the intermediates resulting from them.

In both cases the positive charge can be distributed to five different positions, but these carbocation structures are not equivalent in energy. In the α-case the first two structures still have an intact benzene ring and are consequently much more stable than the remaining three structures. The first two structures contribute much more to the overall resonance hybrid. In the β-case, however, only the first structure has an intact benzene ring; the resulting resonance hybrid has higher energy than in the α-case.

The same conclusion results from application of molecular orbital theory (Section 22.10). The frontier orbital (HOMO) of naphthalene is shown in Figure 30.7. Note that

FIGURE 30.7 HOMO of naphthalene.

the position closer to a node generally has a small magnitude of wave function than a position farther from a node. The α-position has greater wave function magnitude than the β-position and is generally more reactive.

In the nitration reaction the small amount of 2-nitronaphthalene formed is readily removed by recrystallization; hence, the nitration reaction is a satisfactory route to 1-nitronaphthalene. More vigorous nitration conditions give mixtures of 1,5- and 1,8-dinitronaphthalenes. Since the nitro group is a deactivating group, the second nitro group enters the other ring.

Bromination is also an excellent reaction and gives essentially pure 1-bromonaphthalene.

(72–75%)
1-bromonaphthalene

Sulfonation under mild conditions gives the 1-sulfonic acid. However, at higher temperature naphthalene-2-sulfonic acid results. This pattern is the same phenomenon of kinetic versus thermodynamic control that we have seen previously for sulfonations (Section 25.5). The 1-position is the more reactive, but 1-naphthalenesulfonic acid is more hindered and less stable than the C-2 acid because the bulky sulfonic acid group is within the van der Waals radius of the C-8 hydrogen.

naphthalene–1–sulfonic acid   naphthalene–2–sulfonic acid

Under conditions where the sulfonation reaction is reversible, the C-2 acid is the dominant product.

Friedel-Crafts acylation reactions also frequently give mixtures. In general, use of $AlCl_3$ with CS_2 as solvent gives predominantly the α-product, whereas the use of nitrobenzene generally leads to the β-isomer. Separation of the isomers can be difficult or impractical. These generalizations are only approximate. The reaction products depend on the reaction conditions and the concentrations of reagents. These reactions are not simple, and the nature of the rate-determining step can differ for α- and β-reactions.

(81%)
1-benzoylnaphthalene

(90%)
2-acetylnaphthalene

(36%) + (47%)
can be separated by crystallization

EXERCISE 30.8 Suggest two methods each by which naphthalene can be converted efficiently to (a) 1-benzylnaphthalene and (b) naphthalene-2-carboxylic acid.

D. Oxidation and Reduction of Naphthalene

Under many oxidation conditions naphthalene is oxidized to 1,4-naphthoquinone, but the yields are frequently rather poor.

(18–22%)

More vigorous oxidation results in loss of one ring and constitutes one commercial preparation of phthalic anhydride.

phthalic anhydride

Birch reduction (Section 20.6.C) of naphthalene yields 1,4-dihydronaphthalene. Note that in this product an isolated double bond is produced that does not reduce further.

1,4-dihydronaphthalene

Catalytic hydrogenation gives either 1,2,3,4-tetrahydronaphthalene (tetralin) or decahydronaphthalene (decalin) depending on catalyst or conditions.

decalin   tetralin

cis-Decalin (Figure 30.6) is the predominant product of complete hydrogenation. Tetralin and the decalins are high-boiling liquids that find some use as solvents.

EXERCISE 30.9 Suggest efficient syntheses from naphthalene of
(a) 1,2-bis(hydroxymethyl)benzene   (b) 2,3-epoxy-1,2,3,4-tetrahydronaphthalene.

E. Substituted Naphthalenes

Functional groups on a naphthalene ring behave more or less as their benzenoid analogs. For example, nitro groups can be reduced to amines, and bromides can be converted to Grignard or lithium reagents. An especially useful reaction is the fusion of the sulfonic acids with sodium or potassium hydroxide.

2-naphthol

Since both naphthalenesulfonic acids are available by sulfonation under different conditions (page 981), this reaction provides a route to either α-naphthol or β-naphthol.

In the further electrophilic substitution reactions of monosubstituted naphthalenes some simple generalizations can be made.

1. *Meta*-directing substituents in either the 1- or 2-position generally direct to the 5- and 8-positions, the α-positions of the other ring.

2-naphthalenesulfonic
acid

8-nitronaphthalene-
2-sulfonic acid

5-nitronaphthalene-
2-sulfonic acid

2. *Ortho,para*-directing groups in the 1-position direct principally to the 4-position,
   but also occasionally to the 2-position as well.

2-nitro-1-acetylamino-
naphthalene

4-nitro-1-acetylamino-
naphthalene

4-nitro-1-methoxy-
naphthalene

3. *Ortho,para* directors in the 2-position generally direct to the 1-position.

Orange II

Exceptions to these generalizations are not uncommon, especially in Friedel-Crafts
acylations and sulfonation.

(80%)
6-methylnaphthalene-2-sulfonic acid

(60–79%)

One of the important reactions in naphthalene chemistry, the **Bucherer** reaction, involves the interconversion of naphthols and naphthylamines and does not apply generally in benzene chemistry.

2-naphthol   2-naphthylamine

2-Naphthol is readily available from 2-naphthalenesulfonic acid; hence, the Bucherer reaction provides a simple route to 2-naphthylamine which, in turn, can be converted to many other functions via the diazonium ion.

2-Naphthylamine is a powdery solid that at one time was widely used as an important intermediate in dye chemistry. This amine is carcinogenic and is no longer used.

The reaction is reversible and also provides a hydrolytic route from amine to naphthol.

The sulfite or bisulfite ion is essential in this reaction. The amine and naphthol are in equilibrium with a small amount of the imine or keto form, an α,β-unsaturated system that undergoes conjugate addition by bisulfite ion much as in the formation of bisulfite addition compounds of aldehydes and ketones (page 767).

EXERCISE 30.10 Write the most stable resonance structure for nitration of 2-methoxynaphthalene at each of the seven free positions. Explain why nitration occurs primarily at C-1.

30.4 Anthracene and Phenanthrene

A. Structure and Stability

The isomeric tricyclic benzenoid hydrocarbons differ significantly in thermodynamic stability; the linear system, anthracene, is almost 6 kcal mole^{-1} less stable than the angular system, phenanthrene.

$$\Delta H_f^\circ = +55.2 \text{ kcal mole}^{-1}$$

anthracene

$$\Delta H_f^\circ = +49.5 \text{ kcal mole}^{-1}$$

phenanthrene

The empirical resonance energies show a corresponding change; one set of values is 84 kcal mole^{-1} for anthracene and 91 kcal mole^{-1} for phenanthrene. The empirical resonance energy of benzene calculated in the same way is 36 kcal mole^{-1}. The resonance energies of anthracene and phenanthrene are not much more than that of two benzene rings; that is, the third ring contributes relatively little additional resonance stabilization. We shall see that this characteristic is reflected in the reactivities of these hydrocarbons.

B. Preparation of Anthracenes and Phenanthrenes

Anthracene and phenanthrene are both available from coal tar in grades that are suitable for most reactions. Commercial material requires extensive further treatment to obtain the pure hydrocarbons. When pure, anthracene (m.p. 216°C) is colorless and exhibits a beautiful blue fluorescence. This fluorescence is diminished or altered by impurities in the commercial material. Phenanthrene also is a colorless crystalline solid (m.p. 101°C), but it does not fluoresce.

Both ring systems can be built up from simpler compounds. Anthracene and many derivatives are available from phthalic anhydride and benzene compounds.

benzoylbenzoic acid   anthraquinone

Note that intramolecular Friedel-Crafts occurs readily in this case even though the ring already has a carbonyl group.

Anthraquinones can be reduced directly to anthracene by several reducing agents, including sodium borohydride and boron trifluoride etherate.

(73%)

The phenanthrene ring system can be built up from naphthalene.

β-(2-naphthoyl)propionic acid
4-oxo-4-(2-naphthyl)butanoic acid

(91%)
4-(2-naphthyl)-
butanoic acid

(88%)
4-oxo-1,2,3,4-
tetrahydro-
phenanthrene

Note that cyclization occurs exclusively at the 1-position of naphthalene (Section 30.3.E). A similar sequence starting from the 1-substituted naphthalene also gives the phenanthrene ring system.

β-(1-naphthoyl)propionic acid
4-oxo-4-(1-naphthyl)butanoic acid

(70%)
4-(1-naphthyl)butanoic acid

(92–94%)
1-oxo-1,2,3,4-tetrahydro-
phenanthrene

The cyclic ketones can both be converted to phenanthrene by successive reduction, dehydration, and dehydrogenation.

Many substituted phenanthrenes may be synthesized by variations of this general sequence.

EXERCISE 30.11 Show how the two β-naphthoylpropionic acids (page 982) can be used to prepare 1-methylphenanthrene or 4-methylphenanthrene.

C. Reactions

Anthracene and phenanthrene undergo ready oxidation to the corresponding quinones.

(88–91%)
9,10-anthraquinone

(44–48%)
9,10-phenthraquinone

Anthraquinone can be partially reduced to give anthrone.

(82%)
anthrone

Anthrone is the keto form of 9-anthranol; both isomers can be isolated, but anthrone is the stable form.

anthrone   9-anthranol

Both anthracene and phenanthrene can be reduced readily to dihydro compounds.

(75–79%)
9,10-dihydroanthracene

(70–77%)
9,10-dihydrophenanthrene

These reactions show the distinctive reactivity of the 9,10-positions of both compounds, a reactivity inherent in the low resonance stabilization contributed by the third benzene ring (page 986). This reactivity is also demonstrated by the ability of anthracene to undergo Diels-Alder reactions as a diene. The reaction with maleic anhydride is an equilibrium that favors the adduct.

maleic
anhydride

(99%)

A novel reaction of this type is with benzyne (pages 804–805) to give the unusual hydrocarbon triptycene.

(28%)
triptycene

Electrophilic aromatic substitution reactions with anthracene and phenanthrene occur most readily in the 9-position and frequently give disubstituted products.

(83–88%)
9,10-dibromoanthracene

(90–94%)
9-bromophenanthrene

Because of the reactivity of polybenzenoid aromatic hydrocarbons, special conditions must frequently be established for individual reactions. A detailed discussion of this chemistry is beyond the scope of this book.

EXERCISE 30.12 Using resonance structures, suggest why both anthracene and phenanthrene undergo electrophilic attack primarily at the 9-position.

30.5 Higher Polybenzenoid Hydrocarbons

A large number of polybenzenoid hydrocarbons are known, and some are relatively important. Some multiring systems, with their established common names and their numbering systems, are shown below.

chrysene   pyrene   tetracene

fluoranthene   coronene

Some of these hydrocarbons are available from coal tar; others are prepared from simpler systems by building up rings in the manner shown in the preceding section for anthracene and phenanthrene.

Tetracene is an orange compound that shows much of the chemistry of anthracene. Oxidation and reduction occur readily at the 5- and 12-positions, and the hydrocarbon reacts readily as a Diels-Alder diene. Higher linear **acenes** are known: pentacene, with five fused benzene rings in a row, is blue; hexacene is green; and heptacene is a deep greenish black. The higher linear acenes are reactive, air sensitive, and difficult to obtain pure.

Chrysene is similar to phenanthrene in its reactions: it can be oxidized to the 5,6-quinone.

Pyrene is among the most important of these hydrocarbons. Pyrene undergoes the usual electrophilic aromatic substitution reactions such as halogenation, nitration, Friedel-Crafts acylation, and so on. These reactions occur exclusively at the 1-position.

Two numbering systems have been used for pyrene, and care must be taken in reading the literature, particularly the older literature, to establish which system has been used. The system shown here is the accepted IUPAC numbering, but even today references will be found with the older nomenclature.

(78–86%)
1-bromopyrene

Polycyclic systems much larger than coronene are known. The large polycyclic hydrocarbons have low solubility, and few are significant in organic chemistry. Their properties start to approach those of graphite, an allotrope of carbon that consists of infinite planes of benzene rings with the planes separated by 3.4 Å. This distance is usually taken as the total width of the π-electronic system of benzene.

graphite

A number of polycyclic aromatic hydrocarbons are named as **benz**- or **benzo**- derivatives of simpler systems. The position of fusion of the benz- ring is represented by a lowercase italic letter that designates the side around the periphery of the parent system used for the fusion. For example, the sides of anthracene are lettered starting with side *a* between positions 1 and 2.

In this way the following hydrocarbons are derived.

benz[*a*]anthracene

dibenz[*a,j*]anthracene

Some polycyclic aromatic hydrocarbons are highly carcinogenic compounds. Minute amounts painted on the skin of mice will produce skin tumors (epithelioma) in the course of a few months. Some of the most potent of the carcinogenic hydrocarbons are dibenz[a,h]anthracene (but not dibenz[a,c]anthracene), benzo[a]pyrene (but not benzo[e]pyrene), dibenzo[a,i]pyrene, and benzo[b]fluoranthene. These compounds occur in coal tar and in soot. A high incidence of scrotal cancer in chimney sweeps was noticed in England as early as 1775. All of these carcinogenic hydrocarbons have been detected in minute quantity in tobacco smoke.

The way in which these polycyclic aromatic hydrocarbons produce malignant tumors has been actively investigated for several decades, and the overall mechanism is now fairly well understood. The actual carcinogens turn out to be metabolic products of the polycyclic hydrocarbons. After the hydrocarbon enters the organism, it is enzymatically oxidized. This oxidation is a normal cellular function and is intended to render the hydrocarbon more water soluble so that it may be eliminated from the organism. An example is benzo[a]pyrene, which gives rise to the highly carcinogenic diol epoxide shown.

benzo[a]pyrene

The diol epoxides are carcinogenic because they alkylate cellular DNA, causing mutations and an eventual loss of the cell's ability to undergo controlled replication.

Benzo[c]phenanthrene presents a further aspect of interesting chemistry.

benzo[c]phenanthrene

The hydrogen atoms at the 1- and 12-positions interact significantly, and the molecule is forced to twist somewhat from coplanarity. With two additional benzene rings we obtain the spirally fused hydrocarbon hexahelicene.

hexahelicene

If this molecule were planar, two sets of CH groups would have to exist in the same space. In practice the hydrocarbon adopts a spiral structure that is also chiral. The enantiomers of this hydrocarbon have been obtained and have enormous optical rota-

FIGURE 30.8 Stereo structure of 2-methylhexahelicene. [Reproduced with permission from K. N. Trueblood et al., *Acta Cryst.*, **B29**: 223 (1973).]

tions, $[\alpha]_D$ 3700°. The spiral structure has been demonstrated experimentally by the x-ray structure determination of 2-methylhexahelicene as shown in the stereo plot in Figure 30.8.

EXERCISE 30.13 Write the structures of the hydrocarbons named on page 992.

PROBLEMS

1. Name each of the following compounds and show a practical synthesis starting with a suitable benzene derivative.

(a)

(b)

(c)

(d)

(e) Br— —Br

(f)

(g)

(h)

2. 6,6′-Dinitrobiphenyl-2,2′-dicarboxylic acid can be prepared by the Ullmann reaction on 2-iodo-3-nitrobenzoic acid. Give a reasonable preparation of this compound from available materials.

3. Substitution reactions of 2-methylnaphthalene with bulky electrophilic reagents tend to occur at the 6-position. Explain why this position is preferred to the sterically equivalent 7-position.

4. Write out the mechanism for the conversion of 2-naphthol to 2-naphthylamine showing every intermediate involved in the Bucherer reaction.

5. The heat of formation of naphthalene, ΔH_f°, is 36.1 kcal mole^{-1}; ΔH_f° for *trans*-decalin is -43.5 kcal mole^{-1}.
   (a) Calculate the heat of hydrogenation of naphthalene to *trans*-decalin.
   (b) Using the heat of hydrogenation of cyclohexene as a comparison standard, estimate the heat of hydrogenation of naphthalene in the absence of any conjugation stabilization.
   (c) Compare (a) and (b) to derive the corresponding empirical resonance energy of naphthalene.

6. Cadinene, $C_{15}H_{24}$, is a sesquiterpene (Section 34.7) occurring in the essential oils of junipers and cedars. Dehydrogenation gives the naphthalene hydrocarbon cadalene.

   cadinene   cadalene

   (a) What is the IUPAC name for cadalene?
   (b) Give a rational synthesis of cadalene from toluene and any necessary aliphatic compounds.

7. Provide a practical synthesis of each of the following compounds from naphthalene:
   (a) 2-bromonaphthalene   (b) 1-methylnaphthalene
   (c) 1-isopropylnaphthalene   (d) 1-naphthyl propyl ketone
   (e) 2-phenylnaphthalene   (f) 1,2-naphthoquinone
   (g) 1-naphthoic acid   (h) naphthalene-1-*d*

8. Allyl β-naphthyl ether undergoes the Claisen rearrangement to give exclusively 1-allyl-2-naphthol. Give a reasonable explanation for the decided preference of this reaction over the alternative reaction to 3-allyl-2-naphthol.

9. The difference in empirical resonance energies of anthracene and phenanthrene can be accounted for on the basis of resonance structures. There are four Kekulé structures for anthracene and five for phenanthrene.
   (a) Write out both sets of resonance structures for anthracene and phenanthrene.
   (b) For each of the five different carbon-carbon bonds in anthracene, compare the number of resonance structures in which each is single or double and determine the fraction of double bond character (bond order). Compare with the bond lengths predicted using the curve you constructed for Exercise 30.6 with the experimental values determined by x-ray crystal structure techniques as

   1.423
   1.370
   1.396   1.436   1.408

   bond distances in Å

10. Give the expected dominant product or products in mononitration of each of the following compounds.

(a)

(b)

(c)

(d)

(e)

(f)

(g) HO$_3$S—

(h)

(i)

(j)

(k)

(l)

11. Acetylation of phenanthrene with acetyl chloride and AlCl$_3$ in nitrobenzene gives primarily 3-acetylphenanthrene. 2-Acetylphenanthrene is best prepared by Friedel-Crafts acetylation of 9,10-dihydrophenanthrene (note that this hydrocarbon is a biphenyl compound and the 2-position corresponds to the *para*-position of biphenyl) followed by dehydrogenation with Pd/C. Show how to prepare each of the following phenanthrene derivatives.
(a) 2- and 3-phenanthrenecarboxylic acid
(b) 2- and 3-aminophenanthrene
(c) 2- and 3-bromophenanthrene
(d) phenanthrene-2-*d* and phenanthrene-3-*d*

12. (a) Starting from naphthalene or either of the monomethylnaphthalenes show how to pre-pare all five possible methylphenanthrenes. (*Note*: Some of these are more difficult than others.)

(b) α-Methylsuccinic anhydride reacts with naphthalene and $AlCl_3$ in nitrobenzene to give about equal amounts of 4-oxo-4-(1-naphthyl)-2-methylbutanoic acid and 4-oxo-4-(2-naphthyl)-2-methylbutanoic acid. These acids can be separated and used as starting materials for problem (a). Which of the methylphenanthrenes can be prepared in this way?

13. Show how anthraquinone can be prepared from 1,4-naphthoquinone.

14. The following methyl derivatives have been shown to be carcinogenic. Supply an adequate name for each compound.

15. The acidity of fluorene is sufficiently high that it will undergo condensation reactions as do esters in alcoholic sodium ethoxide. Show how such condensation reactions can be utilized for the preparation of the following compounds.
    (a) fluorene-9-carboxylic acid   (b) 9-methylfluorene-9-carboxylic acid
    (c) 9-benzoylfluorene   (d) fluorene-9-carboxaldehyde

16. Suggest a procedure using phase-transfer catalysis for the alkylation of fluorene with *n*-butyl bromide.

17. (a) Write a reasonable mechanism for the following reaction showing all intermediates involved.

    (b) On the basis of this mechanism, what would be the course of reaction for 2-methyl-9-chlorophenanthrene?

18. Give a reasonable mechanism for the following reaction, showing all intermediates involved.

19. 2,6-Naphthoquinone is reduced more readily than 1,2-naphthoquinone. Explain.

20. Steganone is a naturally occurring biphenyl, which was shown by x-ray analysis to have the following structure.

steganone

A synthesis of steganone was carried out, and a product was obtained that was different from steganone. This isomeric product, named isosteganone, was shown to have the same gross structure as steganone and was also shown to have the lactone ring fused trans to the eight-membered ring, as in steganone. What is the nature of the difference between steganone and isosteganone?

21. Triptycene (page 989) is a triarylmethane formally similar to triphenylmethane. Triphenyl-methane is a relatively acidic hydrocarbon with a pK_a of 31.5, whereas the pK_a of triptycene is at least 10 units higher. Explain.

22. How many stereoisomers exist for 1,3-bis-(2-bromo-6-methylphenyl)benzene? Write their structures. Which are chiral?

23. The perinaphthenyl cation is a relatively stable carbocation in which the positive charge can be distributed to six equivalent positions. Write resonance structures showing this equivalency. Use the stability of the perinaphthenyl cation to explain why the 1-position of pyrene is exceptionally reactive in electrophilic substitution reactions.

perinaphthenyl cation

24. We saw on page 983 that vanadium pentoxide-catalyzed air oxidation of naphthalene gives phthalic anhydride. Application of the same reaction to 1-naphthylamine also gives phthalic anhydride. However, 1-nitronaphthalene gives 3-nitrophthalic anhydride. Explain.

Chapter 31

Heterocyclic Compounds

31.1 Introduction

Heterocycles are cyclic compounds in which one or more ring atoms are not carbon (that is, **heteroatoms**). Although heterocyclic compounds are known that incorporate many different elements into cyclic structures (for example, N, O, S, B, Al, Si, P, Sn, As, Cu), we shall consider only some of the more common systems in which the heteroatom is N, O, or S.

Heterocycles are conveniently grouped into two classes, nonaromatic and aromatic. The nonaromatic compounds have physical and chemical properties that are typical of the particular heteroatom. Thus, tetrahydrofuran and 1,4-dioxane are typical ethers, while 1,3,5-trioxane behaves as an acetal.

tetrahydrofuran   1,4-dioxane   1,3,5-trioxane

Pyrrolidine and piperidine are typical secondary amines and the bicyclic compound quinuclidine is a tertiary amine.

pyrrolidine   piperidine   quinuclidine

Since the chemistry of these compounds parallels the chemistry of their acyclic relatives, we shall treat them here only briefly.

The aromatic heterocycles include such compounds as pyridine, where nitrogen replaces one of the CH groups in benzene, and pyrrole, in which the aromatic sextet is supplied by the four electrons of the two double bonds and the lone pair on nitrogen.

pyridine   pyrrole

Other aromatic heterocycles contain more than one heteroatom, and still others contain fused aromatic rings. Examples that we will treat in more detail later include oxazole, indole, and purine.

oxazole   indole   purine

The nomenclature of these heterocyclic series is a vast sea of special names for individual ring systems and trivial names for individual compounds. In the course of developing the chemistry of some important groups of compounds we will treat the associated nomenclature. There is only one naming scheme common to all of these compounds, and it, unfortunately, is used only in cases where alternative nomenclature based on special names is awkward. This scheme is based on the corresponding hydrocarbon. The compound formed by replacing a carbon by a heteroatom is named by an appropriate prefix: **aza** for nitrogen, **oxa** for oxygen, and **thia** for sulfur. For example, the following heterocycles are considered as derivatives of bicyclo[2.2.1]heptane and bicyclo[2.2.0]hexane, respectively.

1-azabicyclo[2.2.1]heptane   2-oxabicyclo[2.2.0]hexane

For saturated, monocyclic heterocycles not containing nitrogen the ring size is designated by a suffix. For three-membered heterocycles the suffix is **-irane**; for four-membered compounds it is **-etane**; for five-membered materials **-olane**; and for six-membered heterocycles the suffix is **-ane**. It should be remembered that this system is not used with nitrogen-containing rings. In addition, most of the simple heterocycles have common names that are in such general use that the systematic names are rarely used. Some examples of this nomenclature are as follows.

1,3-dithiane   oxolane   1,3-dioxolane
(used commonly)   (rarely used)   (used commonly)

The commonly used names for monocyclic rings with a single heteroatom will be discussed in the next section.

31.2 Nonaromatic Heterocycles

A. Nomenclature

Names in common use of some fully saturated heterocycles containing only one heteroatom are shown below.

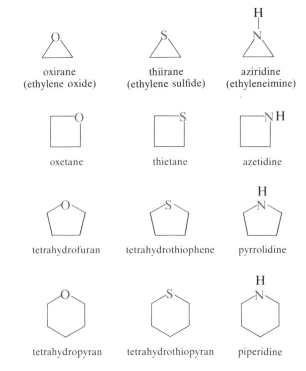

oxirane
(ethylene oxide)

thiirane
(ethylene sulfide)

aziridine
(ethyleneimine)

oxetane

thietane

azetidine

tetrahydrofuran

tetrahydrothiophene

pyrrolidine

tetrahydropyran

tetrahydrothiopyran

piperidine

In naming substituted derivatives, the ring is numbered beginning with the heteroatom.

2,2-dimethyloxirane

3-methylpiperidine

trans-2,4-dimethylthietane

B. Three-Membered Rings

Oxiranes have been discussed previously (Sections 10.11.A and 11.6.E.). Recall that the two most general syntheses are the oxidation of alkenes with peroxyacids and the base-catalyzed cyclization of halohydrins (page 258).

2-methyl-2-propyloxirane

trans-2,3-diphenyloxirane

Aziridines are most commonly prepared by related cyclization reactions. A classical method consists of converting a β-amino alcohol into a β-amino hydrogen sulfate, which is cyclized by treatment with a strong base.

2-phenylaziridine

They may also be prepared by cyclization of β-haloalkylamines and their derivatives. An example is the conversion of an alkene into an aziridine via the iodo isocyanate and iodo carbamate.

cyclohexeneimine

EXERCISE 31.1 (a) Write mechanisms for each step in the foregoing synthesis of cyclohexeneimine from cyclohexene. (b) What is the structure, including stereochemistry, of the product that will be produced if this reaction sequence is applied to *trans*-2-butene?

Thiiranes are most conveniently prepared from the corresponding oxiranes. An especially useful method involves treating the epoxide with sodium thiocyanate. The ensuing reaction is formulated as follows.

cyclohexene sulfide

EXERCISE 31.2 What product results from the reaction of (2R,3R)-2,3-dimethyloxirane with sodium thiocyanate?

The most striking chemical property of the three-membered heterocycles is their extraordinary reactivity, which has its origin in the relief of ring strain that occurs when the ring is cleaved. Recall that oxirane is much more reactive than normal ethers and undergoes ring opening by dilute acid or by base (Section 10.11.A).

$$\triangle\!\!\!\!O + H_2O \xrightarrow[\text{or}]{H^+} HOCH_2CH_2OH$$

Similar reactivity is observed with aziridines and with thiiranes.

$$\underset{C_6H_5}{\overset{\overset{H}{\underset{|}{N}}}{\triangle}} + 2\ HCl \longrightarrow C_6H_5\overset{\overset{Cl}{\underset{|}{}}}{C}HCH_2NH_3{}^+\ Cl^-$$

EXERCISE 31.3 From the data in Appendix I calculate and compare $\Delta H°$ for the following two reactions.

$$CH_3OCH_3 \longrightarrow \triangle\!\!\!\!O + H_2$$

$$CH_3SCH_3 \longrightarrow \triangle\!\!\!\!S + H_2$$

How can you rationalize the result?

C. Four-Membered Rings

The four-membered-ring heterocycles—oxetane, azetidine, and thietane—are rarer, mainly because of the difficulty of preparing four-membered rings (Section 9.8). In some favorable cases the rings may be formed by direct ring closure, but yields in such reactions are often low.

$$\underset{\underset{CH_3}{\overset{|}{\underset{}{}}}{\overset{\overset{CH_3}{\overset{|}{}}}{BrCH_2CCH_2NHCH_3}}} \xrightarrow[100°C]{50\%\ KOH}$$

(80%)
1,3,3-trimethylazetidine

$$ClCH_2CH_2CH_2Cl + Na_2S \xrightarrow{C_2H_5OH}$$

(20–30%)
thietane

Certain four-membered-ring heterocycles may be synthesized by the [2 + 2] cycloaddition of two double bonds. Examples are the formation of β-lactones and β-lactams by the reactions of ketenes with aldehydes and imines, respectively.

$$\underset{O}{\overset{CH_2}{\|}} + \underset{\underset{O}{\|}}{\overset{CH_2}{\overset{\|}{C}}} \xrightarrow[10°C]{ZnCl_2}$$

(88%)
β-propiolactone

$$(C_6H_5)_2C=C=O + C_6H_5CH=NC_6H_5 \longrightarrow$$

(72%)

1,3,3,4-tetraphenyl-
azetidin-2-one

These cycloaddition reactions do not proceed by way of concerted paths. Because a concerted transition state for a [2 + 2] cycloaddition would involve only four π-electrons, such a transition state is not aromatic and does not benefit from the special stabilization that characterizes [4 + 2] cycloaddition transition states, such as the Diels-Alder reaction (Section 20.7). Instead, stepwise mechanisms are involved.

$(C_6H_5)_2C=C=O$ $(C_6H_5)_2C=C=O^-$ $(C_6H_5)_2C-C=O$

$C_6H_5CH=NC_6H_5$ $C_6H_5CH=NC_6H_5$ $C_6H_5C-NC_6H_6$
                                                       H

EXERCISE 31.4 Write a stepwise mechanism for the zinc chloride-catalyzed reaction of ketene with formaldehyde to give β-propiolactone (2-oxetanone). Rationalize the observed mode of addition; that is, why does the reaction not produce 3-oxetanone?

Like the three-membered ring analogs, oxetanes, azetidines, and thietanes are susceptible to acid-catalyzed ring-opening reactions.

$$\square\hspace{-0.6em}_O + C_2H_5OH \xrightarrow[25°C]{trace\ H_2SO_4} C_2H_5OCH_2CH_2CH_2OH$$

(58%)

They are also more reactive than their open-chain relatives in nucleophile reactions but are much less reactive than the analogous three-membered ring compounds. Note the strenuous conditions required for the ring opening of oxetane in the following example.

$$\square\hspace{-0.6em}_O + C_6H_5CH_2S^- Na^+ \xrightarrow[\substack{100°C \\ 6\ hr}]{H_2O} C_6H_5CH_2SCH_2CH_2CH_2 \ \ H$$

(63%)

3-benzylthio-1-propanol

D. Five- and Six-Membered Rings

One source of the saturated five-membered ring heterocycles is reduction of available aromatic compounds derived from furan and pyrrole.

$$+ H_2 \xrightarrow[CH_3CO_2H]{Pt}$$

(94%)

2-butylpyrrole   2-butylpyrrolidine

Many piperidine derivatives may be prepared by hydrogenation of the corresponding pyridine.

(77%)

Aside from reduction of aromatic heterocycles, the main synthetic route to the five-
and six-membered ring saturated compounds is by ring closure of suitable difunctional
compounds.

(75%)

$$BrCH_2CH_2CH_2CH_2Br + C_6H_5NH_2 \xrightarrow{KOH}$$

(100%)

31.3 Furan, Pyrrole, and Thiophene

A. Structure and Properties

The structures of furan, pyrrole, and thiophene would suggest that they have highly
reactive diene character.

furan   pyrrole   thiophene

However, like benzene, they have many chemical properties that are not typical of
dienes. They undergo substitution rather than addition reactions, and they show the
effect of a ring current in their NMR spectra. In short, these heterocycles have characteristics associated with aromaticity.

From an orbital point of view, pyrrole has a planar pentagonal structure in which
the four carbons and the nitrogen have sp^2-hybridization. Each ring atom forms two
sp^2—sp^2 σ-bonds to its neighboring ring atoms, and each forms one sp^2—s σ-bond to
a hydrogen. The remaining p-orbitals on each ring atom overlap to form a π-molecular
system in which the three lowest molecular orbitals are bonding. The six π-electrons
(one for each carbon and two for nitrogen) fill the three bonding orbitals and give the
molecule its aromatic character. Pyrrole (Figure 31.1) is isoelectronic with cyclopentadienyl anion, an unusually stable carbanion that also has a cyclic π-electronic system
with six electrons (Section 21.3.C).

Furan and thiophene have similar structures. In these cases the second lone pair on

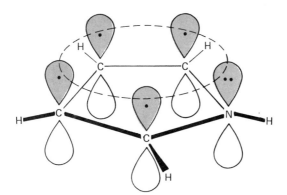

FIGURE 31.1 Orbital structure of pyrrole.

the heteroatom may be considered to occupy an sp^2-orbital that is perpendicular to the π-system of the ring (Figure 31.2).

The aromatic character of these heterocycles may also be expressed by using resonance structures, which show that a pair of electrons from the heteroatom is delocalized around the ring.

This delocalization of the lone-pair electrons away from the heteroatom can be inferred from the dipole moments of these aromatic heterocycles and their nonaromatic counterparts.

1.73 D   1.90 D   1.58 D

0.70 D   0.51 D   1.81 D

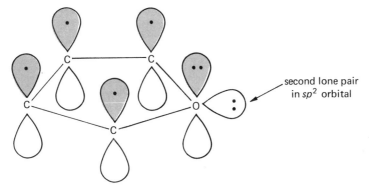

second lone pair
in sp^2 orbital

FIGURE 31.2 Orbital structure of furan.

In the saturated compounds, the heteroatom is at the negative end of the dipole. In the aromatic heterocycles the dipole moment associated with the π-system opposes the σ-moment. As a result the net dipole moment of furan and thiophene is reduced. In pyrrole the π-moment is larger than the σ-moment so that the direction of the net dipole moment is actually reversed from its saturated counterpart!

Empirical resonance energies for furan, pyrrole, and thiophene may be computed from the heats of combustion for the compounds. In all cases, there is a substantial stabilization energy, although of considerably smaller magnitude than for benzene.

Although pyrrole is an amine, it is an extremely nonbasic one because the nitrogen lone pair is involved in the aromatic sextet and is therefore less available for bonding to a proton. The pK_a of its conjugate acid is -4.4. In fact, this pK_a corresponds to a conjugate acid in which protonation has occurred predominantly on carbon rather than on nitrogen.

$$\text{pyrrole} + H^+ \rightleftharpoons \text{conjugate acid}$$

$$pK_a = -4.4$$

EXERCISE 31.5 Using resonance theory, explain why pyrrole protonates on carbon, rather than on nitrogen.

Pyrrole compounds occur widely in living systems. One of the more important pyrrole compounds is the porphyrin hemin, the prosthetic group of hemoglobin and myoglobin (see Figure 29.16). A number of simple alkylpyrroles have played an important role in the elucidation of the porphyrin structures. Drastic reduction of hemin gives a complex mixture from which the four pyrroles—hemopyrrole, cryptopyrrole, phyllopyrrole, and opsopyrrole—have been isolated.

hemopyrrole

cryptopyrrole

phyllopyrrole

opsopyrrole

The function of hemoglobin in an organism is to transport oxygen; 1 g of hemoglobin absorbs 1.35 mL of oxygen at STP, corresponding to exactly one molecule of O_2 per atom of iron. The oxygen binds to the hemoglobin molecule in the vicinity of the iron, and the binding constant is proportional to the partial pressure of oxygen. In the lungs, where the partial pressure of oxygen is high, hemoglobin binds oxygen. In the tissues served by the bloodstream the oxyhemoglobin dissociates back into O_2 and hemoglobin, which returns to the lungs for another load. Carbon monoxide is a poison because it forms a tight complex with the iron of hemoglobin and prevents the iron from binding to oxygen.

The porphyrins are derivatives of porphine, a tetrapyrrole heterocycle, and occur as metal complexes in the active sites of a number of enzymes. The porphine nucleus contains a conjugating system of eighteen π-centers, indicated as the colored line in the structure shown. This system obeys the $4n + 2$ rule and is therefore an aromatic cycle.

porphine

EXERCISE 31.6 One approach to calculating empirical resonance energies is to compare the heats of hydrogenation of furan, pyrrole, and thiophene to tetrahydrofuran, pyrrolidine, and tetrahydrothiophene, respectively, with the heat of hydrogenation of cyclopentadiene to cyclopentane. Apply this method with the data in Appendix I. Rationalize the results using resonance structures.

B. Synthesis

Pyrrole is prepared commercially by the fractional distillation of coal tar or by passing a mixture of furan, ammonia, and steam over a catalyst at 400°C.

Thiophene is prepared industrially by passing a mixture of butane, butenes, or butadiene and sulfur through a reactor heated at 600°C for a contact time of about 1 sec.

Furan, 2-furaldehyde (furfural), 2-furylmethanol, and 2-furoic acid are all inexpensive commercial items.

| furan | 2-furaldehyde furfural | 2-furylmethanol | 2-furoic acid |

The ultimate source of these heterocycles is furfural, which is obtained industrially by the acid hydrolysis of the polysaccharides of oat hulls, corn cobs, or straw. These polysaccharides are built up from pentose units. Dehydration of the pentose may be formulated as follows.

(100%)

In the foregoing mechanism, note that each cationic intermediate is an oxonium ion; simple carbocations are not involved at any point.

Substituted furans, pyrroles, and thiophenes may be prepared by electrophilic substitution on one of the available materials discussed or by a variety of cyclization reactions. The most general is the **Paal-Knorr** synthesis, in which a 1,4-dicarbonyl compound is heated with a dehydrating agent, ammonia, or an inorganic sulfide to produce the furan, pyrrole, or thiophene, respectively.

2,5-hexanedione

2,5-dimethylfuran

2,5-dimethylthiophene

2,5-dimethylpyrrole

EXERCISE 31.7 Write reasonable mechanisms for the formation of 2,5-dimethylfuran and 2,5-dimethylpyrrole from 2,5-hexanedione in the foregoing reactions.

Another general method for the synthesis of substituted pyrroles is the **Knorr pyrrole synthesis**, the condensation of an α-amino ketone with a β-keto ester. The method is illustrated by the following synthesis of diethyl 3,5-dimethylpyrrole-2,4-dicarboxylate.

(57–64%)

The probable mechanism of the Knorr synthesis is as follows.

Notice how each individual step involves either an oxonium ion or an ammonium ion. Again, no unstabilized carbocation is involved.

> **EXERCISE 31.8** Propose syntheses of the following heterocycles from acyclic starting materials.
>
> (a)
>
> 2-methyl-3,5-diethylthiophene
>
> (b)

C. Reactions

The most typical reaction of furan, pyrrole, and thiophene is electrophilic substitution. All three heterocycles are much more reactive than benzene, the reactivity order being pyrrole > furan > thiophene >> benzene. To give some idea of the magnitude of this reactivity order, partial rate factors (reactivities relative to benzene) for tritium exchange with trifluoroacetic acid (page 670) for thiophene are as follows.

Because of this high reactivity, even mild electrophiles suffice to cause electrophilic substitution in these heterocycles. Substitution occurs predominantly at the α-position (C-2).

This orientation is understandable in terms of the mechanism of electrophilic aromatic substitution. The α/β ratio is determined by the relative energies of the transition states leading to the two isomers. As in the case of substituted benzenes (Section 22.6), we may estimate the relative energies of these two transition states by considering the actual reaction intermediates produced by attack at the α- or β-position. The important resonance structures for these two cations are shown below.

The most important of these structures are the two with the positive charge on sulfur because, in these two sulfonium cation structures, all atoms have octets of electrons. Nevertheless, as the sets of resonance structures show, the charge on the cation resulting from attack at the α-position is more extensively delocalized than that for the cation resulting from attack at the β-position. The following examples further demonstrate the generality of α-attack.

(75–92%)
2-acetylfuran

(60%)
2-acetylpyrrole

(75%)
2-iodothiophene

In the last example, note that 2-iodothiophene is the sole product of iodination, even though the reaction is carried out in benzene as solvent; that is, thiophene is so much more reactive than benzene that no significant amount of iodobenzene is formed.

Hydrolytic ring opening is a typical reaction of furans. In essence, the reaction is the reverse of the Paal-Knorr synthesis. Careful hydrolysis of furans can lead to the corresponding 1,4-dicarbonyl compounds in good yield.

(90%)

EXERCISE 31.9   Write a stepwise mechanism for the foregoing reaction.

Pyrroles are polymerized by even dilute acids, probably by a mechanism such as the following.

Thiophenes are more stable and do not undergo hydrolysis.

EXERCISE 31.10 Give reasonable syntheses, starting with the unsubstituted heterocycle in each case, of the following compounds.
(a) 1-(2-pyrryl)-1-propanone   (b) furan-2-*d*   (c) 2-(chloromethyl)thiophene

---

31.4 Condensed Furans, Pyrroles, and Thiophenes

A. Structure and Nomenclature

Benzofuran, indole, and benzothiophene are related to the monocyclic heterocycles in the same way that naphthalene is a benzo derivative of benzene. Carbazole is a dibenzopyrrole, and is analogous to anthracene. In benzofuran, indole, and benzothiophene, the rings are numbered beginning with the heteroatom; carbazole is numbered in a manner analogous to anthracene.

benzofuran   indole   benzothiophene   carbazole

Of the four systems, indoles are by far the most important. Many natural products have indole structures (see Section 34.7).

tryptophan   tryptamine

reserpine

1013

Sec. 31.4
Condensed
Furans,
Pyrroles, and
Thiophenes

From a chemical standpoint the chief effect of fusing the benzene ring onto the simple heterocycle is to increase the stability and to change the preferred orientation in electrophilic substitution from C-2 to C-3 (Section 31.4.C).

B. Synthesis

The most general synthesis of indoles is the **Fischer indole synthesis**, in which the phenylhydrazone of an aldehyde or ketone is treated with a catalyst such as BF$_3$, ZnCl$_2$, or polyphosphoric acid (PPA).

(93%)
1,2,3,4-tetrahydrocarbazole

(73%)
2-phenylindole

The mechanism of the Fischer synthesis has been the subject of much study. The available evidence is in accord with a pathway involving a benzidine-like rearrangement (Section 24.1).

The reaction fails with the phenylhydrazone of acetaldehyde and thus cannot be used to prepare indole itself. However, the phenylhydrazone of pyruvic acid does react to yield indole-2-carboxylic acid, which can be decarboxylated to give indole.

EXERCISE 31.11   Show how each of the following compounds can be prepared by the Fischer indole synthesis.
(a) 2,5-dimethylindole   (b) 4,6-dimethoxyindole
What problems arise in preparation of the following compounds by this method?
(c) 2-ethylindole   (d) 2,4-dimethylindole

C. Reactions

All three condensed heterocycles undergo electrophilic substitution in the heterocyclic ring rather than in the benzene ring. However, each is markedly less reactive than the corresponding monocyclic heterocycle. Some partial rate factors for protodetritiation with trifluoroacetic acid (page 669) are available for benzothiophene and benzofuran.

These values are at least two orders of magnitude smaller than that for the α-position of thiophene (Section 31.3.C).

The preferred orientation in electrophilic substitution reactions in these compounds can be summarized as follows.

1. In benzofuran the most reactive position is C-2.
2. In benzothiophene C-2 and C-3 have comparable reactivities, with C-3 being somewhat the more reactive.
3. In indole the most reactive position is C-3.

The way in which these generalizations apply in practice will be illustrated with some specific examples.

Electrophilic substitution in benzofuran occurs predominantly at C-2, just as in furan itself.

(40%)
2-acetylbenzofuran

If the 2-position is occupied, reaction occurs at C-3.

1015

Sec. 31.4

*Condensed
Furans,
Pyrroles, and
Thiophenes*

(70%)
2-methyl-3-chloromethyl-
benzofuran

The preferred reaction at C-3 in indole and benzothiophene is illustrated by the following reactions.

(97%)
indole-3-carboxaldehyde

(56%)
3-chloromethylbenzothiophene

With benzothiophene other isomers are usually produced as well, but are not always detected or isolated.

These orientation specificities can be rationalized by considering the intermediate ions produced by attack at C-2 and C-3. Reaction at C-2 gives a carbocation in which the charge is distributed to the benzene ring and to the heteroatom; however, the structure with the charge on the heteroatom no longer has a benzene ring. In contrast, reaction at C-3 does not permit effective distribution of charge around the benzene ring, but the electron pair on the heteroatom is utilized efficiently without disruption of the benzene resonance.

The relative reactivities depend on the balance of these contrasting effects. The experimental results suggest that for indole the direct involvement of the basic nitrogen lone pair is much more important than conjugation with the benzene ring, whereas with benzofuran the oxygen lone pair is less basic and the involvement of the benzene ring now dominates. In the case of benzothiophene the two effects are roughly comparable in magnitude.

> **EXERCISE 31.12** From the principles and examples developed in this section, work out whether the 2- or 3-position of carbazole is the more reactive in electrophilic substitution.

31.5 Azoles

A. Structure and Nomenclature

Azoles are five-membered aromatic heterocycles containing two nitrogens, one nitrogen and one oxygen, or one nitrogen and one sulfur. They are named and numbered as shown below. They may be considered as aza analogs of furan, pyrrole, and thiophene in the same way that pyridine is an aza analog of benzene (see Section 31.6).

furan

oxazole
(3-azafuran)

benzene

pyridine
(azabenzene)

oxazole
b.p. 70°C

imidazole
b.p. 263°C
m.p. 90°C

thiazole
b.p. 117°C

isoxazole
b.p. 95°C

pyrazole
b.p. 188°C
m.p. 70°C

isothiazole
b.p. 113°C

From a molecular orbital standpoint the azoles are similar to the simpler aromatic heterocycles. For example, in imidazole each carbon and nitrogen may be considered to be sp^2-hybridized. One nitrogen makes two sp^2—sp^2 σ-bonds to carbon and one sp^2—s σ-bond to hydrogen. The other nitrogen has its lone pair in the third sp^2-orbital. The π-molecular orbital system is made up from the p_z orbitals from each ring atom (Figure 31.3). Six π-electrons (one from each carbon and from one nitrogen, two from the other nitrogen) complete the aromatic shell.

An examination of the physical properties of the simple azoles reveals that imidazole and pyrazole have anomalously high boiling points. They are also the only simple azoles that are solids at room temperature. These properties clearly result from inter-

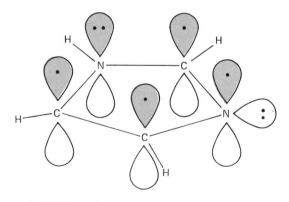

FIGURE 31.3 Orbital structure of imidazole.

molecular hydrogen bonding. With imidazole the hydrogen bonding is of a linear polymer, whereas pyrazole seems to exist largely as the dimer.

Like pyridine (pK_a 5.2; Section 31.6.A), thiazole (pK_a 2.4), pyrazole (pK_a 2.5), and oxazole (pK_a 0.8) are weak bases. As in pyridine, the nitrogen lone pair is in an sp^2-orbital. Recall that greater s-character of lone-pair electrons is associated with heightened stability and lower basicity (Section 12.4). A similar trend is seen with nitrogen acids (Table 31.1).

The higher s-character of the pyridine lone pair compared to aliphatic amines is sufficient to account for a decrease in basicity of several powers of ten. In pyrazole, thiazole, and oxazole the basicity of the nitrogen lone pair is further reduced by the presence of the other heteroatom.

pK_a 2.4 pK_a 0.8 pK_a 2.5

In marked contrast to these results, imidazole seems to be abnormally basic for a compound with sp^2-hybridized nitrogen (pK_a 7.0). The enhanced basicity of imidazole is presumably due to the symmetry of the conjugate acid and the consequent resonance stabilization.

pK_a 7.0

TABLE 31.1 Hybridization and Acidity

Orbital	Carbon Acid	pK_a	Nitrogen Acid	pK_a
sp	$HC\equiv CH$	25	$CH_3C\overset{+}{\equiv}NH$	-10
sp^2	$CH_2=CH_2$	44	$N^+{-}H$	5
sp^3	$CH_3{-}CH_3$	50	$(CH_3)_3\overset{+}{N}H$	10

Its pK_a of 7.0 means that imidazole is half protonated in neutral water. As a result the basicity of imidazole plays an important role in biological processes. The imidazole ring in the amino acid histidine is often involved as a proton acceptor in the active site of enzymes.

histidine

The thiazole ring is also important in nature. It occurs, for example, in vitamin B$_1$, thiamine, a coenzyme required for the oxidative decarboxylation of α-keto acids.

thiamine

A tetrahydrothiazole also appears in the skeleton of penicillin, one of the first and still most important of the broad-spectrum antibiotics.

benzylpenicillin

B. Synthesis

Pyrazoles and isoxazoles may be synthesized by the reaction of hydrazine or hydroxyl-amine with 1,3-dicarbonyl compounds or the equivalent.

(85%)
3,5-dimethylisoxazole

(73–77%)
3,5-dimethylpyrazole

The reaction proceeds through an oxime or hydrazone, which undergoes cyclization. If the dicarbonyl compound is symmetrical, as in the foregoing case, only one product may result, regardless of which carbonyl group undergoes initial attack. If the substrate is not symmetrical, mixtures can result, unless one of the two carbonyl groups is much more reactive to nucleophilic addition than the other, as shown by the following example.

If a substituted hydrazine is used, a 1-substituted pyrazole results.

EXERCISE 31.13 What product is obtained when benzoylacetophenone (1,3-diphenyl-1,3-propanedione) is treated with phenylhydrazine and aqueous HCl?

An alternative synthesis of isoxazoles involves the cycloaddition of a nitrile oxide to an acetylene.

$$CH_3OCCH_2CH_2C\overset{+}{\equiv}N-O^- + CH_3CCH_2CH_2C\equiv CH \longrightarrow$$

(50%)

Nitrile oxides are unstable compounds generated *in situ* by the dehydration of a hydroxamic acid chloride, which is prepared by chlorination of an aldoxime.

An alternative preparation (**Mukaiyama method**) involves dehydration of a nitroalkane.

The reaction of nitrile oxides with alkynes and alkenes is called a **1,3-dipolar cycloaddition**. It is an example of a large class of such cycloaddition reactions that involve six-electron, Hückel transition states and are fully analogous to the Diels-Alder reaction (Sections 20.7, 21.4).

EXERCISE 31.14 Outline a synthesis of 3-ethyl-5-isopropylisoxazole, starting with organic compounds containing five or fewer carbons.

Pyrazoles may also be prepared by a 1,3-dipolar cycloaddition, this time between diazomethane and an acetylene.

$$HC{\equiv}CCOOCH_3 + CH_2N_2 \xrightarrow[0°C]{ether}$$

(80%)
methyl pyrazole-
3-carboxylate

The reaction is formulated in a completely analogous manner.

The initially formed product isomerizes to the more stable aromatic system. 3-Substituted pyrazoles bearing a proton on nitrogen exist in equilibrium with the 5-isomers. Such prototropic equilibria (Section 14.6.A) are generally slow enough so that both isomers are seen in the NMR and CMR spectra. However, the isomerization is usually fast enough that it is not practical to isolate the individual 3- and 5-isomers.

The most general synthesis of the 1,3-azoles is the dehydration of 1,4-dicarbonyl compounds, a form of Paal-Knorr cyclization.

$$C_6H_5\overset{O}{\underset{}{C}}-N\overset{H}{\underset{}{}}CH_2\overset{O}{\underset{}{C}}C_6H_5 \xrightarrow[\Delta]{H_2SO_4}$$

2,5-diphenyloxazole

$$C_6H_5\overset{O}{\underset{}{C}}-N\overset{H}{\underset{C_6H_5}{C}}HCC_6H_5 \xrightarrow[\underset{120°C}{HOAc}]{NH_4{}^+OAc^-}$$

(93%)
2,4,5-triphenylimidazole

$$CH_3\overset{O}{\overset{\|}{C}}CH_2NH\overset{O}{\overset{\|}{C}}CH_3 + P_2S_5 \xrightarrow{120°C}$$

2, 5-dimethylthiazole

EXERCISE 31.15 Write reasonable reaction mechanisms for the foregoing preparations of 2,5-diphenyloxazole and 2,4,5-triphenylimidazole.

C. Reactions

The azoles are markedly less reactive than furan, pyrrole, and thiophene. The reduced reactivity is due to the electronegative azole nitrogen. For the 1,2-azoles the reactivity order is as follows.

Electrophilic substitution takes place exclusively at C-4, whether or not other substituents are at C-3 and C-5.

$$\xrightarrow{\substack{HNO_3, H_2SO_4 \\ 115°C \\ 19\ hr}}$$

(97%)
4-nitroisothiazole

$$\xrightarrow{\substack{HNO_3, H_2SO_4 \\ 70°C}}$$

5-methylisoxazole   4-nitro-5-methylisoxazole

EXERCISE 31.16 We mentioned in Section 31.3.C that the positions in thiophene α to the sulfur are much more reactive than the β-positions toward electrophilic substitution. Explain why the 5-position of isothiazole (α to the sulfur) is *less* reactive than the 4-position (β to the sulfur).

For the 1,3-azoles a similar reactivity order is found.

For imidazoles, which have been studied most extensively, substitution occurs preferentially at C-4 (equivalent to C-5 by proton transfers) rather than at C-2.

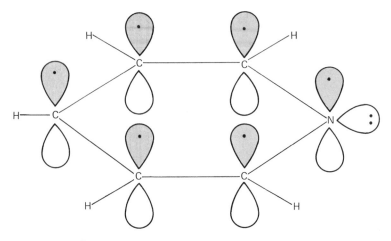

4(5)-nitroimidazole

4(5)-bromoimidazole

When both C-4 and C-5 are blocked, substitution occurs at C-2.

EXERCISE 31.17 Show how each of the following conversions can be accomplished.
(a) 1,4-dimethylimidazole to 5-bromo-1,4-dimethylimidazole
(b) 4-methylimidazole to 2-bromo-4-methyl-5-nitroimidazole

31.6 Pyridine

A. Structure and Physical Properties

Pyridine is an analog of benzene in which one of the CH units is replaced by nitrogen (Figure 31.4). The nitrogen lone pair is located in an sp^2-hybrid orbital that is perpendicular to the π-system of the ring. The effect on the basicity of the nitrogen (pK_a 5.2) has been discussed in Section 31.5.A. Various values have been deduced for the empirical resonance energy of pyridine, but it would appear to be roughly comparable to that of benzene. The resonance stabilization is shown by the two equivalent Kekulé structures and the three zwitterionic forms with negative charge on nitrogen.

FIGURE 31.4 Orbital structure of pyridine.

The surplus negative charge on nitrogen is manifest in the dipole moment of pyridine, which is substantially greater than that of piperidine, the nonaromatic analog. That is, the π-moment is in the same direction as the σ-moment and the net moment is additive.

2.26 D   1.17 D

As the charged resonance structures and the dipole moment show, the ring in pyridine is relatively electron-deficient, a feature that is reflected in many of the reactions of pyridine (Section 31.6.C).

Most alkylpyridines have trivial names that are in common use. The most important are the picolines (methylpyridines) and lutidines (dimethylpyridines). Collidine is the common name of 2,4,6-trimethylpyridine.

pyridine
b.p. 115°C

α-picoline
b.p. 128°C

β-picoline
b.p. 144°C

γ-picoline
b.p. 144°

2,6-lutidine
b.p. 144°C

2,5-lutidine
b.p. 157°C

2,4-lutidine
b.p. 157°C

2,3-lutidine
b.p. 163°C

sym-collidine
b.p. 170°C

B. Synthesis

Pyridine itself and most of the simpler alkylpyridines are available from coal tar distillates. Several syntheses are available for deriving substituted pyridines from other compounds.

The most general technique for constructing the ring is the **Hantzsch pyridine synthesis**. Although numerous variations are known, the simplest consists of the con-

densation of a β-keto ester with an aldehyde and ammonia. The product is a 1,4-dihy-
dropyridine, which is subsequently aromatized by oxidation.

A reasonable mechanism for the Hantzsch reaction is outlined as follows. The first step
is probably a Knoevenagel condensation of the aldehyde (Section 27.7.E) with the
β-keto ester.

(1)

A part of the β-keto ester also condenses with ammonia to form an enamine.

(2) $CH_3\overset{O}{\overset{\|}{C}}CH_2COOCH_3 + NH_3 \longrightarrow CH_3\overset{NH_2}{\overset{|}{C}}=CHCOOCH_3 + H_2O$

The unsaturated keto ester produced in step (1) then undergoes a condensation with the
enamine produced in step (2).

(3)

$$CH_3OOC \quad \overset{CH_3}{\diagup} \quad COOCH_3 \quad \rightleftharpoons \quad CH_3OOC \quad \overset{CH_3}{\diagup} \quad COOCH_3$$

EXERCISE 31.18 The Hantzsch pyridine synthesis is usually carried out with ammonia in alcohol solution, mildly basic conditions. The carbanion intermediates in the reaction are enolate ions with the negative charge delocalized onto oxygen or nitrogen. The foregoing reaction sequence involves a number of protonations and deprotonations. What is the base for deprotonations? Where do the protons come from in the protonation steps? Trace the course of each protonation and deprotonation involved, and write resonance structures to show the stabilization of negative charge in each carbanion intermediate.

C. Reactions

The nitrogen lone pair has basic and nucleophilic properties, although both are diminished by the hybridization effect. Pyridines form salts with acids and are widely used as catalysts and ''acid scavengers'' in reactions where strong acids are produced.

$$R_2CHOH + \quad \bigcirc \!\!-\!SO_2Cl \quad \longrightarrow \quad R_2CHOSO_2\!-\!\bigcirc \quad + \quad \bigcirc$$

pyridinium
chloride

The nitrogen may be alkylated by primary alkyl halides, leading to N-alkylpyridinium salts.

$$\bigcirc + CH_3I \longrightarrow$$

N-methylpyridinium iodide

Pyridines are rather resistant to oxidation, as the following reaction demonstrates.

quinoline   (65–70%)
quinolinic
acid   nicotinic acid
(niacin)

The foregoing reaction provides a route to β-substituted pyridine derivatives. Nicotinic acid is present in minute amounts in all living cells. The corresponding amide, niacinamide, is an essential B vitamin. Nicotinic acid is also produced by oxidation of nicotine, an alkaloid present to the extent of 2–8% in the dried leaves of *Nicotiana tabacum*.

Nicotine is used as an agricultural insecticide, but is also toxic to humans; the fatal dose by ingestion is only 40 mg.

nicotine

Because of its resistance to oxidation, pyridine can even be used as a solvent for chromium trioxide oxidations (**Sarrett procedure**, Section 14.9.A). However, under the proper conditions the nitrogen can be oxidized to the N-oxide, as are other tertiary amines (Section 23.7.E).

(75%)
3-methylpyridine N-oxide

As we shall see, pyridine N-oxides are important synthetic intermediates.

EXERCISE 31.19 For pyridine N-oxide, there are four resonance structures in which all atoms have octet electronic configurations. Write these structures, paying careful attention to formal charges. Be sure to show each nonbonding electron pair as a pair of dots. What do these resonance structures suggest about orientation in the reactions of pyridine N-oxide with electrophiles?

Pyridine is resistant to electrophilic aromatic substitution conditions, not only because of the electron-deficient ring but also because under the acidic conditions of such reactions the nitrogen is protonated or complexed with a Lewis acid. In general, pyridine is less reactive in such reactions than trimethylanilinium ion.

Substitution is achieved only under the most drastic conditions; reaction occurs at C-3, and yields are often poor.

(22%)
3-nitropyridine

(71%)
pyridine-3-sulfonic acid

Alkyl and amino groups activate the ring toward electrophilic substitution. In the alkylpyridines the ring nitrogen directing influence predominates (C-3 or C-5 attack) regardless of the position of alkylation.

β-picoline

5-methylpyridine-3-
sulfonic acid

Amino groups either free or acylated govern the position of further substitution (*ortho* or *para* to the amino).

2-aminopyridine

5-bromo-2-amino-
pyridine

(90%)

ethyl N-(3-pyridyl)-
carbamate

(61%)
ethyl N-(2-nitro-3-pyridyl)-
carbamate

The predominant 3-substitution in pyridine is explainable in terms of the resonance structures of the intermediate ions, and the corresponding transition states, produced by electrophilic attack at the three positions.

Attack at C-2

Attack at C-4

Attack at C-3

Compared with the ion produced from benzene, all three ions from pyridine are destabilized by the inductive effect of the nitrogen, especially if it is protonated or coordinated with a Lewis acid. However, the situation is much worse when attack is at C-2 or
C-4 than at C-3. In the two former cases one of the structures of the intermediate ion
has the positive charge on an electron-deficient nitrogen. Thus the situation in pyridine
is similar to that in nitrobenzene. Electrophilic attack is retarded at all positions, but
especially at C-2 and C-4.

Pyridine N-oxides undergo electrophilic substitution somewhat more readily. Reaction generally occurs at C-4.

(90%)

The N-oxide can often be used as an ''activated'' form of the pyridine. Treatment of
the substituted N-oxide with PCl_3 removes the oxygen.

EXERCISE 31.20 Write the resonance structures for the intermediate cations produced by
reaction of pyridine N-oxide with NO_2^+ at C-2, C-3, and C-4 and use these to explain the
observed orientation in the reaction.

The electron-deficient nature of the pyridine ring is also manifest in the ease with
which pyridines undergo **nucleophilic substitution**. A particularly useful and unusual
example is the synthesis of aminopyridines by the reaction of a pyridine with an alkali
metal amide (**Chichibabin reaction**).

(70–80%)
2-aminopyridine

The reaction is initiated by attack by the nucleophile at C-2 or C-6. Attack occurs at these positions because the negative charge can be delocalized onto the ring nitrogen.

The second step is elimination of hydride ion, which reacts with the aminopyridine to give H_2. The driving force for the elimination of hydride ion is, of course, the formation of the aromatic cycle.

Chichibabin-like reactions are also observed with organolithium compounds.

(50%)
2-phenylpyridine

Diazotization of the 2- and 4-aminopyridines yields the 2- and 4-hydroxypyridines, which exist completely in the keto form (for example, α-pyridone, γ-pyridone).

α-pyridone

γ-pyridone

Even though the simple pyridones exist in the isomeric form with hydrogen attached to nitrogen (amide form), they still have extensive aromatic character, as shown by the important dipolar resonance structure.

EXERCISE 31.21 Suggest a synthesis of 6-phenyl-2-pyridone, starting with pyridine.

A final feature of the pyridine ring is of interest. The methyl groups in α- and γ-picoline are comparable in acidity to those in methyl ketones and readily undergo base-catalyzed reactions. Similar reactions are seen with other pyridines that have alkyl groups at C-2 or C-4.

(80%)
3,4-diethylpyridine

The enhanced acidity at these positions is again attributed to delocalization of negative charge in the intermediate anion into the ring and especially onto the nitrogen.

This side-chain acidity is enhanced in the N-alkylpyridinium compounds.

(60%)

(92%)

EXERCISE 31.22 When 2,3-dimethylpyridine N-oxide is dissolved in methanol-d containing sodium methoxide, three protons are exchanged by deuterium. What is the structure of the product? Explain with the use of resonance structures.

31.7 Quinoline and Isoquinoline

A. Structure and Nomenclature

Quinoline and isoquinoline are benzopyridines. The two compounds are both numbered in the same manner as naphthalene (Section 30.3.A) in such a way that nitrogen gets the smallest possible number.

quinoline
b.p. 238 °C
pK_a 4.8

isoquinoline
b.p. 243 °C
pK_a 5.4

The orbital structures of quinoline and isoquinoline are related to those of pyridine (Section 31.6.A) and naphthalene (Section 30.3.A). Both are weak bases, with pK_as comparable to that of pyridine. Alkaloids based on the quinoline and isoquinoline skeleton are widespread in the plant kingdom (Section 34.7.C).

B. Synthesis

The most general method for synthesizing quinolines is the **Skraup reaction**, in which aniline or a substituted aniline is treated with glycerol, sulfuric acid, and an oxidizing agent such as As_2O_5, ferric salts, or the nitro compound corresponding to the amine used.

(84–91%)

The mechanism of the Skraup reaction probably involves initial dehydration of the glycerol to give acrolein, which undergoes a 1,4-addition by the aniline. The resulting β-anilinopropionaldehyde is then cyclized to a dihydroquinoline, which is finally oxidized to give the product.

(4)

Similar results are obtained if an α,β-unsaturated ketone or aldehyde is substituted for the glycerol.

(73%)
lepidine

If a saturated aldehyde is used, an initial aldol condensation occurs to give an α,β-unsaturated aldehyde that engages in the normal condensation (**Döbner-Miller reaction**).

(32%)
quinaldine

In some of these cases an oxidizing agent is not included; in these cases unsaturated reaction intermediates probably serve as oxidizing agents, but this point has not been established. The Skraup synthesis is extremely versatile; almost any desired quinoline may be prepared by using the proper combination of aniline and aldehyde, so long as the reagents will survive the hot acid conditions.

EXERCISE 31.23 Show how the Skraup synthesis can be used to prepare 6-methoxy-8-nitroquinoline. What problems do you think might exist in the application of this method for the synthesis of 5-methoxyquinoline?

A second general preparation of quinolines is the **Friedländer synthesis**. In this method an *o*-aminobenzaldehyde is condensed with a ketone.

(85%)

The Friedländer synthesis probably involves the following reaction steps.

Although substituted *o*-aminobenzaldehydes are not readily available, the parent compound is, and the reaction occurs smoothly with a variety of aldehydes and ketones. It constitutes a good method for the synthesis of quinolines substituted in the pyridine ring.

EXERCISE 31.24 Show how the Friedländer synthesis may be used to prepare the following quinoline.

Isoquinolines are most easily prepared by a reaction known as the **Bischler-Napieralski synthesis**. An acyl derivative of a β-phenylethylamine is treated with a dehydrating agent to give a dihydroisoquinoline, which is dehydrogenated to the isoquinoline.

EXERCISE 31.25 *p*-Methoxybenzaldehyde is subjected to the following sequence of reactions:

What are the structures of compounds **A** through **E**?

C. Reactions

Quinoline and isoquinoline are considerably more reactive than pyridine in electrophilic substitution reactions. For reactions carried out in strongly acidic solution, reaction occurs on the protonated form, and substitution occurs in the benzene ring at C-5 and C-8.

(52%)   (48%)
5-nitroquinoline   8-nitroquinoline

(90%)   (10%)
5-nitroisoquinoline   8-nitroisoquinoline

As with pyridine N-oxide, quinoline N-oxide undergoes nitration easily; reaction occurs at C-4.

(67%)

Both quinoline and isoquinoline readily undergo nucleophilic substitution reactions of the Chichibabin type.

Like 2- and 4-alkylpyridines, 2- and 4-alkylquinolines and 1-alkylisoquinolines have α-hydrogens that are significantly acidic and enter into base-catalyzed reactions.

(60%)

EXERCISE 31.26 When 1,3-dimethylisoquinoline is treated with NaOCH$_3$ in CH$_3$OD, the protons of the C-1 methyl group are exchanged much more rapidly than those of the C-3 methyl group. Explain.

EXERCISE 31.27 What is the expected product from quinoline in each of the following reactions:
(a) C$_6$H$_5$Li   (b) CH$_3$I, CH$_3$CN
(c) 2 Br$_2$, Ag$^+$, H$_2$SO$_4$ (d) 30% H$_2$O$_2$, acetic acid, 70°C
(e) KMnO$_4$, heat

31.8 Diazines

A. Structure and Occurrence

In this section, we shall take a brief look at another class of heterocycles, the diazines. The three isomeric diazabenzenes are called pyridazine, pyrimidine, and pyrazine.

pyridazine	pyrimidine	pyrazine
b.p. 208°C	b.p. 134°C	b.p. 118°C
pK$_a$ 2.3	pK$_a$ 1.3	pK$_a$ 0.7

In addition to these three diazines, the bicyclic tetraaza compound, purine, is an important heterocyclic system.

purine
m.p. 217°C
pK$_a$ 2.3

These ring systems, particularly those of pyrimidine and purine, occur commonly in natural products. The pyrimidines cytosine, thymine, and uracil are especially important because they are components of nucleic acids, as are the purine derivatives adenine and guanine (Section 34.6).

cytosine   thymine   uracil

adenine   guanine

The purine nucleus also occurs in such compounds as caffeine (coffee and tea) and theobromine (cacao beans).

caffeine   theobromine

B. Synthesis

Pyridazines are prepared by the reaction of hydrazine with 1,4-dicarbonyl compounds.

3,6-dimethylpyridazine

Pyrimidines may be most easily prepared by condensation between 1,3-dicarbonyl compounds and urea or a related substance.

(73%)
2-pyrimidone

(72–78%)
barbituric acid

Note that C-2 oxygenated pyrimidines, like C-2 oxygenated pyridines, exist in the keto form.

Pyrazines result from the dimerization of α-amino carbonyl compounds. The initial dihydropyrazines may be oxidized to obtain the pyrazine.

2,5-dimethylpyrazine

Pyrazines are also obtained from the condensation of 1,2-diamines with 1,2-dicarbonyl compounds. When 1,2-diaminobenzene (*o*-phenylenediamine) is used, the product is a benzopyrazine (quinoxaline). The reaction has been used as a diagnostic test for such 1,2-dicarbonyl compounds.

(85–90%)
quinoxaline

EXERCISE 31.28 Outline syntheses of each of the following compounds.
(a) 3,6-diphenylpyridazine   (b) 4,6-diphenyl-2-pyrimidone
(c) 2,5-diphenylpyrazine

C. Reactions

Because of the second nitrogen in the ring system, the diazines are even less reactive than pyridine toward electrophilic substitution. When activating groups are present on the ring, such substitutions may occur.

(85%)

As with quinoline and isoquinoline, attack on the benzodiazines occurs in the benzene ring.

cinnoline   5-nitrocinnoline   8-nitrocinnoline

quinazoline   6-nitroquinazoline
(56%)

Many other reactions of the diazines and their benzo derivatives are similar to those observed with pyridine, quinoline, and isoquinoline. The following reactions illustrate some of these similarities.

(66%)   (77%)
3-butylpyridazine

(81%)

EXERCISE 31.29 2,5-Dimethylpyrimidine reacts with benzaldehyde and alcoholic KOH to give an adduct, $C_{13}H_{12}N_2$. What is the structure of this material? Write a mechanism rationalizing its formation.

31.9 Pyrones and Pyrylium Salts

Pyrylium cations are isoelectronic with pyridines. The pyrylium cation ring system is an oxonium salt with benzenoid resonance.

pyrylium cation

The parent neutral ring system is that of pyran-2-H or pyran-4-H. In this nomenclature the term "pyran" refers to the hypothetical neutral aromatic ring system; the real molecules must have an extra hydrogen as designated in the name. Although some simple derivatives of the parent pyrans are known, the most important derivatives are an unsaturated ketone, 1,4-pyrone (γ-pyrone), and an unsaturated lactone, 1,2-pyrone (α-pyrone).

| pyran-2-H | pyran-4-H | 1,4-pyrone γ-pyrone | 1,2-pyrone α-pyrone |

Pyrone and pyrylium salt structures are widespread in nature (Section 34.3).

A. Pyrones

Treatment of malic acid with fuming sulfuric acid produces 1,2-pyrone-5-carboxylic acid, which on heating to 650°C decarboxylates to α-pyrone.

HOOCCH$_2$CHOHCOOH $\xrightarrow{\text{fuming H}_2\text{SO}_4}$

malic acid

(60%)
coumalic acid

$\xrightarrow{650°\text{C}}$

(66–70%)
α-pyrone

γ-Pyrones are available by intramolecular cyclization of 1,3,5-triketones.

CH$_3$COCH$_2$COCH$_2$COCH$_3$ $\xrightarrow{\text{POCl}_3}$

2,6-dimethyl-1,4-pyrone

The required triketones are prepared as needed by condensation of a β-diketone with an ester.

$\xrightarrow[\text{2. H}^+]{\text{1. NaH}}$

(77–86%)

$\xrightarrow{\text{H}_2\text{SO}_4}$

(88–98%)

α-Pyrones are dienes and partake readily in Diels-Alder reactions with appropriate dienophiles. The intermediate product decarboxylates thermally, providing a synthesis of substituted benzenes.

The pyrones react with ammonia and primary amines under mild conditions to give the corresponding pyridones.

Pyrones are relatively basic and salts can frequently be isolated. The pK_a of 2,6-dimethyl-1,4-pyrone is 0.4; that is, this pyrone is about as basic as trifluoroacetate ion. The conjugate acid of a pyrone can be considered as a hydroxypyrylium salt.

pK_a = 0.4

EXERCISE 31.30 The first step in the reaction of malic acid with fuming sulfuric acid is decarboxylation to give 3-oxopropanoic acid. Write a reasonable mechanism for the subsequent formation of coumalic acid.

B. Pyrylium Salts

Pyrylium salts can be prepared by treatment of pyrones with Grignard reagents. The intermediate tertiary alcohols are not isolated, but are converted directly with acid to the pyrylium cations.

Alternatively, they are prepared by acid-catalyzed condensations of α,β-unsaturated ketones.

(54–56%)

EXERCISE 31.31 Write a reasonable reaction mechanism for the foregoing reaction. Suggest a method for the preparation of 2,4-dimethyl-6-phenylpyrylium perchlorate.

Pyrylium salts can be useful reagents. They react with nucleophilic reagents at the α-position.

EXERCISE 31.32 Write a reasonable reaction mechanism for the foregoing synthesis of 2,4,6-trimethylnitrobenzene from 2,4,6-trimethylpyrylium perchlorate. Suggest a method for the conversion of 2,6-dimethyl-1,4-pyrone into 2,6-dimethyl-4-phenylnitrobenzene.

PROBLEMS

1. Name each of the following compounds.

(j)

(k)

(l)

(m)

(n)

(o)

(p)

(q)

(r)

(s)

(t)

2. Write a structure for each compound.

(a) 1,2-diphenylaziridine

(b) 2,5-dihydrofuran

(c) 1-methyl-2-pyridone

(d) 8-bromoisoquinoline

(e) 7-methyl-6-aminopurine

(f) 2-aminopurine

(g) (3-indolyl)acetic acid

(h) 4-nitroquinoline-1-oxide

(i) 4-chlorothiophene-2-carboxylic acid

(j) 2-methyl-5-phenylpyrazine

(k) 5-nitroquinoline-2-carboxylic acid

(l) 2-nitrothiazole

(m) 3-cyanoisoxazole

(n) 4,6-dimethyl-1,2-pyrone

3. Outline a synthesis for each of the following compounds.

(a)

(b)

(c)

(d)

(e)

(f)

4. Outline a synthesis for each of the following compounds, starting from non-heterocyclic precursors.

(a)

(b)

(c)

(d)

(e)

(f)

(g)

(h)

(i)

(j)

(k)

(l)

(m)

(n)

(o)

(p)

(q)

(r)

(s)

(t)

(u)

5. Outline a synthesis for each of the following compounds from the corresponding unsubstituted or alkyl-substituted heterocyclic system.

6. Write a reasonable mechanism that explains the following reaction.

Would you expect the analogous reaction to occur with 3-vinylpyridine?

7. *o*-Aminobenzaldehyde is a useful starting material in the Friedländer synthesis of quinolines.
   (a) Propose a synthesis of *o*-aminobenzaldehyde.
   (b) Use *o*-aminobenzaldehyde in the synthesis of the following compounds.

(c) The mechanism of the Friedländer synthesis given on page 1033 was abbreviated. Write out the complete mechanism, showing all of the intermediates involved.

8. The pyridine ring is so inert that Friedel-Crafts reactions fail completely. Suggest a method to synthesize phenyl 3-pyridyl ketone.

9. Predict the major product from each of the following reactions.

(a) $\xrightarrow{\text{HNO}_3}{\text{H}_2\text{SO}_4}$

(b) $\xrightarrow{\text{Br}_2}{\text{HOAc}}$

(c) $\xrightarrow{\text{HNO}_3}{\text{H}_2\text{SO}_4}$

(d) $\xrightarrow{\text{Br}_2}{\text{HOAc}}$

(e) $\xrightarrow{\text{KOH}}$

(f) $\xrightarrow{\text{HNO}_3}{\text{H}_2\text{SO}_4}$

(g) $\xrightarrow{\text{PPA}}{\Delta}$

10. Write a reasonable mechanism for the following reaction.

11. N-Alkylated α-pyridones may be prepared by the oxidation of N-alkylpyridinium salts in basic medium; the usual oxidant is Fe^{3+}, in the form of potassium ferricyanide.

(96%)

Propose a reasonable mechanism for this reaction that accounts for the fact that hydroxide ion is necessary.

12. Pyridine N-oxide reacts with benzyl bromide to give N-benzyloxypyridinium bromide. Treatment of this salt with strong base gives benzaldehyde (92%) and pyridine. Rationalize with a reasonable mechanism.

13. Write a mechanism, showing all steps, that explains the following reaction.

$$CH_3CH_2\overset{\overset{\displaystyle O}{\|}}{C}CH=CHCl + H_2NOH \xrightarrow[\Delta]{EtOH}$$

(60%)   (40%)

14. Pyrrole reacts with ethylmagnesium bromide, followed by methyl iodide, to give a mixture of 2- and 3-methylpyrroles. Rationalize this result, using resonance structures where desirable.

15. Treatment of 4-butyl-5-methylisoxazole with potassium *t*-butoxide, followed by mild acidic workup, provides 3-cyano-2-heptanone. Write a reasonable mechanism for this reaction. Show how the reaction can be used as one step in the conversion of cyclohexanone into 2-cyano-2-methylcyclohexanone.

16. Write a mechanism for the following reaction in which a furan is produced.

$$CH_3\overset{\overset{\displaystyle O}{\|}}{C}CH_2COOEt + CH_3\overset{\overset{\displaystyle O}{\|}}{C}CH_2Cl \xrightarrow[25°C]{pyridine}$$

17. Heats of formation, ΔH_f°, for pyridine and piperidine are $+34.6$ and -11.8 kcal mole^{-1}, respectively. Before these data can be used to estimate the empirical resonance energy of pyridine, we need a value for the heat of hydrogenation of a carbon-nitrogen double bond. Data for several compounds have recently become available that suggest a value of -21 kcal mole^{-1} for ΔH° for the reaction

$$+ H_2 \longrightarrow$$

(a) Use this information together with corresponding results for the heat of hydrogenation of cyclohexene (Appendix I) and derive an empirical resonance energy for pyridine.

(b) An alternative method for calculating the empirical resonance energy is to compare the experimental heat of atomization with that obtained by use of a table of average bond energies, such as that in Appendix III. Compare the value you calculate by this method with the commonly quoted value for the resonance energy of pyridine of 23 kcal mole^{-1}. To get some insight into the source of the discrepancy, compare the calculated and observed heats of atomization of piperidine. How accurate are the results expected from the use of average bond energies?

18. Dipole moments of furan, thiophene, and pyrrole were discussed in Section 31.3.A, and the assignments of directions of the dipoles were presented. Given the following dipole moment data, deduce the directions assigned on page 1005.

0.70 D   1.46 D   0.91 D   1.81 D   6.2 D

2.8 D   1.63 D   0.51 D   1.1 D

19. Given the following dipole moments, deduce the direction of the dipole moment of pyridine. Compared to the dipole moment of piperidine, is this direction reasonable?

2.27 D   3.5 D   1.0 D   0.8 D   1.18 D

20. Umbelliferone is a coumarin derivative present as a glucoside in many plants. It is used commercially as a sun-screen in lotions. Show how it may be synthesized from resorcinol.

21. Papaverine, $C_{20}H_{21}NO_4$ is an alkaloid present in opium and is used as muscle relaxant. It is nonaddicting, but is classified as a narcotic. Reaction with excess hydriodic acid gives 4 moles of CH_3I and shows the presence of four CH_3O groups (Zeisel determination). Oxidation with $KMnO_4$ gives first a ketone, $C_{20}H_{19}NO_5$; continued oxidation gives a mixture from which the compounds shown below were isolated and identified. Deduce the structure of papaverine, and interpret the reactions described.

22. Write a mechanism for the base-catalyzed chlorination of an oxime to give a hydroxamic acid chloride (page 1019).

23. Azulene is an isomer of naphthalene that is characterized by its brilliant blue color. 4,6,8-Trimethylazulene is formed in 43–49% yield when 2,4,6-trimethylpyrylium perchlorate is treated with cyclopentadienylsodium in THF. Write a reasonable reaction mechanism for this reaction.

azulene

Chapter 32

Mass Spectrometry

32.1 Introduction

When a beam of electrons of energy greater than the ionization energy [about 8-13 electron volts (eV) (185-300 kcal mole^{-1}) for most compounds] is passed through a sample of an organic compound in the vapor state, ionization of some molecules occurs. In one form of ionization, one of the valence electrons of the molecule is lost, leaving behind a **radical cation**.

$$e^- + CH_4 \longrightarrow 2\,e^- + [CH_4]^{+\cdot}$$

In CH_4 eight valence electrons bond the four hydrogens to carbon. The symbol $[CH_4]^{+\cdot}$ represents a structure in which seven valence electrons bond the four hydrogens to carbon. The + sign shows that the species has a net positive charge. The · signifies that the species has an odd number of electrons. If a mixture of compounds is bombarded with electrons, a mixture of radical cations differing in mass will obviously be produced.

$$CH_4,\ C_2H_6 \longrightarrow [CH_4]^{+\cdot},\quad [C_2H_6]^{+\cdot}$$

m/z: 16 30

where $m/z \equiv$ mass-to-charge ratio (m is the mass of the molecular radical cation and z is the number of charges).

In practice, even when a pure substance is bombarded with electrons, a mixture of cations is produced. As will be discussed later, some of the ions initially formed break up or **fragment** into smaller ions. For example, methane may give cations with masses of 16, 15, 14, 13, and 12.

$$CH_4 \longrightarrow [CH_4]^{+\cdot},\quad CH_3^+,\quad [CH_2]^{+\cdot},\quad CH^+,\quad [C]^{+\cdot}$$

m/z: 16 15 14 13 12

Lewis structures for these cations are

$$\left[\begin{array}{c} H \\ H:\overset{..}{\underset{..}{C}}\cdot H \\ H \end{array} \right]^{+} \quad \begin{array}{c} H \\ H:\overset{..}{C}{}^+ \\ H \end{array} \quad \left[\begin{array}{c} H \\ H:\overset{..}{C}\cdot \end{array} \right]^{+} \quad H:\overset{..}{C}{}^+ \quad \left[:\overset{..}{C} \right]^{+}$$

Note that the cations having an even number of hydrogens are **radical cations**, whereas the cations having an odd number of hydrogens are normal **carbocations**.

A **mass spectrometer** is an instrument that is designed to ionize molecules, often in the gas phase, separate the ions produced on the basis of their mass-to-charge ratio, and record the relative amounts of different ions produced. A **mass spectrum** is a plot of the data obtained from the mass spectrometer. It is customary for the mass-to-charge ratio (m/z) to be plotted as the abscissa and the number of ions or relative intensity (height of each peak) to appear as the ordinate. Mass spectrometry differs from spectroscopy in that no absorption of light is involved. Nevertheless, it has been called a "spectroscopy" because the mass "spectrum" resembles other kinds of spectra.

EXERCISE 32.1 The ionization energy for methane is greater than that for ethylene. Explain.

32.2 Instrumentation

One of the most common types of mass spectrometer currently in use is the **magnetic sector mass spectrometer**. A sketch of a 90° magnetic sector instrument is shown in Figure 32.1. The sample vapor is introduced at the sample inlet a, usually at low pressure (10^{-5} to 10^{-6} torr). A low pressure is used to minimize the number of collisions between ions and nonionized molecules. Such collisions lead to reactions that produce new ions containing parts of both collision partners. Such ions are often interesting in their own right but lead to difficulties in interpretation of the data. After the sample vapor enters the ion source (detailed in Figure 32.1b) at inlet a, it passes through the electron beam b where ionization occurs. The resulting ions pass out of the ionization chamber and between two charged plates c, which serve to focus the ion

(a)   schematic diagram

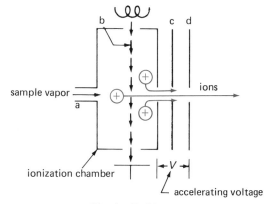

(b)   detail of ion source

FIGURE 32.1 90° sector magnetic deflection mass spectrometer.

beam. There is a difference in potential of several thousand volts between the ionization chamber and the source slit d. In this region, the ions are accelerated and pass through slit d; after traveling a short distance they pass into the magnetic field.

The radius of the path followed by an ion of mass m in a magnetic field depends on its charge ze (e is the electronic charge) and the accelerating potential (V). The energy acquired by an ion accelerated across a potential drop is equal to its kinetic energy.

$$ zeV = \tfrac{1}{2}mv^2 \tag{32-1} $$

In a uniform perpendicular magnetic field of strength $\mathbf{B}$ the ion experiences a centripetal force $\mathbf{B}zev$, where v is the velocity of the ion. Because the ion path is circular, the force on the ion is equal to mv^2/r, where r is the radius of the path followed by the ion.

$$ \mathbf{B}zev = \frac{mv^2}{r} \tag{32-2} $$

$$ r = \frac{mv}{ze\mathbf{B}} \tag{32-3} $$

Most of the ions are singly charged ($z = 1$). As a collection of ions of different masses enters the magnetic field region (f), each ion follows a circular path with a radius given by the foregoing equation. Ions of larger m/z follow a path of greater radius, and ions of lesser m/z follow a path of smaller radius. In the example diagrammed in Figure 32.2 the ions of $m/z = y$ are passing through the collector slit (g) and impinging upon the ion collector (i).

Elimination of the velocity term from equations (32-2) and (32-3) gives

$$ \frac{m}{z} = \frac{\mathbf{B}^2 r^2}{2V} \tag{32-4} $$

This relationship shows that for an ion of given mass-to-charge ratio (m/z), the radius of deflection r can be increased by decreasing $\mathbf{B}$, the magnetic field strength. For example, in the case diagrammed in Figure 32.2 a slight decrease in $\mathbf{B}$ will cause the radius of deflection of all of the ions to increase somewhat. In Figure 32.3 ions of $m/z = y$ no longer pass through the slit and into the collector, but ions of $m/z = x$ do.

Note that the same effect might have been obtained by increasing V slightly or by moving the collector slit slightly to the left. In actual practice this last technique is inconvenient and scanning V has other disadvantages. Scanning of the spectrum is usually achieved by **magnetic scanning**; that is, the accelerating voltage V is kept constant while the magnetic field strength $\mathbf{B}$ is increased. As $\mathbf{B}$ is increased, ions of progressively higher m/z attain the necessary radius of deflection to pass through the collector slit (g) and into the ion collector (i).

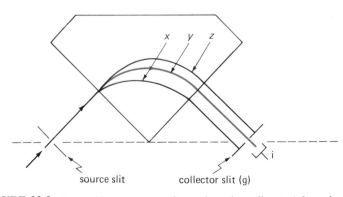

FIGURE 32.2 Ions with $m/z = y$ are focused on the collector i through slit g.

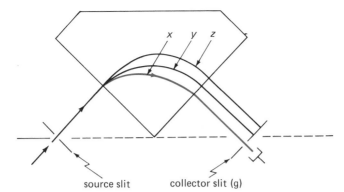

FIGURE 32.3 At lower **B**, ions with $m/z = x$ are now focused on the collector i.

As the ions enter the collector, they impinge upon an electron multiplier detector where a minute current is produced and amplified. The magnitude of this current is proportional to the intensity of the ion beam. The current produced is fed to a computer, which processes the data. The computer may have a stored library of thousands of spectra with which the sample spectrum can be compared. The current produced for various values of m/z is printed in a tabular manner and usually plotted as a bar graph. The most intense peak (the "base peak") is assigned the arbitrary intensity value of 100, and all other peaks are given their proportionate value. A mass spectrum recorded in this manner is shown in Figure 32.4.

EXERCISE 32.2 Note in Figure 32.4 that the most intense peak corresponds to a value of m/z of 43. To what portion of the 2-butanone molecule does such a mass correspond?

32.3 The Molecular Ion: Molecular Formula

The molecular weight of a compound is one datum that can usually be obtained by visual inspection of a mass spectrum. Although the radical cations produced by the initial electron ionization usually undergo extensive fragmentation to give cations of smaller m/z (next section), the particle of highest m/z generally (but not always) corre-

FIGURE 32.4 Mass spectrum of 2-butanone.

sponds to the ionized molecule, and $m/z = M$ for this particle (called the **molecular ion** and abbreviated M^+) gives the molecular weight of the compound.

If the spectrum is measured with a "high-resolution" spectrometer, it is possible to determine a unique molecular formula for any peak in a mass spectrum, including the molecular ion. This is possible because atomic masses are not integers. For example, consider the molecules CO, N_2, and C_2H_4, all of which have a **nominal mass** of 28. The actual masses of the four atomic particles are H = 1.007825, C = 12.000000 (by definition), N = 14.003074, O = 15.994915. Therefore, the actual masses of CO, N_2 and CH_4 are as follows.

$$
\begin{array}{llll}
^{12}C & 12.0000 & ^{14}N_2 & 28.0061 & ^{12}C_2 & 24.0000 \\
^{16}O & 15.9949 & & & ^{1}H_4 & 4.0314 \\
\hline
& 27.9949 & & & & 28.0314
\end{array}
$$

Since a high-resolution spectrometer can readily measure mass with an accuracy of better than 1 part in 100,000, and can separate masses that differ by 1 part in 10,000, the above three masses are readily distinguishable, as shown in Figure 32.5.

Because the mass spectrometer measures the exact m/z for each ion and because most of the elements commonly found in organic compounds have more than one naturally occurring isotope, a given peak will usually be accompanied by several isotope peaks. Table 32.1 shows the common isotopes of some of the elements.

Consider the molecular ion derived from methane. Most of the methane molecules are $^{12}C^{1}H_4$ and have the nominal mass 16. However, a few molecules are either $^{13}C^{1}H_4$ or $^{12}C^{2}H_1{}^{1}H_3$ and have the nominal mass 17. An even smaller number of molecules have both a ^{13}C and an ^{2}H or have two ^{2}H isotopes and therefore have the nominal mass 18. An exact expression for the ratio of isotopic masses $(M + 1)/(M)$ can be derived from probability mathematics but is rather complex. The theoretical intensities of the various isotope peaks may be looked up in special tables compiled for this purpose. However, the contributions of ^{2}H and ^{17}O to $(M + 1)/(M)$ are relatively small

CO N₂   C₂H₄

FIGURE 32.5 High resolution mass spectrum of a mixture of ethylene, nitrogen, and carbon monoxide. The $^{13}CCH_3$ peak is a fragment.

TABLE 32.1 Natural Abundance of Common Isotopes

Element	Abundance, %			
hydrogen	99.985 ^{1}H	0.015 ^{2}H		
carbon	98.893 ^{12}C	1.107 ^{13}C		
nitrogen	99.634 ^{14}N	0.366 ^{15}N		
oxygen	99.759 ^{16}O	0.037 ^{17}O	0.204 ^{18}O	
sulfur	95.0 ^{32}S	0.76 ^{33}S	4.22 ^{34}S	0.014 ^{36}S
fluorine	100 ^{19}F			
chlorine	75.77 ^{35}Cl	24.23 ^{37}Cl		
bromine	50.69 ^{79}Br	49.31 ^{81}Br		
iodine	100 ^{127}I			

The ^{13}C abundance, 1.107%, is the content of oceanic carbonate. Organic compounds in the biosphere run around 1.08% because of isotope effects.

and the ratio is given to a satisfactory approximation for most compounds having few N and S atoms by equation (32-5).

$$\frac{M+1}{M} = \frac{0.01107}{0.98893}c + 0.00015h + 0.00367n + 0.00037o + 0.0080s \quad (32\text{-}5)$$

where M = intensity of the molecular ion (ions containing no heavy isotopes), $M + 1$ = intensity of the molecular ion + 1 peak (ions containing one ^{13}C, ^{2}H, ^{15}N, ^{17}O, or ^{33}S) and c, h, n, o, s = the number of carbons, hydrogens, nitrogens, oxygens, sulfurs.

Using this relationship, we may readily estimate the intensity of the $M + 1$ peak in the mass spectrum of methane.

$$\frac{M+1}{M} = 0.01119(1) + 0.00015(4) = 0.01179$$

Thus the peak at m/z 17 in the mass spectrum of methane should be approximately 1.18% as intense as the peak at m/z 16.

EXERCISE 32.3 Estimate the intensity of the $M + 1$ peak for the following compounds.
(a) decane   (b) 1-decanol   (c) 1-decanamine

Note that the principal contributor to the $M + 1$ peak is ^{13}C. This is partly because of the relatively large relative abundance of ^{13}C (see Table 32.1) and partly because most organic compounds contain many more carbon atoms than they do oxygens or nitrogens. In fact, a useful rule of thumb is that the $M + 1$ peak will be 1.1% for each carbon in the molecule.

A similar relationship may be derived for calculation of the intensity of the $M + 2$ peak. However, in order to obtain an exact figure, a lengthy computation is required. For most compounds the $M + 2$ peak is small. However, for compounds containing chlorine or bromine, the $M + 2$ isotopic peak is substantial. The characteristic doublets observed in the mass spectra of compounds containing chlorine and bromine are an excellent way of diagnosing for the presence of these elements, as shown in Figures 32.6 and 32.7.

One use to which isotope peaks may be put is in approximating the molecular formula of the parent ion in the mass spectrum of an unknown compound. However,

FIGURE 32.6 Mass spectrum of 2-chloropropane.

one must exercise caution when applying the foregoing computations. First, the $M + 1$ peak is generally much less intense than the parent ion. Unless the parent ion is a fairly strong one, its isotope peak may be too weak to measure accurately. Second, intermolecular proton transfer reaction can give $M + 1$ peaks that are not due to isotopes. Third, the presence of a small amount of impurity with a strong peak at $M + 1$ of the sample will interfere with accurate measurement.

EXERCISE 32.4 Sketch the expected appearance of the mass spectrum of 1,2-dibromo-ethane in the region of the molecular ion(s).

32.4 Fragmentation

A. Simple Bond Cleavage

When an electron interacts with a molecule in the ionization chamber of the mass spectrometer, ionization will occur if the impinging electron transfers to the molecule an amount of energy equal to or greater than its ionization potential. The ionization potentials for several organic molecules are given in Table 32.2. When the colliding electron transfers more energy than is required for ionization, a part of the excess

FIGURE 32.7 Mass spectrum of 1-bromopropane.

TABLE 32.2 Ionization Energies

Compound	Ionization Energy, electron volts (eV)
benzene	9.25
aniline	7.70
acetylene	11.40
ethylene	10.52
methane	12.98
methanol	10.85
methyl chloride	11.35

energy will normally be carried away by the radical cation produced in the collision. If the molecular ion gains enough surplus energy, bond cleavage (fragmentation) may occur, with the resultant formation of a new cation and a free radical. Typically, the electron beams employed in the ionization process have an energy of 50-70 eV (1150-1610 kcal mole^{-1}). Since this is far in excess of the typical bond energies encountered in organic compounds (50-130 kcal mole^{-1}), fragmentation is normally extensive.

Consider the case of the simplest hydrocarbon, methane. The mass spectrum of methane is shown in Figure 32.8 in bar graph form as well as tabular form. Note that the base peak (most intense peak) corresponds to the molecular ion (m/z 16). Note also the monoisotopic peak at m/z 17 ($M + 1$), which has an intensity 1.11% that of the molecular ion, within 0.07% of the intensity predicted by theory. Examination of the mass spectrum reveals that cations are also produced and measured that have m/z values of 15, 14, 13, 12, 2, and 1. The following modes of fragmentation may be postulated to explain these various cationic fragments. Initial ionization supplies the molecular ion, with m/z 16.

$$CH_4 + e^- \longrightarrow [CH_4]^{\ddot{+}} + 2e^-$$
$$m/z\ 16$$

Some of these ions move into the accelerating region and are passed into the magnetic field. However, since they possess a large amount of excess energy, many undergo fragmentation before leaving the ionization chamber, giving a methyl cation (m/z 15) and a hydrogen atom.

$$[CH_4]^{\ddot{+}} \longrightarrow CH_3^+ + H\cdot$$
$$m/z\ 15$$

m/z	Intensity
1	3.4
2	0.2
12	2.8
13	8.0
14	16.0
15	86.0
16	100.0
17	1.11

FIGURE 32.8 Mass spectrum of methane.

Occasionally this cleavage occurs in such a way as to produce a methyl radical and a bare proton (m/z 1).

$$[CH_4]^{+\cdot} \longrightarrow CH_3\cdot + \underset{m/z\ 1}{H^+}$$

The fragment CH_3^+ can be accelerated, deflected, and collected as a cation of m/z 15, or it too may undergo fragmentation, giving a hydrogen atom and a new radical cation of m/z 14.

$$CH_3^+ \longrightarrow \underset{m/z\ 14}{[CH_2]^{+\cdot}} + H\cdot$$

Similar events give rise to fragment ions of m/z 13 and 12.

$$[CH_2]^{+\cdot} \longrightarrow \underset{m/z\ 13}{CH^+} + H\cdot$$

$$CH^+ \longrightarrow \underset{m/z\ 12}{[C]^{+\cdot}} + H\cdot$$

Occasionally an ion may eject an ionized hydrogen molecule, giving rise to the weak peak at m/z 2.

$$[CH_4]^{+\cdot} \longrightarrow CH_2 + \underset{m/z\ 2}{[H_2]^{+\cdot}}$$

More complicated alkanes give very complicated spectra, containing a large number of peaks. However, most of these fragment peaks are of low intensity. The more intense fragment peaks have m/z values of $M - 15, M - 29, M - 43, M - 57$, and so on, corresponding to scission of the hydrocarbon chain at various places along its length. The spectrum of n-dodecane, plotted in Figure 32.9, is illustrative. There is a reasonably intense molecular ion (4% of the base peak) at m/z 170. The peak at m/z 155, corresponding to loss of CH_3 ($M - 15$) is so weak as not to be noticeable. However, the peaks at m/z 141 ($M - 29$), 127 ($M - 43$), and so on, are apparent. Note that intensity decreases regularly as mass increases beyond m/z 43 (corresponding to $C_3H_7^+$). The modes of fragmentation responsible for the spectrum of n-dodecane are indicated in Figure 32.10.

FIGURE 32.9 Mass spectrum of n-dodecane.

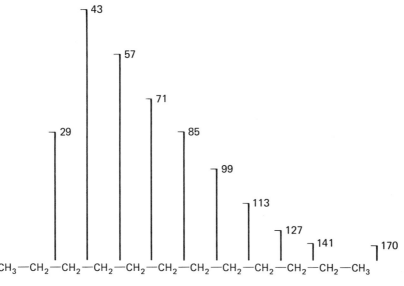

FIGURE 32.10 Fragmentation of *n*-dodecane.

When there is a branch point in the chain, an unusually large amount of fragmentation occurs there because a more stable carbocation results. Thus, in 2-methylpentane, loss of C_3H_7 or CH_3 is much greater than loss of C_2H_5, since the former modes give secondary carbocations, whereas the latter gives a primary carbocation.

The spectrum of 2-methylpentane, plotted in Figure 32.11, illustrates this behavior.

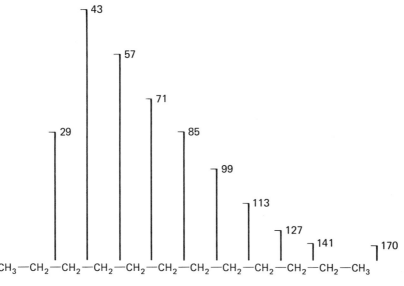

FIGURE 32.11 Mass spectrum of 2-methylpentane.

FIGURE 32.12 Mass spectrum of 3-methylpentane.

On the other hand, the isomeric hydrocarbon 3-methylpentane can cleave in three ways so as to give a secondary carbocation. Two of these cleavages amount to loss of C_2H_5. Correspondingly, the $M - 29$ peak in its spectrum, shown in Figure 32.12, is the most intense peak.

$$\left[\begin{array}{c} CH_3 \\ | \\ CH_3CH_2CHCH_2CH_3 \end{array} \right]^{+\cdot} \longrightarrow CH_3CH_2 \cdot + \begin{array}{c} CH_3 \\ | \\ {}^+CHCH_2CH_3 \end{array}$$
$$m/z\ 86 \qquad\qquad\qquad\qquad m/z\ 57$$

Note that 3-methylpentane cannot undergo a simple cleavage to give an ion with m/z 43. The peak in its spectrum with this value must arise by a process involving some sort of skeletal rearrangement.

The mode of fragmentation in the preceding discussion is common in mass spectrometry. A radical cation usually undergoes bond cleavage in such a manner as to give the *most stable cationic fragment*. What we know about the relative stabilities of various cations from other areas of organic chemistry may often be used to predict how fragmentation will occur in a mass spectrometer. The case of the methylpentanes is a good example of this principle. In Chapter 9 we discussed the S_N1 reactions of alkyl halides to give carbocationic intermediates and found a reactivity order tertiary > secondary > primary. From this order, and other data, we concluded that tertiary carbocations are more stable than secondary ones, which are, in turn, more stable than primary carbocations. Although these results are in solution and mass spectrometry occurs in the vapor phase, we can use our qualitative knowledge of carbocation stabilities to "interpret" the fragmentation pattern of hydrocarbons.

Some of the enthalpy data for ionization of alkyl chlorides given in Table 9.7 on page 179 were actually obtained by mass spectrometric methods.

In alkanes with a quaternary carbon, fragmentation to give tertiary carbocations is so facile that such hydrocarbons frequently give no detectable molecular ion peak. On the other hand, alkenes and aromatic hydrocarbons generally give rather intense molecular ion peaks.

EXERCISE 32.5 What are the principal fragments expected from 3,3-dimethylheptane?

Simple one-bond cleavage is also a prominant fragmentation mode in amines. Cleavage of a bond *adjacent* to a carbon-nitrogen bond gives an alkyl radical and an immonium ion. Primary amines that are not branched at the carbon attached to nitrogen show an intense fragment with m/z 30.

$$[CH_3CH_2CH_2NH_2]^{\ddagger} \longrightarrow CH_3CH_2{\cdot} + CH_2{=}NH_2{}^+$$
$$m/z = 30$$

When the amine is branched at the nitrogen-bearing carbon, an analogous cleavage occurs, leading to a homologous immonium ion; loss of the larger group is preferred.

$$\begin{bmatrix} & CH_3 & \\ & | & \\ CH_3CH_2CH_2CHNH_2 & \end{bmatrix}^{\ddagger} \longrightarrow CH_3CH_2CH_2{\cdot} + CH_3CH{=}NH_2{}^+$$
$$m/z = 44$$

These cleavage patterns are illustrated by the spectra of isobutylamine and *t*-butylamine shown in Figures 32.13 and 32.14.

FIGURE 32.13 Mass spectrum of isobutylamine, $(CH_3)_2CHCH_2NH_2$.

FIGURE 32.14 Mass spectrum of *t*-butylamine, $(CH_3)_3CNH_2$.

B. Two-Bond Cleavage, Elimination of a Neutral Molecule

Some compounds give extremely weak molecular ion peaks. This tends to happen when some form of fragmentation is particularly easy. Such behavior is typical of alcohols, which often give no detectable molecular ion whatsoever. The spectrum of 2-methyl-2-butanol in Figure 32.15 illustrates this phenomenon.

The molecular ion, which would appear at *m/z* 88, is not observed. Instead, sizeable peaks are observed at *m/z* values of 73 (*M* − 15) and 59 (*M* − 29), corresponding to cleavage of the radical ion so as to give stable oxonium ions.

In addition, there is a substantial peak at *m/z* 70, corresponding to loss of water from the molecular ion. This type of fragmentation, in which a radical cation expels a neutral molecule to give a new radical cation, is common with alcohols and ethers.

FIGURE 32.15 Mass spectrum of 2-methyl-2-butanol.

$$\left[CH_3CH_2\underset{\underset{CH_3}{|}}{\overset{\overset{OH}{|}}{C}}CH_3 \right]^{\overset{+}{\cdot}} \xrightarrow{-H_2O} \left[CH_3CH=C\underset{CH_3}{\overset{CH_3}{<}} \right]^{\overset{+}{\cdot}} \quad or \quad \left[CH_3CH_2\underset{}{\overset{\overset{CH_3}{|}}{C}}=CH_2 \right]^{\overset{+}{\cdot}}$$

m/z 70 (center)   m/z 70 (right)

Of course, these new radical cations ions can undergo fragmentation of the type first discussed. The peak at m/z 55 probably arises from such a stepwise path.

$$\left[CH_3CH_2\underset{\underset{CH_3}{|}}{\overset{\overset{OH}{|}}{C}}CH_3 \right]^{\overset{+}{\cdot}} \xrightarrow{-H_2O} \left[CH_3CH_2\overset{\overset{CH_3}{|}}{C}=CH_2 \right]^{\overset{+}{\cdot}} \xrightarrow{-CH_3\cdot} \left[{}^+CH_2-\overset{\overset{CH_3}{|}}{C}=CH_2 \longleftrightarrow CH_2=\overset{\overset{CH_3}{|}}{C}-CH_2{}^+ \right]$$

m/z 70   m/z 55

The m/z 55 fragment is a substituted allyl cation, and the special stability of this ion (Section 19.1.A) is the reason that this fragment is so intense.

When the mass spectrum of an unknown compound does not contain a peak corresponding to the molecular ion, it is easy to be led astray in deducing the structure of the material. However, a careful examination of the mass spectrum of such a compound usually allows one to deduce that elimination of a neutral molecule has occurred and that the even peak of highest m/z is not the molecular ion. As an example, consider the following mass spectrum.

The m/z 70 fragment could be considered to be the molecular ion of a compound with the molecular weight C_5H_{10}, and the m/z 55 fragment would then be due to loss of methyl. However, the rather intense m/z 57 fragment would have to correspond to loss of CH, a mechanistically unreasonable process. Thus, the internal evidence in this mass spectrum suggests that the m/z 70 fragment is not, in fact, a molecular ion.

In addition, the chemist usually has other evidence that might not be consistent with the obvious interpretation of a mass spectrum that does not contain a molecular ion. In the present case, for example, the infrared spectrum contains a strong absorption at 3400 cm^{-1}, strongly suggesting the presence of a hydroxy group. If the m/z 70 fragment *were* the molecular ion of an alcohol, then we would expect a $M - 18$ fragment with m/z 52. The absence of such a peak is further evidence that the spectrum does not contain a molecular ion peak.

There is one other type of fragmentation, also involving expulsion of a neutral molecule that we will develop here. The spectrum of butyraldehyde is plotted in Figure 32.16. The most striking thing about the spectrum is the fact that the base peak (m/z 44) is an even number. Thus it must correspond to expulsion of a molecule, rather than a radical, from the molecular ion. Extensive studies suggest that this fragment arises in the following way.

m/z 72 m/z 44

There is some evidence that suggests that this fragmentation may involve two distinct steps, transfer of a hydrogen atom to the carbonyl oxygen from the γ-carbon followed by scission of the α,β-bond.

This rearrangement reaction is called a **McLafferty rearrangement**. It can provide useful information concerning the structure of isomeric aldehydes and ketones. For example, 2-methylbutanal and 3-methylbutanal both undergo the rearrangement. In the former case one observes an intense peak at m/z 58, but in the latter the rearrangement peak occurs at m/z 44.

m/z 86 m/z 58

m/z 86 m/z 44

EXERCISE 32.7 Ketones and esters also undergo the McLafferty rearrangement. What fragments are expected from each of the following compounds?
(a) 2-butylcyclohexanone   (b) butyl 2,2-dimethylpropanoate

FIGURE 32.16 Mass spectrum of butyraldehyde.

An additional fragmentation common to ketones is cleavage of a bond to the carbonyl group to give a cation of the oxonium ion type.

$$\left[R—\overset{\displaystyle O}{\overset{\|}{C}}—R' \right]^{+} + \xrightarrow{-R'\cdot} \left[R—C≡\overset{..}{O}^{+} \longleftrightarrow R—\overset{+}{C}=\overset{..}{\underset{..}{O}} \right]$$

EXERCISE 32.8 Write equations showing the four principal fragmentation products expected in the mass spectrum of 2-methyl-4-heptanone. There are two different McLafferty rearrangement ions and two different α-cleavages leading to oxonium ions.

PROBLEMS

1. (a) Estimate the relative intensity of the peaks at m/z 112, 114, and 116 in the mass spectrum of 1,2-dichloropropane.
   (b) A compound shows a molecular ion at m/z 138 with a ratio of $(M + 1)/M$ of 0.111. Show how this piece of information can be used to distinguish among the three formulas $C_{10}H_{18}$, $C_8H_{10}O_2$, and $C_8H_{14}N_2$.

2. Estimate the intensity of the $M + 1$ peak, relative to the M^+ peak, for each of the following compounds.
   (a) dimethyl adipate (b) 1,2-diaminonaphthalene
   (c) 1-phenylheptane (d) n-hexacosane ($C_{60}H_{122}$)
   (e) methyl iodide (f) hexafluoroethane

3. The mass spectrum of N-propylaniline has a substantial fragment with m/z 106 ($M - 29$). Account for the fact that N-propyl-p-nitroaniline shows almost no $M - 29$ peak.

4. An unknown compound contains only carbon and hydrogen. Its mass spectrum is shown on page 1064. Propose a structure for the compound.

5. The following mass spectra are of 2,2-dimethylpentane, 2,3-dimethylpentane, and 2,4-di-
methylpentane. Assign structures on the basis of the mass spectra.

6. Identify the following compound from its IR and mass spectra.

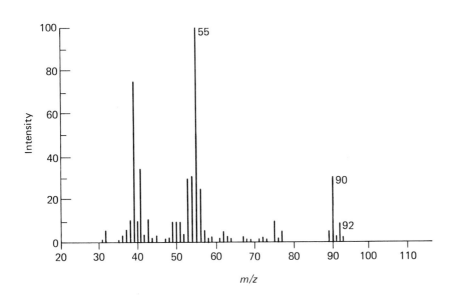

7. Two hydrocarbons were isolated from blue-green algae. The mass spectra of the two hydrocarbons, shown below, provided a clue to their structures. Suggest structures for the two hydrocarbons.

8. An unknown compound gives the following rather simple mass spectrum. What can you deduce about the structure of the compound from this spectrum?

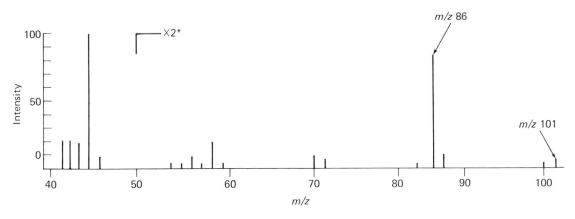

*The vertical scale is expanded by a factor of 2 above *m/z* 50.

The CMR spectrum of the compound shows only two resonances. Can an unambiguous structure be assigned?

9. A compound has infrared absorption at 1710 cm^{-1}. Its mass spectrum is shown on page 1067. Suggest a structure of the compound.

10. Propose a structure for the following compound from its mass spectrum. The IR spectrum shows a strong absorption at 1710 cm^{-1}.

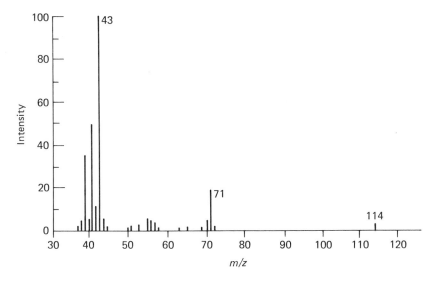

11. An unknown compound shows strong IR absorption at 3400 cm^{-1}. Its mass spectrum is shown below.

Propose a possible structure for the compound. [The IR and NMR spectra of the compound are shown in problem 5, Chapter 15. Confirm your assignment by examination of these spectra.]

12. The mass spectrum of 2-octanone is shown below. Write mechanisms showing the origin of the principal fragments.

13. The following mass spectrum is given by the compound whose NMR and IR spectra are depicted in problem 2, Chapter 23.

Suggest a structure for the compound.

14. The ionization potential of 2-methylbutane is 10.35 eV or 238.7 kcal mole^{-1} (1 eV = 23.06 kcal mole^{-1}); hence, ΔH_f° for 2-methylbutane cation is obtained from ΔH_f° of 2-methylbutane as $-36.9 + 238.7 = 201.8$ kcal mole^{-1}. From the following ΔH_f° values

given for possible fragmentation products of the radical cation, calculate $\Delta H°$ for each of the fragmentation reactions shown.

	$\Delta H_f°$, kcal mole^{-1}		$\Delta H_f°$, kcal mole^{-1}
CH_3^+	260	$CH_3\cdot$	34
$C_2H_5^+$	219	$C_2H_5\cdot$	26
$(CH_3)_2CHCH_2^+$	205	$(CH_3)_2CHCH_2\cdot$	13.5
$(CH_3)_2CH^+$	190	$(CH_3)_2CH\cdot$	17.5
$CH_3CH_2\overset{+}{C}HCH_3$	192	$CH_3CH_2\overset{\cdot}{C}HCH_3$	12

$$\longrightarrow (CH_3)_2CHCH_2\cdot + CH_3^+$$

$$\longrightarrow (CH_3)_2CHCH_2^+ + CH_3\cdot$$

$$\longrightarrow (CH_3)_2CH\cdot + C_2H_5^+$$

$$[(CH_3)_2CHCH_2CH_3]^{\ddagger} \longrightarrow (CH_3)_2CH^+ + C_2H_5\cdot$$

$$\longrightarrow CH_3\cdot + CH_3\overset{+}{C}HCH_2CH_3$$

$$\longrightarrow CH_3^+ + CH_3\overset{\cdot}{C}HCH_2CH_3$$

Chapter 33

The Chemical Literature

33.1 Research Journals

The total knowledge of chemistry is contained in hundreds of thousands of books and journals that are known collectively as **the literature**. New knowledge is communicated to the world for the first time as a **paper** or **communication** in a **research journal**. There are perhaps 10,000 journals that publish original articles on chemical topics, but only about 50 are of general interest to most chemists. Some journals, such as the *Journal of the American Chemical Society*, publish articles in all branches of chemistry. Others, such as the *Journal of Organic Chemistry*, only publish articles dealing with a specific area. A partial listing of typical journals that would be of interest to an organic chemist, with the normal abbreviation printed in italic type, is given below. The language(s) used in each journal is also indicated.

1. *Angewandte Chem*ie (German)
2. *Angewandte Chemie Int*ernational *Ed*ition in *Eng*lish (English)
3. Justus Liebig's *Ann*alen der Chemie (German)
4. *Bull*etin of the *Chem*ical *Soc*iety of *Jap*an (English)
5. *Can*adian Journal of *Chem*istry (English, French)
6. *Chem*ische *Ber*ichte (German)
7. Journal of the *Chem*ical *Soc*iety, *Chem*ical *Commun*ications (English)
8. *Coll*ection of *Czech*oslovak *Chem*ical *Commun*ications (English)
9. *Compt*es *rend*us hebdomadaries, *Ser*ies *C* (French)
10. *Helv*etica *Chim*ica *Acta* (German, French, English)
11. Journal of the *Am*erican *Chem*ical *Soc*iety (English)
12. Journal of the *Chem*ical *Soc*iety, *Dalton Trans*actions (English)
13. Journal of the *Chem*ical *Soc*iety, *Perkin Trans*actions (English)
14. Journal of *Heterocycl*ic *Chem*istry (English)
15. Journal of the *Indian Chem*ical *Soc*iety (English)
16. Journal of *Med*icinal *Chem*istry (English)
17. Journal of *Organometal*lic *Chem*istry (English, German, French)
18. Journal of *Org*anic *Chem*istry (English)
19. *Synthesis* (English)
20. *Syn*thetic *Commun*ications (English)
21. *Tetrahedron* (English, German, French)
22. *Tetrahedron Lett*ers (English, German, French)
23. *Organometallics* (English)

An original article in a research journal may be in the form of a **full paper**, a **note**, or a **communication**. A full paper is a complete report on a research project, with full experimental details and interpretation. It is always accompanied by a short abstract, written by the authors. A note is a final report on a project of smaller scope. It includes experimental details, but has no abstract. A communication is a preliminary report on a finding of unusual significance. Communications are extremely concise, usually less than 1000 words, and have little or no experimental detail. In most cases a communication will be followed later by a full paper after the project has been completed. Some journals, such as *J. Am. Chem. Soc.* and *J. Org. Chem.*, publish both papers and communications, and others, such as *Tetrahedron Lett.* and *J. Chem. Soc., Chem. Commun.*, publish only communications. Research articles are documented with references to the literature, to other research articles, and to books. The traditional form for such a **literature citation** is Author(s), *journal abbreviation*, **volume number**, page number (year). For example,

H. O. House and B. M. Trost, *J. Org. Chem.*, **30**, 2052 (1965).

However, in 1979, the American Chemical Society journals recommended a new form for literature citations. In the newly recommended form the authors' last names are given first, followed by first names and initials, followed by the *journal abbreviation*, **year**, *volume number*, and page number. For example,

House, H. O.; Trost, B. M. *J. Org. Chem.* **1965**, *30*, 2052.

Because of the increase in punctuation required in this system, it has not gained universal favor with chemists. At the present time, both formats are in use.

If a practicing chemist is to keep abreast of the developments in his field, it is essential that he peruse a number of research journals regularly as they appear. All of the journals listed above appear periodically, usually weekly, semimonthly, or monthly. Most chemists regularly scan the tables of contents of a dozen or so journals that publish articles in areas of interest to them.

33.2 Books and Review Articles

The original research journals comprise the **primary literature** of chemistry; they are the ultimate source that must be consulted for authoritative information on any subject. A second category of chemical literature is classed as **secondary literature**. The secondary literature consists of reference books and review articles in which the primary literature is collated and interpreted.

A. Handbooks

There are a number of excellent handbooks that compile data about individual organic compounds. The most extensive and most useful is the *Handbuch der Organischen Chemie*, commonly known as *Beilstein*, after its first editor. *Beilstein* is a multivolume handbook that lists all known organic compounds, together with their physical properties, methods of preparation, chemical properties, and any other available information. The main disadvantage of *Beilstein* is that it is not up to date. All of the literature through 1929 is completely covered, and most classes of compounds are covered through 1959. We shall consider the use of *Beilstein* in Section 33.4.

The Handbook of Chemistry and Physics, published by CRC Press, Inc., Boca Raton, Florida, is revised regularly. It contains a useful collection of data and a copy may be found on the desk of almost every practicing chemist. The most important table for organic chemists is "Physical Constants of Organic Compounds," which occupies a major portion of the book. This table contains the name, formula, color, and several important physical properties for several thousand common organic compounds. Compounds are listed alphabetically by the IUPAC names. A similar volume is Lange's *Handbook of Chemistry*, McGraw-Hill Book Company, New York.

The Dictionary of Organic Compounds, edited by Heilbron, Cook, Bunbury, and Hey, is a five-volume handbook published by Oxford University Press, New York. It contains names, formulas, physical properties, and references for about 40,000 organic compounds. Compounds are listed alphabetically and there is no index.

The Merck Index is published periodically by Merck and Company, Rahway, New Jersey. It concentrates on compounds of medicinal importance, but covers most simple organic compounds, whether or not they have significant physiological properties. In addition to names and formulas, the *Merck Index* lists physical properties, methods of synthesis, physiological properties, and medicinal uses and also gives the generic and trade names for all compounds that are used as drugs.

The Aldrich Catalog of Chemical Compounds has become a useful secondary source for laboratory chemists. This book is primarily a catalog of the more than 16,000 compounds that may be purchased from the Aldrich Chemical Company, Inc.; it is updated annually. However, it also contains physical properties and the *Beilstein* reference for each compound. Furthermore, the entries are cross-referenced to two other reference books that contain NMR and IR spectra. Compounds are listed alphabetically by name and there is a formula index. Users should be cautioned that the nomenclature employed in the Aldrich catalog is a mixture of IUPAC, *Chemical Abstracts*, and trivial.

B. Review Articles

A review article is a survey of a single limited topic. For example, a chemist may assemble all of the information available on a topic by reading the original research articles and condense the information into a review article, frequently with his own interpretation. There are several periodicals that specialize in publishing review articles. A few that are important to organic chemists are

1. *Chemical Reviews* (English)
2. *Chemical Society Reviews* (English)
3. *Angewandte Chemie* (German)
4. *Angewandte Chemie International Edition in English* (English)
5. *Fortschritte der Chemischen Forschung* (German)
6. *Reviews of Pure and Applied Chemistry* (English)
7. *Synthesis* (English)
8. *Organometallic Chemistry Reviews* (English)
9. *Accounts of Chemical Research* (English)

In addition to review journals such as these, there are a number of open-ended serial publications that are published at somewhat irregular intervals in hardbound form. These books are similar in content and format to the normal review journals. A few examples are

1. *Advances in Carbohydrate Chemistry*
2. *Advances in Free Radical Chemistry*
3. *Advances in Photochemistry*
4. *Progress in Physical Organic Chemistry*
5. *Advances in Physical Organic Chemistry*
6. *Organic Reactions*

7. *Progress* in *Organic Chemistry*
8. *Progress* in *Stereochemistry*
9. *Topics* in *Stereochemistry*

Organic Reactions is a particularly important reference source for organic chemists. It is published approximately yearly and contains review articles on general reactions, for example, "The Wittig Reaction" and "The Clemmensen Reaction." The articles are accompanied by extensive tables of applications of the reaction. At the end of each volume there are cumulative subject and author indices.

C. Monographs

There are a large number of excellent books available that provide in-depth surveys of specific areas. The number of such monographs is far too great to list here, and the student is referred to the card catalog in his own library. Several examples, merely to indicate the types of topics covered, are

1. G. I. Frey and R. G. Saxton, *The Chemistry of Cyclooctatetraene and Its Derivatives*, Cambridge University Press, 1978.
2. J. C. Stowell, *Carbanions in Organic Synthesis*, Wiley, New York, 1979.
3. K. Weissermel and H.-J. Arpe, *Industrial Organic Chemistry*, Verlag Chemie, Weinheim and New York, 1978.
4. D. R. Dalton, *The Alkaloids*, Marcel Dekker, Inc., New York and Basel, 1979.
5. *Comprehensive Carbanion Chemistry*, Volume II, E. Buncel and T. Durst, eds., Elsevier, 1984.
6. *Asymmetric Synthesis*, Volume 3, J. D. Morrison, ed., Academic Press, Inc., New York, 1984.

D. Books Covering Methods and Reagents

There are several useful books that are devoted to synthetic methods or to reagents used in organic reactions. *Organic Syntheses* is published by John Wiley & Sons, New York. It is a collection of procedures for the preparation of specific compounds. The work has appeared annually since 1921. The procedures for each 10-year period are collected in cumulative volumes, of which five now exist. The sixth cumulative volume is scheduled for publication in 1985. The procedures in *Organic Syntheses* are submitted by any chemist who wishes to do so and are then tested in the laboratory of a member of the Editorial Board. Although the methods given pertain to specific compounds, an attempt is made to include procedures that have general applicability. For this reason *Organic Syntheses* is a useful source of model procedures when the chemist wishes to carry out a new preparation. The cumulative volumes are each thoroughly indexed, and there is a collective index for the first five cumulative volumes.

Theilheimer, *Synthetic Methods of Organic Chemistry*, S. Karger Verlag, Basel, is an annual compilation of synthetic methods. It is organized by way of a system based upon types of bond formations or bond cleavages. There is an index with each volume and a cumulative index after each fifth volume.

Reagents for Organic Synthesis by L. F. Fieser and M. Fieser (Wiley, New York) is an exceedingly useful compendium of reagents and catalysts used in organic chemistry. In addition to the main volume, ten supplements are now available. The work gives information on how each reagent is prepared, commercial suppliers, and references to its uses.

33.3 Abstract Journals

Abstract journals are periodicals that publish short abstracts of articles that have appeared in the original research journals. There are currently two such publications devoted to the original chemical literature, *Chemical Abstracts* and *Referativnyl Zhurnal* (Russian). A German abstract journal, *Chemisches Zentralblatt*, ceased publication in 1970, but it is frequently useful for retrieving information published before that date.

Chemical Abstracts is published weekly by the American Chemical Society and includes abstracts in English of nearly every paper that contains chemical information, regardless of the original language. Abstracts appear from 3 to 12 months after the appearance of the original paper. The abstracts are grouped into 80 sections, of which sections 21–34 pertain to organic chemistry. Each individual abstract is preceded by the authors' names, the authors' address, the journal citation, and the language of the original article.

Although many chemists use *Chemical Abstracts* routinely to keep abreast of a broad area of chemistry, it is most useful because of its indices. From its beginning in 1907 until 1961 there were annual indices. Since 1962 there have been semiannual indices, covering the periods January–June and July–December. From 1907 until 1956 there were published additional 10-year indices. Since 1957 the cumulative indices have appeared at 5-year intervals. The most recent complete index is the *Tenth Collective Index*, covering the period 1977–1981. Each annual and collective index has a subject index and an author index. Formula indices for the periods 1920–1946, 1947–1956, 1957–1961, 1962–1966, 1967–1971, 1972–1976, and 1977–1981 are also available. The most useful of the indices is the formula index, which can be used to look up specific compounds. The subject index can be used to search for topics (such as "oxidation" or "kinetics") or for specific compounds by name. Although it is easier to search for a specific compound with the formula index, there is frequently merit in using the subject index. For example, the chemist may need information about derivatives of *o*-hydroxybenzoic acid in which there are additional substituents attached to the benzene ring. It would be virtually impossible to carry out such a search with the formula index.

To search *Chemical Abstracts* for information concerning a given compound, one looks up the formula of the compound in each of the collective indices and then in the semiannual indices that have appeared since the last collective index. Following each entry is an abstract number. The abstract numbers are used to locate the abstracts, and these are scanned. If it appears from an abstract that the original paper contains information of use, then this source is consulted.

For example, suppose we wish to know what has been published regarding the carcinogenic (tumor-producing) properties of the hydrocarbon benz[a]anthracene during the period 1967–1971.

benz[*a*]anthracene

Consulting the *Eighth Collective Index*, which covers the period, we find the listing

Benz[*a*]anthracene [56 –55 –3]

[*a*]

Following this listing, there are a number of indexed topics, in alphabetical order. A portion is shown.

bond length and heat of dissocn. of, **69**: 35282v
bond length in, **72**: 6380g
bond lengths and energy levels of, **75**: 5052b
bond order and localization energy of, in excited
   state, polarizability in relation to, **68**: 82565d
bromination of, mechanism of, **66**: 37049m
bud induction by, in tobacco callus culture, **74**:
   2887w
butoxyphenyl siloxanes contg., degradation of, **72**:
   133523f
carbonate dehydratase inhibition by, **67**: 115102k
carcinogenesis by, two –stage process in relation to,
   73: 33378q
carcinogenic activity of
   67: 98520a; **72**: 10910x
   activation energy of elec. conduction in relation
     to, **70**: 42062x
   mol. orbitals in relation to, **72**: 64737q
carcinogenic activity of hydrocarbons and, **72**:
   53064s
carcinogenic and menadione reductase –inducing
   activities of, **68**: 47948j
as carcinogen in human environment, **69**: 25669n
cell invasiveness in presence of, **68**: 103288h
cell protection against dimethylbenzanthracene by,
   aryl hydroxylase formation in, **71**: 122020t
cheese contamination with, from wax coating, **72**:
   109888h
chem. shifts of, mol. orbital calcn. in relation to, **73**:
   55252w

The number after each topic indicates the *Chemical Abstracts* volume number and abstract number where the information will be found. For example, the listing 67:98520a means that abstract 98520 in volume **67** contains information on the carcinogenic activity of benz[a]anthracene. Going to volume **67** of the abstracts (1967), we find the following abstract.

98520a   The carcinogenic activities in mice of compounds related to benz[a]anthracene.   E. Boyland and P. Sims (Roy. Cancer Hosp., London).   *Int. J. Cancer* 2(5), 500–4(1967)(Eng). The carcinogenic activities of 18 aromatic hydrocarbons and their metabolic intermediates were compared after 3–10 s.c. injections of 1 mg. into C57 black mice.   The monohydroxymethyl derivs. of 7,12-dimethylbenz[a]anthracene and some related compds. were active carcinogens, but were much less so than the parent hydrocarbon.   Epoxides formed at the 5,6-bond (K-region) of chrysene, benz[a]anthracene, 7-methylbenz[a]anthracene, and dibenz[a,h]anthracene produced tumors when given at high dose levels, but were not as active as the parent hydrocarbons.   The epoxide derived from phenanthrene was inactive. All of the compds. were prepd. by known methods with the exception of 7,12-dimethylbenz[a]anthracene, dibenz[a,h]anthracene, and chrysene which were obtained com. and 7-(diacetoxymethyl)benz[a]anthracene which was prepd. by heating benz[a]anthracene-7-carboxaldehyde under reflux with Ac₂O for 6 hrs. It sepd. from EtOH in needles, m. 196°.   CTJN

If we desire more complete information, we may consult the original article, which was published in the *International Journal of Cancer Research*, volume 2, on page 500, in 1967.

   In order to use *Chemical Abstracts* efficiently, it helps to have a good command of organic nomenclature. All compounds are listed as derivatives of a parent compound, for example,

$$CH_3\overset{\displaystyle Cl}{\underset{\displaystyle |}{C}}HCH_2CH_2COOH \quad \equiv \quad \text{valeric acid, 4-chloro}$$

$$\equiv \quad \text{2-cyclohexen-1-one, 3-chloro, 2-phenyl}$$

Note that *Chemical Abstracts* does not always use IUPAC nomenclature. At the beginning of each collective index, there is an extensive section dealing with the system of nomenclature used in indexing. In cases where it is not clear which name is used for indexing a particular compound, the formula index is useful. However, the formula index is much more tedious to use because one must often sift through an extensive list of isomers. However, because of the frequency with which the compilers of *Chemical Abstracts* have changed nomenclature systems in recent years, the formula index has become an indispensable aid in searching for more complex structures.

Beginning with the issuance of the volume indices covering the January–June 1972 period, the Subject Index has been issued in three parts: the Chemical Substance Index, the General Subject Index, and the Index Guide. All references to distinct, definable chemical substances are collected in the Chemical Substance Index, and all entries pertinent to any other topics (concepts, processes, organism names, diseases, reactions, generalized classes of compounds, and so on) are found in the General Subject Index. The Index Guide serves to guide the user quickly and efficiently to the proper headings in these two indices. The Index Guide can be used to find a Chemical Substance Index name for trivial, commercial, and other nonsystematically named substances. It represents a compilation of indexing cross-references, preferred index headings, synonyms, and general index notes on thousands of chemical terms and names and should be consulted before using either the Chemical Substance or General Subject Index. The Index Guide is supplemented annually to cover additions and changes that may occur within a volume indexing period.

33.4 *Beilstein*

Beilstein's *Handbuch der Organischen Chemie* is shelved in the reference section of most chemical libraries. There have been four editions of the work and the first three are obsolete. The fourth edition (*vierte Auflage*) consists of a main series (*das Hauptwerk*) and four supplementary series (*erstes, zweites, drittes* and *viertes Ergänzungswerk*). The periods covered by the various series are

Main series	antiquity–1909
First supplement	1910–1919
Second supplement	1920–1929
Third supplement	1930–1949 (incomplete)
Fourth supplement	1950–1959 (incomplete)

The main series consists of 27 volumes (*Bands*), each bound as a separate book. Each supplementary series also consists of 27 volumes, and entries in the supplements are cross-referenced to the main series. Volumes in the supplementary series are sometimes bound as more than one book, and in some cases two or more volumes are bound together.

Compounds are grouped into three major divisions, in the following manner.

Division	Volumes
Acyclishe reihe, Acyclic compounds	1–4
Isocyclishe reihe, Carbocyclic compounds	5–16
Heterocyclishe reihe, Heterocyclic compounds	17–27

There is a fourth minor division—carbohydrates, rubber-like compounds, and carotenoids—contained in volumes 30 and 31, which only appears with the main series. The contents of the various volumes are shown in Table 33.1. In addition, the table indicates which supplements had been completed at the end of 1983. Every conceivable compound can be assigned to a system number, whether or not the compound has been reported in the literature. If one knows the method that is used by the *Beilstein* staff to decide the system number of a given compound, then one can look up the substance in this manner. Unfortunately, the procedure used in assigning system numbers is suffi-

TABLE 33.1 Beilstein's *Handbuch der organischen chemie*

Volume	Contents	System Numbers	Complete through
1	acyclic hydrocarbons, alcohols, ketones	1–151	1959
2	acyclic carboxylic acids	152–194	1959
3	acyclic hydroxy acids, keto acids	195–322	1959
4	acyclic sulfinic acids, amines, phosphines	323–449	1959
5	cyclic hydrocarbons	450–498	1959
6	cyclic alcohols	499–608	1959
7	cyclic ketones	609–736	1959
8	cyclic hydroxy ketones	737–890	1959
9	cyclic acids	891–1050	1949[a]
10	cyclic hydroxy acids, keto acids	1051–1504	1949
11	cyclic sulfinic and sulfonic acids	1505–1591	1949
12	cyclic amines	1592–1739	1949
13	cyclic polyamines, amino alcohols	1740–1871	1949
14	cyclic amino ketones, amino acids	1872–1928	1949
15	cyclic hydroxylamines, hydrazines	1929–2084	1949
16	cyclic azo, phosphines, organometallics	2085–2358	1949
17	heterocyclic, 1 oxygen	2359–2503	1959
18	heterocyclic, 1 oxygen	2504–2665	1959
19	heterocyclic, 2–9 oxygens	2666–3031	1959
20	heterocyclic, 1 nitrogen	3032–3102	1959
21	heterocyclic, 1 nitrogen	3103–3241	1959
22	heterocyclic, 1 nitrogen	3242–3457	1959
23	heterocyclic, 2 nitrogens	3458–3554	1959
24	heterocyclic, 2 nitrogens	3555–3633	1959
25	heterocyclic, 2 nitrogens	3634–3793	1959
26	heterocyclic, 3–8 nitrogens	3794–4187	1959
27	heterocyclic, other ring systems	4188–4720	1929[b]

[a] System numbers 891–949 are complete through 1959.

[b] System numbers 4188–4190 are complete through 1959.

ciently involved that most chemists cannot readily use it. However, the system numbers are also employed for cross-referencing between the Supplements and the Main Series, and they are very useful for finding supplementary information about a given compound after it has been located in the Main Series (or *vice versa*).

Volumes 28 and 29 are a subject index (*Generalsachregister*) and a formula index (*Generalformelregister*), respectively. The most recent indices are part of the fourth supplement and they cover the main series and all four supplements, that is, through 1959. However, these cumulative indices are not available for all volumes (see Table 33.1). For volumes that are not covered by a cumulative index, one must use the cumulative indices published with the Second Supplement (through 1929) and the formula indices published at the end of each *book* (not Volume) of the Third Supplement (through 1949). One cannot rely completely on the indices, because only representative compounds are indexed. However, they are useful to obtain rapidly the approximate location of a compound in the handbook, particularly for heterocyclic compounds. The index listing gives the volume and page numbers where the compound will be found. Bold type indicates the volume number and normal type indicates the page number; supplementary series page numbers are preceded by the appropriate Roman numeral. For example, volume **28** of the second supplementary series contains the listing

Indol **20**, 304, I 121, II 196; **21** II 567.

Thus, we find indole listed on p. 304 in volume **20** of the main series, on p. 121 of volume **20** of the first supplementary series, and on p. 196 of volume **20** of the second supplementary series. The final entry refers to a correction, which appeared on p. 567, at the end of volume **21** of the second supplementary series. We find the same listing in volume **29** of the second supplementary series, which is the formula index, under C_8H_7N, the formula of indole.

Although the *Beilstein* indices are useful, one should become familiar with the basic organizational system of the handbook if it is to be used to best advantage. In each of the first two major divisions—acyclic compounds and carbocyclic compounds—compounds are listed according to the following order of basic classes.

1. Hydrocarbons (*Kohlenwasserstoffe*), RH.
2. Hydroxy compounds (*Oxyverbindungen*), ROH.
3. Carbonyl compounds (*Oxoverbindungen*), $R_2C\!=\!O$.
4. Carboxylic acids (*Carbonsäuren*), RCOOH.
5. Sulfinic acids (*Sulfinsäuren*), RSO_2H.
6. Sulfonic acids (*Sulfonsäuren*), RSO_3H.
7. Selenium acids (*Seleninsäuren* and *Selenosäuren*), $RSeO_2H$ and $RSeO_3H$.
8. Amines (*Amine*), RNH_2, R_2NH, R_3N.
9. Hydroxylamines (*Hydroxylamine*), RNHOH.
10. Hydrazines (*Hydrazine*), $RNHNH_2$.
11. Azo compounds (*Azo-Verbindungen*), $RN\!=\!NH$.

Following these basic classes, there are a further 27 rare classes, which we shall not list.

The handbook begins with acyclic hydrocarbons; the very first entry is methane, CH_4. After all of the derivatives of methane have been listed, one finds ethane, followed by its derivatives, and so on, through all the hydrocarbons having the empirical formula C_nH_{2n+2}. When all alkanes and their substitution derivatives have been listed, hydrocarbons with the formula C_nH_{2n} follow, beginning with ethylene (C_2H_4), and going on up in carbon number. Next are listed hydrocarbons with the formula

C_nH_{2n-2}. In this section we find alkynes and dienes; the first entry is acetylene, C_2H_2. The following group of compounds has the general formula C_nH_{2n-4}, then C_nH_{2n-6}, and so on. Thus, within a class of compounds, such as hydrocarbons, compounds are listed in order of increasing unsaturation. The general formula for the compounds listed on a given pair of pages is printed at the top of the left-hand page.

After all hydrocarbons and their derivatives have been listed, the hydroxy compounds are listed. In the acyclic division, the first hydroxy compound is methanol, CH_3OH, which has the empirical formula $C_nH_{2n+2}O$. Following the alcohols of this formula, one finds alcohols with the formula $C_nH_{2n}O$, and so on. When all mono alcohols have been listed, the diols are listed, beginning with the $C_nH_{2n+2}O_2$ compounds. Next come the triols, tetraols, and so on. When the alcohols have been exhausted, the aldehydes and ketones are listed, and so on down the list of classes of compounds.

Polyfunctional compounds are indexed *under the class that occurs last in the listing*. For example, hydroxycarboxylic acids are indexed under carboxylic acids, amino sulfonic acids under amines, and so on. When three or more of the basic functional groups are present, the same rule applies; a hydroxy amino acid will be found under the amines.

Following each compound in the handbook, one will find its derivatives. The derivatives are of three types and are listed in the following order.

1. FUNCTIONAL DERIVATIVES. These compounds are derivatives of the basic functional group and are hydrolyzable (in principle) to the parent compound. For example, dimethyl ether and methyl nitrate are both considered as functional derivatives of methyl alcohol and are indexed after it.

$$CH_3OCH_3 \xrightarrow{\text{H}_2\text{O}} 2\ CH_3OH$$

$$CH_3ONO_2 \xrightarrow{\text{H}_2\text{O}} CH_3OH + HNO_3$$

2. SUBSTITUTION DERIVATIVES. These are compounds in which a C—H has been replaced by C—X, C—NO, C—NO$_2$, or C—N$_3$. They are listed in the order

1. Halides
   (a) Fluorides, such as CH_3F.
   (b) Chlorides, such as CH_3Cl.
   (c) Bromides, such as CH_3Br.
   (d) Iodides, such as CH_3I.
2. Nitroso derivatives, such as CH_3NO.
3. Nitro derivatives, such as CH_3NO_2.
4. Azido derivatives, such as CH_3N_3.

When there is more than one of the same group attached to the basic compound, the polysubstituted compounds follow the monosubstituted compound. For example, the fluorinated methanes appear in the order CH_3F, CH_2F_2, CHF_3, CF_4. When two different substitution groups are present, the compound is listed under the group that occurs last in the foregoing list. Thus, fluorochloromethane, CH_2FCl, appears immediately after methyl chloride, CH_3Cl; in effect, CH_2FCl is considered as a substitution derivative of CH_3Cl. Likewise, chloronitromethane, $ClCH_2NO_2$, follows nitromethane in the listing. One must be careful not to confuse substitution derivatives with functional derivatives. For example, methyl hypochlorite, CH_3OCl, is listed with the functional derivatives of methyl alcohol because, in principle, it is hydrolyzable to methyl alcohol.

$$CH_3OCl \xrightarrow{\text{H}_2\text{O}} CH_3OH + HOCl$$

3. SULFUR AND SELENIUM COMPOUNDS. These compounds are listed as replacement derivatives under the corresponding oxygen compound. For example, methyl mercaptan, CH_3SH, and dimethyl selenide, $(CH_3)_2Se$, are listed last under the derivatives of methyl alcohol. Similarly, dithioacetic acid, CH_3CS_2H, is found among the final listings that follow acetic acid.

A similar organization is followed with the carbocyclic compounds. For heterocyclic compounds, the same scheme is used, but there is an additional division into *hetero numbers*. Most practicing chemists do not use the hetero numbers but, rather, rely on the subject or formula index to locate the parent heterocycle in the handbook. One must remember that many familiar compounds not normally thought of as heterocyclic compounds indeed are. For example, succinic anhydride will be found in the third division, as a dicarbonyl derivative of the heterocycle tetrahydrofuran.

tetrahydrofuran   succinic anhydride

PROBLEMS

1. Select recent issues of several chemical journals from the current periodicals shelf of your school library. Browse through them and note the form of full papers, notes (in those journals that publish them) and communications.

2. Look up the indicated information in each of the following secondary sources.
  (a) The boiling point and melting point of *p*-bromobenzonitrile in *The Handbook of Chemistry and Physics*.
  (b) The toxicity of nicotine in *The Merck Index*.
  (c) The method of preparation of 9-methylanthracene in *The Dictionary of Organic Compounds*.

3. (a) Find a review article on the Reformatsky reaction in *Organic Reactions*.
  (b) Examine a recent issue of *Chemical Reviews* and note the form of the articles and the type of subjects covered.

4. (a) Find a procedure for the preparation of cyclobutanecarboxylic acid in *Organic Syntheses*.
  (b) Find a leading literature reference to the use of manganese dioxide for the oxidation of allylic alcohols in *Reagents for Organic Synthesis*.

5. (a) Examine a current (unbound) issue of *Chemical Abstracts*. Scan the pages containing Sections 21–34 and note the form and content of the abstracts.
  (b) Using the most recent Author Index, see what papers have been published during that period by A. Streitwieser, Jr., C. H. Heathcock, and P. A. Bartlett.
  (c) Using the 1920–1946 Formula Index, look up 2-hydroxy-1-naphthoic acid.
  (d) Using the most recent Chemical Substance Index, see what sorts of derivatives of *o*-hydroxybenzoic acid are listed.

6. Locate Beilstein's *Handbuch der Organischen Chemie* in your school library. Update Table 33.1 by determining what system numbers have now been completed through 1959. Use the Cumulative Formula Index that is shelved with the Fourth Supplement to look up quinoline. What is its system number?

7. Look up the following compounds in Beilstein's *Handbuch der Organischen Chemie*. Record the melting point and/or boiling point, the system number, and the page number in the main series and each supplementary series where the compound is found.

(a)

(b)

(c)

(d) $ClCH_2CH_2CH_2OH$

(e) $-(CH_2)_{12}COOCH_3$

(f)

(g)

β-eudesmol

(h)

8. Do a complete literature search for each of the following compounds using *Beilstein* to cover the literature up to the time of the most recent *Beilstein* reference and the *Chemical Abstracts* formula indices to cover the literature since that time. Indicate where you looked (with time periods covered) and what references you found. If the original research journals are available in your library, scan the pertinent articles and record any physical constants (e.g., melting point, color, crystal form, spectra). List the references you find in one of the two formats discussed on page 1071, being careful to use the correct journal abbreviations as used by the American Chemical Society journals [see *Chemical Abstracts Service Source Index* (1907–1974 Cumulative)].

(a)

(b) $CH_2{=}CH{-}\overset{\overset{\displaystyle CH_3}{|}}{\underset{\underset{\displaystyle CH_3}{|}}{C}}{-}COCH_3$

(c) $CH_3CH_2CH_2CH_2CH_2\overset{\overset{\displaystyle N_3}{|}}{C}HCH_3$

(d)

Chapter 34

Special Topics

34.1 The Hammett Equation: An Example of a Linear Free Energy Relationship

One of the important areas of research in modern organic chemistry is the elucidation of reaction mechanisms. Because we cannot see the intermediate structures along the path from reactants to products, we must deduce the mechanism of a reaction from indirect evidence. Physical organic chemists make use of many tools in gathering evidence that can be used to draw inferences about the mechanisms of reactions. One of the most useful ideas is the concept that a given structural feature will affect related reactions in more or less the same way. For example, if replacement of a hydrogen by chlorine causes acetic acid to become a stronger acid, then it is reasonable that intro-duction of a chlorine at the α-position of propanoic acid will also result in enhanced acidity. A **linear free energy relationship** is simply a quantitation of this idea. In this section, we shall look briefly at the first and most important linear free energy relation-ship, the Hammett $\sigma\rho$ equation. Since the relationship is based on the acidities of aromatic carboxylic acids, we must first consider the effect of substituents on the acidity of benzoic acid.

A. Acidity of Substituted Benzoic Acids

Phenylacetic acid ($K_a = 4.9 \times 10^{-5}$ M, $pK_a = 4.31$) is somewhat more acidic than acetic acid ($K_a = 1.8 \times 10^{-5}$ M, $pK_a = 4.74$). The sp^2-hybrid carbons of the benzene ring are effectively more electronegative than sp^3-hybrid carbons. This electron-at-tracting effect of a phenyl group was noted earlier in the dipole moment of toluene (Section 20.4). The phenyl group behaves like a normal type of substituent in that the acid-strengthening effect is attenuated rapidly down an alkyl chain, as shown by the acidity data displayed in Table 34.1.

Extrapolating in the other direction, putting the benzene ring still closer to the COOH group, we would expect benzoic acid to be much stronger acid than acetic acid. Benzoic acid ($K_a = 6.3 \times 10^{-5}$ M, $pK_a = 4.20$) is somewhat stronger than acetic

TABLE 34.1 Acidity of Phenylalkanoic Acids

	K_a, M	pK_a
CH_3COOH	1.8×10^{-5}	4.74
C_6H_5COOH	6.3×10^{-5}	4.20
$C_6H_5CH_2COOH$	4.9×10^{-5}	4.31
$C_6H_5CH_2CH_2COOH$	2.2×10^{-5}	4.66
$C_6H_5CH_2CH_2CH_2COOH$	1.8×10^{-5}	4.76

acid, but the difference is much less than an extrapolation from Table 34.1 would suggest. The reason for the difference lies in the conjugation of the benzene ring with the carboxy group. This conjugation is less effective in the negatively charged carboxylate ion and renders the carboxy group effectively less acidic (compare α,β-unsaturated acids, Section 19.3.B).

Quantitative acidity measurements have been obtained for a variety of substituted benzoic acids because of the theoretical significance of aromatic chemistry and especially of the effect of structure on reactivity in these geometrically rigid and well-defined compounds. A number of the available pK_a measurements for *ortho*-, *meta*-, and *para*-substituted benzoic acids are summarized in Table 34.2 and compared with the corresponding substituted acetic acids.

Interesting comparisons may be made by plotting the pK_as of substituted benzoic acids against those of the corresponding acetic acids. Figure 34.1 shows such a plot for *meta*-substituted benzoic acids. A fair linear correlation is obtained, with a slope of about 0.2. That is, substituent effects in the acetic acid series are more pronounced than at the *meta* position of benzoic acid. This relative effect seems reasonable, since the substituent is closer to the carboxylate in the former case.

TABLE 34.2 Acidities of Substituted Benzoic and Acetic Acids

Substituent Y	pK_a at 25°C			
		Y—C_6H_4COOH		
	Y—CH_2COOH	*ortho*	*meta*	*para*
H	4.74	4.20	4.20	4.20
CH_3	4.87	3.91	4.27	4.38
C_2H_5	4.82	3.79	4.27	4.35
F	2.59	3.27	3.86	4.14
Cl	2.85	2.92	3.83	3.97
Br	2.90	2.85	3.81	3.97
I	3.18	2.86	3.85	4.02
CN	2.47	3.14	3.64	3.55
CF_3	3.06		3.77	3.66
HO	3.83	2.98	4.08	4.57
CH_3O	3.57	4.09	4.09	4.47
C_6H_5	4.31	3.46	4.14	4.21
NO_2		2.21	3.49	3.42

FIGURE 34.1 Comparison of acidities of *meta*-substituted benzoic acids with those of corresponding acetic acids.

We have seen previously (Sections 10.4 and 17.4.B) that inductive effects diminish dramatically with distance.

A similar plot of the pK_as of *para*-substituted benzoic acids (Figure 34.2) shows much more scatter. Indeed, the points seem to form no consistent pattern. Electronegative atoms such as the halogens do increase the acidity of both acids, but the oxygen atoms in hydroxy and alkoxy groups cause substantial *decreases* in the acidity of benzoic acid. Moreover, the strongly electron-attracting groups CN and CF$_3$ have a greater effect on the acidity of benzoic acid when they are in the *para* position than when they are in the *meta* position, even though the *para* position is one carbon farther removed from the carboxy group.

FIGURE 34.2 Comparison of acidities of *para*-substituted benzoic acids with those of corresponding substituted acetic acids.

Reason is restored when we recognize that the *para* position is directly conjugated with the reaction center, whereas the *meta* position is not. The pronounced acid-weakening effect of RO and HO groups can be interpreted on the basis of delocalization of nonbonding electron pairs into the ring, which stabilizes the acid.

Comparable delocalization in the conjugate base is less important because the carboxylate group would then bear a double negative charge.

Since the RO group stabilizes the acid more than it does the anion, *acidity is decreased*.

A similar analysis of the enhanced acid-strengthening effect of the electron-attracting groups is possible. For example, the benzene π-electrons are rather polarizable. That is, they can be displaced toward an electron-attracting group or away from an electron-repelling group. In *p*-cyanobenzoic acid, this polarization provides a mechanism for electrostatic stabilization of the anion form. Thus, ionization is facilitated.

In the *meta* isomer such polarization can also operate, but it is not as effective in stabilizing the carboxylate as it is in the *para*-substituted benzoic acid.

Ortho substituents present an additional complication. The steric hindrance provided by the close proximity of substituent and carboxy group prevents the carboxy group from achieving complete coplanarity with the benzene ring. That is, the carboxy group in these compounds is no longer as conjugated with the benzene ring, and the differential stabilization of the carboxylic acid relative to the carboxylate ion is lost. Consequently, all *ortho* substituents, including alkyl groups, cause an increase in the acidity of benzoic acid. Because steric effects are involved as well as electronic effects, there is no useful correlation with the acidities of other substituted acids.

> **EXERCISE 34.1** Using graph paper, plot the pK_as of the *meta*-substituted benzoic acids against the pK_as of the *meta*-substituted phenols (Table 26.1). Note that the points for the comparable *para* substituents generally fall off the *meta* correlation line.

B. The Hammett σρ Equation

Comparison of the acidities of substituted benzoic acids with substituted acetic acids has shown some important parallels but more important differences. We next inquire as to the effect of a substituent in other phenyl compounds compared with the effect in benzoic acid. For example, the acidities of some substituted phenylacetic acids are summarized in Table 34.3. Figure 34.3 shows a plot of these acidities compared with the corresponding benzoic acids.

The *meta* and *para* groups form an excellent linear correlation, but the *ortho* groups deviate substantially. The *meta* and *para* positions are sufficiently removed from the center of reaction that only electronic effects are important; the *ortho* position involves steric effects as well. The important conclusion to be drawn from Figure 34.3 is that in the *meta* and *para* positions the electronic effects of a substituent in one system are proportional to the effects in another. The slope of the line in Figure 34.3, 0.46, shows that a given substituent has only half the effect in modifying the acidity of phenylacetic acid that it has on benzoic acid.

This type of interrelationship has been demonstrated for a wide variety of reactions and equilibria and has been formulated as equation (34-1) by Professor L. P. Hammett. Equation (34-1) is now known as the Hammett equation.

$$\log K_i / K_H = \rho \sigma_i \tag{34-1}$$

In this equation, K_i is the equilibrium or rate constant given by substituent i, compared with that for the unsubstituted compound (substituent = H). The Greek letter sigma,

TABLE 34.3 Acidities of Substituted Phenylacetic Acids

| Substituent, Y | pK_a of Y—$C_6H_4CH_2COOH$ | | |
	ortho	meta	para
H	4.31	4.31	4.31
CH_3	4.35		4.37
F			4.25
Cl	4.07	4.14	4.19
Br	4.05		4.19
I	4.04	4.16	4.18
NO_2	4.00	3.97	3.85
CH_3O			4.36

1087

Sec. 34.1

*The Hammett
Equation: An
Example of a
Linear Free
Energy
Relationship*

FIGURE 34.3 Comparison of acidities of substituted phenylacetic acids with those of corresponding substituted benzoic acids.

σ_i, is a number characteristic of the substituent, whereas rho, ρ, is a number characteristic of the reaction. For the acidities of benzoic acids in water at 25°C, ρ is *defined* as unity; thus, σ_i-values are given directly as the pK_a difference, pK_a(benzoic acid) − pK_a(substituted benzoic acid). Table 34.4 (page 1088) summarizes σ-values for a number of *meta* and *para* substituents. A negative σ-value signifies an electron-donating group; a positive σ-value signifies an electron-attracting group. The larger the magnitude of σ, the greater is the effect of the substituent.

Figure 34.3 corresponds to a Hammett plot with $\rho = 0.46$. The magnitude of ρ indicates the sensitivity of a given equilibrium or reaction to a given substituent. A positive ρ-value signifies that the equilibrium or reaction is aided by electron-attracting substituents. For ionization of phenylacetic acids, the ρ of +0.46 indicates that a given electron-attracting substituent facilitates ionization but has only 0.46 of the effect that the same substituent has in facilitating ionization of benzoic acid.

As another example, the rates of hydrolysis of substituted methyl benzoates by hydroxide ion in aqueous acetone solution form a straight line when plotted against the Hammett σ-constants with a slope (ρ) of 2.23. This result means that substituent groups that facilitate ionization of benzoic acid also facilitate hydrolysis of methyl benzoate. Thus we conclude that the transition state for ester hydrolysis has substantial negative charge (positive ρ indicates stabilization by electron-attracting groups). This result is consistent with our view (Chapter 18) that ester hydrolysis proceeds through an anionic tetrahedral intermediate.

$$Ar-\overset{\overset{\displaystyle O}{\|}}{C}OCH_3 + OH^- \longrightarrow \left[Ar-\underset{\underset{\displaystyle OCH_3}{|}}{\overset{\overset{\displaystyle O^-}{|}}{C}}-OH \right] \longrightarrow ArCO_2^- + CH_3OH$$

Conversely, the reaction of substituted dimethylanilines with methyl iodide in aqueous acetone to give the trimethylanilinium iodide has $\rho = -3.30$. In this case electron-donating substituents help to stabilize the developing positive charge close to the ring and lead to a negative ρ-value.

TABLE 34.4 Hammett Substituent Constants, σ

Group	σ_m	σ_p
CH_3	−0.069	−0.170
$C(CH_3)_3$	−0.10	−0.197
C_6H_5	0.06	−0.01
CF_3	0.43	0.54
CN	0.56	0.660
$COCH_3$	0.376	0.502
NH_2	−0.16	−0.66
NO_2	0.710	0.778
OCH_3	0.115	−0.268
OH	0.121	−0.37
F	0.337	0.062
Cl	0.373	0.227
Br	0.391	0.232
I	0.352	0.18

$$Ar\!-\!N(CH_3)_2 + CH_3I \longrightarrow \left[Ar\!-\!{}^{+}\!\!\overset{\displaystyle CH_3}{\underset{\displaystyle CH_3}{N}}\cdots CH_3 \cdots I^- \right]^{\ddagger} \longrightarrow Ar\!-\!\overset{+}{N}(CH_3)_3 \quad I^-$$

S_N2 transition state

EXERCISE 34.2 Plot the pK_as of *meta*-substituted phenols from Table 26.1 versus the corresponding σ-values and determine ρ. Make a comparable plot for the pK_as of anilinium ions using the data of Table 23.5. Why does a given substituent have a greater effect on ionization of a phenol or an anilinium ion than it does on benzoic acid? Explain using resonance structures where desirable.

EXERCISE 34.3 The pK_as of *m*- and *p*-iodoxybenzoic acids in water at 25°C are 3.50 and 3.44, respectively. Calculate σ_m and σ_p for the iodoxy group, $-IO_2$. Give a rationalization of the approximate magnitude of these σ values on the basis of Lewis structures of the $-IO_2$ group compared to the nitro group.

EXERCISE 34.4 What is the sign of ρ expected for the following reaction?

$$ArCH_2NMe_2 + CH_3I \longrightarrow ArCH_2N(CH_3)_3{}^+ \, I^-$$

EXERCISE 34.5 Compare the expected magnitude of ρ for Exercise 34.4 with that for the following reaction.

$$ArCH_2CH_2NMe_2 + CH_3I \longrightarrow ArCH_2CH_2N(CH_3)_3{}^+ \, I^-$$

EXERCISE 34.6   What is the sign of ρ expected for the following reaction?

$$ArSO_2OCH_3 + C_2H_5O^- \longrightarrow ArSO_3^- + CH_3OC_2H_5$$

EXERCISE 34.7   The first-order rate constants for solvolysis of isopropyl esters of substituted benzenesulfonic acids in 50% aqueous ethanol at 25°C are

Substituent	$10^5 k$, sec^{-1}
H	2.50
p-CH$_3$	1.47
p-Br	7.30
m-NO$_2$	34.2
p-NO$_2$	44.4

Calculate ρ for this reaction and predict the solvolysis rate of isopropyl m-trifluoromethylbenzenesulfonate.

34.2 Transition Metal Organometallic Compounds

Transition metal organometallic chemistry has been an area of incredible growth over the past three decades. Many such compounds are particularly important as catalysts in industrial processes, and research continues for new and better catalysts. The subject is at the interface between organic and inorganic chemistry. In this section we can provide only bare essentials of an introduction to this large, growing, and important field of chemistry.

The transition metals have a partially filled d-orbital shell. The maximum number of electrons in a filled valence shell for an element in the fourth period of the periodic table (the potassium-krypton row) is

$$4s^2 4p^6 3d^{10} = 18$$

Thus there is a tendency for these elements to surround themselves with 18 electrons and achieve an "inert" rare gas electronic configuration, just as elements in the second and third periods strive to achieve an eight-electron configuration. We shall see that a great many transition metal organometallic compounds have structures in which the metal is associated with either 16 or 18 electrons and that many reactions can be rationalized in terms of filling out the inert electron configuration. This "16- or 18-electron rule" provides a useful framework within which to organize the reactions of such compounds.

First we must take up the question of how to "count" the electrons in transition metal organometallic compounds. The abbreviated periodic table in Figure 34.4 shows the elements of groups 1 and 2 and of the three transition series. The numbers at the top of each group correspond to the total number of electrons in the valence shell of an element in that group, regardless of whether the electrons reside in s-, p-, or d-orbitals in the atom itself. The transition elements within the colored box are those to which the 16- or 18-electron rule is most applicable, for reasons that we shall not discuss.

FIGURE 34.4 Periodic table of the elements, showing the number of electrons in the valence shell for each element in the three transition series. The elements within the colored box most often obey the 16-18-electron rule.

In general, electron counting in transition metal compounds works exactly as it does for Lewis structures of second and third period elements except that dative or "donor" bonds are more common with metal systems. Recall that in such a bond two electrons are provided by a suitable donor atom or group, the **ligand**. Both electrons "belong" to the ligand for the purpose of determining formal charges, but do contribute to establishing a rare gas configuration. Common ligands of this type are $H_2\overset{\times}{\underset{\times}{O}}$, $R_2\overset{\times}{\underset{\times}{O}}$, $R_3\overset{\times}{\underset{\times}{N}}$, $R_3\overset{\times}{\underset{\times}{P}}$, $:O{=}\overset{\times}{\underset{\times}{C}}$, in which the donor electron pair is indicated by small xs.

To illustrate the electron-counting procedure, consider the compound molybdenum hexacarbonyl. Six electrons come from the valence shell of the molybdenum atom (Figure 34.4). Each carbon monoxide ligand "donates" two more electrons. Thus the total electronic configuration about the molybdenum in $Mo(CO)_6$ is 18.

$$
\begin{array}{ll}
 & 6 \quad \text{electrons on MO} \\
6 \times 2 = 12 & \text{six CO ligands} \\
 & 18 \quad \text{total electrons}
\end{array}
$$

molybdenum hexacarbonyl
(18 electrons)

None of the 12 carbonyl electrons is counted as "belonging" to Mo; hence, Mo has only the six valence electrons of its own and is formally neutral. Note that these six electrons are not included in the symbolic representation. They would clutter up the diagram; rather, they are implied by the elemental symbol Mo.

A second example is methylmanganese pentacarbonyl. In this compound there are two types of bonds to the metal. The five carbon monoxide ligands each form a "donor" bond in the same manner as the ligands in $Mo(CO)_6$. However, the Mn—CH_3 bond may be viewed as a normal two-electron σ-bond, with one electron being contributed by carbon and one by manganese. Thus Mn has six valence electrons left that are not indicated in the structure—seven from a manganese atom (see Figure 34.4) minus one used in the bond to CH_3. The total electron count is arrived at as shown.

$$
\begin{array}{c}
O \\
C \\
\downarrow \\
OC \cdots \rightarrow Mn \xleftarrow{\cdots} CO \\
OC \nearrow \qquad \nwarrow CH_3 \\
\uparrow \\
C \\
O
\end{array}
$$

methylmanganese pentacarbonyl
(18 electrons)

7	electrons on Mn
-1	Mn electron used in the Mn—CH$_3$ bond
$5 \times 2 = 10$	five CO ligands
2	the Mn—CH$_3$ bonding pair
18	total electrons

In this compound the electrons ''belonging'' to Mn are the six Mn valence electrons, which are not used in bonding and are not shown on the structure, plus one-half of the electrons in the Mn—CH$_3$ σ-bond. Thus the metal is formally neutral.

Another kind of common ligand in transition metal organometallic compounds is the carbon-carbon multiple bond or π-bond of an alkene or alkyne. Accordingly, these groups usually are called π-donors to distinguish them from the σ-donors, the ligands discussed above with lone-pair electrons. The electron count works in the same way. For example, consider the following rhodium compound.

$$
\begin{array}{c}
H \\
Ph_3P \cdots \rightarrow | \quad CH_2 \\
Ph_3P \nearrow Rh \leftarrow \| \\
\uparrow \quad CH_2 \\
C \\
O
\end{array}
$$

9	electrons on Rh
-1	Rh electron used in the Rh—H bond
$2 \times 2 = 4$	two phosphine ligands
2	CO ligand
2	π-bond of ethylene
2	the Rh—H bonding pair
18	total electrons

Again, the formal charge on the metal is zero.

The bonding of ethylene to transition metals ranges from rather weak to quite strong. A strong bond could perhaps be represented as

$$
\begin{array}{c}
\qquad CH_2 \\
M \diagup \quad | \\
\qquad \diagdown CH_2
\end{array}
$$

It is easy to show that both representations give the same electron count.

In all of the examples discussed above the transition metal has achieved an 18-electron configuration and is said to be **coordinatively saturated**.

Transition metal organometallic compounds undergo a wide variety of reactions. Fortunately, almost all known reactions, including various steps in individual reaction mechanisms, can be grouped into five or six basic classes. We shall consider a few of these fundamental reaction types here.

1. Lewis Acid Association-Dissociation. An example is the reaction of tetrakis(triphenylphosphine)nickel with HCl.

$$
\begin{array}{c}
Ph_3P \cdots \rightarrow \quad \xleftarrow{\cdots} Ph_3P \\
Ph_3P \nearrow Ni \nwarrow Ph_3P
\end{array}
\quad + HCl \rightleftharpoons
\left[
\begin{array}{c}
Ph_3P \\
\downarrow \\
Ph_3P \cdots \rightarrow Ni \!-\! H \\
Ph_3P \nearrow \uparrow \\
Ph_3P
\end{array}
\right]^+ Cl^-
$$

(18 electrons) ⠀⠀⠀⠀⠀⠀⠀⠀⠀⠀⠀ (18 electrons)

The forward reaction is association of the metal with the Lewis acid H$^+$. The reverse reaction is dissociation of the Lewis acid from the metal. In Lewis acid association-dissociation the electron count of the metal is unchanged. Another example is the reaction of manganese pentacarbonyl anion with methyl bromide. The reaction may be viewed as a nucleophilic displacement of bromide ion from the alkyl bromide that proceeds by the S_N2 mechanism. However, it also corresponds to association of the manganese with the Lewis acid "CH_3^+."

$$\left[\begin{array}{c} CO \\ \downarrow \\ OC \rightsquigarrow Mn \leftarrow CO \\ \uparrow \\ CO \end{array}\right]^{-} + CH_3-Br \longrightarrow \begin{array}{c} CO \\ \downarrow \\ OC \rightsquigarrow Mn \leftarrow CO \\ \uparrow \quad \searrow CH_3 \\ CO \end{array} + Br^-$$

(18 electrons)   (18 electrons)

2. Lewis Base Association-Dissociation. This is the most common reaction in transition metal organometallic chemistry. An example is seen in the reaction of nickel tetracarbonyl with triphenylphosphine. The reaction mechanism consists of two steps. In the first, a CO ligand dissociates from the nickel, giving the intermediate nickel tricarbonyl. This species has an electron count of 16 and is **coordinatively unsaturated**. This electron-deficient intermediate reacts with triphenylphosphine by Lewis base association.

$$Ni(CO)_4 \longrightarrow Ni(CO)_3 + :CO$$
(18 electrons)   (16 electrons)

$$Ni(CO)_3 + :PPh_3 \longrightarrow Ph_3PNi(CO)_3$$
(16 electrons)   (18 electrons)

In Lewis base association-dissociation *the electron count of the metal changes by* ± 2.

3. Oxidative Addition-Reductive Elimination. Many transition metal organometallic reactions involve the addition of a σ-bond to the metal. An example is the reaction of hydrogen with bis(triphenylphosphine)chloroiridium carbonyl. In this complex, the iridium has a 16-electron configuration. It exists in the coordinatively unsaturated form because the triphenylphosphine ligands are so large. The complex reacts with hydrogen to form two new iridium-hydrogen bonds, giving the 18-electron complex shown. The reaction is called **oxidative addition** because the formal oxidation state of the metal changes from $+1$ to $+3$.

$$\begin{array}{c} Cl \rightsquigarrow \quad \leftarrow PPh_3 \\ \quad Ir \\ Ph_3P \nearrow \quad \searrow CO \end{array} + H_2 \longrightarrow \begin{array}{c} H \\ \downarrow \\ Cl \rightsquigarrow \quad \leftarrow PPh_3 \\ \quad Ir \\ Ph_3P \nearrow \uparrow \searrow H \\ CO \end{array}$$

(16 electrons)   (18 electrons)

The "oxidation state" of a metal in an organometallic compound may be defined in the following manner. Consider only the groups that are σ-bonded (H, R, Cl, CN, OH, etc.). The metal atom is considered to be more electropositive than any of these groups. Therefore it has a formal "oxidation number" of $+1$ for each such σ-bond. Donor ligands are ignored. The oxidation state of the metal is the sum of the oxidation numbers, minus one for each negative charge on the molecule and plus one for each positive charge on the complex. Some transition metal complexes contain more complex π-bonded ligands that cannot be treated in this simplified way, but they are beyond the scope of this introductory discussion.

The reverse of oxidative addition, dissociation of a hydrogen molecule with regeneration of the original iridium complex, is called **reductive elimination**. Note that the electron count of the metal changes by ± 2 in oxidative addition-reductive elimination.

4. Insertion-Deinsertion. Occasionally a donor ligand undergoes **insertion** into a σ-bond from the metal to another atom. In the process a donor bond and a σ-bond are traded for a new σ-bond. Thus the electron count of the metal decreases by two. In the reverse reaction the electron count increases by two. An example of insertion-deinsertion is the rearrangement of the 18-electron complex methylmanganese pentacarbonyl to the 16-electron complex acetylmanganese tetracarbonyl.

methylmanganese pentacarbonyl
(18 electrons)

acetylmanganese tetracarbonyl
(16 electrons)

Now let us briefly examine a few transition metal organometallic reactions and characterize them in terms of the foregoing fundamental transformations. Tris(triphenylphosphine)carbonylrhodium hydride is an effective catalyst for the hydrogenation of alkenes.

$$CH_2{=}CH_2 + H_2 \xrightarrow{\ (Ph_3P)_3RhHCO\ } CH_3CH_3$$

The reaction may be understood in terms of the following stepwise mechanism (for clarity of presentation, the triphenylphosphine ligands are symbolized by L).

(18 electrons)   (16 electrons)

(16 electrons)   (18 electrons)

(18 electrons)   (16 electrons)

(16 electrons)   (18 electrons)

(5) ⇌ + CH_3CH_3

(18 electrons)   (16 electrons)

The mechanism consists of the following sequence of processes.

1. Lewis base dissociation
2. Lewis base association
3. Insertion
4. Oxidative addition
5. Reductive elimination

The products of step 5 are the alkane molecule and the active catalyst, which recycles to step 2 and brings about the hydrogenation of another alkene molecule.

A related catalyst, tris(triphenylphosphine)rhodium chloride, also known as Wilkinson's catalyst, also brings about hydrogenation of alkenes by a mechanism similar to that just described.

tris(triphenylphosphine) rhodium chloride
(Wilkinson's catalyst)

Wilkinson's catalyst also functions to bring about **decarbonylation** of aldehydes.

The reaction mechanism may be formulated as proceeding through the following steps.

(1)

(16 electrons)   (18 electrons)

(2)

(18 electrons)   (16 electrons)

(3)

(16 electrons)   (18 electrons)

(4) $\rightleftharpoons$ + R—H

      (18 electrons)   (16 electrons)

(5) + L $\rightleftharpoons$

      (16 electrons)   (18 electrons)

(6) $\rightleftharpoons$ + CO

      (18 electrons)   (16 electrons)

Like the iridium complex shown on page 1092, Wilkinson's catalyst exists in a coordinatively unsaturated 16-electron state. It can therefore undergo oxidative addition (which changes the electron count of the metal by +2) without prior dissociation of a donor ligand. Thus, the steps are

1. Oxidative addition
2. Lewis base dissociation
3. Deinsertion
4. Reductive elimination
5. Lewis base association
6. Lewis base dissociation

This mechanism is probably a little oversimplified, since there is evidence that free radical pairs may be involved in step 3. Nevertheless, the gross features are no doubt correct.

The simple structural ideas and mechanistic classifications we have introduced are but first steps toward a complete understanding of the rich chemistry of these fascinating compounds.

EXERCISE 34.8 (a) Some transition metals form neutral complexes with carbon monoxide (metal carbonyls); for example, see nickel carbonyl on page 1092. Chromium and iron also form stable carbonyls. Write the expected structures of these compounds.
(b) Other transition metals form stable metal carbonyl anions of the type $M(CO)_n^-$. Write the expected structures of the manganese and cobalt carbonyl anions and explain their stability.

EXERCISE 34.9 The rate of exchange of triphenylphosphine for carbon monoxide in nickel carbonyl is inversely proportional to the pressure of carbon monoxide in contact with the reaction solution

$$Ni(CO)_4 + Ph_3P \longrightarrow Ph_3PNi(CO)_3 + CO$$

Explain.

EXERCISE 34.10 Hydroformylation of alkenes (the "oxo reaction") is an important industrial process. For example, ethylene reacts with hydrogen and carbon monoxide in the presence of hydridocobalt tetracarbonyl to give propionaldehyde.

$$CH_2=CH_2 + CO + H_2 \xrightarrow[100-120°C]{HCo(CO)_4} CH_3CH_2CHO$$

(72%)

Propose a mechanism which is consistent with the "16- or 18-electron rule." Classify each step in your mechanism by reaction type (i.e., Lewis acid association, insertion, etc.).

EXERCISE 34.11 Write a plausible mechanism for the hydrogenation of ethylene with Wilkinson's catalyst. Wilkinson's catalyst also brings about the decarbonylation of acyl halides.

$$CH_3CH_2CH_2CH_2\overset{\overset{O}{\|}}{C}Cl \xrightarrow{(Ph_3P)_3RhCl} CH_3CH_2CH_2CH_2Cl + CO$$

Propose a mechanism for this reaction.

34.3 Organic Coloring Matters

A. Color

As discussed in Section 21.6, all compounds can be excited electronically by electromagnetic radiation. For most organic compounds such transitions are in the ultraviolet region of the spectrum, and such compounds are white and colorless. However, when an electronic transition is in the visible range (about 400-750 nm), the compound will appear to us as colored. The colors perceived for different wavelengths of light are summarized in Table 34.5.

Light of a given wavelength is perceived as the indicated color. However, if that wavelength is *absorbed*, we perceive the complementary color. Some compounds appear to have a yellow color even though their λ_{max} are all in the ultraviolet region. In such cases a "tail" of an absorption band stretches into the visible. Since the light absorbed is violet or blue, we see the compound as the complementary color of yellow.

TABLE 34.5 Color and Wavelength

Wavelength of light, nm	Color	Complementary color
400–430	violet	green-yellow
430–480	blue	yellow
480–490	green-blue	orange
490–510	blue-green	red
510–530	green	purple
530–570	yellow-green	violet
570–580	yellow	blue
580–600	orange	green-blue
600–680	red	blue-green
680–750	purple	green

Intensely colored materials have absorptions in the visible region. For organic compounds, such electronic absorptions are generally $\pi \to \pi^*$ or $n \to \pi^*$ transitions and involve extended π-electronic systems. That is, color in organic compounds is generally a property of π-structure. If the absorption band is narrow or sharp, the color will appear to us as bright or brilliant and clean. A broad absorption band, or more than one band in the visible region, gives colors that we perceive as dull or "muddy."

B. Natural Coloring Matters

A large number of naturally occurring organic compounds are brightly colored. Some find a role in nature because of their color. Examples are the colors of flowers to attract bees and the camouflage of some insects and animals. Not all colors in nature are due to chemicals. Some colors depend on architectural design to produce color by diffraction of light. Examples are the blue feathers of the bluejay and the colors of hummingbirds, peacocks, and some butterflies and beetles. More often, however, specific organic compounds are involved. A few of the important classes of compounds with representative examples will be summarized here.

Anthocyanins provide much of the color of the plant world. They are responsible for the red color of buds and young shoots and for the purple of autumn leaves as the green chlorophyll decomposes with the approach of winter. Their colors depend in part on the pH of their environment. For example, the blue cornflower and red rose have the same anthocyanin, cyanin. The blue color is that of the potassium salt. Anthocyanins are actually present as glycosides. Hydrolysis gives the corresponding anthocyanidins; that is, anthocyanidins are the aglycones of anthocyanins.

Only three anthocyanidins are important: cyanidin (crimson to blue-red flowers, cherries, cranberries), pelargonidin (pelargonium, geranium), and delphinidin (delphinium, pansy, grape). These compounds have the following structures.

cyanidin

pelargonidin

delphinidin

These pyrylium salts (Section 31.9) are generally considered as derivatives of a parent structure, flavone, a nucleus that is widespread in nature.

flavone

In the corresponding glycosides, the sugar units are attached at the 3- and 5-positions.

Carotenoids are also widespread in nature from bacteria and fungi to vegetable and animal life. Examples are β-carotene, which is a precursor for vitamin A, and lycopene, which occurs in tomatoes and ripe fruit.

β-carotene

lycopene

The color of these hydrocarbons clearly comes from $\pi \rightarrow \pi^*$ transitions of the long conjugated system. Note that these compounds are terpenes (Section 34.7). Carotenoids also occur in marine biology, for example, in the skins of fish, sea stars, anemones, corals, and crustaceans, frequently in combination with proteins. Denaturation of the protein in boiling water frees the carotenoid and unmasks its color as in the red color of boiled lobster.

Naphthoquinones and **anthraquinones** also occur in both animal and vegetable worlds. Some examples were given in Section 26.8.A. Echinochrome is a polyhydroxynaphthoquinone that occurs as a red pigment in the sea urchin and sand dollar.

echinochrome

Cochineal is a dried female insect, *Coccus cacti* L., used for a red coloring in food products, cosmetics, and pigments. The principal constituent is carminic acid, a polyhydroxyanthraquinone attached to glucose.

Melanins are complex quinoidal compounds derived from the oxidation and polymerization of tyrosine. Melanins occur in such varied places as feathers, hair, eyes, and the ink of cephalopods. They occur in the skin of all humans, except albinos, and are responsible for the varied skin coloration among the races of man. Albinos and certain white animals lack an enzyme required to convert tyrosine.

Other types of natural pigments include the **ommochromes** (xanthommatin, a yellow pigment from insect eyes), **pterins** (xanthopterin, yellow pigment in butterfly wings), **porphyrins** (hemin, page 963; chlorophyll), and **indigoids** (indigotin or indigo; occurs as glucoside in many plants; used as a blue dye; see next section).

xanthommatin

xanthopterin

chlorophyll a

C. Dyes and Dyeing

Dyes are coloring matters that will bind in some manner to a substrate, usually a fiber or cloth, and are fast to light and to washing. Dyes have been known to man for thousands of years. Early dyes were entirely of natural origin, but common dyes in use today are almost all synthetic. Different methods were and still are used for combining the dye with the fiber. Some of the principal categories follow.

Vat dyes are exemplified by indigo, a highly insoluble blue compound known to the ancient world. It is also the *woad* of ancient Britain. A warm suspension of indigo with other materials was allowed to ferment for several days. This process produced a reduced and soluble "leuco" compound that is colorless. The material to be dyed was immersed in this solution and then exposed to air to reoxidize the leuco base. Indigo is now produced synthetically and is reduced to the leuco form with sodium hydrosulfite. It can be oxidized by exposure to air or more quickly by use of an oxidizing agent such as sodium perborate. The insoluble blue pigment so produced is "locked" within the fiber.

indigotin
indigo

leuco form

Mordant dyes are used in conjunction with a mordant (L. *mordere*, to bite), usually a metal salt that forms an insoluble complex or "lake" with the dye. The dye is applied to fiber or cloth that has been pretreated with a metal salt. An example known to the ancient world was the extract of the madder root, which was mordanted with aluminum salts to produce a color known as turkey red. Other metal salts give different colors. The actual dye that coordinates with the metal is alizarin. Alizarin was first synthesized in 1869, and shortly thereafter synthetically manufactured material drove the natural product from the market with important economic repercussions.

alizarin mordanted with Al^{3+}

Direct dyes can be applied to the fiber directly from an aqueous solution. This process is especially applicable to wool and silk. These fibers are proteins that incorporate both acidic and basic groups that can combine with basic and acid dyes, respectively. An example is mauve, the dye that started the modern synthetic dyestuff industry but is no longer used.

William Henry Perkin was a student at the Royal College of Chemistry when, in 1856 in his home laboratory, at the age of 18, he treated aniline sulfate with sodium dichromate and obtained a black precipitate from which he extracted a purple compound. This material showed promise as a dye and he resigned his position to manufacture it. The product was successful and cloth dyed with mauve was even worn by Queen Victoria. Not long afterward, additional synthetic dyes were synthesized by German chemists and the synthetic dyestuff industry gradually became a German industry. By the time of World War I, almost all of the world production of synthetic dyes was German.

Perkin's success in the discovery of mauve was based on the fact that his "aniline" was impure. It was prepared by nitrating and reducing "benzene" that contained substantial amounts of toluene!

mauve

Mauve is an example of a basic dye that can ion-pair with acidic centers of the fiber. An example of a direct acid dye is benzopurpurin 4B, whose sulfonate ion groups can pair with cationic centers in the fiber.

benzopurpurin 4B

Disperse dyes are used as aqueous dispersions of finely divided dyes or colloidal suspensions that form solid solutions of the dye within the fiber. They are especially useful for polyester synthetic fibers. These fibers have no acidic or basic groups for use with direct dyes and are sensitive to hydrolysis in the strongly alkaline conditions of vat dyeing. Disperse dyes tend to have important limitations. They frequently lack fastness to washing, tend to sublime out on ironing, and are subject to fading with NO_2 or ozone in the atmosphere, a condition known as *gas fading*.

Dyes are also classified on the basis of chemical structure. These structures frequently contain a functional group that is principally involved in the $n \rightarrow \pi^*$ and $\pi \rightarrow \pi^*$ transitions that give rise to the color. Examples of such groups, called **chromophores**, are the azo group, —N=N—, the carbonyl groups in quinones, and extended chains of conjugation. Some of the principal chemical classes of dyes follow.

Azo dyes form the largest chemical class of dyestuffs. These dyes number in the thousands. They consist of a diazotized amine coupled to an amine or a phenol and have one or more azo linkages. An example of a diazo dye, a dye with two azo groups, is direct blue 2B, prepared by coupling tetrazotized benzidine with H-acid (8-amino-1-naphthol-3,6-disulfonic acid) in alkaline solution. If H-acid is coupled with a diazonium ion in dilute acid solution, reaction occurs next to the amino group. Both positions can be coupled to different diazonium salts.

direct blue 2B

couples here in base → ← couples here in acid

H-acid

Triphenylmethane dyes are derivatives of triphenylmethyl cation. They are basic dyes for wool or silk or for suitably mordanted cotton. Malachite green is a typical example that is prepared by condensing benzaldehyde with dimethylaniline and oxidizing the intermediate leuco base.

leuco base

malachite green

Anthraquinone dyes are generally vat dyes as exemplified by alizarin. More complex examples are higher molecular weight compounds prepared by oxidizing anthraquinone derivatives under basic conditions.

2-aminoanthraquinone

indanthrone
indanthrene blue R

Indigoid dyes are also vat dyes, as represented by indigo itself. A dibromoindigo has historical interest as the Tyrian purple of the ancient world. This dye was laboriously isolated from a family of mollusks (*Murex*). Its use was restricted to the wealthy. It is now a relatively inexpensive dye that still finds some use.

Tyrian purple
6,6′-dibromoindigo

Azine dyes are derivatives of phenoxazine, phenothiazine, or phenazine. Mauve and aniline black (pages 711–12) are derivatives of phenazine. Methylene blue is a thiazine derivative used as a bacteriological stain.

methylene blue

Phthalocyanines are used as pigments rather than dyes. An important member of this class is copper phthalocyanine, a brilliant blue pigment that can be prepared by heating phthalonitrile with copper.

copper phthalocyanine

EXERCISE 34.12 The first azo dye found to have a direct affinity for cotton is prepared from tetrazotized benzidine and 4-aminonaphthalene-1-sulfonic acid (naphthionic acid). What is its structure? The dye has λ_{max} = 497 nm but has two bands in mineral acid solution, λ_{max} = 647 and 590 nm. What are the colors of the dye in neutral and acidic solutions?

EXERCISE 34.13 Naphthol Blue Black B is prepared by coupling H-acid with diazotized aniline in basic solution and diazotized *p*-nitroaniline in acidic solution. What is the structure of this dye?

EXERCISE 34.14   Write a reasonable mechanism for the preparation of the leuco base of malachite green.

34.4 Photochemistry

A. Electronically Excited States

Most organic molecules have an even number of electrons with all electrons paired. Within each pair, the opposing electron spins cancel, and the molecule has no net electronic spin. Such an electronic structure is called a **singlet** state. When a ground-state singlet absorbs a photon of sufficient energy, it is converted to an excited singlet state. The process is a **vertical transition**; that is, electronic excitation is so fast that the excited state has the same geometry of bond distances and bond angles as the ground state. The most stable geometry of the excited state often differs from that of the ground state with the result that the excited electronic state is often formed in an excited vibrational state as well. These relationships are illustrated in Figure 34.5. A vertical transition of the type illustrated is also known as a **Franck-Condon** transition.

Figure 34.5 is simplified in showing energy levels as a function of a single bond coordinate. For real molecules, there are many bonds and the resulting pattern of energy levels is multidimensional and complex. Furthermore, there are many excited singlet states, which may be represented collectively as S_i. The lowest excited singlet state is then represented as S_1.

The first formed excited state generally gives up its extra vibrational energy to other bonds in the molecule and falls to the lowest vibrational level of this state. The time required for this process is very short, about 10^{-13} sec, the time required for a single vibration. In the next step, this electronic excited state gives up more energy to other vibrational modes in the molecule or in collisions with solvent and becomes an excited vibrational level of the lowest excited state, S_1. This excited vibrational state again gives up vibrational energy until it reaches the lowest vibrational level of S_1. The change from S_i to S_1 is called **internal conversion** and takes about 10^{-11} sec, or about 10^2 vibrations. Often, the first formed excited state is S_1, particularly when other excited states are much higher in energy.

The lifetime of the S_1 state in its lowest vibrational level is longer, about 10^{-8} to 10^{-7} sec. During this time one of four possibilities can occur. These alternatives are discussed below with the help of a Jablonski diagram (Figure 34.6, page 1106).

1. S_1 can emit a photon and undergo an electronic transition to the ground state, a process called **fluorescence**. Because the excited state has lost energy before fluorescence occurs, the fluorescence photon has less energy than the originally exciting photon. Fluorescent light has longer wavelength than the light required for the original excitation.

2. S_1 can give up energy to other vibrations or to solvent and become an excited vibrational state of the ground state, S_0. This is an internal conversion and is a nonradiative process. The excited vibrational level again gives energy to its environment until it achieves an equilibrium distribution with the lowest vibrational level. The net result of all of these changes is the conversion of the original light quantum into heat.

3. S_1 can undergo internal conversion to an excited vibrational level of the ground state of a different compound, an isomer whose lowest vibrational level of S_0 corresponds to a different geometry than our starting material. Alternatively, S_1 can react on

FIGURE 34.5 Vertical or Franck-Condon electronic transition.

collision with another molecule. In either case, we have achieved a photochemical reaction.

4. S_1 can undergo **intersystem crossing** to the triplet state, T_1. A triplet state is one in which one electron spin has been changed so that the molecule has two electrons that cannot pair. The lowest triplet state is usually of higher energy than the ground state (the rare exceptions are compounds with "ground-state triplets"). Nevertheless, T_1 is of lower energy than S_1. Electrons with the same spin tend to stay apart because of the Pauli principle. As a result, the electrostatic energy of electronic repulsion is less than in comparable singlet states.

In many compounds, the switching of an electronic spin is an improbable process, and triplet states are not important in the photochemistry of such compounds. In certain other compounds, particularly $\pi \rightarrow \pi^*$ states of polycyclic aromatic hydrocarbons and $n \rightarrow \pi^*$ states of many ketones, the process of intersystem crossing is more probable. The process can take as little as 10^{-9} sec. Since the lifetime of S_1 is generally in the range of 10^{-7} to 10^{-8} sec, in such cases almost all of the excited states intersystem cross to T_1.

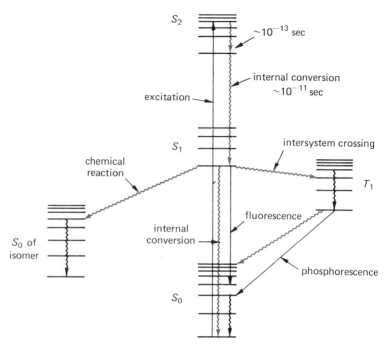

FIGURE 34.6 Jablonski diagram. Nonradiative processes are shown as wavy lines.

Triplet states are fairly long-lived, with lifetimes of greater than 10^{-5} sec, and in some cases up to a second or so. One reason for such long lifetimes is that conversion to S_0 again requires switching an electronic spin. The rate at which intersystem crossing takes place depends in large part on the energy difference between the two states. The energy difference between S_1 and T_1 is generally much less than between T_1 and S_0; hence, the latter intersystem crossing is much less probable.

Triplet states themselves have four possible ways for shedding their excess energy.

1. T_1 can thermally decay to S_0. The net result in this case is again the conversion of a light quantum to heat.

2. T_1 can emit a photon. This process is called **phosphorescence**. As in the case of fluorescence, the wavelength of the phosphorescent light is longer than that of the initially exciting light. Phosphorescence is a low-probability event because of the change in electron spin required. It is generally observed only at low temperature for which thermal events have been slowed.

3. T_1 can convert to T_1 of an isomeric molecule or it can intersystem cross to S_0 of an isomer. Either process results in a photochemical isomerization. Alternatively, T_1 can react on collision with another molecule to provide a photochemical reaction.

4. T_1 can transfer its electronic spin to another molecule and become converted to S_0. This process is called *triplet energy transfer* and is symbolized as

$$T_1 + S_0' \longrightarrow S_0 + T_1'$$

This reaction is actually an equilibrium governed by the usual free energy requirements, but it is usually important only when the reaction shown is exothermic.

B. Photochemical Reactions

Some photochemical reactions involve simple isomerizations. An example is the cis-trans interconversion of alkenes. In this case the excited state involves a twisted double bond (an example is Figure 11.5), and conversion to the ground state has an equal probability of going cis and trans. If a wavelength of light can be chosen at which the trans isomer absorbs and the cis does not, a trans isomer can be converted completely to the cis. In other cases a photochemical *stationary state* is achieved.

trans-stilbene   *cis*-stilbene

The breaking of bonds is a common photochemical reaction. We saw an early example in the dissociation of chlorine to initiate free radical chain reactions (Section 6.3). This reaction is also common for ketones and is called a **Norrish type I** reaction.

$$CH_3COCH_3 \xrightarrow{h\nu} CH_3CO\cdot + CH_3\cdot$$
$$CH_3CO\cdot \longrightarrow CH_3\cdot + CO$$
$$2\,CH_3\cdot \longrightarrow CH_3CH_3$$

For cyclic ketones, the photochemical product is a **diradical** that can undergo further reactions.

Another reaction that ketones can undergo involves intramolecular hydrogen atom transfer via a six-membered-ring transition state to form another diradical. This reaction is called a **Norrish type II** process.

Note the use of an asterisk to indicate an excited *state*. We have previously used this symbol to refer to an antibonding orbital. The asterisk symbolism is used commonly in both contexts.

α,β-Unsaturated carbonyl compounds can undergo photochemical dimerization with the formation of a four-membered ring.

The formation of four-membered rings is also common with dienes.

1,3-cycloheptadiene   bicyclo[3.2.0]hept-6-ene

norbornadiene   quadricyclene
bicyclo[2.2.1]-   tetracyclo[2.2.1.0^{2,6},0^{3,5}]-
hepta-2,5-diene   heptane

Quadricyclene is an unusual hydrocarbon whose trivial name derives from its tetracyclic nature. The compound is considered to be tetracyclic because four carbon-carbon bonds must be broken to obtain an acyclic system. Note how the systematic name is derived from that of the bicyclic parent, bicyclo[2.2.1]heptane. The two additional bridges are both "zero-carbon" bridges, and join C-2 to C-6 and C-3 to C-5, respectively. These additional bridges are included within the bracket that specifies the nature of the cyclic skeleton as the locants 0^{2,6} and 0^{3,5}. This last reaction is a slow process and the compound is formed in low yield. Most of the light quanta absorbed end up as heat, and the **quantum yield** is low. The quantum yield is defined as the number of product molecules divided by the number of light quanta absorbed.

This reaction becomes much more efficient by triplet energy transfer.

(95%)

Norbornadiene is transparent to light of 313 nm wavelength. The ketone, however, absorbs this light in an $n \rightarrow \pi^*$ transition. Intersystem crossing occurs readily to T_1 of the ketone. On colliding with a molecule of norbornadiene, the ketone T_1 gives up its triplet character and is converted back to the ground state. Norbornadiene is converted to its T_1, which undergoes the changes in geometry required to intersystem cross to the ground state of quadricyclene. In this example, the acetophenone functions as a **triplet sensitizer**.

Sensitizers work in the same fashion in photography. The direct photoexcitation of a grain of silver bromide by light (page 831) is an inefficient process and long exposure times would be required. In modern photography, a light photon first excites a dye molecule and its excited state transfers its excitation energy to a silver bromide grain that is then developed as usual. The dye functions as the sensitizer.

The foregoing reactions have as the net result a [2 + 2] cycloaddition, a reaction that is generally not observed as a ground state concerted reaction because of the violation of the Hückel $4n + 2$ rule. The ground state rules for pericyclic reactions are frequently violated in photochemical processes.

Some photochemical reactions involve rather deep-seated rearrangements.

This reaction can be rationalized by the following bond-switching process in the excited state.

Mercury vapor is often used as a photosensitizer.

$$Hg \xrightarrow[\text{(253.7 nm)}]{h\nu} Hg^*$$

$$Hg^* + A \longrightarrow Hg + A^*$$

Small amounts of mercury vapor suffice to make the following reactions preparatively useful.

bicyclo[2.1.1]hexane

tricyclo[3.3.0.0^{2,6}]octane

> **EXERCISE 34.15** For the Norrish type I reaction of 2,2-dimethylcyclohexanone shown on page 1107 show how each of the products is produced.

> **EXERCISE 34.16** Heating (*E,Z*)-cyclonona-1,3-diene gives one stereoisomer of bicyclo[5.2.0]nona-8-ene and photolysis gives the other. Explain.

34.5 Polymer Chemistry

Polymers are large molecules that are generally built up from much smaller units or **monomers**. The *degree of polymerization* refers to the average number of monomer units per polymer molecule. We have encountered polymers frequently in our study of organic chemistry. Especially important are such natural polymers as polysaccharides (Section 28.8) and polypeptides and proteins (Section 29.7). Synthetic polymers have become important components of modern industrial society as vital *materials* of various kinds. These materials may be characterized by their behavior on heating. At high temperatures a polymer is often a viscous liquid in which molecular chains have some mobility relative to each other. At lower temperatures some regions within the polymer (crystallites) may have the regular structure characteristic of crystals. The corresponding phase transition is called the *crystalline melting point*. Alternatively, the polymer may be amorphous, a vitrious or glassy solid at low temperatures in which molecular chains or coils are effectively frozen but not in a regular pattern. Such a phase is characterized by a temperature range referred to as the *glass transition temperature*, T_g.

Synthetic polymers are also catagorized by the type of polymerization reaction used. **Addition** polymers often involve the conversion of multiple bonds in monomers to bonds between the monomer units. Important examples are the polymerization of alkenes and dienes and can involve carbocation, free radical, and carbanion or organometallic intermediates. **Condensation** polymers result from a reaction of monomer units usually accompanied by loss of a small molecule such as water or an alcohol. Examples are the polyesters and polyamides derived from reaction of dicarboxylic acids or esters with diols and diamines, respectively.

A. Carbocation Polymerization of Alkenes

In the case of alkenes, polymerization amounts merely to the exchange of π-bonds for σ-bonds and is thermodynamically feasible. Cationic polymerization is not generally a practical method for preparing useful polymers. The process is used for the dimerization and trimerization of certain alkenes and provides an excellent demonstration of the ways in which monomer units combine to give larger molecules.

As mentioned in Section 11.6.C, isobutylene is absorbed and hydrated by 60-65% aqueous sulfuric acid. Under more vigorous conditions (50% H_2SO_4 at 100°C), the intermediate carbocation can react with alkene to form a new tertiary carbocation. Deprotonation of this new carbocation gives a mixture of alkenes known as ''diisobutylenes.''

$$(CH_3)_3C^+ + (CH_3)_2C{=}CH_2 \xrightarrow{\text{slow}} (CH_3)_3C{-}CH_2{-}\overset{+}{C}(CH_3)_2 \xrightarrow{-H^+}$$

$$(CH_3)_3CCH{=}C(CH_3)_2 + (CH_3)_3CCH_2\overset{\overset{\displaystyle CH_3}{|}}{C}{=}CH_2$$

(20%)　　　　　　　　　　　　(80%)

"diisobutylenes"

Catalytic hydrogenation of this mixture gives 2,2,4-trimethylpentane, the so-called "isooctane" used as a standard for octane ratings of gasolines (Section 6.2). Under still more vigorous conditions isobutylene reacts with sulfuric acid to produce a mixture of trimeric alkenes, "triisobutylenes."

$$3\,(CH_3)_2C{=}CH_2 \xrightarrow{H_2SO_4} CH_3\overset{\overset{\displaystyle CH_3}{|}}{\underset{\underset{\displaystyle CH_3}{|}}{C}}CH_2\overset{\overset{\displaystyle CH_3}{|}}{\underset{\underset{\displaystyle CH_3}{|}}{C}}CH_2\overset{\overset{\displaystyle CH_3}{|}}{C}{=}CH_2 + CH_3\overset{\overset{\displaystyle CH_3}{|}}{\underset{\underset{\displaystyle CH_3}{|}}{C}}CH_2\overset{\overset{\displaystyle CH_3}{|}}{\underset{\underset{\displaystyle CH_3}{|}}{C}}CH{=}\overset{\overset{\displaystyle CH_3}{|}}{C}CH_3$$

"triisobutylenes"

Higher polymers and undesirable tars generally result from the reaction of other alkenes with strong hot acid.

In the absence of suitable alternative nucleophilic compounds to react with the carbocation intermediates, reaction with alkene is the only reaction mode possible. Reaction of isobutylene with a small amount of boron trifluoride occurs at low temperature to produce a high molecular weight polymer.

$$n\,(CH_3)_2C{=}CH_2 \xrightarrow[-200^\circ C]{BF_3} H{-}\left(CH_2{-}\overset{\overset{\displaystyle CH_3}{|}}{\underset{\underset{\displaystyle CH_3}{|}}{C}}\right)_{n-1}{-}CH_2\overset{\overset{\displaystyle CH_3}{|}}{\underset{\underset{\displaystyle CH_2}{||}}{C}}$$

(n = a large number)

Boron trifluoride does not react with alkenes in the rigorous absence of moisture. With traces of water, carbocations are produced. With isobutylene, for example, the intermediate salt, $(CH_3)_3C^+ {}^-BF_3OH$, is produced in low concentration. The anion $^-BF_3OH$ has low nucleophilicity, and the t-butyl cation is free to react with isobutylene to start the cationic polymerization.

In some cases the carbocation will abstract a tertiary hydrogen from an alkane. A reaction of this type is used to produce "isooctane" directly from isobutylene and isobutane.

$$(CH_3)_3CH + (CH_3)_2C{=}CH_2 \xrightarrow[-25^\circ C]{HF} (CH_3)_3CCH_2CH(CH_3)_2$$

2,2,4-trimethylpentane
"isooctane"

A reasonable mechanism for this alkylation reaction is

$$(CH_3)_2C{=}CH_2 \underset{}{\overset{HF}{\rightleftharpoons}} (CH_3)_3C^+ \xrightarrow{(CH_3)_2C{=}CH_2} (CH_3)_3CCH_2\overset{+}{C}(CH_3)_2$$

$$(CH_3)_3CCH_2\overset{+}{C}(CH_3)_2 + (CH_3)_3CH \rightleftharpoons (CH_3)_3CCH_2CH(CH_3)_2 + (CH_3)_3C^+$$

Under these conditions the dimeric carbocation does not react with more isobutylene, but instead abstracts hydrogen from isobutane to provide more *t*-butyl cation to continue the chain of reactions. This is an example of **chain transfer**, a process that occurs generally in addition polymerization and which limits the length of polymer chains.

B. Free Radical Vinyl Polymerization

Radical polymerization is initiated by the addition of free radicals to an alkene double bond as in the reactions discussed in Section 11.6.G. In those reactions, a reagent (HBr, Br$_2$, etc.) is present to react with the intermediate alkyl radical. In the absence of such a reagent the reaction of hydrocarbon radicals with alkenes can become the principal reaction to produce high molecular weight polymer chains. This reaction is an exceedingly important industrial process. Billions of pounds of polyethylene are made annually by this mechanism. The polymerization of ethylene requires high temperature and pressures.

$$n \ CH_2{=}CH_2 \xrightarrow[>100°C; \ 15,000 \ psi]{trace \ O_2 \ or \ peroxides} Y{-}(CH_2CH_2)_n{-}Z$$

where *n* is a large number on the order of 1000

The end groups Y and Z depend on the initiators used and the termination reactions involved. The principal termination steps for ethylene polymerization are disproportionation and combination, as summarized in the following sequence of steps.

$$Y{\cdot} + CH_2{=}CH_2 \longrightarrow Y{-}CH_2{-}CH_2{\cdot}$$

$$YCH_2CH_2{\cdot} + CH_2{=}CH_2 \longrightarrow YCH_2CH_2CH_2CH_2{\cdot} \xrightarrow{etc.} Y(CH_2CH_2)_nCH_2CH_2{\cdot}$$

$$\left.\begin{array}{l} Y(CH_2CH_2)_nCH_2CH_2{\cdot} \\ + \\ Y(CH_2CH_2)_mCH_2CH_2{\cdot} \end{array}\right\} \begin{array}{l} \xrightarrow{disproportionation} Y(CH_2CH_2)_nCH_2CH_3 + Y(CH_2CH_2)_mCH{=}CH_2 \\ \xrightarrow{combination} Y(CH_2CH_2)_nCH_2CH_2CH_2CH_2(CH_2CH_2)_mY \end{array}$$

The product of this so-called "high-temperature polymerization" of ethylene does not have the simple linear structure shown. Ethyl and butyl groups are known to occur along the polymethylene chain, probably because of hydrogen abstraction reactions of the following type.

The result is a **branched chain** polymer. **Linear polyethylene** is made by an entirely different process described later.

Vinyl chloride, tetrafluoroethylene, and styrene are other important monomers used in free radical polymerizations. The Markovnikov addition of radicals to vinyl chloride applies with high specificity so that the product polymer has a complete head-to-tail structure.

$$Y \cdot + CH_2=CHCl \longrightarrow Y-CH_2CHCl \longrightarrow \longrightarrow Y(CH_2CHCl)_nZ$$
polyvinyl chloride

Vinyl chloride is manufactured on an enormous scale, primarily for making polyvinyl chloride, PVC. The 1983 production of PVC was 6.07 billion pounds. Vinyl chloride is manufactured mostly by dehydrochlorination of 1,2-dichloroethane (ethylene dichloride). In 1974 the Occupational Safety and Health Administration concluded that vinyl chloride is a human carcinogen and set maximum limits to exposure.

Polyvinyl chloride is an extremely hard resin. In order to alter the physical properties of the polymer, low molecular weight liquids called **plasticizers** are added in the polymer formulation. Bis-2-ethylhexyl phthalate is one of the compounds added to polyvinyl chloride as a plasticizer. The resulting polymer has a tough leathery or rubber-like texture. It is used in plastic squeeze bottles, imitation leather upholstery, pipes, and so on.

Polytetrafluoroethylene or "Teflon" is a perfluoro polymer having great resistance to acids and organic solvents. It is used to coat "nonstick" frying pans and other cooking surfaces.

$$X-(CF_2CF_2)_n-Y$$
Teflon

Polystyrene is an inexpensive plastic used to manufacture many familiar household items. It is a hard, colorless, somewhat brittle material.

$$\left(\begin{matrix} C_6H_5 \\ | \\ CHCH_2 \end{matrix} \right)_n$$

In the simple formulation of polystyrene, the end groups have been omitted. This simplification is common in the symbolism of polymer chemistry. The end groups constitute a minute portion of a high molecular weight polymer, although their character has a significant effect on the properties of the polymers.

The incorporation of divinylbenzene into the polymerization of styrene provides **cross-linking** because the two vinyl groups can participate in two separate chains and produce a three-dimensional network. Cross-linking has a large effect on physical properties because it restricts the relative mobility of polymer chains. Polystyrene, for example, is soluble in many solvents such as benzene, toluene, and carbon tetrachloride. Even with only 0.1% divinylbenzene, however, the polymer no longer dissolves but only *swells*. This property is important in many uses of polystyrene-derived materials. An example is the polymer used for the Merrifield peptide syntheses (page 949). The 1983 production of polystyrene in its various forms, including copolymers, was 5.55 billion pounds.

Acrylonitrile is another important monomer manufactured in large quantity for use in synthetic fibers and polymers; its 1983 production in the United States was 1.07 million tons. It was once prepared industrially by addition of HCN to acetylene.

$$HC{\equiv}CH + HCN \xrightarrow[NH_4Cl]{CuCl} CH_2=CHCN$$

It is now prepared by a cheaper process that involves the catalytic oxidation of propene in the presence of ammonia.

$$2\ CH_3CH{=}CH_2 + 3\ O_2 + 2\ NH_3 \xrightarrow[\text{catalyst}]{450°} 2\ CH_2{=}CHCN + 6\ H_2O$$

Free radical polymerization of acrylonitrile in aqueous solution gives a polymer that can be spun to give the textile Orlon or Acrilan.

$$CH_2{=}CHCN \longrightarrow {-}\!\!\left(\!CH_2{-}\underset{\underset{CN}{|}}{CH}\!\right)_{\!n}$$

Orlon, Acrilan

The methyl ester of α-methylacrylic acid is also an important monomer. It is prepared from acetone by the following sequence.

$$CH_3COCH_3 + HCN \longrightarrow (CH_3)_2\underset{\underset{OH}{|}}{C}CN \xrightarrow{H_2SO_4} CH_2{=}\underset{\underset{CH_3}{|}}{C}CONH_2 \xrightarrow[H_2SO_4]{CH_3OH} CH_2{=}\underset{\underset{CH_3}{|}}{C}COOCH_3$$

Poly(methyl methacrylate) prepared by free radical polymerization is a stiff transparent plastic known as Lucite or Plexiglas.

$$CH_2{=}\underset{\underset{COOCH_3}{|}}{\overset{\overset{CH_3}{|}}{C}}{-}COOCH_3 \longrightarrow {-}\!\!\left(\!CH_2{-}\underset{\underset{COOCH_3}{|}}{\overset{\overset{CH_3}{|}}{C}}\!\right)_{\!n}$$

poly(methyl methacrylate)
Lucite, Plexiglas

Note that with both acrylonitrile and methyl methacrylate free radical polymerization involves almost exclusively head-to-tail combination of the monomers.

C. Anionic and Organometallic Polymerization

In anionic polymerization, initiation is accomplished by addition of a nucleophile to a carbon-carbon double bond. Simple olefins are inert to most nucleophilic or basic reagents and only when the anion itself is an extremely powerful base such as *t*-butyllithium will addition to the double bond occur.

$$(CH_3)_3C^-\ Li^+ + CH_2{=}CH_2 \longrightarrow (CH_3)_3CCH_2CH_2{}^-\ Li^+$$

Since primary carbanions are more stable than tertiary carbanions, the reaction as shown has favorable thermodynamics. This particular reaction is of limited use because *t*-butyllithium is such a highly reactive compound and decomposes ether rapidly at room temperature.

Other kinds of organometallic intermediates provide rapid polymerization and are much more important. A particularly significant example is a catalyst (**Ziegler-Natta** catalyst) prepared from aluminum alkyls (R_3Al) and titanium tetrachloride. This catalyst polymerizes simple olefins by a mechanism that involves the carbanion character of the carbon-aluminum bond and the ability of the transition metal, titanium, to coordinate with the π-bonds of alkenes. The result is a rapid polymerization reaction that is used extensively with ethylene and propylene. Linear polyethylene, $(CH_2CH_2)_n$, prepared in this way, is more crystalline than high temperature polyethylene and has a higher density and melting point. The long chains of linear polyethylene can lie together in a regular manner in the solid without the defects in regularity imposed by the random branches of the high temperature polymer. Total United States production of polyethylene in 1983 was 13.73 billion pounds, more than one third of which was linear polyethylene.

Polypropylene presents an interesting further aspect of polymer stereochemistry. In addition to polymerization exclusively in a head-to-tail fashion by Ziegler-Natta catalysts, the polymer has the methyl groups entirely on one side of the zigzag backbone.

This isomeric form is called **isotactic**. In isotactic polypropylene there is significant steric hindrance between methyl appendages and the backbone twists regularly to give the polymer a helical structure. Note that the products of free-radical polymerization have a random or **atactic** orientation of substituents. The other possible regular pattern in which substituents alternate on opposite sides of the backbone chain (**syndiotactic**) is rare. The total 1983 production of polypropylene was 4.43 billion pounds.

D. Diene Polymers

Natural rubber consists mostly of polyisoprene in which the double bonds are cis.

The natural latex is not a useful elastomer or rubber but requires a vulcanization process. One such process was discovered by Charles Goodyear in 1839 and involves heating the raw rubber with sulfur. The process appears to involve addition of sulfur units to the double bonds with the production of cross-links between the polymer chains. Because of these cross-links, the polymer resists distortion and tends to return to its original shape.

Elasticity has important structural requirements. If a polymer has regular repeating units, regions of the polymer may pack together by van der Waals forces in a manner similar to crystals. Such polymers are more or less crystalline and tend to be hard solids. Polymers that have flexible and irregular chains tend to be less rigid, but such a polymer is not an elastomer unless it returns to its original shape when the stress is removed. Hence, elastomers tend to have flexible chains with varying amounts of cross-linking.

Some plants produce a polyisoprene with trans double bonds.

$$CH_3 \qquad CH_3$$

This material, known as gutta-percha, is a harder and less elastomeric natural polymer than rubber.

Isoprene polymerizes under the influence of acids or Ziegler-Natta catalysts to a polyisoprene with rubber-like properties. The double bonds in this synthetic polyisoprene are both cis and trans. Synthetic rubbers, however, are derived primarily from butadiene. Buna S or GRS is a **copolymer** of 4-5 moles of butadiene to 1 mole of styrene. In this free radical polymerization, the butadiene adds by cis- and trans-1,4- and 1,2-additions. There are three repeating units in the polymer. Styrene-butadiene copolymers are the principle synthetic rubbers; 1983 production was 4.4 million pounds.

$$-CH-CH_2- \qquad -CH_2CH=CHCH_2- \qquad -CH_2-CH-$$
$$\quad \ |$$
$$\quad C_6H_5 \qquad\qquad\qquad\qquad\qquad\qquad\qquad\qquad CH=CH_2$$

cis and trans

In copolymerization the growing polymer radical has a choice of reacting with two different alkenes. The relative reactivities of the two monomer units are important in determining the composition of the resulting polymer. If one monomer is much more reactive in free radical polymerizations than the other, it will tend to form a **homopolymer** and be consumed before the second monomer starts to become incorporated. Polymers that consist of large segments of homopolymers joined in a copolymer are known as **block** copolymers.

Butadiene is also polymerized with Ziegler-Natta catalysts or by alkali metal catalysts based on alkylsodium formulations or lithium dispersions. Some of these methods are highly specific and give either cis- or trans-1,4- or 1,2-addition. A terpolymer produced from acrylonitrile, butadiene and styrene is an inexpensive plastic known as ABS.

Neoprene is a synthetic elastomer obtained by the free radical polymerization of chloroprene, 2-chloro-1,3-butadiene. Neoprene has unique properties, such as resistance to oils, oxygen, and heat.

Linseed oil is an example of a natural **drying oil** and contains a high percentage of linolenic acid (page 510). Although the unsaturation in this acid is not conjugated, the hardening of linseed oil probably involves conjugated radicals. On exposure to air, the highly unsaturated chain reacts with oxygen and cross-links to give a tough transparent polymer. Oil-based paint is a combination of drying oil with suspended pigment. Varnish also contains such drying oils and also involves the formation of a tough waterproof film by oxygen-promoted free radical cross-linking.

E. Condensation Polymers

Polymers result from the reaction of dicarboxylic acids or derivatives with diols or diamines. For example, an important **polyester** known as Dacron or Terylene is prepared by the reaction of dimethyl terephthalate and ethylene glycol. In one industrial process, the two reactants are heated together and methanol is distilled from the reactor. Polyesters are the major synthetic fiber; 1983 production was 3.54 billion pounds.

$$x \; CH_3OOC\!-\!\!\langle\bigcirc\rangle\!\!-\!COOCH_3 + x \; HOCH_2CH_2OH \xrightarrow{\Delta}$$

$$\left(\!-OOC\!-\!\!\langle\bigcirc\rangle\!\!-\!COOCH_2CH_2\!-\!\right)_x + 2x \; CH_3OH\!\uparrow$$

The best known **polyamide** is nylon 6,6, which is a copolymer formed from 1,6-hexanediamine and adipic acid. The polymer is manufactured by heating an equimolar mixture of the two monomers at 270°C at a pressure of about 10 atm.

$$H_2N(CH_2)_6NH_2 + HOOC(CH_2)_4COOH \xrightarrow[\text{10 atm}]{270°C} \left(\!-NH(CH_2)_6NH\overset{O}{\overset{\|}{C}}(CH_2)_4\overset{O}{\overset{\|}{C}}\!-\!\right)_n + H_2O$$

nylon 6,6

Another form of nylon is nylon 6, which is produced by polymerization of the amino acid 6-aminohexanoic acid. The actual monomer used is the cyclic amide caprolactam. Total 1983 production of various forms of nylon was 2.42 billion pounds.

$$H_2N(CH_2)_5COOH \quad \text{or} \quad \overset{H}{\underset{}{N}}\!\!\bigcirc\!\!\overset{O}{} \longrightarrow \left(\!-NH(CH_2)_5\overset{O}{\overset{\|}{C}}\!-\!\right)_n$$

6-aminohexanoic   caprolactam   nylon 6
acid

Polyurethanes are formed from an aromatic diisocyanate and a diol. One type of diol used is actually a low molecular weight copolymer made from ethylene glycol and adipic acid. When this polymer, which has free hydroxy end groups, is mixed with the diisocyanate, a larger polymer is produced.

$$HOCH_2CH_2OH + HOOC(CH_2)_4COOH \longrightarrow$$

$$HOCH_2CH_2O\left(\!\overset{O}{\overset{\|}{C}}(CH_2)_4\overset{O}{\overset{\|}{C}}OCH_2CH_2O\!\right)_n\!\!H \xrightarrow{\;\;OCN\!\!\bigcirc\!\!NCO\;CH_3\;}$$

$$\left[\!\overset{H}{\underset{-N\!\!\bigcirc}{}}NH\overset{O}{\overset{\|}{C}}OCH_2CH_2O\!\left(\!\overset{O}{\overset{\|}{C}}(CH_2)_4\overset{O}{\overset{\|}{C}}OCH_2CH_2O\!\right)_n\!\!\overset{O}{\overset{\|}{C}}NH\!\right]_x$$

a polyurethane

In the manufacturing process, a calculated amount of water is mixed with the diol. Some of the diisocyanate reacts with the water to give an aromatic diamine and carbon dioxide. The carbon dioxide forms bubbles that are trapped in the bulk of the polymer as it solidifies. The result is a spongy product called **polyurethane foam**. Diamines react with diisocyanates to give **polyureas**.

Note that the polymerization reactions of diisocyanates are not strictly condensation reactions because no small molecules are produced.

EXERCISE 34.17 Vinyl acetate undergoes free radical polymerization. What is the expected structure of the polymer? This polymer can be hydrolyzed to a useful water-soluble polyalcohol. Why is this polyalcohol not produced directly by polymerization of a monomer?

EXERCISE 34.18 When styrene is copolymerized with maleic anhydride under free radical conditions the growing polymer can have two types of radical ends. What are they? The copolymerization of two monomers A and B is characterized by two copolymerization ratios, r_A and r_B, in which r_A is defined as the rate constant for reaction of an A radical end with monomer A divided by the rate constant for reaction with monomer B. If both r_A and r_B equal unity, a random copolymer results. For copolymerization of styrene with maleic anhydride both copolymerization ratios are very small. What does this imply about the structure of the copolymer?

EXERCISE 34.19 Pyromellitic anhydride is the dianhydride of benzene-1,2,4,5-tetracarboxylic acid. It reacts with p-phenylenediamine (p-diaminobenzene) to form a strong condensation polymer stable at high temperatures. What is its structure?

34.6 Nucleic Acids

Nucleic acids are important biomolecules that play a crucial role in the storage of genetic information and in protein biosynthesis. There are two types of nucleic acid, ribonucleic acid (RNA) and deoxyribonucleic acid (DNA). Both are biopolymers in which the repeating monomer units are called **nucleotides**. A nucleotide, in turn, is a

uridylic acid   adenylic acid

sugars:

ribose
(RNA)

2-deoxyribose
(DNA)

phosphate:

phosphate

pyrimidines:

cytosine
(RNA, DNA)

uracil
(RNA)

thymine
(DNA)

purines:

adenine
(RNA, DNA)

guanine
(RNA, DNA)

FIGURE 34.7 Nucleotide building blocks.

complex molecule made up of one unit each of phosphate, a sugar, and a heterocyclic base. For each class of nucleic acid there are four main nucleotide monomers. In RNA the sugar is the pentose ribose and the heterocyclic base is a pyrimidine, uracil or cytosine, or a purine, adenine or guanine (Figure 34.7). The nucleotides themselves are called uridylic acid, adenylic acid, and so on (page 1118).

In DNA the sugar is 2-deoxyribose and the heterocyclic bases are the same except that thymine replaces uracil. The nucleotides are called 2-deoxythymidylic acid, 2-deoxycytidylic acid, and so on.

2-deoxythymidylic acid

Base-catalyzed hydrolysis of a nucleotide removes the phosphate group and yields a **nucleoside**, which is a glycoside formed from the pentose and the heterocyclic base. The nucleosides of RNA are cytidine, uridine, adenosine, and guanosine.

cytidine

uridine

adenosine

guanosine

For DNA the nucleosides are the corresponding 2-deoxy analogs, with 2-deoxythymidine replacing uridine.

2-deoxythymidine

The nucleic acids may be extremely large molecules, with molecular weights of more than a billion. The nucleic acid backbone is a copolymer of phosphoric acid and either ribose or 2-deoxyribose molecules, with one of the four heterocycles, adenine, guanine, cytosine, and uracil (or thymine), linked to C-1 of each of the pentose units (see Figure 34.8). For a segment of DNA such as that illustrated in Figure 34.8, the end of the chain in which phosphate is bonded to C-5 of the pentose is called the 5′-end, and the one in which the phosphate is bonded to C-3 of the pentose is called the 3′-end.

DNA occurs in the nuclei of all cells and is the molecule in which genetic information is stored. In the precise sequence of purine and pyrimidine bases along its phosphodiester backbone, it carries the information necessary for the exact duplication of the cell and, in fact, for the construction of the entire organism. DNA is actually a double-stranded helix of two individual molecules about 20 Å apart. The two chains

FIGURE 34.8 A portion of a deoxyribonucleic acid (DNA) molecule. In this depiction the 5′-end is at the top and the 3′-end is at the bottom.

are held together by reciprocal hydrogen bonding between pairs of bases in opposite positions in the two chains. The molecular geometry is such that adenine forms a strong reciprocal bond to thymine (AT) and guanine to cytosine (GC) (Figure 34.9). The two interwoven chains have exactly complementary structures. Thus, if a segment of one molecule has the base sequence 5′—G—C—A—A—T—G—C—C—3′, then the complementary chain has the corresponding base sequence 3′—C—G—T—T—A—C—G—G—5′, and the two chains are hydrogen-bonded together as symbolized by

$$5' \sim G-C-A-A-T-G-C-C \sim 3'$$
$$3' \sim C-G-T-T-A-C-G-G \sim 5'$$

adenine–thymine bond (AT)

guanine–cytosine bond (GC)

FIGURE 34.9 Base pairs of DNA. The complementary hydrogen bonds responsible for the DNA double helix structure are shown in color. In RNA, analogous pairing exists between adenine and uracil and between guanine and cytosine.

A short section of DNA double helix is represented in Figure 34.10. A spectacular three-dimensional view of a ten base-pair stretch of double helical DNA is shown in Figure 34.11.

Genetic information is passed from cell to cell in a process called **DNA replication**. As one of the essential steps in cell mitosis, the nuclear DNA helices separate. Each of the separate chains then functions as a template upon which another chain exactly complementary to itself is constructed. The end result is that one DNA double helix is

FIGURE 34.10 The DNA double helix is unrolled to show the phosphodiester backbone of the two complimentary strands and the base pairs that hold them together. The backbones run in opposite directions. Each base pair has one purine base, adenine (A) or guanine (G), and one pyrimidine base, thymine (T) or cytosine (C), connected by hydrogen bonds [Illustration copyright © by Irving Geis.]

FIGURE 34.11 Stereo structure of a ten-base-pair stretch of helical DNA. The base sequence of each strand is GCGAATTCGC. [Illustration copyright © by Irving Geis.]

transformed into two. In this way each daughter cell acquires an identical set of nuclear DNA molecules.

The principal function of DNA is as the master blueprint for the production of proteins, the essential catalysts for all cellular reactions. The information regarding primary structure of given proteins is encoded in the exact sequence of the four hetero-cyclic bases along the phosphodiester polymer in various regions of the molecule, known as **genes**. Since proteins are built up from 20 amino acids (Chapter 29), it is necessary that the the **genetic code** have at least this many words. In reality, base triads are used. Since there are four different bases, there are a total of 64 different triads, of which 61 are used to code for the various amino acids and three are "stop" messages. The full genetic code is given in Figure 34.12. For example, the sequence of bases AAA in a gene codes for phenylalanine, GAA for leucine, and so on. As the Figure shows, there is a considerable amount of redundancy in the code, since it has 64 words and only 21 are needed. The third base in each triad is less specific than the first two.

In RNA the pentose units are ribose instead of deoxyribose and uracil (U) replaces thymine (T). Unlike DNA, RNA molecules exist as single strands with rather irregular structures. There are at least three general types. Ribosomal RNA constitutes the major amount and serves a structural and catalytic function. Messenger RNA functions as a template for the actual synthesis of proteins. These molecules are manufactured by the cell by copying the appropriate gene from the DNA molecule into the corresponding sequence with ribonucleic acids. The messenger RNA binds many ribosomes, forming a polyribosome, where protein synthesis occurs. Transfer RNA is also involved in protein synthesis. These small RNA molecules bind to individual amino acids and guide them into place on the growing protein chain. There is one unique transfer RNA for each of the amino acids.

Many fascinating details of DNA and RNA chemistry have been worked out over the last quarter century. Much of the story of the genetic code and how it functions has been unravelled, and much more remains to be learned. It is not appropriate for us to go into the details of the molecular biology of gene transcription and protein synthesis in this introductory chemistry text. We shall, however, take a brief look at one interest-ing facet of nucleic acid chemistry, the method by which DNA primary structure is determined.

	A		G		T		C	
A	AAA	Phe	AGA	Ser	ATA	Tyr	ACA	Cys
	AAG	Phe	AGG	Ser	ATG	Tyr	ACG	Cys
	AAT	Leu	AGT	Ser	ATT	stop	ACT	stop
	AAC	Leu	AGC	Ser	ATC	stop	ACC	Trp
G	GAA	Leu	GGA	Pro	GTA	His	GCA	Arg
	GAG	Leu	GGG	Pro	GTG	His	GCG	Arg
	GAT	Leu	GGT	Pro	GTT	Gln	GCT	Arg
	GAC	Leu	GGC	Pro	GTC	Gln	GCC	Arg
T	TAA	Ile	TGA	Thr	TTA	Asn	TCA	Ser
	TAG	Ile	TGG	Thr	TTG	Asn	TCG	Ser
	TAT	Ile	TGT	Thr	TTT	Lys	TCT	Arg
	TAC	Met	TGC	Thr	TTC	Lys	TCC	Arg
C	CAA	Val	CGA	Ala	CTA	Asp	CCA	Gly
	CAG	Val	CGG	Ala	CTG	Asp	CCG	Gly
	CAT	Val	CGT	Ala	CTT	Asp	CCT	Gly
	CAC	Val	CGC	Ala	CTC	Glu	CCC	Gly

FIGURE 34.12 The genetic code. The third base of each triad is less specific than the first two. In RNA, each word is a complement of the one shown here. For example, the RNA complement of CCC (glycine) is GGG, and that for AAA (phenylalanine) is UUU (uracil replaces thymine).

An efficient method for determining the base sequence in DNA (**sequencing**) is based on a method introduced in 1977 by A. M. Maxam and W. Gilbert. In the **Maxam-Gilbert method** one first labels the end of the DNA chain with a radioactive isotope of phosphorus (^{32}P). Radiolabelling is accomplished by treating the DNA with an enzyme, such as polynucleotide kinase, which transfers a phosphate group from radiolabelled ATP to the 5′-ends of DNA molecules. Other enzymes may also be used to label the chains at the 3′-ends. The purpose of the ^{32}P is to render the end of the DNA chain radioactive, so that autoradiography can be used as an analytical method to detect the presence of DNA molecules.

Radiography is a technique in which radioactivity is used for imaging. Most people are familiar with the use of x-rays for this purpose. In this application of radiography, the x-rays are passed through the object to be examined onto a sheet of photographic film. The degree of exposure of the film is related to the intensity of radiation that passes through various regions of the object. In autoradiography, the substance to be detected is itself radioactive. If an object having various radioactive parts is placed in close contact with a sheet of photographic film, the film will be exposed to a greater or lesser degree depending on the amount of radioactivity in its various parts. Autoradiography is widely used as an analytical method in the following manner. A mixture of radioactive substances is subjected to a chromatographic or electrophoretic separation. The column or plate is then placed in contact with the photographic film and allowed to expose it. When the film is developed, a dark spot or band appears at points corresponding to the positions of radioactive compounds on the chromatogram or electrophoretic gel. An example of an autoradiograph is shown in Figure 34.13.

The radiolabelled DNA is subjected to some reagent that causes base-specific cleavage of the chain. For example, treatment of the specimen with dimethyl sulfate, followed by aqueous base results in specific rupture of the imidazole rings of guanines. When such a sample is treated with piperidine and then aqueous base, the phosphodies-

G A T C G

FIGURE 34.13 Autoradiograph of a sequencing gel. Reading from the bottom, the sequence of this 44-base ribonucleotide is C—C—G—G—G—G—A—T—C—C—G—T—C—G— A—C—C—G—A—G—G—G—A—A—C—G—A—C—G—A—T—C—T—T—G— C—G—G—C—C—A—T—C—G.

ter chain is cleaved at each site occupied by the hydrolyzed guanines. The chemistry of the process may be represented as follows.

In the first step, N-7 of the guanine acts as a nucleophile in an S_N2 reaction with the dimethyl sulfate, giving the resonance-stabilized immonium salt.

The next step is analogous to ester hydrolysis; hydroxide attacks the polar C=N bond, giving an α-amino alcohol that decomposes to a formamide.

Cleavage of the guanine ring renders the glycosidic bond vulnerable, since the nitrogen now bears a hydrogen. Removal of the heterocycle from the phosphodiester occurs by a mechanism such as the following.

With the ribose ring now open, the phosphodiester chain itself is now vulnerable. Rapid hydrolysis of the immonium ion gives an aldehyde having a good leaving group (phosphate) β to the carbonyl. Base-catalyzed elimination breaks the DNA backbone, giving an α,β-unsaturated aldehyde. A second elimination reaction removes the 5' end of the DNA chain from the unsaturated aldehyde.

5′   O=P—O⁻   O   OH H   H   H   O   O=P—O⁻   O   3′   H₂O →   N⁺ H

5′   O=P—O⁻   O   ⁻OH   OH H   H   H   H   CHO   O   O=P—O⁻   O   3′   →

5′   O=P—O⁻   O   OH H   H   H   CHO   HO⁻   +   O⁻   O=P—O⁻   O   3′   →   5′   O=P—O⁻   O⁻   +   OH   CHO

Application of the foregoing chemical cleavage method to a DNA molecule that has been labelled with ^{32}P at the 5′-end produces a complex mixture of fragments. All of the fragments that still contain the 5′-end are radioactive. Of course, there are many fragments that do not contain the 5′-end of the molecule, but since the analytical technique only detects radioactive molecules, these are invisible and of no consequence. Since the cleavage reaction is selective for guanine rings, most of the fragments correspond to rupture adjacent to guanine. An important element of the technique is that cleavage is not total. Thus, a large number of fragments are produced, and most end with a base *that was next to guanine in the intact DNA*. The situation is depicted graphically on page 1129 for a hypothetical 16-base segment of DNA. The radioactive products of this experiment consist mostly of the four fragments shown, plus the intact DNA that did not suffer cleavage.

The mixture is separated using a technique known as gel electrophoresis. In this technique, the molecules travel through a gel at a rate related to the chain length—the smaller the fragment, the more rapidly it moves. Application of autoradiography to the

1129

Sec. 34.7

Natural
Products:
Terpenes,
Steroids, and
Alkaloids

^{32}P—A—A—G—T—C—C—G—C—A—C—T—G—G—T—T—A

intact DNA

| cleavage
↓

^{32}P—A—A

^{32}P—A—A—G—T—C—C

^{32}P—A—A—G—T—C—C—G—C—A—C—T

^{32}P—A—A—G—T—C—C—G—C—A—C—T—G

^{32}P—A—A—G—T—C—C—G—C—A—C—T—G—G—T—T—A

gel reveals the presence of the radioactive fragments as dark lines on the developed film. The distance of the line from the origin is inversely related to the distance of a guanine from the 5′-end of the intact DNA chain. An example of such an autoradiograph is shown in Figure 34.13 on page 1125.

Chemistry such as that described has been developed for cleavage of DNA at each of the other three bases. To fully sequence a DNA molecule, one applies each of the four base-selective cleavage reactions to the radiolabelled DNA and subjects the reaction mixtures to gel electrophoresis. The autoradiographs resulting from these four analyses reveal the presence of every single base in the molecule. In practice, segments of DNA up to 250 bases in length may be sequenced by this method.

EXERCISE 34.20 It is possible to prepare synthetic RNA from any combination of the four nucleotides that one desires. This synthetic RNA can then be used to induce the synthesis of various polypeptides. For example, administration of polyuridylic acid to the bacteria *E. coli* causes it to synthesize polyphenylalanine. What polypeptide is produced by *E. coli* that has been administered polyadenylic acid? What is the expected empirical composition of the polypeptide produced by *E. coli* that has been administered a random 1:1 copolymer of uridylic and guanidylic acids?

EXERCISE 34.21 A second reaction that is used in the Maxam-Gilbert sequencing method involves treatment of the DNA fragment first with hydrazine (H_2NNH_2) and then with piperidine. This pair of reactions results in chain cleavage only at thymine and uracil sites. Write a plausible mechanism that explains the selectivity of the cleavage.

34.7 Natural Products: Terpenes, Steroids, and Alkaloids

Metabolism is the collection of chemical processes by which an organism creates and maintains its substance and obtains energy in order to grow and function. Almost all of these chemical processes involve organic compounds and reactions and naturally fall under the purview of the organic chemist. The metabolic processes of various organisms are varied and complex. In fact, the study of these processes is the subject of an entire discipline of science—biochemistry. However, many of the end products of metabolism are readily isolable organic compounds and have historical importance in organic chemistry. These compounds are grouped together under the broad heading of **natural products**.

There are many different classes of naturally occurring compounds, and some have already been encountered in this book. Some, such as fats (Section 18.12), carbohydrates (Chapter 28), proteins (Chapter 29), and nucleic acids (Section 34.6), have obvious roles in the functioning of organisms. These natural products, together with a relatively small number of related substances, occur in almost all organisms; they are called **primary metabolites**. The processes whereby they are produced are called **primary metabolic processes**. That is, most living organisms, regardless of species, produce the common sugars and sugar derivatives, the common fatty acids, and the simple carboxylic acids.

A second class of natural products is called **secondary metabolites**. They are not necessarily of secondary importance to the organism, but their distribution in nature tends to be much more species-dependent. They are the product of **secondary metabolic processes** of the organism. Examples of such secondary metabolites are the terpenes, the steroids, and the alkaloids. Because of the central role these natural products have played in the development of organic chemistry, we shall briefly examine their structures at this point.

A. Terpenes

The **terpenes** are a class of organic compounds that are the most abundant components of the **essential oils** of many plants and flowers. Essential oils are obtained by distilling the plants with water; the oil that separates from the distillate usually has highly characteristic odors identified with the plant origin. In the days of alchemists this procedure was common. The resulting mixture of organic compounds was thought to be the essence of the plant, hence the term essential oil. As we shall see in Section 34.8, terpenes are synthesized by organisms ("biosynthesized") from acetic acid by way of the important biological intermediate isopentenyl pyrophosphate. Terpene structures may generally be dissected into several "isoprene units."

isopentenyl pyrophosphate   an isoprene unit

Compounds derived from a single isoprene unit are rare in nature. However, compounds composed of two isoprene units are common. These materials are called **monoterpenes**. The simplest acyclic example is geraniol, a constituent of the oil of geranium. A related monoterpene is citronellal, which is responsible for the characteristic aroma of lemon oil.

geraniol   citronellal

Menthol (peppermint oil), β-pinene (turpentine), and camphor (obtained from the wood and leaves of the camphor tree) are examples of cyclic monoterpenes.

1131

Sec. 34.7

Natural
Products:
Terpenes,
Steroids, and
Alkaloids

menthol   β-pinene   camphor

Sesquiterpenes are C_{15} compounds that are composed of three isoprene units. Farnesol, which occurs in the essential oils of rose, acacia, and cyclamen, may be regarded as the parent acyclic alcohol. It has the characteristic odor of lily of the valley and is used in perfumery. A simple monocyclic sesquiterpene is bisabolene, which is found in the oils of bergamot and myrrh.

farnesol   bisabolene

Most terpenes have cyclic or polycyclic structures. A tremendous variety of fascinating structures are known. Examples are nootkatone (aroma of grapefruit), β-santalol (sandalwood oil), guaiol (guaiacum wood), and copaene (copaiba balsam oil).

nootkatone   β-santalol

copaene   guaiol

Diterpenes, C_{20} compounds composed of four isoprene units, include the important visual factor retinal (vitamin A aldehyde) and abietic acid, a component of rosin, the nonvolatile exudate of coniferous trees.

retinal

abietic acid

Terpenes having 25 carbons (sesterterpenes) are rare. However, the C_{30} compounds, or **triterpenes**, are common. An interesting example is squalene, a high-boiling viscous oil that is found in large quantities in shark liver oil. It may be isolated in smaller amounts from olive oil, wheat germ oil, rice bran oil, and yeast, and it is an intermediate in the biosynthesis of steroids (Section 34.8).

squalene

Other triterpenes are polycyclic, such as β-amyrin, a major constituent of the resin of the Manila elemi tree, and cyclolaudenol, a component of the neutral fraction of opium.

β-amyrin

cyclolaudenol

Natural rubber and gutta percha (Section 34.5) are polyterpenes, being made up of a large number of isoprene units.

> In the structural formulas used thus far for terpenes, note that the appendage methyl groups, both in side chains and attached to a cyclic nucleus, are indicated only as lines. This convention is widely used in depicting terpene and steroid structures. Of course, the convention of using a bold line for a methyl substituent that projects upward from the general plane of the ring and a dashed line for a methyl substituent that projects downward from the general plane is still followed.

The elucidation of the structures of the terpenes has provided a fascinating and important chapter in organic chemistry that really started only about a half century ago. Early terpene research led to the recognition of skeletal rearrangements that were among the first examples of carbocation rearrangements. A particularly important example is the camphene hydrochloride-isobornyl chloride rearrangement, which we can recognize as a simple 1,2-alkyl rearrangement.

1133

Sec. 34.7

*Natural
Products:
Terpenes,
Steroids, and
Alkaloids*

camphene
(many essential oils)

camphene hydrochloride

isobornyl chloride

Similar rearrangements are widespread in terpene chemistry. A further example is the rearrangement of longifolene to longifolene hydrochloride. The bond that migrates is shown in color.

longifolene

longifolene
hydrochloride

The stereo structure of longifolene hydrochloride is shown in Figure 34.14.

Synthetic routes to the simpler terpenes are now available, but many of the more complex polycyclic terpenes provide synthetic challenges that intrigue present-day synthetic research chemists.

EXERCISE 34.22 Locate the isoprene units in menthol, β-pinene, camphor, β-santalol, copaene, guaiol, abietic acid, β-amyrin, and longifolene. Note that nootkatone cannot be dissected into three isoprene units. In fact, it has been shown that this sesquiterpene is biosynthesized by a route that involves a 1,2-alkyl rearrangement.

FIGURE 34.14 Stereo structure of longifolene hydrochloride. Note that hydrogens are not shown. [Reproduced with permission from *Molecular Structure and Dimensions*, International Union of Crystallography, 1972.]

B. Steroids

Steroids are tetracyclic natural products that are related to the terpenes in that they are biosynthesized by a similar route. An important example is cholesterol, the major component of human gall stones (Gk., *chole*, bile).

cholesterol

Actually, cholesterol is present in some amount in all normal animal tissues, but it is concentrated in the brain and in the spinal cord. The total amount present in a 180 lb person is 240 g, about $\frac{1}{2}$ lb! It is present partly as the free alcohol and partly esterified with fatty acids.

The structure of cholesterol illustrates the basic steroid skeleton, which is that of a hydrogenated 1,2-cyclopentenophenanthrene having two methyl substituents at C-10 and C-13 and an additional side chain at C-17. The stereochemistry at the various stereocenters is almost invariably that shown, and in subsequent examples we shall not indicate stereochemistry unless it differs from the usual.

1,2-cyclopentenophenanthrene

general steroid ring structure

The tetracyclic steroid nucleus consists of three cyclohexane rings and one cyclopentane ring, each fused to its neighboring ring in a trans manner.

Other steroids are also common constituents of animal tissues and play important roles in normal biological process. Cholic acid, deoxycholic acid, and chenodeoxycholic acid occur in the bile duct. The bile acids exist as amides of the amino acid glycine, H_2NCH_2COOH, or the aminosulfonic acid taurine, $H_2NCH_2CH_2SO_3H$. The sodium salts have a large hydrocarbon region and a highly polar region and function in the cholic acid

deoxycholic acid

chenodeoxycholic acid

intestinal tract as emulsifying agents to promote the absorption of fats. They are a type of biological "soap" (Section 17.4.D).

a bile salt

Estrone, progesterone, testosterone, and androsterone are steroid sex hormones.

estrone

progesterone

testosterone

androsterone

Estrone is an example of an **estrogen**, or female sex hormone. Estrogens are secreted by the ovary and are responsible for the typical female sexual characteristics. Proges-

1135

terone is another type of female sex hormone. It is also produced in the ovary and is the progestational hormone of the placenta and corpus luteum. Testosterone and androsterone are **androgens**, or male sex hormones. They are produced in the testes and are responsible for the typical male sexual characteristics.

One of the most dramatic achievements of synthetic organic chemistry, and one that has already had profound impact on the history and mores of human societies, has been the development of "the pill." Actually, there are a number of different oral contraceptives in use. They are mainly synthetic steroids that interfere in some way with the normal estrus or progestational cycle in the female. One example is norethindrone, also known by the trade name Norlutin.

norethindrone
Norlutin

Steroids are widespread in the plant kingdom as well as in animals. One example is digitalis, a preparation made from the dried seeds and leaves of the purple foxglove. Historically, digitalis was used as a poison and as a medicine in heart therapy. The active agents in digitalis are **cardiac glycosides**, complex molecules built up from a steroid and several carbohydrates. Hydrolysis of digitoxin, one of the cardiac glycosides from digitalis, yields the steroid digitoxigenin.

digitoxigenin

EXERCISE 34.23 On page 1134 is shown a three-dimensional perspective of the basic steroid nucleus. Write similar perspective drawings for the male sex hormone androsterone and the bile acid cholic acid.

C. Alkaloids

Alkaloids constitute a class of basic, nitrogen-containing plant products that have complex structures and possess significant pharmacological properties. The name alkaloid, or "alkali-like," was first proposed by the pharmacist W. Meissner in the early nineteenth century before anything was known about the chemical structures of the compounds.

The first alkaloid isolated in a pure state was morphine, by Sertürner in 1805. The compound occurs in poppies and is responsible for the physiological effect of opium.

1137

Sec. 34.7

*Natural
Products:
Terpenes,
Steroids, and
Alkaloids*

FIGURE 34.15 Stereo structure of codeine hydrobromide. Hydrogens are not shown. [Reproduced with permission from *Molecular Structure and Dimensions*, International Union of Crystallography, 1972.]

morphine

Other members of the morphine family are the O-methyl derivative codeine and the diacetyl derivative heroin.

codeine

heroin

The stereo structure of codeine hydrobromide is shown in Figure 34.15.

Another common family of rather simple alkaloids is related to phenylethylamine. An example is mescaline, which occurs in several species of cactus. It is the active principle of mescal buttons, which were once used by some American Indians in

mescaline

lysergic acid diethylamide
"LSD"

religious rites. It has more recently gained notoriety as an illegal hallucinogen. However, studies have shown that virtually all "mescaline" in street sales is actually LSD (lysergic acid diethylamide), which is an even more potent hallucinogen. Note that both of these hallucinogens contain a β-phenylethylamine grouping, as does amphetamine (page 695).

Another representative alkaloid is the tropane alkaloid cocaine, which has important anesthetic properties.

cocaine

Quinine is an alkaloid from cinchona bark, which has had an important use as an antimalarial agent.

quinine

Nicotine is the chief alkaloid of the tobacco plant.

nicotine

Strychnine and brucine are intricate heptacyclic alkaloids that have been used as rodent poisons. They also find use as resolving agents in organic chemistry (pages 694–95), since they are inexpensive and optically active and form well-defined salts with a variety of organic acids.

strychnine

brucine

Other interesting structures are coniine, the poisonous principle of poison hemlock; sparteine, a constituent of black lupin beans; and lycopodine, a fascinating tetracyclic component of the club moss.

sparteine   coniine   lycopodine

As is obvious from the examples cited, alkaloids typically have potent physiological properties. In fact, this characteristic was partly responsible for the fact that the alkaloids were among the first organic compounds to be isolated in a pure state. Of course, another reason for their early recognition as discrete chemical entities is the fact that they are rather easy to obtain from complex plant material because of their basic nature.

34.8 Biosynthesis

In the previous section, we surveyed the classes of secondary plant metabolites known as terpenes, steroids, and alkaloids. It is not within the scope of this book to go into full details on metabolic processes. However, the elucidation of the pathways by which natural products are constructed by organisms (**biosynthesized**) is a major area of current research. For that reason we shall survey briefly one facet of biosynthesis, that of the terpenes and steroids.

The basic raw material of the higher plants is carbon dioxide. This basic building unit is reduced in a process called **photosynthesis**, to give simple sugars and sugar derivatives.

$$n\,CO_2 + n\,H_2O \longrightarrow (CH_2O)_n + n\,O_2$$

The process described in the foregoing equation is wonderfully complex, and its details have been mostly elucidated. The conversion is catalyzed by the green pigment chlorophyll and various enzymes, and numerous other cellular constituents are involved. The energy required for the functioning of the photosynthetic apparatus is supplied by the light of the sun.

One of the first stable products of photosynthesis that can be identified is 3-phosphoglyceric acid (3-PGA). If $^{14}CO_2$ is "fed" to a plant, the 3-phosphoglyceric acid is labeled initially in the carboxy group.

$$^{14}CO_2 \xrightarrow{\text{photosynthesis}}$$

$$
\begin{array}{c}
^{14}COOH \\
| \\
H-C-OH \\
| \\
CH_2OPOH \\
\end{array}
$$

3-phosphoglyceric acid

This substance is isomerized to 2-phosphoglyceric acid (2-PGA), which undergoes dehydration to give phosphoenolpyruvic acid (PEP). The phosphoenolpyruvic acid is then hydrolyzed to give pyruvic acid and phosphate ion.

$$
\begin{array}{ccc}
\text{COOH} & \text{COOH} & \\
| & | & \\
\text{H—C—OH} & \rightleftharpoons \quad \text{H—C—OPO}_3\text{H}_2 & \longrightarrow \\
| & | & \\
\text{CH}_2\text{OPO}_3\text{H}_2 & \text{CH}_2\text{OH} &
\end{array}
$$

3-PGA   2-PGA   PEP   pyruvic acid

PEP structure: HOOC and OP(OH)$_2$ on C=C; → CH$_3$CCOOH (with =O)

> All of these reactions, like almost all biological reactions, are mediated by enzymes. Enzymes function as catalysts and merely lower the activation energy for a reaction, thereby allowing it to occur more rapidly. An enzyme cannot make a thermodynamically unfavorable process favorable. All biological processes are inherently exothermic. However, just as in any multistep reaction, a given step may be endothermic. In writing reactions in this section, we shall omit the enzymes from the equations.

Pyruvic acid, PEP, 2-PGA, and 3-PGA are all involved in a number of primary metabolic processes that we shall not consider. We shall look only at one reaction of pyruvic acid, a reaction that leads us further down the path from CO$_2$ to the terpenes and steroids. In a complex series of steps, which are generally understood, the α-keto acid is oxidatively decarboxylated and coupled with the SH group of coenzyme A to give a substance known as **acetyl coenzyme A**, or CH$_3$COSCoA.

$$\text{CH}_3\overset{\text{O}}{\overset{||}{\text{C}}}\text{COOH} + \text{coenzyme A} \xrightarrow[\text{steps}]{\text{several}}$$

acetyl coenzyme A, CH$_3$CSCoA (with =O)

Acetyl coenzyme A is a **thiolester**. In essence, it is the biological equivalent of ethyl acetate. The SR group serves two functions; it activates the acetyl group for nucleophilic attack, and it renders the methyl protons more acidic for enolization.

$$\text{CH}_3\overset{\text{O}}{\overset{||}{\text{C}}}\text{SCoA}$$

$$\text{CH}_3-\overset{\text{O}^-}{\underset{\text{N}}{\overset{|}{\text{C}}}}-\text{SCoA}$$

$$^-{:}\,\text{CH}_2-\overset{\text{O}}{\overset{||}{\text{C}}}-\text{SCoA}$$

We have already seen in Section 18.9 how these properties are utilized in the formation of fatty acids. The first step of this process is a biological version of the Claisen condensation, affording acetoacetyl coenzyme A.

$$2 \; CH_3\overset{O}{\overset{\|}{C}}SCoA \; \rightleftharpoons \; CH_3\overset{O}{\overset{\|}{C}}CH_2\overset{O}{\overset{\|}{C}}SCoA \; + \; HSCoA$$
acetoacetyl coenzyme A

This substance reacts with another molecule of acetyl CoA in a form of aldol addition reaction to give β-hydroxy-β-methylglutaryl CoA, or HMG CoA.

$$CH_3\overset{O}{\overset{\|}{C}}CH_2\overset{O}{\overset{\|}{C}}SCoA \; + \; CH_3\overset{O}{\overset{\|}{C}}SCoA \; \longrightarrow \; HO\overset{O}{\overset{\|}{C}}CH_2\underset{\underset{OH}{|}}{\overset{\overset{CH_3}{|}}{C}}CH_2\overset{O}{\overset{\|}{C}}SCoA \; + \; HSCoA$$
β-hydroxy-β-methylglutaryl CoA

The thiolester grouping is reduced, first to a hydroxy aldehydo acid, then to a dihydroxy acid, **mevalonic acid**.

$$HO\overset{O}{\overset{\|}{C}}CH_2\underset{\underset{OH}{|}}{\overset{\overset{CH_3}{|}}{C}}CH_2\overset{O}{\overset{\|}{C}}SCoA \; \xrightarrow{\text{NADPH NADP}^+} \; HO\overset{O}{\overset{\|}{C}}CH_2\underset{\underset{OH}{|}}{\overset{\overset{CH_3}{|}}{C}}CH_2CHO \; \xrightarrow{\text{NADPH NADP}^+}$$

$$HO\overset{O}{\overset{\|}{C}}CH_2\underset{\underset{OH}{|}}{\overset{\overset{CH_3}{|}}{C}}CH_2CH_2OH$$
(R)-3,5-dihydroxy-3-methylpentanoic acid
mevalonic acid

The biological reducing agent in these two reductions is nicotinamide adenine dinucleotide phosphate, **NADPH**.

NADPH

It is classified as a coenzyme and functions with the aid of the enzyme HMG CoA reductase. It functions as a reducing agent in the following manner.

NADPH $\rightleftharpoons$ "H:$^-$" + NADP$^+$

Biological reactions involving oxidation or reduction are conventionally written as indicated, the curved arrow symbolizing that NADPH is consumed and NADP$^+$ is produced in the reaction.

Mevalonic acid is converted, in two steps, into 5-pyrophosphomevalonic acid.

mevalonic acid

5-phosphomevalonic acid

5-pyrophosphomevalonic acid

Phosphorylation is accomplished with the aid of another coenzyme, adenosine triphosphate (**ATP**). The by-product of each phosphorylation step is adenosine diphosphate (**ADP**).

adenosine triphosphate
ATP

adenosine diphosphate
ADP

5-Pyrophosphomevalonic acid is phosphorylated once again to yield 3-phospho-5-pyrophosphomevalonic acid, which undergoes elimination with concommitant decarboxylation to yield isopentenyl pyrophosphate.

3-phospho-5-pyrophosphomevalonic acid

isopentenyl pyrophosphate

Isopentenyl pyrophosphate is the biological "isoprene unit." It undergoes isomerization to γ,γ-dimethylallyl pyrophosphate, which is highly activated toward S_N1 and S_N2 reactions. Coupling of γ,γ-dimethylallyl pyrophosphate with isopentenyl pyrophosphate gives geranyl pyrophosphate.

isopentenyl γ,γ-dimethylallyl
pyrophosphate   pyrophosphate

geranyl pyrophosphate

By successive alkylations of isopentenyl pyrophosphate, farnesyl pyrophosphate and geranylgeranyl pyrophosphate are elaborated. Hydrolysis of these three pyrophosphates yields the acyclic terpene alcohols geraniol, farnesol, and geranylgeraniol.

geranyl pyrophosphate

geraniol
(a monoterpene)

farnesyl pyrophosphate

farnesol
(a sesquiterpene)

geranylgeranyl pyrophosphate

geranylgeraniol
(a diterpene)

The three acyclic pyrophosphates undergo a marvelous assortment of subsequent reactions to yield the cyclic monoterpenes, sesquiterpenes, and diterpenes that are so widespread in the plant kingdom. For example, double bond isomerization, followed by two successive enzyme-catalyzed cyclizations, converts geranyl pyrophosphate into α-pinene, the familiar fragrant principle of turpentine.

α-pinene

The following sequence of steps may be envisioned from farnesyl pyrophosphate to valencene, which is responsible for the aroma and taste of Valencia oranges.

valencene

Similar cyclizations yield the diterpenes. The foregoing metabolic paths are common to many plants. Differences occur mainly in the ways in which geranyl pyrophosphate and farnesyl pyrophosphate are converted into the various terpenes.

Farnesyl pyrophosphate undergoes another biological reaction—reductive coupling. The initial product of this coupling process is a cyclopropylmethyl pyrophosphate, presqualene alcohol pyrophosphate, which is then converted into squalene.

presqualene alcohol pyrophosphate

squalene

The exact mechanism whereby presqualene alcohol pyrophosphate is converted into squalene is still unknown, but it may reasonably be formulated as follows.

where R =

Squalene was once regarded as a curious terpenoid polyene that occurs in shark oil. It is now recognized to be the precursor to the whole family of steroids. Squalene is elaborated by plants by the biosynthetic path outlined previously, beginning with carbon dioxide. In animals its biosynthesis is similar, except that the beginning raw materials are more complicated foodstuffs than carbon dioxide. Oxidation of one of the squalene double bonds yields squalene oxide, which undergoes an enzymatic cyclization. The cyclization is a complex reaction in which the squalene oxide chain must be folded in a precise manner. The initial product is a tetracyclic carbocation, which undergoes the indicated "backbone rearrangement" to afford lanosterol.

squalene

2,3-squalene oxide

lanosterol

Since the oxidation of squalene is an enzymatic process, the squalene oxide is optically active, as is the lanosterol produced by its cyclization. Lanosterol is converted into cholesterol by the loss of the three methyl groups at C-4 and C-14, isomerization of one double bond, and reduction of another double bond.

lanosterol

cholesterol

The exact mechanisms of these final steps have not yet been elucidated, but it is known that the three methyl groups are first oxidized to carboxy groups and then lost as carbon dioxide.

The foregoing discussion illustrates in broad outline the **biosynthesis** of one complex natural product. Similar biosynthetic routes have been elucidated for dozens of other natural products. Many kinds of experiments go into the elucidation of such a pathway, and we do not have space to consider them in detail. One type of experiment that has been extremely useful involves the incorporation of radioactive precursors. We shall illustrate the use of this technique in sorting out the various intermediates involved in the biosynthesis of cholesterol. The pathway proposed above for the final steps is

$$\text{squalene} \longrightarrow \text{2,3-squalene oxide} \longrightarrow \text{lanosterol} \longrightarrow \text{cholesterol}$$

An organism that is producing cholesterol is fed squalene labeled with ^{14}C. After a suitable period cholesterol is isolated, and its radioactivity is determined. Incorporation of the label is taken as evidence that squalene is a biological precursor. Similar experiments may be carried out using labeled squalene oxide and labeled lanosterol. Incorporation studies can also be done to establish the intermediate stages; when labeled squalene oxide is administered, lanosterol is isolated. Studies such as these have been used to work out the entire metabolic path from carbon dioxide to the various terpenes and steroids, at least in gross detail. Many gaps still exist. For example, we still do not know the precise steps that occur between lanosterol and cholesterol.

Incorporation studies can provide even more detailed information on metabolic pathways, as illustrated by the following example. If acetyl coenzyme A, labeled with ^{14}C in the acetyl methyl group, is administered, then the cholesterol produced should have ^{14}C in the positions indicated by black dots if the biosynthetic path outlined in this section is correct.

acetyl CoA

squalene

cholesterol

This experiment has been done, and the cholesterol produced was subjected to a lengthy multistep degradation. The degradation was carried out in such a way that each of the 27 carbons could be examined separately for radioactivity. The label was found precisely where it is predicted to be on the basis of the biosynthetic hypothesis. In particular, the experiment ruled out an earlier hypothesis regarding the possible biosynthesis of cholesterol, which may be summarized as

A more modern method for carrying out such biosynthetic investigations utilizes ^{13}C-labeled precursors, and CMR spectroscopy as the analytical tool. For example, if the foregoing experiment is repeated with acetyl coenzyme A labeled in the methyl group with ^{13}C, the isolated cholesterol will have a CMR spectrum consisting of 15 strong absorptions (those of the 15 carbons indicated by the black dots in the structure on page 1147), and 12 weak absorptions (the natural abundance of ^{13}C in the 12 unmarked carbons of cholesterol). Since the chemical shifts of all 27 carbons in cholesterol have been determined, it is now a trivial exercise to determine the positions of the label.

EXERCISE 34.24 Suppose that a pine seedling is administered acetyl coenzyme A labeled with ^{13}C in the carbonyl position. After an appropriate time, α-pinene is isolated and the CMR spectrum is recorded. How many signals will be observed? Which carbons are labeled with ^{13}C?

EXERCISE 34.25 Another ^{13}C-labeling technique employs acetate in which *both* carbons are ^{13}C. This method is based on the fact that ^{13}C—^{13}C coupling constants are observed, even when the spectrum is measured under conditions such that ^{13}C—^{1}H coupling is not observed. Thus, any ^{13}C that has one ^{13}C neighbor appears as a doublet. Recall that normal, natural-abundance CMR spectroscopy does not show ^{13}C—^{13}C coupling because of the low probability that two such nuclei will be bonded. In the double-label technique, the experiment is carried out in such a way that the natural product of interest is biosynthesized mostly from unlabeled precursor. For example, in a typical experiment the researcher might use 90% unlabeled acetate and 10% acetate in which both carbons are fully labeled with ^{13}C. If such an experiment were carried out with a plant producing farnesol, what would the CMR spectrum of the isolated natural product look like? What spectrum would be observed for valencene isolated from such an experiment?

Appendix I

Heats of Formation

ΔH_f° (gas, 25°C), kcal mole^{-1}

Alkanes

methane	—17.9	2,2-dimethylpropane	—40.3
ethane	—20.2	hexane	—39.9
propane	—24.8	2-methylpentane	—41.8
butane	—30.4	3-methylpentane	—41.1
2-methylpropane	—32.4	2,2-dimethylbutane	—44.5
pentane	—35.1	2,3-dimethylbutane	—42.6
2-methylbutane	—36.9		

Cycloalkanes

cyclopropane	12.7	methylcyclopentane	—25.3
cyclobutane	6.8	methylcyclohexane	—37.0
cyclopentane	—18.4	ethylcyclohexane	—41.0
cyclohexane	—29.5	1,1-dimethylcyclohexane	—43.2
cycloheptane	—28.2	cis-1,2-dimethylcyclohexane	—41.1
cyclooctane	—29.7	trans-1,2-dimethylcyclohexane	—43.0
cyclononane	—31.7	cis-1,3-dimethylcyclohexane	—44.1
cyclodecane	—36.9	trans-1,3-dimethylcyclohexane	—42.2
cubane	148.7	cis-1,4-dimethylcyclohexane	—42.2
		trans-1,4-dimethylcyclohexane	—44.1

Alkenes

ethylene	12.5	2-methyl-1-butene	— 8.6
propene	4.9	2-methyl-2-butene	—10.1
1-butene	— 0.2	cyclobutene	37.5
cis-2-butene	— 1.9	cyclopentene	8.2
trans-2-butene	— 3.0	cyclohexene	— 1.1
2-methylpropene	— 4.3	1-methylcyclohexene	—10.3
1-pentene	— 5.3	cycloheptene	— 2.2
cis-2-pentene	— 7.0	cyclooctene	— 6.5
trans-2-pentene	— 7.9		

Alkynes and Polyenes

acetylene	54.3	cis-1,3-pentadiene	19.1
propyne	44.4	trans-1,3-pentadiene	18.1
1-butyne	39.5	1,4-pentadiene	25.3
2-butyne	34.7	2-methyl-1,3-butadiene	18.1
allene	45.6	cyclopentadiene	31.9
1,2-butadiene	38.8	1,3-cyclohexadiene	25.4
1,3-butadiene	26.1	1,3,5,7-cyclooctatetraene	71.1
1,2-pentadiene	33.6		

Aromatic Hydrocarbons

benzene	19.8	styrene	35.3
toluene	12.0	naphthalene	36.1
o-xylene	4.6	1,2,3,4-tetrahydronaphthalene	7.3
m-xylene	4.1	anthracene	55.2
p-xylene	4.3	9,10-dihydroanthracene	38.2
ethylbenzene	7.1	phenanthrene	49.5

Alcohols

methanol	—48.1	t-butyl alcohol	—74.7
ethanol	—56.2	cyclopentanol	—58.0
allyl alcohol	—29.6	cyclohexanol	—68.4
1-propanol	—61.2	benzyl alcohol	—24.0
2-propanol	—65.1	ethylene glycol	—93.9

Ethers

dimethyl ether	—44.0	1,1-dimethoxyethane	— 93.3
ethylene oxide	—12.6	2,2-dimethoxypropane	—101.9
tetrahydrofuran	—44.0	anisole	— 17.3
diethyl ether	—60.3		

Aldehydes and Ketones

formaldehyde	—26.0	butanal	—49.0
acetaldehyde	—39.7	cyclopentanone	—46.0
propionaldehyde	—45.5	cyclohexanone	—54.0
acetone	—51.9	benzaldehyde	— 8.8
2-butenal	—24.0		

Other Oxygen Compounds

formic acid	— 90.6	benzoic acid	— 70.1
acetic acid	—103.3	acetic anhydride	—137.1
vinyl acetate	— 75.5	furan	— 8.3
methyl acetate	—97.9	phenol	— 23.0
ethyl acetate	—106.3		

Nitrogen Compounds

methylamine	— 5.5	pyridine	34.6
dimethylamine	— 4.7	piperidine	—11.8
trimethylamine	— 5.7	aniline	20.8
ethylamine	—11.4	benzonitrile	51.5
acrylonitrile	44.1	dimethylformamide	—45.8
acetonitrile	17.6	acetanilide	—30.8
propionitrile	12.1	methyl nitrite	—15.8
pyrrole	25.9	nitromethane	—17.9
pyrrolidine	— 0.8	glycine	—93.7

Halogen Compounds

methyl chloride	—20.6	bromobenzene	25.2
methylene chloride	—23.0	chlorobenzene	12.2
chloroform	—24.6	acetyl chloride	—58.4
carbon tetrachloride	—25.2	methyl fluoride	— 56.8
vinyl chloride	8.6	methyl bromide	— 9.1
ethyl chloride	—26.1	methyl iodide	3.4
n-propyl chloride	—31.0	ethyl bromide	—15.2
isopropyl chloride	—33.6	benzyl chloride	4.5

Sulfur Compounds

methanethiol	−5.4	thiirane	19.7
ethanethiol	−11.0	dimethyl sulfoxide	−36.1
dimethyl sulfide	−8.9	dimethyl sulfone	−89.1
dimethyl disulfide	−5.6	thiophene	27.6
thiophenol	26.9	tetrahydrothiophene	−8.1

Inorganic Compounds

CO_2	−94.05	NH_3	−10.9
H_2O	−57.80	CO	−26.42
H_2S	−4.8	H_2NNH_2	22.7
SO_2	−71.0	O_3	34.0
HCl	−22.1	NO_2	7.9
Br_2	7.4	HF	−65.0
HBr	− 8.7	HNO_3	−32.1
I_2	14.9	HNO_2	−18.4
HI	6.3	H_2O_2	−32.53
H_2O_2	−32.5	NO	21.6
		HCN	31.2

Atoms and Radicals

H	52.1	$CH_3\cdot$	35
Li	38.4	$C_2H_5\cdot$	26
C	170.9	$(CH_3)_2CH\cdot$	18
N	113.0	$(CH_3)_3C\cdot$	9
O	59.6	$CH_2{=}CH\cdot$	70
F	18.9	$CH_2{=}CHCH_2\cdot$	39
Cl	28.9	$C_6H_5CH_2\cdot$	48
Br	26.7	$C_6H_5\cdot$	79
I	25.5	$CH_3CO\cdot$	−6
S	65.7	$CH_3CO_2\cdot$	−50
Na	25.8	$CH_3O\cdot$	4
HO	9.4	$C_2H_5O\cdot$	−4
H_2N	44	$HCO\cdot$	9
CN	104	$HOOC\cdot$	−53
SH	34	$CH_3SO_2\cdot$	−61
		$CH_3COCH_2\cdot$	−6
		cyclopropyl$\cdot$	67
		$CH_3OOC\cdot$	−40

Cations and Anions

CH_3^+	262	H^-	34.7
$C_2H_5^+$	219	HO^-	−32.7
$(CH_3)_2CH^+$	187	F^-	−59.5
$(CH_3)_3C^+$	163	Cl^-	−54.5
$CH_2{=}CHCH_2^+$	225	Br^-	−50.9
$C_6H_5CH_2^+$	213	I^-	−45.1
H^+	365.7	CN^-	16
		$CH_3CO_2^-$	−120.5
		NO_2^-	−27.1

Appendix II

Bond-Dissociation Energies

DH°, kcal mole^{-1} for A—B Bonds

A		B: (52.1) H	(18.9) F	(28.9) Cl	(26.7) Br	(25.5) I	(9.4) OH	(44) NH$_2$	(35) Me	(26) Et	(18) i-Pr	(9) t-Bu	(79) Ph	(104) CN
(35)	Methyl	105	110	85	71	57	93	85	90	86	86	84	102	122
(26)	Ethyl	98	108	80	68	53	91.5	82	86	82	81	79	98	118
(21)	Propyl	98	107	81	68	53	92	82	86.5	82	80	79	98	117
(18)	Isopropyl	95	106.5	81	68	53.5	93	82	86	81	79	76	96	116
(9)	t-Butyl	93	110	81	67	52	93	82	84	79	76	71	93	
(79)	Phenyl	111	126	96	80.5	65	111	102	102	97	96	93	115	131
(48)	Benzyl	88		72	58	48	81	71	76	72	71	70	90	
(39)	Allyl	86		68	54	41	78		74	70	70	67		
(−6)	Acetyl	86	119	81	66	49	107		81	76	74	72	93.5	
(−4)	Ethoxy	104					44		83	82			101	
(70)	Vinyl	110		90	78				100	96	95	90	103	130
(52.1)	H	104.2	135.8	103.2	87.5	71.3	119	107	105	98	95	93	111	125

Numbers in parentheses are the heats of formation, ΔH_f°, for the corresponding atom or radical.

Appendix III

Average Bond Energies

Average Bond Energies, kcal mole^{-1}

H	C	N	O	F	Si	S	Cl	Br	I	
104	99	93	111	135	76	83	103	87	71	H
	83[a]	73[b]	86[c]	116[d]	72	65	81	68	52	C
		39	53[e]	65			46			N
			47	45	108		52	48	56	O
				37	135					F
					53		91	74	56	Si
						60	61	52		S
							58			Cl
								46		Br
									36	I

[a] C=C 146, C≡C 200.

[b] C=N 147, C≡N 213.

[c] C=O 176 (aldehydes), 179 (ketones).

[d] In CF$_4$.

[e] In nitrites and nitrates.

Appendix IV

Acid Dissociation Constants

Acidities of Inorganic Acids at 25°C

Name	Formula	pK_a
ammonia		34[a]
ammonium ion	NH_4^+	9.24
boric acid	H_3BO_3	9.24
carbon dioxide	CO_2	6.35[b]
cyanic acid	HOCN	3.46
hydrazinium ion	$H_2NNH_3^+$	7.94
hydrazoic acid	HN_3	4.68
hydriodic acid	HI	−5.2
hydrobromic acid	HBr	−4.7
hydrochloric acid	HCl	−2.2
hydrocyanic acid	HCN	9.22
hydrofluoric acid	HF	3.18
hydrogen peroxide	H_2O_2	11.65
hydrogen selenide	H_2Se	3.89 (11.0)[c]
hydrogen sulfide	H_2S	6.97 (12.9)[c]
hydroxylammonium ion	H_3NOH^+	5.95
hypobromous acid	HOBr	8.6
hypochlorous acid	HOCl	7.53
hypophosphorus acid	H_3PO_2	1.2
nitric acid	$HONO_2$	−1.3
nitrous acid	HONO	3.23
periodic acid	H_3IO_5	1.55 (8.27)[c]
phosphoric acid	$(HO)_3PO$	2.15 (7.20, 12.38)[c]
sulfuric acid	$(HO)_2SO_2$	≈ -5.2 (1.99)[c]
sulfurous acid	$(HO)_2SO$	1.8 (7.2)[c]
thiocyanic acid	HCNS	−1.9

[a] In liquid ammonia.

[b] For the equilibrium $CO_2(aq) = H^+(aq) + HCO_3^-(aq)$.

[c] Second and third acidity constants in parentheses.

Acidities of Organic Acids at 25°C

Acid	pK_a	Acid	pK_a
$CH_3\overset{+}{N}OH$ (N=O)	-11.9	$(CH_3)_2C=\overset{+}{N}OH$ (H)	-1.9
$C_6H_5\overset{+}{N}OH$ (N=O)	-11.3	CH_3SO_3H	≈ -1.2
$C_6H_5\overset{+}{C}\equiv NH$	-10.5	$CH_3C=\overset{+}{N}H_2$ (OH)	≈ 0
$CH_3\overset{+}{C}\equiv NH$	-10.1	$CH_3(CH_2)_3\overset{+}{P}H_3$	0
$CH_3\overset{+}{C}=OH$ (H)	≈ -8	$(CH_3)_2\overset{+}{S}OH$	0
$C_6H_5\overset{+}{C}=OH$ (OH)	-7.3	CF_3COOH	0.2
$(CH_3)_2C=\overset{+}{O}H$	-7.2	picric acid (O_2N, NO_2, NO_2, OH)	0.25
$C_6H_5\overset{+}{C}=OH$ (H)	-7.1		
$CH_3\overset{+}{S}H_2$	-6.8	pyridinium N–OH	0.79
$C_6H_5\overset{+}{O}H_2$	-6.7	$(C_6H_5)_2\overset{+}{N}H_2$	0.8
$C_6H_5\overset{+}{O}CH_3$ (H)	≈ -6.5	$O_2N-C_6H_4-\overset{+}{N}H_3$	1.00
$CH_3\overset{+}{C}=OH$ (OC_2H_5)	-6.5	$C_6H_5\overset{+}{N}H=CC_6H_5$ (OH)	2.17
$C_6H_5N=\overset{+}{N}C_6H_5$ (OH)	-6.45	$CH_3\overset{+}{P}H_3$	≈ 2.5
$C_6H_5\overset{+}{C}CH_3$ (OH)	-6.2	$O_2N-C_6H_4-COOH$	3.42
$CH_3\overset{+}{C}OH$ (OH)	-6.1	$CH_2(NO_2)_2$	3.57
$(CH_3)_2\overset{+}{S}H$	-5.4	$(CH_3)_2\overset{+}{P}H_2$	3.91
$(CH_3)_3\overset{+}{C}OH_2$	-3.8	2,4-dinitrophenol (O_2N, NO_2, OH)	4.09
$(CH_3CH_2)_2\overset{+}{O}H$	-3.6	$C_6H_5\overset{+}{N}H_3$	4.60
$(CH_3)_2CH\overset{+}{O}H_2$	-3.2	$(CH_3)_3\overset{+}{N}OH$	4.7
$C_6H_5N=\overset{+}{N}C_6H_5$ (H)	-2.9	CH_3COOH	4.74
$C_2H_5\overset{+}{O}H_2$	-2.4		
$CH_3\overset{+}{O}H_2$	-2.2		
$C_6H_5\overset{+}{C}=NH_2$ (OH)	-2.0		

Acidities of Organic Acids at 25°C (continued)

Acid	pK_a	Acid	pK_a
	5.29		16.0
		$C_6H_5COCH_3$	16
$(CH_3CO)_3CH$	5.85	$(CH_3)_3COH$	18
	7.0	CH_3COCH_3	20
			20
$O_2N-\!\!\!\!\bigcirc\!\!\!\!-OH$	7.15		23
C_6H_5SH	7.8		
$(CH_3)_3\overset{+}{P}H$	8.65	$CH_3SO_2CH_3$	23
$(CH_3CO)_2CH_2$	9	$CH_3COOC_2H_5$	24.5
$(CH_3)_3\overset{+}{N}H$	9.79	$HC{\equiv}CH$	≈ 25
C_6H_5OH	10.00	CH_3CN	≈ 25
CH_3NO_2	10.21	$(C_6H_5)_3CH$	31.5
CH_3CH_2SH	10.60	$(C_6H_5)_2CH_2$	34
$CH_3\overset{+}{N}H_3$	10.62	$C_2H_5NH_2$	≈ 35
$(CH_3)_2\overset{+}{N}H_2$	10.73	$C_6H_5CH_3$	41
$CH_3COCH_2COOC_2H_5$	11		43
$CH_2(CN)_2$	11.2	$CH_2{=}CH_2$	44
CF_3CH_2OH	12.4		46
$CH_2(COOC_2H_5)_2$	13.3	CH_4	≈ 49
$(CH_3SO_2)_2CH_2$	14	C_2H_6	≈ 50
CH_3OH	15.5		≈ 52
$(CH_3)_2CHCHO$	15.5		
C_2H_5OH	15.9		

Appendix V

Proton Chemical Shifts

Proton Chemical Shifts, δ, ppm, for C—H

Y	CH$_3$Y	CH$_3$—C—Y	CH$_3$—C—C—Y	R—CH$_2$—Y	RCH$_2$—C—Y	R$_2$CH—Y
H	0.23	0.9	0.9	0.9	1.3	1.3
CH=CH$_2$	1.71	1.0		2.0		1.7
C≡CH	1.80	1.2	1.0	2.1	1.5	2.6
C$_6$H$_5$	2.35	1.3	1.0	2.6	1.7	2.9
F	4.27	1.2		4.4		
Cl	3.06	1.5	1.1	3.5	1.8	4.1
Br	2.69	1.7	1.1	3.4	1.9	4.2
I	2.16	1.9	1.0	3.2	1.9	4.2
OH	3.39	1.2	0.9	3.5	1.5	3.9
OR	3.24	1.2	1.1	3.3	1.6	3.6
OAc	3.67	1.3	1.1	4.0	1.6	4.9
CHO	2.18	1.1	1.0	2.4	1.7	2.4
COCH$_3$	2.09	1.1	0.9	2.4	1.6	2.5
COOH	2.08	1.2	1.0	2.3	1.7	2.6
NH$_2$	2.47	1.1	0.9	2.7	1.4	3.1
NHCOCH$_3$	2.71	1.1	1.0	3.2	1.6	4.0
SH	2.00	1.3	1.0	2.5	1.6	3.2
CN	1.98	1.4	1.1	2.3	1.7	2.7
NO$_2$	4.29	1.6	1.0	4.3	2.0	4.4

Proton Chemical Shifts for Y—H

Group Type	δ, ppm
ROH	0.5–5.5
ArOH	4–8
RCOOH	10–13
R$_2$C=NOH	7.4–10.2
RSH	0.9–2.5
ArSH	3–4
RSO$_3$H	11–12
RNH$_2$, R$_2$NH	0.4–3.5
ArNH$_2$, ArRNH	2.9–4.8
RCONH$_2$	5.0–6.5
RCONHR	6.0–8.2
RCONHAr	7.8–9.4

Appendix VI
Symbols and Abbreviations

Å	Ångstrom unit (10^{-8} cm)
Ac	acetyl group, $CH_3CO—$
Ar	aryl radical
$[\alpha]$	specific optical activity
aq.	aqueous
Boc	t-butoxycarbonyl group, $(CH_3)_3COCO—$
n-Bu	n-butyl group, $CH_3CH_2CH_2CH_2—$
t-Bu	t-butyl group, $(CH_3)_3C—$
CMR	^{13}C magnetic resonance
Cbz	benzyloxycarbonyl group, $C_6H_5CH_2OCO—$
D	Debye (10^{-18} esu cm); measure of dipole moment
DCC	dicyclohexylcarbodiimide, $C_6H_{11}N=C=NC_6H_{11}$
δ	chemical shift downfield from TMS, given as ppm
Δ	symbol for heat supplied to a reaction
$\Delta G°$	standard Gibbs free energy of reaction
$\Delta G^{\ddagger}$	Gibbs free energy of activation
$\Delta H°$	standard enthalpy of reaction
$\Delta H_f°$	enthalpy of formation from standard states
$\Delta H^{\ddagger}$	enthalpy of activation
$\Delta S°$	standard entropy of reaction
$\Delta S^{\ddagger}$	entropy of activation
$DH°$	bond dissociation energy
DIBAL	diisobutylaluminum hydride, $[(CH_3)_2CHCH_2]_2AlH$
diglyme	di-2-methoxyethyl ether, $(CH_3OCH_2CH_2)_2O$
DMF	dimethylformamide, $(CH_3)_2NCHO$
DMSO	dimethyl sulfoxide, $(CH_3)_2SO$
DNP	2,4-dinitrophenyl group, $2,4\text{-}(O_2N)_2C_6H_3—$
	or 2,4-dinitrophenylhydrazone, $2,4\text{-}(O_2N)_2C_6H_3NHN=$
E	*entgegen*, opposite sides in (E,Z) nomenclature of alkenes
E1	unimolecular elimination reaction mechanism
E2	bimolecular elimination reaction mechanism
EA	electron affinity
Et	ethyl group, $CH_3CH_2—$
eu	entropy units, cal deg^{-1} $mole^{-1}$
f_i	partial rate factor at position i
glyme	1,2-dimethoxyethane, $CH_3OCH_2CH_2OCH_3$
H	magnetic field
HMPT	hexamethylphosphoric triamide, $[(CH_3)_2N]_3PO$
HOMO	highest occupied molecular orbital
$h\nu$	symbol for light
Hz	Hertz (sec^{-1} or cycles per second)
IP	ionization potential
IR	infrared
J	coupling constant, usually in Hz
k	rate constant for reaction

K	equilibrium constant for reaction
K_a	acid dissociation constant
LDA	lithium diisopropylamide, $LiN[CH(CH_3)_2]_2$
LUMO	lowest unoccupied molecular orbital
Me	methyl group, CH_3-
m/z	mass-to-charge ratio in mass spectrometry
MHz	megaHertz $\equiv 10^6$ Hz
μ	dipole moment
NMR	nuclear magnetic resonance
NR	no reaction; also indicated by $-\!/\!\!\longrightarrow$
Ph	phenyl radical, C_6H_5-
pH	measure of acidity $\equiv -\log [H^+]$
pK_a	measure of acid strength $\equiv -\log K_a$
PMR	proton magnetic resonance
PPA	polyphosphoric acid
ψ	wave function or orbital
R	alkyl or cycloalkyl group
(R,S)	designation of stereochemical configuration
S_N1	unimolecular nucleophilic substitution mechanism
S_N2	bimolecular nucleophilic substitution mechanism
THF	tetrahydrofuran, $\overline{CH_2CH_2CH_2CH_2O}$
TMS	tetramethylsilane, $(CH_3)_4Si$
Ts	tosyl or p-toluenesulfonyl group, p-$CH_3C_6H_4SO_2-$
UV	ultraviolet
X	halogen group
xs	excess
Z	*zusammen*, same side in (E,Z) nomenclature of alkenes
	symbol for flow of electron pair

Index

Boldface numbers indicate primary references.

Bond-Dissociation Energies $DH°$ for A—B Bond, kcal mole^{-1}

A	(52.1) B: H	(28.9) Cl	(26.7) Br	(25.5) I	(9.4) OH	(44) NH$_2$	(35) CH$_3$	(79) C$_6$H$_5$	(104) CN
(35) CH$_3$—	105	85	71	57	93	85	90	102	122
(26) C$_2$H$_5$—	98	80	68	53	91.5	82	86	98	118
(18) i-C$_3$H$_7$—	95	81	68	53.5	93	82	86	96	116
(9) t-C$_4$H$_9$—	93	81	67	52	93	82	84	93	
(79) C$_6$H$_5$—	111	96	80.5	65	111	102	102	115	131
(48) C$_6$H$_5$CH$_2$—	88	72	58	48	81	71	76	90	
(39) CH$_2$=CHCH$_2$—	86	68	54	41	78		74		
(−6) CH$_3$CO—	86	81	66	49	107		81	93.5	
(−4) C$_2$H$_5$O—	104				44		83	101	
(70) CH$_2$=CH—	110	90	78				100	103	130
(52.1) H—	104.2	103.2	87.5	71.3	119	107	105	111	125

Numbers in parentheses: $(\Delta H_f°)$ for A· or B·.

Periodic Table of the Elements

1	2	3	4	5	6	7	8	9	10	11	12	13	14	15	16	17	18
1 **H** 1.008																	2 **He** 4.003
3 **Li** 6.94	4 **Be** 9.01											5 **B** 10.81	6 **C** 12.011	7 **N** 14.01	8 **O** 16.00	9 **F** 19.00	10 **Ne** 20.18
11 **Na** 22.99	12 **Mg** 24.31											13 **Al** 26.98	14 **Si** 28.09	15 **P** 30.97	16 **S** 32.06	17 **Cl** 35.45	18 **Ar** 39.95
19 **K** 39.10	20 **Ca** 40.08	21 **Sc** 44.96	22 **Ti** 47.90	23 **V** 50.94	24 **Cr** 52.00	25 **Mn** 54.94	26 **Fe** 55.85	27 **Co** 58.93	28 **Ni** 58.71	29 **Cu** 63.55	30 **Zn** 65.37	31 **Ga** 69.72	32 **Ge** 72.59	33 **As** 74.92	34 **Se** 78.96	35 **Br** 79.90	36 **Kr** 83.80
37 **Rb** 85.47	38 **Sr** 87.62	39 **Y** 88.91	40 **Zr** 91.22	41 **Nb** 92.91	42 **Mo** 95.94	43 **Tc** 98.91	44 **Ru** 101.07	45 **Rh** 102.91	46 **Pd** 106.4	47 **Ag** 107.87	48 **Cd** 112.40	49 **In** 114.82	50 **Sn** 118.69	51 **Sb** 121.75	52 **Te** 127.60	53 **I** 126.90	54 **Xe** 131.30
55 **Cs** 132.91	56 **Ba** 137.34	57 **La** 138.91	72 **Hf** 178.49	73 **Ta** 180.95	74 **W** 183.85	75 **Re** 186.2	76 **Os** 190.2	77 **Ir** 192.2	78 **Pt** 195.09	79 **Au** 196.97	80 **Hg** 200.59	81 **Tl** 204.37	82 **Pb** 207.19	83 **Bi** 208.98	84 **Po** (209)	85 **At** (210)	86 **Rn** (222)
87 **Fr** (223)	88 **Ra** 226.03	89 **Ac** (227)	104 **(Rf)** (261)	105 **(Ha)** (262)	106 (263)												

Lanthanides

58 **Ce** 140.12	59 **Pr** 140.91	60 **Nd** 144.24	61 **Pm** (145)	62 **Sm** 150.35	63 **Eu** 151.96	64 **Gd** 157.25	65 **Tb** 158.93	66 **Dy** 162.50	67 **Ho** 164.93	68 **Er** 167.26	69 **Tm** 168.93	70 **Yb** 173.04	71 **Lu** 174.97

Actinides

90 **Th** 232.04	91 **Pa** (231)	92 **U** 238.03	93 **Np** (237)	94 **Pu** (244)	95 **Am** (243)	96 **Cm** (247)	97 **Bk** (249)	98 **Cf** (249)	99 **Es** (254)	100 **Fm** (257)	101 **Md** (258)	102 **No** (259)	103 **Lr** (260)

Numbers in parentheses: available radioactive isotope of longest half-life.